The
University of
Chicago
School
Mathematics
Project

Teacher's Edition

VOLUME 1 • CHAPTERS 1–6

Authors

James Flanders
Marshall Lassak
Jean Sech
Michelle Eggerding
Paul J. Karafiol
Lin McMullin
Neal Weisman
Zalman Usiskin

Director of Evaluation

Denisse R. Thompson

The McGraw·Hill Companies

Authors

3rd EDITION AUTHORS

James Flanders
Researcher and Technology Integration
Center for Elementary Mathematics and Science Education
The University of Chicago

Marshall Lassak
Associate Professor of Mathematics and Computer Science
Eastern Illinois University, Charleston, IL

Jean Sech *Mathematics Teacher*
Mattawan High School, Mattawan, MI

Michelle Eggerding *Mathematics Teacher*
Schaumburg High School, Schaumburg, IL

Paul J. Karafiol *Mathematics Teacher*
Walter Payton College Prep High School, Chicago, IL

Lin McMullin *Mathematics Teacher (retired)*
Burnt Hills-Ballston Lake High School, Burnt Hills, NY

Neal Weisman *Mathematics Teacher*
Oak Park/River Forest High School, Oak Park, IL

Zalman Usiskin *Professor of Education*
The University of Chicago

AUTHORS OF EARLIER EDITIONS

Sharon L. Senk
Associate Professor of Mathematics
Michigan State University, East Lansing, MI

Natalie Jakucyn *Mathematics Teacher*
Glenbrook South High School, Glenview, IL

Denisse R. Thompson
Assistant Professor of Mathematics Education
University of South Florida, Tampa, FL

Steven S. Viktora
Chairman, Mathematics Department
New Trier High School, Winnetka, IL

Nils P. Ahbel *Mathematics Teacher*
Kent School, Kent, CT

Suzanne Levin
UCSMP

Marcia L. Weinhold *Mathematics Teacher*
Kalamazoo Area Mathematics and Science Center, Kalamazoo, MI

Rheta N. Rubenstein *Mathematics Department Head*
Renaissance High School, Detroit, MI

Judith Halvorson Jaskowiak *Mathematics Teacher*
John F. Kennedy High School, Bloomington, MN

Gerald Pillsbury
UCSMP

www.WrightGroup.com

Printed in the United State of America.
Send all inquiries to:
Wright Group/McGraw-Hill
P.O. Box 812960
Chicago, IL 60681

ISBN 978-0-07-621393-1
MHID 0-07-621393-5

1 2 3 4 5 6 7 8 9 VHJ 14 13 12 11 10 09

The McGraw-Hill Companies

UCSMP EVALUATION, EDITORIAL, AND PRODUCTION

Director of Evaluation
Denisse R. Thompson
Professor of Mathematics Education
University of South Florida, Tampa, FL

Coordinator of School Relations
Carol Siegel

Executive Managing Editor
Clare Froemel

Production Coordinator
Benjamin R. Balskus

Editorial Staff
Kathryn Rich, Gary Spencer, Carlos Encalada, Evan Jenkins, Currence Monson, Yan Yan Wang, Nathaniel Loman

Evaluation Consultant
Sharon L. Senk, *Professor of Mathematics*
Michigan State University, East Lansing, MI

Evaluation Assistants
Allison Burlock,
Julian Owens, Sophia Zhang, Zhuo Zheng,
Gladys Mitchell, Shravani Pasupneti, Alex Yablon

Production Assistants
Paul Campbell, Gretchen Neidhardt,
Sara Mahoney, Nurit Kirschenbaum

Technology Assistant
Luke I. Sandberg

Since the first two editions of *Advanced Algebra* were published, millions of students and thousands of teachers have used the materials. Prior to the publication of this third edition, the following teachers and schools participated in evaluations of the trial version during 2006–2007.

Clay Brown
Greenwood High School
Greenwood, Arkansas

Kathy Coskey
Glenbrook South High School
Glenview, Illinois

Audra Spicer
New Trier High School
Winnetka, Illinois

Craig Flietstra
Unity Christian High School
Hudsonville, Michigan

Catherine Feuerstein
Westfield High School
Westfield, New Jersey

Michael Buescher
Hathaway Brown School
Shaker Heights, Ohio

Cathy Buckingham
Nolan Catholic High School
Ft. Worth, Texas

Tami Wittkopf
Kewaskum High School
Kewaskum, Wisconsin

The following schools participated in field studies in 1993–1994, 1987–1988, 1986–1987, or 1985–1986 as part of the first edition or the second edition research.

Brentwood School
Los Angeles, California

Boulder High School
Boulder, Colorado

Hernando High School
Brooksville, Florida

Lassiter High School
Marietta, Georgia

Taft High School
Chicago, Illinois

Whitney Young High School
Chicago, Illinois

Kenwood Academy
Chicago, Illinois

Steinmetz Academic Center
Chicago, Illinois

Glenbrook South High School
Glenview, Illinois

Thornton Fractional South High School
Lansing, Illinois

Mt. Zion High School
Mt. Zion, Illinois

Rich South High School
Richton Park, Illinois

Lake Park West High School
Roselle, Illinois

Argo Community High School
Summit, Illinois

Shawnee Mission NW High School
Shawnee, Kansas

Framingham High School
Framingham, Massachusetts

Renaissance High School
Detroit, Michigan

Pontotoc High School
Pontotoc, Mississippi

Sentinel High School
Missoula, Montana

West Genessee High School
Camillus, New York

Lake Oswego High School
Lake Oswego, Oregon

Springfield High School
Springfield, Pennsylvania

Hanks High School
El Paso, Texas

We wish to acknowledge the generous support of the **Amoco (now BP) Foundation** and the **Carnegie Corporation of New York** in helping to make it possible for the first edition of these materials to be developed, tested, and distributed, and the additional support of the **Amoco (now BP) Foundation** for the second edition.

We wish also to acknowledge the contribution of the text *Advanced Algebra with Transformations and Applications*, by Zalman Usiskin (Laidlaw, 1975), to some of the conceptualizations and problems used in this book.

UCSMP: The University of Chicago School Mathematics Project

Introduction to UCSMP

The University of Chicago School Mathematics Project (UCSMP) is a long-term project designed to improve and renovate school mathematics in grades Pre-K through 12. UCSMP began in 1983 with a six-year grant from the Amoco (now BP) Foundation. Since then, additional funding has come from the National Science Foundation, the Ford Motor Company, the Carnegie Corporation of New York, the Stuart Foundation, the General Electric (now Verizon) Foundation, GTE, Citicorp/Citibank, the Exxon Education Foundation, the Illinois Board of Higher Education, the Chicago Public Schools, from royalties, and from publishers of UCSMP materials.

UCSMP received widespread funding from business and industry because both of those communities understand the ramifications of large numbers of young adults leaving school to join the work force lacking the mathematics they need to be successful in the real world.

The UCSMP Pre-K–12 curriculum consists of two vertically articulated programs:

- The nation's leading standards-based Pre-K–6 mathematics program, *Everyday Mathematics,*® and
- The UCSMP secondary component, *UCSMP Grades 6–12.*

The entire UCSMP Pre-K–12 curriculum emphasizes problem solving, everyday applications, the use of technology, and reading in mathematics, while developing and maintaining basic skills.

Throughout the years, the following beliefs have guided the development of the UCSMP program:

UCSMP Pre-K–12 materials are currently being used by an estimated 3.5 to 4 million students in elementary and secondary schools in every state and virtually every major urban area in the United States.

- Mathematics is valuable to the average citizen.
- All students can learn a significant amount of mathematics. By spreading out the traditional four-year secondary curriculum — and more — over additional years, students are given more time to learn the content they need. This smoother pace of instruction means that the average student has a better chance of mastering the content. This keeps students in mathematics rather than weeding them out.
- The curriculum can be more efficient by spending less time on review from previous years and on outmoded content and skills.
- Calculators and computers are powerful tools that make some content more important than before, and other content less important, and allow for the introduction of new content.

Program Organization

Program Overview

Development and testing of University of Chicago School Mathematics Project (UCSMP) materials started in 1983. Field testing and revisions have continued ever since, resulting in the Third Editions of this comprehensive mathematics program.

The UCSMP program is unique in providing a seven-year middle school and high school curriculum. The names of the seven texts around which these years are built are:

- *Pre-Transition Mathematics*
- *Transition Mathematics*
- *Algebra*
- *Geometry*
- *Advanced Algebra*
- *Functions, Statistics, and Trigonometry*
- *Precalculus and Discrete Mathematics*

The UCSMP program emphasizes these features and benefits.

Key Program Features	Advantages	Benefits
ENRICHED CONTENT Wider scope of mathematical content than traditional programs including more statistics in every level, and transformational geometry at every level.	A bridge between algebraic functions and geometric representation	Upgrades student achievement providing continual opportunities for problem solving
PROBLEM-SOLVING Continual emphasis on problem solving with real-world application	Up-to-date curriculum which develops connections to other disciplines	Students are better prepared for jobs in computer related/ technology-based industries
TECHNOLOGY All teachers and students in all courses will be expected to have access to graphing calculators, both in class and for assignments	Up-to-date use of calculators and computers	Real-world experiences and greater understanding of technology
FOUR DIMENSIONS OF UNDERSTANDING The SPUR Approach: Skills, Properties, Uses, Representations	A unique four-dimensional approach to understanding.	Maximizes student performance and fosters independent learning

Program Highlights

In response to various international, national, and state tests since the 1980s, combined with years of research and performance data, the UCSMP project addresses the most current issues in middle school and high school mathematics education.

Guided Instruction and Active Learning

Students learn best when classes are active and dynamic, presenting information through various modes and mediums. Students also learn at different rates and through repeated exposure to topics. Teachers guide students through lessons, activities, and projects that engage students in collaborative discovery of concepts and ideas. Continuous opportunities for review help students master concepts.

New Technology

The use of technology—including calculators, graphing calculators, dynamic geometry systems (DGS), spreadsheets, the Internet, and computer algebra systems (CAS)—is an essential component of the UCSMP Third Editions. Keeping current with modern technology will ensure that our students are well-prepared for the information age.

Real-World Applications

UCSMP uses real-world applications to introduce and develop concepts in lessons from all seven books. Skills that students learn through games and routines in *Everyday Mathematics* are put to the test through dynamic cross-curricular applications in the *UCSMP Grades 6–12* courses so students at various points of understanding can access the mathematics and continue to develop their understanding.

Reading and Writing Mathematics

Reading mathematical text is required throughout all of the UCSMP courses. Students must learn to read and write mathematical language in order to fully understand and communicate mathematical concepts. The familiarity with vocabulary and symbols that develops as students learn to read and write mathematical text will allow students to use any mathematical texts, not just their text books, as tools for understanding.

Multi-dimensional Approach to Understanding

UCSMP provides instruction which utilizes four dimensions of understanding and is unique in organizing the chapter objectives according to these dimensions. This multi-dimensional "SPUR" approach to understanding builds on differentiated instruction, providing continuous support to students despite their particular level of understanding.

SKILLS	Skills understanding means knowing a way to obtain a solution.
PROPERTIES	Properties understanding means knowing properties which you can apply. (Identify or justify the steps in obtaining answer.)
USES	Uses understanding means knowing situations in which you could apply the solving of this equation. (Set up or interpret a solution.)
REPRESENTATIONS	Representations understanding means having a representation of the solving process or a graphical way of interpreting the solution.

Read more about the SPUR approach on pages T20 and T21.

Advanced Algebra

Content

The Third Edition of UCSMP *Advanced Algebra* covers the traditional content of a second algebra course with an approach that applies the geometry students have learned in previous years and utilizes the latest technology for the classroom. Found throughout are activities to develop concepts, many utilizing computer algebra systems. Rich problems and applications abound, many designed to develop and sustain algebra skills.

Advanced Algebra Content Enhanced by Applying Geometry

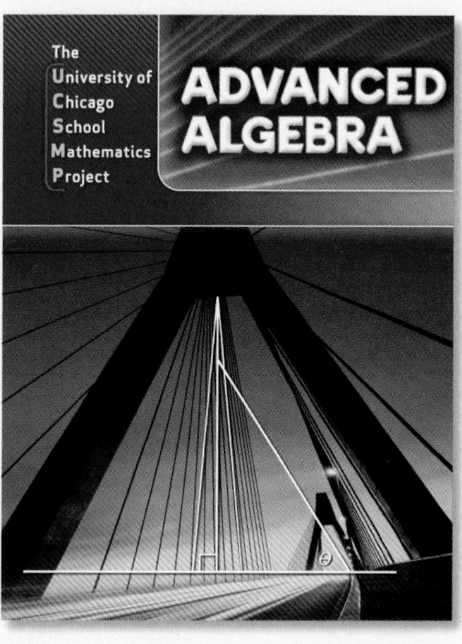

- Review of linear functions and systems utilizing geometric properties of points, lines, and planes
- Analysis of formulas and graphs for quadratic, power, exponential, logarithm, trigonometric, and polynomial functions using reflections, translations, and scale change transformations
- Congruence and symmetry applied in the study of triangle trigonometry
- Geometric applications and representations of all matrix operations
- Continued discussion of the logic of mathematics (definitions, assumed properties, theorems) begun in geometry

Modeling and Applications Carefully Developed

- Detailed examination of the basic properties of a situation that cause it to be modeled by each type of function studied in the course
- Attention given to the use of data in the selection of models
- Careful development of functions of variation and of quadratic relations from data

Rich Problems and Memorable Applications

- Wide variety of problems designed to enhance algebra skills and properties and connect with data and geometry
- Discussion of important aspects of quantitative literacy: investments; loans; lotteries
- Applications to a wide variety of contexts and subject areas, including biology, chemistry, astronomy, history, geography, and music

Use of a Variety of Tools/Technologies in an Activity-Oriented Approach

- Activities, Guided Examples, and Quiz Yourself questions throughout
- Explorations in all lessons; optional projects in all chapters
- Careful balance of mental mathematics, paper-and-pencil skills, and use of technology
- CAS and graphing technology assumed for home use and used to develop algebraic properties, solve problems, and extend content

Part of An Articulated Curriculum

The UCSMP program is flexible, allowing schools to offer the appropriate mathematics to students regardless of their grade level. Students can enter the UCSMP program at any grade, but are advantaged by having had the previous UCSMP courses. The table below shows how *Everyday Mathematics*® and the UCSMP program can be used together beginning at Grade 5. (The percents shown are national percentiles.)

The UCSMP curriculum is appropriate for virtually all students, but not at the same time.

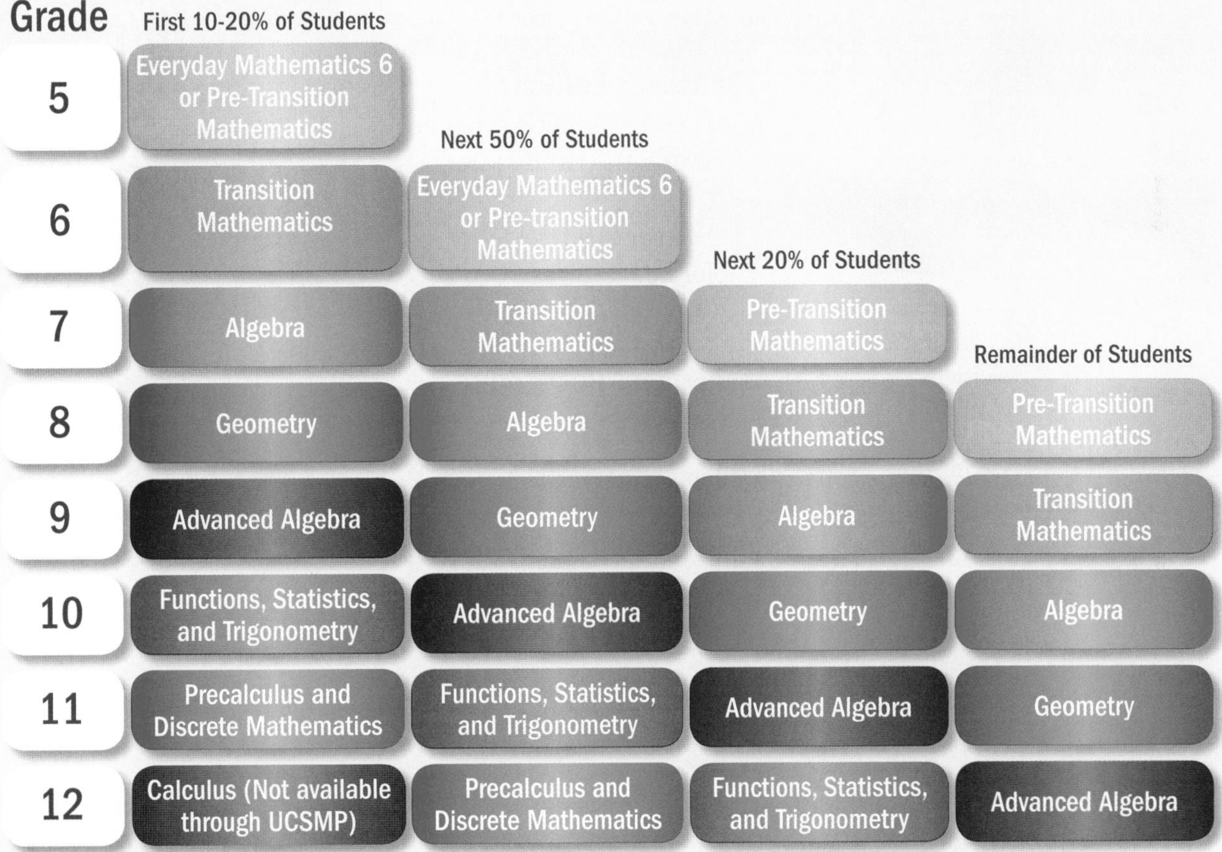

Grade	First 10-20% of Students	Next 50% of Students	Next 20% of Students	Remainder of Students
5	Everyday Mathematics 6 or Pre-Transition Mathematics			
6	Transition Mathematics	Everyday Mathematics 6 or Pre-transition Mathematics		
7	Algebra	Transition Mathematics	Pre-Transition Mathematics	
8	Geometry	Algebra	Transition Mathematics	Pre-Transition Mathematics
9	Advanced Algebra	Geometry	Algebra	Transition Mathematics
10	Functions, Statistics, and Trigonometry	Advanced Algebra	Geometry	Algebra
11	Precalculus and Discrete Mathematics	Functions, Statistics, and Trigonometry	Advanced Algebra	Geometry
12	Calculus (Not available through UCSMP)	Precalculus and Discrete Mathematics	Functions, Statistics, and Trigonometry	Advanced Algebra

UCSMP strongly believes that its curriculum is appropriate for virtually all students, but not at the same time. No student should be deprived of the opportunity to be successful in any of the courses, but no child who is ready should have to wait a year or two to begin the curriculum. The evidence is strong that the national percentiles shown above are good predictors for readiness for the UCSMP program.

Every UCSMP course has been designed so it could be used independently of other UCSMP courses. Testing has verified that any of the UCSMP courses can be taken successfully following the typical prerequisite course in the standard curriculum. However, to take best advantage of these materials, and for them to be appropriate for the greatest number of students, it is preferable to use them in sequence.

Program Components

Each course in the UCSMP program includes the following components.

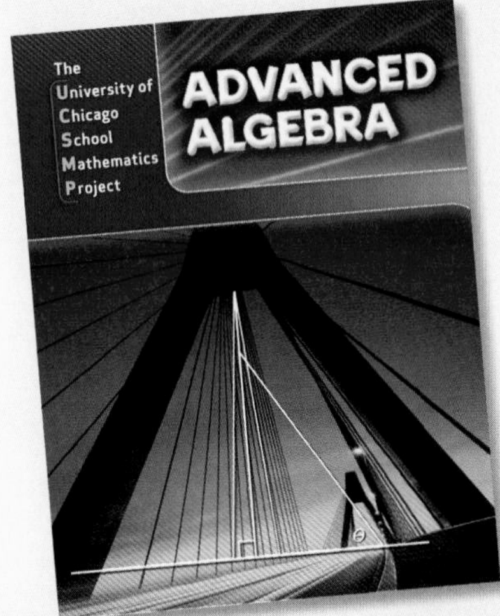

Student Edition

- Hard cover in one volume
- Online version (eSE)
- See pages T12–T15 for key features.

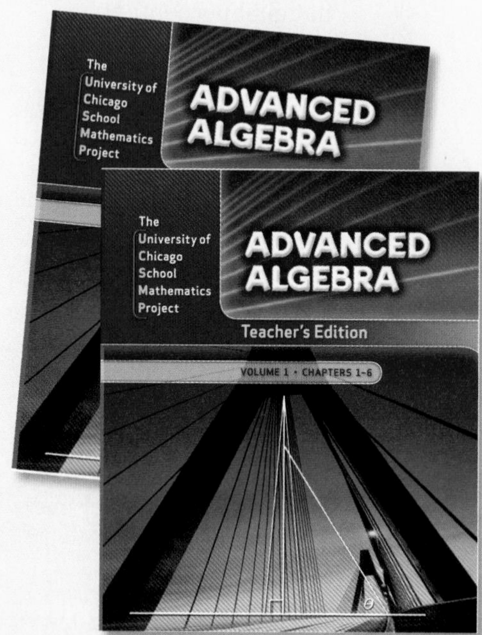

Teacher's Edition

- Hard cover in two volumes
- Electronic version (eTE)
- See pages T16–T17 for key features.

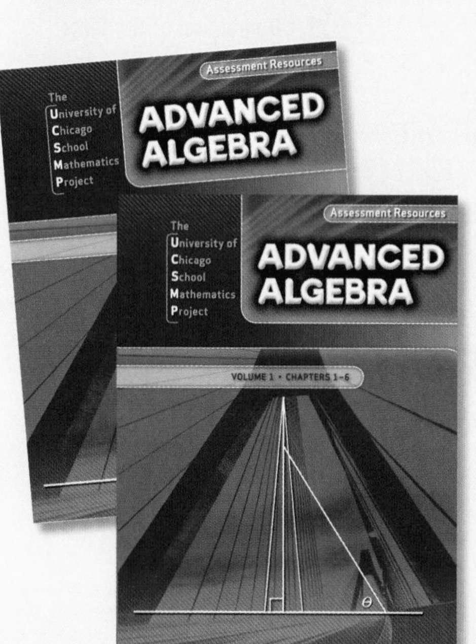

Assessment Resources

- Quizzes
- Chapter Tests
- Comprehensive Tests
- Correlation of SPUR Objectives to Chapter Tests Forms A–D
- Assessment forms

Teaching Resources

- Lesson Masters
- Resource Masters

Electronic Teacher's Edition (eTE)

- CD-ROM of the Teacher's Edition
- Includes all ancillary pages and answers
- Includes Student Edition
- Includes answers and solutions to all SE problems

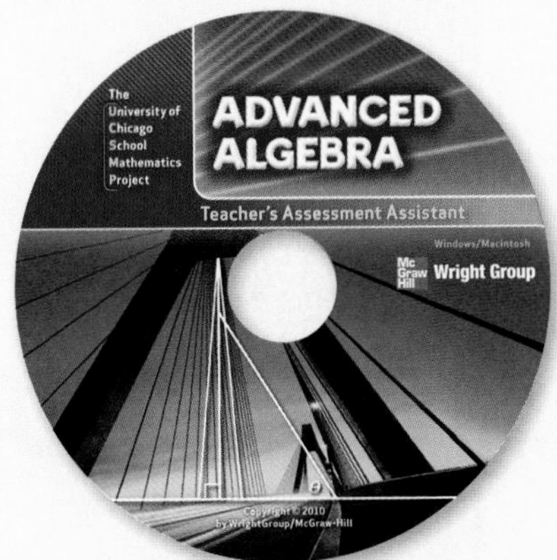

Teacher's Assessment Assistant (TAA)

- Sample assessment items similar to those on Chapter Test Form A
- Ability to create new assessment resources

Hardcover Student Book

Exciting lesson features are shown below.

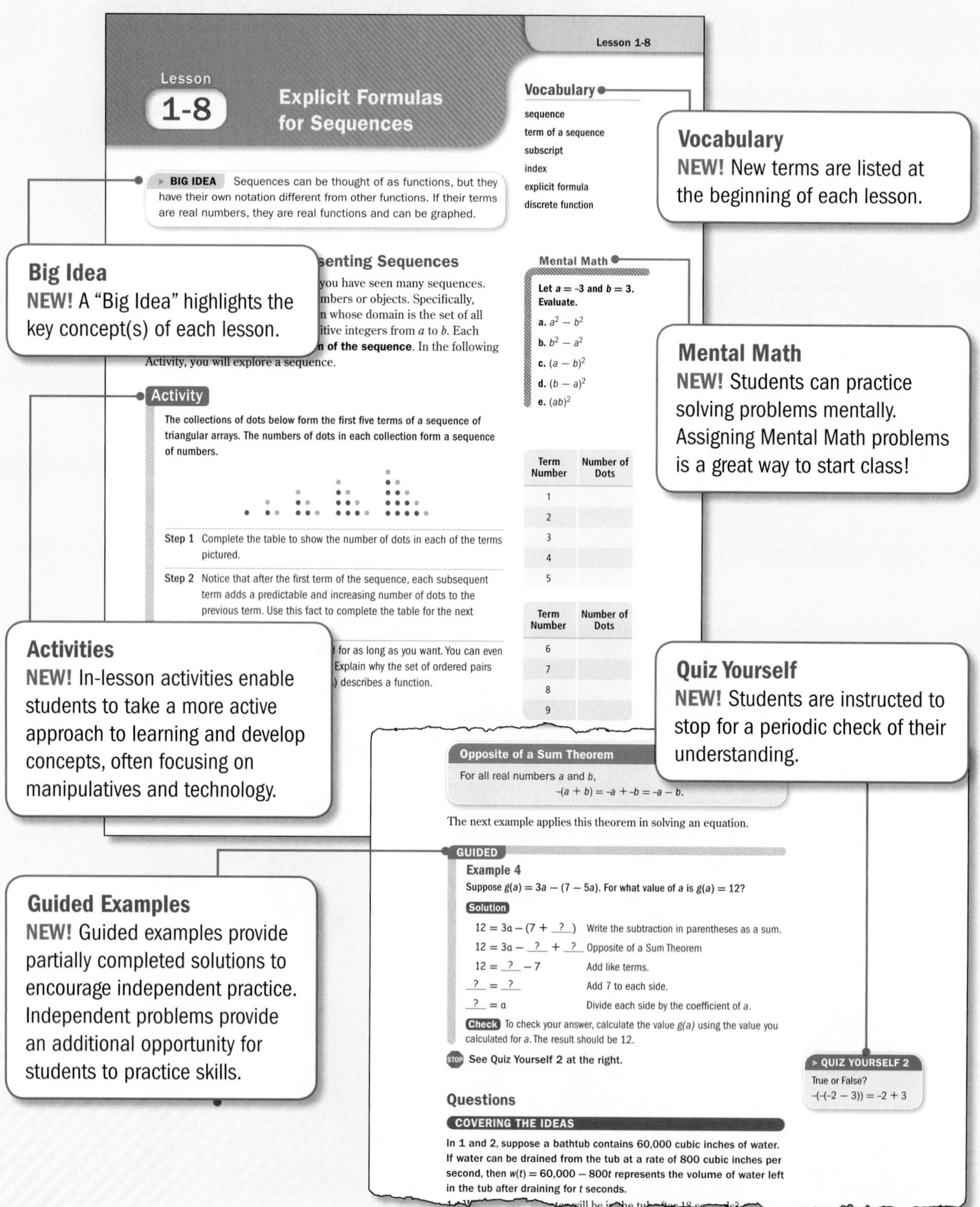

Covering the Ideas
Covering the Ideas questions demonstrate student knowledge of the overall concepts of the lesson.

Applying the Mathematics
Applying the Mathematics questions go beyond lesson examples, with an emphasis on real-world problem solving.

STOP See Quiz Yourself at the right.

In Example 2, P is a function of Y, so Y is the independent variable and P is the dependent variable.

▸ QUIZ YOURSELF
Are there other ordered pairs that show Y is not a function of P? If so, what are they?

Questions

COVERING THE IDEAS

1. In your own words, what is a function?
2. a. What is the difference between a function and a relation?
   b. Give an example of a relation that is not a function.
3. Give the definition and an example of a mathematical model.
4. Consider the table below.

s	–10	–5	0	5	10
t	100	25	0	25	100

   a. Is t a function of s? Explain your answer.
   b. Is s a function of t? Explain your answer.
5. Recall the formula for the circumference of a circle, $C = 2\pi r$. Is C a function of r? Justify your answer.

In 6–8, a relation is graphed. Is the relation a function? How can you ?

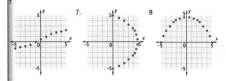

7. 8

APPLYING THE MATHEMATICS

In 13–15, use this information. A bowler's *handicap* is a bonus given to some bowlers in a league. The handicap h is a function of A, the bowler's average score, and is sometimes determined by the formula $h(A) = 0.8(200 - A)$, when $0 < A < 200$.

13. What is the handicap for a bowler whose average is 135?
14. If a bowler has a handicap of 28, what is the bowler's average?
15. What is the domain of the function h?

In 16–19, a. solve the equation by hand, and b. enter the equation into a CAS and solve the resulting equation.

16. $0.05x + 0.12(50000 - x) = 5{,}995.8$
17. $\frac{1}{3}t + \frac{1}{4}t + 6 = t$
18. $\frac{2}{3}p + \frac{1}{2} = p - 3$
19. $0.05z + 0.1(2z) + 0.25(100 - 3z) = 20$
20. Gloria owns a video rental store. Two-fifths of the store items are comedies, one-eighth are horror films, one-fourth are dramas, and the remaining 270 are video games.
    a. How many items are there in total?
    b. How many comedies are there?
    c. How many horror films are there?

In September 1895, the first meeting of the American Bowling Congress met in New York City. The ABC standardized dimensions for bowling balls, pins, and lanes.

Source: www.bowlingmuseum.com

Review
Review questions relate either to previous lessons in the course or to content from earlier courses.

Real-World Applications
Real-world applications to introduce and develop concepts in lessons.

Exploration
Exploration questions ask students to explore ideas.

REVIEW

In 23–26, refer to the graph below. In the graph, x = the year, $I(x)$ = the value in millions of dollars of imports into the United States, and $E(x)$ = the value of exports from the United States, also in millions of dollars. (Lessons 1-3 and 1-4)

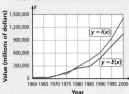

U.S. Trade in Goods and Services

Value (millions of dollars): 1,500,000; 1,200,000; 900,000; 600,000; 300,000; 0

Year: 1960 1965 1970 1975 1980 1985 1990 1995 2000

$y = I(x)$

$y = E(x)$

23. Estimate $I(1995)$.
24. In what unit is the dependent variable of function E measured?
25. In what year(s) was $E(x) > \$500{,}000$ million?
26. A negative *balance of trade* exists when a country's imports are greater than its exports. Write a few sentences comparing the balance of trade for the period 1960–1980 to the balance of trade for the period 1980–2000.
27. A cylindrical soft drink can has a lateral area of about 241 cm^2. If the radius of the can is 3.2 cm, approximate the can's height to the nearest tenth of a cm. (Previous Course)

EXPLORATION

28. Veronica was asked to find the product of two given numbers. By mistake, she added instead of multiplying. Yet she got the right answer! What two different numbers might have been given?

QUIZ YOURSELF ANSWERS

1. No; the owner would

End-of-Chapter Materials

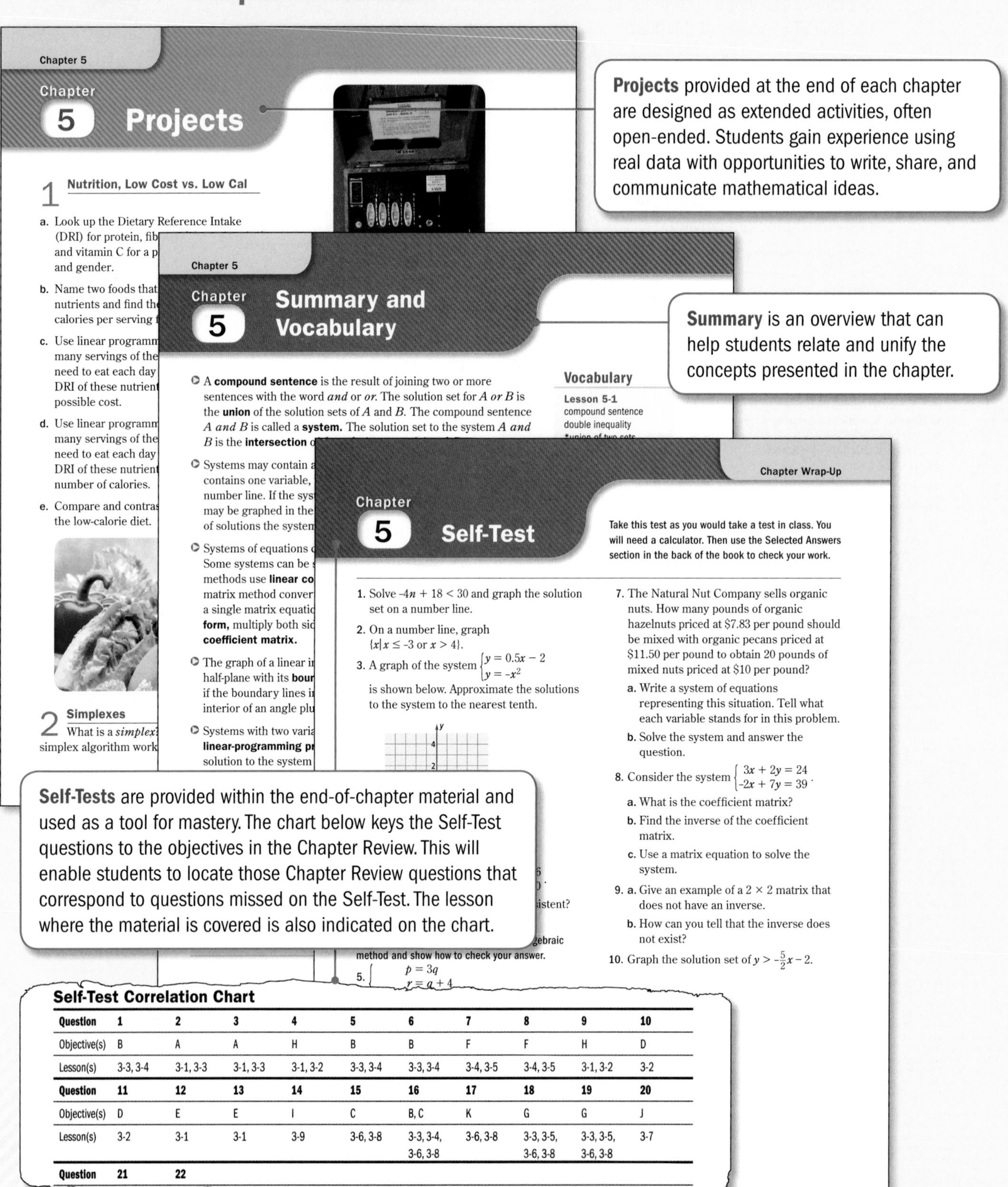

Chapter 5
Chapter 5 Projects
Chapter 5
Chapter 5 Summary and Vocabulary
Chapter Wrap-Up
Chapter 5 Self-Test
Take this test as you would take a test in class. You will need a calculator. Then use the Selected Answers section in the back of the book to check your work.
Self-Test 365

Projects provided at the end of each chapter are designed as extended activities, often open-ended. Students gain experience using real data with opportunities to write, share, and communicate mathematical ideas.

Summary is an overview that can help students relate and unify the concepts presented in the chapter.

Self-Tests are provided within the end-of-chapter material and used as a tool for mastery. The chart below keys the Self-Test questions to the objectives in the Chapter Review. This will enable students to locate those Chapter Review questions that correspond to questions missed on the Self-Test. The lesson where the material is covered is also indicated on the chart.

Self-Test Correlation Chart

Question	1	2	3	4	5	6	7	8	9	10
Objective(s)	B	A	A	H	B	B	F	F	H	D
Lesson(s)	3-3, 3-4	3-1, 3-3	3-1, 3-3	3-1, 3-2	3-3, 3-4	3-3, 3-4	3-4, 3-5	3-4, 3-5	3-1, 3-2	3-2
Question	**11**	**12**	**13**	**14**	**15**	**16**	**17**	**18**	**19**	**20**
Objective(s)	D	E	E	I	C	B, C	K	G	G	J
Lesson(s)	3-2	3-1	3-1	3-9	3-6, 3-8	3-3, 3-4, 3-6, 3-8	3-6, 3-8	3-3, 3-5, 3-6, 3-8	3-3, 3-5, 3-6, 3-8	3-7
Question	**21**	**22**								

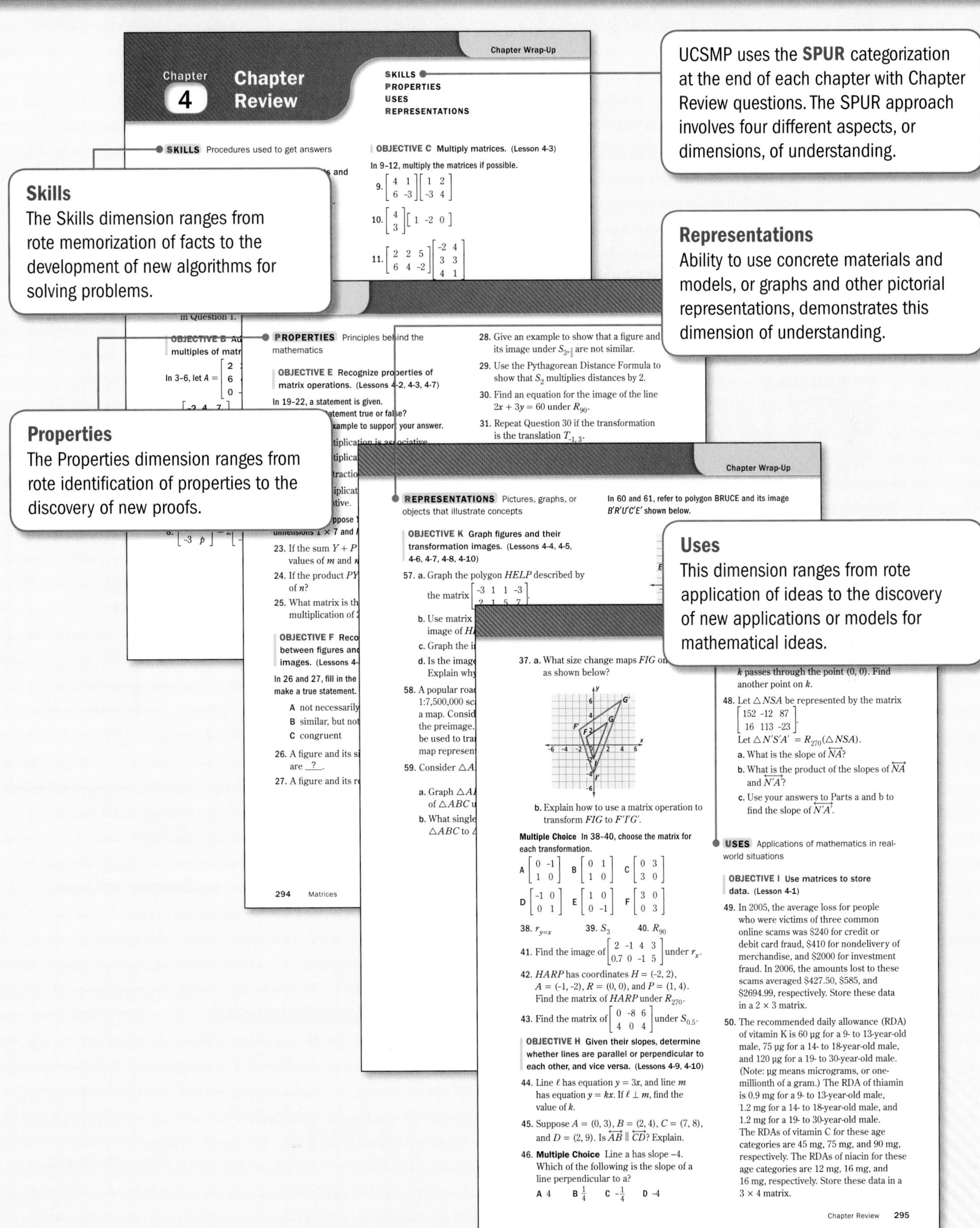

UCSMP uses the **SPUR** categorization at the end of each chapter with Chapter Review questions. The SPUR approach involves four different aspects, or dimensions, of understanding.

Skills
The Skills dimension ranges from rote memorization of facts to the development of new algorithms for solving problems.

Representations
Ability to use concrete materials and models, or graphs and other pictorial representations, demonstrates this dimension of understanding.

Properties
The Properties dimension ranges from rote identification of properties to the discovery of new proofs.

Uses
This dimension ranges from rote application of ideas to the discovery of new applications or models for mathematical ideas.

Four-Step Lesson Format

The Teacher's Edition is an extensive resource that helps address the individual needs of students. The notes within each lesson in the Teacher's Edition provide a variety of teaching ideas, organized around a four-step instructional plan.

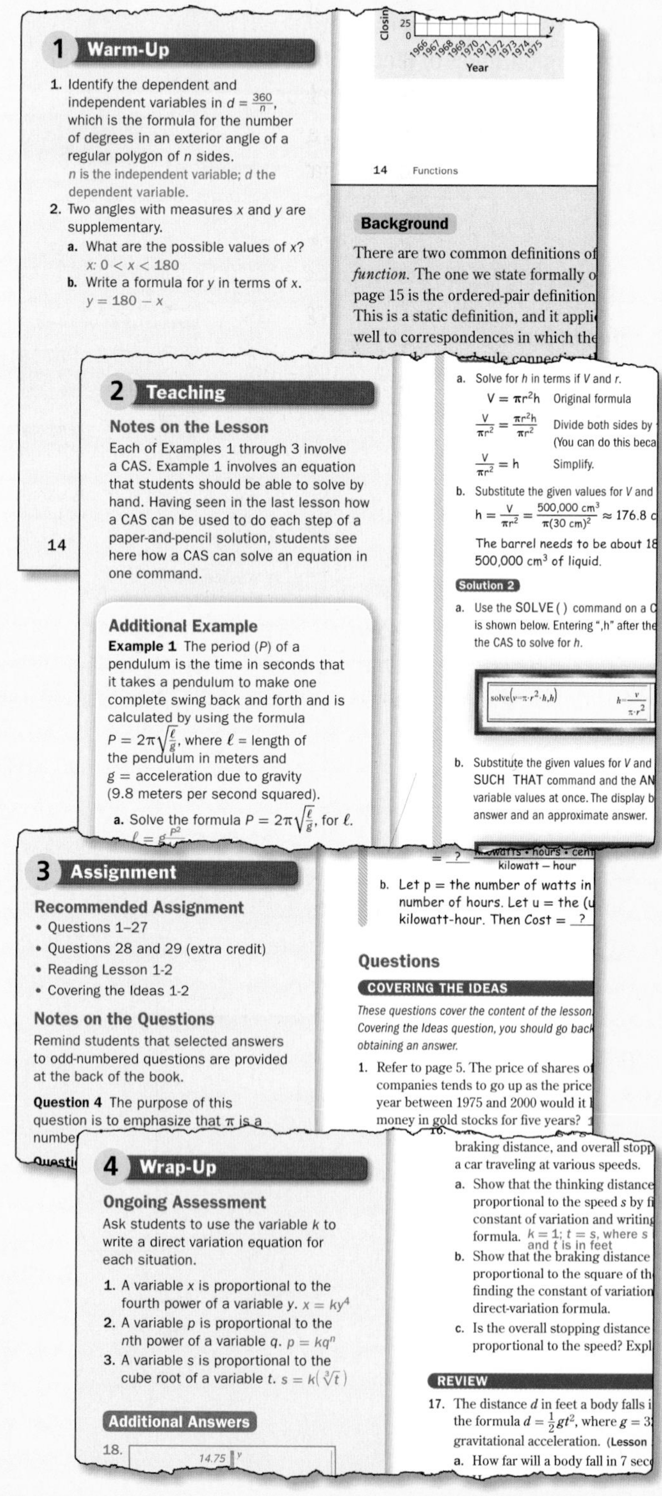

Background provides the rationale for the inclusion of topics or approaches, provides mathematical background, and makes connections between UCSMP courses.

1 Warm-Up provides questions for students to work on as you begin class.

2 Teaching provides overall notes on how to teach and enhance the lesson, including procedures for using the Activities. This section also provides Notes on Examples and Notes on Questions to highlight important aspects of specific examples and questions. Occasionally included are Note-Taking Tips to help students study. Additional Examples, parallel to the Examples in the Student Edition, are included with each lesson for added flexibility.

3 Assignment includes suggested questions to be completed as homework, pointing out those that may be appropriate for extra credit. This section also provides suggested assignments for the next lesson, including reading the lesson and doing the Covering the Ideas section.

4 Wrap-Up includes Ongoing Assessment suggestions that give students an opportunity to informally check their understanding of concepts at the end of each lesson. These options for differentiation generally employ a quick oral and/or written activity.

Differentiation Options

The Teacher's Edition includes many additional options for differentiation to promote universal access, including the following:

ENGLISH LEARNERS

Vocabulary Development

Gives teachers hints and instructional strategies on how to help English language learners and those with weak vocabulary skills gain access to key mathematical concepts.

Accommodating the Learner 

Provides suggestions for adjusting an example, activity, or discussion to make it more accessible to students who may be struggling with a particular concept.

Accommodating the Learner 

Provides suggestions for adjusting an example, activity, or discussion to make it more challenging.

Extension

May be a question, problem, activity, or outside project that extends a concept.

Clearly, all lessons contain more ideas than can be used in one class period — and there are many additional ways to teach each lesson. Depending on the background of students, a challenging activity in one class could be inappropriately easy in another. Teachers should use their professional judgment to select and sequence the activities that are appropriate for the length of a given class period and the needs of their students.

Teachers who have never used group work, manipulatives, or technology often assume that they are very time-consuming. Advanced planning and practice will help with the time management of these very worthwhile activities.

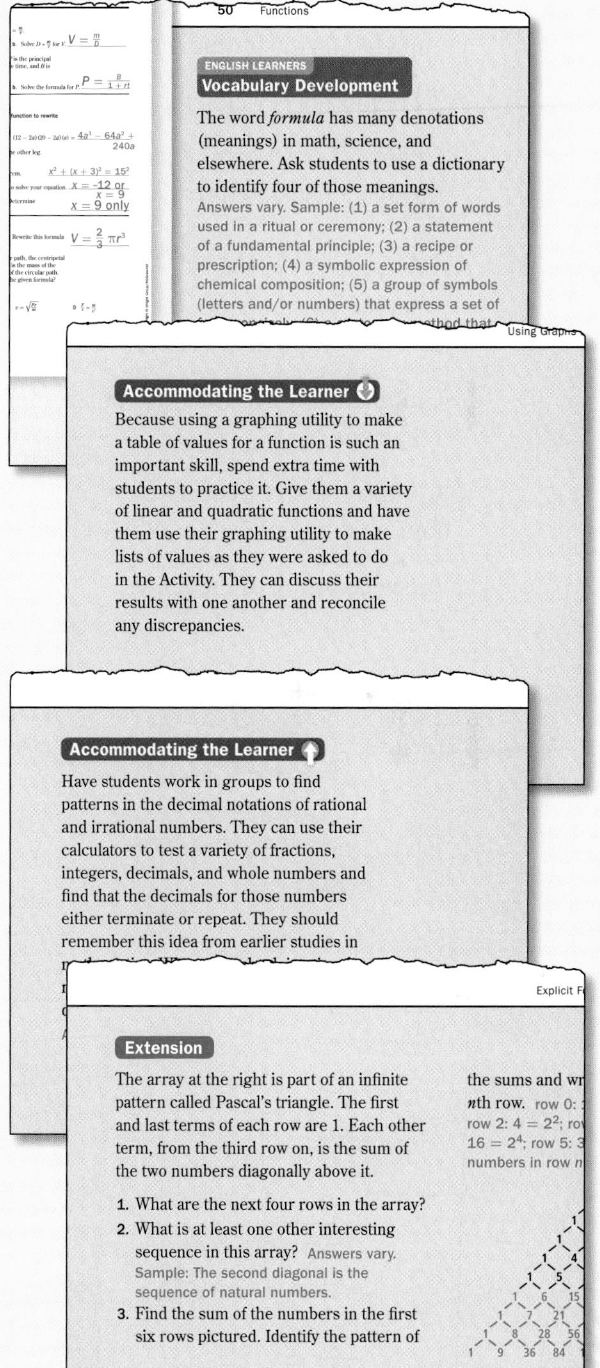

50 Functions

ENGLISH LEARNERS
Vocabulary Development

The word *formula* has many denotations (meanings) in math, science, and elsewhere. Ask students to use a dictionary to identify four of those meanings.
Answers vary. Sample: (1) a set form of words used in a ritual or ceremony; (2) a statement of a fundamental principle; (3) a recipe or prescription; (4) a symbolic expression of chemical composition; (5) a group of symbols (letters and/or numbers) that express a set of

Using Graphs

Accommodating the Learner

Because using a graphing utility to make a table of values for a function is such an important skill, spend extra time with students to practice it. Give them a variety of linear and quadratic functions and have them use their graphing utility to make lists of values as they were asked to do in the Activity. They can discuss their results with one another and reconcile any discrepancies.

Accommodating the Learner

Have students work in groups to find patterns in the decimal notations of rational and irrational numbers. They can use their calculators to test a variety of fractions, integers, decimals, and whole numbers and find that the decimals for those numbers either terminate or repeat. They should remember this idea from earlier studies in

Explicit F

Extension

The array at the right is part of an infinite pattern called Pascal's triangle. The first and last terms of each row are 1. Each other term, from the third row on, is the sum of the two numbers diagonally above it.

1. What are the next four rows in the array?
2. What is at least one other interesting sequence in this array? Answers vary. Sample: The second diagonal is the sequence of natural numbers.
3. Find the sum of the numbers in the first six rows pictured. Identify the pattern of

the sums and wr
*n*th row. row 0:
row 2: $4 = 2^2$; ro
$16 = 2^4$; row 5: 3
numbers in row *n*

Ancillary Materials

Assessment Resources

The *Assessment Resources* booklet provides guidelines for developing an effective assessment program as well as tests and quizzes for every chapter. There are also student-completed forms and teacher-completed forms for individual, group, and class activities.

- Two quizzes per chapter (mostly constructed-response),
- Chapter Tests Forms A and B (parallel forms, mostly constructed-response),
- Chapter Test Form C (performance-based, open-ended),
- Chapter Test Form D (performance-based, assesses multiple objectives with one task)
- Cumulative Form (mostly constructed-response)
- Comprehensive Test (after every three or four chapters, mostly multiple-choice)
- Answers for all of the above

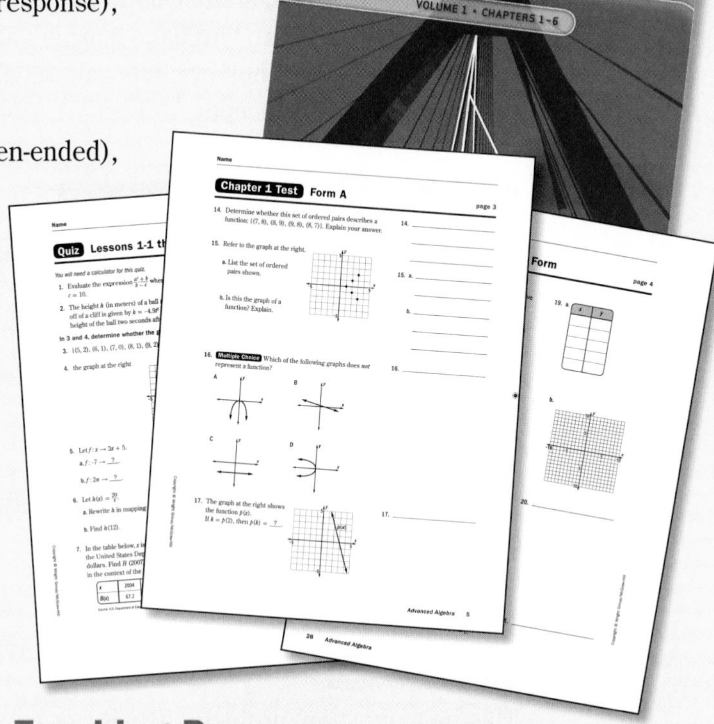

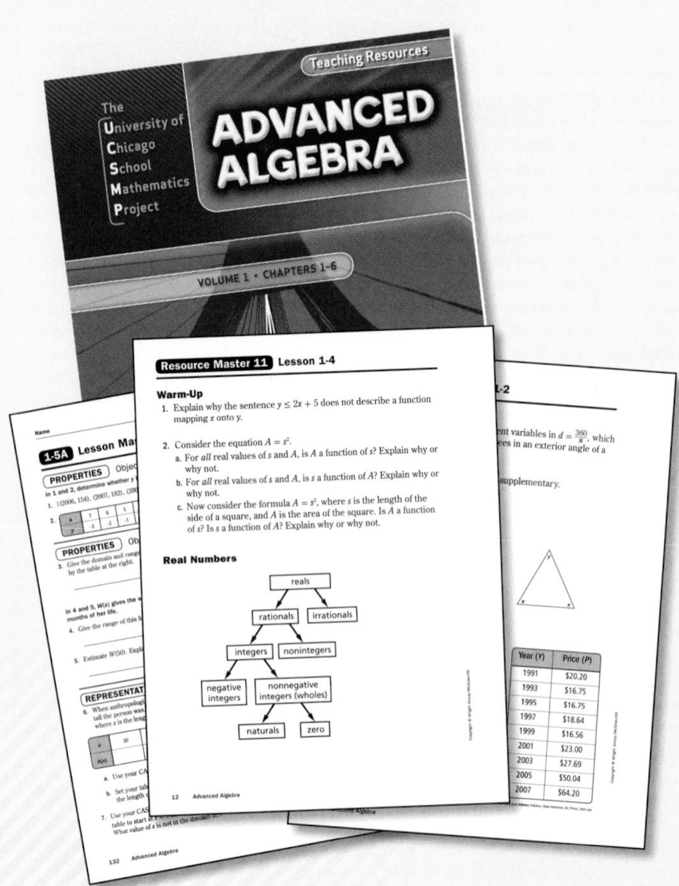

Teaching Resources

- Masters that teachers will want to use many times, such as Coordinate Grids, Centimeter Paper, Spreadsheet, Number Lines, and Dot Paper
- Masters with lesson Warm-Up exercises, Additional Examples, and pictures or art
- Two forms of Lesson Masters per lesson
- Answers for Lesson Masters

electronic Teacher's Edition, CD-Rom (eTE)

The *electronic Teacher's Edition* (eTE) comes in two volumes and includes:

- *Teacher's Edition* pages, with reduced Student Edition (SE) pages
- SE pages without overprinted answers, convenient for projecting on a screen
- *Teaching Resources*
- *Assessment Resources*
- Answer pages for all SE questions
- Worked-out Solutions for all SE questions
- TE margin with text box for writing local standards or notes

electronic Student Edition (eSE)

This is an online version of the SE. Users may access the site *UCSMPmath.com* upon purchasing the Student Edition.

Teacher's Assessment Assistant, CD-Rom (TAA)

- Build quizzes, tests, and worksheets.
- Access test items that mirror those of Chapter Test Forms A and B.
- Create many more test items.
- Print or send worksheets to students electronically.
- Obtain and save results automatically.

Additional Technology

The use of the latest technology has always been an outstanding feature of the UCSMP program. An essential component of UCSMP courses is the use of graphing calculators, spreadsheets, the Internet, and a 3–D geometry system.

Calculators

For home use and during class, students should have access to a graphing calculator and a dynamic geometry system (DGS).

Instructional Planning and Support

The SPUR Approach to Understanding

Since its inception, UCSMP has been known for its SPUR approach to understanding. The SPUR approach involves four different dimensions of understanding to enable students to approach and solve problems in different ways. By approaching problems from different perspectives, students gain an appreciation of the interconnectivity among concepts in mathematics.

The four dimensions of understanding that form this unique SPUR approach are:

Skills

For some, *understanding* mathematics means simply knowing how to get an answer without help from outside sources. In classrooms, when we speak of understanding how to use technology, we mean using technology to do something for us. In *UCSMP Grades 6–12* texts, these are both aspects of the same kind of understanding, the understanding of algorithms (procedures) for getting answers. This dimension of understanding ranges from memorization of basic facts to development of new algorithms. These include doing things mentally, with paper and pencil, or with technology.

The SPUR approach involves four dimensions of understanding to enable students to approach and solve problems in different ways.

Properties

Understanding *why* is at least as important as understanding *how.* Mathematicians often view this kind of understanding as the ultimate goal.

Uses

To the person who applies mathematics, being able to *use* the answer is most important. For example, an understanding of linear equations means being able to apply them appropriately in real situations.

Representations

Students need to be able to represent a concept and work with the concept in that representation in some way. Using concrete materials and models, or graphs and other pictorial representations, demonstrates this dimension of understanding.

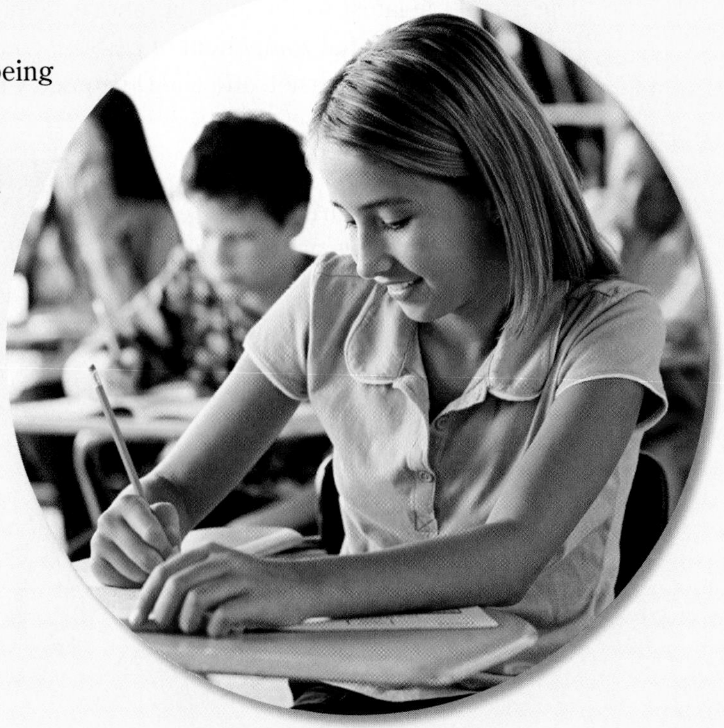

Each dimension of understanding has its easy and difficult aspects. Each can be demonstrated through simple memorization or the highest level of creative thinking. UCSMP believes that the most effective teaching provides students opportunities to demonstrate all of these dimensions.

***UCSMP Grades 6–12* provides instruction which utilizes all four dimensions of understanding in each chapter of each book.**

For a specific example of what understanding means in these four dimensions, consider solving $100 + 5x = 50 + 10x$ and what constitutes evidence of that understanding.

SKILLS	***Skills* understanding means knowing a way to obtain a solution.** Obtain x = 10 by some means.
PROPERTIES	***Properties* understanding means knowing properties which you can apply.** Justify the steps in obtaining the solution.
USES	***Uses* understanding means knowing situations in which you could apply the solving of this equation.** Set up or interpret a solution: If one person has 100 CDs and buys 5 CDs a month, and another person has 50 CDs and buys 10 CDs a month, in how many months will they have the same number of CDs?
REPRESENTATIONS	***Representations* understanding means having a representation of the solution or a graphical interpretation of the solution.** Graph y = 100 + 5x and y = 50 + 10x, and realize that the x-coordinate of the point of intersection is the solution.

UCSMP is unique in organizing the chapter objectives according to these dimensions. The SPUR categorization appears at the end of each chapter with the Chapter Review questions. The Progress Self-Test for each chapter and the Lesson Masters (in the *Teacher's Resources*) are also keyed to the SPUR objectives. The categorization is meant to ensure that the book enables teachers to provide students with opportunities to gain a broader and deeper understanding of mathematics than is normally the case.

It should be noted that the SPUR approach is not a perfect sorter of knowledge; many ideas and many problems involve more than one dimension. Some types of understanding do not fit any of these dimensions exactly. What is important is that students have ample learning opportunities utilizing all four dimensions.

Using the Reading in UCSMP

In order to become an independent learner of mathematics, a student must learn how to learn mathematics from reading. Expect students to read all parts of all lessons – not just the questions and the examples.

At the beginning of the course, the reading may require time in class. Do not expect overnight changes in behavior from students who have never read their math books before. Teachers of students who are using UCSMP materials for the first time report that by the end of the year almost all of their students are reading. Teachers of later UCSMP courses report that this behavior continues without the initial prodding.

Because students may never have been asked to read mathematics, they may ask why they have to read it now. Students must learn to read mathematics because:

- all future courses, not just mathematics courses, require learning through reading;
- jobs and life outside of school require learning through reading;
- the reading relates topics and lessons;
- reading will help students understand the mathematics.

Spend some class time early in the course teaching students how to read mathematics. Guide students through the first few chapters or have them read aloud in class. You might also go over the Covering the Ideas questions orally. Point out how these questions help students understand and remember what they are reading. The answers for these questions can be found directly in the reading or by mimicking worked-out examples.

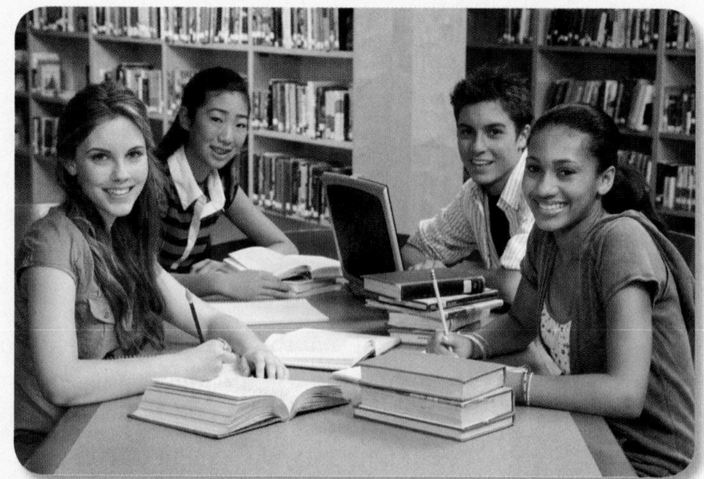

Encourage students to read a math book carefully, paying attention to little words (such as *if, but,* and *not*) that may be crucial to understanding a mathematical statement. Students need to realize that text and graphics are often related and that they should move back and forth from one to the other. Some students may not be able to read 2^5 (2 to the 5th power) or $x + 5 = 9$ (x plus 5 is equal to 9) out loud if they do not have the vocabulary for the math symbols. Thus, it is important to have students read out loud in class, as well as silently and at home.

Writing in Mathematics

UCSMP strongly believes that using writing to help students develop their understanding of mathematics prepares them for their adult roles in an information-rich society—a society where most careers do not consist of uncomplicated, independent tasks.

Through writing, communication of mathematical ideas opens up on a variety of levels. As they write, students apply concepts to their own experiences; construct meaning for mathematical symbols, procedures, and concepts; and internalize meaning as they explore and examine mathematical ideas in words. It also enables teachers to identify incomplete conceptions and overall depth of knowledge.

Writing may consist simply of the steps in answering a question, but to be most effective, it should be more than that. It can include comments about what was being done and why a particular strategy was chosen. The careful examination of thought that writing requires may lead students to see the process of thinking as more important than the ability to quote rules.

Using writing to help students develop their understanding of mathematics prepares them for their adult roles in an information-rich society—a society where most careers do not consist of uncomplicated, independent tasks.

Journal Writing

Journal writing is believed by some to be one of the most effective methods of writing for the purpose of learning mathematics. Informative writing in class and on homework (not necessarily in a bound or spiral notebook) achieves similar results. Journals and informal explorative writing allow students to put concepts in their own words, to speculate on extensions to problems, and to relate material they are learning to what they already know.

In general, undirected journal writing does not provoke as much focus or response from students as carefully and thoughtfully worded prompts. The more concise the prompt, the better. Collect journals and provide feedback regularly to emphasize their importance. Above all, be patient and flexible.

Writing in UCSMP

Writing good explanations and proofs takes time, experience, and guidance. To provide the necessary practice, the UCSMP program has included many questions requiring writing. In each course, UCSMP frequently asks students to explain a solution to a problem or to justify an answer.

Writing good explanations takes time, experience, and guidance. To provide the necessary practice, the UCSMP program has included many questions requiring writing.

Students' explanations may be vague, imprecise, or too brief at first. Encourage greater thoroughness and effectiveness by discussing good explanations in the text. The solutions to the examples in each lesson are excellent models. The portions of the solutions that you may expect students to write are printed in a special font. The *Teacher's Edition* provides Note-Taking Tips to help students become active learners through writing.

Writing on Tests

The recent trend to include open-ended written assessments on high-stakes tests demonstrates the widespread view that good writing in mathematics is an important goal. Incorporate more writing into quizzes and tests by including items that ask students to write about their solutions. Items from the Form C tests (in Assessment Resources) are good examples.

Assessment

Assessing Student Performance in Mathematics

Effective methods of assessment offer students opportunities to demonstrate how they approach problem situations, collect and organize information, formulate and test conjectures, and communicate their mathematical insights. A good assessment program contains tasks that are appropriate to the topics students are learning and provides outcomes valuable to students. Teachers should determine an assessment program that best suits the needs of his or her students.

> **The Assessment Principle**
>
> **"Assessment should support the learning of important mathematics and furnish useful information to both teachers and students."**
> – NCTM *Principles and Standards for School Mathematics,* p. 22.

The assessment process should be a positive experience for students and should:

- Yield feedback on the appropriateness of instructional methods.
- Offer some clues as to how the content or pace of instruction could be modified.
- Identify for students areas for improvement and affirm their success.
- Evaluate student performance for grading purposes.
- Include a variety of assessment techniques.
- Provide opportunities for students to demonstrate their mathematical capabilities in an atmosphere that encourages maximum performance.
- Emphasize what students *do* know, *can* do, and how they think mathematically.
- Motivate students to achieve by using assessment tasks that reflect the value of students' efforts.
- Encourage students to reflect on what they have done.

Good assessment addresses higher-order thinking skills. Teachers should think about:

- Designing assessments that provide a picture of the student as a critical thinker and problem solver.
- Using assessments that identify how the student does mathematics, not just what answer he or she gets.

Assessment Options in UCSMP

The *Assessment Resources* provides a wide variety of assessment and evaluation instruments described to the right. This resource booklet also has answers, evaluation guides, and/or rubrics for all the quizes and tests. The SPUR charts correlate the test items from Chapter Tests Forms A–D to the chapter SPUR objectives.

It should be noted that tests, quizzes, and homework assignments provide only a small picture of what a student may know. In order to help develop your students' abilities with open-ended questions or longer, more elaborate tasks, consider the Exploration questions at the end of each lesson and the Projects at the end of each chapter as part of your assessment tool kit.

Given the requirements of the high-stakes state tests, it is important that students have experiences with the types of items found on state tests, such as multiple-choice items. The multiple-choice items throughout the UCSMP texts and on the included test forms give students experience with this type of assessment.

If your state's assessment includes performance tasks, you may want to assign items from the Form C or Form D test on a regular basis. It is recommended that you score such performance tasks using the rubric applied in your state.

Assessment Instruments

Chapter Quizzes, two per chapter, cover three or four lessons and contain mostly constructed-response items (items for which a student must supply requested information).

Chapter Test Forms A and B are parallel forms and assess every chapter objective in primarily constructed-response format.

Chapter Test Form C consists of 4 to 6 performance-based, open-ended items, many of which assess several chapter objectives simultaneously.

Chapter Test Form D is performance-based and often assesses 5 or more chapter objectives as applied to a single task.

Chapter Test Cumulative Form contains mostly constructed-response items.

Comprehensive Tests, every three or four chapters, are cumulative in nature and consist primarily of multiple-choice items.

Assessment Forms

Student-completed forms

Teacher-completed forms for individual, group, and class activities

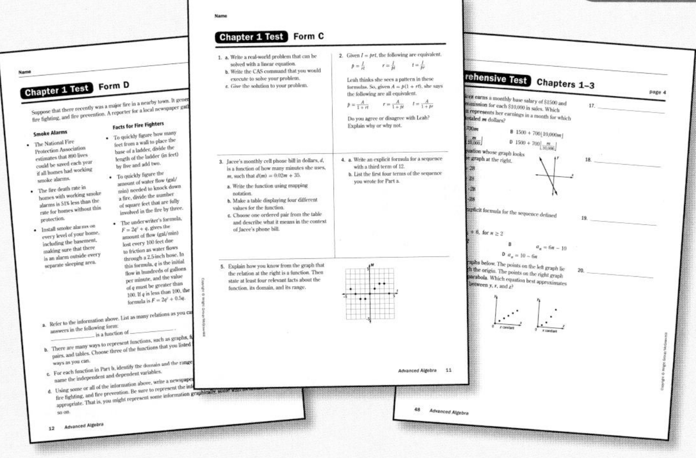

Introduction to the Research

Since 1983, the UCSMP curriculum has been carefully refined through years of field-testing and feedback from users. Teachers throughout the country have discovered that UCSMP materials provide a way for more of their students to be successful, learning more mathematics than with traditional curricula.

The research and development of the three editions of the UCSMP textbooks has involved a sequence of writing and evaluation taking 5–6 years, and three years for the new course *Pre-Transition Mathematics.* Pilot studies, formative evaluations, and national summative evaluations conducted by UCSMP staff use state-of-the-art quantitative and qualitative designs and instruments. Observations, interviews, questionnaires, and a variety of tests are used. Evaluations focus both on the characteristics of teachers, classes, schools, and districts as they implement UCSMP materials and on the performance on traditional, often standardized, and project-made tests of students who used the materials.

The timeline below summarizes the research and development for each of the three editions of UCSMP. More detailed information on the research and development of all three editions of *UCSMP Grades 6–12* and *Everyday Mathematics*® is available from Wright Group at www.wrightgroup.com.

UCSMP Grades 6–12	Pre-1989	1989	1990	1991	1992	1993	1994	1995	1996	1997
Pre-Transition Mathematics										
Transition Mathematics	WRITE ◆ FIELD-TEST ◆ REWRITE ◆ PUBLISH			FEEDBACK ◆ WRITE ◆ FIELD-TEST ◆ PUBLISH – 2nd Ed.						
Algebra	WRITE ◆ FIELD-TEST ◆ REWRITE ◆ PUBLISH			FEEDBACK ◆ WRITE ◆ FIELD-TEST ◆ PUBLISH – 2nd Ed.						
Geometry	WRITE ◆ FIELD-TEST ◆ REWRITE ◆ PUBLISH – 1st Ed.				FEEDBACK ◆ WRITE ◆ FIELD-TEST ◆ PUBLISH – 2nd Ed.					
Advanced Algebra	WRITE ◆ FIELD-TEST ◆ REWRITE ◆ PUBLISH – 1st Ed.				FEEDBACK ◆ WRITE ◆ FIELD-TEST ◆ PUBLISH – 2nd Ed.					
Functions, Statistics, and Trigonometry	WRITE ◆ FIELD-TEST ◆ REWRITE ◆ PUBLISH				FEEDBACK ◆ WRITE ◆ FIELD-TEST ◆ PUBLISH – 2nd Ed.					
Precalculus and Discrete Mathematics	WRITE ◆ FIELD-TEST ◆ REWRITE ◆ PUBLISH				FEEDBACK ◆ WRITE ◆ FIELD-TEST ◆ PUBLISH – 2nd Ed.					

All of the UCSMP studies mentioned were done with students having soft-cover, one-color, multi-section versions of the later published textbooks. Teachers had notes on lessons and chapter tests, but typically had none of the other ancillaries that became available later.

Over the years, UCSMP's research has been cited favorably by organizations charged with evaluating such research. For example, in its publication *On Evaluating Curricular Effectiveness: Judging the Quality of K–12 Mathematics Evaluations* (The National Academies Press, 2004), the Mathematical Sciences Education Board wrote the following in its Conclusions and Recommendations section (p. 202): "The committee was asked to review the 13 NSF-supported curricula and 6 sets of commercially generated curricula. We note that there was considerable variation in the type and extent of evaluation material provided across these 19 curricula. The database of evaluations for the NSF-supported curricula and for UCSMP greatly exceeded the database for the commercially generated materials in quantity and quality."

	1998–2003	2004	2005	2006	2007	2008
			WRITE ◆ FIELD-TEST ◆ REWRITE ◆ PUBLISH – 3rd Ed.			
		WRITE ◆ FIELD-TEST ◆ REWRITE ◆ PUBLISH – 3rd Ed.				
		WRITE ◆ FIELD-TEST ◆ REWRITE ◆ PUBLISH – 3rd Ed.				
				WRITE ◆ FIELD-TEST ◆ REWRITE ◆ PUBLISH – 3rd Ed.		
				WRITE ◆ FIELD-TEST ◆ REWRITE ◆ PUBLISH – 3rd Ed.		
				WRITE ◆ FIELD-TEST ◆ REWRITE ◆ PUBLISH – 3rd Ed.		
				WRITE ◆ FIELD-TEST ◆ REWRITE ◆ PUBLISH – 3rd Ed.		

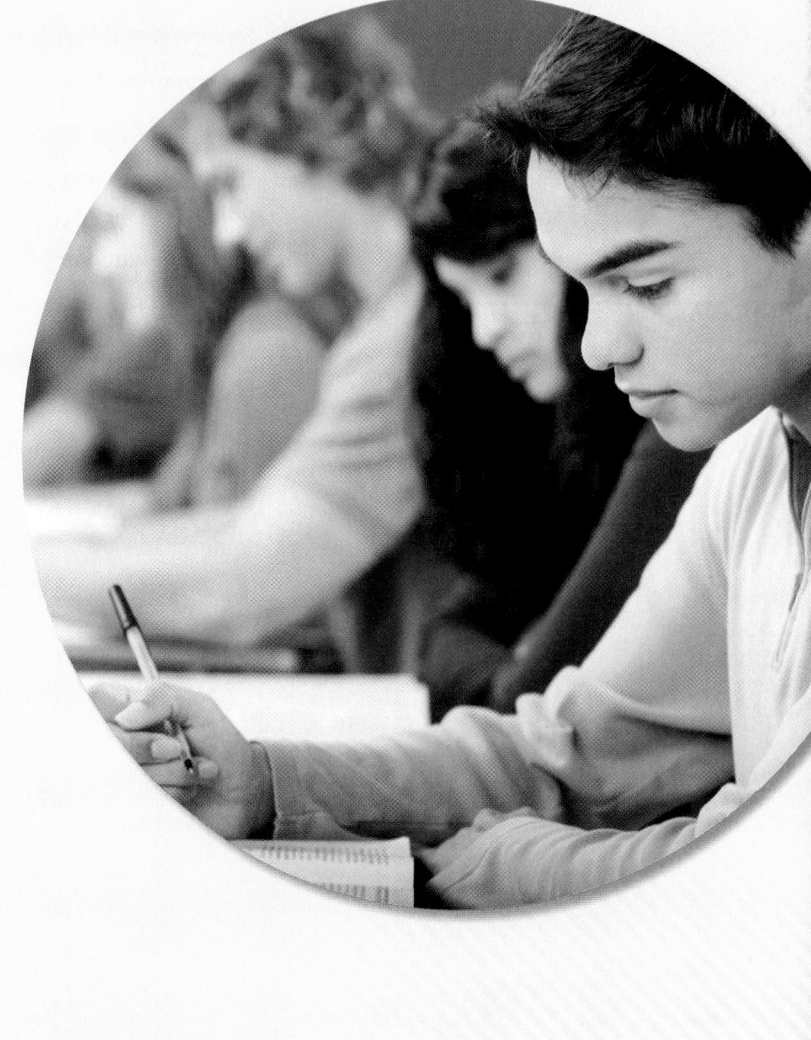

Contents

VOLUME 1

Chapter 3 148
Linear Functions and Sequences

Chapter 4 220
Matrices

Chapter 5 298
Systems

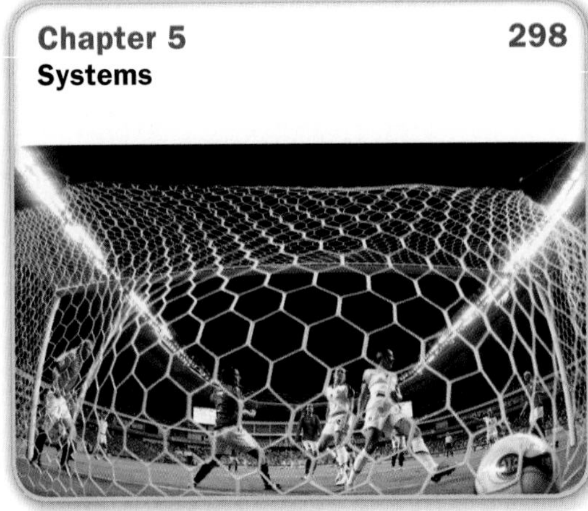

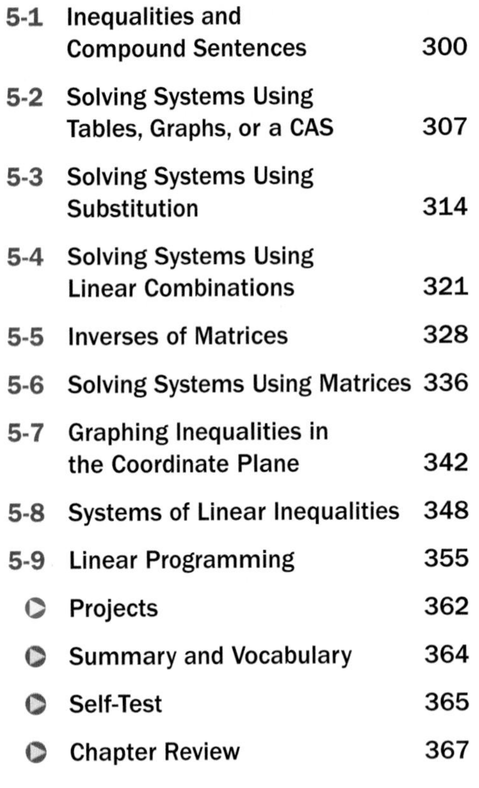

Chapter 6 372
Quadratic Functions

VOLUME 2

Chapter 7 450
Powers

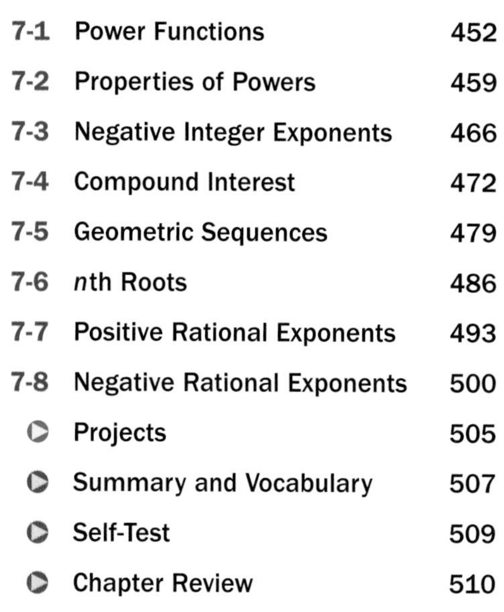

Chapter 8 514
Inverses and Radicals

Chapter 9 578
Exponential and Logarithmic Functions

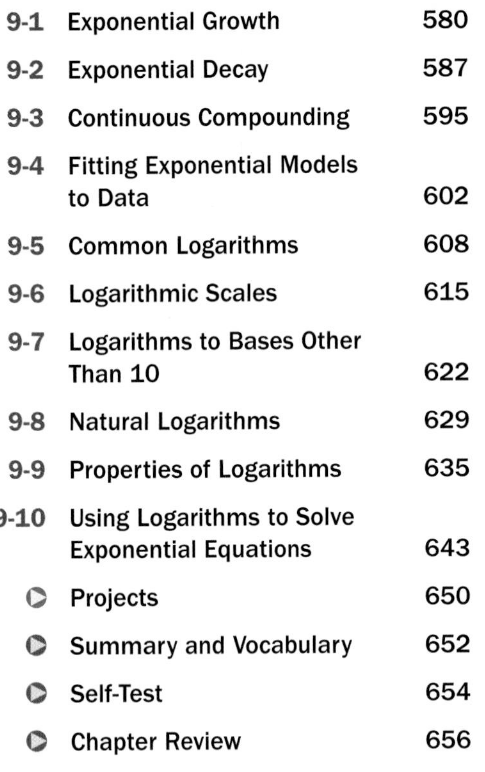

Chapter 10 660
Basic Ideas of Trigonometry

To the Student: Getting Started

Welcome to *Advanced Algebra*! We hope you enjoy this book and find it useful; it was written for you.

Advanced Algebra contains much of the mathematics that educated people around the world use in conversation, and that most colleges want or expect you to have studied. Familiar ideas, such as properties of numbers, graphs, expressions, equations, and inequalities, appear throughout the book. In addition, you will study many topics that may be new to you, including matrices, logarithms, trigonometry, and conic sections. Throughout the course you will use the broad ideas of function and mathematical modeling to help organize ideas.

The name *Advanced Algebra* indicates that the content of this book is related to what you learned in first-year algebra. However, this book is not necessarily more difficult. Some questions may be harder, but you know a lot more than you did then. In particular, you know much more geometry, and you have had a year's more practice with algebra.

Studying Mathematics

A goal of this book is to help you learn mathematics on your own, so that you will be able to deal with the mathematics you see in newspapers and magazines, on television, on any job, and in school. Everything in the book is written with the expectation that you will read it, learn from it, and enjoy that experience.

Not all students learn the same way. You need to find a way that works best for you. Here are a few suggestions.

1. **Mathematics is not a spectator sport.** You can watch an athlete, actor, juggler, or dancer perform, but you cannot replicate their performance without trying, failing, and improving through repeated attempts.

2. **Reading mathematics takes practice.**

- *Read slowly and thoughtfully*, paying attention to each word, graph, table, and symbol. Look up the meaning of any word you do not understand. Use the **QY** (Quiz Yourself) questions to help you check your understanding as you read. The answers to QY questions are found at the end of each lesson.
- *Work examples* yourself as you follow the steps in the text. **Guided Examples** are in most lessons. You should write these examples in a notebook so that you can refer to them throughout the course. Parts of the solutions to examples are written in this font to suggest what to write on your homework paper as a solution to a problem. Many lessons also have **Activities**. You should do these activities to help you understand the mathematics of the lesson.
- *Draw graphs, diagrams, and tables* by hand or with technology when following a complicated example.

3. **Writing mathematics is an important skill.** Writing is a tool for communicating your solutions and

To the Student:
Getting Started

thoughts to others, and can help you understand mathematics, too. Writing good explanations takes practice. Use solutions to the examples in each lesson to guide your writing.

4. **Be persistent.** Not all questions can be answered immediately. If you are struggling with a problem, don't give up! Read the lesson again. Read the question again. Look for examples. If you can, go away from the problem and come back to it a little later.

5. **Develop good study habits.** Many students have found study groups to be helpful. Get the phone numbers or email addresses of a few students in your class, so you can share thoughts about what you are learning. And perhaps most important, ask your teacher for help with important ideas that are still not clear to you after you have worked on them.

Tools Needed for This Book

To be a successful student in this course, you will need lined paper, sharp pencils, erasers, a ruler, and graph paper.

You need technology for use while reading the lessons, doing homework, participating in class, and taking tests. The technology needs to be able to:

1. deal with arithmetic operations, the numbers π and e, square roots, reciprocals (x^{-1} or $\frac{1}{x}$), powers (x^y or x^y), logarithms (log and ln), and trigonometric functions (cos, sin, and tan);
2. graph functions;
3. make lists and tables of values for equations, and calculate statistics on the data in these tables (table generator);
4. manipulate algebraic expressions and solve symbolic equations (a computer algebra system (CAS));
5. construct and manipulate geometric objects (a dynamic geometry system (DGS));
6. operate on matrices; and
7. generate sequences recursively (spreadsheet).

A few calculators have all seven of the above features. Often they are called CAS calculators, though they do much more. Such a calculator will be particularly useful in future mathematics courses and in many courses in college.

Altogether this technology allows you to solve realistic problems without having to do tedious computations, and it enables you to understand better many mathematics ideas. You will begin using technology in Lesson 1-3.

Using Technology

In many places in this book, you have a choice as to whether

paper-and-pencil (✎) or
calculator or computer (🖳)

is the most appropriate technology to solve a problem. Here is some advice.

- Whether you use ✎ or 🖳, take care to copy the problem correctly.
- Do not be content with blindly following a paper-and-pencil procedure or mindlessly pushing buttons on a calculator to solve a problem. Always learn additional ways to do calculations so that you can use them to check your first way. *It is not a good idea to check a problem by merely repeating the same steps you used to solve the problem in the first place.* If you made an error the first

2

time, you are likely to make the same error when you check your work.

- Use the appropriate technology. Avoid using ✐ or 💻 on a problem you should be able to do in your head. If a problem can be solved quickly with a ✐ procedure, try not to use 💻. Do not necessarily use ✐ on a problem that is more appropriate solved with the aid of 💻.
- When using 💻, record what you did in some way so that you can go back and repeat the process if it was a good one, or change the process if it did not work out.

Getting Off to a Good Start

The questions that follow are designed to help you become familiar with *Advanced Algebra*.

We hope you join the hundreds of thousands of students who have enjoyed earlier editions of this book. We wish you much success.

Questions

COVERING THE IDEAS

1. Name four mathematical topics that *Advanced Algebra* includes. Indicate which of these topics are new to you. See margin.
2. What tools other than paper and pencil are needed for this course? See margin.
3. What is a CAS? A CAS is a computer algebra system that can be used to manipulate algebraic expressions and solve symbolic equations.
4. Identify two strategies that you might use to improve your reading comprehension. See margin.
5. What should you do if you cannot answer an assigned question? See margin.
6. Why is it not a good idea to check an answer to a problem by going through the same steps you used to solve the problem? Answers vary. Sample: If I made an error the first time, I am likely to make the same error again.

KNOWING YOUR TEXTBOOK

In 7–10, answer the questions by looking at the Table of Contents, the lessons and chapters of the textbook, or material at the end of the book.

7. Refer to the Table of Contents. What lesson would you read to learn about matrices for reflections? Lesson 4-6
8. Suppose you are working in Lesson 1-8.
   a. Where can you find the answers to the *Guided Example* in the lesson? See margin.
   b. On what page can you find answers to check your work on the Questions? page S17
   c. Answers to which Questions are given? odd-numbered Questions
9. In the *Vocabulary* sections at the end of each chapter, why are some terms marked with an asterisk(*)? See margin.
10. Look at a *Self-Test* at the end of a chapter. What should you do after taking the Self-Test? See margin.

Additional Answers

1. Answers vary. Sample: graphs, equations, matrices, and logarithms; Matrices and logarithms are new to me.
2. erasers, a ruler, graph paper, and technology, either calculator or computer
4. Answers vary. Sample: drawing graphs, diagrams, and tables when following a complicated example; working examples while following the steps in the text
5. Answers vary. Sample: read the lesson again; read the question again; look for examples; or go away from the problem and come back later

8a. on page S17 of the Selected Answers section in the Student Handbook at the back of the book

9. Terms marked with an asterisk (*) indicate that I should be able to give good definitions for those terms.
10. After taking the Self-Test, I should use the Selected Answers section in the back of the book to check my work. The chart keys the Self-Test questions to the objectives in the Chapter Review at the end of the chapter. I can locate those Chapter Review questions that correspond to questions I missed on the Self-Test and the lesson where the material is covered.

Chapter

1 Functions

Chapter Overview

		Local Standards	Pacing (in days)		
			Average	Advanced	Block
1-1	**The Language of Algebra** A Evaluate expressions and formulas, including correct units in answers.		1	0.75	0.5
1-2	**Relations and Functions** G Determine whether a given relation is a function.		1	0.75	0.5
1-3	**Function Notations** B Use mapping and *f*(*x*) notation for functions. J Evaluate and interpret values of functions in real-world situations.		1	0.75	0.5
	QUIZ 1		0.5	0.5	0.25
1-4	**Graphs of Functions** H Determine the domain and range of a function. J Evaluate and interpret values of functions in real-world situations. L Use a graphing utility to graph functions and generate tables for functions.		1	0.75	0.5
1-5	**Using Graphs and Tables of Functions** G Determine whether a given relation is a function. H Determine the domain and range of a function. L Use a graphing utility to graph functions and generate tables for functions.		1	0.75	0.5
1-6	**Solving Equations** C Solve and check linear equations. K Use linear equations to solve real-world problems.		1	0.75	0.5
	QUIZ 2		0.5	0.5	0.25
1-7	**Rewriting Formulas** D Solve formulas for their variables. F Use a CAS to solve equations or expand expressions. I Describe relationships between variables in a formula.		1	0.75	0.5
1-8	**Explicit Formulas for Sequences** E Find terms of sequences. L Use a graphing utility to graph functions and generate tables for functions.		1	0.75	0.5
		Self-Test	1	0.75	0.5
		Chapter Review	2	1	0.5
		Test	1	1	0.5
		TOTAL	13	9.75	6

Technology Resources

Teacher's Assessment Assistant, Ch. 1
Electronic Teacher's Edition, Ch. 1

Differentiated Options  Universal Access

	Accommodating the Learner	Vocabulary Development	Ongoing Assessment	Materials
1-1	pp. 8, 12	p. 9	group, p. 13	
1-2	pp. 15, 17	p. 18	oral, p. 19	
1-3	pp. 21, 23	p. 22	group, p. 25	CAS
1-4	pp. 29, 30	p. 28	group, p. 32	CAS or graphing calculator
1-5	pp. 35, 36		group, p. 39	CAS or graphing calculator
1-6	pp. 42, 43		group, p. 46	
1-7	pp. 48, 49	p. 50	group, p. 52	
1-8	pp. 55, 56	p. 54	group, p. 59	

Objectives

	Lessons	Self-Test Questions	Chapter Review Questions
Skills			
A Evaluate expressions and formulas, including correct units in answers.	1-1	12	1-4
B Use mapping and $f(x)$ notation for functions.	1-3	1, 2, 3, 6	5-10
C Solve and check linear equations.	1-6	9, 10, 11	11-18
D Solve formulas for their variables.	1-7	7, 8, 14	19-24
E Find terms of sequences.	1-8	19	25-28
F Use a CAS to solve equations or expand expressions.	1-7	25	29-31
Properties			
G Determine whether a given relation is a function.	1-2, 1-5	16, 17, 18	32-37
H Determine the domain and range of a function.	1-4, 1-5	4, 5, 13, 15, 23	38-46
I Describe relationships between variables in a formula.	1-7	28	47-49
Uses			
J Evaluate and interpret values of functions in real-world situations.	1-3, 1-4	22, 24	50-56
K Use linear equations to solve real-world problems.	1-6	27	57-60
Representations			
L Use a graphing utility to graph functions and generate tables for functions.	1-4, 1-5, 1-8	20, 21	61-66

Resource Masters Chapter 1

Resource Master 1, Graph Paper (page 2), can be used with Lessons 1-1, 1-4, 1-5, 1-7, and 1-8.

Resource Master 5 Lesson 1-1

Warm-Up

1. Refer to the Chapter Opener on pages 4 and 5. Work in small groups and write down what you think the value of gold might be today and give at least one reason for your prediction. Collect the predictions from other groups and graph them; then calculate the mean, median, and mode. Then go to the Internet or to a daily newspaper's financial section to see how close the predictions you collected are to the actual value.
2. Think of another object whose value changes dramatically over time. These objects are often called *collectibles*, and there exist catalogues that give the values of the more common collectibles. Have you seen such books?

Additional Examples

1. Maria collects stamps. She already has 860 stamps in her collection. She plans to buy 20 stamps each month. How many stamps will Maria have after m months?
2. Find the value of $2\sqrt{a^2 - c^2} + c + \sqrt{b^2 - a^2 + c^2}$ when $a = 5$, $b = 6$, and $c = 4$.
3. A kilowatt-hour is a kilowatt of power used for 1 hour. A 15-watt energy-saving spiral bulb gives the same amount of brightness as a regular 60-watt bulb. What does it cost to have a 15-watt bulb turned on for 33 hours at 9.53¢ per kilowatt-hour?

Resource Master for Lesson 1-1

Resource Master 6 Lesson 1-1

Algebraic Sentences

Symbol	Meaning
=	is equal to
<	is less than
>	is greater than
≤	is less than or equal to
≥	is greater than or equal to
≠	is not equal to
≈	is approximately equal to

Rules for Order of Operations

1. Perform operations within parentheses or other grouping symbols from the innermost group out.
2. Within grouping symbols, or if there are no grouping symbols:
   a. Take powers from left to right.
   b. Multiply and divide in order from left to right.
   c. Add and subtract in order from left to right.

Resource Master for Lesson 1-1

Resource Master 7 Lesson 1-2

Warm-Up

1. Identify the dependent and independent variables in $d = \frac{360}{n}$, which is the formula for the number of degrees in an exterior angle of a regular polygon of n sides.
2. Two angles with measures x and y are supplementary.
   a. What are the possible values of x?
   b. Write a formula for y in terms of x.

Additional Examples

1. Two angles in an isosceles triangle, as shown at the right, have the same measure x. The measure of the third angle is y. This relationship can be modeled by the equation $y = 180 - 2x$. Which of x or y is the dependent variable and which is the independent variable? Explain your answer.

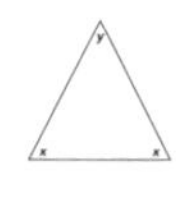
y
x
x

2. The average annual price P of crude oil per barrel in the year Y is given in the table at the right.
   a. Is Y a function of P? Why or why not?
   b. Is P a function of Y? Why or why not?

Year (Y)	Price (P)
1991	$20.20
1993	$16.75
1995	$16.75
1997	$18.64
1999	$16.56
2001	$23.00
2003	$27.69
2005	$50.04
2007	$64.20

Source: http://www.inflationdata.com/inflation/Inflation_Rate/Historical_Oil_Prices_Table.asp

Resource Master for Lesson 1-2

Resource Master 8 Lesson 1-2

Vocabulary Development: Relations and Functions

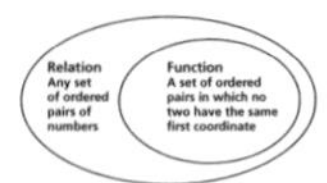
Relation
Any set of ordered pairs of numbers
Function
A set of ordered pairs in which no two have the same first coordinate

Question 13

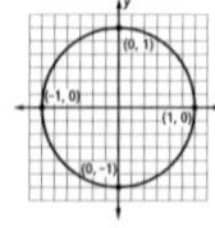
(0, 1)
(-1, 0)
(1, 0)
(0, -1)
y
x

Resource Master for Lesson 1-2

Resource Master 9 Lesson 1-3

Warm-Up

1. If $f(x) = 3x^4 - 2x^2$, find $f(1)$, $f(2)$, and $f(\sqrt{5})$.
2. If $f: x \to 3x^4 - 2x^2$, find $f(1)$, $f(2)$, and $f(\sqrt{5})$.
3. For the function f of Warm-Up Questions 1 and 2, find a value of x for which $f(x) < 0$.

Additional Examples

1. If $T(F) = \frac{5}{9}(F - 32)$, evaluate $T(86)$.
2. Let $f: x \to x + \frac{x^2}{20}$. Evaluate $f(10)$ and $f(s) + f(10)$.

Resource Master for Lesson 1-3

Resource Master 10 Lesson 1-3

Question 17

x	$h(x)$	$g(x)$	$h(x) - g(x)$
-4	16	0.06	15.94
-2			
-0.5			
0.5			
2.5			
3			
3.5			
4.5			
10	100		

Resource Master for Lesson 1-3

Resource Master 11 Lesson 1-4

Warm-Up

1. Explain why the sentence $y \leq 2x + 5$ does not describe a function mapping x onto y.

2. Consider the equation $A = s^2$.
   a. For *all* real values of s and A, is A a function of s? Explain why or why not.
   b. For *all* real values of s and A, is s a function of A? Explain why or why not.
   c. Now consider the formula $A = s^2$, where s is the length of the side of a square, and A is the area of the square. Is A a function of s? Is s a function of A? Explain why or why not.

Real Numbers

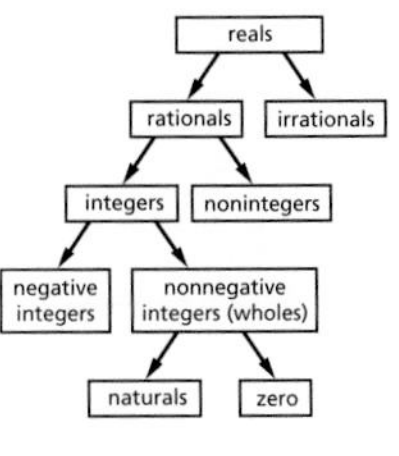

Resource Master for Lesson 1-4

Resource Master 12 Lesson 1-5

Warm-Up

Suppose the point (t, d) stands for the distance d in meters that a boat is from a pier t minutes from now. Graph the following situation. The boat is now at the pier. The boat moves away from the pier at a constant rate for 5 minutes until it is 300 meters from the pier. It drops anchor there and stays there for 10 minutes. Then it goes back to shore at a constant rate and gets back in 7 minutes.

Additional Example

1. The graph below gives the distances Maria traveled during a 7-hour trip. She drove some and then visited an historical museum. After visiting the museum, Maria drove some more and then stopped for dinner before returning home.

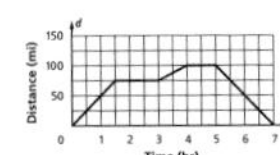

   a. Which variable is a function of the other variable? Express this relationship in $f(x)$ notation.
   b. State the domain and range of the function.
   c. Estimate Maria's distance from home after 3.5 hours and write your answer using $f(x)$ notation.
   d. Estimate how much time it took Maria to first be 100 miles from home.
   e. What is the significance of the left horizontal line segment? Estimate its endpoints.

Resource Master for Lesson 1-5

Resource Master 13 Lesson 1-5

Additional Example

2. Robert Wadlow is the tallest person in medical history whose height has been substantiated. At birth, he was of normal height. The table below gives his height h at various ages a, where $h = f(a)$.

Age (yr)	8	10	16	18	22
Height (m)	1.9	2.0	2.4	2.5	2.7

Sources: http://www.altonweb.com; http://www.guinnessworldrecords.com/

   a. What is the domain of the function defined by this table?
   b. What is the range of this function?
   c. Find $f(16)$. What does this represent?
   d. For what value of a does $f(a) = 2.7$?

Questions 1–3

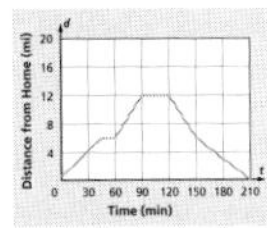

Question 17

r	-3	-2	-1	0	1	2	3
s							

Resource Master for Lesson 1-5

Resource Master 14 Lesson 1-6

Warm-Up

1. A concert group plans to visit 4 cities on a tour. One third of the total distance the group travels is from its home city to the first city. One-fifth of the total distance is from the first city to the second. It is 273 miles from the second city to the third city and 441 miles back home. Find the total distance traveled.

2. Suppose $f(n) = 8n - (4 - 2n)$. For what value of n is $f(n) = 3356$?

Additional Examples

1. In the board game Monopoly®, you purchase four houses and a hotel on Illinois Avenue for a one time cost of \$750. You will earn rent of \$1100 each time another player lands on the property. If i players land on Illinois Avenue, then your profit is $f(i) = 1100i - 750$.
   a. What is your profit after 1 player lands on Illinois Avenue?
   b. How many players must land on Illinois Avenue so that your profit is at least \$15,000?

2. Suppose you just received a \$50,000 inheritance. At first, you decide to invest some of the money in a certificate of deposit account that earns 6% and the rest in a savings account that earns 4%. If x dollars are invested at 6%, then $E(x) = 0.06x + 0.04(50{,}000 - x)$ gives the interest earned in 1 year. If you want to earn \$2500 in the first year, how much money should be placed in each account?

Resource Master for Lesson 1-6

Resource Master 15 Lesson 1-6

Additional Examples

3. Suppose during a 2007–2008 regular season NBA game involving the Boston Celtics, Kevin Garnett scored $\frac{1}{3}$ of Boston's points in the game, and Ray Allen scored $\frac{1}{4}$ of the points. The rest of the players scored 60 points. Write an equation to model the situation; then determine how many points Boston scored in this game.

4. Suppose $h(y) = 13y - (26 - 3y)$. For what value of y is $h(y) = 100$?
   Solution $100 = 13y - (26 - 3y)$
   Write the subtraction in the parentheses as a sum:
   $100 = 13y - (26 + \_\_)$
   Apply Opposite of a Sum Theorem: $100 = 13y - \_\_ + \_\_$
   Add like terms: $100 = \_\_ - \_\_$
   Add 26 to each side: $\_\_ = \_\_$
   Divide each side by 16: $\_\_ = y$

Resource Master for Lesson 1-6

Resource Master 16 Lesson 1-7

Warm-Up

1. a. Solve the formula $A = \ell w$ for w.
   b. Solve the formula $A = \ell w$ for ℓ.
   c. Which formula gives w in terms of A and ℓ?

2. A line has the equation $5x - 3y = 10$. Find an equation for this line as a formula for y in terms of x.

Additional Examples

1. The period (P) of a pendulum is the time in seconds that it takes a pendulum to make one complete swing back and forth and is calculated by using the formula $P = 2\pi\sqrt{\frac{\ell}{g}}$, where ℓ = length of the pendulum in meters and g = acceleration due to gravity (9.8 meters per second squared).
   a. Solve the formula $P = 2\pi\sqrt{\frac{\ell}{g}}$, for ℓ.
   b. What is the approximate length of a pendulum whose period is 1 minute?

2. Because the density of air consumed by scuba divers increases as they dive deeper, they consume more air the deeper they dive. The formula $t = \frac{30s}{d + 30}$ is used by some scuba divers to estimate the number of minutes (t) of air they will have at a depth (d) if they consume a tank of air at the surface surface in s minutes. Solve the formula for d in terms of t and s.

3. A certain ancient pyramid has a volume of x cubic meters. Each side of its base is 231 meters.
   a. Solve $V = \frac{1}{3}Bh$ for h.
   b. Assume that the pyramid has a volume of 2,614,689 cubic meters. What is its height?

Resource Master for Lesson 1-7

Resource Master 17 Lesson 1-8

Warm-Up

Consider the following sentence: "Was it a cat I saw?" Read the sentence several times and determine if there is anything special about the sentence.

Additional Examples

1. Consider the formula $t_n = 3^n - 4$.
   a. Assuming $n \geq 1$, what are the first four numbers in the sequence defined by this formula?
   b. Evaluate t_{10} and explain what it means.

2. Alfonso has invested \$750 for 1 year at 8% annual interest.
   a. If the interest is compounded semiannually, how much will he have at the end of 1 year? .
   b. How much money will Alfonso have at the end of the second and third years (assuming no withdrawals)?
   c. How much money will he have after 10 years (assuming no withdrawals)?

Resource Master for Lesson 1-8

Resource Master 18 Lesson 1-8

Activity, Step 1

Term Number	Number of Dots
1	
2	
3	
4	
5	

Activity, Step 2

Term Number	Number of Dots
6	
7	
8	
9	

Extension

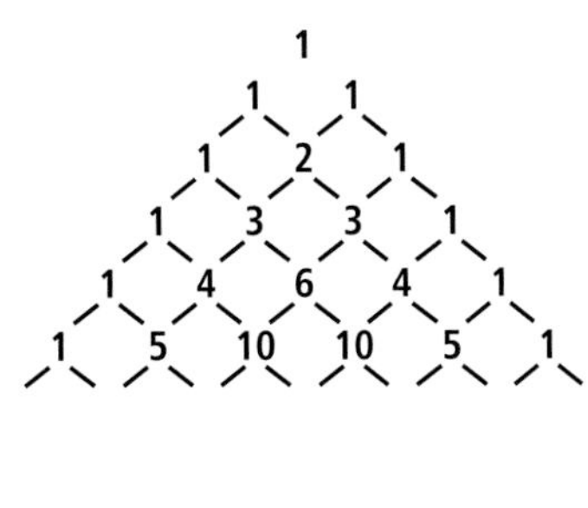

Resource Master for Lesson 1-8

Chapter 1

Pacing

Each lesson in this chapter is designed to be covered in 1 day. At the end of the chapter, you should plan to spend 1 day to review the Self-Test, 1 to 2 days for the Chapter Review, and 1 day for a test. You may wish to spend a day on projects and possibly a day is needed for quizzes. This chapter should therefore take 12 to 14 days. We strongly advise you not to spend more than 15 days on this chapter.

Overview

Before beginning this chapter, make certain that your students have read "To you, the student" so they know what materials they are expected to have.

It is assumed that students have access to Computer Algebra System (CAS) technology, which includes graphing calculators, dynamic geometry systems (DGSs), and a computational ability that far exceeds standard scientific calculators. Students will need CAS capabilities for the Activity in Lesson 1-3, and CAS technology is used throughout the remainder of the book.

Students will often not be told when to use a calculator because the appropriate occasions for paper-and-pencil work vary among students, depending on the problem. They should, however, be instructed to use calculators *when appropriate*. We expect that they will need to use calculators in class, for homework, with projects, and on tests. We do not generally give instructions to use technology, even when a particular technology might be needed, because we wish students to view these tools as naturally as they view paper and pencil. Mental Math questions do not require paper and pencil or a calculator. Students are expected to read this book. Students who have studied from previous UCSMP texts should be accustomed to reading mathematics. Others may not be and will

Chapter 1 Functions

Contents

Gold holds a special significance in almost all cultures around the world. It has long symbolized wealth and power, and it has always held great economic value. Unlike most other metals, gold is often found alone in the form of nuggets in a wide range of geographic areas, so it was likely the first metal used by early human beings. Since its discovery, gold has seen a wide range of uses, from ornamentation, to currency (the first gold coins were created in Turkey around 700 BCE), to modern scientific, technological, and medical applications.

Gold was once used to define the value of currency. In 1879, the United States dollar was set so that $20.67 was equal to one troy ounce of gold. It remained at this exact value until 1933, when President Roosevelt devalued the dollar as part of an attempt to

Chapter 1 Overview

Chapter 1 reviews concepts of elementary algebra within the context of functions. Formulas and sequences are used to introduce language and important notation.

Functions are a fundamental concept that describe relationships among variables. Students will use functions throughout this book and in virtually every mathematics course they take after *Advanced Algebra*. Students are already familiar with many functions, including linear functions they studied in earlier algebra work and transformations they studied in geometry. But they are likely not to have had much work with $f(x)$ notation, mapping notation, and the language of functions.

Lesson 1-1 reviews the language of expressions and sentences in algebra. Lessons 1-2 and 1-3 introduce the terminology and notation associated with all functions. Lessons 1-4 and 1-5 relate this language to graphs of functions and to tables of function values. Lessons 1-6 and 1-7 deal with solving equations.

combat the Great Depression. Since then, the price of gold has varied.

In 1976, one troy ounce of gold was worth \$145.10. By 1980, the price had more than quadrupled, to \$641.20. By 1985, it had dropped to about half of its 1980 value. The price of gold at the end of each year from 1960 to 2005 is displayed in the graph below.

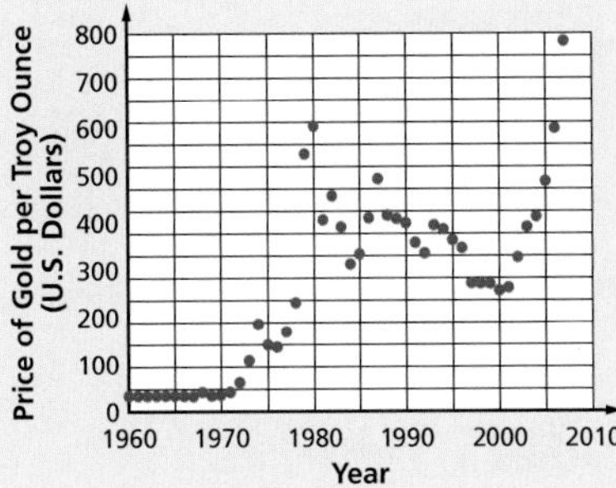

Each point on the graph represents a pair of numbers: the year and the closing price of gold in that year. From this graph it is difficult to predict the future value of gold. However, when a graph has a pattern, you can often describe its values with a formula, and you may be able to estimate future values with some confidence.

This graph represents a *function*. Functions exist whenever the value of one or more variables determines the value of another variable. The study of functions is basic to the study of all mathematics. In this chapter, you will see how to describe functions with words, tables, graphs, and symbols in order to solve a wide variety of problems.

Lesson 1-8 introduces a special type of function, the sequence, with explicit formulas for the nth term.

The strong geometric flavor in Chapter 1, with graphs and visual patterns, continues throughout the book, which serves three purposes: (1) Many students profit greatly from a visual representation of concepts they are learning. (2) Blending geometry with algebra shows the interrelationships between these two branches of mathematics. (3) Students' knowledge of geometry is reviewed and enhanced.

The end-of-chapter material, optional in many books, is an integral part of this book and should not be skipped.

need to adjust to this expectation. Specific suggestions are given throughout this chapter to assist you in teaching students to read mathematics.

Using Pages 4–5

These pages describe a function in two ways: in prose and with a graph.

You might mention that there are two other common ways to describe functions: with an equation or a table. This function, because it is not particularly predictable, is not described with an equation. Students will see descriptions of functions with equations beginning in Lesson 1-2.

Draw attention to the list of lesson titles so that students have an idea of what they will be studying in Chapter 1. Point out the two themes: a review of solving equations and new material on functions.

Some students may wonder about the effects of inflation on the price of gold. The prices given here do not consider the effect of inflation. Taking inflation into account, the price of over \$450 for an ounce of gold in 1979 is higher than the price of over \$500 in 2005. Almanacs and the Internet contain tables that can be used to modify the prices here to take inflation into account. See, for example, http://www.goldprice.org/.

Chapter 1 Projects

At the end of each chapter, you will find projects related to the chapter. At this time you might want to have students look over the projects on pages 60 and 61. You might want to have students tentatively select a project on which to work. Then, as students read and progress through the chapter, they can finalize their project choices.

Sometimes students might work alone. At other times, you might let them collaborate with classmates for a presentation and discussion. We recommend that you allow for diversity and encourage students to use their imaginations when presenting their projects. As students work on projects throughout the year, they should see many uses of mathematics in the real world.

Lesson 1-1

GOAL

Immerse students into algebra through the translation and evaluation of algebraic expressions.

SPUR Objectives

The SPUR Objectives for all of Chapter 1 are found in the Chapter Review on pages 66–69.

A Evaluate expressions and formulas, including correct units in answers.

Materials/Resources

- Lesson Masters 1-1A and 1-1B
- Resource Masters 1, 5, and 6

HOMEWORK

Suggestions for Assignment

- Questions 1–27
- Questions 28 and 29 (extra credit)
- Reading Lesson 1-2
- Covering the Ideas 1-2

Local Standards

1 Warm-Up

1. Refer students to the Chapter Opener on pages 4 and 5. Have students work in small groups and ask each group to list what the value of gold might be today and give at least one reason for their prediction. Collect and graph the predictions; then have students calculate the mean, median, and mode. (Note: If you are teaching more than one section of UCSMP *Advanced Algebra,* compare the results among your classes.) Tell students to find gold prices on the Internet or in a daily newspaper's financial section and determine how close their predictions are to the actual value.

Lesson 1-1 The Language of Algebra

Vocabulary

variable
algebraic expression
expression
algebraic sentence
evaluating an expression
order of operations
vinculum
equation
formula

▸ BIG IDEA Algebra is a language with expressions and sentences. There are precise rules for evaluating algebraic expressions so that the meaning and values of expressions are unambiguous.

The language of algebra uses numbers and variables. It lets you describe patterns and relationships between quantities. A **variable** is a symbol that can be replaced by any one of a set of numbers or other objects. When variables stand for numbers, and numbers and variables are combined using the operations of arithmetic, the result is called an **algebraic expression**, or simply an **expression**. For instance, the expression $\frac{s^2\sqrt{3}}{4}$ for the area of an equilateral triangle with side length s uses the variable s and the number $\frac{\sqrt{3}}{4}$. The expression for the volume of a cone with radius r and height h is $\frac{1}{3}\pi r^2 h$. That expression involves the variables r and h and the numbers π and $\frac{1}{3}$. Both expressions involve the operations of multiplication and powering.

Mental Math

a. What is the area of a square with perimeter 28 inches? 49 in^2

b. What is the area of a rectangle with length 6 cm and perimeter 20 cm? 24 cm^2

c. What is the width of a rectangle with length 12 ft and area 108 ft^2? 9 ft

d. What is the length of a rectangle with width 25 mm and perimeter 130 mm? 40 mm

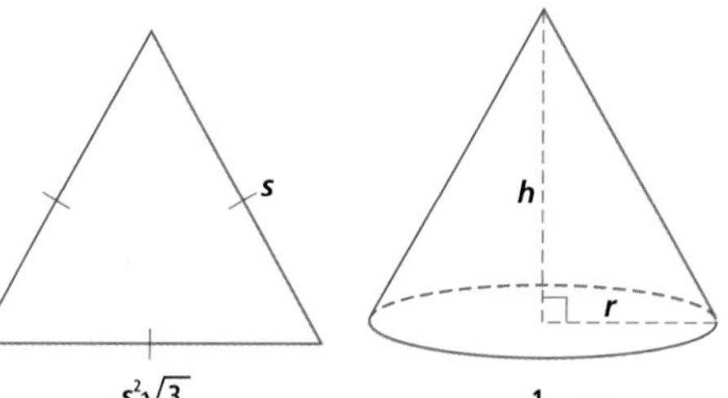

$A = \frac{s^2\sqrt{3}}{4}$ $V = \frac{1}{3}\pi r^2 h$

An **algebraic sentence** consists of expressions related with a verb in symbolic form. Common verbs are shown in the table at the right:

Examples of algebraic sentences are $A = \pi r^2$, $A \approx 3.14 \cdot r^2$, $a + b = b + a$, and $3x + 9 < 22$.

Symbol	Meaning
$=$	is equal to
$<$	is less than
$>$	is greater than
$\leq$	is less than or equal to
$\geq$	is greater than or equal to
$\neq$	is not equal to
$\approx$	is approximately equal to

Background

There are three basic ways to translate a statement from English into algebra: word-for-word direct translation, patterning, and using models. We assume students are familiar with word-for-word translation from previous courses. Example 1 illustrates patterning. Questions 19–24 in this lesson review models for operations that students in UCSMP *Pre-Transition Mathematics, Transition Mathematics,* and *Algebra* learned previously.

The evaluation of expressions and formulas is considered as review at this point, but the inclusion of the unit analysis in Example 3 may be new for students who have not studied from previous UCSMP courses.

Writing Expressions and Sentences

From your earlier study of algebra, you have gained experience writing expressions and sentences, modeling real situations, and evaluating expressions or sentences. In Example 1 below, part of the solution is written using this typestyle. This style is used to indicate what you might write on your homework paper as the solution to the problem.

Example 1

Joseph has a collection of 1,380 comic books and buys 17 new titles every month. If Joseph continues collecting comic books in this way, how many comic books will he have after *m* months?

The first American comic book was *The Adventures of Obadiah Oldbuck*, by Rudolphe Töpffer, published in 1842.

Solution Make a table. Beginning with 1,380 comic books, in each month there will be an increase to Joseph's collection of 17 issues.

Months from Now	Number of Comics
1	$1380 + 1 \cdot 17$
2	$1380 + 2 \cdot 17$
3	$1380 + 3 \cdot 17$
4	$1380 + 4 \cdot 17$

Notice in this table that the arithmetic in the right column is not carried out. This makes the pattern easier to see. The number in the left column, which gives the number of months, is always in a particular place in the expression in the right column. You should see the following pattern.

$m \qquad 1380 + m \cdot 17$

Because of the Commutative Property of Multiplication, $m \cdot 17 = 17m$. So, after m months, Joseph will have $1380 + 17m$ comic books.

Check Pick a value for *m* not in the table and substitute it in $1380 + 17m$. We pick $m = 5$, indicating 5 months from now, and get $1380 + 17m = 1380 + 17 \cdot 5 = 1{,}465$ comic books. Then calculate the number of comics 5 months from now using the table. The table shows that in 4 months, Joseph would have $1380 + 4 \cdot 17 = 1{,}448$ comics. Add 17 for the fifth month to get $1448 + 17 = 1{,}465$. It checks.

You could also describe the situation in Example 1 with the sentence $C = 1380 + 17m$, where C is the number of comic books after m months.

2. Now ask students to think of another object whose value changes dramatically over time. Answers vary. Sample: stamps, rare coins, art objects, collector's cards
These objects are often called *collectibles,* and various catalogues give the values of the more common collectibles. Ask your students if they have seen such books.

2 Teaching

Reading mathematics will be a new expectation for students not familiar with UCSMP texts, and this lesson has been designed to get them off to a successful start in mathematical reading. To read well, a student must read carefully, watching for important terms and symbols. We strongly recommend *not* discussing this lesson until students have had an opportunity to read it and try the questions on their own. If there is time in class, give students time to read.

Writing expressions and sentences Emphasize that algebraic sentences include both inequalities and equations. The statement "x is a natural number" is also a sentence (with verb "is"), but it is not an algebraic sentence because it does not have algebraic expressions on each side of the verb. The statement "x equals five" *is* an algebraic sentence even though it is not written with algebraic symbolism.

Example 1 Students who have studied from previous UCSMP texts have seen the type of patterning found in Example 1 many times. Point out to students that the approach to translation found here (making a table, looking for patterns, and drawing a conclusion) is an ideal problem-solving technique that often works when other methods fail. Furthermore, this technique works even when the expression is quite complicated.

Additional Example

Example 1 Maria collects stamps. She already has 860 stamps in her collection. She plans to buy 20 stamps each month. How many stamps will Maria have after *m* months?
$860 + 20m$

Notes on the Lesson

Example 2 A guided example such as Example 2 guides students through solving a problem. The expression being evaluated here is the one found in the Quadratic Formula and provides answers to two questions: (1) Have all your students studied the Quadratic Formula? (2) Can your students do evaluations of this type?

Additional Example

Example 2 Find the value of $2\sqrt{a^2 - c^2} + c + \sqrt{b^2 - a^2 + c^2}$ when $a = 5$, $b = 6$, and $c = 4$.

Solution

Substitute:

$2\sqrt{a^2 - c^2} + c + \sqrt{b^2 - a^2 + c^2} =$

$2\sqrt{\underline{\ ?\ }^2 - \underline{\ ?\ }^2} + \underline{\ ?\ } + \sqrt{\underline{\ ?\ }^2 - \underline{\ ?\ }^2 + \underline{\ ?\ }^2}$

5; 4; 4; 6; 5; 4

Compute the powers:

$2\sqrt{\underline{\ ?\ } - \underline{\ ?\ }} + 4 + \sqrt{\underline{\ ?\ } - \underline{\ ?\ } + \underline{\ ?\ }}$

25; 16; 36; 25; 16

Subtract and add as indicated:

$2\sqrt{\underline{\ ?\ }} + 4 + \sqrt{\underline{\ ?\ }}$ 9; 27

Compute the square roots:

$2 \cdot \underline{\ ?\ } + 4 + 3\sqrt{\underline{\ ?\ }}$ 3; 3

Simplify: $\underline{\ ?\ } + 4 + \underline{\ ?\ } = \underline{\ \ ?\ \ }$

6; $3\sqrt{3}$; $10 + 3\sqrt{3}$

STOP See Quiz Yourself 1 at the right.

Quiz Yourself (QY) questions are designed to help you follow the reading. You should try to answer each Quiz Yourself question before reading on. The answer to the Quiz Yourself is found at the end of the lesson.

QUIZ YOURSELF 1

In the situation of Example 1, how many comic books would Joseph have after 6 years?

Evaluating Expressions and Formulas

Substituting numbers for the variables in an expression and calculating a result is called **evaluating the expression**. In the expression $1380 + 17m$ in Example 1, we multiplied the value of m by 17 and then added 1380. We were using the standard rules for **order of operations** to evaluate the expression.

Rules for Order of Operations

1. Perform operations within parentheses or other grouping symbols from the innermost group out.
2. Within grouping symbols, or if there are no grouping symbols:
   a. Take powers from left to right.
   b. Multiply and divide in order from left to right.
   c. Add and subtract in order from left to right.

GUIDED

Example 2

A Guided Example is an example in which some, but not all of the work is shown. You should try to complete the example before reading on. Answers to Guided Examples are in the Selected Answers section at the back of this book.

Find the value of $\frac{-b - \sqrt{b^2 - 4ac}}{2a}$ when $a = 3$, $b = -1$, and $c = -4$.

Solution

Step 1 Substitute: $\frac{-b - \sqrt{b^2 - 4ac}}{2a} = \frac{? - \sqrt{?^2 - 4 \cdot ? \cdot ?}}{2 \cdot ?}$ 1; -1; 3; -4; 3

Step 2 In both the fraction and the radical symbol ($\sqrt{\ }$), the bar (—) is a grouping symbol. (The bar is called a **vinculum**.) The square root vinculum is inside the fraction vinculum, so work inside the square root first.

Compute the power and then do the multiplications followed by the subtraction. (Watch the sign!)

$= \frac{? - \sqrt{?}}{2 \cdot ?}$ 1; 49; 3

Accommodating the Learner

When applying the rules for the order of operations, students sometimes forget that fraction bars and square-root symbols act as grouping symbols. Give students the expressions shown at the right. Have them identify which part of each expression should be evaluated first. Then have them evaluate each expression.

1. $8 + \frac{3}{(5 - 3)}$ 5 – 3; 9.5
2. $16 - 7\sqrt{25 - 9}$ 25 – 9; -12
3. $5 - \frac{(3 + 5)}{8}$ 3 + 5; 4
4. $\frac{0}{7} + \sqrt{4}$ $\frac{0}{7}$; 2

Step 3 Now compute the square root and subtract in the fraction's numerator. Then multiply in the fraction's denominator.

$= \frac{?}{?}$ -6; 6

Step 4 You may wish to rewrite the fraction in lowest terms.

$=$ _?_ -1

 **See Quiz Yourself 2 at the right.**

▸ QUIZ YOURSELF 2

Evaluate $88 - 16 \div 2 \cdot 3^{6-4}$.

An **equation** is a sentence stating that two expressions are equal. A **formula** is an equation stating that a single variable is equal to an expression with one or more different variables on the other side. The single variable on one side of a formula is said to be written *in terms of* the other variables. Below are some examples.

$x = \frac{b \pm \sqrt{b^2 - 4ac}}{2a}$	both an equation and the Quadratic Formula
$A = \pi r^2$	both an equation and a formula
$y = 3x + 4$	both an equation and a formula
$a + b = b + a$	an equation that is not a formula
$x = 15$	an equation that is not a formula

Formulas are useful because they express important ideas with very few symbols and can be easily applied to many situations.

Example 3 shows how to evaluate an expression with more than one variable taken from a real situation. It also illustrates how to work with units in evaluating expressions.

GUIDED

Example 3

A kilowatt-hour is one kilowatt of power used for one hour.

a. What does it cost to have a 60-watt bulb turned on for 33 hours at a cost of 9.53¢ per kilowatt-hour?

b. Give a formula for the cost in terms of the three numbers in the problem.

Solution

a. Cost = 60 watts • _?_ hours • _?_ $\frac{\text{cents}}{\text{kilowatt-hour}}$ 33; 9.53

You need to change 60 watts to kilowatts. Since 1 kilowatt = 1000 watts, $1 = \frac{1 \text{ kilowatt}}{1000 \text{ watts}}$. This fraction is a *conversion factor.*

Thus, 60 watts = 60 watts • $\frac{1 \text{ kilowatt}}{1000 \text{ watts}}$ = _?_ kilowatts. $\frac{6}{100}$, or 0.06

Cost = _?_ kilowatts • _?_ hours • _?_ $\frac{\text{cents}}{\text{kilowatt-hour}}$ 0.06; 33; 9.53

(continued on next page)

Notes on the Lesson

Example 3 Most chemistry and physics teachers will be very appreciative if you take some time to discuss unit analyses like the one found here.

Additional Example

Example 3 A kilowatt-hour is a kilowatt of power used for 1 hour. A 15-watt energy-saving spiral bulb produces the same amount of brightness as a regular 60-watt bulb. What does it cost to have a 15-watt bulb turned on for 33 hours at 9.53¢ per kilowatt-hour?

Solution

Cost = 15 watts · _?_ hours · _?_ $\frac{\text{cents}}{\text{kilowatt-hour}}$ 33; 9.53

Change 15 watts to kilowatts: 1 kilowatt = 1,000 watts. Thus, 15 watts · $\frac{1 \text{ kilowatt}}{1000 \text{ watts}}$ = _?_ kilowatt. 0.015

Cost = _?_ kilowatt · _?_ hours · _?_ $\frac{\text{cents}}{\text{kilowatt-hour}}$ = _?_ cents 0.015; 33; 9.53; 4.72

Cost = _?_ 4.72 cents

ENGLISH LEARNERS

Vocabulary Development

Write the following terms on the board: *variable, expression, algebraic expression, algebraic sentence, equation, formula,* and *vinculum.* To the right of the terms, write the following: $8(3 + 5)$, $\frac{5n}{2}$, $8x + 12 = 17$, $a - 4 < 12$, and $d = \frac{1}{2}gt^2$.

Review with students the various terms and have volunteers identify each instance of the terms in the second list you have written. Supply values for the variables and then review the rules for the *order of operations.* Have students *evaluate* the expressions and the formula and solve the equations and inequality.

3 Assignment

Recommended Assignment

- Questions 1–27
- Questions 28 and 29 (extra credit)
- Reading Lesson 1-2
- Covering the Ideas 1-2

Notes on the Questions

Remind students that selected answers to odd-numbered questions are provided at the back of the book.

Question 4 The purpose of this question is to emphasize that π is a number, not a variable.

Questions 5 and 6 This is the first of many questions in the text asking students to write their own examples. These tasks help students to understand what is given and what is to be found and give them sensitivity to the type of information that is required in a problem. See also Question 24.

1-1A Lesson Master

Questions on SPUR Objectives
See Student Edition pages 66–69 for objectives.

VOCABULARY

1. Identify all of the variables in each expression or sentence.
   a. $V = \frac{4}{3}\pi r^3$ V, r
   b. $d = \frac{1}{2}a \cdot t^2 + v \cdot t$ d, a, v, t

In 2 and 3, determine whether each sentence is a. an equation and b. a formula. Write *yes* or *no*.

2. $F = m \cdot a$ a. yes b. yes
3. $2x - 7y \geq 8$ a. no b. no

SKILLS Objective A

4. Evaluate each expression when $a = 3$, $b = -7$, and $c = 2$.
   a. $a + 2bc =$ −25
   b. $(a + b)(c - 4) =$ 8
   c. $ab^{c+1} =$ −1029
   d. $\frac{(\frac{1}{3}ab)^c}{\sqrt{a-c}} =$ 49
5. Evaluate each expression for $x = 1.2$, $y = -\frac{3}{4}$, and $z = \sqrt{2}$. Round to the nearest thousandth.
   a. $x^2 + y^2 + z^2 =$ 4.003
   b. $(x + y + z)^2 =$ 3.475
   c. $z^2 + x \div y =$ 0.4
   d. $\frac{z^2 + x}{y} =$ −4.267
6. Use $V = \frac{1}{3}\pi r^2 h$ to find the volume of an ice cream cone with radius 2 cm and height 9 cm. Round to the nearest whole number and include units. 38 cm³
7. The acceleration g due to gravity at a particular location is given by $g = \frac{2d}{t^2}$, where d is the distance an object falls in t seconds. On the moon, an astronaut drops a rock. It falls 2 meters in 1.6 seconds. Find the value of g rounded to the nearest tenth. Include units. $g = 1.6 \frac{m}{sec^2}$
8. A compact fluorescent bulb uses 13 watts to produce the same light as a 60-watt incandescent bulb. At 11.3¢ per kilowatt-hour, how much money will the compact fluorescent save over the 5000-hour life of the bulb? $26.56

Notice that the units are multiplied and divided as if they were numbers.

$= \underline{\ ?\ } \frac{\text{kilowatts} \cdot \text{hours} \cdot \text{cents}}{\text{kilowatt} - \text{hour}} = \underline{\ ?\ }$ cents 18.87; 18.87

b. Let p = the number of watts in the bulb. Let t = the number of hours. Let u = the (unit) cost in cents per kilowatt-hour. Then Cost = ? . $\frac{ptu}{1000}$

Questions

COVERING THE IDEAS

These questions cover the content of the lesson. If you cannot answer a Covering the Ideas question, you should go back to the reading for help in obtaining an answer.

1. Refer to page 5. The price of shares of stock in gold-mining companies tends to go up as the price of gold goes up. In what year between 1975 and 2000 would it have been best to put your money in gold stocks for five years? 1975
2. In your own words, describe the difference between an equation and a formula.
3. In your own words, describe the difference between an expression and an equation.
4. a. Name all the variables in $\pi\left(\frac{d}{2}\right)^2$. *d*
   b. Classify $\pi\left(\frac{d}{2}\right)^2$ as an equation, formula, expression, or sentence. Explain your answer.
5. Give an example of an algebraic expression not found in the reading.
6. Give an example of an algebraic sentence not found in the reading.
7. Consider the sentence $c^2 = a^2 + b^2$.
   a. Is this sentence an equation? Why or why not?
   b. Is this sentence a formula? Why or why not?
8. Evaluate $\frac{-b + \sqrt{b^2 - 4ac}}{2}$ when $a = -5$, $b = 30$, and $c = -25$. 1
9. Paula has collected 6 years of back issues of the magazine *Nature Today and Tomorrow. Nature Today and Tomorrow* prints 51 issues per year. If Paula reads two issues per day, how many issues will Paula have left to read after m months? Consider that the average month has 30 days. $306 - 60m$

2. Answers vary. Sample: Equations and formulas are both algebraic sentences with equal signs. A formula has a single variable on one side, but an equation can have more than one variable on each side, or no variable at all.

3. Answers vary. Sample: An equation must include an equal sign, but an algebraic expression does not include a verb.

4b. Expression; it does not include a verb in symbolic form, so it cannot be an equation, formula, or sentence.

5. Answers vary. Sample: e^{rt}

6. Answers vary. Sample: $I = p \cdot e^{rt}$

7a. Yes; it is an algebraic sentence that includes an equal sign.

7b. Answers vary. Sample: Yes; it can be considered a formula solved for c^2.

10. a. Evaluate $12 \div 3 \cdot 5^{(4-2)} + 76$. 176
    b. Indicate the order in which you applied the five operations in Part a.

10b. First do the subtraction inside the parentheses, then take the power, then divide, then multiply, and then add.

11. Refer to Example 3. Find the cost of operation of a central air conditioner that uses 3.5 kilowatts and runs for 12 hours a day for one week at a cost of 9.53¢ per kilowatt-hour. $28.02

APPLYING THE MATHEMATICS

These questions extend the content of the lesson. You should study the examples and explanations if you cannot answer the question. For some questions, you can check your answers with the ones in the Selected Answers section at the back of this book.

12. a. The expression $\frac{6^2 - 7}{5}$ is not equivalent to the expression $6 \cdot 6 - 7 \div 5 \cdot 5$. Why not? Use the order of operations to justify your answer.
    b. Insert parentheses into the second expression to make it equivalent to the first expression. $(6 \cdot 6 - 7) \div (5 \cdot 5)$

12a. According to the Order of Operations, the value of the first expression is $\frac{29}{25}$ because the fraction bar acts as a grouping symbol. The value of the second expression is 29.

13. a. If a person owns C comic books and buys 31 new comics every month, how many comic books will this person have after t years?
    b. If a person owns C comic books and buys b new comics every month, how many comic books will this person have after t years?

13a. $C + 372t$

13b. $C + 12bt$

14. Yuma used 1,040 ft of fence to enclose the rectangular pasture shown below. One side borders a river where there is already a thick hedge. That side needed no fencing.

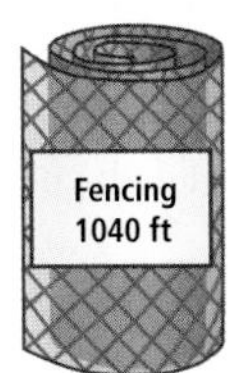

    a. Let x be the width of the pasture as labeled. Write an expression for L, the length of the pasture, in terms of x. $1040 - 2x$
    b. Write an expression for the area of the pasture in terms of L and x. xL
    c. Write an expression for the area of the pasture in terms of x only. $x(1040 - 2x)$
    d. Suppose Yuma wants the pasture to enclose at least 60,000 square feet. Write a sentence relating your answer in Part c to the area the fence must enclose. $x(1040 - 2x) \geq 60{,}000$

Notes on the Questions

Questions 19–23 We teach modeling in UCSMP texts. Modeling requires the ability to find mathematics that describes the real situation. A model for an operation is a general pattern that includes many of the uses of that operation. Students who have studied from UCSMP *Pre-Transition Mathematics, Transition Mathematics,* and *Algebra* will be familiar with the following models:

- *Addition:* put-together, slide
- *Subtraction:* take-away, comparison, slide
- *Multiplication:* area, size change, rate factor, repeated addition
- *Division:* rate, ratio comparison
- *Powering:* growth, repeated multiplication

In this course, students will also see models for functions. Encourage students who are having difficulty with these questions to substitute numerical values for the variables. For example, after substitution, Question 19 might read as follows: "You download 20 files in 40 minutes. What is your rate of download?" Then the answer is $\frac{1}{2}$ file per minute, or 2 minutes per file, and the operation is division.

In 15–17, evaluate each expression to the nearest tenth when $x = 7.2$, $y = \sqrt{3}$, and $z = -2$.

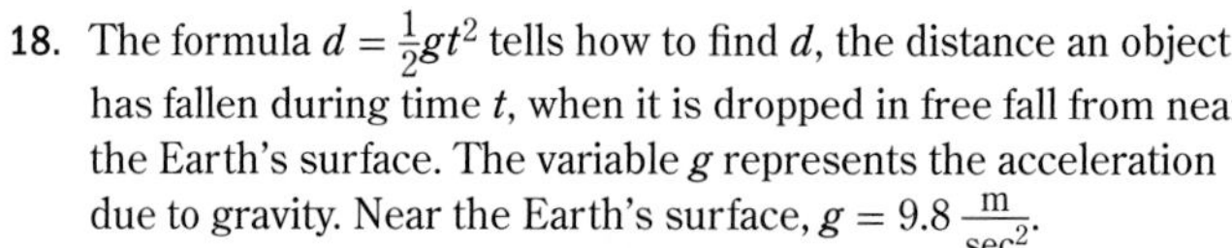

15. $\frac{10x}{y^4 - z^3}$ 4.2 16. $\frac{x}{y^2} + z$ 0.4 17. $y - x^2 - z$ -48.1

In May 2008, NASA sent Phoenix to Mars, looking for evidence of life.

18. The formula $d = \frac{1}{2}gt^2$ tells how to find d, the distance an object has fallen during time t, when it is dropped in free fall from near the Earth's surface. The variable g represents the acceleration due to gravity. Near the Earth's surface, $g = 9.8 \frac{\text{m}}{\text{sec}^2}$.
    a. About how far will a rock fall in 5 seconds if it is dropped close to the Earth's surface? 122.5 m
    b. About how far will a rock fall in 5 seconds if it is dropped near the surface of the moon, where $g = 1.6 \frac{\text{m}}{\text{sec}^2}$? 20 m
    c. Looking at the results of Parts a and b, notice that the smaller g-value on the moon resulted in the rock falling a shorter distance. What conjecture might you make about the g-value on Mars in relation to Earth, if a rock dropped close to the surface of Mars fell 46.25 m in 5 seconds?

18c. Mars's g-value is smaller than Earth's.

REVIEW

Every lesson contains review questions to practice ideas you have studied earlier.

In 19–23, tell which expression, (a) $x + y$, (b) $x - y$, (c) $y - x$, (d) xy, (e) $\frac{x}{y}$, or (f) $\frac{y}{x}$, correctly answers the given question. (Previous Course)

19. You download x files in y minutes. What is your rate of download in files per minute? (e)
20. Toy cars are made x times the size of the actual car they represent. If the original car is y feet long, what is the length of the related toy car? (d)
21. You had x dollars, but after paying for lunch you have y dollars left. How much did lunch cost? (b)
22. Mindy gave Jian x marbles. Then Jian lost some of his marbles. If he has y marbles left, how many of his marbles did Jian lose? (b)
23. Destinee walked x mph for y hours. How many miles did she walk? (d)
24. Write examples of situations different from those in this lesson that lead to each expression you did not use as an answer in Questions 19–23. (Previous Course)

24. Answers vary. Sample: (a) You have x dollars in your pocket and you find y dollars on the street. How much do you have now? (c) You owe your mom x dollars, and you get paid y dollars at your job. How much will you have when you pay her back? (f) You have y slices of pizza and x people sharing the meal. How many slices will each person get?

Accommodating the Learner

After completing the lesson, have students look through their other textbooks—for example, biology, chemistry, physics, and social studies—to find formulas. Then have students explain in writing what each formula means, what each variable represents, and when or how the formula is used.

25. **Multiple Choice** Which sentence correctly relates the angle measures in the figure below? **(Previous Course)** C

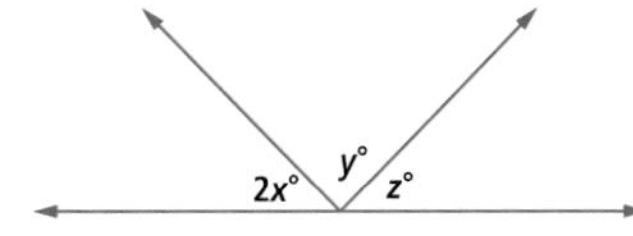

A $x + y + z = 180$ B $x = 90 - y - z$

C $2x + y + z = 180$ D none of these

26. What name is given to the polygon that is the shape of a stop sign? **(Previous Course)** octagon

27. a. Solve $2x = 4x + 18$ for x. $x = -9$

b. Check your work. **(Previous Course)**

EXPLORATION

These questions ask you to explore topics related to the lesson. Sometimes you will need to use references found in a library or on the Internet.

28. The graph of gold prices on page 5 looks distinctly different before and after 1971. Describe this difference in your own words. Do research on the Internet or at a library to find out what event happened to affect gold prices, and explain why this event caused the pattern of the graph to change.

29. Silver is another economically important metal. Using the information from the Internet or a library, make a graph of silver prices since 1960 similar to the graph of gold prices on page 5. Does your graph of silver prices follow the same patterns as the graph of gold prices?

Yes; silver prices rose dramatically at about the same time as gold, and their prices seem to follow the same patterns. Silver is generally much less expensive than gold, however.

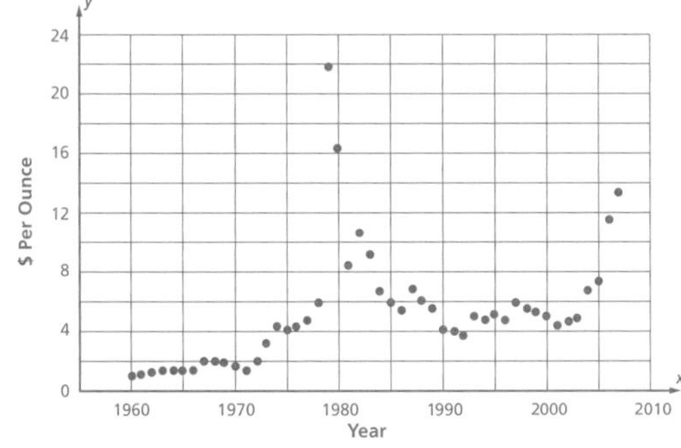

27b. $2(-9) = 4(-9) + 18$;
$-18 = -36 + 18$;
$-18 = -18$
The answer checks.

28. Answers vary. Sample: Before 1971, the price of gold is relatively stable. After 1971, it increases rapidly. Until 1971, gold was directly linked to the value of the dollar. Anyone could exchange their dollars for gold at any time, at a fixed exchange rate. But by 1971, foreign governments had more U.S. dollars than the U.S. could cover with their supply of gold. So, then-President Richard Nixon decided to "close the gold window." People could no longer come to the U.S. Treasury and exchange their currency for gold. The exchange rate for gold was no longer fixed. The value of the dollar dropped, and this allowed the price of gold to skyrocket.

QUIZ YOURSELF ANSWERS

1. 2604

2. 16

Notes on the Questions

Questions 25 and 26 These questions deal with topics from geometry. At appropriate times, geometric concepts, examples, and applications are used in the text. Students usually enjoy learning how algebra and geometry are connected. Those students who have not completed a geometry course will need additional help with the geometric content in this book, as we assume that students have completed a full geometry course prior to this course.

4 Wrap-Up

Ongoing Assessment

Have students work in pairs. Ask one student to write an algebraic expression involving three different variables and designate a value for each variable. Have the other student evaluate the expression for the given values. Then have students reverse roles. Encourage students to use the four basic operations as well as powering and finding square roots in their expressions. Students should demonstrate an ability to write and evaluate algebraic expressions.

Project Update

Project 1, *Value over Time,* on page 60 relates to the content of this lesson.

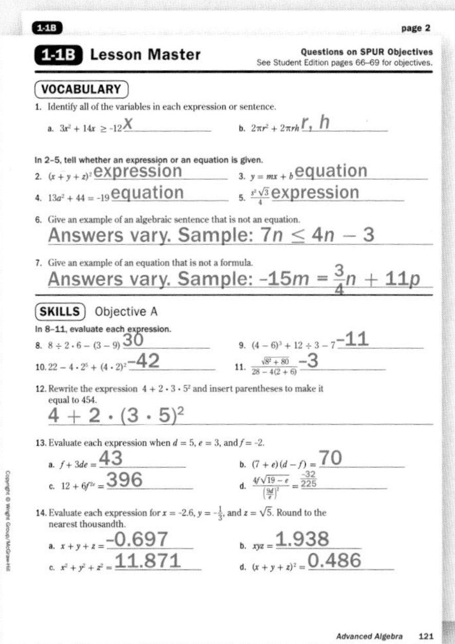

1-1B page 2

1-1B Lesson Master

Questions on SPUR Objectives
See Student Edition pages 66–69 for objectives.

VOCABULARY

1. Identify all of the variables in each expression or sentence.

a. $3x^2 + 14x \geq -12$ x

b. $2\pi r^2 + 2\pi rh$ r, h

In 2–5, tell whether an expression or an equation is given.

2. $(x + y + z)^2$ expression

3. $y = mx + b$ equation

4. $13a^2 + 44 = -19$ equation

5. $\frac{s^2\sqrt{3}}{4}$ expression

6. Give an example of an algebraic sentence that is not an equation.
Answers vary. Sample: $7n \leq 4n - 3$

7. Give an example of an equation that is not a formula.
Answers vary. Sample: $-15m = \frac{3}{4}n + 11p$

SKILLS Objective A

In 8–11, evaluate each expression.

8. $8 \div 2 \cdot 6 - (3 - 9)$ 30

9. $(4 - 6)^3 + 12 \div 3 - 7$ -11

10. $22 - 4 \cdot 2^5 + (4 \cdot 2)^2$ -42

11. $\frac{\sqrt{8^2 + 80}}{28 - 4(2 + 6)}$ -3

12. Rewrite the expression $4 + 2 \cdot 3 \cdot 5^2$ and insert parentheses to make it equal to 454.
$4 + 2 \cdot (3 \cdot 5)^2$

13. Evaluate each expression when $d = 5$, $e = 3$, and $f = -2$.

a. $f + 3de =$ 43

b. $(7 + e)(d - f) =$ 70

c. $12 + 6f^{2e} =$ 396

d. $\frac{4f\sqrt{19 - e}}{\left(\frac{9d}{e}\right)^2} = \frac{-32}{225}$

14. Evaluate each expression for $x = -2.6$, $y = -\frac{1}{3}$, and $z = \sqrt{5}$. Round to the nearest thousandth.

a. $x + y + z =$ -0.697

b. $xyz =$ 1.938

c. $x^2 + y^2 + z^2 =$ 11.871

d. $(x + y + z)^2 =$ 0.486

Advanced Algebra 121

Lesson 1-2

GOAL

Introduce and apply the basic vocabulary associated with functions: *function, independent variable,* and *dependent variable.*

SPUR Objectives

G Determine whether a given relation is a function.

Materials/Resources

- Lesson Masters 1-2A and 1-2B
- Resource Masters 7 and 8

HOMEWORK

Suggestions for Assignment

- Questions 1–20
- Question 21 (extra credit)
- Reading Lesson 1-3
- Covering the Ideas 1-3

Local Standards

1 Warm-Up

1. Identify the dependent and independent variables in $d = \frac{360}{n}$, which is the formula for the number of degrees in an exterior angle of a regular polygon of n sides.
   n is the independent variable; d the dependent variable.
2. Two angles with measures x and y are supplementary.
   a. What are the possible values of x?
   x: $0 < x < 180$
   b. Write a formula for y in terms of x.
   $y = 180 - x$

Lesson 1-2 Relations and Functions

Vocabulary

relation
function
dependent variable
independent variable
input, output
is a function of
maps
mathematical model

▸ **BIG IDEA** Functions are the mathematical models of relationships between two variables.

You saw a graph of the yearly closing prices of gold at the beginning of this chapter. The closing prices for 1966 to 1975 are given in the following table.

Year y	Closing Price p (in dollars)
1966	35.4
1967	35.5
1968	43.5
1969	35.4
1970	37.6
1971	43.8
1972	65.2
1973	114.5
1974	195.2
1975	150.8

Two graphs of these data are shown below.

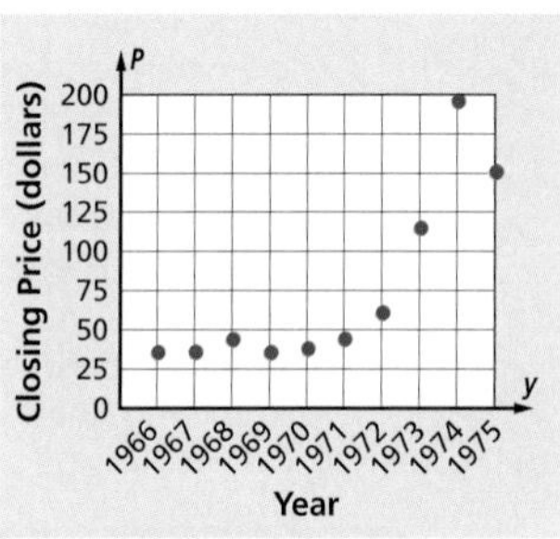

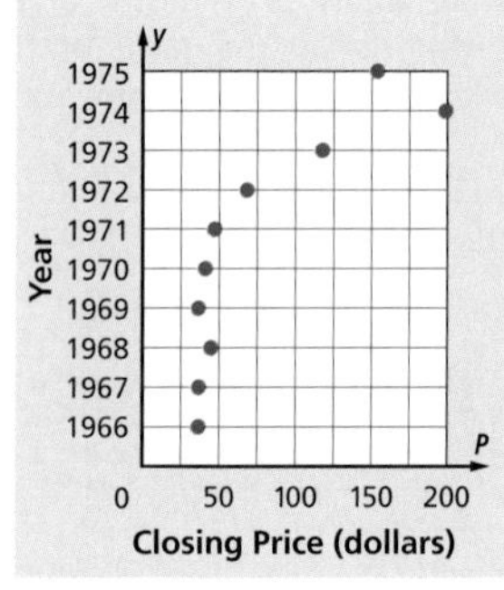

Mental Math

Rewrite the expression as the power of a single variable, if possible.

a. $x^7 \cdot x^2$ x^9

b. $\frac{a^7}{a^2}$ a^5

c. $d^8 + d^4$ not possible

d. $n^{16} \cdot \frac{n^3}{n^5}$ n^{14}

Background

There are two common definitions of *function.* The one we state formally on page 15 is the ordered-pair definition. This is a static definition, and it applies well to correspondences in which there is no mathematical rule connecting the independent and dependent variables, as with the function that maps a person onto his or her social security number. A more active definition is that a function is a correspondence between two variables in which no value of the independent variable corresponds to more than one value of the dependent variable.

The graph on the left on the previous page shows the ordered pairs (y, p) in the set {(1966, 35.4), (1967, 35.5), (1968, 43.5), (1969, 35.4), (1970, 37.6), (1971, 43.8), (1972, 65.2), (1973, 114.5), (1974, 195.2), (1975, 150.8)}. The graph on the right shows the ordered pairs (p, y) in the set {(35.4, 1966), (35.5, 1967), (43.5, 1968), (35.4, 1969), (37.6, 1970), (43.8, 1971), (65.2, 1972), (114.5, 1973), (195.2, 1974), (150.8, 1975)}.

Each of these sets of ordered pairs and their graphs shows the relationship between the variables y and p. In general, a **relation** is any set of ordered pairs. Any correspondence or pairing between two variables can be written as a set of ordered pairs. In the relation (y, p) graphed on the left, no two ordered pairs have the same first coordinate. Each value of y relates to *one and only one* value of p. A relation having this property describes a *function*.

Definition of Function

A **function** is a set of ordered pairs (x, y) in which each first component x of the pair is paired with exactly one second component y.

In the relation (y, p), the variable p is the **dependent variable** because finding its value depends on knowing the value of y. The variable y is the **independent variable**. Sometimes the independent variable values of a function are called **inputs** and the dependent variable values are called **outputs**.

When the relationship between two quantities is a function, we say that the dependent variable (the second component) **is a function of** the independent variable (the first component). In our gold example, the price of gold at the end of the year is a function of the year.

We also say that the function **maps** each value of the independent variable onto the corresponding value of the dependent variable. Because of this property, every function is a relation, and we can reword the definition of function given earlier.

Definition of Function (reworded)

A **function** is a relation in which no two ordered pairs have the same first component y.

Not every relation is a function. Consider the relation with the ordered pairs (p, y). Both (35.4, 1966) and (35.4, 1969) are in this relation. That is, if the closing price of gold is 35.4, the year could be either 1966 or 1969. Because of this ambiguity, y is not a function of p.

2 Teaching

Notes on the Lesson

The table, graph, and list of ordered pairs of closing prices of gold illustrate three ways of describing a relation. Ask: *How do each of these methods help to identify a relation as a function?*

- *table:* No value in the left column corresponds to more than one value in the right column.
- *graph:* No vertical line contains more than one piece of data. (*Note:* This test applies to functions described with Cartesian (rectangular) coordinates but not to functions described with polar coordinates.)
- *ordered pairs:* No first component is paired with more than one second component.

The situation with gold could be viewed as not being a function if there were two values of gold at the end of a year, say, values found on gold exchanges in two different countries. Being a function is quite special because it means that there is a unique value of the dependent variable for each value of the independent variable.

Example 1 In this case, it could be argued that either x or y could be the independent variable. You might have been asked to subtract y from both sides of the equation, resulting in $x = 90 - y$. Here, y is the independent variable, and x is the dependent variable.

Note-Taking Tips

You might want students to add the table from the Background (page 15) to their journals.

You might want to give students the following table to help them understand the three origins of functions and how the components are related.

Origin	Domain = set of possible values of	Range = set of possible values of
Formula	independent variable	dependent variable
Table	first row left column	second row right column
Computer	input	output

Accommodating the Learner

Some students have difficulty determining whether one variable is a function of another. Encourage them to remember that if y is a function of x, each value of x is paired with only one value of y. Students can ask themselves this question: "Is any value of x paired with more than one value of y?" If the answer is *no, y is* a function of x. If the answer is *yes, y is not* a function of x.

Notes on the Lesson

Example 2 You might note that time (in this case, the year) is often an independent variable.

Additional Example

Example 1 Two angles in an isosceles triangle have the same measure x. The measure of the third angle is y. This relationship can be modeled by the equation $y = 180 - 2x$. Which of x or y is the dependent variable and which is the independent variable? Explain your answer.

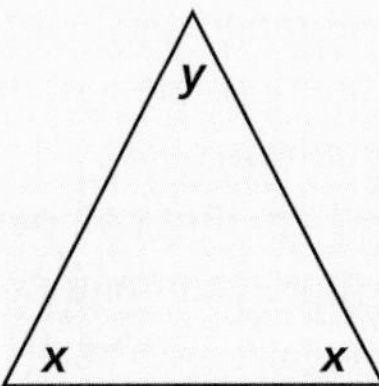

In this equation, y is the dependent variable because finding its value depends on knowing the value of x. This means that the independent variable is x.

Example 2 The average annual price P of crude oil per barrel in the year Y is given in the following table.

Year (Y)	Price (P)
1991	\$20.20
1993	\$16.75
1995	\$16.75
1997	\$18.64
1999	\$16.56
2001	\$23.00
2003	\$27.69
2005	\$50.04
2007	\$64.20

Source: http://www.inflationdata.com/inflation/Inflation_Rate/Historical_Oil_Prices_Table.asp

a. Is Y a function of P? Why or why not? Y is not a function of P because $P = \$16.75$ is paired with two different years, 1993 and 1995.

b. Is P a function of Y? Why or why not? P is a function of Y because each year is paired with only one value of P.

The table and list of ordered pairs in the situation about gold prices are examples of *mathematical models* of the yearly gold prices. A **mathematical model** for a real situation is a description of that situation using the language and concepts of mathematics. Often the situation has to be simplified for the mathematical model. In the case of gold, since the price of gold is always changing, we used the closing price of the end of the year. Sometimes models are created to describe properties of mathematical objects.

Example 1

In a right triangle, the sum of the measures of the two acute angles is 90 degrees. Suppose x is the degree measure of one acute angle, and y is the degree measure of the other, as shown in the drawing at the right.

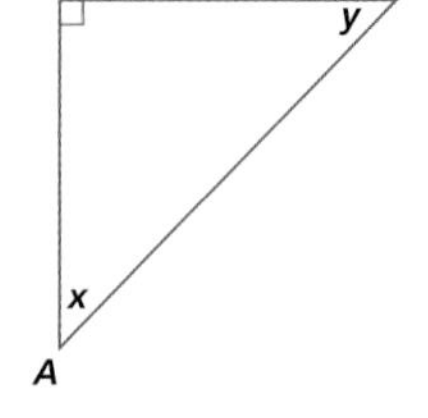

You can write an algebraic sentence to describe this situation.

$$x + y = 90$$

Now you can subtract x from both sides of this equation to get y alone on one side.

$$y = 90 - x$$

In this question, which of x or y is the dependent variable and which is the independent variable? Explain your answer.

Solution In this formula, y is the dependent variable because finding its value depends on knowing the value of x. This means that the independent variable is x.

A function can be described in words, by a formula, or in a graph or table.

Example 2

The percentage P of the adult U.S. population aged 25 and over who had earned a 4-year college degree by the year Y is given in this table.

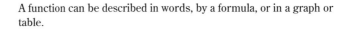

Year (Y)	1986	1988	1990	1992	1994	1996	1998	2000	2002	2004	2006
Percent (P)	19	20	21	21	22	24	24	26	27	28	28

a. Is Y a function of P? Why or why not?

b. Is P a function of Y? Why or why not?

Solution

a. Think: If Y is a function of P, then for each value of P there should be only one value of Y. So Y is not a function of P because $P = 21$ is paired with two different years, $Y = 1990$ and $Y = 1992$.

Extension

You might use this activity after discussing the lesson. Provide students with tape measures or string and metric rulers. Write the following formulas on the board:

Male: $h = 69.089 + 2.238F$

Female: $h = 61.412 + 2.37F$

Explain that the height of adult humans is a function of their bone lengths, and these formulas can be used to estimate height based on bone size. In the formula, h is the height in centimeters of an adult human, and F is the length in centimeters of his or her femur (thigh bone). Have students measure the distance from their knees to their hip joints and then evaluate the formula to see how accurately the formulas approximate their own heights.

b. P is a function of Y because each year is paired with only one value of P. That is, there was a unique percentage of graduates each of these years.

STOP See Quiz Yourself at the right.

In Example 2, P is a function of Y, so Y is the independent variable and P is the dependent variable.

▸ QUIZ YOURSELF

Are there other ordered pairs that show Y is not a function of P? If so, what are they?

Questions

COVERING THE IDEAS

1. In your own words, what is a function?
2. a. What is the difference between a function and a relation?
   b. Give an example of a relation that is not a function.
3. Give the definition and an example of a mathematical model.
4. Consider the table below.

s	–10	–5	0	5	10
t	100	25	0	25	100

   a. Is t a function of s? Explain your answer.
   b. Is s a function of t? Explain your answer.
5. Recall the formula for the circumference of a circle, $C = 2\pi r$. Is C a function of r? Justify your answer.

In 6–8, a relation is graphed. Is the relation a function? How can you tell?

6. 7. 8

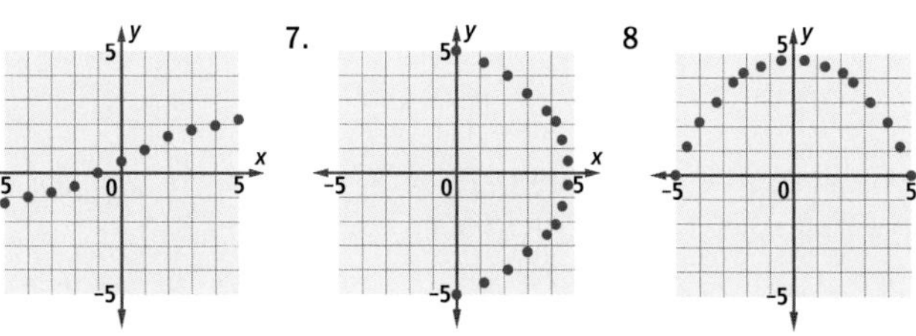

4a. Yes; every value of s is associated with only one value of t.

4b. No; there would be two different s values generated by $t = 25$ or $t = 100$.

5. Yes; for every ordered pair (r, C), each value of r determines only one value for C.

6. Yes; there is only one y-value for every x-value.

7. No; one x-value generates two different y-values.

8. Yes; there is only one y-value for every x-value.

1. Answers vary. Sample: A function is a set of ordered pairs where no two pairs have the same first coordinate.

2a. Answers vary. Sample: A function is a type of relation, but not all relations are functions. If a relation is a set of ordered pairs where two points have the same first component, it is not a function.

2b. Answers vary. Sample: $y = 3$

3. Answers vary. Sample: A mathematical model is a description of a real situation using the language and concepts of mathematics. For example, the equation $x + y + z = 180$ models the relationship among the angle measures in a triangle.

3 Assignment

Recommended Assignment

- Questions 1–20
- Question 21 (extra credit)
- Reading Lesson 1-3
- Covering the Ideas 1-3

Notes on the Questions

Question 5 If the formula were solved for r, we would say that r is a function of C.

Question 7 Go back to the definition of a function. Emphasize that no two points on the graph of a function can have the same first coordinate. This brings home the importance of the definition of a term.

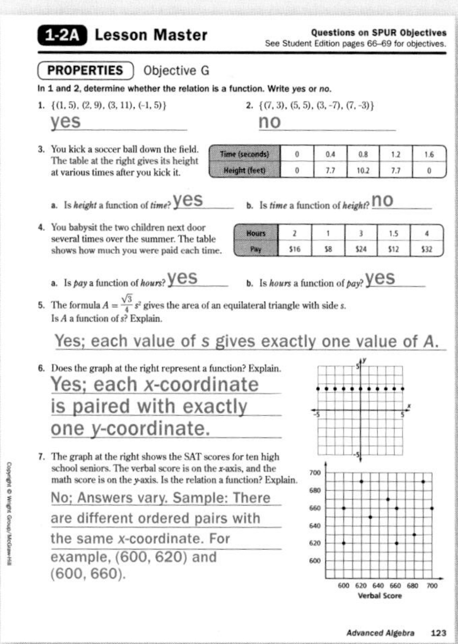

1-2A Lesson Master

Questions on SPUR Objectives
See Student Edition pages 66–69 for objectives.

PROPERTIES Objective G

In 1 and 2, determine whether the relation is a function. Write *yes* or *no*.

1. {(1, 5), (2, 9), (3, 11), (-1, 5)} yes
2. {(7, 3), (5, 5), (3, -7), (7, -3)} no

3. You kick a soccer ball down the field. The table at the right gives its height at various times after you kick it.

Time (seconds)	0	0.4	0.8	1.2	1.6
Height (feet)	0	7.7	10.2	7.7	0

   a. Is *height* a function of *time*? yes
   b. Is *time* a function of *height*? no

4. You babysit the two children next door several times over the summer. The table shows how much you were paid each time.

Hours	2	1	3	1.5	4
Pay	\$16	\$8	\$24	\$12	\$32

   a. Is *pay* a function of *hours*? yes
   b. Is *hours* a function of *pay*? yes

5. The formula $A = \frac{\sqrt{3}}{4}s^2$ gives the area of an equilateral triangle with side s. Is A a function of s? Explain.
   Yes; each value of s gives exactly one value of A.

6. Does the graph at the right represent a function? Explain.
   Yes; each x-coordinate is paired with exactly one y-coordinate.

7. The graph at the right shows the SAT scores for ten high school seniors. The verbal score is on the x-axis, and the math score is on the y-axis. Is the relation a function? Explain.
   No; Answers vary. Sample: There are different ordered pairs with the same x-coordinate. For example, (600, 620) and (600, 660).

Advanced Algebra 123

Accommodating the Learner ↑

Give students the following equations. Have them describe the graph of the equation and determine whether y is a function of x and explain why.

1. $x^2 + y = 9$ The graph of $x^2 + y = 9$ is a parabola with $y = 9$ when $x = 0$ and $x = \pm 3$ when $y = 0$. Yes; for each value of x, there is only one value of y.
2. $x^2 + y^2 = 64$ The graph of $x^2 + y^2 = 64$ is a circle that intersects the x- and y-axes at 8 and -8. No; for each value of x, there are two values of y.
3. $x^2 + 4y^2 = 144$ The graph of $x^2 + 4y^2 = 144$ is an ellipse that intersects the y-axis at 6 and -6 and the x-axis at 12 and -12. No; for each value of x between -12 and 12 there are two values of y.

You might have students sketch the graphs or use a graphing calculator to verify their answers.

Notes on the Questions

Question 9 Ask: Why is the formula $D = \frac{180(n-2)}{n}$? The sum of the measures of the angles of any n-gon is $180(n - 2)$. Because each of the n angles in a regular n-gon has the same measure, divide the sum by n to find the measure of one angle.

Question 13 When the unit circle is described in terms of rectangular coordinates, as here, then it is not the graph of a function. When it is described in polar coordinates as $\{(r, \theta): r = 1\}$, then the set of points on the unit circle is a function because θ is viewed as the independent variable in polar coordinate situations.

APPLYING THE MATHEMATICS

9. Let D be the degree measure of each interior vertex angle in a regular polygon with n sides. The formula $D = \frac{180(n-2)}{n}$ gives D as a function of n.
   a. Identify the dependent variable. Explain your answer.
   b. Find the number of degrees in one of the interior angles of a regular hexagon. 120
   c. Draw a regular hexagon. Check that your answer to Part b is correct either by using a protractor, or by giving a logical argument based on the Triangle-Sum Theorem, which states that the sum of the measures of the angles of a triangle is 180°.

10. The table below shows data about some of the costs of running a vehicle. Y = year, T = the average cost (cents) per mile of owning and operating the vehicle, and G = the average cost (cents) per mile of gasoline for the vehicle. (The data assume an average of 15,000 vehicle-miles per year.)
    a. Is T a function of Y? Explain your answer.
    b. Is Y a function of G? Again, explain your answer.

Y = Year	T = Average Cost per Mile to Own and Operate (in cents)	G = Average Cost per Mile for Gasoline (in cents)
1985	23.2	5.6
1990	33.0	5.4
1991	37.3	6.6
1992	38.8	5.9
1993	38.7	5.9
1994	39.4	5.6
1995	41.2	5.8
1996	42.6	5.6
1997	44.8	6.6
1998	46.1	6.2
1999	47.0	5.6
2000	49.1	6.9
2001	51.0	7.9
2002	50.2	5.9
2003	51.7	7.2
2004	56.2	6.5
2005	52.2	9.5
2006	52.2	8.9

Source: American Automobile Association

9a. D is the dependent variable. You cannot know the measure of the interior vertex angles if you do not know how many sides the polygon has.

9c. Answers vary. Sample: A regular hexagon can be split into six equilateral triangles. Each of the triangles has interior angles that sum to 180°. Since they are equilateral, they are also equiangular. So, each interior angle of each triangle has measure 60°. Therefore, each interior angle of the hexagon has measure 120°.

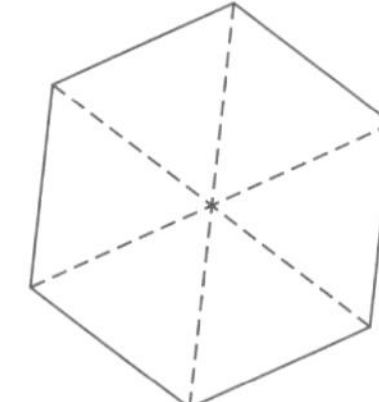

10a. Yes; every value of Y has only one corresponding value of T.

10b. No; a single value of G, for example 5.6, is paired with multiple values of Y.

ENGLISH LEARNERS

Vocabulary Development

To help students differentiate between a *relation* and a *function*, discuss the definitions of these terms. Both relations and functions are sets of ordered pairs. A *relation* is *any* set of ordered pairs, but a *function* is a *special* set of ordered pairs in which no two different ordered pairs have the same first coordinate. The Venn diagram at the right may help students visualize the difference.

Relation
Any set of ordered pairs of numbers

Function
A set of ordered pairs in which no two ordered pairs have the same first coordinate

In 11 and 12, find the value of the dependent variable for the given value of the independent variable.

11. $p = 3x^2, x = -5$ $p = 75$
12. $d = -6b^2 + 2b - 8, b = 5.6$ $d = -184.96$
13. Recall from geometry that the *unit circle* is the circle with center (0, 0) and radius 1. A graph of the unit circle is given at the right. Is the unit circle a graph of a function? Explain your answer.

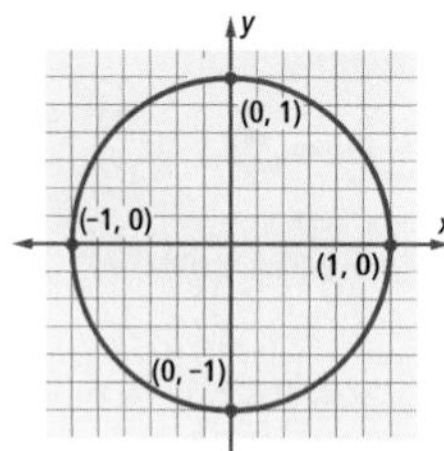

13. No; it is not the graph of a function because there are two *y*-values for every *x*-value except -1 and 1.

REVIEW

A lesson reference following a review question indicates a place where the idea of the question is discussed.

14. **Multiple Choice** Which of the following equations are formulas? There may be more tha``n one correct answer. **(Lesson 1-1)**
    A $A = \pi r^2$ B $Ax + By = C$ A, B, C
    C $E = mc^2$ D $(x - a)(x + a) = x^2 - a^2$

In 15–20, state the answer in terms of the variables given. (Previous Course)

15. Farid bought *m* blank CDs for a total of *b* dollars. What was his cost per CD? $\frac{b}{m}$ dollars
16. Butter normally costs *n* dollars per pound. If butter is on sale for *s* dollars per pound, how much will you save?
17. How many different outfits can be made from *K* skirts and *L* shirts? *KL* outfits
18. A bank pays you *I* interest on *P* dollars of savings. How much do you have altogether? $P + I$ dollars
19. If a recipe for *m* people requires *g* eggs, how many eggs will a recipe for *n* people require? $\frac{g}{m}n$ eggs
20. If a website has *h* hits now and is getting *m* hits an hour, how many hits will it have in all, *t* hours from now? $h + mt$ hits

16. $n - s$ dollars per pound

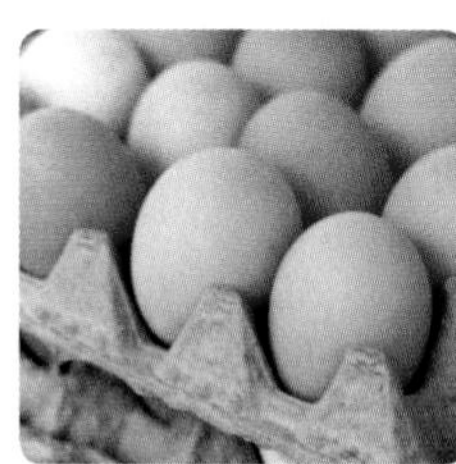

In 2007, the average per capita egg consumption in the United States was 253.8 eggs

EXPLORATION

21. The word *function* has several meanings beside the definition given in this lesson. Discuss the similarities and differences between the mathematical definition of function and its nonmathematical definitions.
Answers vary. Sample: One common nonmathematical meaning refers to the assigned role of a person or thing. This is somewhat similar to the mathematical definition because a mathematical function is about the assigned relationship between two variables. However, this definition says nothing about the way that relationship is constructed. Function can also mean a social gathering. This is unrelated to the mathematical definition. Finally, a function can mean that something is dependent on some other factors. This is closest to the mathematical definition.

QUIZ YOURSELF ANSWER

Yes; (24, 1996) and (24, 1998)

Notes on the Questions

Question 14 Ask students for the variables in choice B; they may not realize that *c*, being the speed of light, is a constant and that *m* is the independent variable.

Questions 15–20 These questions continue the theme of Questions 19–24 in Lesson 1-1.

Question 19 One way to answer this question is to think of eggs per person as a unit. The recipe requires $\frac{g}{m}$ eggs per person, so it requires *n* times that for *n* people.

4 Wrap-Up

Ongoing Assessment

Ask students to describe a relation between two variables that is a function and make a table showing at least five ordered pairs for the function. Then ask them to describe a relation between two variables that is *not* a function and make a table showing at least five ordered pairs for that relation. Students should demonstrate that they understand what is and what is not a function.

Project Update

Project 2, *Functions and Graphs on the Internet,* on page 60 relates to the content of this lesson.

Have students work in pairs to define sets of ordered pairs that illustrate both relations and functions.

Spend some time discussing the difference between *independent* and *dependent* variables. Students should be able to identify the difference based on the everyday definitions of the two terms.

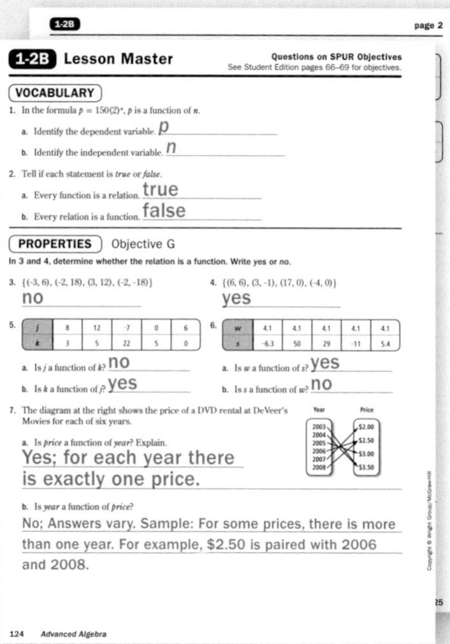

1-2B page 2

1-2B Lesson Master

Questions on SPUR Objectives
See Student Edition pages 66–69 for objectives.

VOCABULARY

1. In the formula $p = 150(2)^n$, p is a function of n.
   a. Identify the dependent variable. p
   b. Identify the independent variable. n
2. Tell if each statement is *true* or *false*.
   a. Every function is a relation. true
   b. Every relation is a function. false

PROPERTIES Objective G

In 3 and 4, determine whether the relation is a function. Write *yes* or *no*.

3. {(-3, 6), (-2, 18), (3, 12), (-2, -18)}
   no
4. {(6, 6), (3, -1), (17, 0), (-4, 0)}
   yes

5.

j	8	12	-7	0	6
k	3	5	22	5	0

   a. Is *j* a function of *k*? no
   b. Is *k* a function of *j*? yes

6.

w	4.1	4.1	4.1	4.1	4.1
s	-6.3	50	29	-11	5.4

   a. Is *w* a function of *s*? yes
   b. Is *s* a function of *w*? no

7. The diagram at the right shows the price of a DVD rental at DeVeer's Movies for each of six years.

Year: 2003, 2004, 2005, 2006, 2007, 2008
Price: $2.00, $2.50, $3.00, $3.50

   a. Is *price* a function of *year*? Explain.
   Yes; for each year there is exactly one price.
   b. Is *year* a function of *price*?
   No; Answers vary. Sample: For some prices, there is more than one year. For example, $2.50 is paired with 2006 and 2008.

124 Advanced Algebra

Lesson

1-3

GOAL

Introduce the two main notations for a function *f*: Euler's $y = f(x)$ notation and the arrow or mapping notation $f: x \rightarrow y$.

SPUR Objectives

B Use mapping and $f(x)$ notation for functions.

J Evaluate and interpret values of functions in real-world situations.

Materials/Resources

- Lesson Masters 1-3A and 1-3B
- Resource Masters 9 and 10
- Quiz 1
- CAS

HOMEWORK

Suggestions for Assignment

- Questions 1–25
- Question 26 (extra credit)
- Reading Lesson 1-4
- Covering the Ideas 1-4

Local Standards

1 Warm-Up

1. If $f(x) = 3x^4 - 2x^2$, find $f(1)$, $f(2)$, and $f(\sqrt{5})$. 1, 40, 65
2. If $f: x \rightarrow 3x^4 - 2x^2$, find $f(1)$, $f(2)$, and $f(\sqrt{5})$. 1, 40, 65
3. For the function f of Warm-Up Questions 1 and 2, find a value of x for which $f(x) < 0$. Answers vary. Sample: 0.5

Lesson 1-3

Function Notations

Vocabulary

$f(x)$ notation

argument of a function

value of a function

mapping notation

BIG IDEA A function f may be written as a set of ordered pairs $(x, f(x))$, described in $f(x)$ notation by an equation $y = f(x)$, or defined by the mapping $f: x \rightarrow y$.

Mental Math

a. How much would 15 cans of tuna cost if each can costs 59 cents? $8.85

b. How much would 15 frozen dinners cost if each dinner costs $5.90? $88.50

c. How much would 1.5 pounds of mixed nuts cost at a price of $5.90 per pound? $8.85

d. How much would 4.5 pounds of mixed nuts cost at a price of $5.90 per pound? $26.55

Consider these three equations:

$$y = 90 - x,$$
$$y = 1.8x + 32,$$
$$y = \sqrt{25 - x^2}.$$

The first equation relates the degree measures x and y of the two acute angles in a right triangle. The second equation converts a temperature x in degrees Celsius into a temperature y in degrees Fahrenheit. The third equation gives the length y of one leg of a right triangle with another leg of length x and hypotenuse of length 5. Each formula is easy to use, but when they are all together on the page, all the x's and y's can be confusing. To avoid this confusion, you can use **$f(x)$ notation.** If A names the angle function, T names the temperature conversion function, and L names the formula for leg length, you can write:

$A(x) = 90 - x$ $A(x)$ is read "A of x."

$T(x) = 1.8x + 32$ $T(x)$ is read "T of x."

$L(x) = \sqrt{25 - x^2}$ $L(x)$ is read "T of x."

Now each function can be simply referred to by its name: A, T, or L. Any letter or string of letters (such as ABS or $SQRT$) or letters and numbers (such as $T1$) can name a function.

$f(x)$ notation

The symbol $f(x)$ is read "f of x". It does *not* mean f times x. This notation is attributed to Leonhard Euler (pronounced "oiler"), an extraordinary Swiss mathematician. In 1770, Euler wrote what is considered the most influential algebra book of all time, *Vollständige Anleitung zur Algebra (Complete Introduction to Algebra).* In honor of him, $f(x)$ notation is also called "Euler's notation."

Leonhard Euler (1707–1783)

Background

Some students may wonder why special notations are needed for functions. Why not use formulas, as in Lessons 1-1 and 1-2? There are at least three reasons why function notation is convenient. (1) It allows us to distinguish between several functions of the same variable. In this lesson we note how easy it is to identify and distinguish three functions A, T, and L. It would be confusing if we used y for the second coordinate of each. (2) Function notation enables us to concisely define operations with functions (for example, composition, which is introduced later in this course) and study properties (for example, the odd and even functions that are studied in later courses). (3) Function notation shows us clearly which variable is the independent variable.

You can combine $f(x)$ notation with a descriptive name for the independent variable. If you replace x with C for degrees Celsius, function T above is described by

$$T(C) = 1.8C + 32.$$

The letter C is the independent variable, or input, and $T(C)$ names the dependent variable, or output. T is the name of the function which multiplies the input C by 1.8 and adds 32.

You may also think of the function as

$$T(\ ) = 1.8(\ ) + 32.$$

The same variable, number, or expression is placed in the ( ) wherever the ( ) appears. What is written in the parentheses is called the **argument of the function**; the result is called the **value of the function**.

Example 1

If $T(C) = 1.8C + 32$, evaluate $T(20)$.

Solution Substitute 20 for C in the equation $T(C) = 1.8C + 32$.

$T(20) = 1.8(20) + 32$
$T(20) = 36 + 32$
$T(20) = 68$

Check Look at a thermometer with both Celsius and Fahrenheit scales to see that 20°C = 68°F.

 **See Quiz Yourself 1 at the right.**

QUIZ YOURSELF 1

In the function A on page 20, calculate $A(32)$.

Computer Algebra Systems (CAS)

In this course, you will often use a *computer algebra system* (CAS). Computer algebra systems have many uses. They allow you to define and find values of functions and expressions, simplify and solve algebraic equations and inequalities, and perform operations with algebraic expressions. Computer algebra systems use $f(x)$ notation to define functions and $f1, f2, f3$, and so on to name the functions to be graphed. Once defined, you can use these names on the home screen to find values of the function such as $f1(17)$ or $f3(\pi)$. The following Activity shows how to define and evaluate functions on a CAS.

2 Teaching

Notes on the Lesson

f(x) notation In some mathematical expositions, the expression $f(x)$ names a function. We consider this loose language because it blurs the distinction between a function and its values. In this book, we may *describe* a function with the equation $f(x) = x + 2$, but we name the function by the single letter f. We reserve $f(x)$ to stand for the second component of the ordered pairs of the function.

Thus, to avoid confusion, the text does not, for example, define a distance function d with the equation $d(t) = rt$ and then also use the formula $d = rt$ in the same discussion. Unfortunately, graphing calculators do not always make this distinction. As pointed out in the lesson, some graphers use the variable names $f1$, $f2$, and so on, to refer to the dependent variable. Once defined, these same names can be used on the home screen of some graphers to find specific values of the graphed functions, such as $f1(17)$, $f2(12)$, and so on. If this is the case for the graphers used in your classroom, point this out to your students.

We sometimes call $f(x)$ notation "Euler's $f(x)$ notation" to emphasize that symbols are invented by people.

Additional Example

Example 1 If $T(F) = \frac{5}{9}(F - 32)$, evaluate $T(86)$. 30

Computer algebra systems (CAS) Throughout this course, we introduce capabilities of a CAS as they connect with particular content. Here we show how to define a function so that the CAS can obtain values of the function. Graphing calculators can produce values of functions if you type in the formula for the function value. However, a CAS can do this symbolically, not just numerically. Thus the Activity on page 22 shows an exact value for $f(\pi)$ and an exact value in terms of c for $f(3c)$. This powerful capability of a CAS makes it useful for generating algebraic and numerical patterns.

Students who have studied from the 3rd edition of UCSMP *Algebra* have already used $N(S)$ for the number of elements in a set and $P(E)$ for the probability of an event, and they will have seen $f(x)$ notation from the middle of the year on. Students who have studied from the 3rd edition UCSMP *Geometry* have used $T(P)$ for the image of a point under a transformation. Consequently, $f(x)$ notation may be quite familiar to some students.

Accommodating the Learner

Some students may have difficulty with the function concept. You might help them by illustrating the idea with a "function machine," a machine that takes a number (the input) and operates on it. The number that emerges from the machine is the output.

Have students relate this idea to $f(x)$ notation by thinking of the "f" as the function machine and "x" as the input, or argument, of the function. Then $f(x)$ stands for the output or value of the function.

Notes on the Lesson

Mapping notation for functions
Mapping notation makes the distinction between a function and its values quite clear, and it is consistent with geometric applications of transformations in which r_m stands for a reflection over line m and $r_m(P)$ stands for the image of point P under the reflection. Mapping notation stresses the fact that a domain value determines a range value. $f(x)$ notation is used when there are sentences to solve.

Activity

MATERIALS CAS

Let f be the function that gives the length of one leg of a right triangle with a hypotenuse of 5 in terms of x, the length of the other leg.

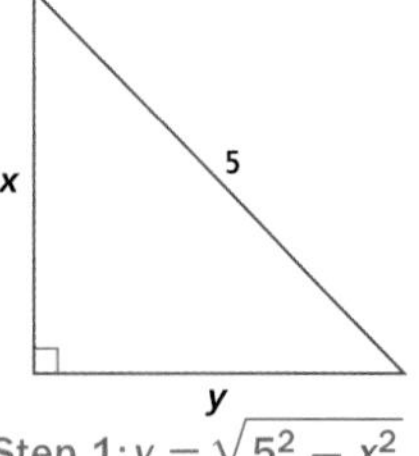

Step 1 Find an equation for y in terms of x.

Step 1: $y = \sqrt{5^2 - x^2}$

Step 2 Put your calculator in REAL (not complex) mode. Define the function f on your CAS using the equation you found in Step 1. The entry is made on the command line and the CAS may write the expression in a different form for easier reading. Here is what one calculator shows.

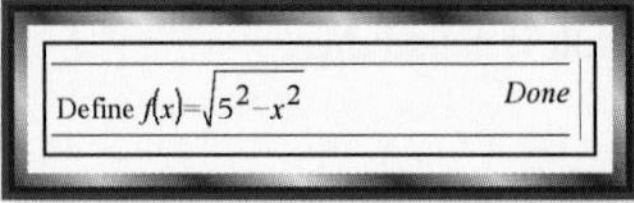

Step 3 Use your CAS to evaluate $f(4)$, $f(2.95)$, $f(\pi)$, and $f(3 \cdot c)$. One CAS shows the following results.

Step 3: 3; 4.03702;
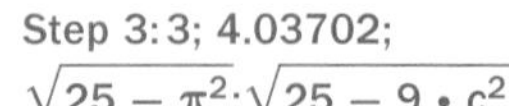
$\sqrt{25 - \pi^2}$; $\sqrt{25 - 9 \cdot c^2}$

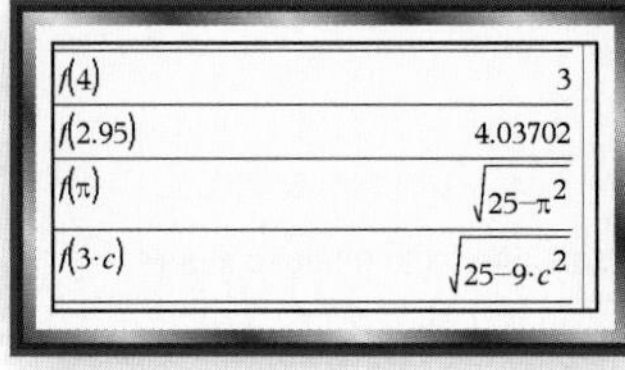

Step 4 Use your CAS to evaluate $f(6)$. Write a brief explanation of the result.

Step 4: Answers vary. Sample: Error: Nonreal answer. 25 – 36 = -11, for which there exists no real square root.

See Quiz Yourself 2 at the right.

▸ QUIZ YOURSELF 2
Use your CAS to find the values of $f(2)$ and $f(-2)$.

Mapping Notation for Functions

In the Activity, the function f is described by $f(x) = \sqrt{5^2 - x^2}$. Another notation, called **mapping notation**, is sometimes used for functions. Mapping notation uses a colon (:) and an arrow (→). The function from the Activity would be written in mapping notation as follows:

$$f{:}\, x \rightarrow \sqrt{5^2 - x^2}\,.$$

This is read, "the function f maps x onto $\sqrt{5^2 - x^2}$." For $f(4) = 3$, in mapping notation we write

$$f{:}\, 4 \rightarrow 3.$$

ENGLISH LEARNERS
Vocabulary Development

To reinforce the function notations taught in this lesson, reproduce the table at the right on the board. Have volunteers come forward and write the corresponding function notations for the equation. Then write a function in one of the two function notations in the appropriate column and have volunteers translate it into the other forms. Repeat until all students have had an opportunity to participate.

Formula	$f(x)$ Notation	Mapping Notation $f{:}\, x \rightarrow y$
$y = 3x^2 - 5$		

Example 2

Let $f: x \rightarrow \sqrt{5^2 - x^2}$. Evaluate $f(3)$ and $f(r) - f(3)$.

Solution 1 Substitute 3 for x.

$f(3) = \sqrt{5^2 - 3^2} = 4$

Substitute r for x. $\sqrt{5^2 - x^2} = \sqrt{5^2 - r^2} = \sqrt{25 - r^2}$

$f(r) = \sqrt{5^2 - r^2} = \sqrt{25 - r^2}$

So $f(3) = 4$ and $f(r) - f(3) = \sqrt{25 - r^2} - 4$.

Solution 2 Use a CAS. Define $f(x)$. Then evaluate $f(3)$ and $f(r) - f(3)$, as shown at the right.

Define $f(x)=\sqrt{5^2-x^2}$	*Done*
$f(3)$	4
$f(r)-f(3)$	$\sqrt{25-r^2}-4$

Questions

COVERING THE IDEAS

In 1–3, how is each read?

1. $f(x)$ f of x
2. $T: a \rightarrow a^2 + 3a + 4$ The function T maps a onto $a^2 + 3a + 4$.
3. $A(x) = \frac{1}{2}x(5 - x)$ A of x equals $\frac{1}{2}x$ times the quantity 5 minus x.

In 4–8, suppose $f(x) = \sqrt{25 - x^2}$. Evaluate the expression. If necessary, round to the nearest hundredth.

4. $f(0)$ 5
5. $f(\sqrt{2})$ 4.80
6. $f(-5)$ 0
7. $6 \cdot f\left(-\frac{1}{2}\right)$ 29.85
8. $f(a) - f(b)$ $\sqrt{25 - a^2} - \sqrt{25 - b^2}$

In 9–11, use the function with equation $T(C) = 1.8C + 32$.

9. Evaluate $T(86)$. 186.8
10. Write this function in mapping notation. $T: C \rightarrow 1.8C + 32$
11. What would you enter into your CAS command line to define the function T? Answers vary. Sample: define $t(c) = 1.8c + 32$
12. Is the value of a function the dependent or the independent variable? dependent

In 13–14, let $g: x \rightarrow 12 - 2x$.

13. **Fill in the Blank**
    a. $g: 12 \rightarrow$ _?_ -12
    b. $g: -3 \rightarrow$ _?_ 18
14. Rewrite the function g using $f(x)$ notation. $g(x) = 12 - 2x$

Additional Example

Example 2 Let $f: x \rightarrow x + \frac{x^2}{20}$. Evaluate $f(10)$ and $f(s) + f(10)$. $f(10) = 15$; $f(s) = s + \frac{s^2}{20}$, so $f(s) + f(10) = s + \frac{s^2}{20} + 15$

3 Assignment

Recommended Assignment

- Questions 1–25
- Question 26 (extra credit)
- Reading Lesson 1-4
- Covering the Ideas 1-4

Notes on the Questions

Questions 1–3 These questions provide an opportunity to work for correct use of language. Ask students to read aloud what they have written on their papers so that others in the class can learn what language is appropriate and what is not.

Accommodating the Learner

Refer students to Question 17. Have them repeat Parts a and b by using $g(x) = 3^x$ and $h(x) = x^3$. Have them use these values for x: -4, -3, -2, -1, 0, 1, 2, 3, and 4 and round answers to the nearest hundredth.

a.

x	h(x)	g(x)	h(x) – g(x)
-4	-64	0.01	-64.01
-3	-27	0.04	-27.04
-2	-8	0.11	-8.11
-1	-1	0.33	-1.33
0	0	1	-1
1	1	3	-2
2	8	9	-1
3	27	27	0
4	64	81	-17

b. No; the table shows that $g(x) \geq h(x)$.

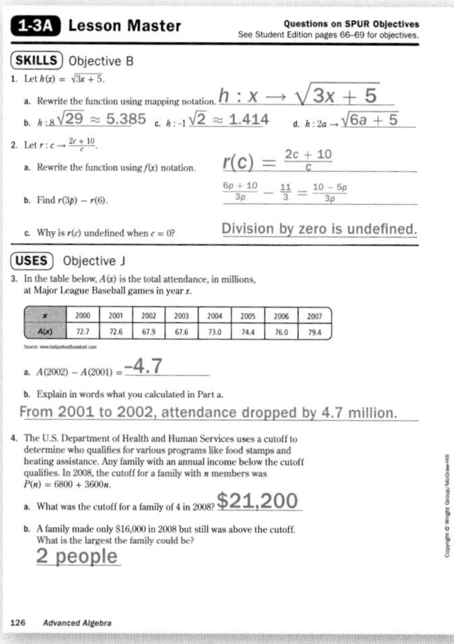

1-3A Lesson Master

Questions on SPUR Objectives
See Student Edition pages 66–69 for objectives.

SKILLS Objective B

1. Let $h(x) = \sqrt{3x + 5}$.
   a. Rewrite the function using mapping notation. $h: x \rightarrow \sqrt{3x + 5}$
   b. $h: 8$ $\sqrt{29} \approx 5.385$
   c. $h: -1$ $\sqrt{2} \approx 1.414$
   d. $h: 2a \rightarrow$ $\sqrt{6a + 5}$
2. Let $r: c \rightarrow \frac{2c + 10}{c}$.
   a. Rewrite the function using $f(x)$ notation. $r(c) = \frac{2c + 10}{c}$
   b. Find $r(3p) - r(6)$. $\frac{6p + 10}{3p} - \frac{11}{3} = \frac{10 - 5p}{3p}$
   c. Why is $r(c)$ undefined when $c = 0$? Division by zero is undefined.

USES Objective J

3. In the table below, $A(x)$ is the total attendance, in millions, at Major League Baseball games in year x.

x	2000	2001	2002	2003	2004	2005	2006	2007
A(x)	72.7	72.6	67.9	67.6	73.0	74.4	76.0	79.4

Source: www.ballparksofbaseball.com

   a. $A(2002) - A(2001) =$ −4.7
   b. Explain in words what you calculated in Part a. From 2001 to 2002, attendance dropped by 4.7 million.
4. The U.S. Department of Health and Human Services uses a cutoff to determine who qualifies for various programs like food stamps and heating assistance. Any family with an annual income below the cutoff qualifies. In 2008, the cutoff for a family with n members was $P(n) = 6800 + 3600n$.
   a. What was the cutoff for a family of 4 in 2008? $21,200
   b. A family made only $16,000 in 2008 but still was above the cutoff. What is the largest the family could be? 2 people

126 Advanced Algebra

Notes on the Questions

Question 17 You may want to have students use an algebraic spreadsheet for Part a. Only when $x = 4$ do the functions g and h have the same value.

APPLYING THE MATHEMATICS

In 15 and 16, let $V(r) = \frac{4}{3}\pi r^3$.

15. a. What is the argument of the function V? r
    b. What is the value of the function V when $r = 6$? 288π
    c. What is the value of the function V when the argument is $3R$? $36\pi R^3$
16. What argument of the function V produces a value of $\frac{4}{3}\pi$? 1
17. Define $g(x) = 2^x$ and $h(x) = x^2$ on your CAS.
    a. Complete the following table. (When necessary, round to the nearest hundredth.)

x	$h(x)$	$g(x)$	$h(x) - g(x)$
-4	16	0.06	15.94
-2	? 4	? 0.25	? 3.75
-0.5	? 0.25	? 0.71	? -0.46
0.5	? 0.25	? 1.41	? -1.16
2.5	? 6.25	? 5.66	? 0.59
3	? 9	? 8	? 1
3.5	? 12.25	? 11.31	? 0.94
4.5	? 20.25	? 22.63	? -2.38
10	100	? 1024	? -924

    b. Is $h(x) > g(x)$ for all values of x? Explain based on the results of your table.
    c. The g and h functions in your CAS remain stored in memory until you either replace them with new definitions or delete them. Find out how to check the variable and function contents of your CAS memory.
    d. Are g and h stored as functions in your CAS memory? How can you tell?
    e. Delete the h function from your CAS memory. What happens now when you use your CAS to evaluate $h(8)$?

17b. No; the table shows, for example, that $h(-0.5) < g(-0.5)$.

17c. Answers vary. Sample: The var key should display the currently stored variables and functions in your CAS memory.

17d. Answers vary. Sample: Yes; the calculator uses a different icon to represent stored functions and stored variables.

17e. The calculator does not evaluate the function.

In 18–20, use the table below, in which *x* is the year and *p*(*x*) is the average price (in cents) of one gallon of unleaded gasoline during the year *x*.

x	1997	1998	1999	2000	2001	2002	2003	2004	2005	2006
p(*x*)	123.4	105.9	116.5	151.0	146.1	135.8	159.1	188.0	229.5	258.9

Source: http://www.economagic.com

Regular Gasoline 409 9/10
Plus Gasoline 419 9/10
Premium Gasoline 429 9/10

18. a. Evaluate $p(2006) - p(2005)$. 29.4
    b. Explain in words what you have just calculated.
    c. What does the answer to Part a mean about the price of gasoline?
19. For what values of *x* is $p(x) > 150$?
20. Solve $p(x) = 116.5$ for *x*. 1999
21. Given that $g: x \to |-x| + (x - 2)^3$, evaluate.
    a. $g(4)$ 12
    b. $g(-4)$ -212
    c. $g(2.376)$ 2.42916
    d. $g(4b)$ $|4b| + (4b - 2)^3$

18b. the change in average price of a gallon of gasoline between 2005 and 2006

18c. The average price increased by 29.4 cents from 2005 to 2006.

19. 2000, 2003, 2004, 2005, 2006

REVIEW

22. Is *y* a function of *x*? Why or why not? **(Lesson 1-2)**

x	0	1	-1	2	-2
y	0	1	1	8	8

Yes; each value of *x* is paired with a single value of *y*.

23. Amy has three sisters and two brothers. Suppose she writes out the relation of all pairs (*x*, *y*) where *x* and *y* are siblings of hers and *x* is *y*'s brother. Is this relation a function? **(Lesson 1-2)**

23. No; because one brother has more than one sibling.

24. Berto is saving money for a car. He has $657 in his account. He plans on saving $50 each week. How much will he have **(Lesson 1-1)**
    a. after 11 weeks? $1207
    b. after *n* weeks?

24b. $657 + 50n$ dollars

25. a. Give an equation for the horizontal line through (-4, 6).
    b. Give an equation for the vertical line through (-4, 6).
    c. Write equations for the horizontal line and the vertical line that intersect at (*h*, *k*). **(Previous Course)**

25a. $y = 6$
25b. $x = -4$
25c. $y = k$, $x = h$

EXPLORATION

26. Leonhard Euler contributed to all branches of mathematics. Various theorems, formulas, and functions are named after him. Research Euler's *totient function* and write a paragraph about it.

Answers vary. Sample: Euler's totient function gives, for a given positive integer *n*, the number of positive integers less than or equal to *n* that are coprime to *n*. Coprime means that two numbers have no common factor other than 1. The totient function is represented by the Greek letter ϕ (phi) and is written ϕ(*n*).

QUIZ YOURSELF ANSWERS

1. $A(32) = 58$
2. $f(2) \approx 4.58$; $f(-2) \approx 4.58$

Notes on the Questions

Question 25 Even at this level, there are students who are confused by the meanings of "horizontal" and "vertical."

Question 26 There is much to be said. Euler was probably the most prolific mathematician of all time. In the books of the UCSMP series, Euler's name is likely mentioned more often than any other mathematician, not only because he made many mathematical discoveries but also because he wrote the algebra text to which most current algebra textbooks can trace their origins.

4 Wrap-Up

Ongoing Assessment

Have students work in pairs. Have one student use *f*(*x*) notation to write a function. Have the other student read the function aloud and use mapping notation to write the same function. Have the first student give a value for the variable and the second student evaluate the function. Then have students reverse roles and repeat the activity. Students should demonstrate an understanding of both *f*(*x*) and *f*: *x* → notations and the language appropriate to them and successfully evaluate a function.

Administer Quiz 1 (or a quiz of your own) after students complete this lesson.

Project Update

Project 2, *Functions and Graphs on the Internet,* on page 60 relates to the content of this lesson.

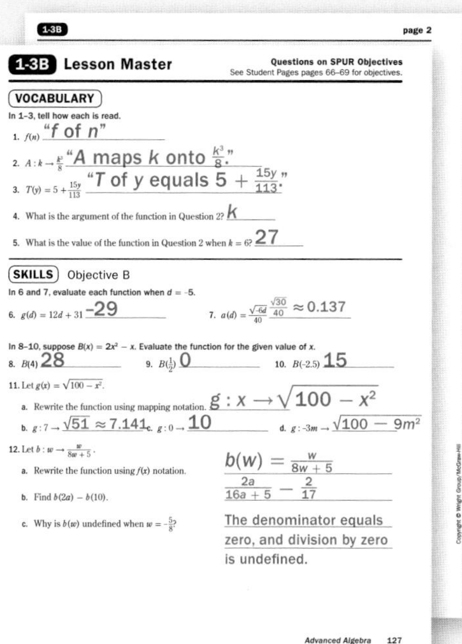

1-3B page 2

1-3B Lesson Master

Questions on SPUR Objectives
See Student Pages pages 66–69 for objectives.

VOCABULARY

In 1–3, tell how each is read.

1. $f(n)$ "f of n"
2. $A: k \to \frac{k^3}{8}$ "A maps k onto $\frac{k^3}{8}$."
3. $T(y) = 5 + \frac{15y}{113}$ "T of y equals $5 + \frac{15y}{113}$."
4. What is the argument of the function in Question 2? k
5. What is the value of the function in Question 2 when $k = 6$? 27

SKILLS Objective B

In 6 and 7, evaluate each function when $d = -5$.

6. $g(d) = 12d + 31$ −29
7. $a(d) = \frac{\sqrt{-6d}}{40}$ $\frac{\sqrt{30}}{40} \approx 0.137$

In 8–10, suppose $B(x) = 2x^2 - x$. Evaluate the function for the given value of *x*.

8. $B(4)$ 28
9. $B(\frac{1}{2})$ 0
10. $B(-2.5)$ 15

11. Let $g(x) = \sqrt{100 - x^2}$.
    a. Rewrite the function using mapping notation. $g: x \to \sqrt{100 - x^2}$
    b. $g: 7 \to$ $\sqrt{51} \approx 7.141$
    c. $g: 0 \to$ 10
    d. $g: -3m \to$ $\sqrt{100 - 9m^2}$

12. Let $b: w \to \frac{w}{8w + 5}$.
    a. Rewrite the function using $f(x)$ notation. $b(w) = \frac{w}{8w + 5}$
    b. Find $b(2a) - b(10)$. $\frac{2a}{16a + 5} - \frac{2}{17}$
    c. Why is $b(w)$ undefined when $w = -\frac{5}{8}$? The denominator equals zero, and division by zero is undefined.

Advanced Algebra 127

Lesson 1-4

GOAL

Make and read graphs; give the graphical interpretation of the domain and range of a function and the concept of function notation.

SPUR Objectives

H Determine the domain and range of a function.

J Evaluate and interpret values of functions in real-world situations.

L Use a graphing utility to graph functions and generate tables for functions.

Materials/Resources

- Lesson Masters 1-4A and 1-4B
- Resource Masters 1 and 11
- CAS or graphing calculator

HOMEWORK

Suggestions for Assignment

- Questions 1–26
- Question 27 (extra credit)
- Reading Lesson 1-5
- Covering the Ideas 1-5

Local Standards

1 Warm-Up

1. Explain why the sentence $y \leq 2x + 5$ does not describe a function mapping x onto y. One x-value corresponds to many y-values.
2. Consider the equation $A = s^2$.
   a. For *all* real values of s and A, is A a function of s? Explain why or why not. Yes; for every value of s, there is exactly one value of A.
   b. For *all* real values of s and A, is s a function of A? Explain why or why not. No; the same nonzero value of A has two values of s. For example, if $A = 25$, $s = 5$ or $s = -5$.

Lesson 1-4 Graphs of Functions

Vocabulary

real function
domain of a function
set-builder notation
range of a function
trace
standard window
natural numbers
counting numbers
whole numbers
integers
real numbers
rational numbers
irrational numbers

▸ **BIG IDEA** Because a *real function* is a set of ordered pairs of real numbers, it can be graphed on the coordinate plane.

A **real function** is a function whose independent and dependent variables stand only for real numbers. You can graph a real function on a rectangular coordinate graph. If $y = f(x)$, then the coordinates of points on the graph have the form (x, y) or $(x, f(x))$.

Mental Math

Refer to $\triangle ABC$ below. Estimate to the nearest integer.

a. BC 2 units

b. the area of $\triangle ABC$ 1 square unit

c. the perimeter of $\triangle ABC$ 5 units

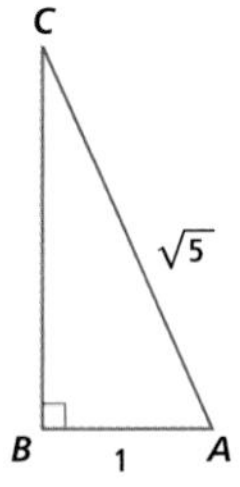

An Example from Driver's Education

When a driver attempts to stop a car, the distance d the vehicle travels before stopping is a function of the car's speed x and can be modeled by the equation $d = x + \frac{x^2}{20}$. If we give the name C to the function giving the stopping distance, then $C(x) = x + \frac{x^2}{20}$. Several ordered pairs of this function C are shown in the table below.

Speed (mph) = x	0	10	20	30	40	50	60	70
Car's Stopping Distance (ft) = $C(x)$	0	15	40	75	120	175	240	315

On the following page are two graphs relating the data above. The graph at the left is a graph of the function C for values of x from 0 to 70. All the points on it are of the form $(x, C(x))$. To find the value of $C(60)$ from the graph, start at 60 on the x-axis. Read up to the curve and then across to find the value on the y-axis. So, $C(60) = 240$. Notice that this agrees with the value in the table above.

The graph at the right includes the graph of a second function S. S maps the speed x of an SUV (sport utility vehicle) onto its stopping distance $S(x)$ at that speed. Using function notation helps distinguish the y-coordinates of the graphs when more than one function is displayed.

Background

One of the advantages of the ordered-pair definition of a function is that when the components of the ordered pairs are real numbers, the coordinate graph is a natural geometric representation. Students have graphed equations before, and we expect that some of this lesson will be review.

We introduce the term *real function* for a function whose domain and range contain real numbers only. Real functions can be graphed in the coordinate plane; other functions cannot.

Domain and range of a function Students should be familiar with the names for the different domains mentioned on page 29. Some books define the natural numbers to include 0; the choice really is arbitrary. Zero might even be called a counting number, for it is the count of a set with no elements, for example, the number of living dinosaurs. The idea of the domain of a variable may be new to students; this concept, however, is quite important and will arise repeatedly during problem-solving

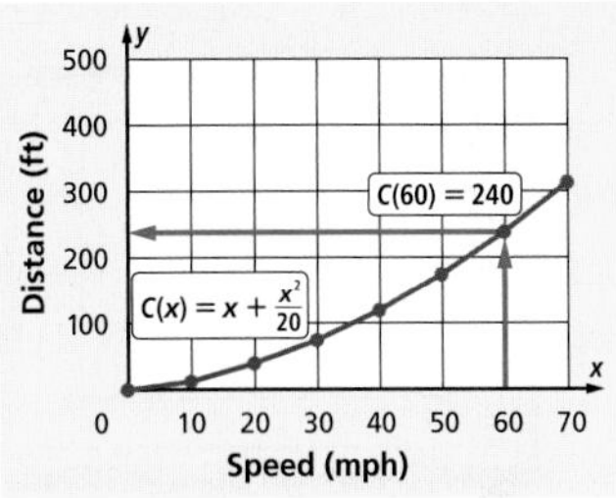

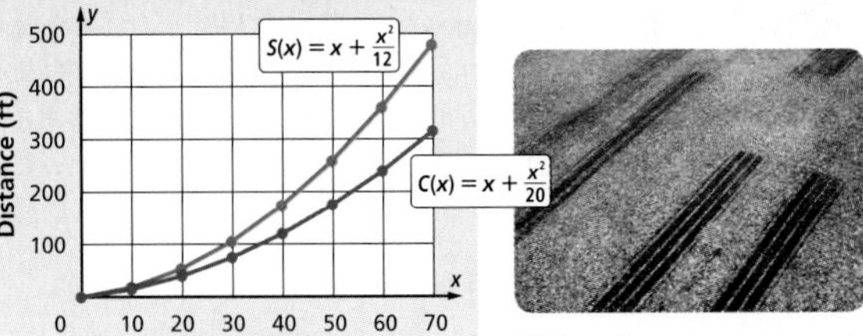

Skid marks on a road caused by heavy braking.

Domain and Range of a Function

For the functions C and S on the previous page, the situation and table determine what values of the independent and dependent variables to include in the graph. The set of allowable values for the independent variable is called the **domain of the function**. Allowable speeds for both C and S are from 0 to 70 mph, so the domain for each is $\{x|\ 0 \le x \le 70\}$. This notation, called **set-builder notation**, is read "the set of all x such that 0 is less than or equal to x and x is less than or equal to 70." Some people write $\{x\!: 0 \le x \le 70\}$ for set-builder notation.

The **range of a function** is the set of values for the dependent variable that can result from all possible substitutions for the independent variable. According to the table, when x has values from 0 to 70, the values of $C(x)$ range from 0 to 315. So the range of C is $\{y|\ 0 \le y \le 315\}$. For these values of x, the graph shows that values of $S(x)$ range from 0 to about 480. So the range of S is $\{y|\ 0 \le y \le 480\}$.

When graphing a function on a graphing utility, you need to consider its domain and range in order to get an appropriate picture. The *window* of the graph must be large enough for you to see what you want to see, but not so large that the graph is too tiny. In this Activity you will learn how to set your grapher's window and use its TRACE feature to further examine the functions C and S.

Activity

MATERIALS CAS or graphing calculator

Step 1 Locate your grapher's place for entering equations to be graphed.

Step 2 Enter $x + \frac{x^2}{20}$ for the first function and $x + \frac{x^2}{12}$ for the second function. A possible display is shown at the right.

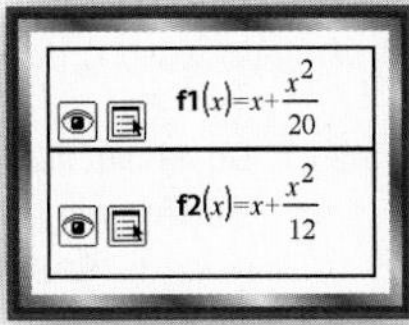

(continued on next page)

activities. A common domain in addition to those listed on page 29 is the set of positive real numbers.

The hierarchy on page 29 abbreviates the names of sets in a common way. We say "the reals" for "the set of real numbers." Emphasize that each set in this hierarchy is a subset of the ones above it to which it is connected.

c. Now consider the formula $A = s^2$, where s is the length of the side of a square, and A is the area of the square. Is A a function of s? Is s a function of A? Explain why or why not. Yes; because length and area are positive quantities only, for every value of s, there is exactly one value of A, and for every value of A, there is exactly one value of s.

2 Teaching

Notes on the Lesson

An example from driver's education Here we see an advantage of function notation. We are able to distinguish the *car* stopping-distance function C from the *SUV* stopping-distance function S merely by using a different letter.

Domain and range of a function Emphasize that when the graph of a function is given, the domain can be determined by scanning along the horizontal axis, and the range can be determined by scanning along the vertical axis. The skill of scanning along one dimension is also useful for deciding whether a relation is a function and when working with inverses later in this book.

Point out that the domain and range of a function may be restricted to a subset of the real numbers, either by the mathematical expressions in the function or the particular context in which the function is being applied. For example, the driver's education application restricts x to the set of nonnegative real numbers because x represents speed. We picked a maximum value of 70 for x because that is the maximum legal speed in many states.

Activity Go through this Activity on pages 27–29 slowly, making certain that students understand each step before going on. Even though students should have their own calculators, you should have them work in pairs. If one student does not see where a particular feature is on his or her calculator, the other student may be able to help.

Step 3 Set the viewing window large enough to show the graphs of both C and S. Because the range of S is larger, use its domain and range for the window. Your graphs should now look similar to the ones shown at the right.

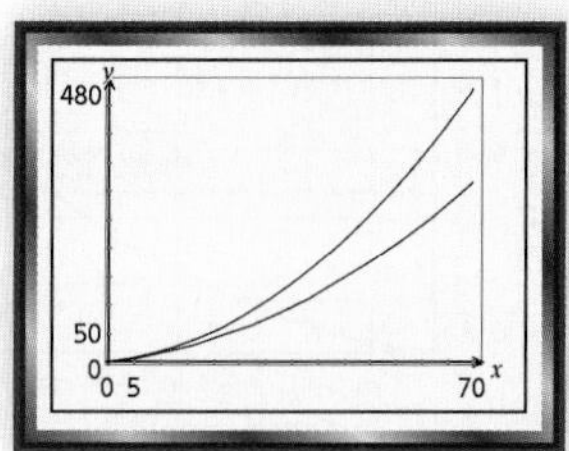

Step 4 The **TRACE** feature on your grapher allows you to estimate input and output values, much as you would on a graph drawn by hand. Trace along the graphs within the window, as shown. The numbers on the screen are the approximate x- and y-coordinates of the point on the graph where the TRACE marker is currently placed. Which ordered pair on the graph of function S appears at the right edge of the window?
(70, 478.33)

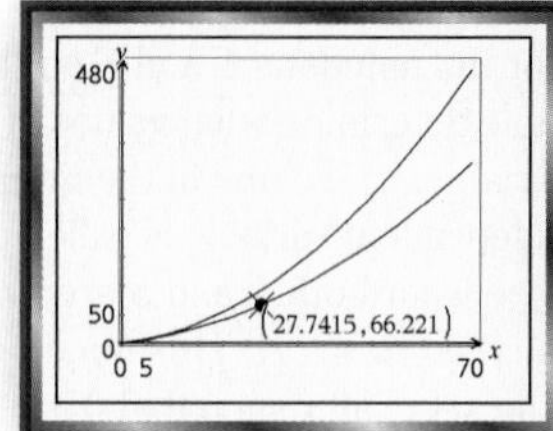

Step 5 The upper limit of allowable speeds in the table for C is 70 because that is the maximum speed limit in many parts of the U.S. However, some states have limits up to 75 mph. Continue tracing the C and S functions off the right side of the viewing window to estimate $C(75)$ and $S(75)$. Then define a new window which allows you to see allowable values of $C(x)$ and $S(x)$ over the domain $\{x|\ 0 \leq x \leq 75\}$.
$C(75) = 356.25$, $S(75) = 543.75$; new window: $0 \leq x \leq 75$, $0 \leq y \leq 545$

Step 6 Your grapher has a default window, often called the **STANDARD WINDOW**, that shows all four quadrants at a reasonably close scale. On many calculators, the default window is where $\{x|\ -10 \leq x \leq 10\}$, $\{y|\ -10 \leq y \leq 10\}$; and the x-scale and the y-scale are both 1. This means that both the horizontal (x) axis and the vertical (y) axis are viewable from –10 to 10, with 1 unit between tick marks. Find and use the standard window to graph C and S, as shown at the right.

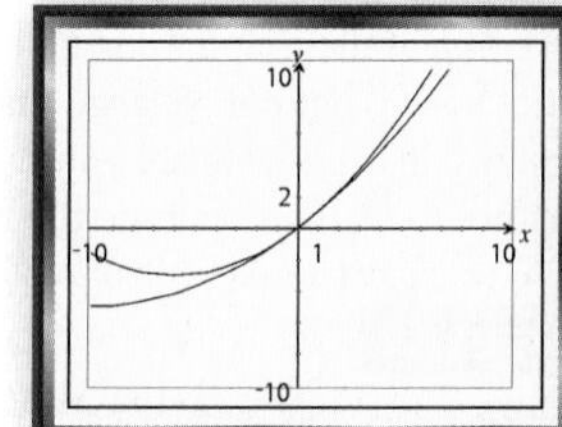

Step 7 Do all the ordered pairs displayed in this window of the graphs make sense in the situations of car and SUV speeds? Explain your answer.
No; you do not need to consider negative values because cars and SUVs cannot travel at a negative speed or stop in a negative number of feet.

ENGLISH LEARNERS
Vocabulary Development

Give students a copy of the table from the Background in Lesson 1-2 (see page 15). Discuss the terms and how they relate to each other and to the origins of functions. Stress that *range* in this sense does not have the same meaning as range in statistical terms.

If time permits, you could also write headings corresponding to the labels in the hierarchy of real numbers on the board. Have volunteers supply numbers and then have the class identify the sets to which they belong.

Step 8 Trace along the graphs of the C and S functions beyond the left edge of the standard window. You will see that the graphs of these functions are in Quadrants I, II, and III. Set the viewing window as specified below.

$-40 \le x \le 40$ x scale = 5
$-40 \le y \le 40$ y scale = 5

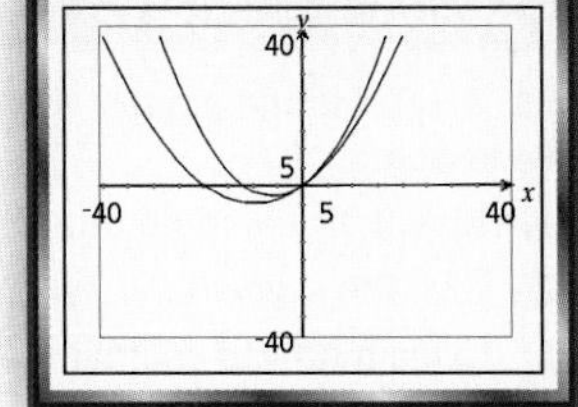

Step 9 Trace along the graphs of C and S again to estimate the minimum value of each function.

Step 9. Minimum value of $C \approx -5$; minimum value of $S \approx -3$

Negative speeds and negative distances are not reasonable measures. However, when you examine the graphs of the C and S functions without regard to stopping distances, you see that the functions are defined for negative values of x and y. When examining functions outside of real situations, it is common practice to identify the largest possible domain and its associated range.

Since there exist minimum values for $C(x)$ and $S(x)$, the biggest range for C is about $\{y| \ y \ge -5\}$ and for S it is about $\{y| \ y \ge -3\}$. But even if you imagine the graphs extending forever to the right and left, there do not seem to be minimum or maximum values for x. So x can be any real number, and we say that the domain of both C and S is the set of all *real numbers*, or the set of all reals.

Some sets of numbers that you are probably familiar with are frequently used as domains and often appear as ranges.

The set of **natural numbers** or **counting numbers** $\{1, 2, 3, 4, 5, ...\}$
The set of **whole numbers** $\{0, 1, 2, 3, 4, 5, ...\}$
The set of **integers** $\{..., -3, -2, -1, 0, 1, 2, 3, ...\}$
The set of **real numbers** (those numbers that can be represented by decimals)

Samples: 0, 1, -7, 35 million, 2.34, π, $\sqrt{5}$

The set of **rational numbers** (those numbers that can be represented as ratios of the form $\frac{a}{b}$, where a and b are integers and $b \ne 0$)

Samples: 0, 1, -7, $\frac{2}{3}$, $1\frac{9}{11}$, $-\frac{34}{10}$, 0.0004, $-9.6\overline{18}$, $\sqrt{16}$

The set of **irrational numbers** (real numbers that are not rational)

Samples: π, $\sqrt{5}$, $\sqrt{10}$, e

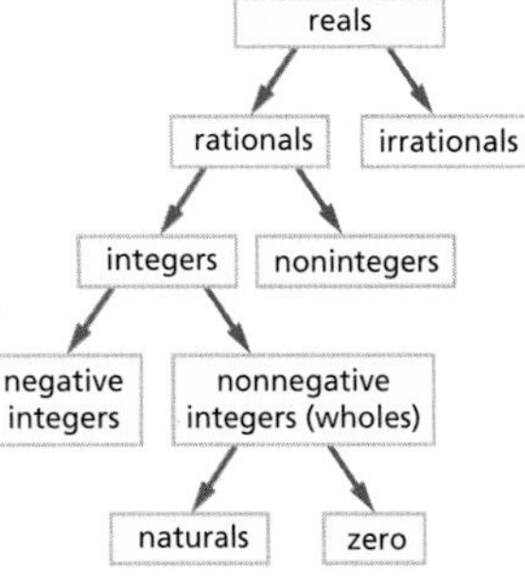

The diagram at the right shows how each set of numbers relates to the others. A number in any set is also in any set in the path above it. For example, an integer is also a rational number and a real number, but not all integers are whole numbers or natural numbers.

 **See Quiz Yourself at the right.**

QUIZ YOURSELF

Give an example of a negative rational number that is not an integer.

Notes on the Lesson

When reading the hierarchy for the sets of numbers on this page, students should stop their reading to ask: Is there a natural number that is NOT a whole number? no Is there a real number that is NOT positive? yes; zero or any negative number Encourage students to continue asking questions of this type as they complete the lesson.

Accommodating the Learner

Have students work in groups to find patterns in the decimal notations of rational and irrational numbers. They can use their calculators to test a variety of fractions, integers, decimals, and whole numbers and find that the decimals for those numbers either terminate or repeat. They should remember this idea from earlier studies in mathematics. When they check irrational numbers, however, they will find that the decimals neither terminate nor repeat.

Answers vary. Check students' work.

3 Assignment

Recommended Assignment

- Questions 1–26
- Question 27 (extra credit)
- Reading Lesson 1-5
- Covering the Ideas 1-5

Notes on the Questions

Students will routinely use graphing utilities throughout the year. Sometimes homework and/or test questions ask students to sketch the results of their graphers. It is a good idea to set some ground rules for making these sketches. When making sketches, students should show a fairly accurate representation of some critical points (if they exist): *x*-intercepts, *y*-intercepts, and relative maxima or minima.

We suggest covering all the questions in order.

1-4A Lesson Master

Questions on SPUR Objectives
See Student Edition pages 66–69 for objectives.

PROPERTIES Objective H

In 1 and 2, use the graph of $P(x)$ at the right.

1. Give the domain and range of $P(x)$.
   domain: $\{x \mid -3 \le x \le 4\}$; range: $\{y \mid 2 \le y \le 5\}$
2. Find $P(-2)$ and $P(3)$.
   $P(-2) = 2$; $P(3) = 4$

USES Objective J

In 3 and 4, the height h (in feet) of a ball t seconds after it is dropped from a 20-story building is given by $h(t) = 225 - 16t^2$. Find the indicated value and explain what it means in context.

3. $h(3)$ 81; after three seconds, the ball will be 81 feet high.
4. $h(3.75)$ 0; the ball will hit the ground 3.75 seconds after it is dropped.

REPRESENTATIONS Objective L

In 5 and 6, graph the function on your grapher's standard window. Use the graph to a. estimate the value of the function when $x = 2$, and b. find the domain and range of the function.

5. $f(x) = x^2 + 2x - 3$
   a. 5
   b. domain: all real numbers; range: $\{y \mid y \ge -4\}$
6. $g(x) = 3 - \sqrt{x + 4}$
   a. $3 - \sqrt{6} \approx 0.55$
   b. domain: $\{x \mid x \ge -4\}$; range: $\{y \mid y \le 3\}$

Questions

COVERING THE IDEAS

In 1–3, refer to the graphs of functions *C* and *S* at the beginning of this lesson.

1. Give their common domain. $\{x \mid 0 \le x \le 70\}$
2. Give the range of *S*. $\{y \mid 0 \le y \le 315\}$
3. Explain how to estimate $C(45)$ from the graph.

In 4–6, refer to the Activity.

4. Use your grapher's TRACE feature to estimate $C(55)$. 206.25
5. Assume you are in a state with a maximum speed limit of 55 mph. Define a window which shows all allowable values of $C(x)$ and $S(x)$ over the domain $\{x \mid 0 \le x \le 55\}$.
6. What is the standard window on your grapher?

In 7 and 8, the graph of a function is given. From the graph, determine the function's domain and range. Use set-builder notation.

7. 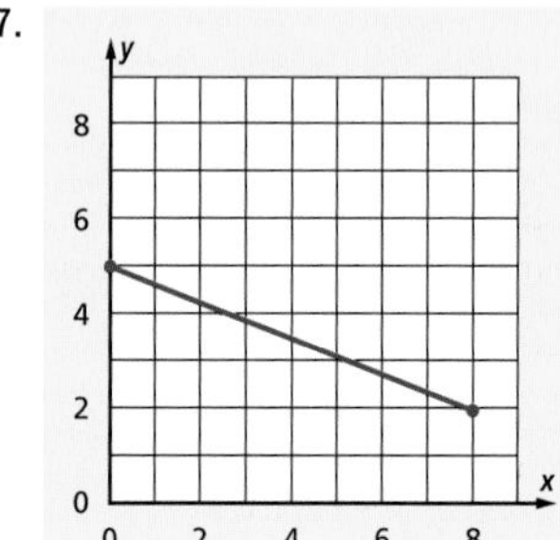

8. 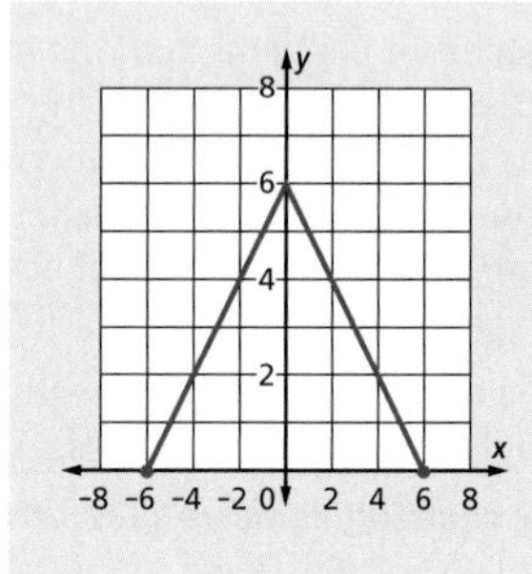

In 9–11, identify each number as an integer, a rational number, an irrational number, or a real number. A number may belong to more than one set.

9. –97
10. $\frac{23}{47}$
11. $-\sqrt{18}$
12. Name a rational number that is not an integer.
13. Name a real number that is an integer and not positive.
14. Name a real number that is an irrational number between 0 and 1.

3. Use the TRACE function on your graphing utility to estimate $C(45)$.

5. Answers vary. Sample: $0 \le x \le 55$, $0 \le y \le 310$

6. Answers vary. Sample: $-20 \le x \le 20$, $-15 \le y \le 15$

7. $\{x \mid 0 \le x \le 8\}$; $\{y \mid 2 \le y \le 5\}$

8. $\{x \mid -6 \le x \le 6\}$; $\{y \mid 0 \le y \le 6\}$

9. integer, rational number, real number

10. rational number, real number

11. irrational number, real number

12. Answers vary. Sample: $\frac{3}{7}$

13. Answers vary. Sample: –29

14. Answers vary. Sample: $\frac{\sqrt{3}}{2}$

Accommodating the Learner

Have students study again the table referenced in Vocabulary Development to help them distinguish between the *domain* and the *range* of a function. They can use this aid as well: In alphabetical order, domain comes before range, just as domain represents the set of first coordinates of a function and range represents the set of second coordinates.

APPLYING THE MATHEMATICS

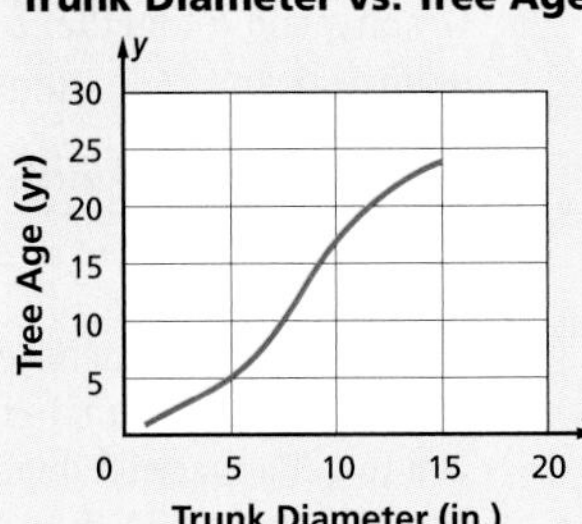

15. The graph at the right shows the relationship between the age of a grapefruit tree and the diameter of its trunk. Let $A(d)$ be the age of a grapefruit tree whose diameter is d inches.
   a. Estimate the range of A. $\{y \mid 0 \le y \le 24\}$
   b. Estimate $A(10)$ from the graph. 17 years
   c. What diameters correspond to a tree aged between 10 and 20 years? $7 \le d \le 12$
   d. Sketch a graph of this relation with age on the x-axis and diameter on the y-axis. Is this the graph of a function? See margin.

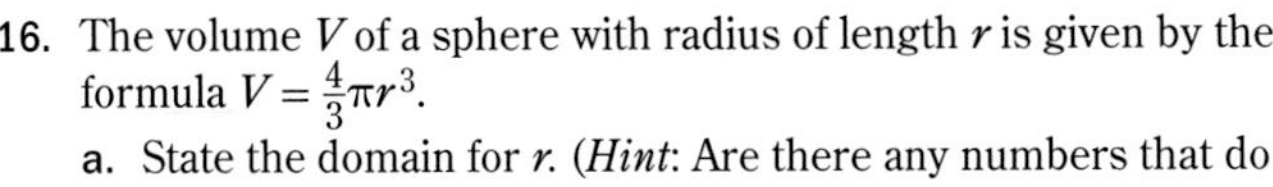

16. The volume V of a sphere with radius of length r is given by the formula $V = \frac{4}{3}\pi r^3$.
   a. State the domain for r. (*Hint*: Are there any numbers that do not make sense for the value of the radius?) $\{r \mid r \ge 0\}$
   b. Find the volume of a beach ball with a 15 cm radius. Round your answer to the nearest tenth. 14,137.2 cm^3

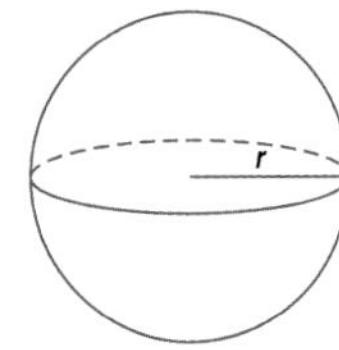

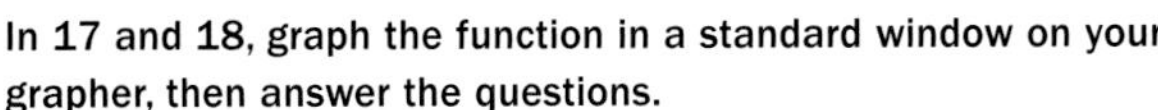

In 17 and 18, graph the function in a standard window on your grapher, then answer the questions.

17. $f(x) = 5$
   a. What is $f(15)$? 5
   b. State the domain and range of f.
18. $g(x) = -2x^2 - 7$
   a. What is the maximum value of g? -7
   b. State the domain and range of g.
19. On your grapher or CAS, graph the function $f(x) = \frac{4}{1 + x}$.
   a. Use your grapher to estimate $f(0)$. Check your answer using algebra. 4
   b. For what value of x is $f(x) = \frac{1}{2}$? Use your grapher and check your answer using algebra. $x = 7$

17b. $\{x \mid x$ is a real number$\}$; $\{y \mid y = 5\}$

18b. $\{x \mid x$ is a real number$\}$; $\{y \mid y \le -7\}$

Additional Answers

15d. yes

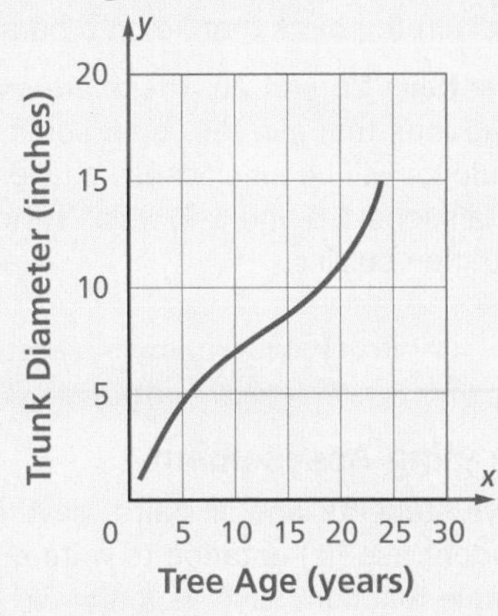

Notes on the Questions

Question 24 Some students may know that $f(n) = 0.5n(n - 3)$. So, if this function were graphed, it would be a set of discrete points that lie on a parabola.

Questions 25 and 26 These are simple equations that can tell you if some students will be significantly challenged by Lessons 1-6 and 1-7, which review equation solving.

4 Wrap-Up

Ongoing Assessment

Have students work in pairs. Have each student use $f(x)$ notation to write a simple function, such as $f(x) = 3x - 9$ or $f(x) = 4x^2 - 2$, and exchange papers. Each student should graph the function on his or her graphing utility and then give the domain and range of the function. If possible, have them give the maximum and/or minimum as well. Then have them check each other's work. Students should demonstrate an understanding of the domain and range of a function and determine maximum and minimum values.

Project Update

Project 2, *Functions and Graphs on the Internet,* on page 60 relates to the content of this lesson.

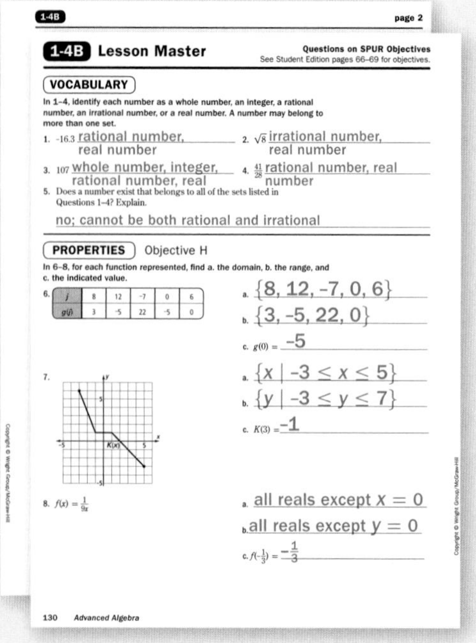

1-4B page 2

1-4B Lesson Master — Questions on SPUR Objectives. See Student Edition pages 66–69 for objectives.

VOCABULARY

In 1–4, identify each number as a whole number, an integer, a rational number, an irrational number, or a real number. A number may belong to more than one set.

1. -16.3 rational number, real number
2. $\sqrt{8}$ irrational number, real number
3. 107 whole number, integer, rational number, real number
4. $\frac{41}{28}$ rational number, real number
5. Does a number exist that belongs to all of the sets listed in Questions 1–4? Explain. no; cannot be both rational and irrational

PROPERTIES Objective H

In 6–8, for each function represented, find a. the domain, b. the range, and c. the indicated value.

6.

j	8	12	-7	0	6
$g(j)$	3	-5	22	-5	0

a. $\{8, 12, -7, 0, 6\}$
b. $\{3, -5, 22, 0\}$
c. $g(0) = -5$

7. a. $\{x \mid -3 \le x \le 5\}$
b. $\{y \mid -3 \le y \le 7\}$
c. $K(3) = -1$

8. $f(x) = \frac{1}{9x}$
a. all reals except $x = 0$
b. all reals except $y = 0$
c. $f(-\frac{1}{3}) = -\frac{1}{3}$

130 Advanced Algebra

20. Refer to Question 17 in Lesson 1-3, where you were asked to compare functions with equations $g(x) = 2^x$ and $h(x) = x^2$.
    a. Graph g and h together on your grapher in the window defined below. See margin.

xmin	xmax	xscale	ymin	ymax	yscale
–5	5	1	–2	15	1

    b. In this window, sometimes $h(x) > g(x)$ and sometimes $g(x) > h(x)$. Your grapher has a ZOOM feature which allows you to get a magnified view of certain regions of your graph. Use ZOOM and TRACE to approximate values of x for which $h(x) > g(x)$. $x < -0.77$ and $x > 2$

21. A formula for the height h of an object in free fall t seconds after its release from a height of 25 feet is $h = -16t^2 + 25$.
    a. Graph this equation on your grapher. Sketch the graph. (Most graphers use x for the independent variable, and $y1$, $y2$, etc. for the dependent variables, so you must substitute x for t and y for h when entering this equation.) See margin.
    b. Use the TRACE feature on your grapher to estimate the height of the object after 1.1 seconds. 5.64 ft

In an egg drop, contestants build contraptions to protect an egg to be dropped from a certain height. The winning contraption will protect the egg from breaking.

REVIEW

22. Suppose that for all x, $d(x) = 2x^3 - x + 3$. Evaluate. **(Lesson 1-3)**
    a. $d(2)$ 17 b. $d(-2)$ -11 c. $d(\pi r)$ $2(\pi r)^3 - \pi r + 3$

23. Use a CAS to find $S(100)$ when $S(n) = \frac{n(n+1)}{2}$. **(Lesson 1-3)** 5050

24. Let n = the number of sides of a polygon and $f(n)$ = the number of its diagonals. The figures below show that $f(4) = 2$ and $f(5) = 5$. Find $f(3)$ and $f(6)$. **(Lesson 1-3)** $f(3) = 0$, $f(6) = 9$

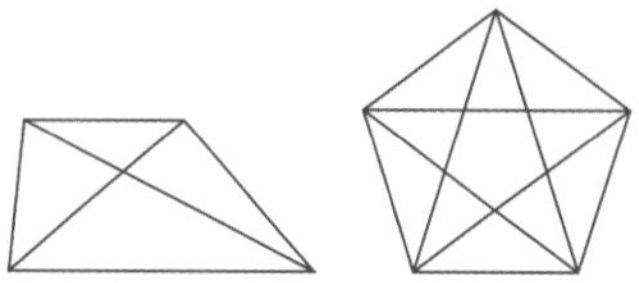

In 25 and 26, solve and check. (Previous Course)

25. $\frac{1}{3}r - 27 = 60$ 26. $2x = \frac{3}{2}x + 4$

25. $r = 261$; $\frac{1}{3}(261) - 27 = 60$

26. $x = 8$; $2(8) = \frac{3}{2}(8) + 4$

EXPLORATION

27. Find a coordinate graph in a newspaper or magazine. Does it represent a function? Why or why not? If it is a function, identify the domain and range of the function. Answers vary. Check students' answers.

QUIZ YOURSELF ANSWER

Answers vary. Sample: $-\frac{4}{5}$

Additional Answers

20a.

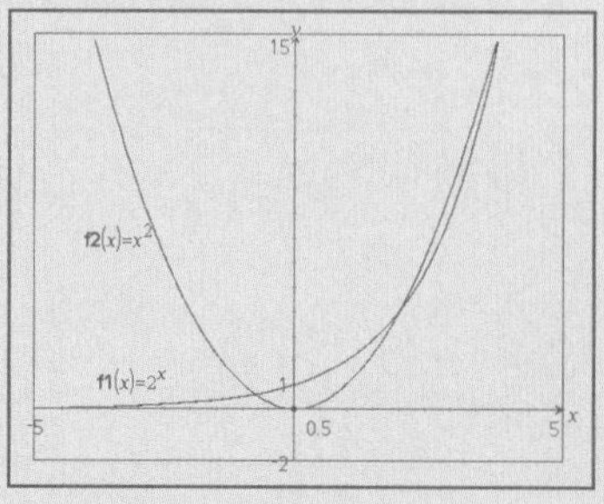

21a.

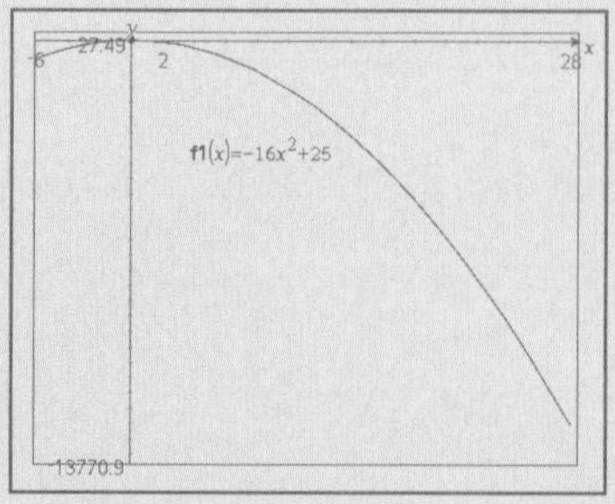

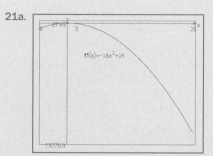

Lesson 1-5 Using Graphs and Tables of Functions

▸ **BIG IDEA** The graph of a function can tell a story and from it you can learn great deal about the function.

When a graph is plotted in the (x, y) coordinate plane, x is the independent variable, and y is the dependent variable. Time is often an independent variable, as in Example 1.

Mental Math

Suppose Berta drove 280 miles in four hours.

a. What was her average speed? 70 mph

b. Berta drove for another 30 minutes at the same speed. How far has she traveled in all? 315 miles

c. Berta stopped for a half-hour for lunch, then drove another 210 miles at the same speed. How long did she drive after lunch? 3 hours

d. If Berta started her trip at 9:30 A.M., at what time did she arrive at her destination? 5:30 P.M.

GUIDED

Example 1

Frank Furter rode his bicycle to Chuck Roast's house to plan a back-to-school picnic. The boys then rode a short distance to the park and then back to Frank's house. The graph below models Frank's trip where t is time in minutes and d is Frank's distance from home in miles.

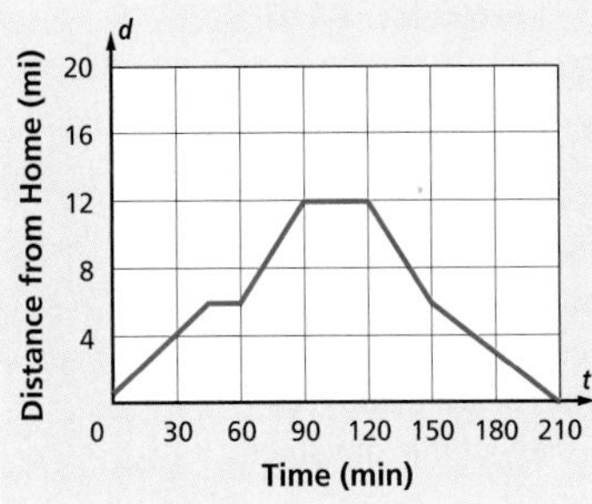

Use the graph of Frank's bicycle trip to answer the following questions.

a. **Which variable is a function of the other variable? Express this relationship in $f(x)$ notation. (Give the function the name f.)**

b. **State the domain and range of the function in this situation.**

c. **Estimate Frank's distance from home after 60 minutes, and write your answer using $f(x)$ notation.**

d. **Estimate how much time it took Frank to first reach 12 miles from home. Write your answer using $f(x)$ notation.**

e. **What is the significance of the left horizontal line segment? Estimate its endpoints, and describe it using $f(x)$ notation.**

(continued on next page)

Lesson 1-5

GOAL

Discuss how graphs can tell stories and how to use technology to create lists of function values.

SPUR Objectives

G Determine whether a given relation is a function.

H Determine the domain and range of a function.

L Use a graphing utility to graph functions and generate tables for functions.

Materials/Resources

- Lesson Masters 1-5A and 1-5B
- Resource Masters 1, 12, and 13
- CAS or graphing claculator

HOMEWORK

Suggestions for Assignment

- Questions 1–23
- Question 24 (extra credit)
- Reading Lesson 1-6
- Covering the Ideas 1-6

Local Standards

Background

This is a relatively easy lesson for students who have experience with graphing technology.

Example 1 We say that the graph "models" Frank's bicycle trip. It is a model because of its simplicity. No person can ride a bicycle at the same exact rate for 30 minutes, but the graph shows that he maintained constant speeds (the slopes of the lines) for as long as an hour. Make certain that students realize what each segment on the graph means.

Activity The "Table Step" is called a "t-step" or "Δt" on some calculators. It is an important aspect to the generation of a table of values. Notice that the QY on page 36 asks for a smaller increment to generate more values.

1 Warm-Up

Suppose the point (t, d) stands for the distance d in meters that a boat is from a pier t minutes from now. Graph this: The boat is at the pier now. It moves away from the pier at a constant rate for 5 min until it is 300 m from the pier. It drops anchor there and stays there for 10 min. Then it goes back to shore at a constant rate and gets back in 7 min.

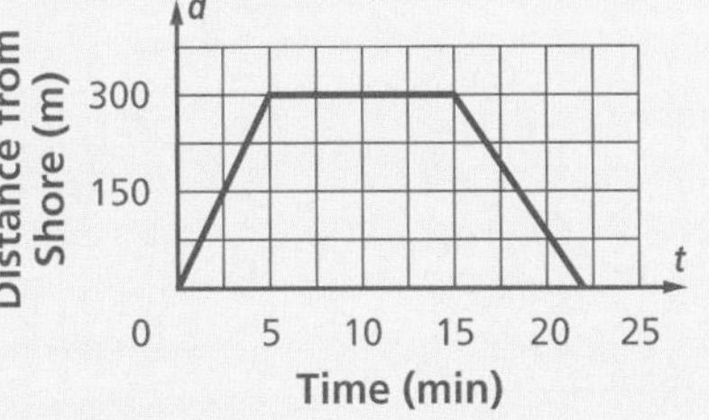

2 Teaching

Notes on the Lesson

Example 1 Here is a type of situation that students will have seen in previous UCSMP courses and perhaps other courses. Those who have not seen such a situation may be looking for a formula because the segments are connected. Point out that the graph, not a formula, defines the function here. To emphasize how much information is contained in this graph, you might ask students to write the story that the graph tells about Frank's bicycle trip in those 3.5 hours.

Creating and reading tables on a grapher It is possible that some of your students have never made a list, even if they have used a graphing calculator or other graphing utility. If so, you will have to go through this Activity on page 35 slowly. This is such an important skill that you should ensure that all students work through the Activity. You will likely need to be more specific about the directions for the model of calculator you are using in class to ensure that all students can find the table settings and change them when appropriate.

Solution

a. The time t is on the horizontal axis, and the distance d is on the vertical axis. So, the distance from home d is a function of the length of time t since Frank left home.
In $f(x)$ notation, __?__ = f(__?__). *d; t*

b. The domain is the set of possible values of the independent variable.
The domain is {t| __?__ ≤ t ≤ __?__} minutes. 0; 210
The range is the set of values attained by the dependent variable.
The range is {d| __?__ ≤ d ≤ __?__} miles. 0; 12

c. When $t = 60$, $d \approx$ __?__. The distance is about __?__ miles. 6; 6
In $f(x)$ notation, f(__?__) ≈ __?__ miles. 60; 6

d. The leftmost point on the graph at $d = 12$ is (90, 12). It took about __?__ minutes for Frank to ride 12 miles away from home. 90
In $f(x)$ notation, f(__?__) = 12 miles. 90

e. From about $t =$ __?__ to about $t =$ __?__ minutes, Frank's distance remained constant at about 6 miles. This shows that Frank stayed at Chuck's house for about 15 minutes. One explanation is that it might take time for Chuck to get ready to leave for the park. 45; 60
In $f(x)$ notation, for __?__ ≤ t ≤ __?__, f (__?__) = 6 miles. 45; 60; *t*

Creating and Reading Tables on a Grapher

Sometimes it is helpful to represent the ordered pairs of a function in a table. In previous courses, you may have found values for tables by substituting values into a formula. For example, if $y = 15 - 4x$ and $x = -2$, then $y = 15 - 4(-2) = 23$, and the ordered pair is (-2, 23). In the previous lesson, you used your grapher's TRACE feature to find ordered pairs. Your grapher can also generate a table of values automatically.

Activity

MATERIALS CAS or graphing calculator

Suppose a puddle of water is evaporating and its depth $D(t)$ in inches after t days is given by the formula $D(t) = 6 - \frac{1}{16}t^2$.

Step 1 Enter the equation into your grapher.

Step 2 Set up a table to start at $x = -5$ and to generate values in increments of 1. If your grapher needs an end value, use $x = 5$.

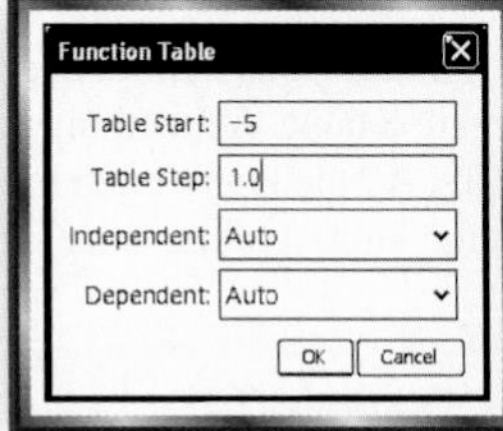

Step 3 Your table should be similar to the one to the right. If necessary, you can see more values in the table by scrolling with the up and down arrows on your grapher.

x	f1(x):=
	6−1/16.
-5.	4.4375
-4.	5.
-3.	5.4375
-2.	5.75
-1.	5.9375
0.	6.
-5.	

Step 4 The values in the x column represent which variable in this problem?
The values in the $f(x)$ column represent which variable in this problem?
Do all of the ordered pairs in the table realistically model the puddle of water situation? Why or why not?

Step 4. t days; $D(t)$ inches; no; negative values of x do not make sense because x represents elapsed time.

Step 5 Determine the water depth after 6 days. Write your answer in $D(t)$ notation. $D(6) = 3.75$ in.

Step 6 When is the water depth 5.75 inches? Write your answer in $D(t)$ notation. $D(2) = 5.75$ in.

Recall that a function *can* have two or more ordered pairs with the same second coordinate. For instance, in the table from the Activity, when $f(x) = 5$, then $x = -4$ or 4. However, only $x = 4$ models a real number of days.

Accommodating the Learner

Because using a graphing utility to make a table of values for a function is such an important skill, spend extra time with students to practice it. Give them a variety of linear and quadratic functions and have them use their graphing utility to make lists of values as they were asked to do in the Activity. They can discuss their results with one another and reconcile any discrepancies.

Additional Example

Example 1 The graph below gives the distances Maria traveled during a 7-hour trip. She drove some and then visited an historical museum. After visiting the museum, Maria drove some more and then stopped for dinner before returning home.

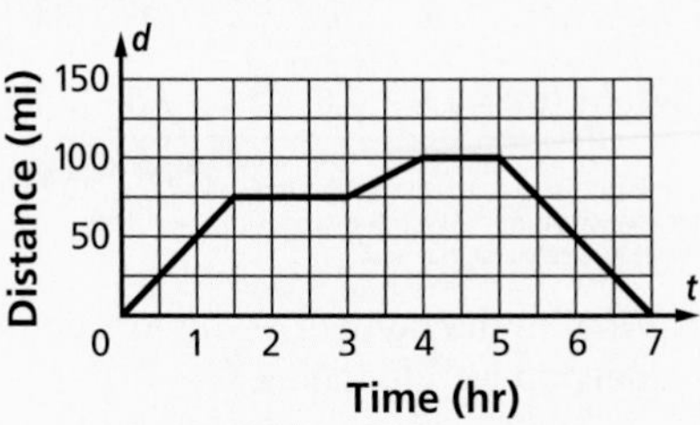

a. Which variable is a function of the other variable? Express this relationship in $f(x)$ notation.

b. State the domain and range of the function.

c. Estimate Maria's distance from home after 3.5 hours and write your answer using $f(x)$ notation.

d. Estimate how much time it took Maria to first be 100 miles from home.

e. What is the significance of the left horizontal line segment? Estimate its endpoints.

Solution

a. The distance d is a function of the time t since Maria left home: ___?___ = f(___?___). d; t

b. The domain is $\{t \mid$ ___?___ $\le t \le$ ___?___$\}$ hours. 0; 7 The range is $\{d \mid$ ___?___ $\le d \le$ ___?___$\}$ miles. 0; 100

c. When $t = 3.5$, $d =$ ___?___. The distance is about ___?___ miles. 75; 75 In symbols, f(___?___) = ___?___ miles. 3.5; 75

d. The left-most point on the graph at $d = 100$ is (4, 100). It took about ___?___ hours for Maria to travel 100 miles away from home. 4

e. From about $t =$ ___?___ to about $t =$ ___?___ minutes, Maria's distance remained constant at about 75 miles. This shows that Maria stopped and stayed at the museum for about $1\frac{1}{2}$ hours. 1.5; 3
For ___?___ $\le t \le$ ___?___, f(___?___) = 75 miles. 1.5; 3; t

Additional Example

Example 2 Robert Wadlow is the tallest person in medical history whose height has been substantiated. At birth, he was of normal height. The table below gives his height h at various ages a, where $h = f(a)$.

Age (yr)	8	10	16	18	22
Height (m)	1.9	2.0	2.4	2.5	2.7

Sources: http://www.altonweb.com/history/wadlow/; http://www.guinnessworldrecords.com/records/human_body/extreme_bodies/tallest_man.aspx

a. What is the domain of the function defined by this table? {8, 10, 16, 18, 22}

b. What is the range of this function? {1.9, 2.0, 2.4, 2.5, 2.7}

c. Find $f(16)$. What does this represent? 2.4; At age 16, Robert Wadlow was 2.4 m tall.

d. For what value of a does $f(a) = 2.7$? 22

Note: If students have trouble visualizing 2.7 meters, tell them that this height corresponds to 8 feet 11 inches.

3 Assignment

Recommended Assignment

- Questions 1–23
- Question 24 (extra credit)
- Reading Lesson 1-6
- Covering the Ideas 1-6

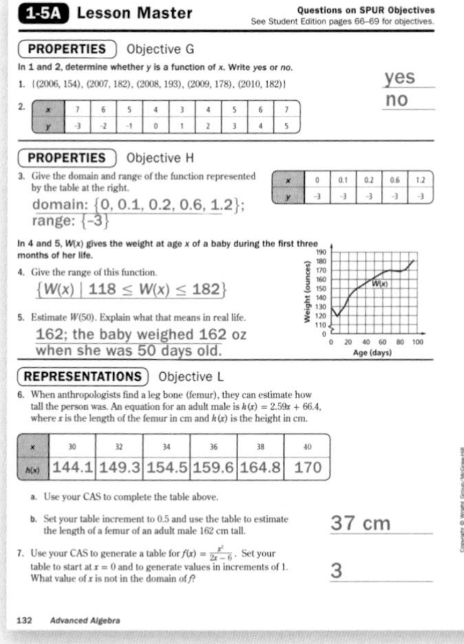

1-5A Lesson Master — Questions on SPUR Objectives. See Student Edition pages 66–69 for objectives.

PROPERTIES Objective G

In 1 and 2, determine whether y is a function of x. Write *yes* or *no*.

1. {(2006, 154), (2007, 182), (2008, 193), (2009, 178), (2010, 182)} yes

2. no

x	7	6	5	4	3	4	5	6	7
y	-3	-2	-1	0	1	2	3	4	5

PROPERTIES Objective H

3. Give the domain and range of the function represented by the table at the right.
domain: {0, 0.1, 0.2, 0.6, 1.2}; range: {-3}

x	0	0.1	0.2	0.6	1.2
y	-3	-3	-3	-3	-3

In 4 and 5, $W(x)$ gives the weight at age x of a baby during the first three months of her life.

4. Give the range of this function.
$\{W(x) \mid 118 \le W(x) \le 182\}$

5. Estimate $W(50)$. Explain what that means in real life.
162; the baby weighed 162 oz when she was 50 days old.

REPRESENTATIONS Objective L

6. When anthropologists find a leg bone (femur), they can estimate how tall the person was. An equation for an adult male is $h(x) = 2.59x + 66.4$, where x is the length of the femur in cm and $h(x)$ is the height in cm.

x	30	32	34	36	38	40
h(x)	144.1	149.3	154.5	159.6	164.8	170

a. Use your CAS to complete the table above.

b. Set your table increment to 0.5 and use the table to estimate the length of a femur of an adult male 162 cm tall. 37 cm

7. Use your CAS to generate a table for $f(x) = \frac{x^2}{2x - 6}$. Set your table to start at $x = 0$ and to generate values in increments of 1. What value of x is not in the domain of f? 3

132 Advanced Algebra

Unlike graphs in which smooth or *continuous* curves show the ordered pairs at *all* values of the domain and range, tables give a *discrete* view of a function that shows only some of the ordered pairs. For example, your table in the Activity only shows the ordered pairs for integer values of x. To find more pairs, you can change the table increment in the table setup.

STOP See Quiz Yourself at the right.

A function does not need to be defined by a formula in order to create a table. A function can be defined simply as a set of ordered pairs. A function defined by a set of ordered pairs has a domain and range limited to the values in the ordered pairs.

▶ QUIZ YOURSELF

Find two other ordered pairs for the puddle function D by changing the table increment to 0.5.

Example 2

In 2000, the Centers for Disease Control and Prevention (CDC) found the mean height h in centimeters for girls in the U.S. at various ages a where $h = f(a)$. Some of these data are given in the table below.

a	2	4	6	8	10
h	85	101	115	127	138

a. What is the domain of the function defined by this table?

b. What is the range of this function?

c. Find $f(6)$. What does this represent?

d. For what value of a does $f(a) = 138$?

The average height of adult women in the United States in 2002 was 5′ 3.75″.

Solution

a. The domain is the set of values the independent variable a can have. The domain is {2, 4, 6, 8, 10}.

b. The range is the set of possible values of the dependent variable h. The range is {85, 101, 115, 127, 138}.

c. $f(6) = 115$. At age 6, girls in the U.S. have an average height of 115 cm.

d. $f(a) = 138$ when $a = 10$.

Questions

COVERING THE IDEAS

In 1–3, refer to the graph in Example 1.

1. How far from home was Frank when he ended his trip? How does the graph show this?

2. Estimate $f(75)$ and explain what it means.

1. 0 miles; The graph shows this because the rightmost point is (210, 0), and the coordinate 0 indicates distance from home.

2. $f(75) \approx 9$. This means that after 75 minutes, Frank was 9 miles from home, on the way from Chuck's house to the park.

Accommodating the Learner

Lesson 1-2 presented the differences between relations and functions. A relation is any set of ordered pairs, whereas as function is a set of ordered pairs in which there is one unique y component for each x component.

Show students the diagram at the right. Ask: Which graph is a relation and which graph is a function? Explain your rationale.

a.

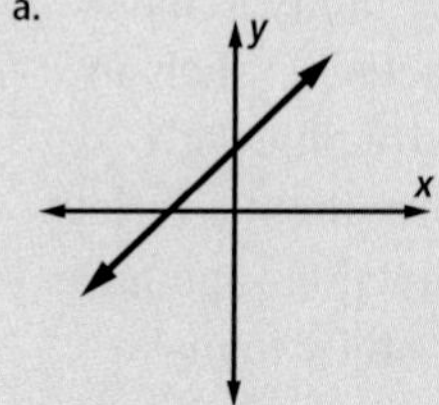

b.

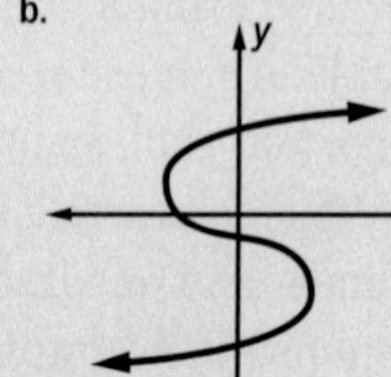

c.

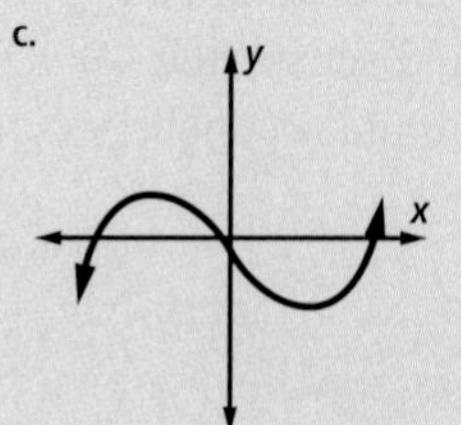

d.

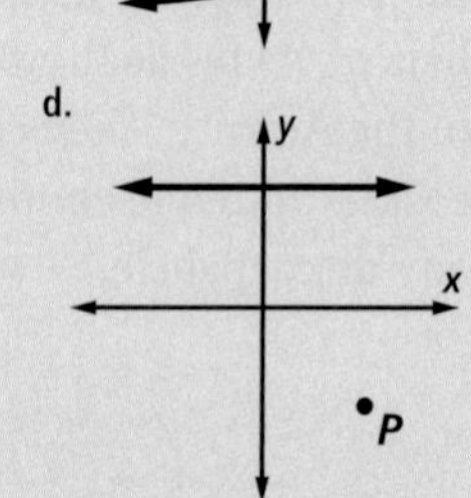

3. What is the maximum value of $f(t)$? 12

In 4–6, refer to the following table of values for the function with equation $s = f(t)$.

s	–3	–2	0	4	9
t	9	4	0	16	81

4. What is the domain of this function? What is the range?
5. Find each of the following:
   a. $f(16)$ 4
   b. $f(4)$ -2
6. For what value of t does $f(t) = 9$? 81

In 7 and 8, refer to the Activity.

7. Change the table increment to 0.2.
   a. What is the depth of the water after 3.6 days? 5.19 in.
   b. When does the depth reach 4.04 inches? After 5.6 days
8. Can you find an increment to show all the ordered pairs of D? Why or why not?
9. Use your grapher to make a table of values for $f(x) = 9 - x^2$ that begins at $x = 1$ and has increments of 0.5. List the first five ordered pairs in the table.

4. domain: {0, 4, 9, 16, 81}; range: {-3, -2, 0, 4, 9}

8. No; you could always break it into smaller units of time.

9. (1, 8); (1.5, 6.75); (2, 5); (2.5, 2.75); (3, 0)

APPLYING THE MATHEMATICS

10. The graph below shows the distances $M(t)$ and $P(t)$ that Maria and Pia traveled during a 40-km bike race.

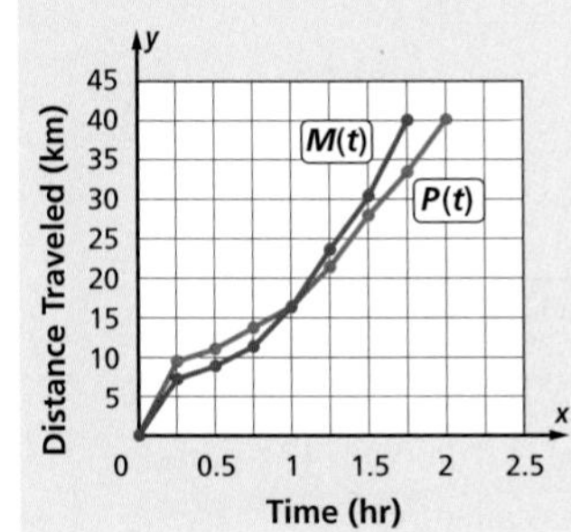

   a. Estimate $P(0.5) - M(0.5)$. What does this quantity represent?
   b. Find a value of t such that $M(t) = P(t)$. What is happening at this moment?
   c. Do $M(t)$ and $P(t)$ have the same domain? Why or why not?

10a. 2; Pia is 2 km ahead of Maria after half an hour.

10b. $t = 1$; Maria and Pia are the same distance in the race at this time.

10c. No; Maria completes the race in 1.75 hr, but Pia takes 2 hr to complete it.

Notes on the Questions

Questions 10 and 14–16 The ability to understand and answer these questions is not just a mathematical skill; it is a consumer skill as well. Graphs like these are found throughout the print media.

Graphs a and c are functions because each x-value has one unique y-value. Graphs b and d are relations, but they are not functions. In graph b, an x-value near the y-axis has more than one y-value. In graph d, there exists a point on the horizontal line that shares the x-value of point P. Two different y-values correspond to this x-value.

Notes on the Questions

Question 16 Notice how helpful function notation is in this question.

In 11–13, a set of ordered pairs is given in a table. Is the set a function? If it is, give its domain and range. If it is not, explain why not.

11.

x	y
-3	-0.1
-2	-0.06
-1	-0.03
0	0
1	0.03
2	0.06
3	0.1

12.

x	y
0	-6
1	-4
2	-2
3	0
2	2
1	4
0	6

13.

x	y
-6	0
-4	1
-2	2
0	3
2	2
4	1
6	0

11. Yes; domain: {-3, -2, -1, 0, 1, 2, 3}; range: {-0.1, -0.06, -0.03, 0, 0.03, 0.06, 0.1}

12. No; there is more than one value for *y* assigned to certain values for *x*

13. Yes; domain: {-6, -4, -2, 0, 2, 4, 6}; range: {0, 1, 2, 3}

In 14–16, refer to the table and graph below. They give information about the number of farms and the average size (in acres) of these farms across the United States from 1995 to 2005.

Year	1995	1996	1997	1998	1999	2000	2001	2002	2003	2004	2005
Number of Farms (thousands)	2,200	2,190	2,190	2,190	2,190	2,170	2,160	2,160	2,130	2,110	2,100

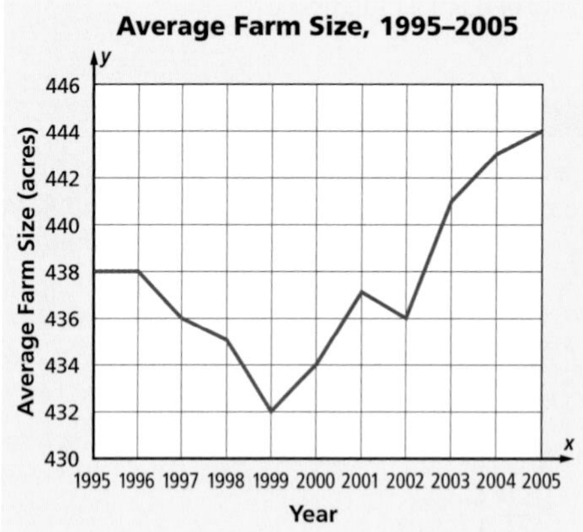

14. If the average size function is called A, what is $A(2000)$? 434 acres

15. If the function giving the number of farms is called N, find $N(2002)$. 2,160,000

16. a. Calculate $A(2004) \cdot N(2004) - A(1996) \cdot N(1996)$. -24,490,000
    b. Explain in words what the computation in Part a represents.

16b. Overall, the area taken up by farms in the United States decreased by 24,490,000 acres between 1996 and 2004.

17. For the equation $s = 4 - r^2$:

   a. Find the values of s which correspond to the given values of r.

r	-3	-2	-1	0	1	2	3
s	? -5	? 0	? 3	? 4	? 3	? 0	? -5

   b. Plot (r, s) on a coordinate graph for each of the values in the table. Is s a function of r? Explain. See margin.

   c. Plot (s, r) on a coordinate graph for each of the values in the table. Is r a function of s? Explain. See margin.

In 2007, the high school graduation rate in France was 85%.

REVIEW

In 18 and 19, use this information. In the United States many teachers grade tests on a scale of 1–100. In France it is common to grade tests on a scale of 1–20 (with 20 being the highest). Suppose G is a function that converts a grade in the American system to a grade $G(x)$ in the French system. (Lesson 1-4)

18. Write an expression for $G(x)$. $G(x) = \frac{x}{5}$

19. Give a reasonable domain and range for the function G.

20. Write out the elements of the set $\{S|\ S$ is a state in the United States, and S does not share a border with any other state$\}$. (Lesson 1-4)

21. Consider all ordered pairs of the form $(x, 2x - \pi x^2)$. Do these ordered pairs describe a function? If they do, describe this function using mapping notation. If they do not, explain why not. (Lessons 1-3, 1-2)

22. The formula for the surface area of a sphere with radius R is $A = 4\pi R^2$.

   a. Write the function mapping R onto A in $f(x)$ notation.

   b. Which is the dependent variable and which is the independent variable? (Lessons 1-3, 1-2)

23. The radius of the planet Neptune is approximately 24,750 kilometers. Estimate its surface area to the nearest million square kilometers. (Previous Course)

EXPLORATION

24. Think about your trips to and from school yesterday. Draw a graph similar to the graph in Example 1 to model your trip. What is your independent variable? What is your dependent variable? Are there any horizontal lines on your graph? If so, what do they represent? If not, why not?

19. $\{x|\ 0 \le x \le 100\}$; $\{G(x)|\ 0 \le G(x) \le 20\}$

20. Hawaii, Alaska

21. Yes; $f: x \rightarrow 2x - \pi x^2$

22a. $A(R) = 4\pi R^2$

22b. A is the dependent variable, R is the independent variable.

23. 7,698,000,000 km^2

24. Answers vary. Sample: The independent variable is time, the dependent variable is distance from home. The horizontal lines represent time spent in one place.

QUIZ YOURSELF ANSWER

Answers vary. Samples: (1.5, 5.8594); (2.5, 5.6094).

Notes on the Questions

Question 20 In topological terms, the existence of such sets S in the United States means that the United States is disconnected.

Question 24 This question should be assigned to everyone, and you might have students volunteer to tell their stories. It is fun and educational, too.

4 Wrap-Up

Ongoing Assessment

Have students work in pairs. Have each student write a simple equation, such as $f(x) = x^2 - 4$ or $f(x) = x^3$. Have partners exchange papers and use a graphing utility to generate a table of values for the function each is working with. The table should begin at $x = 1$ with increments of 0.5. Have them list the first five ordered pairs in the table. Students should be able to use their graphing utilities to correctly find values of a given function.

Project Update

Project 2, *Functions and Graphs on the Internet,* on page 60 relates to the content of this lesson.

Additional Answers

17b. Yes; each value of r is paired with a single value of s.

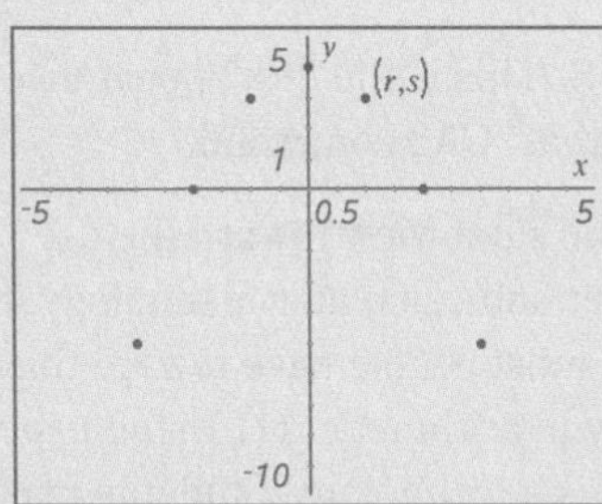

17c. No; certain values of s are paired with more than one value of r.

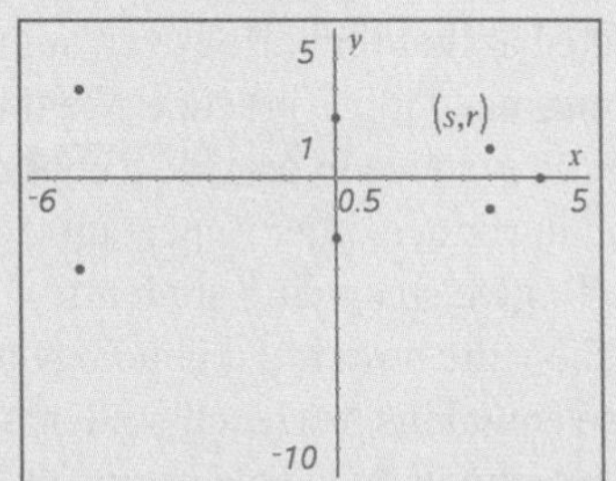

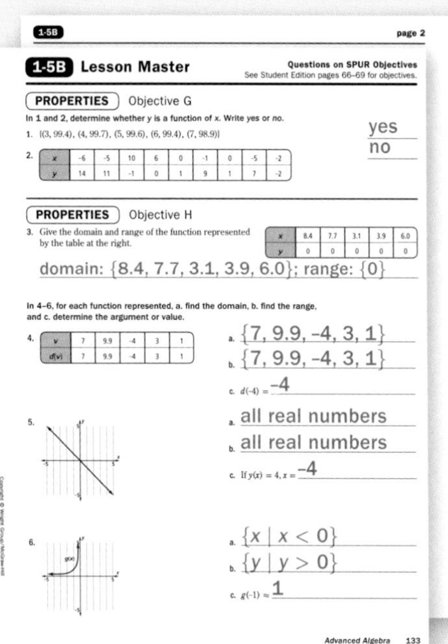

1-5B page 2

1-5B Lesson Master

Questions on SPUR Objectives
See Student Edition pages 66–69 for objectives.

PROPERTIES Objective G

In 1 and 2, determine whether y is a function of x. Write *yes* or *no*.

1. $\{(3, 99.4), (4, 99.7), (5, 99.6), (6, 99.4), (7, 98.9)\}$ yes

2. no

x	-6	-5	10	6	0	-1	0	-5	-2
y	14	11	-1	0	1	9	1	7	-2

PROPERTIES Objective H

3. Give the domain and range of the function represented by the table at the right.

x	8.4	7.7	3.1	3.9	6.0
y	0	0	0	0	0

domain: $\{8.4, 7.7, 3.1, 3.9, 6.0\}$; range: $\{0\}$

In 4–6, for each function represented, a. find the domain, b. find the range, and c. determine the argument or value.

4.

v	7	9.9	-4	3	1
$d(v)$	7	9.9	-4	3	1

a. $\{7, 9.9, -4, 3, 1\}$

b. $\{7, 9.9, -4, 3, 1\}$

c. $d(-4) =$ −4

5.

a. all real numbers

b. all real numbers

c. If $y(x) = 4$, $x =$ −4

6.

a. $\{x \mid x < 0\}$

b. $\{y \mid y > 0\}$

c. $g(-1) \approx$ 1

Advanced Algebra 133

Lesson 1-6

GOAL

Review the Distributive Property and the solving of linear equations in the context of functions. Show that the Distributive Property works with fractions and decimals as well as integers.

SPUR Objectives

C Solve and check linear equations.

K Use linear equations to solve real-world problems.

Materials/Resources

- Lesson Masters 1-6A and 1-6B
- Resource Masters 14 and 15
- Quiz 2

HOMEWORK

Suggestions for Assignment

- Questions 1–27
- Questions 28 and 29 (extra credit)
- Reading Lesson 1-7
- Covering the Ideas 1-7

Local Standards

1 Warm-Up

1. A concert group plans to visit 4 cities on a tour. One-third of the total distance the group travels is from its home city to the first city. One-fifth of the total distance is from the first city to the second. It is 273 miles from the second city to the third city and 441 miles back home. Find the total distance traveled. Let d = total distance traveled in miles. $\frac{1}{3}d + \frac{1}{5}d + 273 + 441 = d$; $d = 1530$; 1530 miles
2. Suppose $f(n) = 8n - (4 - 2n)$. For what value of n is $f(n) = 3356$? $n = 335.6$

Lesson 1-6 Solving Equations

BIG IDEA By solving $y = f(x)$ for x you can find the value of x that leads to a particular value of y.

Suppose you are studying a function f. Two key questions often arise.

1. Given a value of x, what is the value of $f(x)$?
2. Given a value of $f(x)$, what is the value of x?

In the previous lesson, you learned how to answer these questions using graphs and tables. If the function is described with an equation, then answering the first question usually involves evaluating an expression. Answering the second question usually involves solving an equation. Example 1 illustrates these two situations. The expressions and equations are easy enough that you should be able to work with them by hand, but we also show how to use a CAS on the same questions since a CAS is useful for more complicated problems.

Mental Math

a. How many outfits can you make with 4 t-shirts and 5 pairs of pants, if one of the pairs of pants cannot be worn with two of the shirts? 18

b. How many outfits can you make with 4 blouses, 5 skirts, and 6 pairs of shoes? 120

c. How many outfits can you make with 4 shirts, x pairs of pants, y pairs of shoes, and 7 ties? $28xy$

Example 1

In the board game Monopoly®, Boardwalk is the most expensive property. The one-time cost of the property plus a hotel is $1,400, while the rent earned from another player landing on it is $2,000. If n = the number of players landing on Boardwalk, then $f(n) = 2000n - 1400$ is the owner's total profit after n players have landed on the property.

a. What will be the owner's profit after 4 people land on Boardwalk?

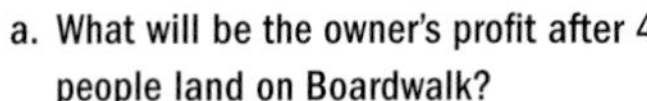

b. Is it possible for the owner to make exactly $10,000 in profit?

Solution 1

a. The profit is given by $f(4)$.
$f(n) = 2000n - 1400$
So, $f(4) = 2000 \cdot 4 - 1400 = 6600$.
The owner's profit will be $6,600.

Background

Earlier texts of the UCSMP series stressed the solving of linear equations, and mastery was expected at that time. However, some students may need more practice. We try to distribute the practice to provide a continual review and introduce other important concepts. To give struggling students help and show the power of technology to solve these equations, we teach students to use CAS technology to solve equations. In particular, in Solution 2 of Example 1, students see that a CAS can emulate the steps of the paper-and-pencil algorithm for solving an equation.

Example 3 This is the first appearance of the "such that" CAS command.

We have the same view toward the use of computer and calculator technology in algebra as most people have toward this technology in arithmetic. (1) Using paper and pencil is a technology. Students make mistakes with it at least as often as they make mistakes with more sophisticated

b. The question asks you to find n when $f(n) = 10{,}000$. Substitute for $f(n)$ and solve the equation.

$$2000n - 1400 = 10{,}000$$
$$2000n - 1400 + 1400 = 10{,}000 + 1400 \quad \text{Add 1400 to both sides.}$$
$$2000n = 11{,}400$$
$$n = 5.7 \quad \text{Divide both sides by 2000.}$$

The property owner needs 5.7 people to land on Boardwalk. So it is not possible to earn exactly $10,000 in profit.

Solution 2 Use a CAS.

a.

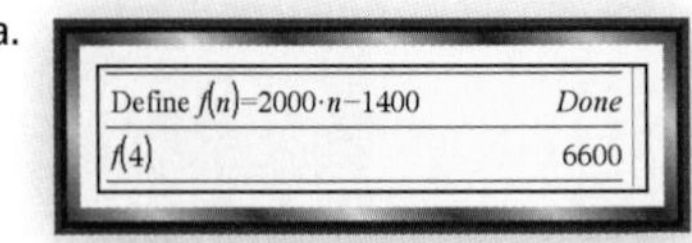

Define $f(n)=2000\cdot n-1400$ Done
$f(4)$ 6600

b.

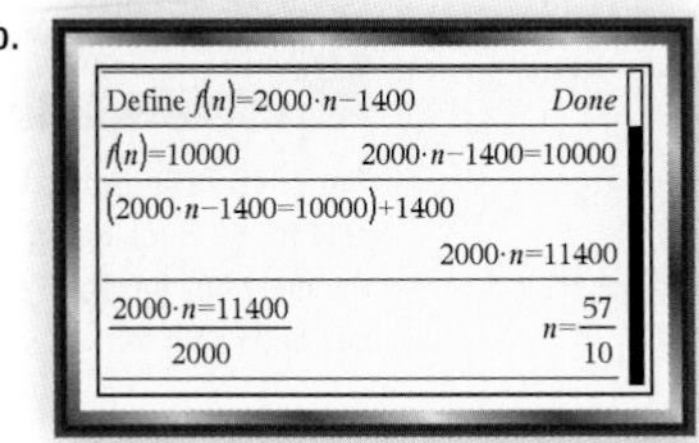

Define $f(n)=2000\cdot n-1400$ Done
$f(n)=10000$ $2000\cdot n-1400=10000$
$(2000\cdot n-1400=10000)+1400$ $2000\cdot n=11400$
$\frac{2000\cdot n=11400}{2000}$ $n=\frac{57}{10}$

$\frac{57}{10}$ is not an integer, so it is not possible for an owner to earn exactly $10,000 in profit.

STOP See Quiz Yourself 1 at the right.

Recall that when you subtract (or add the opposite of) a number from each side of an equation, you are applying the Addition Property of Equality to find an *equivalent,* but simpler, equation. There are many other properties that are frequently applied when solving equations. The properties of real numbers used in algebra are listed in Appendix A. Skim this Appendix now, and refer to it whenever you need to check the meaning or name of a particular property. The next three examples explore how one of these properties, the Distributive Property, can be used to solve equations.

Distributive Property

For all real numbers a, b, and c,
$$c(a + b) = ca + cb.$$

QUIZ YOURSELF 1

Can the owner make exactly $12,000 in profit? Explain.

technology. They also sometimes overuse paper-and-pencil technology just as they sometimes overuse electronic technology. (2) Students should be able to do some tasks in their head, and they should be able to do some tasks with paper and pencil. Here they learn how to use technology to do these tasks. Furthermore, there are some tasks that are more appropriately done "in your head," some for which it is reasonable to expect paper-and-pencil competency, and some that wisely should be done with technology. (3) In all cases, it is useful if a student has enough knowledge to use one technology to check results found with another technology.

1-6

2 Teaching

Notes on the Lesson

Example 1 We strongly recommend having students go through these steps using a CAS. Notice how this CAS (and most others) can treat an equation as an object. In the third line of the solution to Part b, 1400 is added to the equation. This is shorthand for adding 1400 to both sides of the equation. Similarly, in the last line, the equation is divided by 2000, shorthand for dividing both sides of the equation by 2000. You may be uncomfortable with this notation when you first see it, but the power of the CAS to emulate both efficient and inefficient equation-solving steps makes the CAS very useful as a learning tool.

If you have students who are struggling with these equations, you might start with an equation such as $4 - 3x = 8x + 14$. Now have students use their CAS to add or subtract various expressions to or from both sides. For example, what happens when you add 4? $8 - 3x = 8x + 18$ Subtract $3x$? $4 - 6x = 5x + 14$ Add –4? $-3x = 8x + 10$ Adding –4 *does* yield a simpler equation. The CAS thus can instruct students in what paper-and-pencil steps to take.

Additional Example

Example 1 In the board game Monopoly®, you purchase four houses and a hotel on Illinois Avenue for a one-time cost of $750. You will earn rent of $1100 each time another player lands on the property. If i players land on Illinois Avenue, then your profit is $f(i) = 1100i - 750$.

a. What is your profit after 1 player lands on Illinois Avenue? $350

b. How many players must land on Illinois Avenue so that your profit is at least $15,000? at least 15 players

Example 2 In previous UCSMP courses, students were taught that if there is a tax of, say 21%, then the total value can be calculated by multiplying by 1.21: $P + 0.21P = 1.21P$. Similarly, if there is a discount of 7%, then the total value after discount is found by multiplying by 0.93: $P - 0.07P = 0.93P$. These are examples of the Size-Change Model for Multiplication, and they are helpful if not necessary for understanding exponential growth. If students do not understand the construction of the equation in Example 2, note that total cost is an application of the Putting-Together Model for Addition, and the equation reads *value of first card plus value of second card equals $550*.

When justifications are given for the steps in solving an equation, one must read both across and down—across to see the justification and down to see how each step follows from the previous one. It is important in equation solving to not be distracted by all the steps and examine only how each step follows from the one previous. Reading the solution to an equation in this manner differs markedly from reading a proof.

There are three ways of writing justifications: (1) Name the property, such as the "Multiplication Property of Equality." (2) Describe the property with variables, as in "If $a = b$, then $ac = bc$." (3) Indicate what was done, as in "Multiply each side by $\frac{1}{28}$." Students should be able to give any of these types of justifications; we tend to give either the first or the third type.

Additional Example

Example 2 Suppose you just received a $50,000 inheritance. At first, you decide to invest some of the money in a certificate of deposit account that earns 6% and the rest of the money in a savings account that earns 4%. If x dollars are invested at 6%, then $E(x) = 0.06x + 0.04(50{,}000 - x)$ gives the interest earned in 1 year. If you want to earn $2500 in the first year, how much money should be placed in each account?

Solution Solve for x when given $E(x) = 0.06x + 0.04(50{,}000 - x)$.

$0.06x + 0.04(50{,}000 - x) = 2500$

Distribute 0.04:
$0.06x + \underline{\ ?\ } - \underline{\ ?\ } = 2500$
2000; $0.04x$

Add like terms: $\underline{\ ?\ } + \underline{\ ?\ } = 2500$
2000; $0.02x$

Subtract 2000 from both sides:
$\underline{\ ?\ } = \underline{\ ?\ }$ $0.02x$; 500

Divide each side by 0.02: $x = \underline{\ ?\ }$
$25,000

$50{,}000 - x = \underline{\ ?\ }$ $25,000

By investing $25,000 in each account, you will earn $2500 in the first year.

Using the Distributive Property

In Example 2, the Distributive Property is used to solve an equation containing parentheses.

GUIDED

Example 2

Darius had $500 to spend at the baseball card convention. He decided to spend all his money buying the rookie cards of his two favorite players. At the end of the season, Darius found that the first card increased in value by 21%, while the second card decreased in value by 7%. He spent d dollars on the first card, so he spent $(500 - d)$ dollars on the second card.

So,

$$T(d) = 1.21d + 0.93(500 - d)$$

gives the total value of the two cards. If Darius's cards were worth $550 at the end of the season, how much did he spend on each card?

The 1909 T206 Honus Wagner sold for $2.8 million in 2007, the most any baseball card has been sold for.

Solution 1 You are given that $T(d) = 550$, and asked to find d. Solve an equation.

$1.21d + 0.93(500 - d) = 550$		
$1.21d + \underline{\ ?\ } - \underline{\ ?\ } = 550$	Distribute the 0.93.	465; $0.93d$
$\underline{\ ?\ } + \underline{\ ?\ } = 550$	Add like terms.	$0.28d$; 465
$\underline{\ ?\ } = \underline{\ ?\ }$	Subtract 465 from each side.	$0.28d$; 85
$d \approx \underline{\ ?\ }$	Divide each side by 0.28.	303.57
$500 - \underline{\ ?\ } = \underline{\ ?\ }$	Find the cost of the other card.	303.57; 196.43

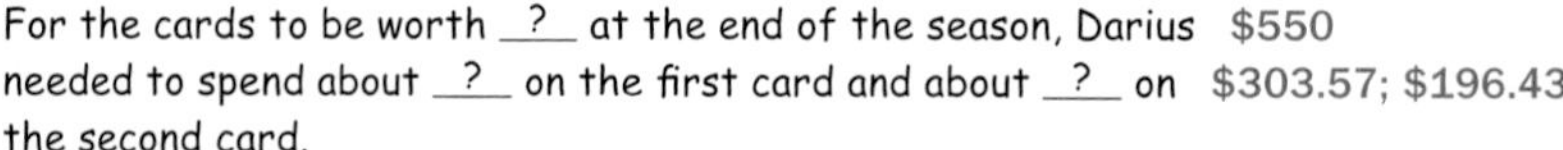

For the cards to be worth __?__ at the end of the season, Darius needed to spend about __?__ on the first card and about __?__ on the second card. $550; $303.57; $196.43

Solution 2 Enter the equation in a CAS. The CAS automatically simplifies the equation to get one of the steps in Solution 1. You can then solve this equation.

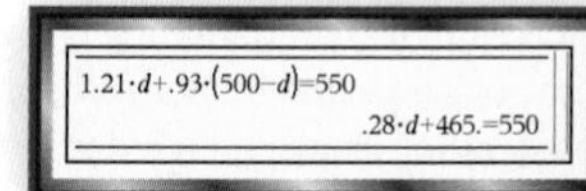

Clearing Fractions in Equations

Often, an equation modeling a real situation will involve fractions. If you want to clear an equation of fractions for simplicity, multiply each side of the equation by a common multiple of the denominators. If there is more than one term on either side of the equation, you will then need to apply the Distributive Property. Example 3 illustrates this procedure.

Accommodating the Learner

Give students the following problem to solve: Water that passes through a purification system can reach a storage tank through Pipe A or Pipe B. Pipe A can fill the storage tank in 20 minutes, while it takes Pipe B 30 minutes to fill the same tank. How long will it take to fill the tank if both pipes are used simultaneously? 12 minutes

Example 3

In game 5 of the 2006 NBA Finals between Miami and Dallas, Dirk Nowitzki scored $\frac{1}{5}$ of Dallas's points and Josh Howard scored $\frac{1}{4}$ of Dallas's points. The rest of the Dallas Mavericks scored a total of 55 points. How many points did Dallas score?

Dirk Nowitzki, of the Dallas Mavericks.

Solution Write an equation to model the situation, then solve it.

If P = the total number of points scored by Dallas in the game, then Dirk scored $\frac{1}{5}$ of P, Josh scored $\frac{1}{4}$ of P, and the rest of the team scored 55 points. So, $P = \frac{1}{5}P + \frac{1}{4}P + 55$.

To clear the fractions in this equation, multiply both sides by a common multiple of the denominators 4 and 5. One common multiple is 20.

$20P = 20\left(\frac{1}{5}P + \frac{1}{4}P + 55\right)$

$20P = 4P + 5P + 1100$ Distribute the 20.

$20P = 9P + 1100$ Combine like terms.

$11P = 1100$ Subtract $9P$ from each side.

$P = 100$ Divide each side by 11.

So, the Dallas Mavericks scored 100 points, with Dirk scoring $\frac{1}{5}(100) = 20$ points and Josh scoring $\frac{1}{4}(100) = 25$ points.

Check Use the SUCH THAT command on your CAS to verify that the computed solution is true. On the CAS pictured here this function is represented by a vertical bar |.

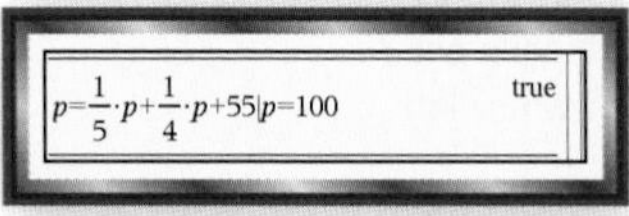

In words, this display reads "p equals one-fifth p plus one-fourth p plus 55 such that p equals 100 is true", so it checks. Sometimes "such that" is read "with."

Opposite of a Sum Theorem

From the Distributive Property and the fact that $-1 \cdot x = -x$ for all x, you can deduce that
$-(a + b) = -1 \cdot (a + b) = -1 \cdot a + -1 \cdot b = -a + -b = -a - b$.

This result is the Opposite of a Sum Theorem.

Accommodating the Learner

You may need to remind students that solving an equation involves writing a series of equivalent equations. Explain that *equivalent equations* are equations with the same solutions. Suggest that students cover the right columns, or reasons, in the solutions on Examples 2 and 3. Then have them explain how one equivalent equation is obtained from the previous one.

Notes on the Lesson

Clearing fractions in equations
A frequent problem students have when "clearing fractions" from an equation containing fractions on only one side is to use multiplication only on that side of the equation. Use Example 3 to illustrate that each side of an equation can be thought of as having implicit parentheses. Thus, the equation to be solved is $P = (\frac{1}{5}P + \frac{1}{4}P + 55)$. Stress that the Multiplication Property of Equality is applied to *both* sides, so both sides need to be multiplied by 20 or a multiple of 20 to clear fractions.

We show one way to use a CAS to check this problem. A second way available on some CASs is to have the calculator do each step of the paper-and-pencil solution, as in Example 1. Begin with $(\frac{1}{5}P + \frac{1}{4}P + 55 = P)$. Enter $(\frac{1}{5}P + \frac{1}{4}P + 55 = P)*20$; the machine will multiply both sides by 20, giving the result. This capability enables students to use a CAS to practice a skill they should have without the technology. A third way to check with a CAS is to use a "Solve" command. However, the "Solve" command should not be used as a solution method.

Additional Example

Example 3 Suppose during a 2007–2008 regular season NBA game involving the Boston Celtics, Kevin Garnett scored $\frac{1}{3}$ of Boston's points in the game, and Ray Allen scored $\frac{1}{4}$ of the points. The rest of the players scored 60 points. Write an equation to model the situation; then determine how many points Boston scored in this game. $p = \frac{1}{3}p + \frac{1}{4}p + 60$, where p = the total points scored by Boston; 144

Opposite of a Sum Theorem Of the many special cases of the Distributive Property, we identify the Opposite of a Sum Theorem because subtracting a binomial or other polynomial gives students so much trouble.

Additional Example

Example 4 Suppose $h(y) = 13y - (26 - 3y)$. For what value of y is $h(y) = 100$?

Solution $100 = 13y - (26 - 3y)$

Write the subtraction in the parentheses as a sum:
$100 = 13y - (26 + \underline{\ ?\ })$ -3y

Apply Opposite of a Sum Theorem:
$100 = 13y - \underline{\ ?\ } + \underline{\ ?\ }$ 26; 3y

Add like terms: $100 = \underline{\ ?\ } - \underline{\ ?\ }$
16y; 26

Add 26 to each side: $\underline{\ ?\ } = \underline{\ ?\ }$
126; 16y

Divide each side by 16: $\underline{\ ?\ } = y$
7.875

3 Assignment

Recommended Assignment

- Questions 1–27
- Questions 28 and 29 (extra credit)
- Reading Lesson 1-7
- Covering the Ideas 1-7

1-6A Lesson Master

Questions on SPUR Objectives
See Student Edition pages 66–69 for objectives.

SKILLS Objective C

In 1–6, a. solve the equation, and b. check your answer by hand or with a CAS.

1. $2a - 7 = 5a + 17$
   a. $a = -8$
   b. $2(-8) - 7 = 5(-8) + 17$
2. $5 + 3(c - 9) = 12.5$
   a. $c = 11.5$
   b. $5 + 3(11.5 - 9) = 12.5$
3. $4(2n + 3) = 6 - (n - 2)$
   a. $n = -\frac{4}{9}$
   b. $4(2(-\frac{4}{9}) + 3) = 6 - (-\frac{4}{9} - 2)$
4. $0.15n + 0.03(8000 - n) = 576$
   a. $n = 2800$
   b. $0.15(2800) + 0.03(8000 - 2800) = 576$
5. $\frac{2}{5} = \frac{18}{x + 3}$
   a. $x = 42$
   b. $\frac{2}{5} = \frac{18}{42 + 3}$
6. $\frac{2}{3}x + \frac{1}{4}x = x - 3.75$
   a. $x = 45$
   b. $\frac{2}{3}(45) + \frac{1}{4}(45) = 45 - 3.75$

USES Objective K

7. Devon split $4000 between a savings account paying 2% interest and a Certificate of Deposit paying 5% interest. If he put x dollars in the savings account, the total interest he will earn in the first year will be $I(x) = 0.02x + 0.05(4000 - x)$. If this money grows to $4155 at the end of the year, how much did he put in the savings account? $1500
8. Sheryl spent one-fourth of the money she made at her summer job on entertainment and one-fifth on transportation. She saved half of her earnings for college, and spent the remaining $150 on clothes. How much did she make at her summer job? $3000
9. You have exactly $120 to spend on new school clothes, including 6% sales tax. What is the most that the clothes themselves can cost? $113.20

Advanced Algebra 135

Opposite of a Sum Theorem

For all real numbers a and b,
$$-(a + b) = -a + -b = -a - b.$$

The next example applies this theorem in solving an equation.

GUIDED

Example 4

Suppose $g(a) = 3a - (7 - 5a)$. For what value of a is $g(a) = 12$?

Solution

$12 = 3a - (7 + \underline{\ ?\ })$ Write the subtraction in parentheses as a sum. -5a

$12 = 3a - \underline{\ ?\ } + \underline{\ ?\ }$ Opposite of a Sum Theorem -7; 5a

$12 = \underline{\ ?\ } - 7$ Add like terms. -8a

$\underline{\ ?\ } = \underline{\ ?\ }$ Add 7 to each side. 19; 8a

$\underline{\ ?\ } = a$ Divide each side by the coefficient of a. 2.375

Check To check your answer, calculate the value $g(a)$ using the value you calculated for a. The result should be 12.

 See Quiz Yourself 2 at the right.

QUIZ YOURSELF 2

True or False? $-(-(-2 - 3)) = -2 + 3$

Questions

COVERING THE IDEAS

In 1 and 2, suppose a bathtub contains 60,000 cubic inches of water. If water can be drained from the tub at a rate of 800 cubic inches per second, then $w(t) = 60{,}000 - 800t$ represents the volume of water left in the tub after draining for t seconds.

1. What volume of water will be in the tub after 18 seconds? 45,600 in^3
2. After how many seconds will the tub be empty? 75 seconds

In 3 and 4, assume Jamila has a collection of 200 nickels and dimes. If n is the number of nickels in her collection, then $c(n) = 0.05n + 0.10(200 - n)$ represents the face value amount of money her collection is worth.

3. Evaluate $c(122)$. What does the answer mean in the context of this problem?
4. Solve $c(n) = 19.15$. What does the answer mean in the context of this problem?

3. 13.9; if she has 122 nickels, her collection is worth $13.90.
4. $n = 17$; if her collection is worth $19.15, she has 17 nickels.

In 5–7, an equation is given. Solve the equation and check your solution using the SUCH THAT command on a CAS.

5. $4y + 50 = 5y + 42$
6. $2z + 2 = 2 - 6z$
7. $4 = \frac{6}{x}$

In 8 and 9, identify a common multiple of the denominators and solve the equation.

8. $\frac{h}{6} + \frac{h}{10} = 1$
9. $\frac{1}{8}x + \frac{2}{3}x = 5$

10. **Fill in the Blank** According to the Opposite of a Sum Theorem, $-(3 - 9y) =$ __?__.

In 11 and 12, an equation is given.

a. Solve each equation.

b. Check your work.

11. $3x - (x + 1) = 7$
12. $5n - (9 - 5n) = 9$

5. $y = 8$
6. $z = 0$
7. $x = 1.5$
8. Answers vary. Sample: 30; $h = \frac{15}{4}$
9. Answers vary. Sample: 24; $x = \frac{120}{19}$
10. $-3 + 9y$

11a. $x = 4$

11b. $3(4) - (4 + 1) = 7$

12a. $n = \frac{9}{5}$

12b. $5\left(\frac{9}{5}\right) - \left(9 - 5\left(\frac{9}{5}\right)\right) = 9$

APPLYING THE MATHEMATICS

In 13–15, use this information. A bowler's *handicap* is a bonus given to some bowlers in a league. The handicap *h* is a function of *A*, the bowler's average score, and is sometimes determined by the formula $h(A) = 0.8(200 - A)$, when $0 < A < 200$.

13. What is the handicap for a bowler whose average is 135? 52
14. If a bowler has a handicap of 28, what is the bowler's average? 165
15. What is the domain of the function h? $0 < A < 200$

In September 1895, the first meeting of the American Bowling Congress met in New York City. The ABC standardized dimensions for bowling balls, pins, and lanes.

Source: www bowlingmuseum.com

In 16–19, a. solve the equation by hand, and b. enter the equation into a CAS and solve the resulting equation.

16. $0.05x + 0.12(50000 - x) = 5{,}995.8$ $x = 60$
17. $\frac{1}{3}t + \frac{1}{4}t + 6 = t$ $t = \frac{72}{5}$
18. $\frac{2}{3}p + \frac{1}{2} = p - 3$ $p = \frac{21}{2}$
19. $0.05z + 0.1(2z) + 0.25(100 - 3z) = 20$ $z = 10$
20. Gloria owns a video rental store. Two-fifths of the store items are comedies, one-eighth are horror films, one-fourth are dramas, and the remaining 270 are video games.
    a. How many items are there in total? 1,200
    b. How many comedies are there? 480
    c. How many horror films are there? 150
21. Suppose $f(n) = \frac{n-1}{n+2}$.
    a. What is $f(18)$? $\frac{17}{20}$
    b. If $f(n) = \frac{46}{49}$, find n. $n = 47$

Notes on the Questions

Questions 8 and 9 Point out that you could multiply by any common multiple of the denominators, and the fractions would be cleared, but the numbers would be greater.

Questions 13–15 This formula may be remembered by some students who studied from UCSMP *Algebra*.

Question 21b Did any students do this in their heads? Notice that, in the formula for $f(n)$, the numerator and denominator differ by 3. Because they differ by 3 in the value of $f(n)$, it must be that $n - 1 = 46$.

Question 22 This problem should be done without solving the sentences.

Notes on the Questions

Questions 23–26 Many people are surprised at the size of the trade deficit.

Question 27 Many students, even after completing a full year of geometry, often encounter difficulties in answering questions about surface area and volume. Yet in the real world, objects are 3-dimensional. The ideas of volume and surface area are also important in calculus. The formula needed here is $A = 2\pi rh$, a special case of the more general formula for cylindrical figures, including prisms. Lateral area is the product of their height and the perimeter of their base.

Question 28 You might ask more advanced students for a rule that will find and graph all such pairs of numbers. $xy = x + y$ implies that $y = \frac{x}{x-1}$ if $x \neq 1$. So for each value of x other than 1, there exists a unique value of y.

4 Wrap-Up

Ongoing Assessment

Have students work in pairs. Have each student write two equations similar to those in Questions 5–9 or 16–19. Have students exchange papers and solve their partners' equations. Tell students to show all the steps and a check. Students should provide equations of the type requested and demonstrate an ability to solve and check those equations.

Administer Quiz 2 (or a quiz of your own) after students complete this lesson.

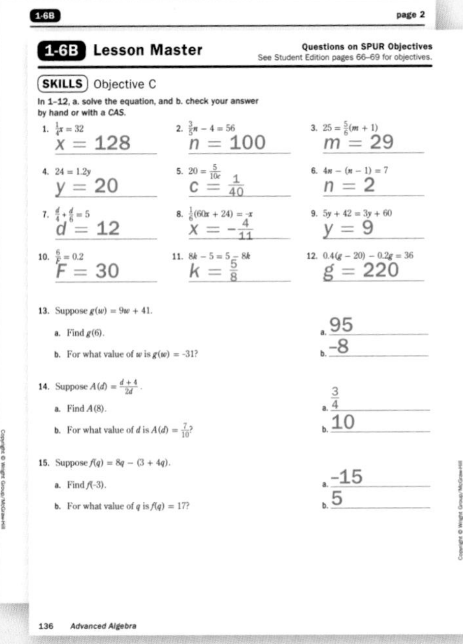

1-6B page 2

1-6B Lesson Master

Questions on SPUR Objectives
See Student Edition pages 66–69 for objectives.

SKILLS Objective C

In 1–12, a. solve the equation, and b. check your answer by hand or with a CAS.

1. $\frac{1}{4}x = 32$ $x = 128$
2. $\frac{3}{5}n - 4 = 56$ $n = 100$
3. $25 = \frac{5}{6}(m + 1)$ $m = 29$
4. $24 = 1.2y$ $y = 20$
5. $20 = \frac{5}{10c}$ $c = \frac{1}{40}$
6. $4n - (n - 1) = 7$ $n = 2$
7. $\frac{d}{4} + \frac{d}{6} = 5$ $d = 12$
8. $\frac{1}{6}(60x + 24) = -x$ $x = -\frac{4}{11}$
9. $5y + 42 = 3y + 60$ $y = 9$
10. $\frac{6}{F} = 0.2$ $F = 30$
11. $8k - 5 = 5 - 8k$ $k = \frac{5}{8}$
12. $0.4(g - 20) - 0.2g = 36$ $g = 220$

13. Suppose $g(w) = 9w + 41$.
    a. Find $g(6)$. a. 95
    b. For what value of w is $g(w) = -31$? b. -8

14. Suppose $A(d) = \frac{d+4}{2d}$.
    a. Find $A(8)$. a. $\frac{3}{4}$
    b. For what value of d is $A(d) = \frac{7}{10}$? b. 10

15. Suppose $f(q) = 8q - (3 + 4q)$.
    a. Find $f(-3)$. a. -15
    b. For what value of q is $f(q) = 17$? b. 5

136 Advanced Algebra

22. **Multiple Choice** Which of the following sentences are equivalent to $3(x - 7) = \frac{5}{2}$? There may be more than one correct answer. A, C

    A $3x - 21 = \frac{5}{2}$ B $3x - 21 = \frac{5}{21}$ C $x - 7 = \frac{5}{6}$

REVIEW

In 23–26, refer to the graph below. In the graph, x = the year, $i(x)$ = the value in millions of dollars of imports into the United States, and $E(x)$ = the value of exports from the United States, also in millions of dollars. (Lessons 1-3 and 1-4)

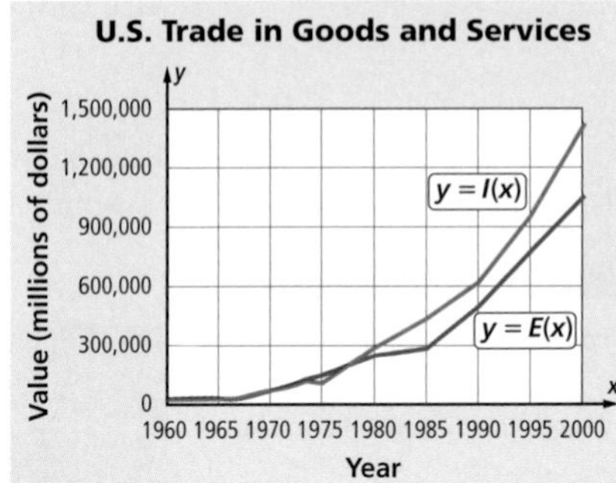

23. Estimate $I(1995)$.
24. In what unit is the dependent variable of function E measured?
25. In what year(s) was $E(x) > \$500,000$ million?
26. A negative *balance of trade* exists when a country's imports are greater than its exports. Write a few sentences comparing the balance of trade for the period 1960–1980 to the balance of trade for the period 1980–2000.
27. A cylindrical soft drink can has a lateral area of about 241 cm^2. If the radius of the can is 3.2 cm, approximate the can's height to the nearest tenth of a cm. **(Previous Course)** 12.0 cm

EXPLORATION

28. Veronica was asked to find the product of two given numbers. By mistake, she added instead of multiplying. Yet she got the right answer! What two different numbers might have been given?
29. The graph for Questions 23–26 only displays the values of U.S. imports and exports through the year 2000. Research on the Internet to find more recent import and export data. What can you say about trends in imports, exports, or balance of trade by looking at the more recent data? See margin.

23. about \$1,000,000 million
24. millions of dollars
25. 1990 through 2000
26. Answers vary. Sample: Between 1960 and 1980, the dollar value of imports into the United States and exports from the United States were roughly equal. Thus, there was an equal balance of trade. However, beginning around 1980, and continuing through 2000, the value of imports exceeded exports, and the United States had a negative balance of trade.
28. Answers vary. Sample: $4, \frac{4}{3}$ (They could be any two numbers of the form $x, \frac{x}{x-1}$.)

QUIZ YOURSELF ANSWERS

1. No; the owner would need 6.7 people to land on Boardwalk to get exactly \$12,000 profit.
2. false

Additional Answers

29. Answers vary. Sample:

Year	Exports (in millions)	Imports (in millions)	Balance of Trade (in millions)
2001	1,004,896	1,370,022	(365,126)
2002	974,721	1,398,446	(423,725)
2003	1,017,757	1,514,672	(496,915)
2004	1,157,250	1,769,341	(612,092)
2005	1,283,070	1,997,441	(714,522)
2006	1,445,703	2,204,225	(758,522)
2007	1,621,808	2,333,420	(711,612)

Source: www.census.gov/foreign-trades/statistics/historical/index.html

U.S. imports and exports values increase in a manner that is consistent with previous values. Though these trends remain roughly the same, the negative balance of trade substantially increases as both values continue on their paths of divergence.

Lesson 1-7 Rewriting Formulas

Vocabulary

equivalent formulas

BIG IDEA Every formula defines one variable in terms of other variables; by using equation-solving properties you can manipulate a formula so that any one of the variables is defined in terms of the rest of the variables.

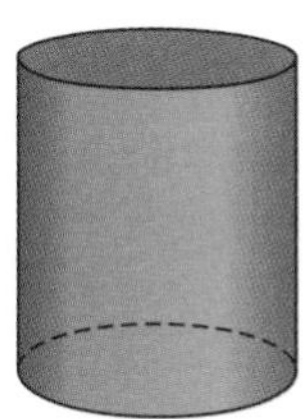

The volume V of a cylindrical barrel is given by the formula $V = \pi r^2 h$, where r is the barrel's radius and h is the barrel's height. This formula gives the volume V in terms of r and h. If you have values for r and h, you can use this formula to calculate V. For instance, if a barrel has radius 30 cm and height 100 cm, then

$$V = \pi(30 \text{ cm})^2(100 \text{ cm})$$
$$= 90{,}000\pi \text{ cm}^3$$
$$\approx 283{,}000 \text{ cm}^3.$$

In some situations it is useful to solve a formula for one of the other variables. Example 1 illustrates how to convert a formula to a more useful form.

Mental Math

The 180-member marching band is going on a field trip. Suppose that one bus can transport 50 students.

a. How many buses are needed to transport the band members? 4

b. One chaperone for every 10 students is going on the trip. Now how many buses are needed? 4

c. The instruments take up 15 seats on one of the buses. Now how many buses are needed? 5

Example 1

Justin Case is an engineer for a barrel manufacturing company. He wants to design a cylindrical barrel to contain 500,000 cm^3 of liquid and is considering several different radii and heights. To do this, it is useful to solve the volume formula for h in terms of r.

a. Solve the formula $V = \pi r^2 h$ for h in terms of V and r.

b. Find the height of a barrel with radius 30 cm that will contain 500,000 cm^3 of liquid.

(continued on next page)

Lesson 1-7

GOAL

Emphasize the importance of solving a formula for some variable other than the original isolated variable. This lesson also provides another day to work on solving open sentences.

SPUR Objectives

D Solve formulas for variables in them.

F Use a CAS to solve equations or expand expressions.

I Describe relationships between variables in a formula.

Materials/Resources

- Lesson Masters 1-7A and 1-7B
- Resource Masters 1 and 16

HOMEWORK

Suggestions for Assignment

- Questions 1–20
- Question 21 (extra credit)
- Reading Lesson 1-8
- Covering the Ideas 1-8

Local Standards

1 Warm-Up

1. **a.** Solve the formula $A = \ell w$ for w. $w = \frac{A}{\ell}$

   b. Solve the formula $A = \ell w$ for ℓ. $\ell = \frac{A}{w}$

   c. Which formula gives w in terms of A and ℓ? a

2. A line has the equation $5x - 3y = 10$. Find an equation for this line as a formula for y in terms of x. $y = \frac{5x}{3} - \frac{10}{3}$

Background

The statement of Example 1 **1** gives the motivation for rewriting formulas. Students need to understand that such manipulations make subsequent evaluations of the formula much easier. It is not uncommon for manuals in the trades to give three formulas where one would suffice, so a manual might give $d = rt$, $r = \frac{d}{t}$, and $t = \frac{d}{r}$, as if they were somehow mysteriously related. Of course, the relationship is not mysterious at all.

Emphasize to students that when a formula is solved for a particular variable, the same properties for solving an equation are used. Consequently, this lesson contains no new properties.

Some students have great trouble solving equations when the coefficients themselves are variables. Point out that solving these kinds of equations is often easier than solving equations with numerical coefficients because less arithmetic is involved.

2 Teaching

Notes on the Lesson

Each of Examples 1 through 3 involve a CAS. Example 1 involves an equation that students should be able to solve by hand. Having seen in the last lesson how a CAS can be used to do each step of a paper-and-pencil solution, students see here how a CAS can solve an equation in one command.

Additional Example

Example 1 The period (P) of a pendulum is the time in seconds that it takes a pendulum to make one complete swing back and forth and is calculated by using the formula $P = 2\pi\sqrt{\frac{\ell}{g}}$, where ℓ = length of the pendulum in meters and g = acceleration due to gravity (9.8 meters per second squared).

a. Solve the formula $P = 2\pi\sqrt{\frac{\ell}{g}}$, for ℓ. $\ell = g\frac{P^2}{4\pi^2}$

b. What is the approximate length of a pendulum whose period is 1 minute? $\approx$ 893.65 m

Sources: http://hyperphysics.phy-astr.gsu.edu/hbase/pend.html; http://www.glenbrook.k12.il.us/gbssci/phys/Class/1DKin/U1L5b.html

Note-Taking Tips

Encourage students to include in their journals the steps for making computations on a CAS.

Solution 1

a. Solve for h in terms if V and r.

$V = \pi r^2 h$ Original formula

$\frac{V}{\pi r^2} = \frac{\pi r^2 h}{\pi r^2}$ Divide both sides by πr^2. (You can do this because $r \neq 0$.)

$\frac{V}{\pi r^2} = h$ Simplify.

b. Substitute the given values for V and r.

$h = \frac{V}{\pi r^2} = \frac{500{,}000 \text{ cm}^3}{\pi(30 \text{ cm})^2} \approx 176.8 \text{ cm}$

The barrel needs to be about 180 cm high to contain 500,000 cm^3 of liquid.

Solution 2

a. Use the SOLVE( ) command on a CAS to solve for h. One CAS display is shown below. Entering ",h" after the formula in the command line tells the CAS to solve for h.

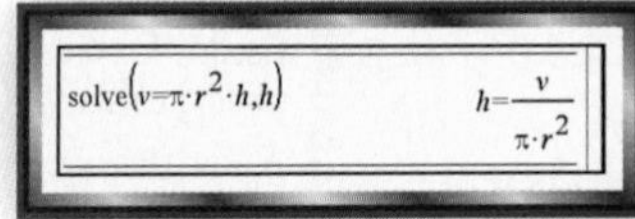

b. Substitute the given values for V and r to find h. We use the SUCH THAT command and the AND connector to enter both variable values at once. The display below shows both an exact answer and an approximate answer.

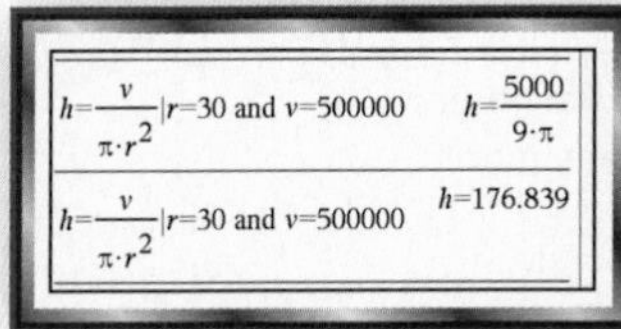

See Quiz Yourself 1 at the right.

QUIZ YOURSELF 1

Find h when $V = 500{,}000 \text{ cm}^3$ and $r = 32$ cm.

The formulas $V = \pi r^2 h$ and $h = \frac{V}{\pi r^2}$ are *equivalent formulas* because any V, r, and h that satisfy one of them also satisfies the other. Two formulas are **equivalent formulas** when the values of the variables that satisfy them are the same.

Accommodating the Learner

Some students may have difficulty identifying what each variable in a formula represents. For example, in the formula $d = rt$, say: "distance equals rate times time." For a formula like $A = \frac{1}{2}bh$, you could draw a triangle with an altitude and write the letters b and h in different colors.

Example 2

The formula $c = \frac{65t}{r - 65}$ computes the number c of hours needed for one car driving r miles per hour to catch up to another car that is t hours ahead and driving at 65 mph. Solve the formula for t in terms of c and r.

Solution Solve the formula for t by hand. Compare these steps to the computations on a CAS.

By hand **On a CAS**

$c = \frac{65t}{r - 65}$ Write down the formula (at left) and enter it on a CAS (at right).

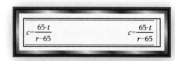

$c \cdot (r - 65) = 65t$ Multiply each side by $(r - 65)$. You may see the word ANS on your screen before you push ENTER. ANS refers to the last thing displayed on the CAS. In this case, it is the whole formula for c.

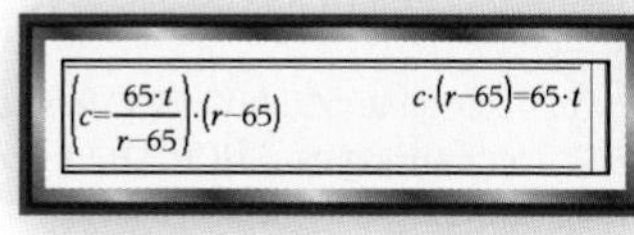

$cr - 65c = 65t$ Use the Distributive Property. The CAS shown here does this by using the EXPAND( ) command.

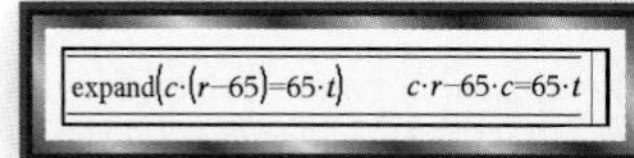

$\frac{cr - 65c}{65} = t$ Divide each side by 65.

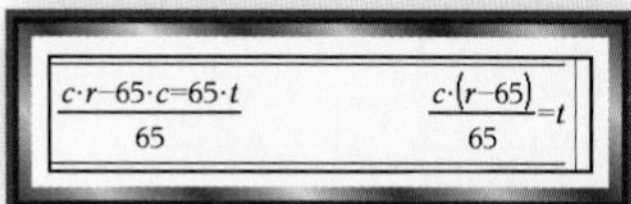

The formula is solved for t in terms of c and r. The result is the same, whether done by hand or with CAS.

 See Quiz Yourself 2 at the right.

> **QUIZ YOURSELF 2**
>
> a. Why is $c = \frac{65t}{r - 65}$ undefined when $r = 65$?
>
> b. Find t if $r = 70$ and $c = 10$. Explain your result in the context of the problem.

Using a CAS as an aid when solving equations has some advantages. It can be faster and more efficient than computing by hand. Using a CAS can also simplify the process for solving for a variable in an equation, especially when that variable's exponent is greater than 1, or when there is more than one variable, as Example 3 illustrates. The process can also be simplified by substituting values for some of the variables to *reduce* the problem to a function of a single variable.

Notes on the Lesson

Example 2 This is a more difficult equation and demonstrates that a CAS can show a solution that may not look the same as the solution found by hand. In this case, the formula for t is rewritten (using the EXPAND( ) command) without necessarily solving for a particular variable. You might note that, as a check of the expression for t, students can use unit analysis. In units, $\frac{cr}{65}$ is hours (c) multiplied by miles per hour (r) divided by miles per hour (65), resulting in hours; from this are subtracted hours (c), and the result is hours (t).

Students may wonder where the original equation $c = \frac{65t}{d - 65}$ came from. Because $r = \frac{d}{t}$ or, equivalently, $d = rt$, we get $t = \frac{d}{r}$. The catch-up time c is thus the catch-up distance divided by the catch-up rate. The other family is $65t$ ahead, so that is the catch-up distance. The catch-up rate is the difference between the catch-up family's rate and the other family's rate, $r - 65$.

Additional Example

Example 2 Because the density of air consumed by scuba divers increases as they dive deeper, they consume more air the deeper they dive. The formula $t = \frac{30s}{d + 30}$ is used by some scuba divers to estimate the number of minutes (t) of air they will have at a depth (d) in sea water, if they consume a tank of air at the surface in s minutes. Solve the formula for d in terms of t and s. $d = 30\frac{s}{t} - 30$

Additional Example 2 Recreational scuba diving depth is limited to 120 feet. For most divers the limiting factor for the duration of a dive is the amount of nitrogen absorbed by the body, not the amount of available air.

Accommodating the Learner

Electricity can be described as the flow of electrons through a conductor. Electricity flows more freely through some conductors than others. The force opposing the flow of electricity is called resistance and is measured in ohms. In electrical circuits, resistance (a resistor) can be applied in a series mode or in a parallel mode. When two or more resistors are connected in series, the total resistance in the circuit is the sum of the individual resistances. So $R_T = R_1 + R_2 + R_3 + \ldots + R_n$. If the resistors are connected in parallel, the total resistance is still the sum, but now the formula is

$$\frac{1}{R_T} = \frac{1}{R_1} + \frac{1}{R_2} + \frac{1}{R_3} + \ldots + \frac{1}{R_n}.$$

A parallel circuit has one branch in series. If the total resistance is 2.25 ohms, $R_1 = 3$ ohms, and $R_2 = 4$ ohms, what is R_3 if R_2 and R_3 are connected in series?

Hint: Have students solve the equation $\frac{1}{R_T} = \frac{1}{R_1} + \frac{1}{R_2 + R_3}$ for R_3. 5 ohms

Sources: http://physics.bu.edu/py106/notes/Circuits.html; http://physics.bu.edu/~duffy/PY106/Resistance.html

Notes on the Lesson

Example 3 In Part b, one variable is fixed. This is a hard concept for some students, as the answer does not contain the same variables as the original formula. The CAS highlights the substitution and can make it easier to understand what was done.

Additional Example

Example 3 A certain ancient pyramid has a volume of x cubic meters. Each side of its base is 231 meters.

a. Solve $V = \frac{1}{3}Bh$ for h. $h = \frac{3V}{B}$

b. Assume that the pyramid has a volume of 2,614,689 cubic meters. What is its height? 147 m

3 Assignment

Recommended Assignment

- Questions 1–20
- Question 21 (extra credit)
- Reading Lesson 1-8
- Covering the Ideas 1-8

1-7A Lesson Master — Questions on SPUR Objectives. See Student Edition pages 66–69 for objectives.

SKILLS Objective D

1. Density is defined as mass divided by volume, or $D = \frac{m}{V}$.
   a. Solve $D = \frac{m}{V}$ for m. $m = DV$
   b. Solve $D = \frac{m}{V}$ for V. $V = \frac{m}{D}$
2. The simple interest formula is $B = P + Prt$ where P is the principal (the amount borrowed), r is the interest rate, t is the time, and B is the total amount repaid.
   a. Solve the formula for t. $t = \frac{B-P}{Pr}$
   b. Solve the formula for P. $P = \frac{B}{1+rt}$

SKILLS Objective F

In 3 and 4, use the CAS ENTER X,T,Θ,n PRGM ALPHA DEL function to rewrite the expression.

3. $-(2x + 5y - 7) =$ $-2x - 5y + 7$
4. $(12 - 2a)(20 - 2a)(a) =$ $4a^3 - 64a^2 + 240a$
5. In a right triangle, one leg is 3 inches longer than the other leg. The hypotenuse is 15 inches long.
   a. Set up an equation using the Pythagorean Theorem. $x^2 + (x + 3)^2 = 15^2$
   b. Use the CAS SIN ON LOG VARS ENTER command to solve your equation. $x = -12$ or $x = 9$
   c. You should have gotten two answers in Part b. Determine which (if either) is a solution to the problem. $x = 9$ only

PROPERTIES Objective I

6. The formula for the volume of a cone is $V = \frac{1}{3}\pi r^2 h$. Rewrite this formula for a cone whose height is twice its radius. $V = \frac{2}{3}\pi r^3$
7. **Multiple Choice** If an object is moving in a circular path, the centripetal force F on the object is given by $F = \frac{mv^2}{r}$, where m is the mass of the object, v is the object's velocity, and r is the radius of the circular path. Which, if any, of these equations are equivalent to the given formula? B and C

   A $Fm = rv^2$ B $\frac{F}{m} = \frac{v^2}{r}$ C $v = \sqrt{\frac{Fr}{m}}$ D $\frac{F}{r} = \frac{m}{v^2}$

138 Advanced Algebra

Example 3

a. Solve $V = \pi r^2 h$ for r.

b. Assume a fixed volume of 500,000 cm^3. Write the formula for r in terms of h only.

Solution

a. Solve the formula for r on a CAS. The CAS result at the right shows two different values for r.

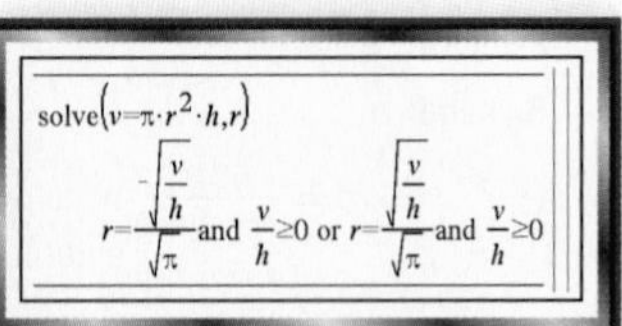

So either $r = \frac{-\sqrt{\frac{V}{h}}}{\sqrt{\pi}}$ or $r = \frac{\sqrt{\frac{V}{h}}}{\sqrt{\pi}}$.

The first expression is negative, which is impossible in this situation, since $r > 0$.

So, $r = \frac{\sqrt{\frac{V}{h}}}{\sqrt{\pi}}$. You could also write this as $r = \frac{\sqrt{V}}{\sqrt{h\pi}}$.

b. Substitute 500,000 for V. This can be done by hand, or by using the SUCH THAT command on a CAS.

Notice that the CAS simplified $\sqrt{500000}$ but left the answer in exact form. So $r = 500 \cdot \frac{\sqrt{2}}{\sqrt{h \cdot \pi}}$ is a formula for r in terms of h.

The volume formula solved for r is substantially more complicated than the formula solved for h. The added complexity is not surprising because in the original formula, r was squared, and h was not.

Questions

COVERING THE IDEAS

In 1–2, refer to the formula $V = \pi r^2 h$ in the lesson.

1. What is the volume of a cylindrical barrel of radius 5 cm and height 25 cm? $\approx$ 1,963.5 cm^3
2. The formula $\frac{V}{\pi r^2} = h$ is solved for _?_. h
3. Graph the function from Example 3b giving r in terms of h when V is assumed to be 500,000. Use a window that shows x and y values as large as 100. See margin.

In 4 and 5, complete the sentence "_?_ is written in terms of _?_" for the given formula.

4. $A = s^2$ (area of a square) A; s
5. $V = \frac{1}{3}Bh$ (volume of a pyramid) V; B and h

ENGLISH LEARNERS

Vocabulary Development

The word *formula* has many denotations (meanings) in math, science, and elsewhere. Ask students to use a dictionary to identify four of those meanings. Answers vary. Sample: (1) a set form of words used in a ritual or ceremony; (2) a statement of a fundamental principle; (3) a recipe or prescription; (4) a symbolic expression of chemical composition; (5) a group of symbols (letters and/or numbers) that express a set of facts concisely; (6) a customary method that leaves little room for originality.

Ask: Why is a formula important in mathematics? Answers vary. Sample: Formulas provide a way to calculate specific values, such as volume and area.

6. Refer to the formula $c = \frac{65t}{r - 65}$ from Example 2. Assume the first car has a 2-hour head start over the second car. Find the second car's catch up time for each speed. Explain what your answers mean in the context of the problem.
   a. 75 mph b. 85 mph c. 45 mph

7. Refer to Example 2. Solve the formula for *r*. $r = \frac{65t}{c} + 65 = 65\left(\frac{t}{c} + 1\right)$

APPLYING THE MATHEMATICS

8. Imagine you are riding in the second car in the situation of Example 2. Let *t* be the number of hours head start the other car had at a speed of 65 $\frac{\text{mi}}{\text{hr}}$. Let *c* be the number of hours it will take you to catch up at a rate $r\frac{\text{mi}}{\text{hr}}$. So, in time *c*, you will have traveled *rc* miles, while the other car will have traveled $65(t + c)$ miles. Thus, when you catch up, $rc = 65(t + c)$. Solve for *c*. $c = \frac{65t}{r - 65}$

9. **Multiple Choice** Which formula is easiest to use if you want to find *W* and you are given *G* and *k*? B
   A $G = 17Wk$ B $W = \frac{G}{17k}$ C $k = \frac{G}{17W}$

10. **Multiple Choice** In chemistry, a given mass and volume of gas will satisfy the equation $\frac{T_1}{P_1} = \frac{T_2}{P_2}$, where P_1 and T_1 are the pressure and temperature at one time, and P_2 and T_2 are the pressure and temperature at another time. Which is an equivalent formula solved for P_2? D
   A $P_2 = \frac{T_2 T_1}{P_1}$ B $P_2 = \frac{T_1}{P_1 T_2}$ C $P_1 = \frac{P_2 T_1}{T_2}$ D $P_2 = \frac{P_1 T_2}{T_1}$

In 11 and 12, the *pitch P* of a gabled roof is a measure of the steepness of the slant of the roof. Pitch is the ratio of the vertical rise *R* to half the *span S* of the roof: $P = \frac{R}{0.5\,S}$. (The span is the longest horizontal distance from one side of the roof to the other.)

11. a. Solve the pitch formula for *S*. $S = \frac{R}{0.5P}$
    b. If a builder wants a roof to have a pitch of $\frac{6}{15}$ and a rise of 8 feet, what must be the span of the roof? 40 feet

12. The photograph at the right shows the roof of the Throne Hall of the Cambodian Royal Palace in Phnom Penh. Using the interior triangle, measure the rise and span of the roof and estimate its pitch.

13. If $y = kx^2$ and $y = 12$ when $x = 4$, solve for *k*. $k = 0.75$

6a. $c = 13$; If the first car has a 2-hr head start and travels at 65 mph, the second car, traveling at 75 mph, will catch up in 13 hr.

6b. $c = 6.5$; If the first car has a 2-hr head start and travels at 65 mph, the second car, traveling at 85 mph, will catch up in 6.5 hr.

6c. $c = -6.5$; If the first car has a 2-hr head start and travels at 65 mph, the second car, traveling at 45 mph, will never catch up.

12. rise ≈ 1.0 in., span = 1.25 in., pitch ≈ 1.6

Additional Answers

3.

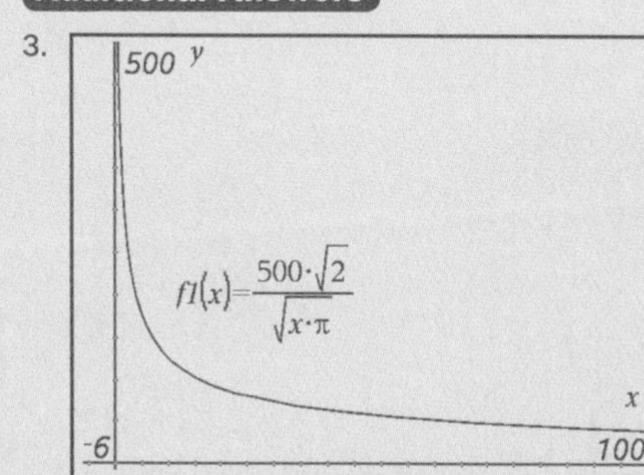

1-7

Notes on the Questions

Question 8 One derivation of the formula relating *r, t,* and *c* is in the Notes on the Lesson for Example 2. This question contains a derivation of an equivalent formula.

Question 12 Students may not realize that they are supposed to measure the lengths *on the picture* and from that determine the rise and span. You might ask why this would give the same pitch as the actual building's measurements. The picture and the actual building are similar, so the ratios of sides on the two are equal.

4 Wrap-Up

Ongoing Assessment

Have students work in pairs. Ask each student to write a formula learned in a previous mathematics course or in a science course. Then have them exchange papers and rewrite the formula in terms of other variables in the formula. Students should demonstrate an ability to rewrite formulas in terms of any variable.

Project Update

Project 4, *Cooking a Turkey,* and Project 5, *Height and Area of an Isosceles Triangle,* on page 61 relate to the content of this lesson.

Additional Answers

19a.

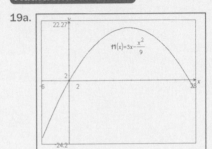

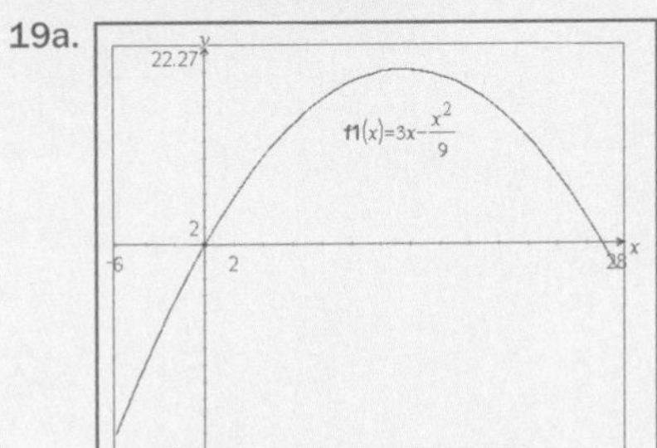

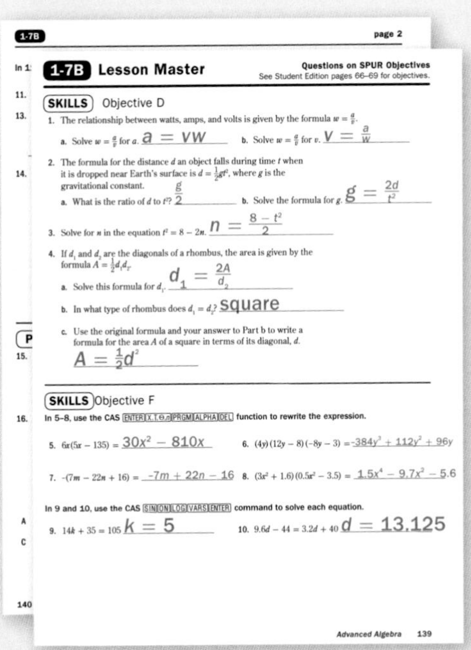

1-7B page 2

1-7B Lesson Master Questions on SPUR Objectives
See Student Edition pages 66–69 for objectives.

SKILLS Objective D

1. The relationship between watts, amps, and volts is given by the formula $w = \frac{a}{v}$.
   a. Solve $w = \frac{a}{v}$ for a. $a = vw$
   b. Solve $w = \frac{a}{v}$ for v. $v = \frac{a}{w}$
2. The formula for the distance d an object falls during time t when it is dropped near Earth's surface is $d = \frac{1}{2}gt^2$, where g is the gravitational constant.
   a. What is the ratio of d to t^2? $\frac{g}{2}$
   b. Solve the formula for g. $g = \frac{2d}{t^2}$
3. Solve for n in the equation $t^2 = 8 - 2n$. $n = \frac{8 - t^2}{2}$
4. If d_1 and d_2 are the diagonals of a rhombus, the area is given by the formula $A = \frac{1}{2}d_1d_2$.
   a. Solve this formula for d_1. $d_1 = \frac{2A}{d_2}$
   b. In what type of rhombus does $d_1 = d_2$? square
   c. Use the original formula and your answer to Part b to write a formula for the area A of a square in terms of its diagonal, d. $A = \frac{1}{2}d^2$

SKILLS Objective F

In 5–8, use the CAS ENTER X,T,Θ,n PRGM ALPHA DEL function to rewrite the expression.

5. $6x(5x - 135) =$ $30x^2 - 810x$
6. $(4y)(12y - 8)(-8y - 3) =$ $-384y^3 + 112y^2 + 96y$
7. $-(7m - 22n + 16) =$ $-7m + 22n - 16$
8. $(3x^2 + 1.6)(0.5x^2 - 3.5) =$ $1.5x^4 - 9.7x^2 - 5.6$

In 9 and 10, use the CAS SIN ON LOG VARS ENTER command to solve each equation.

9. $14k + 35 = 105$ $k = 5$
10. $9.6d - 44 = 3.2d + 40$ $d = 13.125$

Advanced Algebra 139

14. The formula $C = \pi d$ gives the circumference of a circle in terms of its diameter d.
    a. Solve this formula for π. $\pi = \frac{C}{d}$
    b. Use your result in Part a to write an English sentence that gives the definition of π.

In 15 and 16, use the formula $A = \frac{1}{2}h(b_1 + b_2)$ for the area A of a trapezoid with bases of length b_1 and b_2 and height h.

15. Solve the formula for b_1. $b_1 = \frac{2A}{h} - b_2$
16. a. In the original formula, how does the value of A change if the values of b_1 and b_2 are switched? To what geometrical situation does this correspond?
    b. How does the original formula change if $b_1 = b_2$? To what geometrical situation does this correspond?
    c. How does the original formula change if $b_2 = 0$? To what geometrical situation does this correspond?

REVIEW

17. Solve the equation. **(Lesson 1-6)**
    a. $\frac{5}{8}x = 10$ $x = 16$
    b. $\frac{5}{8}x + 30 = 10$ $x = -32$
    c. $\frac{5}{8}x + 30 = 10 + \frac{1}{3}x$ $x = -\frac{480}{7}$
18. Describe how you would use your calculator to generate a table for the function with equation $y = x^2 - 2x$ and with values starting at -5 in increments of 0.1 **(Lesson 1-5)**
19. a. Graph the function f when $f(x) = 3x - \frac{x^2}{9}$ for all real numbers x. 19a. See margin.
    b. What are its domain and range?
    c. What is its range if its domain is restricted to $\{x| 2 \le x \le 6\}$? **(Lesson 1-4)** $\{f(x)| \frac{50}{9} \le f(x) \le 14\}$
20. The velocity v of an object that starts from rest and accelerates at rate a over a distance d is given by the formula $v = \sqrt{2ad}$. What is the velocity of an object which started at rest and accelerated at 6 $\frac{m}{s^2}$ over a distance of 6.75 m? **(Lesson 1-1)** 9 $\frac{m}{s}$

EXPLORATION

21. Formulas with three or more variables are common in science and financial applications. Find such a formula and describe what its variables represent and what it computes. See margin.

14b. π is equal to the circumference of a circle divided by its diameter.

16a. The value of A will not change. This corresponds to a reflection over a line parallel to the bases.

16b. The formula becomes $A = bh$. The figure is now a parallelogram.

16c. The formula becomes $A = \frac{1}{2}bh$.The figure is now a triangle.

18. Answers vary. Sample: First, define the function. Then, open a function table application, and insert the function. Set the starting value for x to be -5, and the step to be 0.1.

19b. All real numbers; all real numbers ≤ 20.25

QUIZ YOURSELF ANSWERS

1. $h \approx 155.4$ cm

2a. The denominator of the fraction would be zero, and division by zero is not defined.

b. $t = \frac{10}{13}$. A car driving 70 $\frac{mi}{hr}$ will need 10 hours to catch up with a car driving 65 $\frac{mi}{hr}$ that had a $\frac{10}{13}$-hour head start.

Additional Answers

21. Answers vary. Sample: In chemistry, the ideal gas law is $PV = nRT$, where P stands for absolute pressure, V stands for volume of a container, n stands for the amount of substance of gas, R stands for the ideal gas constant, and T stands for the absolute temperature. The Law describes the state of an ideal gas, and generally represents the relationship between things like pressure, volume, and temperature.

Lesson 1-8 Explicit Formulas for Sequences

Vocabulary

sequence
term of a sequence
subscript
index
explicit formula
discrete function

BIG IDEA Sequences can be thought of as functions, but they have their own notation different from other functions. If their terms are real numbers, they are real functions and can be graphed.

Recognizing and Representing Sequences

In previous mathematics courses you have seen many sequences. A *sequence* is an ordered list of numbers or objects. Specifically, a **sequence** is defined as a function whose domain is the set of all positive integers, or the set of positive integers from a to b. Each item in a sequence is called a **term of the sequence**. In the following Activity, you will explore a sequence.

Mental Math

Let $a = -3$ and $b = 3$. Evaluate.

a. $a^2 - b^2$ 0

b. $b^2 - a^2$ 0

c. $(a - b)^2$ 36

d. $(b - a)^2$ 36

e. $(ab)^2$ 81

Activity

The collections of dots below form the first five terms of a sequence of triangular arrays. The numbers of dots in each collection form a sequence of numbers.

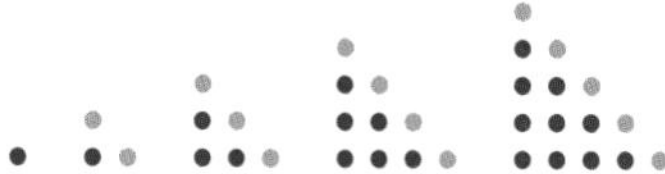

Step 1 Complete the table to show the number of dots in each of the terms pictured.

Term Number	Number of Dots
1	1
2	3
3	6
4	10
5	15

Step 2 Notice that after the first term of the sequence, each subsequent term adds a predictable and increasing number of dots to the previous term. Use this fact to complete the table for the next four terms.

Term Number	Number of Dots
6	21
7	28
8	36
9	45

Step 3 This process can be continued for as long as you want. You can even think of it as going on forever. Explain why the set of ordered pairs (term number, number of dots) describes a function.
For each term number there corresponds only one number of dots.

Background

Sequences appear early in this book because they (1) provide a good vehicle for reviewing subscripts, which we need; (2) involve formulas; (3) are examples of functions; (4) are important in developing and identifying patterns, which is an effective problem-solving strategy; and (5) are interesting to students.

An algebraic description of sequences will be new to most students. However, given a sequence, most students will be able to see the next term in the pattern. Most students have seen subscripted variables, such as x_1, y_1, x_2, and y_2, as coordinates of points or in the formula for the slope of a line. However, they may not be familiar with the concept of a subscript as a counter or as a way to identify a particular term.

Students who have studied from previous UCSMP books should be familiar with the sequence of triangular numbers in the Activity.

Lesson 1-8

GOAL

Introduce sequences as functions and the subscript notation for the *n*th term of sequences.

SPUR Objectives

E Find terms of sequences.

L Use a graphing utility to graph functions and generate tables for functions.

Materials/Resources

- Lesson Masters 1-8A and 1-8B
- Resource Masters 1, 17, and 18

HOMEWORK

Suggestions for Assignment

- Questions 1–20
- Question 21 (extra credit)
- Self-Test

Local Standards

1 Warm-Up

Write the following sentence on the board: "Was it a cat I saw?" Ask students to read the sentence several times and determine if there is anything special about the sentence. The sentence is a pattern called a palindrome, which reads the same forward and backward.

2 Teaching

Notes on the Lesson

Notation is often the greatest difficulty that students have with sequences. Often they cannot read the notation and are in the same position you might be in if you had to read a letter written in an unfamiliar language. You may wish to pick phrases and sentences from this lesson and ask students to read them. Here are two examples: (1) $T_n = \frac{n(n+1)}{2}$ is read "*T* sub *n* equals the quantity *n* times the quantity *n* plus one all divided by 2." (2) $p_n = \left(\frac{1}{2}\right)^n$ is read "*p* sub *n* equals one-half to the *n*th power."

Students also need to see that *n* serves two purposes in this notation. In $t_n = 2n - 1$, the expression $2n - 1$ defines a pattern used to generate the terms. Here, *n* is the independent variable. In t_n, *n* also indicates that the dependent variable *t* depends on *n*. Point out the following analogies:

Name of Function	Independent Variable	Value of Function
f	x	$f(x)$
t	n	t_n

In general, be careful that you do not get bogged down in this lesson. There is opportunity for more work with subscripted variables in the Chapter Review.

The sequence you explored in the Activity is the sequence of *triangular numbers*. This sequence defines a function whose domain is the set of all positive integers. If you call this function T, then $T(1) = 1$, $T(2) = 3$, $T(3) = 6$, … . A notation for sequences more common than $f(x)$ notation is to put the argument in a *subscript*. A **subscript** is a label that is set lower and smaller than regular text. Using subscripts, $T_1 = 1$, $T_2 = 3$, $T_3 = 6$, … . The notation $T_3 = 6$ is read "T sub three equals six." The subscript is often called an **index** because it *indicates* the position of the term in the sequence.

See Quiz Yourself 1 at the right.

QUIZ YOURSELF 1

What are T_4 and T_5?

Writing Explicit Formulas for Sequences

Many sequences can be described by a rule called an **explicit formula** for the *n*th term of the sequence. Explicit formulas are important because they can be used to calculate any term in the sequence by substituting a particular value for *n*.

To find an explicit formula for the *n*th triangular number T_n, you can use the fact that the area of a triangle is half the area of a rectangle.

Notice that each triangular array of dots can be arranged to be half of a rectangular array.

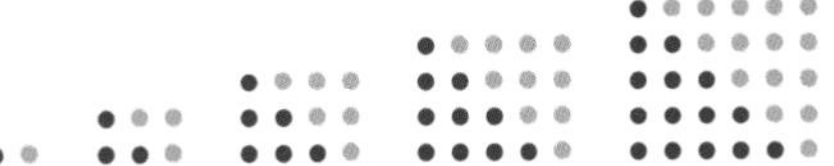

For instance, the number of dots representing the 4th triangular number is half the number of dots in a 4 by 5 rectangular array.

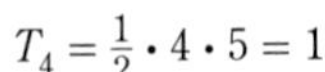

$$T_4 = \frac{1}{2} \cdot 4 \cdot 5 = 10$$

5

4

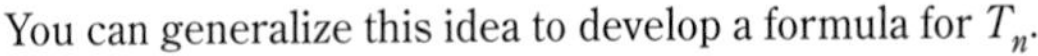

You can generalize this idea to develop a formula for T_n.

Term Number	Value of Term (number of dots)
1	$T_1 = \frac{1}{2} \cdot 1 \cdot 2 = 1$
2	$T_2 = \frac{1}{2} \cdot 2 \cdot 3 = 3$
3	$T_3 = \frac{1}{2} \cdot 3 \cdot 4 = 6$
4	$T_4 = \frac{1}{2} \cdot 4 \cdot 5 = 10$
⋮	⋮
n	$T_n = \frac{1}{2} \cdot n \cdot (n+1)$

ENGLISH LEARNERS

Vocabulary Development

Explain that the prefix *sub-* means "under" or "below." You might use a drawing of a submarine—a boat that operates under water—or a subway—an underground railroad. Similarly, a subscript is a number or letter written below and to the right of a term to indicate the position of the term. So in t_{120}, for example, 120 is the subscript indicating that t_{120} is the 120th term in a sequence.

The number of dots in the nth rectangle is $n(n + 1)$. T_n is half that.

$$T_n = \frac{1}{2} \cdot n \cdot (n + 1) = \frac{n(n + 1)}{2}$$

Thus an explicit formula for the number of dots in the nth term is

$$T_n = \frac{n(n + 1)}{2}.$$

 **See Quiz Yourself 2 at the right.**

▸ QUIZ YOURSELF 2

What is the 15th triangular number? The 100th triangular number?

Example 1

Suppose you flip a fair coin until it comes up tails. The probability that you will not have had an outcome of tails after n flips is given by the sequence $p_n = \left(\frac{1}{2}\right)^n$.

a. **Compute and graph the first four terms of this sequence.**

b. **Evaluate p_{20}, and explain what it represents.**

Solution

a. Substitute 1, 2, 3, and 4 for n in the formula and graph the ordered pairs (n, p_n).

$p_1 = \left(\frac{1}{2}\right)^1 = \frac{1}{2}$

$p_2 = \left(\frac{1}{2}\right)^2 = \frac{1}{4}$

$p_3 = \left(\frac{1}{2}\right)^3 = \frac{1}{8}$

$p_4 = \left(\frac{1}{2}\right)^4 = \frac{1}{16}$

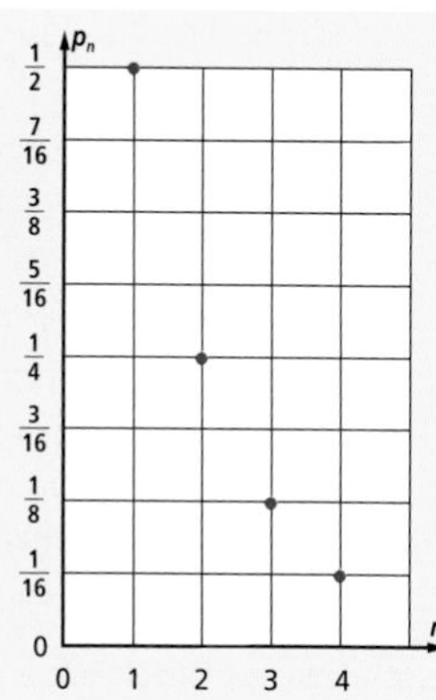

b. Substitute $n = 20$ into the formula.

$p_{20} = \left(\frac{1}{2}\right)^{20} = \frac{1}{1{,}048{,}576}$

p_{20} is the probability that you will not have had an outcome of tails after 20 flips.

 **See Quiz Yourself 3 at the right.**

▸ QUIZ YOURSELF 3

Write $p_n = \left(\frac{1}{2}\right)^n$ using function notation.

Using Explicit Formulas for Sequences

Sequences arise naturally in many situations in science, business, finance, and other areas. Example 2 looks at a sequence in finance.

Additional Example

Example 1 Consider the formula $t_n = 3^n - 4$.

a. Assuming $n \geq 1$, what are the first four numbers in the sequence defined by this formula? -1, 5, 23, 77

b. Evaluate t_{10} and explain what it means. 59,045; t_{10} represents the 10th number in the sequence defined by $3^n - 4$.

Accommodating the Learner

To help students learn the concepts of this lesson, use the following activities for the sequence of increasing odd positive numbers 1, 3, 5, 7, ..., $2n - 1$, that is, the sequence with formula $t_n = 2n - 1$.

a. Have students identify the third term and then write it symbolically. 5; $t_3 = 5$ Do similar exercises with other terms.

b. Ask students to provide the symbolic translation of "the fifth term of the sequence is 9." $t_5 = 9$ Point out that the symbolic description is much more compact than words.

c. Give students a statement such as $t_5 = 9$ and have them read it aloud. t sub five equals nine, or the value of the fifth term is nine.

d. Indicate that t_n represents the general or nth term of the sequence. By giving n a value, a specific term of the sequence is indicated. Which term of the sequence is 847? Solve $t_n = 2n - 1 = 847$ to find $n = 424$.

Notes on the Lesson

Example 2 The table output in Solution 2 may show rounded answers.

Additional Example

Example 2 Alfonso has invested \$750 for 1 year at 8% annual interest.

a. If the interest is compounded semiannually, how much will he have at the end of 1 year?

b. How much money will Alfonso have at the end of the second and third years (assuming no withdrawals)?

c. How much money will he have after 10 years (assuming no withdrawals)?

Solution

a. Use the equation $T = p(1 + r)^t$, where T is the total principal and interest in the account, p is the principal, r is the interest rate divided by the number of times interest is compounded, and t is the number of times the interest is compounded times the number of years.

$T_1 = p(1 + r)^t = \underline{\ ?\ }(1 + \underline{\ ?\ })^{\underline{?}}$

$= \underline{\ ?\ }$ 750; $\frac{0.08}{2}$; 2; \$811.20

b. $T_2 = \underline{\ ?\ }(1 + \underline{\ ?\ })^{\underline{?}} = \underline{\ ?\ }$

\$811.20; $\frac{0.08}{2}$; 2; \$877.40

$T_3 = \underline{\ ?\ }(1 + \underline{\ ?\ })^{\underline{?}} = \underline{\ ?\ }$

\$877.40; $\frac{0.08}{2}$; 2; \$949.00

c. Follow the sequence started in Part b. $T_{10} = \underline{\ ?\ }(1 + \underline{\ ?\ })^{\underline{?}}$

$= \underline{\ ?\ }$

949.00; $\frac{0.08}{2}$; 14; \$1643.36

Source: http://cs.selu.edu/~rbyrd/math/regular/

GUIDED

Example 2

It is common for people to save money in savings accounts such as Certificates of Deposites (CDs) that yield a high interest rate paid once a year. Suppose you deposited \$28,700 and expected a 4.1% interest rate to be *compounded* annually. Then the formula $S_n = 28{,}700(1.041)^{n-1}$ gives your total savings at any time during the year leading up to the *n*th anniversary.

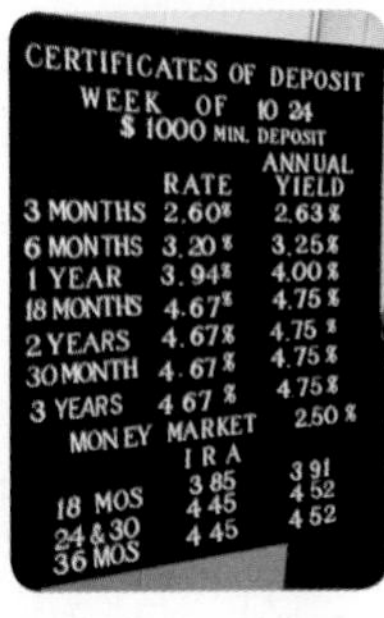

Rates for Certificates of Deposit

a. Compute the first five terms of the sequence.

b. Compute the hundredth term of the sequence.

c. What does your answer to Part b mean in the context of this problem?

Solution 1

a. Define the sequence using function notation on a CAS and compute the first five values.

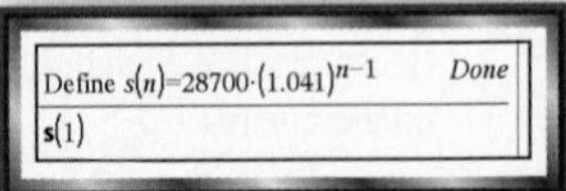

$S(1) = \underline{\ ?\ }$ 28,700

$S(2) = \underline{\ ?\ }$ 29,876.70

$S(3) = \underline{\ ?\ }$ 31,101.64

$S(4) = \underline{\ ?\ }$ 32,376.81

$S(5) = \underline{\ ?\ }$ 33,704.26

b. Compute $S(100)$ in the same way.

$S(100) = \underline{\ ?\ }$ 1,532,865.74

c. This sequence gives the total savings at the end of the *n*th year. So, $S(100) = \underline{\ ?\ }$ means that on the 100th anniversary of the account opening, there will be $\underline{\ ?\ }$ in the account. 1,532,865.74; \$1,532,865.74

Solution 2

a. Enter the formula into a grapher and generate a table to view the first five values.

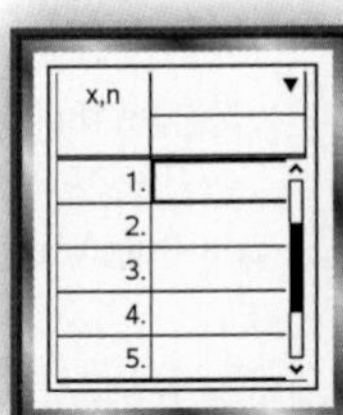

The table start value is $n = \underline{\ ?\ }$. 1

The increment is $\underline{\ ?\ }$. 1

The table end value is $n = \underline{\ ?\ }$. 5

b. Scroll down to see the value of $S(n)$ when $n = 100$.

$S(100) = \underline{\ ?\ }$ 1,532,865.74

c. After 100 years, there will be $\underline{\ ?\ }$ in the account. \$1,532,865.74

Accommodating the Learner

Have students find the next term in each sequence and explain how they determined this term.

1. 1, 2, 9, 28, 65, … 126; one more than the cube of whole numbers: $0^3 + 1 = 1$; $1^3 + 1 = 2$, $2^3 + 1 = 9$, and so on
2. 2, 4, 7, 12, 19, 30 … 43; the differences between two adjacent terms are the consecutive primes: $4 - 2 = 2$; $7 - 4 = 3$, $12 - 7 = 5$, and so on
3. 1, 2, 2, 4, 8, 32, … 256; each term after the second term is the product of the two previous terms.
4. 8, 5, 2, -1, -4, … -7; each term is three less than the preceding term.

A sequence is an example of a *discrete function*. A **discrete function** is a function whose domain can be put into one-to-one correspondence with a finite or infinite set of integers, with gaps, or intervals, between successive values in the domain. The graphs of discrete functions consist of unconnected points. The gaps in the domain of a sequence are the intervals between the positive integers. The graph of gold prices on page 5 and the graph in Example 1 of this lesson are both examples of graphs of discrete functions.

Questions

COVERING THE IDEAS

1. Consider the increasing sequence 1, 3, 5, 7, ... of positive odd numbers.
   a. 13 is the 7th __?__ of the sequence. term
   b. If this sequence is called D, what is D_{11}? 21
2. Consider the equation $a_{11} = 22.83$.
   a. Which number is the subscript? 11
   b. What does the *number that is not the subscript* represent? the term
   c. Which term of the sequence is this? 11th
   d. Rewrite the equation using function notation. $a(11) = 22.83$
   e. Rewrite the equation in words. a sub 11 equals 22.83.

In 3 and 4, consider the sequence T of triangular numbers in the Activity on page 53.

3. Compute the 20th triangular number. 210
4. If $T_n = 15$, what is the value of n? 5
5. a. Draw a possible next term in the sequence at the right.
   b. How many dots does it take to draw each of the first 5 terms?
   c. Determine an explicit formula for the sequence S_n if S_n = the number of dots in the nth term. $S_n = n^2$

5a. (5 × 5 array of dots)

5b. 1, 4, 9, 16, 25

6. Consider the sequence h whose first six terms are 231, 120, 91, 66, 45, 28.
   a. What number is the 4th term? 66
   b. How is the sentence "$h_5 = 45$" read? h sub 5 equals 45.
   c. h_6 = __?__ 28

In 7 and 8, an explicit formula for a sequence is given. Write the first four terms of the sequence.

7. $a_n = 7.3 - 3n$ 4.3, 1.3, -1.7, -4.7
8. $S_n = \frac{n(n+1)(2n+1)}{6}$ (sum of the first n squares) 1, 5, 14, 30

3 Assignment

Recommended Assignment

- Questions 1–20
- Question 21 (extra credit)
- Self-Test

Notes on the Questions

Question 5 This very easy question is a test to see whether any students have entirely missed an idea of the lesson.

Extension

The array at the right is part of an infinite pattern called Pascal's triangle. The first and last terms of each row are 1. Each other term, from the third row on, is the sum of the two numbers diagonally above it.

1. What are the next four rows in the array?
2. What is at least one other interesting sequence in this array? Answers vary. Sample: The second diagonal is the sequence of natural numbers.
3. Find the sum of the numbers in the first six rows pictured. Identify the pattern of the sums and write an expression for the nth row. row 0: $1 = 2^0$; row 1: $2 = 2^1$; row 2: $4 = 2^2$; row 3: $8 = 2^3$, row 4: $16 = 2^4$; row 5: $32 = 2^5$; The sum of the numbers in row n is $S_n = 2^n$

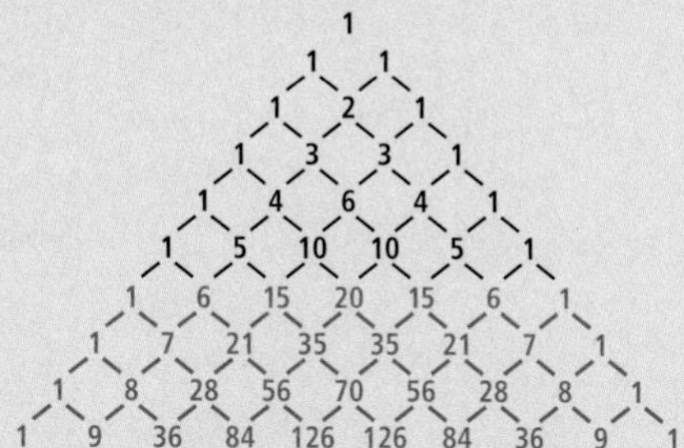

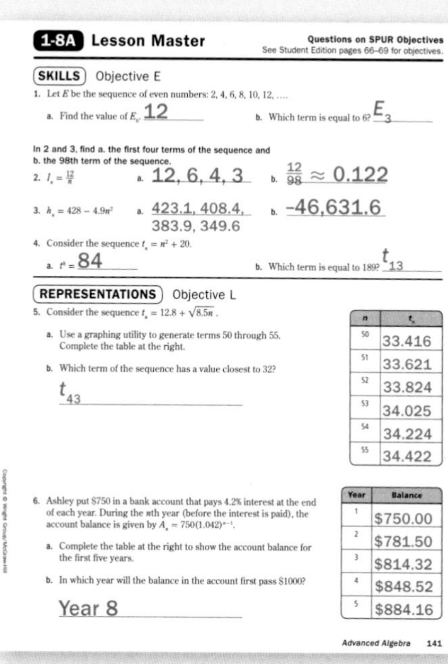

1-8A Lesson Master

Questions on SPUR Objectives
See Student Edition pages 66–69 for objectives.

SKILLS Objective E

1. Let E be the sequence of even numbers: 2, 4, 6, 8, 10, 12, ...
   a. Find the value of E_6. 12
   b. Which term is equal to 6? E_3

In 2 and 3, find a. the first four terms of the sequence and b. the 98th term of the sequence.

2. $l_n = \frac{12}{n}$ a. 12, 6, 4, 3 b. $\frac{12}{98} \approx 0.122$
3. $h_n = 428 - 4.9n^2$ a. 423.1, 408.4, 383.9, 349.6 b. −46,631.6
4. Consider the sequence $t_n = n^2 + 20$.
   a. t_8 = 84
   b. Which term is equal to 189? t_{13}

REPRESENTATIONS Objective L

5. Consider the sequence $t_n = 12.8 + \sqrt{8.5n}$.
   a. Use a graphing utility to generate terms 50 through 55. Complete the table at the right.
   b. Which term of the sequence has a value closest to 32? t_{43}

n	t_n
50	33.416
51	33.621
52	33.824
53	34.025
54	34.224
55	34.422

6. Ashley put $750 in a bank account that pays 4.2% interest at the end of each year. During the nth year (before the interest is paid), the account balance is given by $A_n = 750(1.042)^{n-1}$.
   a. Complete the table at the right to show the account balance for the first five years.
   b. In which year will the balance in the account first pass $1000? Year 8

Year	Balance
1	$750.00
2	$781.50
3	$814.32
4	$848.52
5	$884.16

Advanced Algebra 141

Notes on the Questions

Questions 10 and 11 An interesting aspect is how a small difference in the recursive relation makes a huge difference in the sequence that is determined.

Additional Answers

9a.

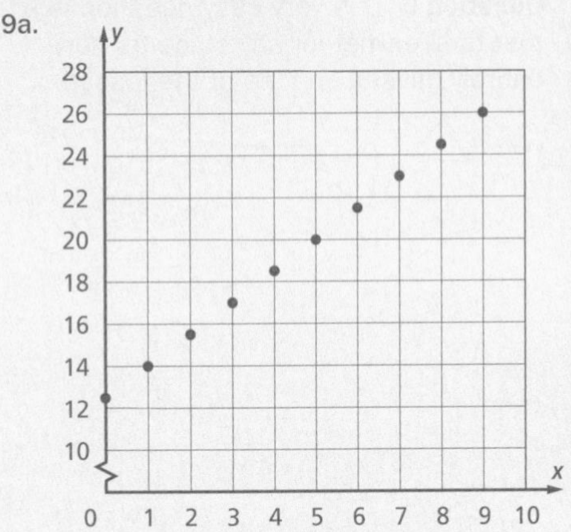

11a.

Term Number	Value of term
4	$C_4 = \frac{4^2(4+1)^2}{4} = 100$
5	$C_5 = \frac{5^2(5+1)^2}{4} = 225$
6	$C_6 = \frac{6^2(6+1)^2}{4} = 441$
7	$C_7 = \frac{7^2(7+1)^2}{4} = 784$

9. Refer to Solution 2 of Example 2. 9a. See margin
   a. Graph the values from the table with the anniversary n on the horixontal axis and the total savings S_n on the vertical axis.
   b. Should the points on the graph be connected? Why or why not? Relate your answer to the domain of the function.

9b. No; non-integer values are not part of the domain of the function.

10. a. **Multiple Choice** Which could be a formula for the nth term of the sequence 3, 9, 27, 81, … ? C
   A $t_n = 3n$ B $t_n = 3n^3$ C $t_n = 3^n$
   b. For the choices not used, write the first four terms of the sequence being represented. A: 3, 6, 9, 12; B: 3, 24, 81, 192

APPLYING THE MATHEMATICS

11. a. Generate a table of the 4th through 7th terms of the sequence C defined by $C_n = \frac{n^2(n+1)^2}{4}$. See margin.
   b. This sequence gives the sum of the first n cubes. What does C_7 represent? the sum of the first seven cubes

In Questions 12 and 13, consider the story *Anno's Magic Seeds* by Mitsumasa Anno (1992). It is the story of Jack, who receives two magic seeds. A person who eats one of these seeds will be full for one year, and planting a seed yields two seeds.

12. Jack begins the first year with two magic seeds. He eats one and plants the other. It grows and produces two seeds at the start of the second year. In this second year, Jack repeats his behavior by eating one seed and planting the other to get two seeds for the start of the third year. Jack continues the trend each year, eating one seed and planting the remaining seed to get two for the following year.
   a. Create a table and a graph illustrating the relationship between the year and the number of seeds Jack has at the beginning of the year for the first five years. See margin.
   b. Does this situation determine a function? Why or why not?
   c. Does this situation determine a sequence? Why or why not?

12b. Yes; for each year there corresponds one number of seeds.

12c. Yes; the function is defined over the natural numbers.

13. Suppose Jack decides to forgo eating a seed in the first year and instead plants both seeds to end up with four seeds at the start of the second year. In the second year, Jack eats one seed and plants the remaining three to end up with six seeds at the start of the third year. The third year, Jack eats one seed and plants the remaining five to end up with ten seeds at the start of the fourth year. Jack continues his behavior of eating one seed and planting what is left.

Additional Answers

12a.

Year	Seeds
1	2
2	2
3	2
4	2
5	2

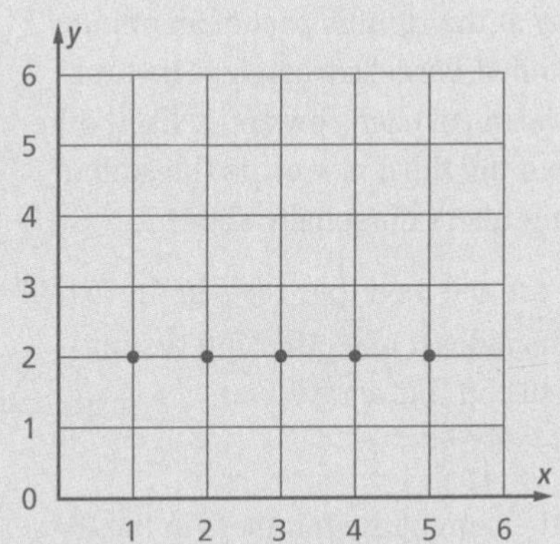

a. Write the first six ordered pairs that relate the year to the number of seeds. (1, 2), (2, 4), (3, 6), (4, 10), (5, 18), (6, 34)

b. Find an explicit formula for the number of seeds at the beginning of the nth year, for all $n > 1$. $S_n = 2 + 2^{n-1}$, for all $n > 1$

14. Some common bacterial cells, such as *E. coli,* can divide and double every 20 minutes. The doubling process takes place when a microbe reproduces by splitting to make 2 cells. Each of these cells then splits in half to make a total of 4 cells. Each of these 4 cells then splits to make a total of 8, and so on. Each splitting is called a *generation*. If a colony begins with 125 microbes, the equation $P_n = 125(2)^{n-1}$ gives the number of microbes in the nth generation (assuming all microbes survive).

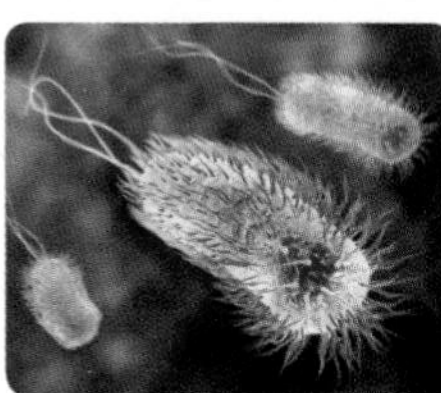

E. coli cells

a. Calculate the first three terms of the sequence.

b. Identify the independent variable and dependent variable of the function.

REVIEW

15. Solve for s in the formula $d = 7s - 13$. **(Lesson 1-7)** $s = \frac{d + 13}{7}$

16. The measure θ of an exterior angle of a regular polygon is given by $\theta = \frac{360}{n}$, where n is the number of sides of the polygon. Solve for n in terms of θ. **(Lesson 1-7)** $n = \frac{360}{\theta}$

In 17 and 18, an equation is given. (Lesson 1-6)

a. Solve the equation.

b. Check your answer.

17. $5r - (2r + 1) = 6$

18. $7t - (9 - 4t) = 9$

19. A medium pizza costs \$12.50 plus \$1.50 for each topping. If C is the total cost of the pizza and t is the number of toppings ordered, then $C(t) = 12.50 + 1.50t$ gives c as a function of t. **(Lesson 1-4)**

a. Specify the domain of this function.

b. Write the four smallest numbers in the range of this function.

c. Graph this function. See margin.

20. **Fill in the Blank** Let $h: a \to a^3 + 2$. Then $h: -3 \to$ _?_.
(Lesson 1-3) -25

EXPLORATION

21. Triangular numbers have many curious properties. For example, a triangular number can never end with the digits 2, 4, 7, or 9. Find one more property of the triangular numbers.

14a. $P_1 = 125$, $P_2 = 250$, $P_3 = 500$

14b. n is the independent variable (the number of generations); P_n is the dependent variable (the number of microbes).

17a. $r = \frac{7}{3}$

17b. $5\left(\frac{7}{3}\right) - \left(2\left(\frac{7}{3}\right) + 1\right) = 6$

18a. $t = \frac{18}{11}$

18b. $7\left(\frac{18}{11}\right) - \left(9 - 4\left(\frac{18}{11}\right)\right) = 9$

19a. t must be a whole number.

19b. 12.5, 14, 15.5, 17

21. Answers vary. Sample: Every triangular number is either divisible by 3 or has a remainder of 1 when divided by 9.

QUIZ YOURSELF ANSWERS

1. $T_4 = 10$; $T_5 = 15$
2. 120; 5050
3. $p(n) = \left(\frac{1}{2}\right)^n$

Notes on the Questions

Question 21 A Web site with many properties of these numbers is http://www.shyamsundergupta.com/triangle.htm.

4 Wrap-Up

Ongoing Assessment

Have students work in pairs. Tell each student to write a formula with no more than two operations and list the first five terms generated by the formula. Then have students exchange papers and give the 10th term of the sequence. Students should demonstrate an ability to write formulas for sequences and evaluate the formula for a specific term.

Project Update

Project 3, *Triangular Numbers,* on page 60 relates to the content of this lesson.

Additional Answers

19c.

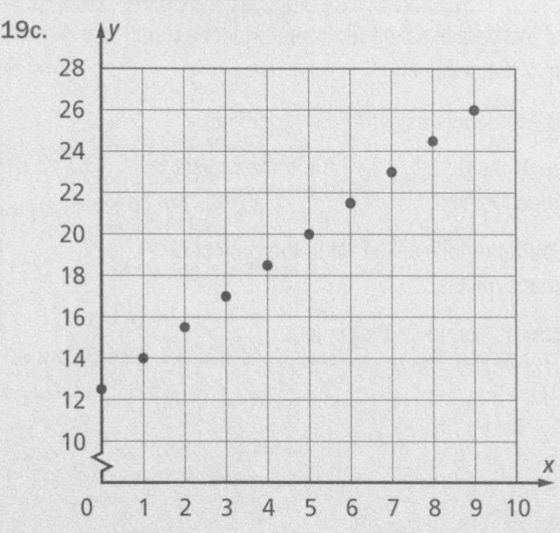

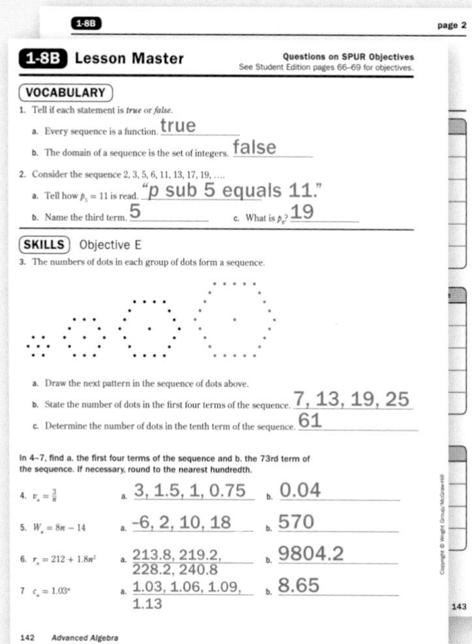

1-8B page 2

1-8B Lesson Master

Questions on SPUR Objectives
See Student Edition pages 66–69 for objectives.

VOCABULARY

1. Tell if each statement is *true* or *false*.
   a. Every sequence is a function. true
   b. The domain of a sequence is the set of integers. false
2. Consider the sequence 2, 3, 5, 6, 11, 13, 17, 19, ….
   a. Tell how $p_5 = 11$ is read. "p sub 5 equals 11."
   b. Name the third term. 5
   c. What is p_8? 19

SKILLS Objective E

3. The numbers of dots in each group of dots form a sequence.
   a. Draw the next pattern in the sequence of dots above.
   b. State the number of dots in the first four terms of the sequence. 7, 13, 19, 25
   c. Determine the number of dots in the tenth term of the sequence. 61

In 4–7, find a. the first four terms of the sequence and b. the 73rd term of the sequence. If necessary, round to the nearest hundredth.

4. $v_n = \frac{3}{n}$ a. 3, 1.5, 1, 0.75 b. 0.04
5. $W_n = 8n - 14$ a. -6, 2, 10, 18 b. 570
6. $r_n = 212 + 1.8n^2$ a. 213.8, 219.2, 228.2, 240.8 b. 9804.2
7. $c_n = 1.03^n$ a. 1.03, 1.06, 1.09, 1.13 b. 8.65

142 *Advanced Algebra* 143

Chapter 1

The projects relate to the content of the lessons of this chapter as follows:

Project	Lesson(s)
1	1-1
2	1-2, 1-3, 1-4, 1-5
3	1-8
4	1-7
5	1-7

1 Value over Time

Students should be sure that the objects they select are ones for which information will be easy to obtain. The price of a share of stock, an ounce of gold, or a barrel of oil is easy to track because the data appear either in daily newspapers or on the Internet. Prices of used computers or cars, for example, might be published, but not on a regular basis.

2 Functions and Graphs on the Internet

Encourage students to identify the types of graphs they find (vertical bar graphs, horizontal bar graphs, line graphs, broken line graphs, and so on). Have students print out the page where the graph appears and share the purpose of the graph with the class.

3 Triangular Numbers

Internet resources that students might consult for triangular numbers include http://www.mathematische-basteleien.de/triangularnumber.htm, http://www.shyamsundergupta.com/triangle.htm, http://planetmath.org/encyclopedia/TriangularNumbers.html, and http://mathworld.wolfram.com/TriangularNumber.html. For pentagonal numbers, selected Web sites include http://www.math-magic.com/misc/pentagonal.htm, http://www.math.sdu.edu.cn/mathency/math/p/p204.htm, and http://mathworld.wolfram.com/PentagonalNumber.html.

Chapter 1 Projects

A project represents an opportunity for you to extend your knowledge of a topic related to the material of this chapter. You should allow more time for a project than you do for typical homework questions.

1 Value over Time

Recall the first pages of the chapter describing the fluctuation of gold prices over time. Find an object, such as a painting masterpiece, whose value has tended to increase over time. Find another object, such as a new car, whose value usually decreases over time. In tables and graphs, record values of these objects over reasonable domains. Write a paragraph explaining why the values increase in one case while decreasing in the other.

Van Gogh's Bedroom at Aries, 1889 (oil on canvas), Vincent Van Gogh

2 Functions and Graphs on the Internet

Search for coordinate graphs on the Internet. Find six to eight graphs you think are interesting. Look for a variety of subjects and shapes of graphs. For each graph, tell whether it represents a function. Identify its domain and range. Make up at least one question that can be answered by the graph.

3 Triangular Numbers

Triangular numbers appear in several mathematical applications and have many interesting properties.

a. Research the applications and properties of triangular numbers and prepare a report on your findings.

b. Pentagonal numbers are similar to triangular numbers. Draw the first five geometric representations of the pentagonal sequence using dots and find an explicit formula for the nth term.

Project Rubric

Advanced	Student correctly provides all of the details asked for in the project as well as additional correct independent conclusions.
Proficient	Student correctly provides all of the details asked for in the project.
Partially proficient	Student correctly provides some of the details asked for in the project or provides all details with some inaccuracies.
Not proficient	Student correctly provides few of the details asked for in the project or provides all details with many inaccuracies.
No attempt	Student makes little or no attempt to complete the project.

4 Cooking a Turkey

The amount of time it takes to cook a turkey depends on several factors, such as the turkey's weight. Use the Internet to find at least three different tables or formulas for cooking times for turkey. Compare the tables and formulas and explain which factors each table or formula takes into account.

5 Height and Area of an Isosceles Triangle

Consider the triangle below, with two sides of length 10, base of length x, and height h.

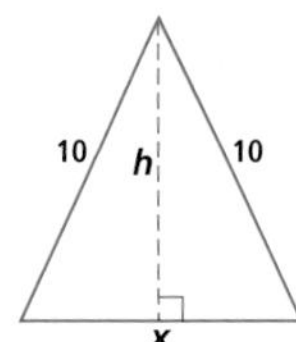

a. Find a formula for h in terms of x. What is the domain of this function? (*Hint:* Use the Triangle Inequality.)

b. Use your graphing utility to graph the function you found in Part a over its domain. How does h change as x changes?

c. Find a formula for the area of the triangle in terms of x only.

d. Use your graphing utility to graph the function you found in Part c. Draw a sketch of the graph.

e. How does the area of the triangle change as x changes? Use the TRACE command on your grapher to find the value of x when the area of the triangle is the largest.

f. Find the value of h when the area of the triangle is the largest. Draw a sketch of the triangle of largest area.

Notes

4 Cooking a Turkey

A cooking time calculator can be found on the Butterball Turkey Web site at http://www.butterball.com. Sample roasting charts can be found at http://www.eatturkey.com, http://homecooking.about.com/library/archive/blturkey7.htm, and many more Web sites.

5 Height and Area of an Isosceles Triangle

The Triangle Inequality is as follows: The sum of the lengths of any two sides of a triangle is greater than the length of the third side.
That is, in $\triangle ABC$,

$AB + BC > AC$
$BC + AC > AB$
$AB + AC > BC$

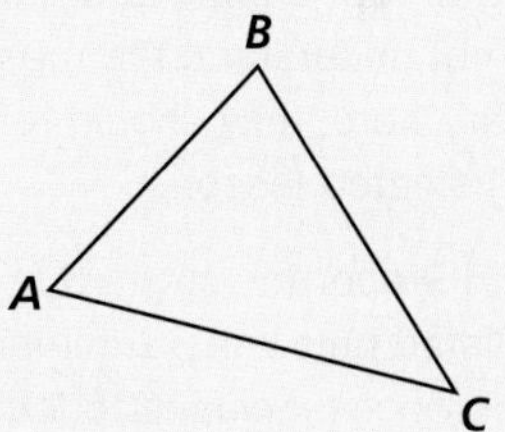

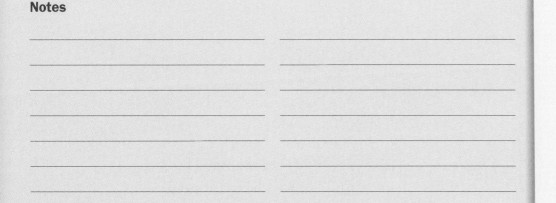

Sample answers for projects are in the Solution Manual in the Electronic Teacher's Edition.

Chapter 1

Summary and Vocabulary

The Summary gives an overview of the entire chapter and provides an opportunity for students to consider the material as a whole. Thus, the Summary can be used to help students relate and unify the concepts presented in the chapter.

Vocabulary words and symbols are listed by lesson to provide a checklist of concepts that students must know. Emphasize to students that they should read the vocabulary list carefully before starting the Self-Test on pages 64–65. If students do not understand the meaning of a vocabulary word, they should refer back to the indicated lesson.

Theorems and Properties covered in the chapter are listed below the Summary with page references included to lead students back to the location in the chapter where the theorem or property is stated.

Chapter 1 Summary and Vocabulary

In the columns at the right are the most important terms and phrases for this chapter. You should be able to give a general description and a specific example of each and a precise definition for those marked with an asterisk (*).

- The language of algebra is based on numbers and **variables**. These are combined in **expressions**, and two or more expressions connected by a verb make up an **algebraic sentence**.

- **Formulas** are equations stating that a single variable is equal to an expression with one or more variables on the other side. Formulas are evaluated and can be rewritten using the rules for the **order of operations** and properties of equality.

- A **function** is defined as a set of ordered pairs in which each first coordinate can be paired with exactly one second coordinate. The first coordinate of the ordered pair is the **independent variable**; the second coordinate is the **dependent variable**. Thus, a function pairs two variables in such a way that each value of the independent variable corresponds to exactly one value of the dependent variable. The **domain** of a function is the set of possible values for the independent variable, while the **range** is the set of values obtained for the dependent variable. Many functions are **mathematical models** of real situations or other mathematical properties.

- Functions can be used to represent situations where one value of an ordered pair is known and the other unknown. They can also be used to describe situations in which objects are transformed or otherwise mapped onto other objects. Each of these types of situations may arise in everyday contexts and in all branches of mathematics.

- Functions are often named with a single letter. Euler's $f(x)$ **notation** $f(x) = x + 20$, and the **mapping notation** $f: x \rightarrow x + 20$, both describe the same function. Graphing utilities use $f(x)$ notation and often name functions y_1, y_2, y_3, and so on. A CAS defines functions with $f(x)$ notation, but also accepts equations and formulas that are not solved for one variable.

Vocabulary

1-1
*variable
algebraic expression
expression
algebraic sentence
evaluating an expression
order of operations
vinculum
*equation
*formula

1-2
relation
*function
*independent variable
*dependent variable
input, output
is a function of
maps
mathematical model

1-3
*$f(x)$ notation
argument of a function
value of a function
mapping notation

1-4
real function
*domain of a function
*range of a function
set builder notation
trace
standard window
*natural numbers
*counting numbers
*whole numbers
*integers
rational numbers
real numbers
irrational numbers

- Along with words and formulas, functions are also represented by tables and graphs.

x	y
–2	18
–1	19
0	20
1	21
2	22

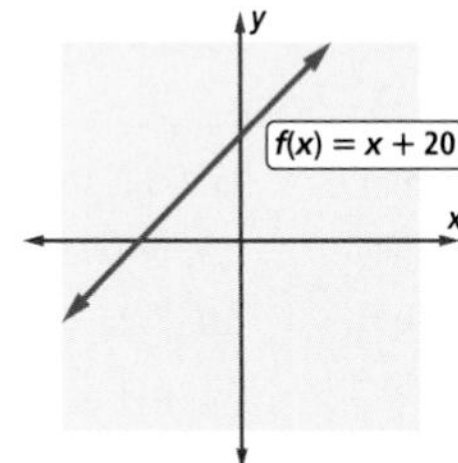

- A **sequence** is a function whose domain is the set of all positive integers or the set of positive integers from a to b. Sequences may be defined with an **explicit formula** in which the nth **term** can be calculated directly from n. In a sequence S, the nth term is identified as S_n.

Theorems and Properties

Distributive Property p. 41
Opposite of a Sum Theorem p. 44

Vocabulary

1-7
equivalent formulas

1-8
*sequence
term of a sequence
subscript
index
*explicit formula
discrete function

Summary and Vocabulary 63

Self-Test

For the development of mathematical competence, feedback and correction, along with the opportunity for practice, are necessary. The Self-Test provides the opportunity for feedback and correction; the Chapter Review provides additional opportunities for practice. We cannot overemphasize the importance of these end-of-chapter materials. It is at this point that the material gels for many students, allowing them to solidify skills and understanding. In general, student performance should improve after these pages.

Assign the Self-Test as a one-night assignment. Worked-out solutions for all questions are in the Selected Answers section of the student book. Encourage students to take the Self-Test honestly, grade themselves, and then be prepared to discuss the test in class.

Advise students to pay special attention to those Chapter Review questions (pages 66–69) that correspond to the questions they missed on the Self-Test.

Chapter 1 Self-Test

Take this test as you would take a test in class. You will need a calculator. Then use the Selected Answers section in the back of the book to check your work.

1. If $f(x) = x^2 - 4^x$, find $f(-1.5)$ to the nearest hundredth. 7.13

2. Suppose that f is a function and a is a real number. Describe the difference in the statements "$f(a) = 7$" and "$f(7) = a$." See margin.

3. The table below defines the function g. Find $g(-2)$ and $g(2)$. $g(-2) = 17$ and $g(2) = 3$

r	-1	-2	-1	0	1	2	3
$g(r)$	6	17	15	2	-4	3	-2

In 4 and 5, let f be the function graphed below.

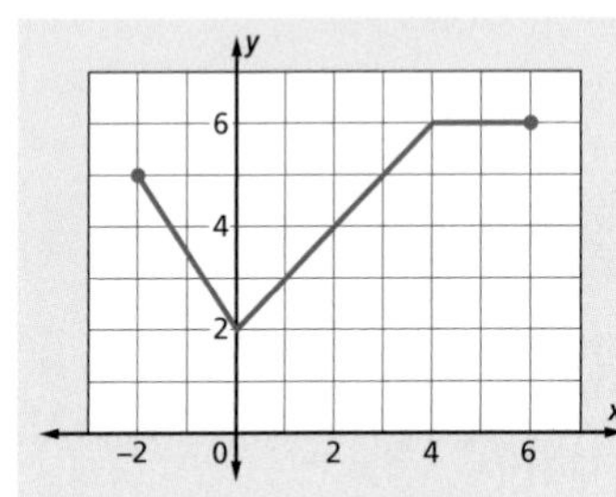

4. Find the domain and range of f. See below.

5. Use the graph to estimate each of the following:
   a. $f(3)$ 5
   b. All values of x such that $f(x) = 4$. $x = -1.3$ and $x = 2$

6. Suppose $S: n \to \frac{n}{2}(3(n-1))$. Evaluate $S(10)$. 135

7. Which formula below is solved for c? B
   A $A = \frac{1}{2}c_1c_2$
   B $c = 2\pi r$
   C $a^2 + b^2 = c^2$

8. Suppose you travel m miles in 4 hours. Write a formula that gives your speed s in miles per hour. $s = \frac{m}{4}$

In 9–11, solve for the variable. 9–11. See margin.

9. $5(7x - 4) = 50$

10. $3.2a = 0.75 + 1.2a$

11. $p + 0.2(1200 - p) = 244.4p$

In 12–14, use the formula $V = \frac{1}{3}\pi r^2h$ for the volume of a cone.

12. Find the volume of the cone at right to the nearest cubic centimeter. 101 cm^3

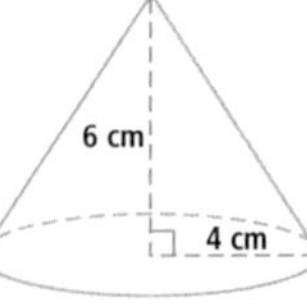

13. Suppose $h = 6$ and the domain of the volume function is $0 < r \le 10$. What is the range of the function? $\{V \mid 0 < V \le 200\pi\}$

14. a. Solve this formula for h in terms of V and r. See margin.
    b. Solve this formula for r in terms of V and h. See margin.

15. A function f contains only the points (0, 7), (4, 8), (8, 9) and (16, 11). Give its domain and range. See margin.

16. **Multiple Choice** Which of the following are graphs of functions? B, C

A
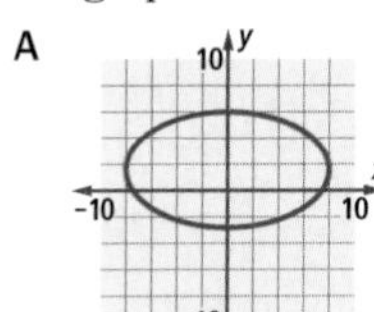

B
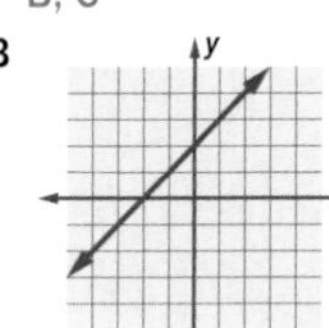

C
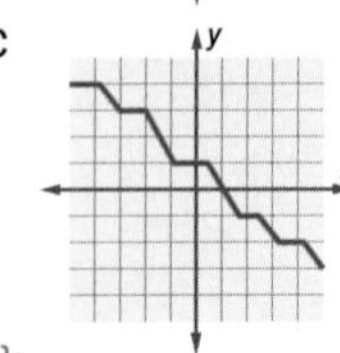

D
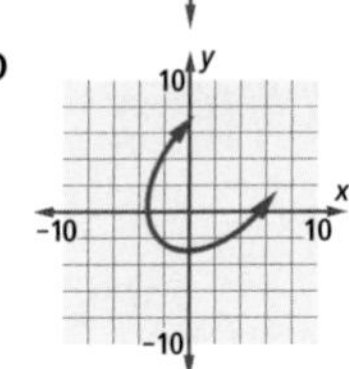

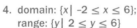

4. domain: $\{x \mid -2 \le x \le 6\}$; range: $\{y \mid 2 \le y \le 6\}$

Additional Answers

2. The first statement says that the value of the function $f(x)$ evaluated at $x = a$ is 7, whereas the second statement says that value of the function $f(x)$ evaluated at $x = 7$ is a.

9. $5(7x - 4) = 50$; $7x - 4 = 10$; $7x = 14$; $x = 2$

10. $3.2a = 0.75 + 1.2a$; $2a = 0.75$; $a = 0.375$

11. $p + 0.2(1200 - p) = 244.4p$;
$p + 0.2 \cdot 1200 - 0.2p = 244.4p$;
$240 = 244.6p$; $p = 0.981$

14a. $V = \frac{1}{3}\pi r^2h$; $h = \frac{V}{\left(\frac{1}{3}\right)\pi r^2}$; $h = \sqrt{\frac{3V}{\pi r^2}}$

14b. $V = \frac{1}{3}\pi r^2h$; $r^2 = \frac{3V}{\pi h}$; $r = \sqrt{\frac{3V}{\pi h}}$

15. domain: {0, 4, 8, 16}; range: {7, 8, 9, 11}

In 17 and 18, determine whether the relation is a function. Justify your answer. See margin.

17. {(9, 7), (7, 5), (18, 12), (9, 4)}

18.

x	0	1	2	4
y	0	2	3	3

(Consider x to be the independent variable.)

19. a. Write the first five terms of the sequence $a_n = -4^n + 2$. See margin.

b. What is a_7? -16,382

20. Use a graphing utility to graph the function $f(t) = 6 - t^2$ with a domain $\{t | -5 \le t \le 5\}$. 20–20a. See margin.

a. What is the range of this function?

b. To the nearest hundredth, estimate where $f(t) = 0$. $x \approx -2.45$ and $x \approx 2.45$

21. Create a table for $y = -3 \cdot \left(\frac{1}{2}\right)^x$ with a start value of $x = -6$, a table increment of 2 and, if necessary, an end value of 2.

a. List the first five ordered pairs in the table. See margin.

b. For what value of x does $y = -0.75$? $x = 2$

22. The following table of values represents the wind chill index for various temperatures when there is a 10 mph wind. Use the table to answer the following questions.

A = Actual temperature (°F)	30	20	10	0	-10	-20	-30
W(A) = Wind-chill index (°F)	21	9	-4	-16	-28	-41	-53

Source: National Oceanic and Atmospheric Administration

Let A = the actual temperature and let W be the name of the function that maps A onto the wind-chill index. 22a. See margin.

a. Evaluate $W(10)$ and explain what it means in terms of the wind chill.

b. For what value of A does $W(A) = -41$? $A = -20$

23. Refer to the graph at the right. See margin.

a. List the ordered pairs in the graph.

b. Is this a function? Explain why or why not.

c. State the domain and range.

24. The population, $P(y)$ in millions, of a certain city is modeled by the function with equation $P(y) = 2 \cdot 1.005^y$, where y is the year minus 2000 (for example, in 2006, $y = 6$). How many more people will be living in the town in the year 2020 than in 2006? about 149,000 more people

25. **Multiple Choice** What CAS command would you use to rewrite the expression $(a^2 + 1)(a + 1)(a - 1)$? C

A SOLVE()
B FUNCTION()
C EXPAND()
D DEFINE()

26. The probability of tossing a six-sided die and rolling a 3 n times in a row can be represented by the sequence $p_n = \left(\frac{1}{6}\right)^n$. What is the probability of rolling a 3 four times in a row? about 0.000772

27. On a recent flight between St. Louis and Los Angeles, $\frac{1}{4}$ of the tickets sold were for seats in business class, $\frac{1}{10}$ in first class, and the remaining 195 tickets were in coach class. How many tickets were sold altogether? See margin.

28. The Pythagorean Theorem states that if a and b are the legs of a right triangle and c is its hypotenuse, then $a^2 + b^2 = c^2$. What happens to the value of c if you switch the values of a and b? See margin.

Notes on the Questions

Question 19 The sequence formula $a_n = -4^n + 2$ always yields negative values for a_n. Students may be surprised by this because they typically do not realize there is a difference between $(-4)^n$ and -4^n. You may have to explain to students why $(-4)^n$ is not always equal to -4^n. In the order of operations, powers take precedence over multiplication, and taking the opposite is viewed as multiplication by -1.

Question 24 Students need to put their calculator in decimal (or approximate) mode. Otherwise, on some calculators, students may see an "overflow" result.

Additional Answers

21.

x	-6	-4	-2	0	2
y	-192	-48	-12	-3	-0.75

21a. The first five ordered pairs are (-6, -192), (-4, -48), (-2, -12), (0, -3), and (2, -0.75).

22a. $W(10) = -4$; the wind-chill index with a 10 mph wind at 10°F is -4°F.

23a. (-1, 0), (0, 2), (1, 3), (2, 2), (3, 0)

23b. Yes; there is only one y-value for each x-value.

23c. domain: {-1, 0, 1, 2, 3}; range: {0, 2, 3}

27. $T = \frac{1}{4}T + \frac{1}{10}T + 195$; $T = \frac{7}{20}T + 195$; $\frac{13}{20}T = 195$; $T = \frac{20}{13} \cdot 195 = 300$; 300 tickets

28. The value of c does not change because $a^2 + b^2 = b^2 + a^2 = c^2$. This corresponds to the geometric situation of a reflection, where the orientation of the triangle shifts, but its lengths do not change.

Additional Answers

17. No; it is not a function because $x = 9$ corresponds to both $y = 7$ and $y = 4$.

18. Yes; it is a function; each x-value defines just one y-value.

19a. $a_1 = -4^1 + 2 = -2$; $a_2 = -4^2 + 2 = -14$; $a_3 = -4^3 + 2 = -62$; $a_4 = -4^4 + 2 = -254$; $a_5 = -4^5 + 2 = -1022$

20.

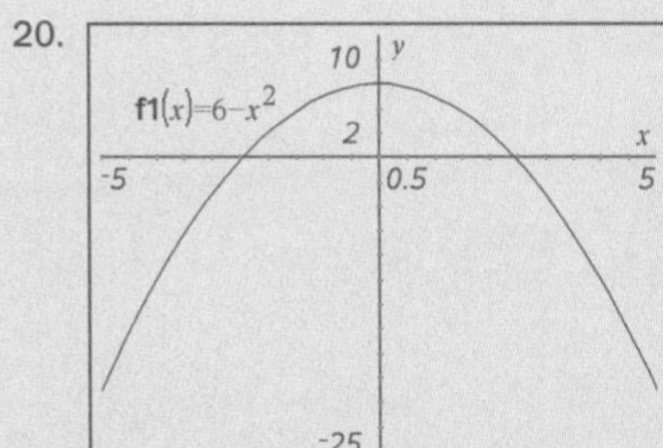

20a. $\{f(t) \mid -19 \le f(t) \le 6\}$

Chapter Review

The main objectives for the chapter are organized in the Chapter Review under the four types of understanding this book promotes: Skills, Properties, Uses, and Representations.

Whereas end-of-chapter material may be considered optional in some texts, in UCSMP *Advanced Algebra* we have selected these objectives and questions with the expectation that they will be covered. Students should be able to answer these questions with about 85% accuracy after studying the chapter.

You may assign these questions over a single night to help students prepare for a test the next day or you may assign the questions over a two-day period. If you work the questions over two days, we recommend assigning the evens for homework the first night so that students get feedback in class the next day, and then assigning the odds the night before the test because the answers are provided to the odd-numbered questions in the Selected Answers section at the back of the book.

It is effective to ask students which questions they still do not understand and use the day as a total class discussion of the material that the class finds most difficult.

Resources

- Assessment Resources: Chapter 1 Test Forms A–D

Technology Resources

Teacher's Assessment Assistant, Ch. 1
Electronic Teacher's Edition, Ch. 1

Chapter 1 Chapter Review

SKILLS
PROPERTIES
USES
REPRESENTATIONS

SPUR stands for Skills, Properties, Uses, and Representations. The Chapter Review Questions are grouped according to the SPUR Objectives in this chapter.

SKILLS Procedures used to get answers

OBJECTIVE A Evaluate expressions and formulas, including correct units in answers. (Lesson 1-1)

1. Evaluate $100 \cdot (1 + r)^t$ when $r = 0.06$ and $t = 3$. 119.1016
2. If $m = \frac{4y(y+2)}{9}$, find m when $y = 16$. $m = 128$
3. If $d = \frac{1}{2}gt^2$, find d when $g = 9.8\frac{\text{m}}{\text{sec}^2}$ and $t = 3$ sec. $d = 44.1$ m
4. Evaluate $\frac{n}{2^{2(n-1)}}$ when $n = 4$. $\frac{1}{16}$

OBJECTIVE B Use mapping and $f(x)$ notation for functions. (Lesson 1-3)

5. If $f(x) = -5x + 10$, what is $f(5)$? -15
6. **Fill in the Blank** Suppose $g: t \rightarrow t - 2t^3$. Then $g: -1 \rightarrow$ __?__. 1

In 7 and 8, a function is described by an equation.
a. Rewrite the function in mapping notation.
b. Evaluate the function at $x = 9$.

7. $h(x) = 12x - 2\sqrt{x}$ 7–8. See margin.
8. $j(x) = 3 - 4 \cdot 2^x$

In 9 and 10, a function is given in mapping notation.
a. Rewrite the function in $f(x)$ notation.
b. Evaluate the function at $x = 8$.

9. $f: x \rightarrow 4 - 27x$ 9–10. See margin.
10. $c: x \rightarrow \frac{\sqrt{2x}}{5}$

OBJECTIVE C Solve and check linear equations. (Lesson 1-6)

In 11–18, solve and check.

11. $12x = \frac{4}{5}$ $x = \frac{1}{15}$; $12\left(\frac{1}{15}\right) = \frac{4}{5}$
12. $\frac{3}{8}(b + 5) = 9$ $b = 19$; $\frac{3}{8}(19 + 5) = 9$
13. $-\frac{5}{3} = \frac{4}{3} - v$ $v = 3$; $-\frac{5}{3} = \frac{4}{3} - 3$
14. $L = 2L - (6 - 6L)$ $L = \frac{6}{7}$; $\frac{6}{7} = 2\left(\frac{6}{7}\right) - \left(6 - 6\left(\frac{6}{7}\right)\right)$
15. $-s + 5s = 4(2s + 3)$ $s = -3$; $3 + 5(-3) = 4(2(-3) + 3)$
16. $0.02(800z + 50) = -500 - 24z$ See margin.
17. $\frac{m}{8} + \frac{m}{6} - 2 = -3m$ See margin.
18. $y - 8(y + 5) = 13y$ $y = -2$; $-2 - 8(-2 + 5) = 13(-2)$

OBJECTIVE D Solve formulas for their variables. (Lesson 1-7) 19–23. See margin.

19. Solve for t in the formula $x = 12 - 6t$.
20. Solve for q in the formula $E = \frac{kq}{r^2}$.
21. Solve for h in the formula $A = \frac{1}{3}(\pi r_1^2 h - \pi r_2^2 h.)$
22. Solve for n in the formula $t = a + (n - 1)d$.
23. Explain why the equation $s = \frac{4\pi}{\sqrt{2bds}}$ is not solved for s.
24. **Multiple Choice** Which of the following is not a formula solved for the volume, radius, or height of a cylindrical barrel? C
A $V = hr^2 \cdot \pi$ B $\frac{V}{\pi r^2} = h$
C $r^2 = \frac{V}{h\pi}$ D $\sqrt{\frac{V}{\pi h}} = r$

OBJECTIVE E Find terms of sequences. (Lesson 1-8)

In 25 and 26, write the first five terms of the sequence. These sequences are defined for all integers $n \geq 1$.

25. $a_n = -3 - 6n$ -9, -15, -21, -27, -33
26. $b_n = -5 \cdot 2^n$ -10, -20, -40, -80, -160
27. If $c_n = n^2 - n$, find $c_4 + c_3$. 18
28. When $d_n = (-0.5)^n$, find $3d_2 + d_1$. 0.25

Additional Answers

7a. $h: x \rightarrow 12x - 2\sqrt{x}$
7b. 102
8a. $j: x \rightarrow 3 - 4 \cdot 2^x$
8b. -2045
9a. $f(x) = 4 - 27x$
9b. -212
10a. $c(x) = \frac{\sqrt{2x}}{5}$
10b. $\frac{4}{5}$
16. $z = \frac{-501}{40}$; $0.02\left(800\left(-\frac{501}{40}\right) + 50\right) = -500 - 24\left(\frac{501}{40}\right)$
17. $m = \frac{48}{79}$; $\left(\frac{48}{79 \cdot 8}\right) + \left(\frac{48}{79 \cdot 6}\right) - 2 = -3\left(\frac{48}{79}\right)$
19. $t = \frac{12 - x}{6}$
20. $q = \frac{Er^2}{k}$
21. $h = \frac{3A}{\pi(r_1^2 - r_2^2)}$
22. $n = \frac{t - a + d}{d}$
23. Answers vary. Sample: It is not solved for s because s appears on both sides of the equal sign.

OBJECTIVE F Use a CAS to solve equations or expand expressions. (Lesson 1-7)

29. Use the SOLVE() function on your CAS to solve the formula for the volume of a cone, $V = \frac{1}{3}\pi r^2 h$, for r. What two solutions does it give? Which one is the correct formula for r? See margin.

In 30 and 31, suppose that while solving an equation for the variable c on a CAS, you encounter the intermediate equation $5 + 5r + ab = 5c$. 30. See margin.

30. What should you enter next? Finish solving this equation on your CAS.

31. **Multiple Choice** A student solving the equation obtains the CAS result $c = \frac{1}{5}(ab + 5r + 5)$. What CAS command will yield a simplified solution? B

A ANS*5 B EXPAND(ANS)

C ANS/5 D SOLVE(ANS, c)

PROPERTIES Principles behind the mathematics

OBJECTIVE G Determine whether a given relation is a function. (Lessons 1-2, 1-5)

In 32-33, determine whether the given table or set of ordered pairs describes y as a function of x.

32. 

x	1	3	5	7	9
y	3	5	7	9	1

yes

33. $\{(0, 3), (1, -2), (2, -1), (1, 2), (-1, 5)\}$ no

In 34-37, determine whether the given graph represents the graph of a function. Justify your answer. 34-37. See margin.

34.

35.

36.

37.

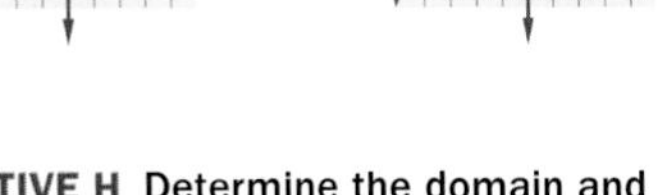

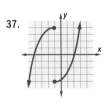

OBJECTIVE H Determine the domain and range of a function. (Lessons 1-4, 1-5)

In 38-43, find the domain and range of the function described by the given table, set of ordered pairs, equation, or graph. 38-44. See margin.

38.

t	2	3	5	7	11
$e(t)$	1	2	3	4	5

39. $\{(0, -1), (1, -1), (2, -1), (-1, -1), (-2, -1)\}$

40. $f(x) = x^2$

41. $g(y) = 3y^5$

42. 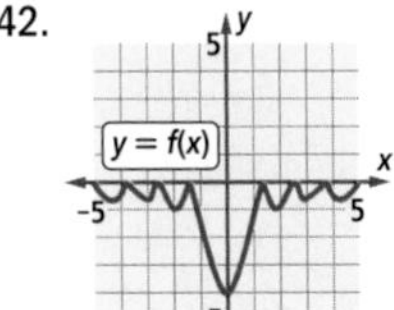

43. 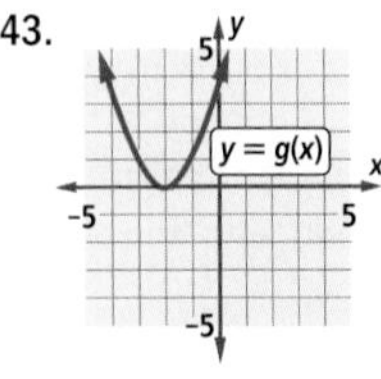

44. From the graph in Question 42, find the approximate values of x for which $f(x) = 0$.

45. What is $g(-3)$ in Question 43? $g(-3) = 1$

Chapter 1 Review

Additional Answers

29. $r = -\frac{\sqrt{3 - v}}{\sqrt{h\pi}}$ or $r = \frac{\sqrt{3 - v}}{\sqrt{h\pi}}$; $\frac{\sqrt{3 - v}}{\sqrt{h\pi}}$

30. [ANS]/[5]; $\frac{5r + ab + 5}{5} = c$

34. No; some x-values define more than one y-value.

35. Yes; each x-value defines a single y-value.

36. Yes; each x-value defines a single y-value.

37. No; an x-value defines two y-values.

38. $\{2, 3, 5, 7, 11\}$; $\{1, 2, 3, 4, 5\}$

39. $\{-2, -1, 0, 1, 2\}$; $\{-1\}$

40. all real numbers; all nonnegative real numbers

41. all real numbers; all real numbers

42. $\{x \mid -5 \le x \le 5\}$, $\{f(x) \mid -4 \le f(x) \le 0\}$

43. all real numbers; all nonnegative real numbers

44. $x = -5, x = -3.75, x = -2.5, x = -1.25, x = 1.25, x = 2.5, x = 3.75, x = 5$

Additional Answers

46.

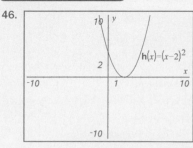

47. If m_1 and m_2 are switched, F has the same value. This implies that the magnitude of the gravitational force that m_2 exerts on m_1 is equal to that exerted by m_1 on m_2.

48. $V = \ell^3$; the rectangular box is a cube.

50. \$63,181; \$92,834; \$136,403; \$200,421

52b. $d(2) = 64$; the ball can fall only a maximum of 60 ft.

53a.

Time (months)	Balance (dollars)
1	200
2	235
3	270
4	305
5	340
6	375

54. the population of Minnesota in 1970

55. 629,672; the difference between the population of Wisconsin and the population of Minnesota in 1980

56. 471,906; the amount the population of Wisconsin grew between 1990 and 2000

61a.

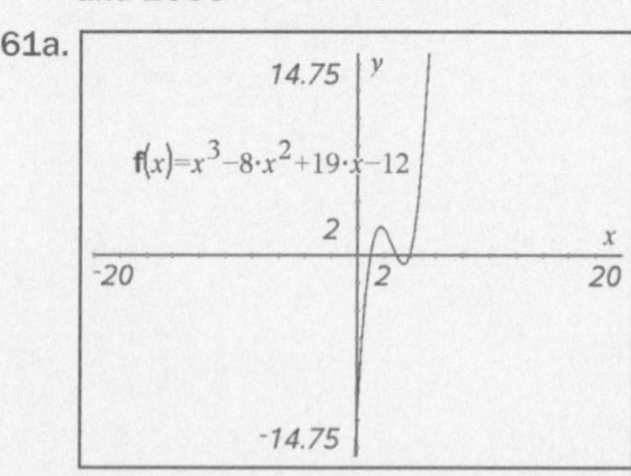

61b. $x = 1, x = 3, x = 4$

46. Graph the function $h(x) = (x - 2)^2$ on a grapher using a standard window, and use the graph to determine the function's domain and range. See margin.

OBJECTIVE I Describe relationships between variables in a formula. (Lesson 1-7)

47. Isaac Newton's Law of Universal Gravitation states that every object exerts a gravitational force on every other object. The formula $F = \frac{Gm_1m_2}{r^2}$ gives the magnitude of the gravitational force F that a body of mass m_1 exerts on a body of mass m_2 if they are a distance r apart. G is the gravitational constant. What happens to the value of F if m_1 and m_2 are switched? What does this imply about the force that the body of mass m_2 exerts on the body of mass m_1? See margin.

48. Rewrite the formula $V = \ell wh$, for the volume of a rectangular box with length ℓ, width w, and height h, in terms of ℓ when $w = \ell = h$. What situation does this formula represent? See margin.

49. **Multiple Choice** Given $x \neq 0$, $y \neq 0$, and $k \neq 0$, which of the following formulas is equivalent to the formula $y = \frac{k}{x}$? D

A $k = \frac{y}{x}$ B $x = ky$ C $y = \frac{x}{k}$
D $x = \frac{k}{y}$ E $k = \frac{x}{y}$

USES Applications of mathematics in real-world situations

OBJECTIVE J Evaluate and interpret values of functions in real-world situations. (Lessons 1-3, 1-4) 50. See margin.

50. Michelle's annual salary is \$43,000. She gets an increase of 8% at the end of each year. The sequence $a_n = 43{,}000 \cdot 1.08^n$ gives Michelle's salary in the nth year. At this growth rate, what will Michelle's salary be in the 5th, 10th, 15th, and 20th years?

51. The formula $S(x) = x + \frac{x^2}{20}$ relates a car's stopping distance $S(x)$ in feet to the car's speed x in miles per hour. Determine how many more feet it takes a car traveling at 85 mph to stop than a car traveling at 55 mph. 240 ft

52. The distance in feet $d(t)$ a dropped object falls in t seconds is given by the function $d(t) = 16t^2$. Suppose you drop a ball from a height of 60 feet. 52b. See margin.

a. About how far will the ball fall in 1.3 seconds? 27.04 ft

b. Find $d(2)$. Explain why this result does not make sense in this situation.

53. Janelle opened a savings account with \$200. Each month she adds \$35 to her account. 53a. See margin.

a. Create a table with the amounts in her account for the first six months.

b. Write a formula for the sequence giving her savings account balance at the end of each month. $B(t) = 200 + 35(t - 1)$

In 54–56, let $M(x)$ and $W(x)$ be the populations of Minnesota and Wisconsin, respectively, in the year x. 54–56. See margin.

Year x	Population of Minnesota $M(x)$	Population of Wisconsin $W(x)$
1970	3,806,103	4,417,821
1980	4,075,970	4,705,642
1990	4,375,099	4,891,769
2000	4,919,479	5,363,675

Source: U.S. Census Bureau

54. What does $M(1970)$ represent?

55. Calculate $W(1980) - M(1980)$. What does this represent?

56. Calculate $W(2000) - W(1990)$. What does this represent?

Additional Answers

62a.

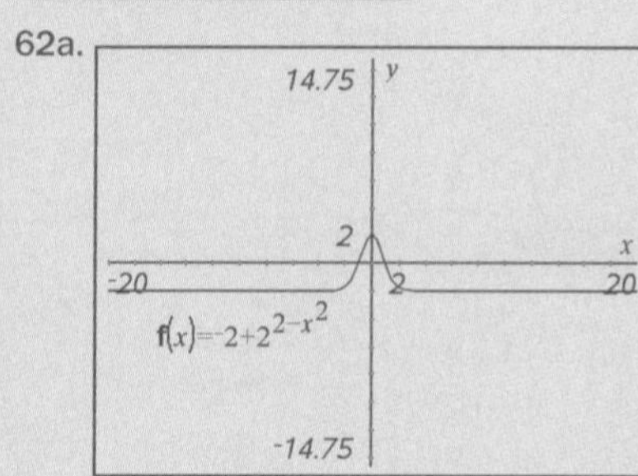

62b. $x = -1, x = 1$

63.

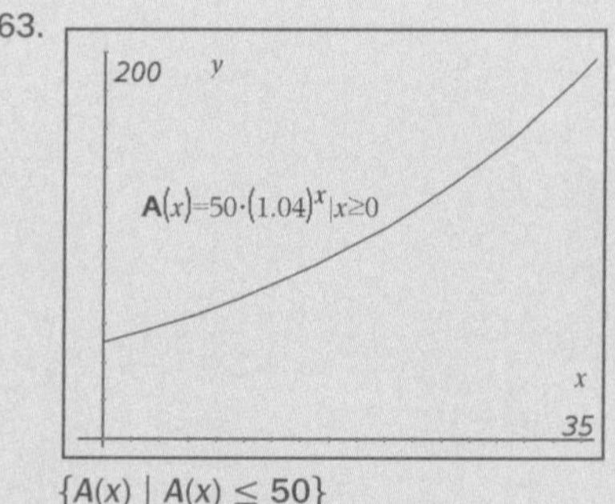

$\{A(x) \mid A(x) \leq 50\}$

OBJECTIVE K Use linear equations to solve real-world problems. (Lesson 1-6)

57. Suppose a baby blue whale weighs 4,000 lb at birth and gains 200 lb a day while nursing. A formula that gives its weight W after d days of nursing is $W = 4000 + 200d$.
   a. Write an equation that can be used to find the number of days d a young blue whale has been nursing if it weighs W lb.
   b. Use your answer to Part a to find d for $W = 14{,}000$. a. $d = \frac{W - 4000}{200}$; b. 50 days
58. At George Washington High School, all students are in grade 10, 11, or 12. This year $\frac{3}{10}$ of the students are in grade 10, 400 students are in grade 11, and $\frac{1}{5}$ of all students are in grade 12. How many students are at George Washington High this year? 800 students
59. Cara wants to park her car in a parking lot that charges \$6 for the first hour and \$1.50 for each additional hour. So the cost c in dollars to park for h hours is $c = 6 + 1.5(h - 1)$. How long can Cara park if she has \$20? (Parking time is always rounded up to the next hour, so if she parks for 70 minutes, she must pay for 2 hours.) 10 hours
60. Frederick is paying off a \$3,000 loan in installments of \$160 per month. So the amount left to pay in dollars after m months will be $3000 - 160m$. After how many full months will Frederick be out of debt? 19 months

REPRESENTATIONS Pictures, graphs, or objects that illustrate concepts

OBJECTIVE L Use a graphing utility to graph functions and generate tables for functions. (Lessons 1-4, 1-5, 1-8)

In 61 and 62, a function is given.

a. Use a graphing utility to graph f in the standard window.

b. Use your graph to find all values of x when $f(x) = 0$. 61–66. See margin.

61. $f(x) = x^3 - 8x^2 + 19x - 12$
62. $f(x) = -2 + 2^2 - x^2$
63. Use a graphing utility to graph A when $A(t) = 50 \cdot 1.04^t$, with the domain restricted to $\{t| \ t \geq 0\}$. What is the range of this function?
64. Use a graphing utility to graph B when $B(t) = 50 \cdot 0.96^t$, with the domain restricted to $\{t| \ t \geq 0\}$. What is the range of this function?

In 65 and 66, a function f is given.

a. Create a table for f with a start value of 1 and a table increment of 0.2. List the first five ordered pairs in the table.

b. Give a value of x for which f(x) is within 0.05 of -0.4.

c. **Multiple Choice** What appears to be true of $f(x)$?

A $f(x)$ is always positive.

B $f(x)$ is always negative.

C $f(x)$ starts off positive and becomes negative.

D none of the above

65. $f(x) = 2^x - 4^x + 3^x$
66. $f: x \rightarrow \frac{2x - 1}{6 - 5x}$

Assessment

Evaluation The *Assessment Resources* provide four forms of the Chapter 1 Test. Forms A and B present parallel versions of a short-answer format. Form C consists of four to six short-response questions that cover the SPUR objectives from Chapter 1. Form D offers performance assessment that covers a subset (or even just one) of the SPUR objectives for the chapter.

Feedback After students have taken the test for Chapter 1 and you have scored the results, return the tests to students for discussion. Class discussion on the questions that caused trouble for most students can be very effective in identifying and clarifying misunderstandings. You might want to have them note the items they missed and work either in groups or at home to correct them. It is important for students to receive feedback on every chapter test, and we recommend that students see and correct their mistakes before proceeding too far into the next chapter.

Suggestions for Assignment Assign Lesson 2-1 for homework the evening of the test. It gives students work to do after they have completed the test and keeps the class moving. If you do not do this, you may cover one less chapter over the course of the year.

Additional Answers

64.

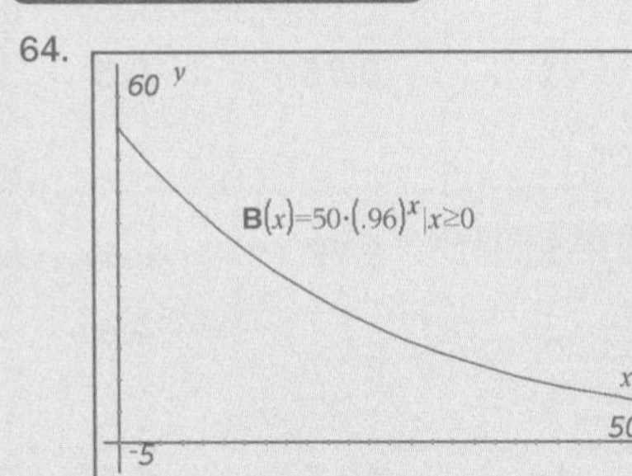

$\{B(x) \mid 0 \leq B(x) \leq 50\}$

65a.

x	f(x)
1	1
1.2	0.757
1.4	0.330
1.6	-0.359
1.8	-1.419

65b. 1.6

65c. C

Additional Answers

66a.

x	f(x)
1	1
1.2	undefined
1.4	-1.8
1.6	-1.1
1.8	-0.867

66b. Answers vary. Sample: –5

66c. D

Chapter

2 Variation and Graphs

Chapter Overview

		Local Standards	Pacing (in days) Average	Advanced	Block
2-1	**Direct Variation** **A** Translate variation language into formulas and formulas into variation language. **B** Solve variation problems. **F** Recognize variation situations. **G** Solve real-world variation problems.		1	0.75	0.5
2-2	**Inverse Variation** **A, B, F, G** See 2-1.		1	0.75	0.5
2-3	**The Fundamental Theorem of Variation** **D** Use the Fundamental Theorem of Variation.		1	0.75	0.5
	QUIZ 1		0.5	0.5	0.25
2-4	**The Graph of $y = kx$** **C** Find slopes and rates of change. **E** Identify the properties of variation functions. **I** Graph variation equations. **J** Identify variation equations from graphs.		1	0.75	0.5
2-5	**The Graph of $y = kx^2$** **C, E, I, J** See 2-4.		1	0.75	0.5
2-6	**The Graphs of $y = \frac{k}{x}$ and $y = \frac{k}{x^2}$** **E** Identify the properties of variation functions. **I** Graph variation equations. **J** Identify variation equations from graphs.		1	0.75	0.5
	QUIZ 2		0.5	0.5	0.25
2-7	**Fitting a Model to Data I** **H** Fit an appropriate model to data.		1	0.75	0.5
2-8	**Fitting a Model to Data II** **D** Use the Fundamental Theorem of Variation. **H** Fit an appropriate model to data.		1	0.75	0.5
2-9	**Combined and Joint Variation** **A** Translate variation language into formulas and formulas into variation language. **B** Solve variation problems. **G** Solve real-world variation problems.		1	0.75	0.5
		Self-Test	1	0.75	0.5
		Chapter Review	2	1	0.5
		Test	1	1	0.5
		TOTAL	14	10.5	6.5

Technology Resources

Teacher's Assessment Assistant, Ch. 2

Electronic Teacher's Edition, Ch. 2

Differentiated Options  Universal Access

	Accommodating the Learner	Vocabulary Development	Ongoing Assessment	Materials
2-1	pp. 75, 77	p. 74	written, p. 78	
2-2	pp. 81, 82	p. 83	group, p. 85	
2-3	p. 88	p. 89	oral, p. 92	
2-4	pp. 96, 99	p. 95	group, p. 99	
2-5	pp. 101, 102	p. 103	written, p. 105	
2-6	pp. 107, 108	p. 108	oral, p. 113	
2-7	pp. 116, 117	p. 117	group, p. 120	
2-8	pp. 123, 124	p. 123	oral, p. 128	
2-9	p. 131	p. 132	written, p. 135	

Objectives

Skills	Lessons	Self-Test Questions	Chapter Review Questions
A Translate variation language into formulas and formulas into variation language.	2-1, 2-2, 2-9	1-3	1-8
B Solve variation problems.	2-1, 2-2, 2-9	4	9-12
C Find slopes and rates of change.	2-4, 2-5	7	13-18
Properties			
D Use the Fundamental Theorem of Variation.	2-3, 2-8	5, 6, 17	19-26
E Identify the properties of variation functions.	2-4, 2-5, 2-6	8, 10	27-34
Uses			
F Recognize variation situations.	2-1, 2-2	11	35-42
G Solve real-world variation problems.	2-1, 2-2, 2-9	18	43-48
H Fit an appropriate model to data.	2-7, 2-8	15, 16, 19	49-51
Representations			
I Graph variation equations.	2-4, 2-5, 2-6	9, 12, 13	52-57
J Identify variation equations from graphs.	2-4, 2-5, 2-6	14	58-61

Resource Masters Chapter 2

Resource Master 1, Graph Paper (page 2), can be used with Lesson 2-8. **Resource Master 2, Four Quadrant Graph Paper** (page 3), can be used with Lessons 2-4 and 2-5. **Resource Master 3, Automatic Grapher Grids** (page 4), can be used with Lessons 2-5 and 2-6.

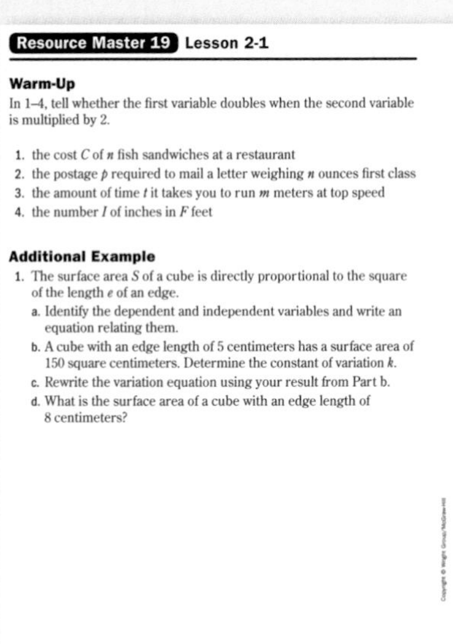

Resource Master 19 Lesson 2-1

Warm-Up

In 1–4, tell whether the first variable doubles when the second variable is multiplied by 2.

1. the cost C of n fish sandwiches at a restaurant
2. the postage p required to mail a letter weighing n ounces first class
3. the amount of time t it takes you to run m meters at top speed
4. the number I of inches in F feet

Additional Example

1. The surface area S of a cube is directly proportional to the square of the length e of an edge.
   a. Identify the dependent and independent variables and write an equation relating them.
   b. A cube with an edge length of 5 centimeters has a surface area of 150 square centimeters. Determine the constant of variation k.
   c. Rewrite the variation equation using your result from Part b.
   d. What is the surface area of a cube with an edge length of 8 centimeters?

Resource Master for Lesson 2-1

Resource Master 20 Lesson 2-1

Additional Example

2. Suppose m varies directly as the fifth power of p. If $m = 96$ when $p = 2$, find m when $p = 5$.
   Solution Write an equation with variables m, p, and k that describes the variation.
   ____ $= k \cdot$ ____^{5}
   Given that $m = 96$ when $p = 2$, find k.
   ____ $= k \cdot$ ____^{5}; ____ $= k \cdot$ ____, so $k =$ ____.
   Rewrite the formula using the value of k found above and $p = 5$ and solve for m.
   $m =$ ____ $\cdot$ ____^{5}
   $m =$ ____
   So, when $p = 5$, $m =$ ____.

Question 15

s	1	2	3	4	5	6	7	8	9	10
S.A.										

Resource Master for Lesson 2-1

Resource Master 21 Lesson 2-2

Warm-Up

In 1–4, tell whether the first variable is halved when the second variable is multiplied by 2.

1. The rent R for an apartment is split evenly among n people.
2. The distance d you travel in a car if you are going at a constant speed s.
3. The time t it will take to get to a destination if you travel at a rate r.
4. The distance d between n evenly spaced buttons from the top to the bottom of a particular shirt.

Additional Examples

1. The number of units u in a length varies inversely with the length ℓ of the unit. Write an equation that expresses this relationship.
2. Using the seesaw in Example 2, suppose Kerry weighs 34 kilograms and is 1.8 meters from the pivot. If Madison weighs 38 kilograms, how far from the pivot should she sit to balance Kerry?
3. In Example 3, suppose the intensity of light 6 meters from a light source is 30 lumens. Find the constant of variation and determine the intensity of the same light 9 meters from its source.
   Solution Write an equation relating d, the distance from the light source, and I, the light's intensity:
   $I = \frac{k}{\_\_\_\_}$.
   To find k, substitute $d =$ ____ and $I =$ ____ into your equation and solve for k.
   ____ $= \frac{k}{\_\_\_\_}$, so ____ $= k$
   Using that value of k, evaluate the formula for I when $d = 9$ meters.
   $I =$ ____ $=$ ____ lumens.

Resource Master for Lesson 2-2

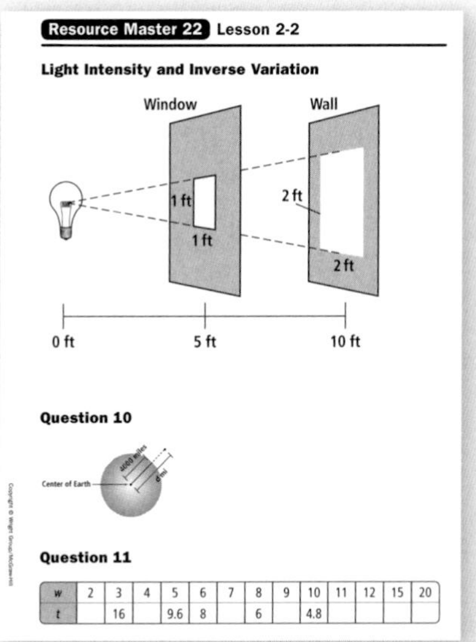

Resource Master 22 Lesson 2-2

Light Intensity and Inverse Variation

Question 10

Question 11

w	2	3	4	5	6	7	8	9	10	11	12	15	20
t		16		9.6	8		6		4.8				

Resource Master for Lesson 2-2

Resource Master 23 Lesson 2-3

Warm-Up

1. You are getting logs for a fireplace. One log is 30 centimeters long, and a second log of the same thickness is 60 centimeters long. If the first log weighs 5 kilograms, what will the second log weigh?
2. You are shown two solid cubes of wood of the same type. The first is 6 inches on a side, and the second is 15 inches on a side. You pick up the first block which weighs 12 pounds. Explain why most people would need help to pick up the second block.

Additional Examples

1. Use the information in Example 1 and the Activity. If the wrappers for the mini pops cost 2.25 cents each, how much does a wrapper for a super jumbo pop cost?
2. In a parade, the height of a float varies directly with the square of the length of the vehicle that supports the float. This year's vehicles are 3 times as long as the vehicles used 10 years ago. Estimate how the height of this year's floats compares to the height of the floats 10 years ago.
   Solution Letting $\ell =$ the length of the vehicle and $h =$ the height of the float, an equation for the variation function is $h = k\ell^2$. When ℓ is multiplied by ____, h is multiplied by ____. So this year's floats are about ____ times as tall as the floats 10 years ago.

Resource Master for Lesson 2-3

Resource Master 24 Lesson 2-3

Activity, Steps 1 and 2

Size	Mean Radius r (cm)	r^3 (cm^3)	Ratio of Radius to Mini's Radius	Ratio of r^3 to Mini's r^3	Production Cost Estimate
Mini	0.7	0.343	1:1	1:1	$\frac{1}{2}$ cent
Regular	1.4				
Jumbo	2.1				
Super Jumbo	2.8				

Activity, Step 4

Size	Radius r (cm)	Ratio of r^3 to Mini's r^3	Number of Pops n in a Carton
Mini	0.7	1:1	270
Regular	1.4		
Jumbo	2.1		
Super Jumbo	2.8		

Question 8

x	1	2	3	4	6	8	9
y							

Resource Master for Lesson 2-3

Resource Master 25 Lesson 2-4

Warm-Up

Manually graph a set of points (x, y) such that $y = -2.5x$. What is the slope of the line?

Additional Example

Determine the slope of a line with equation $d = \frac{5}{7}w$, where w is the independent variable (in weeks) and d is the dependent variable (in days).

Question 17

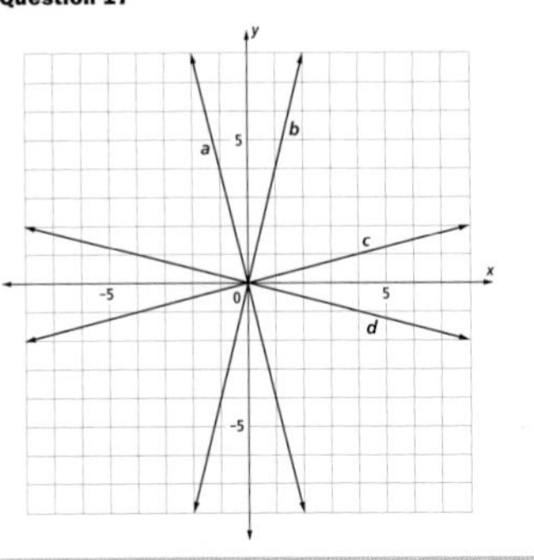

Resource Master for Lesson 2-4

Resource Master 27 Lesson 2-5

Resource Master 26 Lesson 2-5

Warm-Up

1. A parabola is the graph of the equation $y = kx^2$ and contains the point (4, 6).
   a. What is the value of k?
   b. Name at least three other points on this parabola.
2. What is an equation for the reflection image of the parabola of Warm-Up Question 1 over the x-axis?
3. What is an equation for the reflection image of the parabola of Warm-Up Question 1 over the y-axis?

Additional Example

Find the following rates of change for the relation $d = \frac{1}{20}s^2$ and describe what each means in terms of braking distance.

a. r_3, the rate of change from (10, 5) to (20, 20)
b. r_4, the rate of change from (20, 20) to (50, 125)

Resource Masters for Lesson 2-5

Resource Master 28 Lesson 2-6

Warm-Up

Chiliad High School has 1000 students. (A *chiliad* is a group of one thousand.) The school is holding a talent show and is inviting the families of all the students. A mailing will go to the families. It is estimated that it would take one person 15 seconds to fold the insert, stuff it into an envelope, and seal the envelope. If s students volunteer to stuff envelopes to get the mailing out, how many minutes t will it take to have all the envelopes ready for mailing?

Additional Examples

1. If p is a constant, what are the domain and range of a function with equation $y = \frac{p}{x}$?
2. a. Graph $y = \frac{36}{x^2}$ in a window with $\{x \mid -6 \le x \le 6\}$ and $\{y \mid -10 \le y \le 10\}$. Sketch the graph on your paper. Then clear the screen and graph $y = -\frac{36}{x^2}$ in the same window.
   b. Describe the symmetry of each graph.

Resource Master for Lesson 2-6

Resource Master 30 Lesson 2-6

Resource Master 29 Lesson 2-6

The Graph of $y = \frac{k}{x}$

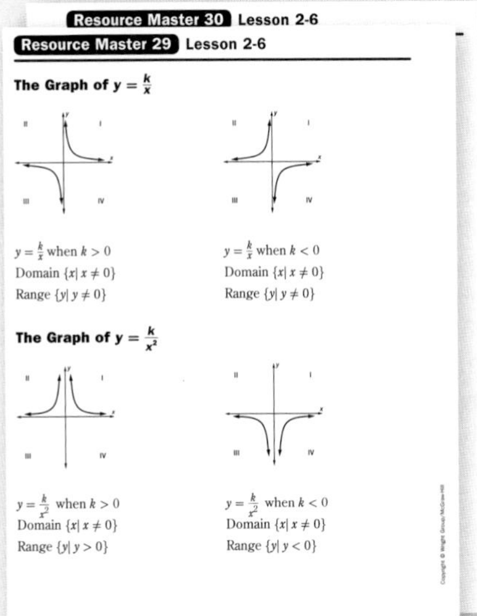

Resource Masters for Lesson 2-6

Resource Master 31 Lesson 2-7

Warm-Up

Caroline North measured how far a marble rolled down a ramp in 1 through 5 seconds. She obtained the following data:

Time (seconds)	1	2	3	4	5
Distance (inches)	0.3	1.2	2.6	4.9	7.6

Find an equation of variation relating time t and distance D.

Additional Examples

1. Find a variation equation to describe these data:

x	1	1.5	2	2.5	3
y	3.2	2.25	12.8	20	28.8

Solution A graph of the data will suggest the formula $y = kx^2$. Substitute one of the ordered pairs into the formula to find k. The easiest pair to use is (1, 3.2).

____ = k(____)^2

k = ____

So, a variation equation describing the data is y = ____x^2.

2. a. Use the Fundamental Theorem of Variation to determine an appropriate model that relates x and y in this table.

x	60	65	72	75	83	91	99	107
y	2.5	2.31	2.08	2	1.81	1.65	1.52	1.4

   b. Predict the value of x for $y = 100$.

Resource Master for Lesson 2-7

Resource Master 32 Lesson 2-7

Guided Example 1

Time in Air t (sec)	1	1.5	2	2.5	3
Observed Distance Fallen d (m)	4.9	11.0	19.6	30.6	44.1
Predicted Distance Fallen d (m)					

Resource Master for Lesson 2-7

Resource Master 33 Lesson 2-8

Warm-Up

1. How are walking speed s and distance walked d related?
2. If the distance walked is kept constant, how are time t and speed s related to each other?
3. From Warm-Up Questions 1 and 2, how are walking speed, distance walked, and time walked related?

Additional Examples

1. Verify that P varies directly with q for these data.

P	1	2	3	4	5	6
q	4.5	9	13.6	17.9	22.5	27.1

2. Using the data given in the table below, use the Converse of the Fundamental Theorem of Variation to determine how G varies with m and write a variation equation for the situation. What is the value of k?

G	1	2	3	4	5	6
m	5	20	45	80	125	180

Resource Master for Lesson 2-8

Resource Master 35 Lesson 2-8

Resource Master 34 Lesson 2-8

Additional Example

3. Using the data given in the table below, use the Converse of the Fundamental Theorem of Variation to determine how R varies with s. Find the constant of variation k to verify the relationship between R and s.

R	1	2	3	4	5	6
s	350	175	117	88	70	58

Solution Select three data points from the table such that s_2 is double the value of s_1 and s_3 is triple the value of s_1:

(s_1, R_1) = (____, ____), (s_2, R_2) = (____, ____),

(s_3, R_3) = (____, ____).

$\frac{R_2}{R_1}$ = ____, so as s doubles, R is divided by ____.

$\frac{R_3}{R_1}$ = ____, so as s triples, R is divided by ____.

So r varies ____ as ____, and $R = \frac{k}{\_\_\_\_}$.

Now select a data point from the table and use it to find k.

____ $= \frac{k}{\_\_\_\_}$, so ____ $= k$

Use k to write a variation formula for R as a function of s: ____.

Verify the relationship by filling in the values of R in this table:

R	1	2	3	4	5	6
s						

Compare your results to the original data. Based on this comparison, you can confirm that R varies ____ as ____.

Resource Masters for Lesson 2-8

Resource Master 37 Lesson 2-9

Resource Master 36 Lesson 2-9

Warm-Up

Use the bicycle gear formula $S = \frac{kRF}{B}$. Consider three gear settings: (1) the front gear has 22 teeth, and the back gear has 30 teeth; (2) the front gear has 44 teeth, and the back gear has 30 teeth; (3) the front gear has 44 teeth, and the rear gear has 11 teeth.

1. The ratio $\frac{F}{B}$ is called the *gear ratio*. Which of the three settings has the highest gear ratio?
2. At the same number of pedal revolutions, which of these gear settings will cause a bicycle to travel the farthest?
3. At the same number of pedal revolutions, compare how far a bicycle will travel at setting 1 than at setting 3.
4. Explain why R is in the numerator of this formula.

Additional Examples

1. A bicyclist is pedaling at 85 revolutions per minute using a front gear with 39 teeth and a back gear with 13 teeth. At these settings, she is traveling 21 miles per hour. Describe how her speed would change if she decreased her pedaling to 60 revolutions per minute.
2. The hyperfocal length H in yards varies directly with the square of the focal length L in inches and inversely with the selected aperture f.
   a. Write a general variation equation to model this situation.
   b. Find the value and unit of k when the hyperfocal length of a 1.75-inch lens is 12 yards and the aperture is set at 9.
   c. Write a variation formula for the situation using your answer to Part b.
   d. Find the hyperfocal length needed (in yards) if you want to shoot with a 12-inch lens at an aperture setting of 2.5. Include the units.

Resource Masters for Lesson 2-9

Chapter 2

Pacing

Each lesson in this chapter is designed to be covered in 1 day. At the end of the chapter, you should plan to spend 1 day to review the Self-Test, 1 to 2 days for the Chapter Review, and 1 day for a test. You may wish to spend a day on projects and possibly a day is needed for quizzes. This chapter should therefore take 14 to 18 days. We strongly advise you not to spend more than 18 days on this chapter.

Overview

Open this chapter by asking students to suggest examples of situations that are related in such a way that if one condition changes, it causes changes in other conditions. List the examples that students suggest, such as the following: The amount you pay for fresh fish at a supermarket depends on the weight of the fish. Point out those that exemplify variation formulas (the fish-cost relationship is an example of direct variation) and tell students that such relationships will be the focus of this chapter. You can use the direct variation situations to lead into a discussion of Lesson 2-1.

Lesson 2-1 introduces a four-step procedure for solving variation equations. We use that procedure to solve variation problems, rather than proportions, to help emphasize the point that variation relationships are functions.

Chapter 2

Variation and Graphs

Contents

As you ride your bicycle on level ground, you control the speed by moving the pedals. The faster you pedal, the more revolutions R the pedals make each minute, and the faster the bicycle travels. However, an experienced cyclist knows that speed is also dependent upon the *gear ratio* between the numbers of teeth on the front and back gears. Increasing the number F of front-gear teeth increases speed, but increasing the number B of back-gear teeth reduces the speed. Thus, speed varies as R, F, and B change. But how does it vary?

Chapter 2 Overview

Chapter 2 has three interrelated ideas: (1) equations of variation; (2) graphical representations of variation equations; and (3) modeling data using variation equations.

Lessons 2-1 and 2-2 introduce direct and inverse variation, respectively, and Lesson 2-3 explores how a change in one variable in a variation equation affects the other variable.

Lessons 2-4 through 2-6 concentrate on graphing equations of variation. Some of this material, namely the graph of $y = kx$ and possibly the graph of $y = kx^2$, may be a review for your students. Slope is interpreted as a measure of the rate of change between points on a graph, for nonlinear graphs as well as linear graphs.

Lessons 2-7 and 2-8 introduce the idea of mathematical modeling from data—more

Suppose Mario knows that when he is pedaling at 80 revolutions per minute (rpm) with 35 teeth on the front gear and 15 teeth on the back gear, he travels at 14.5 miles per hour. How would his speed be affected if he increases his revolutions to 100 rpm? You will learn how to answer this question in this chapter about *variation*, that is, how one quantity changes as others are changed.

71

specifically, modeling using equations of variation. These lessons strengthen the work done with graphing earlier in the chapter and help establish modeling as a major theme of this book.

Lesson 2-9 discusses the difference between combined variation and joint variation. Combined variation refers to direct and inverse variations occurring together, whereas joint variation refers to one quantity varying directly as the product of two or more independent variables, with no inverse variation. Thus, Lesson 2-9, which returns to a discussion of the language of variation, summarizes many of the ideas in the chapter.

Using Pages 70–71

A simple application to bicycling considers the speed (in revolutions per minute) of pedaling. At a given gear, if you pedal twice as fast for some period of time, you will go twice as far in that time. Gears affect how many times the wheels rotate for each rotation of the pedals. A gear uses a chainwheel (sprocket), and the relative rotation speeds of the wheels and pedals depend on the number of teeth in the gear. A 10-speed bike has 2 gears in the front and 5 in the back ($2 \times 5 = 10$); some of today's mountain bikes have 24 speeds, with 3 gears in the front and 8 in the back ($3 \times 8 = 24$). The rider can use "derailleurs" to move the chain from one chainwheel to another, changing the front and the back independently.

The relationship between the speed R of pedaling, the number of teeth F on the front gear, the number of teeth B on the back gear, and the speed S of the bike is an example of combined variation. The combined variation equation, $S = k\frac{RF}{B}$, is explored in Lesson 2-9.

Chapter 2 Projects

At the end of each chapter, you will find projects related to the chapter. At this time you might want to have students look over the projects on pages 136 and 137. You might want to have students tentatively select a project on which to work. Then, as students read and progress through the chapter, they can finalize their project choices.

Sometimes students might work alone. At other times, you might let them collaborate with classmates for a presentation and discussion. We recommend that you allow for diversity and encourage students to use their imaginations when presenting their projects. As students work on projects throughout the year, they should see many uses of mathematics in the real world.

Lesson 2-1

GOAL

Introduce the language and logic of direct variation.

SPUR Objectives

A Translate variation language into formulas and formulas into variation language.

B Solve variation problems.

F Recognize variation situations.

G Solve real-world variation problems.

Materials/Resources

- Lesson Masters 2-1A and 2-1B
- Resource Masters 19 and 20

HOMEWORK

Suggestions for Assignment

- Questions 1–23
- Question 24 (extra credit)
- Reading Lesson 2-2
- Covering the Ideas 2-2

Local Standards

1 Warm-Up

In 1–4, tell whether the first variable doubles when the second variable is multiplied by 2.

1. the cost C of n fish sandwiches at a restaurant yes
2. the postage p required to mail a letter weighing n ounces first class no
3. the amount of time t it takes you to run m meters at top speed no
4. the number I of inches in F feet yes

Lesson 2-1 Direct Variation

Vocabulary

varies directly as

direct-variation equation

constant of variation

direct-variation function

directly proportional to

BIG IDEA When two variables x and y satisfy the equation $y = kx^n$ for some constant value of k, we say that y varies directly as x^n.

Mental Math

a. Which is larger: $\frac{7}{9}$ or $\frac{7}{10}$? $\frac{7}{9}$

b. Which is closer to $\frac{1}{2}$: $\frac{3}{5}$ or $\frac{4}{7}$? $\frac{4}{7}$

c. Which is closer to zero: $\frac{1}{2} - \frac{1}{3}$ or $\frac{1}{3} - \frac{1}{4}$? $\frac{1}{3} - \frac{1}{4}$

d. Which is closer to 1: $\frac{1}{2} + \frac{1}{4} + \frac{1}{6}$ or $\frac{1}{3} + \frac{1}{5} + \frac{1}{7}$ $\frac{1}{2} + \frac{1}{4} + \frac{1}{6}$

When possible, Lance puts his bike into its highest gear for maximum speed. In highest gear, the ratio of the number of front-gear teeth to the number of back-gear teeth is $\frac{52 \text{ teeth}}{11 \text{ teeth}} \approx 4.73$. This means that as Lance turns the pedals one complete revolution, the back wheel turns almost 5 times. So if w is the number of back-wheel turns per minute and p is the number of pedal turns per minute, then

$$w = \frac{52}{11}p.$$

If Lance starts pedaling twice as fast, then the back wheel will also turn twice as fast as it previously did. We say that w **varies directly as** p, and we call $w = \frac{52}{11}p$ a **direct-variation equation**. In a direct variation, both quantities increase or decrease together.

Suppose Lance changes to a lower gear with a gear ratio of $\frac{42 \text{ teeth}}{21 \text{ teeth}} = 2$. A direct-variation equation for this situation is $w = 2p$.

Recall the formula $A = \pi r^2$ for the area of a circle. This, too, is a direct-variation equation; as the radius r increases, the area A also increases. In this case, A varies directly as r^2. Often this wording is used: the area A varies directly as the *square* of r.

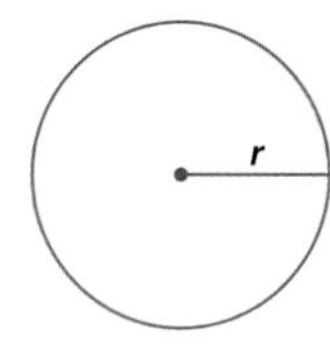

$A = \pi r^2$

Direct-Variation Functions

The formulas $w = \frac{52}{11}p$, $w = 2p$, and $A = \pi r^2$ are all of the form $y = kx^n$, where k is a nonzero constant, called the **constant of variation**, and n is a positive number. These formulas all describe *direct-variation functions*.

Background

Direct variation functions When students are given a formula with one variable isolated on one side, they usually understand that the variables are related: As the variable on one side of the equation changes, so does the variable on the other side. Lesson 2-1 focuses on a particular way that the dependent variable changes.

The terms *dependent variable* and *independent variable* are key in thinking about variation. It is usually clear in a real-world situation which variable is the independent variable and which is the dependent variable. However, in an abstract situation, the labeling of variables as independent and dependent may be arbitrary.

Some people like to think of direct variation in terms of doubling: If the independent variable doubles, then the dependent variable doubles. The converse is also true: If $f(2x) = 2f(x)$ for all real numbers x, then f is a direct variation function.

Definition of Direct-Variation Function

A **direct-variation function** is a function that can be described by a formula of the form $y = kx^n$, with $k \neq 0$ and $n > 0$.

When y varies directly as x^n we also say that y is **directly proportional to** x^n. For instance, the formula $A = \pi r^2$ can be read "the area of a circle is directly proportional to the square of its radius." Here $n = 2$ and $k = \pi$, so π is the constant of variation.

QY1

If you know one point (x, y) of a direct-variation function, you can determine k and, thus, know precisely the function.

The formula $A = \pi r^2$ is one example of a general theorem from geometry: in a set of similar figures (in this case, circles), area is proportional to the square of length. Likewise, in a set of similar figures, volume is proportional to the cube of edge length. Example 1 is an instance of that theorem.

▶ QY1

Identify the constant of variation and the value of n in the formula $w = \frac{52}{11}p$.

Example 1

The volume V of a regular icosahedron is directly proportional to the cube of the length ℓ of an edge.

a. Identify the dependent and independent variables and write an equation relating them.

b. A regular icosahedron with an edge length of 4 cm has a volume of about 140 cm^3. Determine the constant of variation k.

c. Rewrite the variation equation using your result from Part b.

d. Approximate to the nearest cubic centimeter the volume of an icosahedron with an edge length of 5 cm.

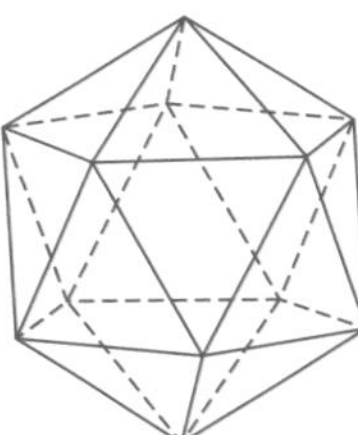

Regular Icosahedron (20 faces)

Solution

a. Because V is directly proportional to ℓ, the dependent variable is V and the independent variable is ℓ. In this problem $n = 3$, so an equation for the direct variation is $V = k\ell^3$, where k is a constant.

b. To determine k, substitute $V = 140$ cm^3 and $\ell = 4$ cm into your direct-variation equation from Part a.

$$140 \text{ cm}^3 = k \cdot (4 \text{ cm})^3$$

$$140 \text{ cm}^3 = (64 \text{ cm}^3) \cdot k$$

$$k = \frac{140 \text{ cm}^3}{64 \text{ cm}^3} = 2.1875$$

(continued on next page)

2 Teaching

Notes on the Lesson

Direct-variation functions It is important that students realize that the phrases *varies directly as* and *is directly proportional to* are synonymous. (See also the Vocabulary Development note on page 74.) A similar situation holds true in Lesson 2-2 for the phrases *varies inversely as* and *is inversely proportional to*.

You can motivate this lesson's exploration of direct variation, including the definitions and uses of the terms, by using familiar examples such as those in the Warm-Up, others suggested by your students, or the following:

- The cost of gas for a car varies directly as the amount of gas purchased.
- The amount of sales tax varies directly as the total price of the goods purchased.
- The amount of calories in a sector of an apple pie varies directly as the angle measure of the sector.
- The volume of a sphere varies directly as the cube of its radius.

An algorithm (procedure) for solving variation problems is described after Example 1 and then applied in Example 2 and the Activity. Stress the steps of the procedure, as illustrated in Example 1:

1. Write the general variation formula.
2. Use the formula to find k.
3. Write the formula with the value of k in it.
4. Use that formula to answer the question.

This algorithm is very efficient for solving these problems.

Activity It is not necessary to solve direct variation problems using technology, but the technology mimics the process by which direct variation problems can be solved and provides a general application of that process. (A similar technology activity for inverse variation appears in Lesson 2-2, so time spent here discussing *dirk* and *dvar* can have a payoff there.)

Additional Examples

Example 1 The surface area S of a cube is directly proportional to the square of the length e of an edge.

a. Identify the dependent and independent variables and write an equation relating them. e is the independent variable, and S is the dependent variable; $S = ke^2$

b. A cube with an edge length of 5 centimeters has a surface area of 150 square centimeters. Determine the constant of variation k. $k = 6$

c. Rewrite the variation equation using your result from Part b. $S = 6e^2$

d. What is the surface area of a cube with an edge length of 8 centimeters? 384 cm^2

Example 2 Suppose m varies directly as the fifth power of p. If $m = 96$ when $p = 2$, find m when $p = 5$.

Solution Write an equation with variables m, p, and k that describes the variation.

_?_ $= k \cdot$ _?_ ^{5} m; p

Given that $m = 96$ when $p = 2$, find k.

_?_ $= k \cdot$ _?_ ^{5}; _?_ $= k \cdot$ _?_, so $k =$ _?_. 96; 2; 96; 32; 3

Rewrite the formula using the value of k found above and $p = 5$ and solve for m.

$m =$ _?_ $\cdot$ _?_ ^{5} 3; 5

$m =$ _?_ 9375

So, when $p = 5$, $m =$ _?_. 9375

c. Substitute $k = 2.1875$ to get a formula relating the edge length and volume.

$V = 2.1875\ \ell^3$

d. Evaluate your formula when $\ell = 5$ cm.

$V = 2.1875(5\text{ cm})^3 \approx 270\text{ cm}^3$

Direct-Variation Functions

The four parts of Example 1 illustrate a procedure you can use to solve variation problems. First, write a general equation that describes the variation. Next, substitute the given values into the general equation and solve for k. Then use the k-value to write the variation function. Finally, evaluate the function at the specified point to find the missing value.

Guided Example 2 illustrates how to use this procedure to solve a typical direct-variation problem.

GUIDED

Example 2

Suppose b varies directly as the sixth power of g. If $b = 729$ when $g = 2$, find b when $g = 10$.

Solution Write an equation with variables b, g, and k that describes the variation.

_?_ $= k \cdot$ _?_ ^{6} b; g

Find the constant of variation. You are given that $b = 729$ when $g = 2$. Substitute these values into the variation formula to find k.

_?_ $= k \cdot$ _?_ ^{6} 729; 2

_?_ $= k \cdot$ _?_ 729; 64

_?_ $= k$ $\frac{729}{64}$

Now rewrite the variation formula using the value of the constant you found.

_?_ $=$ _?_ $\cdot$ _?_ ^{6} b; $\frac{729}{64}$; g

Finally, use the formula to find b when $g = 10$.

$b =$ _?_ $\cdot$ _?_ ^{6} $\frac{729}{64}$; 10

$b =$ _?_ 11,390,625

So, when $g = 10$, $b =$ _?_. 11,390,625

ENGLISH LEARNERS

Vocabulary Development

Help students understand the point, also made in the Notes on the Lesson on page 73, that various phrases in this lesson *all have the same meaning:* "*w* and *p* are directly proportional"; "*w* is directly proportional to *p*"; "*w* varies directly with *p*"; and "*w* varies directly as the first power of *p*."

Activity

You can solve direct-variation problems on a CAS by defining two functions. The first function calculates the constant of variation *k*. The second function calculates values of the direct-variation function using that *k* and a value of the independent variable.

Step 1 Plan your first function.

a. Give a meaningful name to the function so you can use it in the future. We call the first function *dirk*, short for *direct-variation k-value*.

b. Think about the inputs you need to calculate *k* and give them names. In Part b of Example 1, you used initial values of the independent and dependent variables and the value of the exponent to calculate *k*. Good names for the initial values of the independent and dependent variables are *xi* and *yi*, respectively. We call the exponent *n*, as in the direct-variation formula $y = kx^n$.

c. Generalize the result of solving for *k* in Part b of Example 1. In the Example,

$xi = 4, yi = 140, n = 3$, and $k = \frac{140}{4^3}$.

So, in general, $k = \frac{yi}{xi^n}$.

Step 2 Clear the values for *xi*, *yi*, *k*, and *n* in the CAS memory. Then define the *dirk* function using its three inputs and the general formula for *k* you found above.

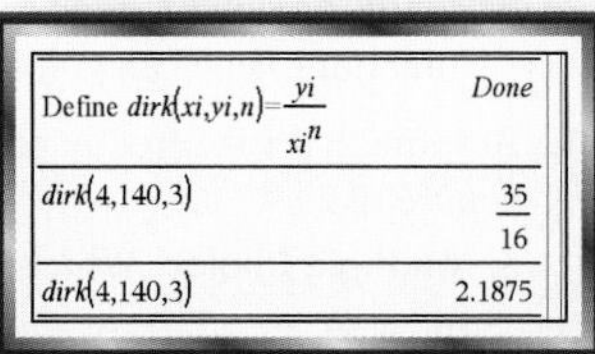

Step 3 Use the *dirk* function to calculate *k* for the situation in Example 1. The input values are $xi = 4$, $yi = 140$, and $n = 3$. The display at the right shows the value of *k* in both fraction and decimal form.

Step 4 A good name for the second function is *dvar*, for *direct variation*. There are three inputs for this function also: another known value *x* for the independent variable, the constant of variation *k*, and the exponent *n*. Clear *x* from the CAS memory and define *dvar* using the general form of the direct-variation formula, as shown at the right.

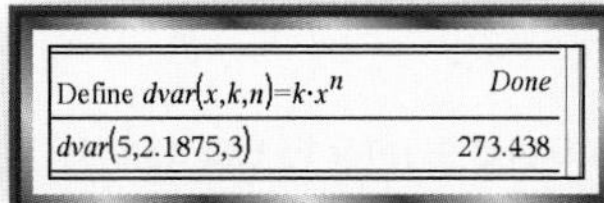

Step 5 Use *dvar* to find the missing function value for $x = 5$, $k = 2.1875$, and $n = 3$. Compare your answer to Part d of Example 1.

QY2

You may use ***dirk*** and ***dvar*** to answer the Questions.

> **QY2**
> Use *dirk* and *dvar* to check your answers to Example 2.

Note-Taking Tips

As students make notes about this lesson, you may want to ask them to think of some familiar formulas from math and determine whether they represent direct variation. Some examples are as follows:

- $C = \pi d$, $C = 2\pi r$
  (*C* varies directly with *d* or *r*.)
- $A = \pi r^2$, $A = s^2$
  (*A* varies directly with r^2 or with s^2.)
- $P = 2\ell + 2w$, $c^2 = a^2 + b^2$
  (not direct variation)

Accommodating the Learner

Ask students to look up conversion formulas, from simple ones, such as between miles and kilometers, to more complex ones, such as between car speed and braking distance. Ask them to report to the class how to interpret those formulas as direct variation equations. Ask them to explain why some conversion formulas, such as between degrees Fahrenheit and degrees Celsius, do not represent direct variation equations. **Answers vary. Sample: The zero values do not correspond.**

3 Assignment

Recommended Assignment

- Questions 1–23
- Question 24 (extra credit)
- Reading Lesson 2-2
- Covering the Ideas 2-2

Notes on the Questions

Although students are allowed to use *dirk* and *dvar* to answer these questions, they should be able to answer the questions without using that technology.

Question 2 This question provides an opportunity to review several formulas for area and volume learned in geometry. In general, if all the figures covered by a formula are similar (in the geometric sense of the word), such as the icosahedron of Example 1 or squares or spheres, then there exists a direct variation formula for their perimeter, area, or volume. Spheres have a surface area formula of the form $y = kx^2$ and a volume formula of the form $y = kx^3$. In the former case, $k = 4\pi$. In the latter case, $k = \frac{4\pi}{3}$. Because all rectangular solids are not similar, their surface area and volume formulas are not simple direct variations. (The volume formula for a rectangular solid is an example of joint variation, which is explored in Lesson 2-9.)

2-1A Lesson Master

Questions on SPUR Objectives
See Student Edition pages 143–147 for objectives.

SKILLS Objective A

In 1 and 2, write a variation equation representing the situation.

1. y varies directly as the third power of x. $y = kx^3$
2. The area A of a regular hexagon is directly proportional to the square of the length s of a side. $A = ks^2$
3. **Fill in the Blanks** If $v = \frac{2}{3}w^4$, then <u>V</u> varies directly as the <u>4th</u> power of <u>W</u>, and <u>$\frac{2}{3}$</u> is the constant of variation.

SKILLS Objective B

4. Suppose y varies directly as x, and y is 12 when x is 2.4. Find y when x is 9.1. 45.5
5. Suppose A is directly proportional to the cube of c, and $A = 192.8$ when $c = 1.2$. Find A when c is 9.1. $\approx 84{,}079$
6. Suppose S is directly proportional to the square of r, and $S = 100\pi$ when $r = 5$. Find the constant of variation. 4π

USES Objective F

In 7–9, determine whether the two variables are (approximately) directly proportional.

7. The height of a batted baseball and the time after it is hit. no
8. The amount of rain that falls and the number of hours it has been raining. yes

USES Objective G

9. Camille babysits for her neighbors. One week they paid her \$20 for $2\frac{1}{2}$ hours. If the pay is directly proportional to the hours worked, how much would she make for 4 hours of babysitting? \$32
10. The amount of electric power generated by a windmill varies directly as the cube of the wind speed. A particular windmill generates 640 watts of power when the wind is 8 miles per hour.
    a. Find the constant of variation and use it to write a variation formula. $\frac{5}{4}$, $p = \frac{5}{4}s^3$
    b. How much power will the windmill generate in a 12-mph wind? 2160 watts

144 Advanced Algebra

Questions

COVERING THE IDEAS

1. Provide an example of direct variation from everyday life.
2. Give an example of a direct-variation function from geometry.
3. **Fill in the Blanks** In the function $y = 5x^2$, _?_ varies directly as _?_, and _?_ is the constant of variation. y; x^2; 5
4. Suppose pay varies directly as time worked and Paul makes \$400 for working 25 hours.
   a. What is the constant of variation? 16
   b. How much will Paul make for working 32 hours? \$512
5. The lengths of the femur and tibia within a species of mammal are typically directly proportional. If the femur of one household cat is 116.0 mm long and its tibia is 122.8 mm long, how long is the tibia of a cat whose femur is 111.5 mm long? 118.1 mm

femur

tibia

6. Suppose $s = 4.7t$.
   a. Find s when $t = 3.1$. 14.57
   b. Is this an equation for a direct-variation function? How can you tell?
7. Assume that y is directly proportional to the square of x.
   a. **Multiple Choice** Which equation represents this situation? B
      A $y = 2x$ B $y = kx^2$ C $x = ky^2$ D $y = 2x^k$
   b. **Multiple Choice** It is also true that x is directly proportional to B
      A the square of y. B the square root of y.
      C twice y. D half of y.

In 8 and 9, refer to Example 1.

8. What is the volume of a regular icosahedron with an edge of length 2 cm? 17.5 cm^3
9. Use the `solve` command on a CAS to find the length of the edge of a regular icosahedron with a volume of 20 cm^3. 2.09 cm
10. Suppose W varies directly as the fourth power of z, and $W = 27$ when $z = 3$.
    a. Find the constant of variation. $\frac{1}{3}$
    b. Find W when $z = 9$. 2,187
11. Suppose y varies directly as the cube of x, and $y = 27.6$ when $x = 0.5$. Find y when $x = 3.2$. 7,235.1744

1. Answers vary. Sample: The weekly salary of a person varies directly with how many hours that person works that week.

2. Answers vary. Sample: $V = \frac{4}{3}\pi r^3$

6b. Yes; the equation is of the form $y = kx^n$, with $n = 1$ and $k = 4.7$.

Extension

Discuss with students that pairs of exchange rates such as $i = 12f$ and $f = \frac{1}{12i}$ (to convert between inches and feet) are variation equations with constants that are reciprocals. Then tell students to find two currency exchange rates, such as the rates for converting between U.S. dollars and Euros or between U.S. dollars and Mexican pesos. Ask students to find out if the constants of variation for those pairs of exchanges are reciprocals and, if they are not, to explain why.

Answers vary. Sample: Most currency exchange rates include some profit margin for the company that provides the exchange. That profit margin shows up as a lower exchange rate than the official cross-currency rate.

12. Suppose f is a function defined by $f(x) = \frac{x^3}{7}$. Is f a direct-variation function? Justify your answer.

12. Yes; $f(x)$ varies directly with the cube of x, and $\frac{1}{7}$ is the constant of variation.

APPLYING THE MATHEMATICS

13. When lightning strikes in the distance, you do not see the flash and hear the thunder at the same time. You first see the lightning, then you hear the thunder.
   a. Write an equation to represent the following situation: The distance d (in miles) from the observer to the flash varies directly as the time t (in seconds) between seeing the lightning and hearing the thunder. $d = kt$
   b. Suppose that lightning strikes a point 4 miles away and that you hear the thunder 20 seconds later. How far away has lightning struck if 12 seconds pass between seeing a flash and hearing its thunder? 2.4 miles

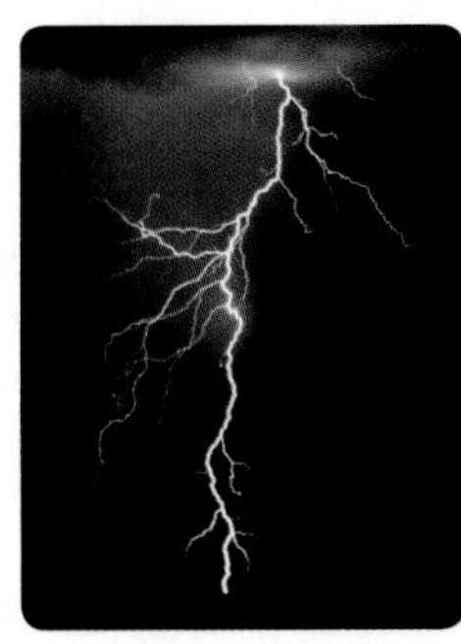

14. The speed of sound in air is about 1,088 feet per second.
   a. Convert the speed of sound to miles per second.
   b. Write the relationship between the number of miles sound travels and the number of seconds it takes sound to travel that distance as a direct variation. Be sure to identify what your variables represent.
   c. Use your answer from Part b to find the time it takes sound to travel four miles in air. 19.4 seconds

14a. 0.206 mile per second

14b. $m = 0.206s$, where m is the number of miles sound travels in s seconds

15. Refer to the formula S.A. $= 6s^2$ for the surface area of a cube with an edge of length s.
   a. Complete the table at the right.
   b. How many times as large is the area when $s = 4$ as when $s = 2$? 4
   c. How many times as large is the area when $s = 6$ as when $s = 3$? 4
   d. How many times as large is the area when $s = 10$ as when $s = 5$? 4
   e. **Fill in the Blank** Relate the length of the edge to the surface area of the cube. When the edge length doubles, the surface area __?__. quadruples
   f. **Fill in the Blank** When the edge length triples, the surface area __?__. increases by a factor of 9

s	S.A.
1	? 6
2	? 24
3	? 54
4	? 96
5	? 150
6	? 216
7	? 294
8	? 384
9	? 486
10	? 600

Notes on the Questions

Question 5 Paleontologists and forensic scientists use the property that bones are directly proportional to each other to determine the height of a person or animal from just a few bones.

Question 14c Some students may multiply 0.206 mile per second by 4 miles. These students need to think of the units for the answer. The question asks for an answer in *time;* therefore, students must calculate 4 miles ÷ 0.206 mile/second, which "cancels" the mile units.

Accommodating the Learner

Show students these two statements:

1. For $m = 3p$, when p is doubled from A to __?__, then m is __?__ from __?__ to __?__.

2. For $q = 3r^2$, when r is doubled from B to __?__, then q is __?__ from __?__ to __?__.

Ask them to complete Statement 1 three times, starting with three different values for A, then complete Statement 2 three times, starting with three different values for B. Ask students to describe their results.

Answers vary. Sample: For any values for A and B, m is doubled, and q is quadrupled (multiplied by 4).

4 Wrap-Up

Ongoing Assessment

Ask students to use the variable k to write a direct variation equation for each situation.

1. A variable x is proportional to the fourth power of a variable y. $x = ky^4$
2. A variable p is proportional to the nth power of a variable q. $p = kq^n$
3. A variable s is proportional to the cube root of a variable t. $s = k(\sqrt[3]{t})$

Additional Answers

18.

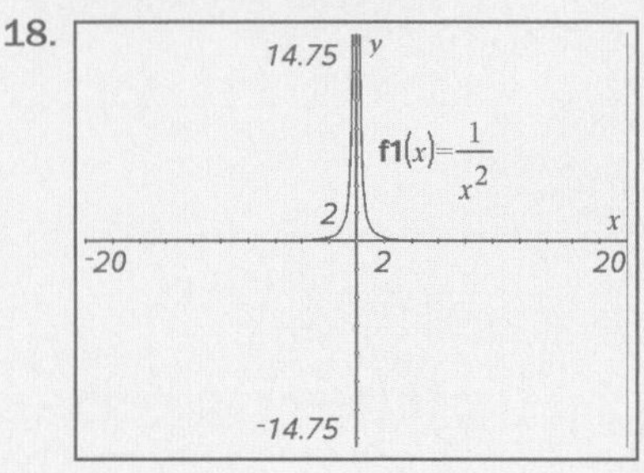

all real numbers except 0

21a. Answers vary. Sample:

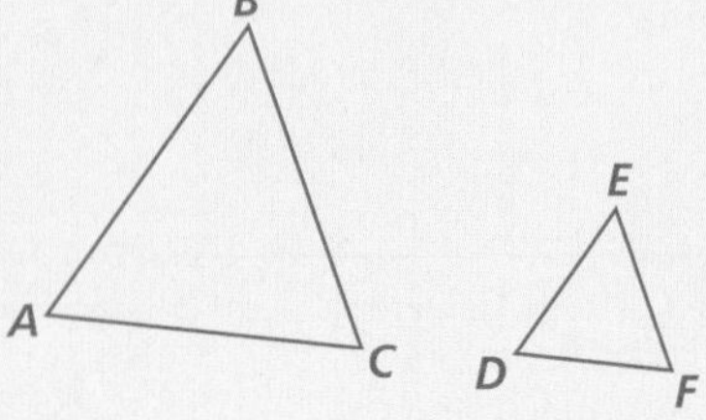

2-1B page 2

2-1B Lesson Master

Questions on SPUR Objectives
See Student Edition pages 143–147 for objectives.

VOCABULARY

In 1–3, use the direct variation equation $V = \frac{4}{3}\pi r^3$ to identify the

1. *constant of variation.* $\frac{4}{3}$
2. *independent variable.* r
3. *dependent variable.* V

SKILLS Objective A

In 4–8, write a variation equation representing the situation.

4. a varies directly as the cube of b. $a = kb^3$
5. T is directly proportional to the fourth power of S. $T = kS^4$
6. The actual distance D between two towns is directly proportional to d, the distance between them on a map. $D = kd$
7. A person's weight w varies directly as the cube of his or her height h. $w = kh^3$
8. Real-estate taxes T are directly proportional to property value V. $T = kV$
9. Write the variation equation $y = kx^3$ in words. y varies directly as the cube of x.

SKILLS Objective B

10. m is directly proportional to n. If $m = 48$ when $n = 12$, find m when $n = 3$. $m = 12$
11. y varies directly as the square of x. If $y = 63$ when $x = 3$, find y when $x = 9$. $y = 567$
12. s varies directly as g^4, and $s = 64$ when $g = 2$.
    a. Find the constant of variation k. $k = 4$
    b. Find s when $g = 3$. $s = 324$
13. c varies directly as the cube of d, and $c = 32$ when $d = 4$.
    a. Find the constant of variation k. $k = 0.5$
    b. Find c when $d = 5$. $c = 62.5$

146

Advanced Algebra 145

16. The table at the right gives a typical thinking distance, braking distance, and overall stopping distance for a car traveling at various speeds.
    a. Show that the thinking distance t is directly proportional to the speed s by finding the constant of variation and writing a direct-variation formula. $k = 1$; $t = s$, where s is in mph and t is in feet
    b. Show that the braking distance b is directly proportional to the square of the speed s by finding the constant of variation and writing a direct-variation formula.
    c. Is the overall stopping distance d directly proportional to the speed? Explain how you know.

Speed	Thinking Distance	Braking Distance	Overall Stopping Distance
20 mph	20 ft	20 ft	40 ft
30 mph	30 ft	45 ft	75 ft
40 mph	40 ft	80 ft	120 ft
50 mph	50 ft	125 ft	175 ft
60 mph	60 ft	180 ft	240 ft
70 mph	70 ft	245 ft	315 ft

16b. $k = \frac{1}{20}$; $b = \frac{s^2}{20}$, where b is in feet and s is in mph

16c. No; since $d = t + b$, and they do not vary directly by the same power, no direct-variation formula can be written.

REVIEW

17. The distance d in feet a body falls in t seconds is given by the formula $d = \frac{1}{2}gt^2$, where $g = 32\ \frac{\text{ft}}{\text{sec}^2}$ is the constant of gravitational acceleration. **(Lesson 1-4)**
    a. How far will a body fall in 7 seconds? 784 feet
    b. How long did a body fall if it traveled 83 feet? 2.28 seconds
18. Graph the function f with the equation $f(x) = \frac{1}{x^2}$ in a standard window. What is the domain of f? **(Lesson 1-4)** See margin.
19. In the table at the right, is y a function of x? Justify your answer. **(Lesson 1-2)** No; $x = -1$ is paired with two different y-values.

x	y
-1	1
-1	-1
-4	2
0	0
-18	-4

20. A dime has a diameter of 17.91 mm. **(Lesson 1-1)**
    a. You place 15 dimes in a row. What is the length of your row of dimes? 268.65 mm
    b. Write an expression to describe what happens to the length of your row of dimes when you remove x dimes.

20b. $268.65 - 17.91x$

21. Suppose $\triangle ABC \sim \triangle DEF$ (that is, the two triangles are similar).
    a. Sketch a possible diagram of this situation. See margin.
    b. What can you say about the ratios $\frac{AB}{BC}$ and $\frac{DE}{EF}$? **(Previous Course)** They are equal.

In Questions 22 and 23, write the expression as a power of 5. (Previous Course)

22. $5^2 \cdot 5^3$ 5^5
23. $(5 \cdot 5)^3$ 5^6

EXPLORATION

24. Use the Internet to find some common gear ratios that are used for different speed settings on racing bikes. Write and solve a direct-variation problem involving one of these gear ratios. See margin.

QY ANSWERS

1. $\frac{52}{11}$ is the constant of variation, and $n = 1$.
2. *dirk* gives $k \approx 11.39$, and *dvar* shows that $b = 11{,}390{,}625$ when $g = 10$. So, the answers check.

Additional Answers

24. Answers vary. Sample: A bike with a gear ratio of 0.73 to 1 moves at 3.4 mph when a bicyclist pedals at 75 rpm. Assume speed varies directly with the gear ratio when the bicyclist pedals at a constant number of revolutions per minute. Find a direct variation function to represent the situation. Use it to find the speed that a bike with a gear ratio of 1.6 to 1 moves if the bicyclist continues to pedal at 75 rpm. [If r = the gear ratio and s = speed in miles per hour, $s = 4.66r$. When $r = 1.6$, $s = 7.45$ mph.]

Lesson 2-2 Inverse Variation

Vocabulary

inverse-variation function

varies inversely as

inversely proportional to

▸ **BIG IDEA** When two variables x and y satisfy the equation $y = \frac{k}{x^n}$ for some constant value of k, we say that y varies inversely as x^n.

The Condo Care Company has been hired to paint the hallways in a condominium community. A few years ago, it took 8 workers 6 hours (that is, 48 worker-hours) to do this job. If w equals the number of workers and t equals the time (in hours) that each worker paints, then the product wt is the total number of hours worked. Since it takes 48 worker-hours to finish the job,

$$wt = 48, \text{ or } t = \frac{48}{w}.$$

Certain combinations of w and t that could finish the job are given below.

Number of Workers w	1	3	5	6	8	12	15
Time t (hr)	48	16	9.6	8	6	4	3.2

 QY1

Mental Math

Let $g(x) = 2x^2$. Find:

a. $g(2)$ 8

b. $g(0.4)$ 0.32

c. $g(3n)$ $18n^2$

d. $g(3n) - g(2) + g(1)$ $18n^2 - 6$

▸ **QY1**

If 20 workers were to divide the painting job equally, how many hours would each one have to paint?

Inverse-Variation Functions

The formula $t = \frac{48}{w}$, which determines the values in the table above, has the form $y = \frac{k}{x^n}$ where $k = 48$ and $n = 1$. This is an example of an *inverse-variation function*.

Definition of Inverse-Variation Function

An **inverse-variation function** is a function that can be described by a formula of the form $y = \frac{k}{x^n}$, with $k \neq 0$ and $n > 0$.

Background

Definition of inverse variation If two variables x and y satisfy the equation $y = \frac{k}{x}$, then y varies inversely as x. If $y = \frac{k}{x^2}$, then y varies inversely as x^2. Regardless of the exponent of x, we call the relationship between x and y an inverse variation. Whenever three quantities are related so that one is a product of the other two, such as in the area formula $A = bh$ for a rectangle, you can solve for one of the factors (for example, $\frac{A}{h} = b$) to get an inverse-variation relationship. So if the area of a rectangle is fixed, the length of the rectangle is inversely proportional to its width.

An inverse-square situation Why are inverse-square relationships associated with light and sound intensity? The set of points at a given distance from a given point is a sphere. If a sound leaves a source at a given time, that sound becomes dispersed as the surface of a sphere. The area of the sphere is related to its radius

(continued on next page)

Lesson 2-2

GOAL

Introduce and explore the language and concept of inverse variation.

SPUR Objectives

A Translate variation language into formulas and formulas into variation language.

B Solve variation problems.

F Recognize variation situations.

G Solve real-world variation problems.

Materials/Resources

- Lesson Masters 2-2A and 2-2B
- Resource Masters 21 and 22

HOMEWORK

Suggestions for Assignment

- Questions 1–22
- Question 23 (extra credit)
- Reading Lesson 2-3
- Covering the Ideas 2-3

Local Standards

1 Warm-Up

In 1–4, tell whether the first variable is halved when the second variable is multiplied by 2.

1. The rent R for an apartment is split evenly among n people. yes
2. The distance d you travel in a car if you are going at a constant speed s. No; this is a direct variation.
3. The time t it will take to get to a destination if you travel at a rate r. yes
4. The distance d between n evenly spaced buttons from the top to the bottom of a particular shirt. No; d varies inversely as $n - 1$, not n.

2 Teaching

Notes on the Lesson

Example 2 In some regions, another name for a seesaw is a teeter-totter. On a seesaw, the product of the weight of a person times the distance from that person to the pivot (or *fulcrum*) on one side must equal the product on the other side. Notice that the constant of variation has the unit meter-kilograms. This emphasizes the fact that the variables have units associated with them, and by keeping track of the units, solving the problem becomes clearer.

Additional Examples

Example 1 The number of units u in a length varies inversely with the length ℓ of the unit. Write an equation that expresses this relationship. $u = \frac{k}{\ell}$

Example 2 Using the seesaw in Example 2, suppose Kerry weighs 34 kilograms and is 1.8 meters from the pivot. If Madison weighs 38 kilograms, how far from the pivot should she sit to balance Kerry? about 1.6 m

For the inverse-variation function with equation $y = \frac{k}{x^n}$, we say y **varies inversely as** x^n, or y is **inversely proportional to** x^n. In an inverse variation, as either quantity increases, the other decreases. In the painting example, as the number of workers increases, the number of hours each must work decreases.

As with direct variation, inverse variation occurs in many kinds of situations.

Example 1

The speed S of a bike varies inversely with the number B of back-gear teeth on the rear wheel. Write an equation that expresses this relationship.

Solution Use the definition of an inverse-variation function. In this case, $n = 1$. So,

$$S = \frac{k}{B}.$$

Solving Inverse-Variation Problems

Many scientific principles involve inverse-variation functions. For example, imagine that a person is sitting on one end of a seesaw. According to the *Law of the Lever*, in order to balance the seesaw another person must sit a certain distance d from the pivot (or fulcrum) of the seesaw, and that distance is inversely proportional to his or her weight w. Algebraically, $d = \frac{k}{w}$. Since d is inversely proportional to w, as d increases, w will decrease. This means a lighter person can balance the seesaw by sitting farther from the pivot, or a heavy person can balance the seesaw by sitting closer to the pivot.

Example 2

Ashlee and Sam are trying to balance on a seesaw. Suppose Sam, who weighs 42 kilograms, is sitting 2 meters from the pivot. Ashlee weighs 32 kilograms. How far away from the pivot must she sit to balance Sam?

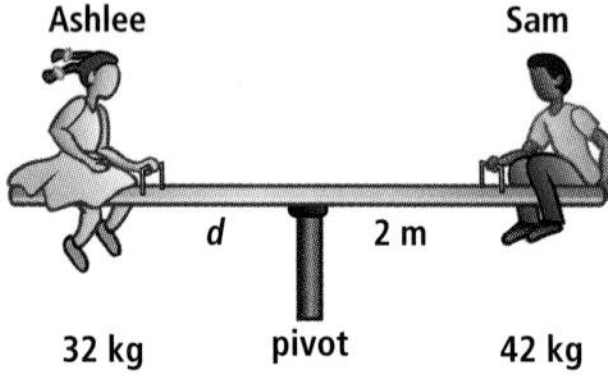

by the formula $A = 4\pi r^2$, so at any given point on the sphere, the volume of sound at that point is inversely proportional to the square of the radius.

Example 3 Of all the variation relationships in the physical world, the inverse-square laws are among the most important because they occur so frequently. It is primarily because of these applications that inverse variation is taught.

Solution Let d = a person's distance (in meters) from the pivot. Let w = that person's weight (in kilograms).

First write a variation equation relating *d* and *w*. From the *Law of the Lever*,

$$d = \frac{k}{w}.$$

To find *k*, substitute Sam's weight and distance from the pivot into $d = \frac{k}{w}$ and solve for *k*.

$$2\text{m} = \frac{k}{42 \text{ kg}}$$
$$k = 2 \text{ m} \cdot 42 \text{ kg}$$
$$k = 84 \text{ meter-kilograms}$$

Substitute the value found for *k* into the formula.

$$d = \frac{84}{w}$$

Substitute Ashlee's weight into the formula above to find the distance she must sit from the pivot.

$$d = \frac{84}{32} = 2.625 \text{ m}$$

Ashlee must sit about 2.6 meters away from the pivot to balance Sam.

Check Since $d = \frac{k}{w}$, $k = dw$. So the product of Ashlee's distance from the pivot and her weight should equal the constant of variation. Does 2.625 meters • 32 kilograms = 84 meter-kilograms? Yes, the numbers and the units agree.

QY2

> ▸ **QY2**
> If Saul takes Sam's place on the seesaw and Saul weighs 55 kg, what is the new constant *k* of variation?

An Inverse-Square Situation

Just as one variable can vary directly as the square of another, one variable can also vary inversely as the square of another. For example, in the figure on the next page, a spotlight shines onto a wall through a square window that measures 1 foot on each side. Suppose the window is 5 feet from the light and the wall is 10 feet from the light. The light that comes through the window will illuminate a square on the wall that is 2 feet on a side. The same light that comes through the 1-square foot window now covers 4 square feet.

Note-Taking Tips

To help students compare the equations and relationships in this lesson with those in Lesson 2-1, encourage them to include the following information in their notes:

direct variation $y = kx$: Because $\frac{y}{x} = k$, the *quotient* of the variables is constant.

inverse variation $y = \frac{k}{x}$: Because $xy = k$, the *product* of the variables is constant.

inverse-square variation $y = \frac{k}{x^2}$: Because $x^2y = k$, the *product* of x^2 and y is constant.

Accommodating the Learner ↑

Have students work in small groups. Ask them to think about a seesaw situation in which persons *A* and *B* are sitting on one side of the pivot and person *C* is on the other side. Using W_P and D_P to represent the weight *W* and distance-from-pivot *D* for person *P*, ask students to find an equation that can represent the situation. Then ask students to find values of *W* and *D* for each person so the two sides of the seesaw balance. $W_AD_A + W_BD_B = W_CD_C$; Answers vary. Sample: $W_A = 100$, $D_A = 4$, $W_B = 100$, $D_B = 2$, $W_C = 100$, and $D_C = 6$.

Additional Example

Example 3 In Example 3, suppose the intensity of light 6 meters from a light source is 30 lumens. Find the constant of variation and determine the intensity of the same light 9 meters from its source.

Solution Write an equation relating *d*, the distance from the light source, and *I*, the light's intensity: $I = \frac{k}{?}$ d^2

To find *k*, substitute $d =$ __?__ and $I =$ __?__ into your equation and solve for *k*. 6^2; 30

$\underline{?} = \frac{k}{?}$, so $\underline{?} = k$ 30; 6^2; 1080

Using that value of *k*, evaluate the formula for *I* when $d = 9$ meters.

$I = \underline{?} = \underline{?}$ $\frac{1080}{9^2}$; $13.\overline{3}$

Since the same amount of light illuminates four times the area, the intensity of light on the wall is $\frac{1}{4}$ of its intensity at the window. As distance from the light source increases, the area the light illuminates increases, and the intensity of the light decreases. This is an example of inverse variation: the intensity *I* of light is inversely proportional to the square of the distance *d* from the light source.

$$I = \frac{k}{d^2}$$

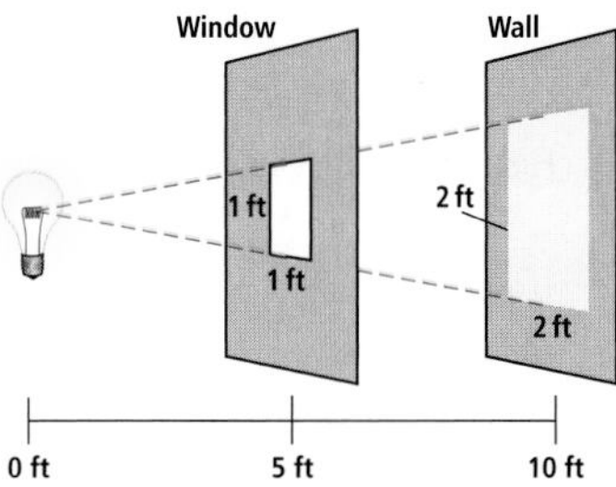

GUIDED

Example 3

Suppose the intensity of the light 4 meters from a light source is 40 lumens. (A lumen is the amount of light that falls on a 1-square foot area that is 1 foot from a candle.) Find the constant of variation and determine the intensity of the same light 6 meters from its source.

Solution Write an equation relating *d* and *I*, where *d* = the distance from the light source in meters and *I* = the light's intensity in lumens.

$$I = \frac{k}{?} \quad d^2$$

To find *k*, substitute $d =$ __?__ and $I =$ __?__ into your equation and solve for *k*. 4; 40

$\underline{?} = \frac{k}{?}$ 40; 4^2

$\underline{?} \cdot \underline{?} = k$ 40; 16

$\underline{?} = k$ 640

Substitute *k* back into the equation to find the inverse-variation formula for this situation.

$I = \frac{?}{d^2}$ 640

Evaluate this formula when $d = 6$ meters.

$I = \frac{?}{?}$ 640; 6^2

$I = \underline{?}$ lumens 17.8

As you did in Lesson 2-1 for direct-variation problems, you can define functions on your CAS to help solve inverse-variation problems.

Accommodating the Learner

Before students begin the section on inverse-square variation, you may want to review the property that an exponent applies only to its base, not to any factors or coefficients of the base. For example, an expression such as $\left(\frac{k}{x}\right)^2$ is equal to $\frac{k^2}{x^2}$ because the base for the exponent 2 is $\frac{k}{x}$, while an expression such as $k\left(\frac{1}{x}\right)^2$ is equal to $k\left(\frac{1}{x^2}\right)$ or $\frac{k}{x^2}$ because the base for the exponent 2 is $\frac{1}{x}$.

Activity

MATERIALS CAS

Step 1 Clear all variable values on your CAS.

Define the function *ink(xi, yi, n)* = $xi^n \cdot yi$.

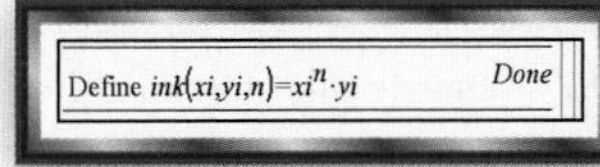

Define ink(xi,yi,n)=xi^n·yi
Done

This function calculates the constant of variation *k* from three inputs: an *initial* independent variable value *xi*, an *initial* dependent variable value *yi*, and the exponent *n*.

Step 2 Define the function *invar(x, k, n)* = $\frac{k}{x^n}$.

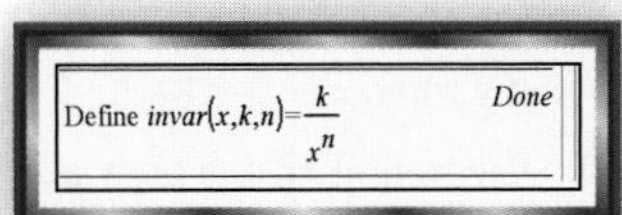

This function calculates an inverse-variation value from three inputs: *any* independent variable value *x*, the constant of variation *k* calculated by *ink*, and the exponent *n*.

Step 3 Check your solution to Example 3 by using *ink* to find *k* for $xi = 4$, $yi = 40$ and $n = 2$. Use *invar* with the appropriate inputs to verify the rest of your solution.

Questions

COVERING THE IDEAS

1. **Fill in the Blank** In the Condo Care Company problem at the beginning of this lesson, the time to finish the job varies inversely as the __?__. number of workers
2. **Fill in the Blank** The equation $s = \frac{k}{r^2}$ means *s* varies inversely as __?__. the square of *r*
3. **Multiple Choice** Assume *k* is a nonzero constant. Which equation does *not* represent an inverse variation? A

   A $y = kx$ B $xy = k$ C $y = \frac{k}{x}$ D $y = \frac{k}{x^2}$
4. Refer to Example 1. Find the constant of variation if you are pedaling 21 mph and have 11 teeth on the back gear. 231
5. Refer to Example 2. If Sam sits 2.5 meters from the pivot, how far away from the pivot must Ashlee sit to balance him? 3.28 m
6. Suppose the seesaw at the right is balanced.
   a. Find the missing distance. 3.5 ft
   b. If the 80 lb person sits farther from the pivot, which side of the seesaw will go up?
   the side opposite the 80 lb person

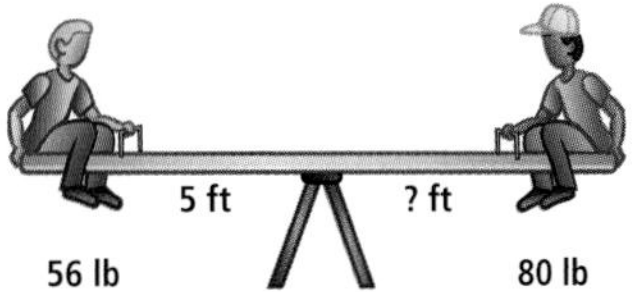

3 Assignment

Recommended Assignment

- Questions 1–22
- Question 23 (extra credit)
- Reading Lesson 2-3
- Covering the Ideas 2-3

ENGLISH LEARNERS
Vocabulary Development

Some students may be confused because the term *inverse* is also used in mathematics with conditional statements (the inverse of "if *p*, then *q*" is "if not-*p*, then not-*q*"). Help students understand that although "inverse" is a natural term for each situation (because an inverse statement reverses the truth value of the hypothesis and conclusion, while inverse variation reverses the position of the independent variable from a numerator to a denominator), this is a situation where the term has different meanings in different contexts.

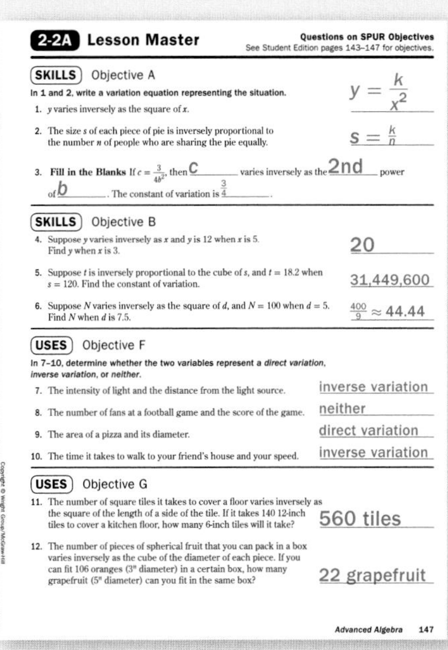

2-2A Lesson Master

Questions on SPUR Objectives
See Student Edition pages 143–147 for objectives.

SKILLS Objective A

In 1 and 2, write a variation equation representing the situation.

1. *y* varies inversely as the square of *x*. $y = \frac{k}{x^2}$
2. The size *s* of each piece of pie is inversely proportional to the number *n* of people who are sharing the pie equally. $s = \frac{k}{n}$
3. **Fill in the Blanks** If $c = \frac{3}{4b^2}$, then __c__ varies inversely as the __2nd__ power of __b__. The constant of variation is $\frac{3}{4}$.

SKILLS Objective B

4. Suppose *y* varies inversely as *x* and *y* is 12 when *x* is 5. Find *y* when *x* is 3. 20
5. Suppose *t* is inversely proportional to the cube of *s*, and $t = 18.2$ when $s = 120$. Find the constant of variation. 31,449,600
6. Suppose *N* varies inversely as the square of *d*, and $N = 100$ when $d = 5$. Find *N* when *d* is 7.5. $\frac{400}{9} \approx 44.44$

USES Objective F

In 7–10, determine whether the two variables represent a direct variation, inverse variation, or neither.

7. The intensity of light and the distance from the light source. inverse variation
8. The number of fans at a football game and the score of the game. neither
9. The area of a pizza and its diameter. direct variation
10. The time it takes to walk to your friend's house and your speed. inverse variation

USES Objective G

11. The number of square tiles it takes to cover a floor varies inversely as the square of the length of a side of the tile. If it takes 140 12-inch tiles to cover a kitchen floor, how many 6-inch tiles will it take? 560 tiles
12. The number of pieces of spherical fruit that you can pack in a box varies inversely as the cube of the diameter of each piece. If you can fit 106 oranges (3" diameter) in a certain box, how many grapefruit (5" diameter) can you fit in the same box? 22 grapefruit

Advanced Algebra 147

Notes on the Questions

Question 10 Explain that *d* is the distance from the *center* of Earth to the astronaut, not from the *surface* of Earth to the astronaut.

Questions 14 and 15 These are not exact variations but "impressionistic variations."

Question 17 It is essential that students realize that weight varies directly with volume, so weight varies directly with the cube of height. The answer may surprise some students. Very tall basketball players should weigh quite a bit; a 7-footer should not weigh $\frac{7}{6}$ as much as a 6-footer, but $\left(\frac{7}{6}\right)^3$ as much. This is related to the Fundamental Theorem of Similarity, which students may have encountered in geometry: If two figures are similar, then the ratio of their volumes equals the cube of the ratio of similitude, and the ratio of their areas equals the square of the ratio of similitude. Also, suggest that students convert both height measurements to inches before answering the question.

7. Refer to Example 3. Find the intensity of the light 9 meters from the source. How does this compare to the intensity of the light 6 meters from the source?

7. 7.9 lumens; it is approximately 0.44 times as intense (or, it is 2.25 times softer).

APPLYING THE MATHEMATICS

8. Translate this statement into a variation equation.
   The time *t* an appliance can run on 1 kilowatt-hour of electricity is inversely proportional to the wattage rating *w* of the appliance. $t = \frac{k}{w}$

9. If *y* varies inversely as x^3, and $y = 12$ when $x = 5$, find the value of *y* when $x = 2$. 187.5

10. The weight *W* of a body above the surface of Earth varies inversely as the square of its distance *d* from the center of Earth. Use 4,000 miles for the radius of Earth.

Center of Earth
4000 miles
d mi

   a. Write an inverse-variation function to model this situation. $W = \frac{k}{d^2}$
   b. When an astronaut is 300 miles above Earth, what is the value of *d*? 4300 miles
   c. Suppose an astronaut weighs 170 pounds on the surface of Earth. What will the astronaut weigh in orbit 300 miles above Earth? 147.1 pounds
   d. What will be the astronaut's weight 2,000 miles above the surface of Earth? 75.6 pounds

11. Consider again the Condo Care Company situation at the beginning of the lesson.
   a. Complete the table below by filling in the missing values.

w	2	3	4	5	6	7	8	9	10	11	12	15	20
t	? 24	16	? 12	9.6	8	? 6.9	6	? 5.3	4.8	? 4.4	? 4	? 3.2	? 2.4

   b. **Fill in the Blank** Compare the values of *t* when $w = 2$ and $w = 4$. Also compare the values of *t* when $w = 4$ and $w = 8$, and again when $w = 6$ and $w = 12$. Make a conjecture. When the number of people working doubles, the mean time each person needs to work ___?___. is halved
   c. **Fill in the Blank** Follow a similar procedure to complete the following conjecture. When the number of people working triples, the mean time ___?___. is divided by 3
   d. Prove your conjecture from Part b or Part c.

11d. $t = \frac{48}{w}$, so $\frac{\frac{48}{3w}}{\frac{48}{w}} = \frac{48 \cdot w}{48 \cdot 3w} = \frac{1}{3}$

Extension

Ask students to use a physics text or other source (or even Question 16 in Lesson 2-6 of this chapter) to find the equation called "Newton's Law of Gravitation." Ask them to explain how that equation represents inverse-square variation. $F = \frac{GmM}{r^2}$, where *F* is the force of attraction between two bodies with masses *m* and *M*, *r* is the distance between them, and *G* is a constant; the gravitational force between two bodies varies inversely as the square of the distance between them.

Fill in the Blank In 12–15, complete the sentence with the word *directly* or *inversely*.

12. The surface area of a sphere varies __?__ as the square of its radius. directly
13. The number of hours required to drive a certain distance varies __?__ as the speed of the car. inversely
14. My hunger roughly varies __?__ as the time since I last ate. directly
15. My hunger roughly varies __?__ as the amount of food I have eaten. inversely

REVIEW

16. At Percy's Priceless Pizza, the price of a pepperoni pizza is proportional to the square of its diameter. If Percy charges \$11.95 for a 10-inch diameter pizza, how much does Percy charge for a 14-inch pizza? **(Lesson 2-1)** \$23.42
17. At 7'7" and 303 pounds, Gheorghe Muresan was one of the tallest people ever to play professional basketball. For people with similar body shapes, weight varies directly with the cube of height. How much would you expect someone with Gheorghe's body shape to weigh if that person were 5'10"? **(Lesson 2-1)** 137.9 lb
18. If $f(d) = 3d^3$ for all d, find $f(2x)$. **(Lesson 1-3)** $24x^3$

In 19 and 20, simplify and indicate the general property. (Previous Course)

19. $\frac{x^{11}}{x^4}$
20. $(2x)^4$

21. At a certain time of day, a 13' tree casts a shadow 7' long.
    a. Draw a picture of this situation and mark a right triangle in your picture. See margin.
    b. A nearby tree is 18' tall. How long would its shadow be at the same time of day? **(Previous Course)** 9.7 feet
22. In the figure at the right, line ℓ is parallel to line m. Find x. **(Previous Course)** $x = 36$

EXPLORATION

23. The *inverse-square law* in physics governs the way various things happen as distance varies, such as how the light intensity decreases as the distance from the source increases, as discussed in Example 3. Research the inverse-square law, and find three other situations where it applies.

Other examples of the inverse-square law include all forms of electromagnetic radiation (which includes light), gravity, sound, and the electrical force or repulsion between two electrically charged particles.

19. x^7; Quotient of Powers Property $\frac{x^m}{x^n} = x^{m-n}$

20. $16x^4$; Power of a Product Property $(xy)^m = x^m \cdot y^m$

Gheorghe Muresan on defense against John Shasky

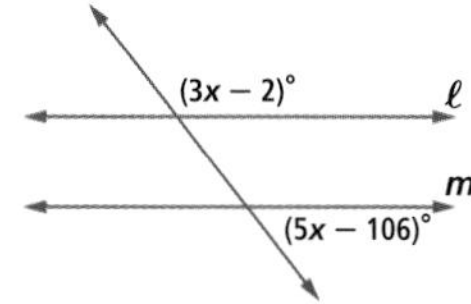

QY ANSWERS

1. 2.4 hours
2. 110 meter-kilograms

4 Wrap-Up

Ongoing Assessment

Ask students to work in small groups with the variation equations $y = \frac{k}{x}$, $q = \frac{k}{p^2}$, and $s = \frac{k}{r^3}$. Ask them to use the value $k = 100$ and find two ordered pairs for the variables x and y, p and q, and r and s that satisfy the three equations. Answers vary. Sample: $(x, y) = (1, 100), (2, 50)$; $(p, q) = (1, 100), (2, 25)$; $(r, s) = (1, 100), (2, 12.5)$

Project Update

Project 1, *The Law of the Lever*, on page 136 relates to the content of this lesson.

Additional Answers

21a.

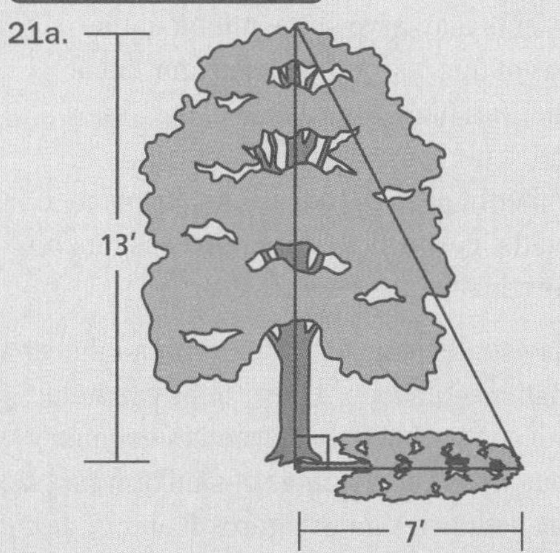

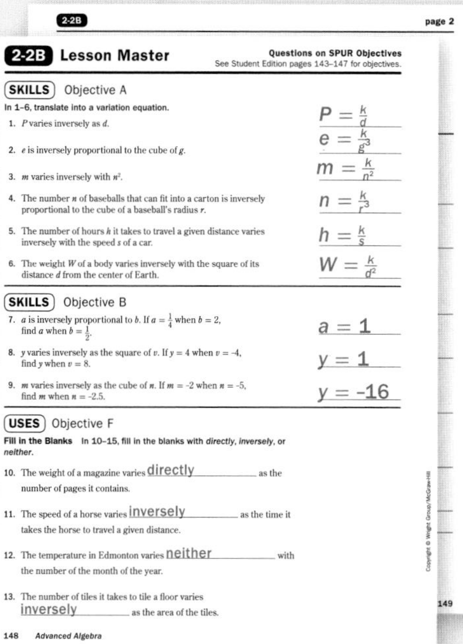

2-2B page 2

2-2B Lesson Master

Questions on SPUR Objectives
See Student Edition pages 143–147 for objectives.

SKILLS Objective A

In 1–6, translate into a variation equation.

1. P varies inversely as d. $P = \frac{k}{d}$
2. e is inversely proportional to the cube of g. $e = \frac{k}{g^3}$
3. m varies inversely with n^2. $m = \frac{k}{n^2}$
4. The number n of baseballs that can fit into a carton is inversely proportional to the cube of a baseball's radius r. $n = \frac{k}{r^3}$
5. The number of hours h it takes to travel a given distance varies inversely with the speed s of a car. $h = \frac{k}{s}$
6. The weight W of a body varies inversely with the square of its distance d from the center of Earth. $W = \frac{k}{d^2}$

SKILLS Objective B

7. a is inversely proportional to b. If $a = \frac{1}{4}$ when $b = 2$, find a when $b = \frac{1}{2}$. $a = 1$
8. y varies inversely as the square of v. If $y = 4$ when $v = -4$, find y when $v = 8$. $y = 1$
9. m varies inversely as the cube of n. If $m = -2$ when $n = -5$, find m when $n = -2.5$. $y = -16$

USES Objective F

Fill in the Blanks In 10–15, fill in the blanks with *directly*, *inversely*, or *neither*.

10. The weight of a magazine varies directly as the number of pages it contains.
11. The speed of a horse varies inversely as the time it takes the horse to travel a given distance.
12. The temperature in Edmonton varies neither with the number of the month of the year.
13. The number of tiles it takes to tile a floor varies inversely as the area of the tiles.

148 *Advanced Algebra*

149

Lesson 2-3

GOAL

Discuss the Fundamental Theorem of Variation.

SPUR Objectives

D Use the Fundamental Theorem of Variation.

Materials/Resources

- Lesson Masters 2-3A and 2-3B
- Resource Masters 23 and 24
- Quiz 1

HOMEWORK

Suggestions for Assignment

- Questions 1–23
- Question 24 (extra credit)
- Reading Lesson 2-4
- Covering the Ideas 2-4

Local Standards

1 Warm-Up

1. You are getting logs for a fireplace. One log is 30 centimeters long, and a second log of the same thickness is 60 centimeters long. If the first log weighs 5 kilograms, what will the second log weigh? 10 kg; the second log has the same thickness, so its weight is directly proportional to its length.

Lesson 2-3 The Fundamental Theorem of Variation

BIG IDEA When y varies directly as x^n, multiplying x by c causes y to be multiplied by c^n; when y varies inversely as x^n, multiplying x by c causes y to be divided by c^n.

In previous lessons, you explored the effects of doubling or tripling the length s of the edge of a cube on the surface area S.A. of the cube. You also explored the effects of doubling or tripling the value of w on the value of t in the equation $t = \frac{48}{w}$. In this lesson you will see how to generalize the findings of these problems.

This Activity explores how changes in the independent variable result in changes in the dependent variable in two different variation functions.

Mental Math

Claudia is building an in-ground pool in her back yard. The pool is 12 feet wide and 20 feet long.

a. If the pool is 5 feet deep, how much water can it hold? 1200 ft^3

b. Claudia is building a cement walkway 2 feet wide around the pool. If she builds a fence around the walkway, how long will the fence be? 80 ft

c. If she places a fence post every 4 feet around the walkway, how many posts will she need? 20

Activity

Fruit Roll Industries makes mini and regular fruit pops and is considering making larger jumbo pops. Assume the production cost p of a fruit pop varies directly with the volume V of candy on the stick. So, $p = k_0 \cdot V$. Also assume that a pop is approximately a sphere, so $V = \frac{4}{3}\pi r^3$, where r is the mean radius of pops of a particular size. Then $p = k_0 \cdot \frac{4}{3}\pi r^3$. Since $\frac{4}{3}$, π, and k_0 are all constants, $\frac{4}{3}\pi k_0$ is a constant and we can write $p = kr^3$. This means that p varies directly with the cube of r.

Step 1 Make a table like the one below based on the estimated radius of different-size pops. Fill in the blank cells in all columns except the one labeled Production Cost Estimate.

Size	Mean Radius r (cm)	r^3 (cm^3)	Ratio of Radius to Mini's Radius	Ratio of r^3 to Mini's r^3	Production Cost Estimate
Mini	0.7	0.343	1:1	1:1	$\frac{1}{2}$ cent
Regular	1.4	? 2.744	? 2:1	? 8:1	?
Jumbo	2.1	? 9.261	? 3:1	? 27:1	?

National Lollipop Day is celebrated on July 20.

Background

Students may have some notion of the ideas of this lesson, especially for linear direct variation. For instance, they know that if a person buys three times the number of posters than originally planned, then the cost will be three times as much as originally budgeted.

Many students have trouble with nonlinear variation situations. These steps can help them apply what they learned in geometry about areas and volumes of similar figures. Start with two similar figures F and F'. If x is the ratio of similitude, then the area of F' varies directly as the square of x, and the volume of F' varies directly as the cube of x. Going the other way, if the volume of a carton is kept constant, then the number n of objects of a given volume that can fit in the carton is inversely proportional to the cube of the volume of the object. In the Activity, these geometric theorems are verified by computation. In Examples 1 and 2, they are verified from formulas.

Step 2 Compare r and r^3 for the mini and regular pops.

a. The radius of the regular pop is _?_ times as big as the mini pop, but r^3 for the regular pop is _?_ times as big as for the mini pop. Since p varies directly as r^3, p is proportional to r^3. So, the cost of production of a regular pop should be _?_ times that of the mini, pop, or _?_ cents. 2; 8; 8; 4

b. Make the same comparisons for the mini and jumbo pops. The jumbo cost should be _?_ times the mini cost, or _?_ cents. Note that when the mini's radius is multiplied by 3 to get the jumbo radius, you can find the cost of the jumbo pop by multiplying the cost of the mini pop by _?_ to the third power. 27; 13.5; 3

c. Suppose there is a super jumbo pop with a radius of 2.8 cm. Fill in the table to find the estimated cost of production? Justify your answer.

Step 2c. 32 cents; The radius ratio is 4, so the cost ratio is 4^3. $4^3\left(\frac{1}{2}\text{ cent}\right) =$ $64\left(\frac{1}{2}\text{ cent}\right) = 32$ cents

Size	Mean Radius r (cm)	r^3 (cm^3)	Ratio of Radius to Mini's Radius	Ratio of r^3 to Mini's r^3	Production Cost Estimate
Super Jumbo	2.8	? 21.952	? 4:1	? 64:1	? 32 cents

Step 3 Complete the following sentence to generalize your findings: If the production cost varies directly as r^3, and r is multiplied by a number c, then the cost is multiplied by _?_. c^3

Step 4 Suppose there is only one size of carton used for fruit pop shipments and each carton contains fruit pops of only one size. As the radius of the fruit pop gets larger, what happens to the number of pops that fit in the carton? The number n of pops that fit in a carton varies _?_ as the cube of the radius. inversely Algebraically, $n = \frac{k}{r^3}$.

a. Make a table like the one below and fill in the ratio column.

Size	Radius r (cm)	Ratio of r^3 to Mini's r^3	Number of Pops n in a Carton
Mini	0.7	1:1	270
Regular	1.4	? 8:1	? 33
Jumbo	2.1	? 27:1	? 10
Super Jumbo	2.8	? 64:1	? 4

b. Note that since n varies inversely as r^3, n will _?_ as r^3 increases. Since r^3 for the regular pop is _?_ r^3 for the mini pop, $\frac{270}{?} =$ _?_ regular pops will fit in a carton. Write this number in the table. decrease; 8; 8; 33

(continued on next page)

2. You are shown two solid cubes of wood of the same type. The first is 6 inches on a side, and the second is 15 inches on a side. You pick up the first block, which weighs 12 pounds. Explain why most people would need help to pick up the second block. The second block weighs 187.5 lb. This is because the first block has a volume of 216 in^3, while the second block has a volume of 3375 in^3, or 15.625 times the volume of the first block. Thus, it is 15.625 times the weight.

2 Teaching

Notes on the Lesson

Activity This Activity may take a good deal of time, but it covers all the main ideas of the lesson. You should have students work on it in pairs or small groups. Stop after all students have the first table completed to ensure that all students are on the right track. *Note:* Tell students to disregard the space taken up by the sticks when calculating the number of fruit pops that will fit in a carton.

The Fundamental Theorem of Variation Part b of the theorem (which students are asked to prove in Question 17) can be considered a special case of Part a, where n is negative. For instance, if $n = -2$ and y varies directly as x^n, then $y = kx^{-2} = \frac{k}{x^2}$ or y varies inversely as x^2.

Notes on the Lesson

The Fundamental Theorem of Variation

The proof of Part a of the Fundamental Theorem of Variation is difficult for many students to follow because six variables are being considered (c, k, n, y, y_1, and y_2). You might want to rewrite this in a form more familiar from geometry, namely,

- Given: y varies directly as x^n; x is multiplied by c.
- Prove: y is multiplied by c^n.

Then review the proof on page 88.

Note-Taking Tips

Ask students to break the Fundamental Theorem of Variation into two parts: the equations and the descriptions of how y changes for specific changes in x. Encourage them to include specific descriptions in their notes, such as the following: For $w = kd^3$, when d is multiplied by 2, then w is multiplied by 2^3 or 8; for $w = kd^n$, when d is multiplied by a, then w is multiplied by a^n.

c. Note that when the mini's radius is multiplied by 3 to get the jumbo's radius, you can find the number of jumbo pops that fit in the carton by __?__ the number of mini pops by __?__ to the __?__ power. You can find the number of super jumbo pops by __?__ the number of mini pops by __?__ to the __?__ power. Use this information to complete the rightmost column of the table. dividing; 3 third dividing; 4; third

Step 5 Complete the following sentence to generalize your findings: If the number of pops in a carton varies inversely as r^3, and r is multiplied by a number c, then the number of pops is divided by __?__. c^3

 QY1

QY1

If an all-day giant pop has a radius that is 5 times the radius of the mini pop, what is its production cost?

The generalizations you made in Steps 3 and 5 of the Activity are instances of the *Fundamental Theorem of Variation*. In your generalizations, $n = 3$. In the theorem, n can be any positive number.

The Fundamental Theorem of Variation

1. If $y = kx^n$, that is, y varies *directly* as x^n, and x is multiplied by c, then y is multiplied by c^n.
2. If $y = \frac{k}{x^n}$, that is, y varies *inversely* as x^n, and x is multiplied by a non-zero constant c, then y is divided by c^n.

Proof of 1 Let y_1 = original value before multiplying x by c

$y_1 = kx^n$ definition of direct variation

Let y_2 = value when x is multiplied by c

To find y_2, x must be multiplied by c.

$y_2 = k(cx)^n$ definition of y_2

$y_2 = k(c^n x^n)$ Power of a Product Postulate

$y_2 = c^n(kx^n)$ Associative and Commutative Properties of Multiplication

$y_2 = c^n y_1$ substitution of y_1, for kx^n

Proof of 2 The proof of this part is left for you to do in Question 17.

 QY2

QY2

If y varies *inversely* as x, and x is divided by c, what is the effect on y?

Accommodating the Learner ↑

Ask students to consider the variation equations $y_1 = a(2x)^n$ and $y_2 = b(3x)^n$. Ask them to explain what happens to y_1 and y_2 if x is doubled, tripled, halved, or quartered. y_1 is multiplied by $2^n \cdot 2^n$ or 4^n, by $2^n \cdot 3^n$ or 6^n, by 1, or by $\frac{1}{2^n}$, respectively; y_2 is multiplied by $3^n \cdot 2^n$ or 6^n, by $3^n \cdot 3^n$ or 9^n, by $\left(\frac{3}{2}\right)^n$, or by $\left(\frac{3}{4}\right)^n$, respectively.

Accommodating the Learner ↓

Ask students to look at Part a of the Fundamental Theorem of Variation, replacing the variables n and c, respectively, with 2 and 3, and then with $\frac{1}{2}$ and 3, and rewrite Part a for each choice of n and c. Then ask students to repeat the same steps for Part b of the theorem.

Example 1

Fruit Roll Industries needs a cost estimate for the wrappers of the new super jumbo pop. Because the pop is roughly a sphere, the area of the wrapper is a multiple of the surface area of a sphere, where $S.A. = 4\pi r^2$. So, the cost w of a wrapper varies directly with the surface area. The company knows the wrappers for the mini pops cost 1.5¢ each. How much do the wrappers of the super jumbo pop cost?

Solution Because the cost w_1 of a mini pop wrapper varies directly with the surface area, $w_1 = kr^2$ when r is the radius of the mini pop. In the Activity, the radius of the super jumbo pop was 4 times as long as the radius of the mini pop, or $4r$. So, if w_2 is the cost of a super jumbo pop wrapper, $w_2 = k(4r)^2$. Then

$w_2 = k(4^2r^2)$ Power of a Product Property

$w_2 = 16(kr^2)$ Associative and Commutative Properties of Multiplication

$w_2 = 16w_1$ Substitution of w_1 for kr^2

So, the cost of a super jumbo pop wrapper is 16, or 4^2, times the cost of a mini pop wrapper. Because a mini pop wrapper costs 1.5¢, a super jumbo pop wrapper costs 16(1.5) = 24¢.

GUIDED

Example 2

Generally, the weight of a land animal of a particular type varies directly with the cube of its femur diameter. Phoberomys, an extinct rodent that lived over 5 million years ago, is an ancestor of the modern guinea pig. Its femur diameter is 18 times that of today's average guinea pig. Estimate how the weight of this ancient rodent compares to the weight of a modern guinea pig.

This is what a Phoberomys may have looked like.

Illustration by Carin L. Cain © Science

Solution 1 Let d = the animal's femur diameter and w = the animal's weight. Since weight varies directly as the cube of femur diameter, an equation for the variation function is $w = kd^3$. Now apply the Fundamental Theorem of Variation. When d is multiplied by __?__, w is multiplied by __?__^{3} = __?__. Thus, the ancient rodent Phoberomys weighed about __?__ times as much as a modern guinea pig. 18; 18; 5832; 5832

(continued on next page)

Additional Examples

Example 1 Use the information in Example 1 and the Activity. If the wrappers for the mini pops cost 2.25 cents each, how much does a wrapper for a super jumbo pop cost? 36 cents

Example 2 In a parade, the height of a float varies directly with the square of the length of the vehicle that supports the float. This year's vehicles are 3 times as long as the vehicles used 10 years ago. Estimate how the height of this year's floats compares to the height of the floats 10 years ago.

Solution Letting ℓ = the length of the vehicle and h = the height of the float, an equation for the variation function is $h = k\ell^2$. When ℓ is multiplied by __?__, h is multiplied by __?__. So this year's floats are about __?__ times as tall as the floats 10 years ago. 3; 9; 9

ENGLISH LEARNERS

Vocabulary Development

The first paragraph of the lesson includes the phrase *generalize the findings*. You may want to discuss terms such as *generalize, specific, pattern,* and *example,* including in the discussion how *specific examples* are related to *patterns* and how *generalized statements* are related to *specific results*.

Extension

Ask students to calculate the ratio of the volume of a sphere to its surface area for a sphere with a radius of 6 inches, a sphere with a radius of 12 inches, and a sphere with a radius of 18 inches. Ask them to describe any patterns they find. In general, $\frac{V}{S.A.} = \frac{\frac{4}{3}\pi r^3}{4\pi r^2} = \frac{r}{3}$; the ratio is always one-third of the radius.

Solution 2 Set the problem up as in Example 1.

An equation for the variation function is $w = kd^3$. Let w_1 = the weight of the guinea pig, d = the femur diameter of the guinea pig, and w_2 = the weight of Phoberomys with femur diameter $18d$.

$$w_1 = kd^3$$
$$w_2 = k(\underline{\ ?\ })^3 \quad 18d$$
$$= k(\underline{\ ?\ }d^3) \quad 18^3$$
$$= 18^3(\underline{\ ?\ }) \quad kd^3$$
$$= 18^3 w_1$$
$$= \underline{\ ?\ }w_1 \quad 5832$$

So, $w_2 \approx 5800w_1$. Phoberomys weighed about ___?___ times as much as the modern guinea pig. 5832

A modern adult male guinea pig weighs about 2 pounds. So, with this model, an estimate of Phoberomys' weight is 11,600 pounds, or almost 6 tons! Other measurements of Phoberomys show that the $w = kd^3$ model overestimates the weight of the rodent. A better model is $w = kd^{2.5}$. You will study noninteger exponents in a later chapter.

Questions

COVERING THE IDEAS

In 1 and 2, refer to the Activity.

1. What is the production-cost estimate of a jumbo pop? 13.5 cents
2. How many super jumbo pops fit in a carton? 4

In 3 and 4, consider the formula $S.A. = 4\pi r^2$ for the surface area of a sphere from Example 1.

3. **Fill in the Blank** The pairs $(2, 16\pi)$ and $(4, 64\pi)$ represent (r, s) for two spheres. They are instances of this pattern: if the radius r is doubled, the surface area is multiplied by ___?___. 4
4. Show that the Fundamental Theorem of Variation is true for the points in Question 3. $4 = 2 \cdot 2$; $64\pi = 16\pi \cdot 2^2$
5. **Fill in the Blank** If $y = kx^n$, and x is divided by c, then y is ___?___. divided by c^n
6. **Fill in the Blank** If $y = \frac{k}{x^n}$, and x is multiplied by c $(c \neq 0)$, then y is ___?___. divided by c^n

3 Assignment

Recommended Assignment

- Questions 1–23
- Question 24 (extra credit)
- Reading Lesson 2-4
- Covering the Ideas 2-4

Notes on the Questions

Questions 3 and 4 When one variable varies directly as the square of another, then the graph of the pairs of the values of the variables is a parabola with vertex (0, 0).

2-3A Lesson Master

Questions on SPUR Objectives
See Student Edition pages 143–147 for objectives.

PROPERTIES Objective D

1. Suppose y varies directly as x. What is the effect on y if x is
   a. doubled? y is doubled. b. divided by 5? y is divided by 5.
   c. tripled? y is tripled. d. increased by 12%? y is increased by 12%.
2. Suppose d varies inversely as the square of t. What is the effect on d if t is
   a. doubled? d is divided by 4. b. divided by 4? d is multiplied by 16.
   c. halved? d is multiplied by 4. d. multiplied by a? d is divided by a^2.
3. Suppose p is directly proportional to the fourth power of r. What is the effect on p if r is
   a. quadrupled? p is multiplied by 256. b. divided by 10? p is divided by 10,000.
   c. divided by c? p is divided by c^4. d. multiplied by b? p is multiplied by b^4.
4. Suppose y is inversely proportional to the nth power of x. What is the effect on y if x is
   a. doubled? y is divided by 2^n. b. divided by 3? y is multiplied by 3^n.
   c. divided by c? y is multiplied by c^n. d. multiplied by d? y is divided by d^n.

In 5–7, suppose the weight of an animal varies directly as the cube of its height or length.

5. A baby snake is $\frac{1}{6}$ as long as an adult. How do their weights compare?
   The adult snake weighs 6^3 or 216 times as much as the baby snake.
6. A male lion is 1.15 times as tall as a female lion. How do their weights compare?
   The male lion weighs 1.15^3 or ≈ 1.52 times as much as the female lion.
7. A songbird is one third as tall as a hawk. How do their weights compare?
   The hawk weighs 3^3 or 27 times as much as the songbird.

Fill in the Blanks In 8–10, suppose the radius of a sphere is tripled. Find the change in the characteristic.

8. The volume of the sphere is multiplied by 3^3 or 27.
9. The diameter of the sphere is multiplied by 3.
10. The surface area of the sphere is multiplied by 3^2 or 9.

150 Advanced Algebra

7. Refer to Example 2. Suppose the diameter of the femur bone of another ancient rodent is 3.2 times that of the modern guinea pig. Compare the weight of this ancient rodent to the weight of a modern one.

In 8–10, suppose $y = 3x^4$.

8. Complete the table of values at the right.
9. Describe the change in y when x is doubled. Explain your reasoning.
10. When answering the question, "Describe the change in y when x is divided by 3," Laura's response was "y is multiplied by $\frac{1}{81}$." Do you agree with Laura? Why or why not? Yes; y is divided by 3^4, or 81.
11. The volume of a cube varies directly with the cube of its edge length.
    a. If the edge length is multiplied by 8, what effect does that have on the volume? The volume is multiplied by 512.
    b. If the edge length is divided in half, what effect does that have on the volume? The volume is divided by 8.

7. The ancient rodent was $3.2^3 = 32.8$ times as heavy.

x	y
1	? 3
2	? 48
3	? 243
4	? 768
6	? 3888
8	? 12,288
9	? 19,683

9. When x is doubled, y is multiplied by 16. This is because $16 = 2^4$.

APPLYING THE MATHEMATICS

12. Marta went to the farmer's market to buy oranges. The oranges that are 3 inches in diameter cost 25 cents per dozen. The oranges that are 4 inches in diameter are 50 cents per dozen. Marta chose the 3-inch oranges. Did she make the more economical decision? Explain your answer? See margin.
13. The Brobdingnagians in Jonathan Swift's *Gulliver's Travels* are similar to us, but they are 12 times as tall.
    a. How would you expect the weight of these giants to compare to our weight?
    b. How would you expect their surface area to compare to ours?
14. The inverse square law for light intensity, $I = \frac{k}{d^2}$, models the relationship between distance d from a light source and the intensity I of the light. See margin.
    a. When Booker is working at his computer, he is twice the distance from the floor lamp in his room as he is when he is working at his desk. Compare the light intensity of the floor lamp at his computer to the intensity at his desk. Justify your answer.
    b. Suppose Booker moves his computer so that it is three times as far from the floor lamp as his desk. Compare the intensity of the lamp light at his computer and his desk. Justify your answer.

13a. Their weight would be about 12^3, or 1728, times as great.

13b. Their surface area would be about 12^2, or 144, times as great.

Additional Answers

12. No; because the radius of the larger oranges was $\frac{4}{3}$ times the radius of the smaller oranges, this means that their volume was $\left(\frac{4}{3}\right)^3$ or about 2.37 times as great. Because their volume more than doubled, paying only twice the price of the smaller oranges would have been the better deal.

14a. The light intensity at his computer is one-fourth the intensity at his desk. We see this from the inverse-square law for light intensity, which shows that $I = \frac{k}{(2d)^2} = \frac{1}{4}\left(\frac{k}{d^2}\right)$.

14b. If he moves his computer, the light intensity at his computer will now be one-ninth the intensity at his desk. We see this from the inverse-square law for light intensity, which shows that $I = \frac{k}{(3d)^2} = \frac{1}{9}\left(\frac{k}{d^2}\right)$.

Notes on the Questions

Questions 5–11 These questions may be difficult for some students. Suggest that they substitute numbers for the variables to examine specific examples before reaching conclusions to the questions asked. *Examining specific cases* before forming a general conclusion is a good problem-solving strategy that students should know. For instance, in Question 9, pick a value for x, say 10. Then $y = 30{,}000$. Now double x to 20. Then $y = 480{,}000$, 16 times as great. The key is to notice that $16 = 2^4$. You can help develop students' intuition by using algebra to arrive at the answers. This more general approach may be discussed after students have worked through specific examples with numbers. Here is an algebraic solution: Start with $y = 3x^4$. Replacing x with $2x$, then $y = 3(2x)^4 = 3 \cdot 16x^4 = 48x^4$. Because $\frac{48x^4}{3x^4} = 16$, y is multiplied by 16 when x is doubled.

Additional Answers

17. Let $y_1 =$ original value before multiplying x by c.
Let $y_2 =$ value when x is multiplied by c.

To find y_2, x must be multiplied by c.

$y_1 = \frac{k}{x^n}$ definition of inverse variation

$y_2 = \frac{k}{(cx)^n}$ definition of y_2

$y_2 = \frac{k}{c^n x^n}$ Power of a Product Postulate

$y_2 = \frac{1}{c^n} \cdot \frac{k}{x^n}$ Associative and Commutative Properties of Multiplication

$y_2 = \frac{1}{c^n} \cdot y_1$ substitution of y_1 for $\frac{k}{x^n}$

$y_2 = \frac{y_1}{c^n}$ definition of division

Notes on the Questions

Question 16 We ignore the hole because the ratio of the radius of the hole on larger CDs to the hole on smaller CDs is not 5 : 3.

4 Wrap-Up

Ongoing Assessment

Show students the equations $y_1 = mx^3$, $y_2 = \frac{n}{x^4}$, and $y_3 = \left(\frac{1}{p}\right)x^5$, telling them that m, n, and p are constants. Ask students to describe how the variables vary together. Answers vary. Sample: y_1 varies directly with the cube of x; y_2 varies inversely with the fourth power of x, and y_3 varies directly with the fifth power of x.

Administer Quiz 1 (or a quiz of your own) after students complete this lesson.

In 15 and 16, refer to the illustration of the micro- and standard-size CDs at the right. The radius of the standard CD is 5 inches and the radius of the micro CD is 3 inches.

A standard and micro CD.

15. What is the ratio of the circumferences of the larger to the smaller CD? 5:3
16. Use the Fundamental Theorem of Variation to calculate the ratio of the surface areas of the larger to the smaller CD, assuming the CDs had no hole in the center. 25:9
17. Complete the proof of Part 2 of the Fundamental Theorem of Variation. See margin.

REVIEW

18. Translate this statement into a variation equation: The number of oranges that fit into a crate is inversely proportional to the cube of the radius of each orange. **(Lesson 2-2)** $N = \frac{k}{r^3}$
19. **Multiple Choice** Most of the power of a boat motor results in the generation of a wake (the track left in the water). The engine power P used in generating the wake is directly proportional to the seventh power of the boat's speed s. Which equation models this variation? **(Lesson 2-1)** C

    A $P = 7s$ B $s = kP^7$ C $P = ks^7$ D $P = k^7s$
20. Suppose V varies directly as the third power of r. If $V = 32$ when $r = 8$, find V when $r = 5$. **(Lesson 2-1)** $\frac{125}{16} \approx 7.8$
21. a. If one blank CD costs c cents, how much do n blank CDs cost? **(Lesson 1-1)** cn cents

    b. If two blank CDs cost d cents, how much do m blank CDs cost? **(Lesson 1-1)** $\frac{d}{2}m$ cents
22. ***Skill Sequence*** Find all solutions. **(Previous Course)**

    a. $x^2 = 25$ b. $25y^2 = 36$ c. $3z = \frac{25}{3z}$
23. In the diagram at the right, $\triangle DIG \sim \triangle ART$. Find TR. **(Previous Course)** 10.85

22a. $x = 5$ or -5
22b. $y = \frac{6}{5}$ or $-\frac{6}{5}$
22c. $z = \frac{5}{3}$ or $-\frac{5}{3}$

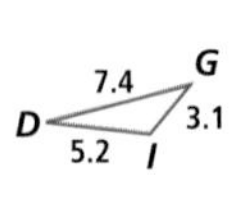

EXPLORATION

24. Go to the store or use the Internet to find a product that comes in two different sizes (for example, a regular and a large-screen television). Compare prices of the smaller and larger versions of the product. Using the Fundamental Theorem of Variation, decide whether the prices of the two products are in the proper ratio. Explain your decision. What factors other than size might affect the price? See margin.

QY ANSWERS

1. 62.5 cents
2. y is multiplied by c.

Additional Answers

24. Answers vary. Sample: A 26 in. flat-panel LCD television costs \$450. A 42 in. flat-panel LCD television costs \$1300. These measures refer to the longest diagonal of the screen. It would be reasonable for the prices to vary directly as the area of the screen, and the area of the screen should vary directly as the square of the diagonal. So, if c is the cost and d is the length of the diagonal, we have $c = kd^2$. The diagonal of the larger television is $\frac{42}{26} \approx 1.6$ times as long as the diagonal of the smaller television. According to the Fundamental Theorem of Variation, the price of the larger television should be $1.6^2 = 2.56$ times as high as the price as the smaller television. But the larger television's price is actually $\frac{1300}{450} \approx 2.89$ times as high as the smaller television's price. However, there may be other factors in the cost. For example, the larger a LCD screen is, the more expensive it is to manufacture. Also, the televisions may be different brands and have different audio or video features.

2-3B Lesson Master Questions on SPUR Objectives
See Student Edition pages 143–147 for objectives.

VOCABULARY

1. **Fill in the Blank** If y varies directly as x, and x is multiplied by c, then y is multiplied by c.
2. **Fill in the Blank** If y varies inversely as x^n and x is multiplied by a nonzero constant c, then y is divided by c^n.

PROPERTIES Objective D

In 3–6, suppose that in the given variation situations the value of x is doubled. How is the value of y changed if

3. y varies directly as x^3? y is multiplied by $2^3 = 8$.
4. y varies directly as x^4? y is multiplied by $2^4 = 16$.
5. y varies inversely as x^2? y is divided by $2^2 = 4$.
6. y varies inversely as $\sqrt{x}$? y is divided by $\sqrt{2}$.

In 7–10, suppose that in the given variation situations the value of x is tripled. How is the value of y changed if

7. y varies directly as x? y is tripled.
8. y varies inversely as x? y is divided by 3.
9. y varies directly as x^2? y is multiplied by $3^2 = 9$.
10. y varies inversely as x^3? y is divided by $3^3 = 27$.

In 11–16, suppose that a varies directly as the fourth power of b. How does the value of a change if

11. b is doubled? a is multiplied by $2^4 = 16$.
12. b is quadrupled? a is multiplied by $4^4 = 256$.
13. b is multiplied by 5? a is multiplied by $5^4 = 625$.
14. b is multiplied by 6? a is multiplied by $6^4 = 1296$.

Advanced Algebra 151

Lesson 2-4 The Graph of $y = kx$

Vocabulary

rate of change

slope

BIG IDEA The graph of the set of points (*x*, *y*) satisfying $y = kx$, with *k* constant, is the line containing the origin and having slope *k*.

Mental Math

Consider this set of numbers: −17, 512, $-\sqrt{2}$, $\frac{7}{11}$, 0.0145.

a. Find the median of this set. 0.0145

b. Which numbers in the set are irrational? $-\sqrt{2}$

c. Which numbers are rational but not integers? $\frac{7}{11}$ and 0.0145

d. Which numbers are not in the domain of *f* if $f(x) = \sqrt{4 - x^2}$? 17 and 512

Recall from the Questions in Lesson 2-1 that the distance *d* you are from a lightning strike varies directly with the time *t* elapsed between seeing the lightning and hearing the thunder. The formula $d = \frac{1}{5}t$ describes this situation for the values given in that lesson. This direct-variation function can also be represented graphically. A table and a graph for the equation $d = \frac{1}{5}t$ are shown here.

Time *t* (sec)	0	5	10	15	20	25	30
Distance *d* (mi)	0	1	2	3	4	5	6

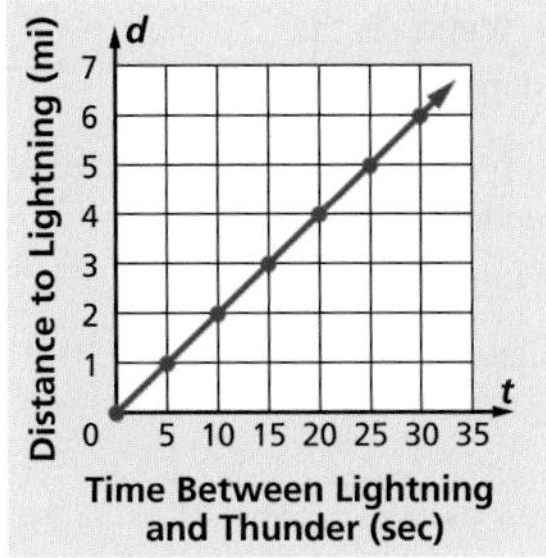

Background

Most of this lesson should be a review for students. It covers graphs of lines through the origin and the slope of such lines.

There are two important ideas to emphasize in this lesson: (1) Slope is a rate of change (an idea that is extended to nonlinear curves in the next lesson), and (2) there are common features in the graphs of all equations of the form $y = kx$. Students should recognize quickly what the graphs of important functions should look like. We also expect the reverse: Students should be able to look at a graph and determine what kind of linear equation can represent that graph. (This idea is extended in Lessons 2-7 and 2-8 to $y = \frac{k}{x}$ and $y = \frac{k}{x^2}$.)

(continued on next page)

Lesson 2-4

GOAL

Review graphs of lines through the origin; review the idea of slope.

SPUR Objectives

C Find slopes and rates of change.

E Identify the properties of variation functions.

I Graph variation equations.

J Identify variation equations from graphs.

Materials/Resources

- Lesson Masters 2-4A and 2-4B
- Resource Masters 2 and 25

HOMEWORK

Suggestions for Assignment

- Questions 1–26
- Question 27 (extra credit)
- Reading Lesson 2-5
- Covering the Ideas 2-5

Local Standards

1 Warm-Up

Ask students to manually graph a set of points (*x*, *y*) such that $y = -2.5x$. Then ask for the slope of the line. Answers vary. Check students' work.

(*Note:* Students' comfort with these two tasks will give you an indication of how much time you may need to discuss this lesson. Also, be sure that students realize that, for a linear graph, the slope of the graph *does not* depend on the points selected for calculating it.)

2 Teaching

Notes on the Lesson

For reasonably prepared students, you may be able to proceed directly to the Questions.

The slope of a line If students have not had much experience with slope, give some numerical examples and include the units. For instance, in the Example, you can calculate the slope as $\frac{5 \text{ miles} - 2 \text{ miles}}{25 \text{ seconds} - 10 \text{ seconds}}$, which gives $\frac{1}{5}$ mile/second as the answer. Discuss the *meaning* of slope as a rate. In this case, the slope is the speed (in miles/second) at which thunder travels, which is the speed of sound in air.

A common error students make when calculating slope is inverting the ratio. As a mnemonic device, you may want to suggest that students think of slope as $\frac{\text{rise}}{\text{run}}$, or better yet $\frac{\text{"ryse"}}{\text{run}}$ to help remember that the change in vertical distance (y) is in the numerator of the slope fraction.

If students have studied from UCSMP *Pre-Transition Mathematics, Transition Mathematics,* or *Algebra,* they will have seen the Comparison Model for Subtraction (that $a - b$ is the amount by which a exceeds b) and the Rate Model for Division (that $\frac{a}{b}$ is the rate of a's per b's). A special case of comparison is change; that is, $a - b$ is the change from b to a. Thus, the slope formula is literally a rate formed from two changes. This explains why there is subtraction and division in the slope formula.

Note that the domain of this function is the set of nonnegative real numbers, and the range is also the set of nonnegative real numbers. When all real-world solutions to the equation $d = \frac{1}{5}t$ are plotted in the coordinate plane, the graph is a ray starting at the origin and passing through the first quadrant. There are no points on the graph of $d = \frac{1}{5}t$ in any other quadrants.

QY1

> **QY1**
> Explain why there could be no real-world solutions in Quadrants II, III, or IV.

The Slope of a Line

Recall that the steepness of a line is measured by a number called the *slope*. The slope of a line is the **rate of change** of y with respect to x and can be calculated using the coordinates of two points on the line. Let (x_1, y_1) and (x_2, y_2) be the two points. Then $y_2 - y_1$ is the vertical change (the change in the dependent variable), and $x_2 - x_1$ is the horizontal change (the change in the independent variable). The slope, or rate of change, is the quotient of these changes.

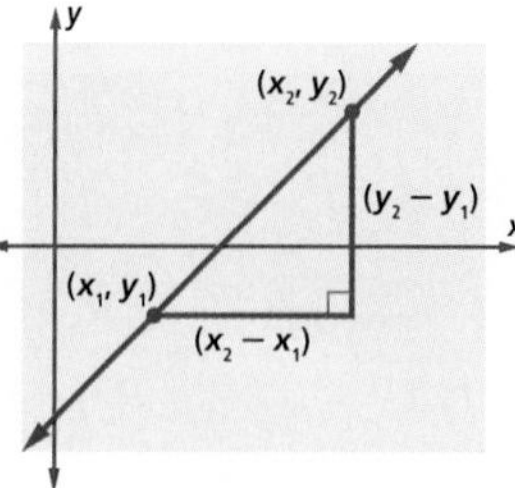

$$\text{slope} = \frac{\text{change in vertical distance}}{\text{change in horizontal distance}}$$

$$= \frac{\text{change in dependent variable}}{\text{change in independent variable}}$$

$$= \frac{y_2 - y_1}{x_2 - x_1}$$

Definition of Slope

The **slope** of the line through the two points (x_1, y_1) and (x_2, y_2) is $\frac{y_2 - y_1}{x_2 - x_1}$.

Example

Determine the slope of the line with equation $d = \frac{1}{5}t$, where t is the independent variable time (in seconds) and d is the dependent variable distance (in miles).

Solution Use the definition of slope. Because d is on the vertical axis and t is on the horizontal axis, the ordered pairs are of the form (t, d).

Find two points on the line; either point can be considered (t_1, d_1). Here we use $(t_1, d_1) = (10, 2)$ and $(t_2, d_2) = (15, 3)$.

$$\text{slope} = \frac{d_2 - d_1}{t_2 - t_1} = \frac{3 \text{ mi} - 2 \text{ mi}}{15 \text{ sec} - 10 \text{ sec}} = \frac{1}{5} \frac{\text{mi}}{\text{sec}}$$

Activity Moving a *slider* changes the value of a parameter and shows the effect of that change. Students have probably seen sliders when they download something from the Internet. The incrementally filling rectangle is a slider that keeps track of the time and/or amount of download completed. Even if students are familiar with the content of the lesson, we encourage doing the Activity because it shows how to deal with a slider in a mathematical context.

Refer to the graph at the beginning of this lesson. Notice that for every change of 5 units to the right, there is a change of 1 unit up. This is equivalent to saying that for every change of 1 horizontal unit, there is a change of $\frac{1}{5}$ of a vertical unit. Notice that because of the difference in units, you cannot visually see the slope as $\frac{1}{5}$.

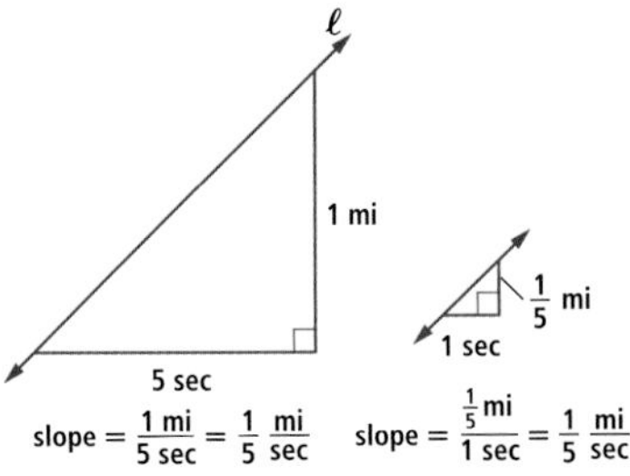

 QY2

The Slope of $y = kx$

Observe from the Example that the graph of $y = \frac{1}{5}x$ has slope $\frac{1}{5}$. This is an instance of the following theorem.

Slope of $y = kx$ Theorem

The graph of the direct-variation function with equation $y = kx$ has constant slope k.

Proof Let (x_1, y_1) and (x_2, y_2) be any two distinct points on $y = kx$, with $k \neq 0$. Since the points are on the line,

$y_1 = kx_1$ substitution

and $y_2 = kx_2$

Now solve this system of equations for k.

$y_2 - y_1 = kx_2 - kx_1$ Subtraction Property of Equality

$y_2 - y_1 = k(x_2 - x_1)$ Distributive Property

$\frac{y_2 - y_1}{x_2 - x_1} = k$ Division Property of Equality

So by the definition of slope, k is the slope of the line through these points.

Thus, k is the slope of the line with equation $y = kx$.

▶ **QY2**

What is the slope of the line through (9, 36) and (25, 100)?

Additional Example

Example Determine the slope of a line with equation $d = \frac{5}{7}w$, where w is the independent variable (in weeks) and d is the dependent variable (in days). $\frac{5}{7}$

Note-Taking Tips

Discuss with students the usefulness of subscripted variables to express the definition of slope. Students should realize that using two y variables and two x variables makes it clear which values in ordered pairs are in the numerator and which values are in the denominator of the fraction. The corresponding order of the subscripts is a reminder of how to substitute the two ordered pairs into the definition.

ENGLISH LEARNERS

Vocabulary Development

Some students may need guidance pronouncing subscripted variables. You may want to discuss both subscripted variables and variables with superscripts (exponents), so students make a clear distinction between, say, x_2 (x-sub-two or x-two) and x^2 (x squared or x to the second power). Be sure students realize that x^2 indicates an operation (square the value of x), while x_2 represents a particular, single value.

Notes on the Lesson

Activity Notice that the graphs of $y = kx$ and $y = -kx$ are reflection images of each other over both the x-axis and the y-axis. It may not be obvious that the graphs of $y = kx$ and $y = \left(\frac{1}{k}\right)x$ are reflection images of each other over the line $y = x$. This is because switching the axes switches x and y, and if $y = kx$, then $x = \left(\frac{1}{k}\right)y$. (Students will encounter this idea again when they study inverse functions.) In Step 4, students should realize that for any point A with coordinates $(1, y)$, the y-value of this ordered pair is the same as k and the slope of the line. Make sure students do not mistakenly conclude that the slope always equals the y-coordinate of any point on the line. Question 13 addresses this possible misunderstanding.

All the lines with equation $y = kx$, where k is any real number, make up a family of lines through the origin with different slopes k. They are all direct-variation functions. In general, the domain of a function with equation $y = kx$ is the set of real numbers, and the range is the set of real numbers.

To explore how the value of k affects the graph of $y = kx$, you can graph $y = kx$ using several different values of k. This approach lets you view several graphs simultaneously and compare them. The graphs of $y = kx$ for four different values of k are shown on the axes below.

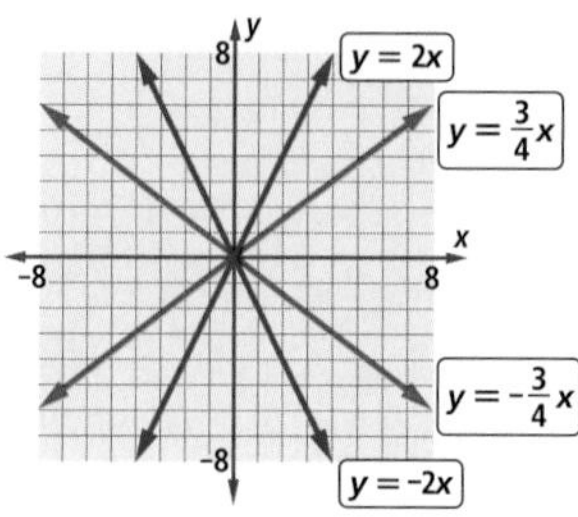

Activity

MATERIALS CAS, graphing calculator, or variation graph application

In this Activity, you will vary k to see how the graph of $y = kx$ changes.

Step 1 Consider the family of curves $y = kx$. Examine the graph for various positive values of k. Describe, in terms of slope, how the graph of the line $y = kx$ behaves for values of $k > 0$. How is the steepness of the graph affected as k increases?

Step 2 Examine the graph for various negative values of k. Describe, in terms of slope, how the graph of the line $y = kx$ behaves for values of $k < 0$. How is the steepness of the graph affected as k decreases?

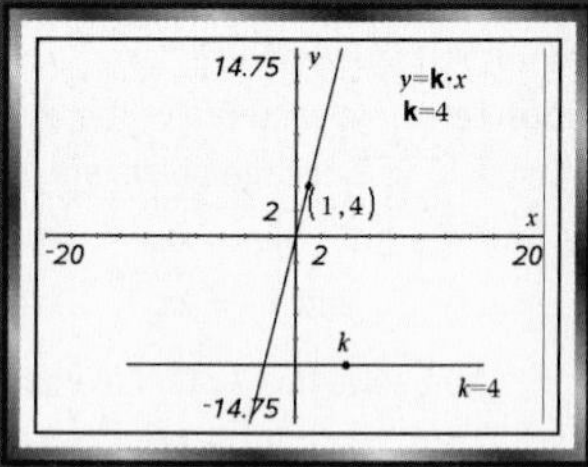

Step 3 Describe the graph of the line $y = kx$ when $k = 0$.

Step 4 Choose any k and note the coordinates of the point $A = (1, k)$ on the graph. A always has x-coordinate 1, but its y-coordinate changes with the value of k. Use the coordinates of point A and the fact that the line passes through the origin to find the slope of the line.

Compare this slope to the y-coordinate of A and the value of k. What do you notice?

Step 1. The value of y increases with respect to x. The graph becomes steeper.

Step 2. The value of y decreases with respect to x. The graph becomes steeper in a downward direction.

Step 3. The graph is horizontal.

Step 4. Answers vary. Sample: Let $k = 3$. Then $y_1 = 3$. Slope $= 3$. They are all the same number.

Accommodating the Learner

Have students work in small groups. One student identifies a value for x, and a second student identifies a value for y. Then all students in the group should calculate $k = \frac{y}{x}$, write the equation $y = kx$ (using the calculated k value), and graph the equation. Students should check each other's work before repeating the activity, with different students identifying x and y values. Answers vary. Check students' work.

Questions

COVERING THE IDEAS

1. By definition, $\frac{y_2 - y_1}{x_2 - x_1}$ is the slope of the line through which points? (x_1, y_1) and (x_2, y_2)

2. Use the expression $\frac{y_2 - y_1}{x_2 - x_1}$ for the slope of a line.
   a. Let $(x_1, y_1) = (2, 4)$ and $(x_2, y_2) = (4.2, -5.3)$. Find the slope of the line through these two points. slope $\approx$ -4.23
   b. Let $(x_1, y_1) = (4.2, -5.3)$ and $(x_2, y_2) = (2, 4)$. Again, find the slope of the line through these points. Compare your answer to your answer to Part a. slope $\approx$ -4.23; They are the same.
   c. Mingmei incorrectly calculated the slope of the line through $(x_1, y_1) = (4.2, -5.3)$ and $(x_2, y_2) = (2, 4)$ as follows: $\frac{4 - (-5.3)}{4.2 - 2} \approx 4.23$. What error did she make? How does her answer compare to the answer you found in Part b?
   d. Given any two points $A = (c, d)$ and $B = (j, k)$, is the slope of the line through A and B the same as the slope of the line through B and A? Explain using the results you found in Parts a and b.

3. **Fill in the Blanks** Slope = $\frac{\text{change in the \_?\_ variable}}{\text{change in the \_?\_ variable}}$

4. **Fill in the Blanks** A slope of $-\frac{2}{5}$ means that for every change of 5 units to the right there is a change of _?_ units _?_. It also means that for every change of 1 horizontal unit there is a vertical change of _?_ unit. 2; down; $-\frac{2}{5}$

5. In the graph of $d = \frac{1}{5}t$, the slope of the line is $\frac{1}{5}$. Write a sentence to describe this slope in the context of lightning and thunderstorms, using the appropriate units.

6. In the lesson, a triangle is drawn to show that a line has slope $\frac{1}{5}$. Draw a similar diagram that shows that a line has a slope of $\frac{7}{3}$. See margin.

7. **Fill in the Blanks** The graph of $y = kx$ slants up as you read from left to right if k is _?_. It slants down as you read from left to right if k is _?_. positive; negative

8. When k is negative, in which quadrants is the graph of $y = kx$? II and IV

9. **Fill in the Blanks** The graph of every direct-variation function $y = kx$ is a _?_ with slope _?_ and passing through the point _?_. line; k; (0, 0)

2c. She divided by $(x_1 - x_2)$ instead of $(x_2 - x_1)$; her answer is the opposite of the correct answer.

2d. Yes; reversing the order of the points changes the sign in both the numerator and the denominator, so there is no change in the final value.

3. dependent; independent

5. For every 5 seconds it takes to hear thunder, you are 1 mile farther away from where the lightning struck.

3 Assignment

Recommended Assignment

- Questions 1–26
- Question 27 (extra credit)
- Reading Lesson 2-5
- Covering the Ideas 2-5

Notes on the Questions

Question 4 The second sentence gives an alternative fundamental conception of slope to "rise over run," namely that the slope of a line is the distance that a point on the line moves up (or down) when it moves one unit to the right. The advantage of this conception is that it emphasizes that the slope of a line is a single number.

Question 5 The answer should have something to do with lightning and thunder time and distance and is best if it involves the single number $\frac{1}{5}$, not merely the two numbers 1 and 5.

Additional Answers

6.

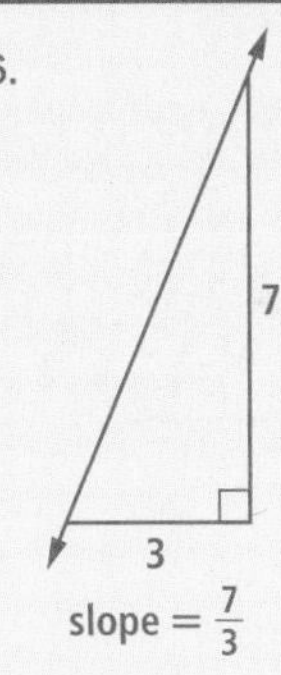

slope = $\frac{7}{3}$

Extension

Ask students to show the graph, in Quadrant I only, of a line of the form $x + y = k$, where k is a positive number. Tell them to divide the line segment into an even number of congruent segments (say 6, 8, or 10) and find the slopes of the lines joining each dividing point with the origin. Ask students how many dividing points there are and to describe some patterns in the slopes.

Answers vary. Sample: The number of dividing points is one fewer than the number of congruent segments, so the number of dividing points is odd; the slope for the "middle" point is 1, and as you go away from that middle point, in both directions, the slopes are reciprocals.

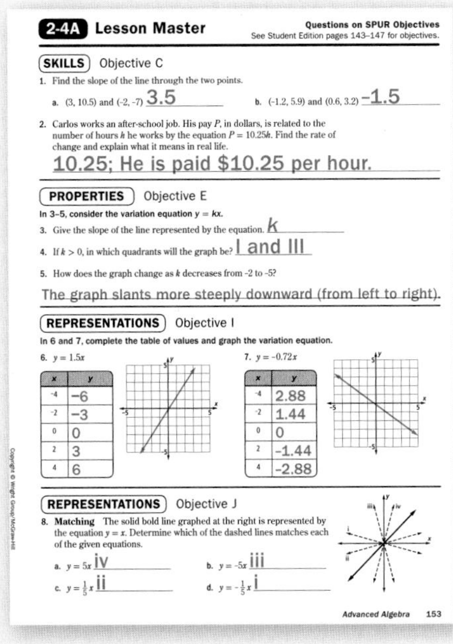

2-4A Lesson Master

Questions on SPUR Objectives
See Student Edition pages 143–147 for objectives.

SKILLS Objective C

1. Find the slope of the line through the two points.
   a. (3, 10.5) and (-2, -7) 3.5
   b. (-1.2, 5.9) and (0.6, 3.2) −1.5

2. Carlos works an after-school job. His pay P, in dollars, is related to the number of hours h he works by the equation $P = 10.25h$. Find the rate of change and explain what it means in real life.
   10.25; He is paid $10.25 per hour.

PROPERTIES Objective E

In 3–5, consider the variation equation $y = kx$.

3. Give the slope of the line represented by the equation. k
4. If $k > 0$, in which quadrants will the graph be? I and III
5. How does the graph change as k decreases from -2 to -5?
   The graph slants more steeply downward (from left to right).

REPRESENTATIONS Objective I

In 6 and 7, complete the table of values and graph the variation equation.

6. $y = 1.5x$

x	y
-4	−6
-2	−3
0	0
2	3
4	6

7. $y = -0.72x$

x	y
-4	2.88
-2	1.44
0	0
2	-1.44
4	-2.88

REPRESENTATIONS Objective J

8. **Matching** The solid bold line graphed at the right is represented by the equation $y = x$. Determine which of the dashed lines matches each of the given equations.
   a. $y = 5x$ iv
   b. $y = -5x$ iii
   c. $y = \frac{1}{5}x$ ii
   d. $y = -\frac{1}{5}x$ i

Advanced Algebra 153

Notes on the Questions

Question 12 The ordered pairs were purposely chosen to prevent students from calculating the slope solely by counting squares on a grid, where each tick mark represents one unit.

Question 15 For many students, the answer will be obvious without a graph, but the graph confirms the intuition.

APPLYING THE MATHEMATICS

In 10–12, compute the rate of change for the given situation. Include units where appropriate.

10. An escalator drops 2 feet for every 7 seconds traveled. $-\frac{2}{7}$ feet per second
11. A car travels forward 60 miles every hour. 60 miles per hour
12. A line passes through the points $\left(-2, \frac{1}{3}\right)$ and $\left(\frac{2}{5}, 10\right)$. about 4.03
13. Refer to Step 4 of the Activity. Find an additional point B on the line $y = kx$ for your chosen value of k. Calculate the slope of the line using points A and B. Compare this to the slope you calculated using A and O. How do the slopes compare to each other and to k?
14. Bicycle manufacturers have found that, for the average person and a given style of bicycle, the proper seat height h varies directly with the inseam measurement i of the rider's pants.
    a. If the seat height is 27 inches for an inseam of 25 inches, determine an equation for the variation function. $h = 1.08i$
    b. Should the domain and range be all real numbers? Why or why not?
    c. What is the slope of the graph of this function? 1.08
    d. What does the slope represent in this situation?
15. Plot the points (3, 1), (9, 3), (12, 6) on a coordinate plane. Do these points lie on a line that represents a direct-variation function of the form $y = kx$? If so, compute the rate of change of that function. If not, explain why not. See margin.
16. The federal minimum wage was \$5.15/hr between 1997 and the summer of 2007.
    a. Determine the direct-variation function that calculates the amount of money m that someone earned (before taxes) by working w hours at this minimum wage. $m = 5.15w$
    b. A typical work week has 40 hours. Determine a reasonable domain and range for the function that maps time worked in a week onto the amount earned.
    c. Sketch a detailed graph of the function. See margin.
    d. In July 2009, the minimum wage increased to \$7.25 an hour. Describe how the graph of the function would change.
17. The graph at the right shows the four equations $y = 4x$, $y = -4x$, $y = \frac{1}{4}x$, and $y = -\frac{1}{4}x$. Match each graph with its equation.
    17. a: $y = -4x$; b: $y = 4x$; c: $y = \frac{1}{4}x$; d: $y = -\frac{1}{4}x$

13. Answers vary. Sample: For $k = 3$, $A = (1, 3)$. The point $B = (2, 6)$ is also on the line $y = 3x$. Using A and B, the slope is $\frac{6-3}{2-1} = 3$. This is the same slope found using A and O, and it is equal to k.

14b. No; the inseam measurement cannot be less than or equal to 0 or else the person would not have legs, and it cannot be too large, because people do not grow indefinitely. The same restrictions apply to the seat height.

14d. For every inch increase in inseam, seat height should increase by 1.08 inches.

16b. Answers vary. Sample: domain: $\{w \mid 0 \le w \le 60\}$; range: $\{m \mid 0 \le m \le 309\}$

16d. The slope of the line would increase, so the graph would be steeper.

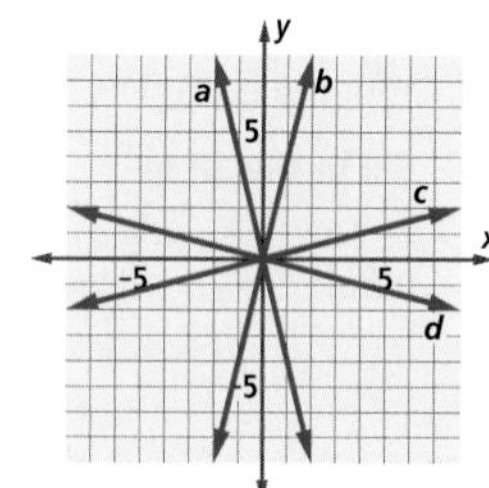

Additional Answers

15. No; the rate of change between the first two points is $\frac{1}{3}$, and the rate of change between the second and third points is 1.

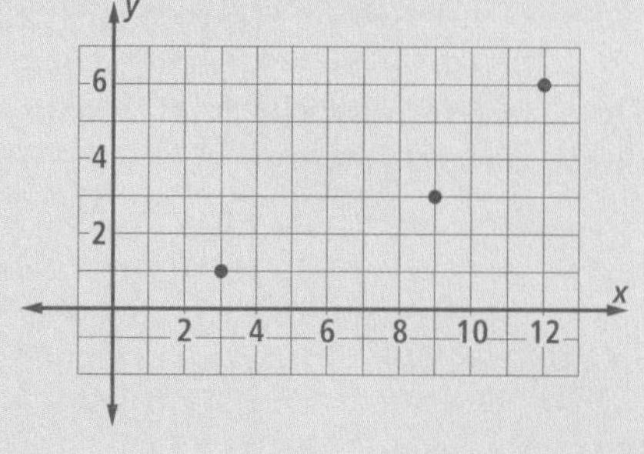

16c.

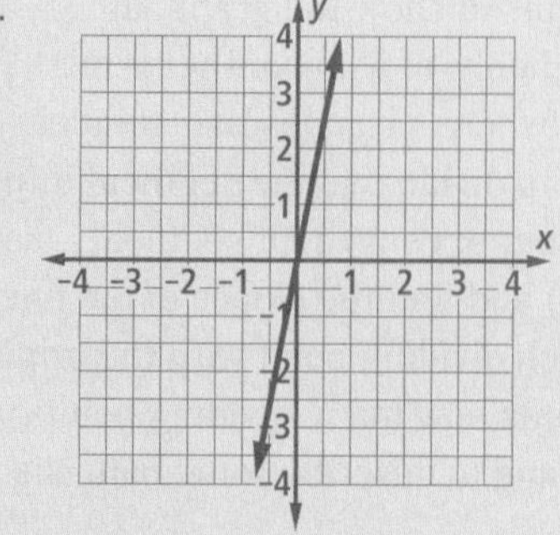

18. Below is a graph of $y = kx$. Explain how similar triangles can be used to show that the slope of the line is the same no matter which points are chosen to find the slope.

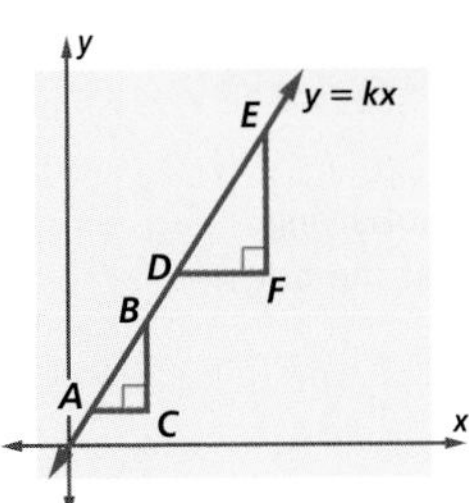

18. The ratio of the legs for both triangles will be the same, meaning the slope is the same.

19. To program the formula for slope into a CAS, use the DEFINE command and enter slope(x1, y1, x2, y2) $= \frac{y_2 - y_1}{x_2 - x_1}$. Then use your programmed formula to find the slope of the line through the given points.

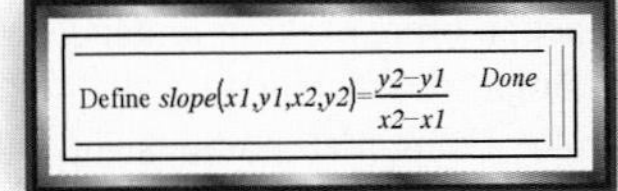

Define slope(x1,y1,x2,y2)=y2−y1 / x2−x1 Done

a. (152, 278) and (194, 360) $\frac{41}{21}$ b. (8.4, -3.6) and (6, 10) $-\frac{17}{3}$

REVIEW

20. In the variation function $W = \frac{k}{d^3}$, what is the effect on W if
   a. d is tripled? W would be multiplied by $\frac{1}{27}$.
   b. d is halved? (Lesson 2-3) W would be multiplied by 8.

21. Assume that the cost of a square cake varies directly as the square of the length of a side. What would be the ratio of the cost of a 6-inch square cake to a 10-inch square cake? (Lesson 2-3) 9:25

In 22–25, state whether the equation is of a direct-variation function, an inverse-variation function, or neither. (Lessons 2-1, 2-2)

22. $y = -\frac{3}{x}$ inverse
23. $y = -\frac{x}{3}$ direct
24. $y = -\frac{3}{x^2}$ inverse
25. $y = x - 3$ neither

26. Ohm's Law, $I = \frac{V}{R}$, relates current I (in amperes) to voltage V (in volts) and resistance R (in ohms). (Lesson 1-7)
   a. Solve this formula for R. $R = \frac{V}{I}$
   b. Solve this formula for V. $V = RI$

EXPLORATION

27. Each of the following terms is a synonym for *slope*. Research each term to find out who might use each one.
   a. marginal cost economist
   b. pitch architect
   c. grade engineer
   d. rise over run mathematician

QY ANSWERS

1. In Quadrants II, III, and IV, t or d or both would be negative. The distance d cannot be negative, and the thunder cannot occur before the lightning, so the time t cannot be negative.
2. $\frac{100 - 36}{25 - 9} = \frac{64}{16} = 4$

4 Wrap-Up

Ongoing Assessment

Have students work in groups. Taking turns, each student should write an equation of the form $y = kx$, where k is a positive or negative integer, fraction, or decimal. The other students then describe the graph of the equation. Answers vary. Sample: For each integer value of k, the ordered pairs $(1, k)$ and $\left(\frac{1}{k}, 1\right)$ are on the line $y = kx$.

Accommodating the Learner

Have students work in small groups. Taking turns, each student writes a positive or negative decimal or irrational number as a value of k. Then all students in the group find the ordered pairs of the form (1, __?__) and (__?__, 1) that are on the graph of $y = kx$. For each value of k, the ordered pairs $(1, k)$ and $\left(\frac{1}{k}, 1\right)$ are on the line $y = kx$.

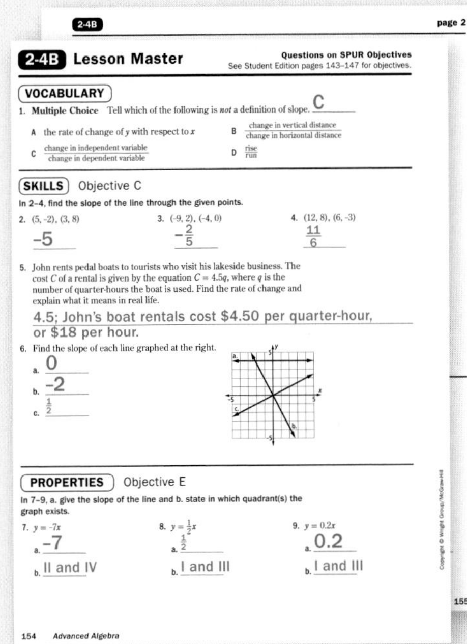

2-4B page 2

2-4B Lesson Master

Questions on SPUR Objectives
See Student Edition pages 143–147 for objectives.

VOCABULARY

1. **Multiple Choice** Tell which of the following is *not* a definition of slope. C
   A the rate of change of y with respect to x
   B $\frac{\text{change in vertical distance}}{\text{change in horizontal distance}}$
   C $\frac{\text{change in independent variable}}{\text{change in dependent variable}}$
   D $\frac{\text{rise}}{\text{run}}$

SKILLS Objective C

In 2–4, find the slope of the line through the given points.

2. (5, -2), (3, 8) -5
3. (-9, 2), (-4, 0) $-\frac{2}{5}$
4. (12, 8), (6, -3) $\frac{11}{6}$

5. John rents pedal boats to tourists who visit his lakeside business. The cost C of a rental is given by the equation $C = 4.5q$, where q is the number of quarter-hours the boat is used. Find the rate of change and explain what it means in real life.
   4.5; John's boat rentals cost $4.50 per quarter-hour, or $18 per hour.

6. Find the slope of each line graphed at the right.
   a. 0
   b. -2
   c. $\frac{1}{2}$

PROPERTIES Objective E

In 7–9, a. give the slope of the line and b. state in which quadrant(s) the graph exists.

7. $y = -7x$ a. -7 b. II and IV
8. $y = \frac{1}{2}x$ a. $\frac{1}{2}$ b. I and III
9. $y = 0.2x$ a. 0.2 b. I and III

Copyright © Wright Group/McGraw-Hill

155

154 Advanced Algebra

Lesson

2-5 The Graph of $y = kx^2$

Vocabulary

parabola

vertex of a parabola

reflection-symmetric

line of symmetry

▸ **BIG IDEA** The graph of the set of points (x, y) satisfying $y = kx^2$, with k constant, is a parabola with vertex at the origin and containing the point $(1, k)$.

In Lesson 1-4, you studied functions whose values gave the stopping distances of a vehicle at various speeds. Stopping distance includes reaction time, braking distance, and other factors. Braking distance is simply the distance needed to stop a vehicle after applying the brake. Using mathematics you will study in calculus, it can be proved that braking distance varies directly with the square of a vehicle's speed. In Question 16 of Lesson 2-1, you found that the formula $d = \frac{1}{20}s^2$ describes this relation for a typical car. The table and graph below represent this relation.

Speed s (mph)	Braking Distance d (ft)
0	0
10	5
20	20
30	45
40	80
50	125
60	180
70	245

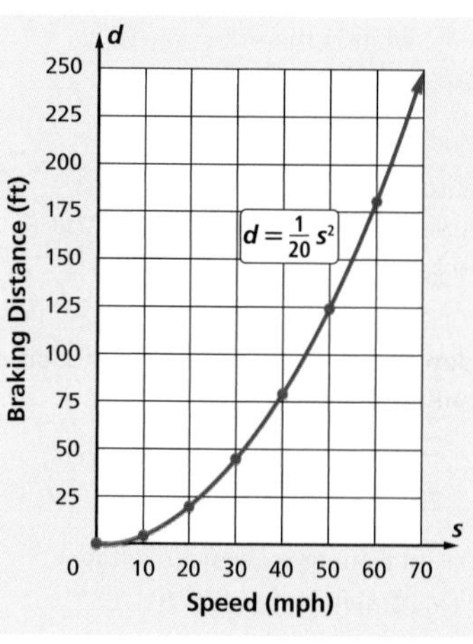

Rates of Change

The points on the graph above do not lie on a straight line. You can verify this by calculating the slopes of the lines through different pairs of points on the graph and seeing that they are not equal.

Mental Math

Suppose that packs of gum cost 39 cents each.

a. What will be your change if you pay for two packs with a \$1 bill? 22 cents

b. What will be your change if you pay for eight packs with a \$5 bill? \$1.88

c. What will be your change if you pay for twenty packs with a \$10 bill? \$2.20

d. Now suppose you want 20 packs and the store is having a buy-three-packs, get-one-free sale. What will be your change if you pay with a \$10 bill? \$4.15

Lesson

2-5

GOAL

Extend the idea of slope as "rate of change" to nonlinear graphs; introduce some of the properties of parabolas.

SPUR Objectives

C Find slopes and rates of change.

E Identify the properties of variation functions.

I Graph variation equations.

J Identify variation equations from graphs.

Materials/Resources

- Lesson Masters 2-5A and 2-5B
- Resource Masters 2, 3, 26, and 27

HOMEWORK

Suggestions for Assignment

- Questions 1–19
- Question 20 (extra credit)
- Reading Lesson 2-6
- Covering the Ideas 2-6

Local Standards

1 Warm-Up

1. A parabola is the graph of the equation $y = kx^2$ and contains the point (4, 6).
   a. What is the value of k? $\frac{3}{8}$
   b. Name at least three other points on this parabola. Answers vary. Sample: (0, 0), $\left(1, \frac{3}{8}\right)$, $\left(-1, \frac{3}{8}\right)$
2. What is an equation for the reflection image of the parabola of Warm-Up Question 1 over the x-axis? $y = -\frac{3}{8}x^2$
3. What is an equation for the reflection image of the parabola of Warm-Up Question 1 over the y-axis? $y = \frac{3}{8}x^2$

Background

This lesson uses the important ideas that constant slope is a characteristic of linear relations, and nonconstant slope is a characteristic of nonlinear relations.

Another key concept is how the graph of $y = kx^2$ is affected by the sign and magnitude of k. Given a value for k, students should be able to quickly sketch the graph of $y = kx^2$. Graphing utilities can provide a quick way for students to check their graphs.

Most of the important properties of parabolas will be studied later in this book. In this lesson, the focus is that students learn how to graph $y = kx^2$ quickly, how to tell whether the graph opens up or down, and how the value of k affects how fast the graph goes up (or down). The Activity is invaluable for that.

Example 1

Find the following rates of change and explain what each means in terms of braking distance.

a. r_1, the rate of change from (20, 20) to (40, 80)

b. r_2, the rate of change from (40, 80) to (60, 180)

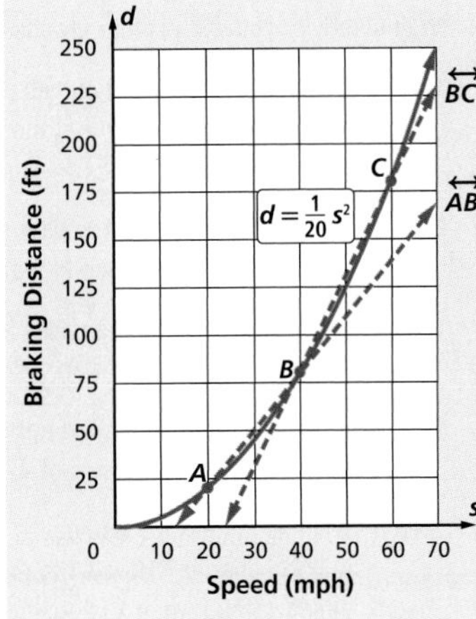

Solution

a. Use the definition of slope.

$$r_1 = \frac{80 \text{ ft} - 20 \text{ ft}}{40 \text{ mph} - 20 \text{ mph}} = \frac{60 \text{ ft}}{20 \text{ mph}} = \frac{3 \text{ ft}}{\text{mph}}$$

This means that, on average, when driving between 20 mph and 40 mph, for every increase of 1 mph in speed, you need 3 more feet to stop your car.

b. Similarly, $r_2 = \frac{180 \text{ ft} - 80 \text{ ft}}{60 \text{ mph} - 40 \text{ mph}} = \frac{100 \text{ ft}}{20 \text{ mph}} = 5 \frac{\text{ft}}{\text{mph}}$.
So on average, between $s = 40$ and $s = 60$, for every change of 1 mph (the horizontal unit), there is a change of 5 feet of braking distance (the vertical unit).

Check Look at the points on the graph. Let $A = (20, 40)$, $B = (40, 80)$, and $C = (60, 180)$. Is $\overleftrightarrow{BC}$ steeper than $\overleftrightarrow{AB}$? Yes, it is.

QY1

▸ QY1

Calculate the average rate of change between $A = (20, 40)$ and $C = (60, 180)$ in Example 1 and explain what it means.

The rate of change between different pairs of points on the graph of $d = \frac{1}{20}s^2$ is not constant. Two conclusions can be drawn:

1. The graph of $d = \frac{1}{20}s^2$ is not a line.
2. A single number does not describe the slope of the whole graph.

Notice that the slope is larger where the graph is steeper, meaning the braking distance increases more and more rapidly as the speed increases.

The equation $d = \frac{1}{20}s^2$ represents a direct-variation function of the form $y = kx^2$. All graphs of equations of this form share some properties. You should be able to sketch graphs of any equation of this form.

2 Teaching

Notes on the Lesson

Example When discussing the graph shown on page 100, point out that the scales on the axes are different, which makes it difficult to estimate the slope from the picture. Use this example to stress to students the importance of considering the scales on the axes *before* making assumptions about slope. Remind them that they should always consider the scales when reading any graph. Be sure students understand that because a parabola is not a line, the rate of change between points on it *does* depend on the particular points chosen for calculating it.

Additional Example

Example Find the following rates of change for the relation $d = \frac{1}{20}s^2$ and describe what each means in terms of braking distance.

a. r_3, the rate of change from (10, 5) to (20, 20) **1.5 ft/mph; on average, when driving between 10 mph and 20 mph, for each increase of 1 mph in speed, you need 1.5 more feet to stop your car.**

b. r_4, the rate of change from (20, 20) to (50, 125) **3.5 ft/mph; on average, between $s = 20$ and $s = 50$, for every change of 1 mph, there is a change of 3.5 ft of braking distance.**

Accommodating the Learner

As students look at the table of (s, d) values on page 100, it may be useful for them to check that all the ordered pairs in the table satisfy the formula $d = \frac{1}{20}s^2$.

Note-Taking Tips

When students calculate the slope for two points on a graph (as they do in the Example and Questions 1, 15b, and 16), encourage them to write the two ordered pairs and label them "used these two ordered pairs." That note can help students explain their work, recall their steps when they review their work, and help identify sources of errors.

Notes on the Lesson

Activity This Activity involves a slider. Point out in Step 4 that the result when $k = 0$ is not a parabola, which is why the text following the Activity has the restriction $k \neq 0$.

In some books the reflection symmetry of figures is defined in terms of coordinates. These parabolas would be said to be reflection-symmetric because when (x, y) is on the graph, so is $(-x, y)$. Notice on page 102 that we do *not* define reflection symmetry algebraically in terms of coordinates. That is because *reflection symmetry is a geometric property of figures from which algebraic formulas for reflection images can be deduced.* All students who have taken previous UCSMP courses have been introduced to reflections and should recall that reflection symmetry is a property of many figures, including rectangles, isosceles triangles, circles, and regular polygons. For students encountering reflections for the first time, connect reflections with folding over the line of symmetry.

Activity

MATERIALS CAS, graphing calculator, or variation graph application

In this Activity, you will explore graphs of the family of curves $y = kx^2$.

Step 1 Consider the family of curves $y = kx^2$. The graph has point $A = (1, k)$ on it. Verify that the coordinates for point A are correct by substituting $x = 1$ into $y = kx^2$. $y = k(1)^2$, so $y = k$.

Step 2 Grab and drag point A to vary the shape of the graph. Since point A has y-coordinate k, the value of k *varies* as you drag A.

Step 3 When $k > 0$, and k increases in value, how does the graph of $y = kx^2$ change? It becomes narrower.

Step 4 When $k = 0$, describe the appearance of the graph $y = kx^2$. What are the coordinates of A? It becomes the x-axis. $A = (1, 0)$.

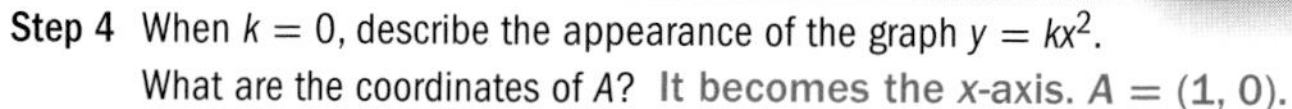

Step 5 When $k < 0$,and k decreases in value, how does the graph of $y = kx^2$ change? How is the graph of $y = kx^2$ different when k is negative from when k is positive? It becomes narrower. When k is negative, the graph is reflected over the x-axis.

The Graph of $y = kx^2$

All of the graphs in the family of curves with the equation $y = kx^2$ with $k \neq 0$ are **parabolas**. No matter what value is chosen for k, the parabola passes through the point (0, 0). This point is the parabola's **vertex**. Further, each parabola in this family coincides with its reflection image over the y-axis. Thus, each parabola is **reflection-symmetric**, and the y-axis is called the **line of symmetry**.

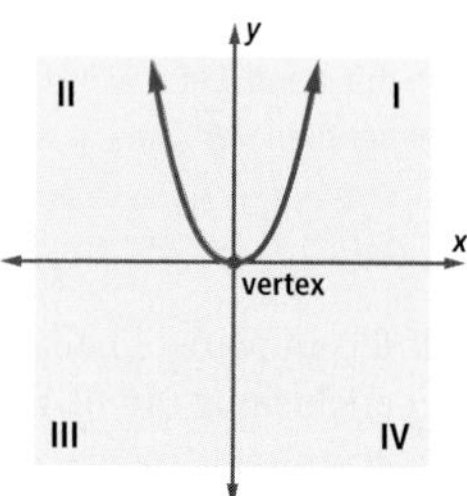

$y = kx^2, k > 0$
parabola opens up
Domain: the set of all reals
Range: the set of nonnegative reals

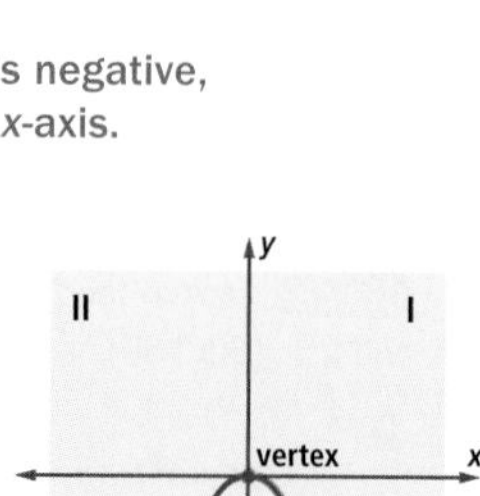

$y = kx^2, k < 0$
parabola opens down
Domain: the set of all reals
Range: the set of nonpositive reals

In general, the domain of the function with equation $y = kx^2$ is the set of all real numbers. As you saw in the Activity, when $k > 0$, the range is the set of nonnegative real numbers, and the graph of the function is a parabola that *opens up*. That is, the vertex of the parabola is its *minimum* point. When $k < 0$, the range is the set of nonpositive real numbers and the corresponding parabola *opens down*. That is, the vertex of the parabola is its *maximum* point.

READING MATH

Parabola (a curve) and *parable* (a story) come from the same Greek word *parabolē* meaning "comparison." The *parabola* is named for a comparison of two distances that are equal.

Accommodating the Learner

Point out to students that another description of slope is "average rate of change." Ask them to identify several Quadrant I points on $y = x^2$, such as (1, 1), (2, 4), (3, 9), and (4, 16), and then compare the slope determined by the first and last pair (1, 1) and (4, 16) to the "average" of the slopes using the consecutive pairs (1, 1) and (2, 4), (2, 4) and (3, 9), and (3, 9) and (4, 16). What conclusions can they draw?

Answers vary. Sample: The average of the slopes using all the integers between 1 and 4 (that is, using (1, 1) and (2, 4), (2, 4) and (3, 9), and (3, 9) and (4, 16)), is $\frac{3+5+7}{3} = 5$, which is the same as the slope for (1, 1) and (4, 16). However, if you use just the pairs (1, 1) and (3, 9) and (3, 9) and (4, 16), the average of the slopes is $\frac{4+7}{2} = 5.5$, which is not the same as the slope for (1, 1) and (4, 16).

 QY2

The equation $y = kx^2$ is not the only equation whose graph is a parabola. You will study other equations leading to parabolas in Chapter 6.

> ▶ **QY2**
> Without using a graphing utility, sketch rough graphs of $y = -2x^2$ and $y = 2x^2$ on the same set of axes.

Questions

COVERING THE IDEAS

In 1 and 2, refer to the formula $d = \frac{1}{20}s^2$ relating speed and braking distance.

1. Find the average rate of change between each pair of points and explain what it means.
   a. (10, 5) and (20, 20)
   b. (50, 125) and (60, 180)
   c. (a, b) and (c, d)
2. Your answers to Questions 1a and 1b should be different numbers. What does that tell you about the graph of $d = \frac{1}{20}s^2$? The graph is not a line.
3. Name the type of curve that results from graphing $y = kx^2$ $(k \neq 0)$. parabola
4. Explain what it means to say that the graph of $y = kx^2$ is symmetric to the y-axis.
5. Suppose $k < 0$. State the domain and range of the function $f: x \rightarrow kx^2$.
6. Refer to the Activity. Describe how the graph of $y = kx^2$ changes in each situation. a. It becomes more and more narrow.
   a. k increases from 1 to 10
   b. k decreases from 1 to 0
7. For what values of k does the graph of $y = kx^2$
   a. open up? $k > 0$
   b. open down? $k < 0$

In 8 and 9, one variable varies directly as another.
a. Name the variables.
b. Name the constant of variation.

8. $S.A. = 4\pi r^2$ (surface area of a sphere) a. $S.A.$, r; b. 4π
9. $A = \frac{s^2}{4}\sqrt{3}$ (area of an equilateral triangle) a. A, s; b. $\frac{\sqrt{3}}{4}$

1a. 1.5; As speed increases from 10 to 20 miles per hour, braking distance increases by 1.5 ft for each mph, on average.

1b. 5.5; As speed increases from 50 to 60 miles per hour, braking distance increases by 5.5 ft for each mph, on average.

1c. $\frac{d-b}{c-a}$; As speed increases from a to c miles per hour, braking distance increases by $\frac{d-b}{c-a}$ ft for each mph, on average.

4. If reflected over the y-axis, it would produce an identical graph.

5. domain: set of all real numbers; range: $\{y | \; y \leq 0\}$

6b. It becomes increasingly wider.

ENGLISH LEARNERS

Vocabulary Development

The discussion and description of parabolas on page 102 provides a natural opportunity to review the terms *domain* and *range* for functions.

3 Assignment

Recommended Assignment

- Questions 1–19
- Question 20 (extra credit)
- Reading Lesson 2-6
- Covering the Ideas 2-6

Notes on the Questions

Question 6 It is common to say that graphs of parabolas get wider or thinner. This is not actually the case, for all parabolas are similar. Some parabolas look wider because we are viewing less of them—that is, they are *bigger* (but not wider) parabolas. In particular, when graphed on the same axes, the parabola $y = \frac{1}{a}x^2$ is a times the size of the parabola $y = x^2$. You can see the similarity of all parabolas by separately graphing two parabolas with equations $y = kx^2$ and $y = mx^2$, $k \neq m$, on different calculators. By zooming in on the vertex of each one, students can see that the curves are congruent to each other.

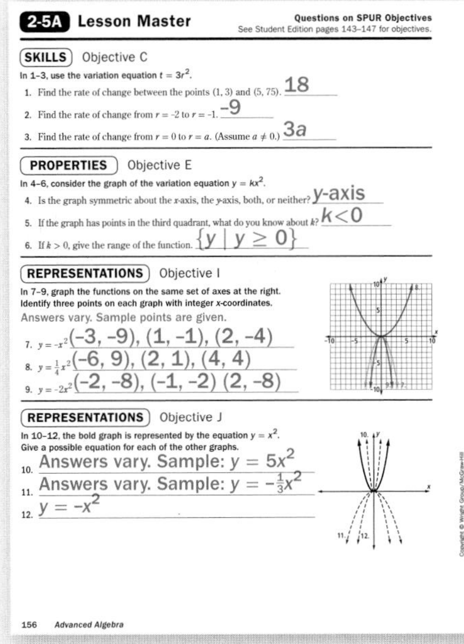

2-5A Lesson Master

Questions on SPUR Objectives
See Student Edition pages 143–147 for objectives.

SKILLS Objective C

In 1–3, use the variation equation $t = 3r^2$.

1. Find the rate of change between the points (1, 3) and (5, 75). 18
2. Find the rate of change from $r = -2$ to $r = -1$. −9
3. Find the rate of change from $r = 0$ to $r = a$. (Assume $a \neq 0$.) $3a$

PROPERTIES Objective E

In 4–6, consider the graph of the variation equation $y = kx^2$.

4. Is the graph symmetric about the x-axis, the y-axis, both, or neither? y-axis
5. If the graph has points in the third quadrant, what do you know about k? $k<0$
6. If $k > 0$, give the range of the function. $\{y \mid y \geq 0\}$

REPRESENTATIONS Objective I

In 7–9, graph the functions on the same set of axes at the right. Identify three points on each graph with integer x-coordinates.
Answers vary. Sample points are given.

7. $y = -x^2$ (−3, −9), (1, −1), (2, −4)
8. $y = \frac{1}{4}x^2$ (−6, 9), (2, 1), (4, 4)
9. $y = -2x^2$ (−2, −8), (−1, −2) (2, −8)

REPRESENTATIONS Objective J

In 10–12, the bold graph is represented by the equation $y = x^2$. Give a possible equation for each of the other graphs.

10. Answers vary. Sample: $y = 5x^2$
11. Answers vary. Sample: $y = -\frac{1}{3}x^2$
12. $y = -x^2$

156 Advanced Algebra

Notes on the Questions

Question 12 You might ask if any student in your class is a photography expert and can describe how exposure affects the quality of a picture.

Additional Answers

12a.

f	E
1.0	0.000167
1.4	0.000233
2.0	0.000333
2.8	0.000467
4.0	0.000667
5.6	0.000933

12c. 

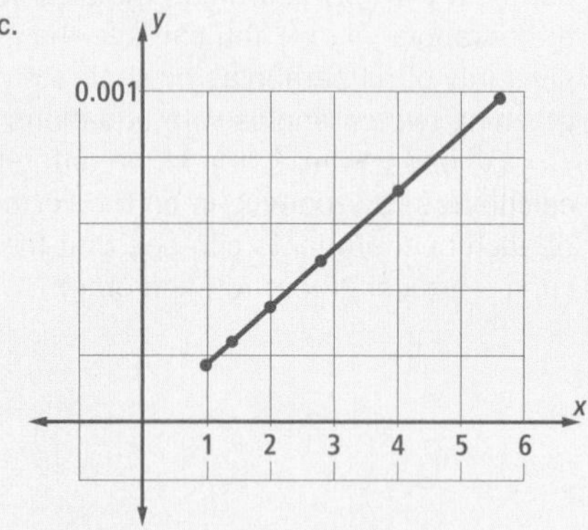

0.0008

12e. By averaging answers. From the table use E when $f = 4$ and $f = 5.6$: $E = \frac{0.002667 + 0.005227}{2} = \frac{0.007894}{2} \approx 0.0039$. By the graph, $E = 0.0038$. By the equation, $E = \frac{1}{6000}(4.8)^2 \approx 0.0038$. If the graph is a line, all the methods are effective. If the graph is a parabola, the averaging method is less accurate than the other two methods.

APPLYING THE MATHEMATICS

10. **Matching** Match each equation with the proper graph. Assume each graph has the same scale.
a. $y = \frac{1}{4}x^2$ iii b. $y = -3x$ i c. $y = -2x^2$ iv 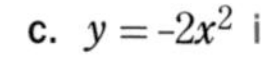 d. $y = 2x^2$ ii

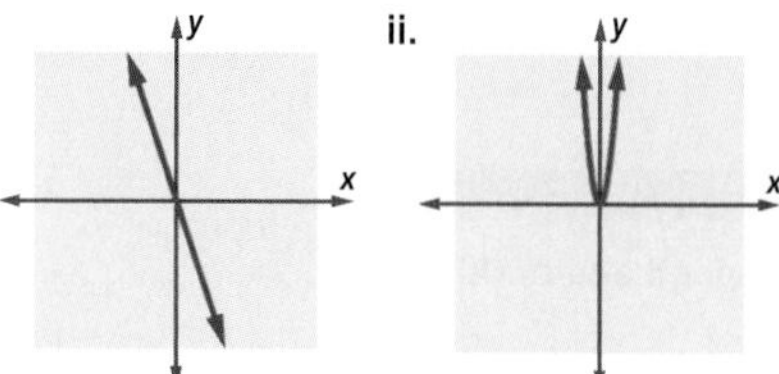

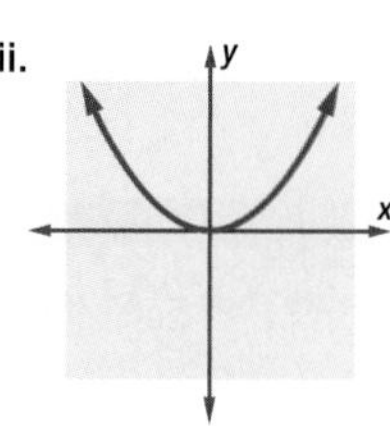

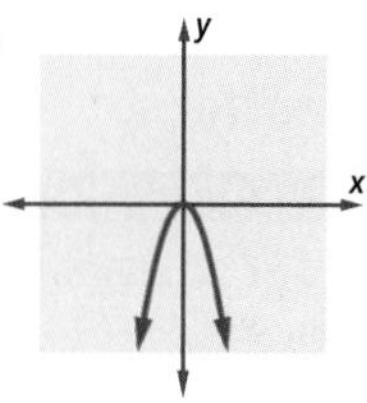

11. a. Explain why the point (0, 0) is on the graph of $y = kx^2$ for all values of k.

11a. Substituting (0, 0) into $y = kx^2$ gives the true statement $0 = 0$ for all values of k.

b. Explain how to use the point $(1, f(1))$ to determine the value of k if $f(x) = kx^2$.

11b. Substitute 1 for x: $f(1) = k(1)^2 = k$, so $k = f(1)$ in this equation.

12. On some cameras, you can control the diameter of the aperture, or the opening through which light passes to the film, by setting an f-stop. You also control the ***exposure***, or the length of time the aperture is open, to ensure that the proper amount of light reaches the film. Let E be the exposure (in seconds) and f be the f-stop of a camera. Suppose you know that E varies directly as either f or f^2, and the constant of variation is $\frac{1}{6000}$.

a. Assume that E varies directly as f, so $E = \frac{1}{6000}f$. Make a table of ordered pairs for this function. For values of f use 1, 1.4, 2, 2.8, 4, and 5.6. See margin.

b. Using a special camera, you set an f-stop of 4.8. Use your table to find two values close to the required exposure. Average the two values to make an estimate of E for $f = 4.8$. 0.0008

c. Graph the ordered pairs from the table on a coordinate grid and connect the points with a smooth curve. Use the graph to estimate the required exposure. See margin.

d. Using the variation equation, determine the actual exposure required for an f-stop of 4.8. How do the three values you found for the exposure compare? $E = \frac{1}{6000}(4.8) = 0.0008$; the three values are equal.

e. Repeat Parts a–d, but this time assume that E varies directly as f^2, so $E = \frac{1}{6000}f^2$. How do the three values you found for the exposure compare? How does the shape of the graph affect the accuracy of these methods for estimating E? See margin.

Extension

As an extension of Question 6, point out that the graph of $y = 1x^2$ contains the point (2, 4). Ask students to find the values of k so that the graph of $y = kx^2$ contains (1, 4), (3, 4), or (4, 4). Students can continue this investigation, identifying a point (a, a^2) on $y = x^2$ and then finding the values of k so that the graph of $y = kx^2$ contains $(1, a^2)$, $(2, a^2)$, $(3, a^2)$, $(4, a^2)$, and so on.

For equations of the form $y = kx^2$, $y = 4x^2$ contains (1, 4); $y = \left(\frac{4}{9}\right)x^2$ contains (3, 4); and $y = \left(\frac{1}{4}\right)x^2$ contains (4, 4); for equations of the form $y = kx^2$, $y = a^2x^2$ contains $(1, a^2)$; $y = \left(\frac{a^2}{4}\right)x^2$ contains $(2, a^2)$; $y = \left(\frac{a^2}{9}\right)x^2$ contains $(3, a^2)$; and $y = \left(\frac{a^2}{16}\right)x^2$ contains $(4, a^2)$.

13. The maximum load a beam can safely support varies directly as its width. A contractor suggests replacing an 8''-wide beam that can hold 6000 pounds with two 4''-wide beams made of the same material as the 8'' beam, one next to the other. Can the two 4'' beams replace a single 8'' beam safely? Justify your answer. See margin.

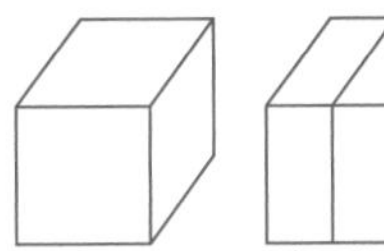

14. Suppose (3, 5) is on the graph of $y = kx^2$. Is this sufficient information to determine k? If so, find k. If not, why not? yes; $k = \frac{5}{9}$

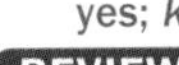

REVIEW

15. Consider the following four equations. **(Lesson 2-4, Previous Course)**

$y = 3x \qquad y = \frac{1}{3}x \qquad y = -\frac{1}{3}x \qquad y = -3x$

a. Graph the equations on one set of axes. See margin.

b. Find the slope of each line. 3; $\frac{1}{3}$; $-\frac{1}{3}$; -3

c. Give the equations of two lines that appear to be perpendicular. $y = \frac{1}{3}x$; $y = -3x$ or $y = -\frac{1}{3}x$; $y = 3x$

16. Find the slope of a submarine dive if the submarine drops 1,200 feet while moving forward 4,000 feet. **(Lesson 2-4)** $-\frac{3}{10}$

17. Consider the sequence t defined by $t_n = 3n^2 - 2n + 2$. **(Lessons 1-2, 1-5, 1-8)**

a. What is the domain of the sequence?

b. Use your CAS to generate a table containing the first forty terms of this sequence. Write down the last five.

18. Onida's annual salary is \$42,000. She gets an increase of 6% at the end of each year. The formula $a_n = 42{,}000(1.06)^n$ gives Onida's salary a_n at the end of the nth year. **(Lesson 1-8)**

a. Find Onida's salary at the end of each year for the first five years.

b. What would Onida's salary be after 20 years with this company?

19. a. Write a letter of the alphabet that has exactly one line of symmetry.

b. Write a letter of the alphabet that has exactly two lines of symmetry. **(Previous Course)**

EXPLORATION

20. The f-stop settings on a camera are related to the diameter of the aperture of the camera. Increasing the f-stop decreases the diameter of the aperture. Research to find out the relationship between these two variables. See margin.

17a. The domain of any sequence is the set of positive numbers.

17b. 3818, 4035, 4258, 4487, 4722

18a. \$44,520; \$47,191; \$50,023; \$53,024; \$56,205

18b. \$134,700

19a. Answers vary. Samples: A, B, C, D, E, K, M, T, U, V, W, Y;

19b. Answers vary. Samples: H, I, O, X

QY ANSWERS

1. 3.5 $\frac{\text{ft}}{\text{mph}}$; when you are driving between 20 mph and 60 mph, on average, for every increase of 1 mph, there is an increase of 3.5 ft in braking distance.

2.

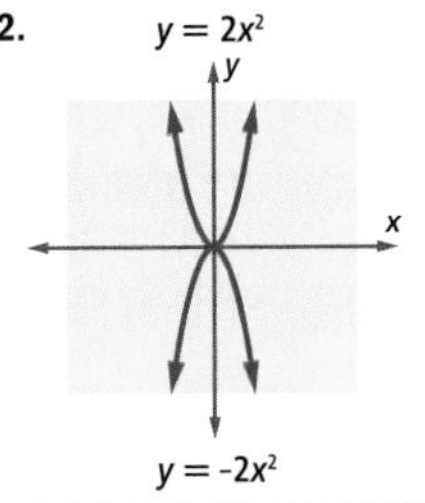

4 Wrap-Up

Ongoing Assessment

Ask students to write equations of the form $y = kx^2$ for two parabolas—one that opens up and one that opens down. Then ask students to find the coordinates of three ordered pairs on each graph. Answers vary. Check students' work.

Additional Answers

20. Answers vary. Sample: The aperture and f-stop are inversely related. The aperture is the size of the lens opening. The f-stops that are set on a camera are a set of fixed focal lengths that determine the size of the aperture diameter. As the f-stop increases, the aperture diameter is reduced. Adjusting the f-stop changes the size of the aperture, with the intention of changing the amount of light that reaches the lens.

Additional Answers

13. Yes; each 4-in. beam will be half as strong as the 8-in. beam because strength is directly proportional to width.

15a.

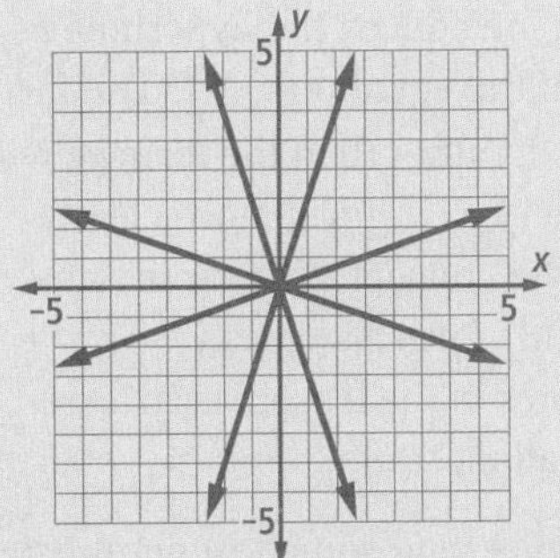

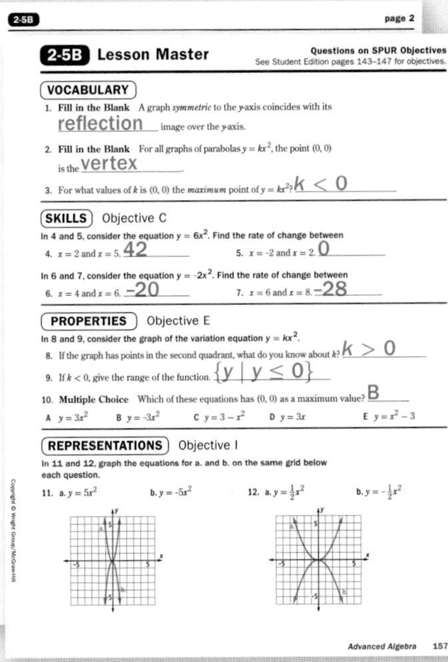

2-5B page 2

2-5B Lesson Master Questions on SPUR Objectives See Student Edition pages 143–147 for objectives.

VOCABULARY

1. Fill in the Blank A graph *symmetric* to the *y*-axis coincides with its reflection image over the *y*-axis.

2. Fill in the Blank For all graphs of parabolas $y = kx^2$, the point (0, 0) is the vertex

3. For what values of k is (0, 0) the *maximum* point of $y = kx^2$? $k < 0$

SKILLS Objective C

In 4 and 5, consider the equation $y = 6x^2$. Find the rate of change between

4. $x = 2$ and $x = 5$. 42 5. $x = -2$ and $x = 2$. 0

In 6 and 7, consider the equation $y = -2x^2$. Find the rate of change between

6. $x = 4$ and $x = 6$. −20 7. $x = 6$ and $x = 8$ −28

PROPERTIES Objective E

In 8 and 9, consider the graph of the variation equation $y = kx^2$.

8. If the graph has points in the second quadrant, what do you know about k? $k > 0$

9. If $k < 0$, give the range of the function. $\{y \mid y \leq 0\}$

10. Multiple Choice Which of these equations has (0, 0) as a maximum value? B

A $y = 3x^2$ B $y = -3x^2$ C $y = 3 - x^2$ D $y = 3x$ E $y = x^2 - 3$

REPRESENTATIONS Objective I

In 11 and 12, graph the equations for a. and b. on the same grid below each question.

11. a. $y = 5x^2$ b. $y = -5x^2$ 12. a. $y = \frac{1}{2}x^2$ b. $y = -\frac{1}{2}x^2$

Advanced Algebra 157

Lesson 2-6

GOAL

Discuss the graphs of inverse linear variation $\left(y = \frac{k}{x}\right)$ and the graphs of inverse-square variation $\left(y = \frac{k}{x^2}\right)$.

SPUR Objectives

E Identify the properties of variation functions.

I Graph variation equations.

J Identify variation equations from graphs.

Materials/Resources

- Lesson Masters 2-6A and 2-6B
- Resource Masters 3 and 28–30
- Quiz 2

HOMEWORK

Suggestions for Assignment

- Questions 1–24
- Question 25 (extra credit)
- Reading Lesson 2-7
- Covering the Ideas 2-7

Local Standards

1 Warm-Up

Chiliad High School has 1000 students. (A *chiliad* is a group of one thousand.) The school is holding a talent show and is inviting the families of all the students. A mailing will go to the families. It is estimated that it would take one person 15 seconds to fold the insert, stuff it into an envelope, and seal the envelope. If s students volunteer to stuff envelopes to get the mailing out, how many minutes t will it take to have all the envelopes ready for mailing? $t = \frac{250}{s}$

Lesson 2-6 The Graph of $y = \frac{k}{x}$ and $y = \frac{k}{x^2}$

Vocabulary

hyperbola
branches of a hyperbola
vertical asymptote
horizontal asymptote
discrete set
inverse-square curve

BIG IDEA The graph of the set of points (x, y) satisfying $y = \frac{k}{x}$, with k constant, is a hyperbola with the x- and y-axes as asymptotes; the graph of the set of points (x, y) satisfying $y = \frac{k}{x^2}$ looks somewhat similiar but is closer to the axes.

In previous lessons you explored the graphs of the equations of the direct-variation functions $y = kx$ and $y = kx^2$. Activity 1 explores the quite different graph of the equation of an inverse-variation function, $y = \frac{k}{x}$.

Mental Math

m∠1 = 72. What is m∠2 if

a. ∠1 and ∠2 are supplementary? 108

b. ∠1 and ∠2 are the two acute angles in a right triangle? 18

c. ∠1 and ∠2 are vertical angles? 72

d. ∠1 and ∠2 form a linear pair? 108

Activity 1

MATERIALS graphing utility

Step 1 Graph the function $y = \frac{10}{x}$ in a standard window. The resulting graph has points only in Quadrants I and III.

Step 2 Trace along the graph starting from a positive value of x and moving to the right. You can trace beyond the window edge if you want. It may also help if you zoom in on the graph for large values of x. Describe what happens to y as x increases in value. y approaches 0.

Step 3 Now trace to the left starting from a negative value of x. Describe what happens to y as x decreases in value. y approaches 0.

Step 4 Does the graph of $y = \frac{10}{x}$ ever intersect the x-axis? If it does, give the coordinates of any point(s) of intersection. If it does not, explain why not. No; the numerator is 10, thus y could never equal 0.

Step 5 Now trace closer and closer to x = 0 from both the positive and negative directions. Does the graph of $y = \frac{10}{x}$ ever intersect the y-axis? If it does, give the coordinates of any point(s) of intersection. If it does not, explain why not.

Step 6 Graph $y = \frac{k}{x}$ for a few nonzero values of k other than 10. Trace along the graphs past the edges of the standard window and near x = 0. Do all the graphs have the same behavior as x gets very far from 0 and very close to 0?

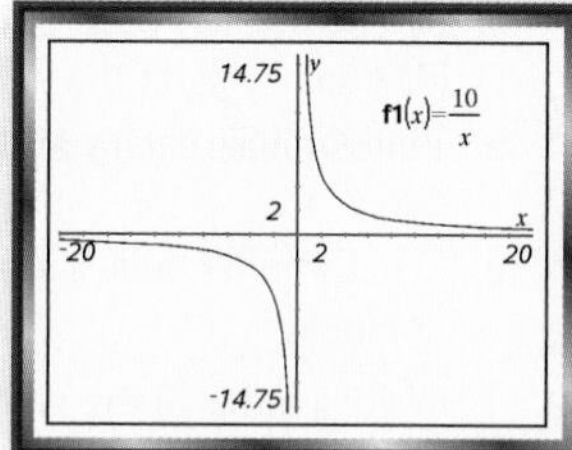

Step 5: No; it is not possible to divide by 0, so 0 is not in the domain of the function.

Step 6: See margin for graph. Yes, the graphs have the same behavior. None of the graphs intersect the x- or y-axis.

Background

This lesson introduces the hyperbola as the graph of the equation $y = \frac{k}{x}$. The form $y = \frac{k}{x}$ is used, rather than the form $xy = k$, because the "y = ..." form more clearly expresses the concept of linear inverse variation. This form also leads naturally, later in the lesson, to inverse-square variation.

Many students (and some teachers) have difficulty graphing $y = \frac{k}{x}$ and $y = \frac{k}{x^2}$ accurately enough so the differences between them are noticeable. A graphing utility can be particularly useful here to demonstrate that the inverse square curve hugs the axes more than the hyperbola does. The differences between the graphs are important because, starting in Lesson 2-7, students are asked to choose between the two equation forms to model a data set.

The Graph of $y = \frac{k}{x}$

The graph of every function with an equation of the form $y = \frac{k}{x}$, where $k \neq 0$, is a **hyperbola**. In Activity 1 you graphed the hyperbola $y = \frac{10}{x}$. All hyperbolas with equation $y = \frac{k}{x}$ share some properties. For example, the functions they represent all have the same domain and range.

▶ READING MATH

Hyperbola (a curve) and *hyperbole* (an exaggeration) come from the same Greek word *hyperbolē* meaning "excess." Like *parabola*, *hyperbola* refers to a comparison of two distances; however, one of these distances is "in excess" of the other.

Example 1

What are the domain and range of the function with equation $y = \frac{k}{x}$?

Solution To find the domain, think: What values can x have? You can substitute any number for x except 0 into the equation $y = \frac{k}{x}$.

So, the domain of the function with equation $y = \frac{k}{x}$ is $\{x | x \neq 0\}$.

To find the range, think: What values can y have? Recall from the Activity that y can be positive or negative, large or small. But if $y = 0$, you would have $0 = \frac{k}{x}$, or $0 \cdot x = k$, which is impossible because, in the formula $y = \frac{k}{x}$ for a hyperbola, k cannot be zero. So, the range of the function with equation $y = \frac{k}{x}$ is $\{y | y \neq 0\}$.

The graphs in the $y = \frac{k}{x}$ family of curves share another property. Each hyperbola in this family consists of two separate parts, called **branches**. When $k > 0$, the branches of $y = \frac{k}{x}$ lie in the first and third quadrants; if $k < 0$, the branches lie in the second and fourth quadrants, as shown below.

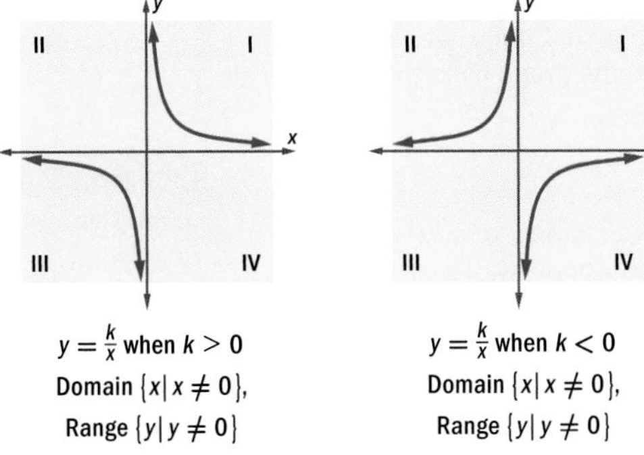

$y = \frac{k}{x}$ when $k > 0$
Domain $\{x | x \neq 0\}$,
Range $\{y | y \neq 0\}$

$y = \frac{k}{x}$ when $k < 0$
Domain $\{x | x \neq 0\}$,
Range $\{y | y \neq 0\}$

Asymptotes

When $x = 0$, $y = \frac{k}{x}$ is undefined, so, the curve does not cross the y-axis. However, when x is *near* 0, the function is defined.

2 Teaching

Notes on the Lesson

This lesson can be taught by going through the two Activities. They parallel each other, and each emphasizes the fact that the axes are asymptotes; that is, the branches of each kind of curve get closer and closer to the axes without ever touching them.

Additional Example

Example 1 If p is a constant, what are the domain and range of a function with equation $y = \frac{p}{x}$?
domain: $\{x | x \neq 0\}$; range: $\{y | y \neq 0\}$

Additional Answers

Activity 1

Step 6:

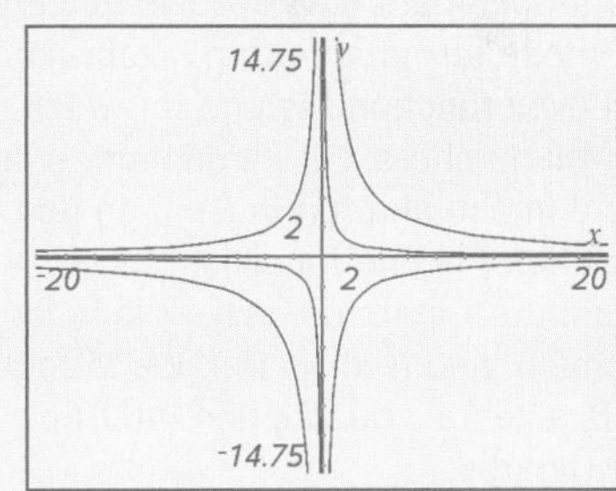

Accommodating the Learner

Before students read about the graph in Activity 1, ask them to complete the table of ordered pairs for the function $y = \frac{10}{x}$ at the right. Then, when they look at the graph in Activity 1, ask them to show where their ordered pairs appear on the graph.

x	y
-10	? -1
-5	? -2
? -2	-5
-1	? -10
? 1	10
? 2	5
5	? 2
10	? 1
20	? 0.5

Notes on the Lesson

You may want to introduce the terminology of *even function* and *odd function* in this lesson. By definition, an *even function* is a function that is reflection-symmetric to the *y*-axis; it gets its name from the fact that the direct variation *power functions* of the form $y = kx^n$, where *n* is an even integer (positive or negative), are reflection-symmetric to the *y*-axis. An *odd function* is a function that is point-symmetric about the point (0, 0); it gets its name from the fact that the direct variation *power functions* of the form $y = kx^n$, where *n* is an odd integer (positive or negative), have this symmetry. Point symmetry can be described as 2-fold rotation symmetry; it describes a figure that is its own image under a rotation of 180° (a half turn). A figure that is point-symmetric looks the same upside down as it does right side up. The definitions of these terms are often algebraic: An even function *f* is one for which, for all numbers *x* in its domain, $-x$ is in its domain, and $f(x) = f(-x)$; an odd function *f* is one for which, for all numbers *x* in its domain, $-x$ is in its domain, and $f(-x) = -f(x)$. We introduce this algebraic description later in the course.

You found in Activity 1 that for $y = \frac{k}{x}$, $k > 0$, as *x* approaches zero from the positive direction, the *y*-value gets larger and larger. Similarly, as *x* approaches zero from the negative direction, the *y*-value gets smaller and smaller (more and more negative). As the values of *x* get closer and closer to a certain value *a*, if the values of the function get larger and larger or smaller and smaller, then the vertical line with equation $x = a$ is called a **vertical asymptote** of the graph of the function. The *y*-axis is a vertical asymptote to the graph of $y = \frac{k}{x}$, for $k \neq 0$.

Similarly, the *x*-axis is a **horizontal asymptote** of the curve $y = \frac{k}{x}$. As *x* gets very, very large (or very, very small), the value of *y* gets closer and closer to zero.

In some situations, only one branch of a hyperbola is relevant. For instance, recall the Condo Care Company example of Lesson 2-2. The time *t* it takes to complete the job and the number of workers *w* are related by the equation $t = \frac{48}{w}$. A table of values for this equation is shown below, along with a graph of the points in the table at the right. Because you cannot have a negative number of workers, there are no points in Quadrant III.

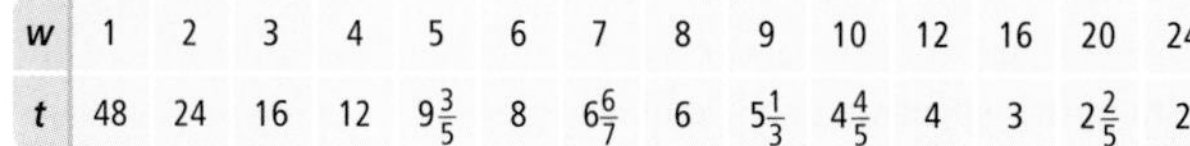

w	1	2	3	4	5	6	7	8	9	10	12	16	20	24
t	48	24	16	12	$9\frac{3}{5}$	8	$6\frac{6}{7}$	6	$5\frac{1}{3}$	$4\frac{4}{5}$	4	3	$2\frac{2}{5}$	2

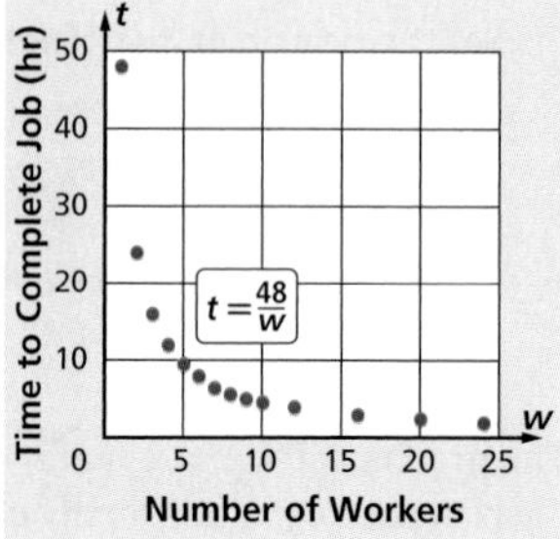

In this example the function has a *discrete* domain, the set of positive integers. A **discrete set** is one in which there is a positive distance greater than some fixed amount between any two elements of the set. Because the number of workers is an integer, it does not make sense to connect the points of this graph. Thus, the graph consists of a set of discrete points on one branch of the hyperbola $y = \frac{48}{x}$.

QY

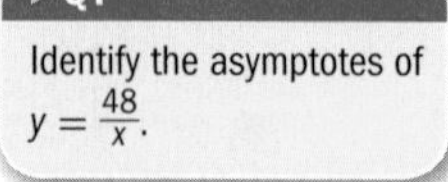

▶ QY

Identify the asymptotes of $y = \frac{48}{x}$.

Activity 2 explores the graphs of a different family of inverse-variation functions, those with equation $y = \frac{k}{x^2}$. We call the graph of such an inverse-variation function an **inverse-square curve**.

Activity 2

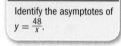

Step 1: It is not possible for the function values to be negative, since the denominator must be positive.

Step 1 Graph the function $y = \frac{10}{x^2}$ in a standard window. The resulting graph appears in Quadrants I and II. Why do you think this graph does not appear in Quadrants III or IV?

Step 2 Trace along the curve to a positive value of *x*. Continue tracing to the right. Describe what happens to *y* as *x* increases. y approaches 0.

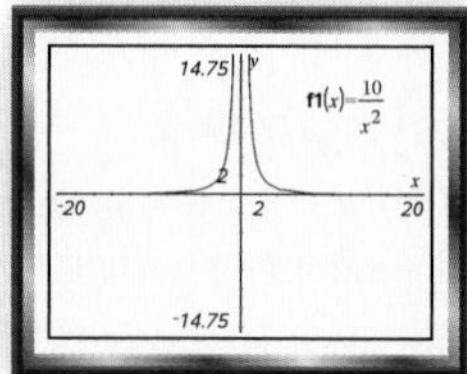

Accommodating the Learner

After students have sketched graphs for the equations $y = \frac{k}{x}$ and $y = \frac{k}{x^2}$ for positive and negative values of *k*, ask them how the graphs of $y = \left|\frac{k}{x^2}\right|$ and $y = -\left|\frac{k}{x^2}\right|$ are similar to the graphs of $y = \frac{k}{x}$ and $y = \frac{k}{x^2}$.

The graphs contain two branches of a hyperbola, like the graphs of $y = \frac{k}{x}$, but the branches appear in Quadrants I and II or in Quadrants III and IV, as do the graphs of $y = \frac{k}{x^2}$.

ENGLISH LEARNERS

Vocabulary Development

It will probably be clear to most students that they will need to learn the main vocabulary terms in this lesson: *hyperbola, branches,* and *asymptote.* Be sure they also pay attention to the definition of *discrete.* You may want students to become familiar with the term *continuous* to help them understand *discrete.*

Step 3 Now trace to a negative value of x. Continue tracing to the left. Describe what happens to y as x decreases. y approaches 0.

Step 4 Does the graph of $y = \frac{10}{x^2}$ ever intersect the x-axis? If it does, give the coordinates of the point(s) of intersection. If it does not, explain why not. No; the numerator is 10, thus y could never equal 0.

Step 5 Does the graph of $y = \frac{10}{x^2}$ ever intersect the y-axis? If it does, give the coordinates of the point(s) of intersection. If it does not, explain why not. No; it is not possible to divide by 0.

Step 6 Trace the graph close to $x = 0$ from both the positive direction and the negative direction. How does the graph behave near $x = 0$? Why does it behave this way?

Step 6: It goes to infinity. The denominator keeps getting smaller, causing the function values to become greater and greater.

The Graph of $y = \frac{k}{x^2}$

Example 2 examines the graph of $y = \frac{k}{x^2}$ for two values of k, one positive value and one negative value.

Example 2

a. Graph $y = \frac{24}{x^2}$ in a window with $\{x | -5 \le x \le 5\}$ and $\{y | -10 \le y \le 10\}$. Sketch the graph on your paper. Then clear the screen and graph $y = -\frac{24}{x^2}$.

b. Describe the symmetry of each graph.

Solution

a. The graphs below were generated using a graphing utility.

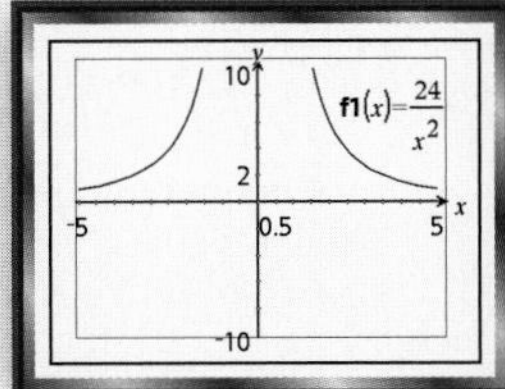

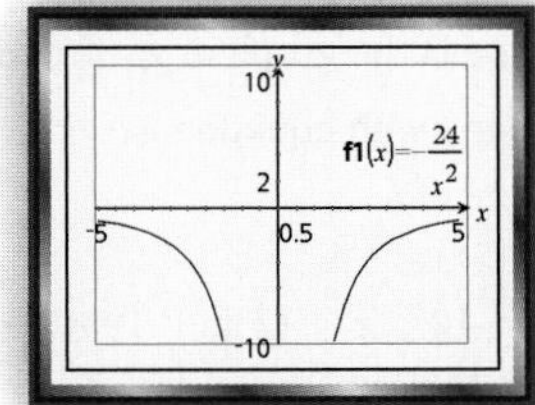

b. If either graph were reflected over the y-axis, the preimage and the image would coincide. So, each graph is symmetric about the y-axis.

Notice that the inverse-square curve, like a hyperbola, has two distinct branches. These two branches, however, do not form a hyperbola because the shape and relative position of the branches differ from a hyperbola. The domain of every inverse square function is $\{x | x \neq 0\}$. The range depends on the value of k. When k is positive, the range is $\{y | y > 0\}$. When k is negative, the range is $\{y | y < 0\}$. Graphs of the two types of inverse-square curves are shown on the next page.

Additional Example

Example 2

a. Graph $y = \frac{36}{x^2}$ in a window with $\{x | -6 \le x \le 6\}$ and $\{y | -10 \le y \le 10\}$. Sketch the graph on your paper. Then clear the screen and graph $y = -\frac{36}{x^2}$ in the same window.

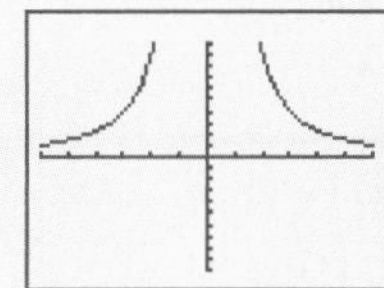

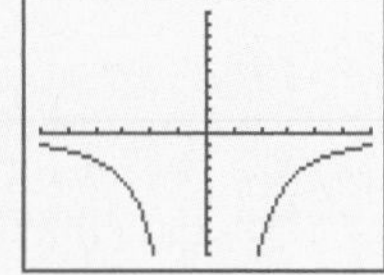

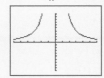

b. Describe the symmetry of each graph. Each graph is symmetric about the y-axis.

Note-Taking Tips

Encourage students to include several examples of hyperbolas in their notes, with annotations identifying the branches and asymptotes of each graph. Students should think about explaining a topic in their notes as being similar to explaining it to another student because organizing information in an explanation is perhaps the best way to learn and remember a topic.

Extension

Have students expand on the idea that the graph of a hyperbola gets closer and closer to an asymptote. Have students work in small groups. Taking turns, one student should write an equation for a hyperbola, such as $y = \frac{25}{x}$, and another student should write a "small" number, such as 0.001. Then all students in the group should find a value of x for which y is less than 0.001. If $x \ge 25{,}000$, then $y \le 0.001$. Students should check each other's work and then repeat the activity for another hyperbola and another small number. (*Note:* A formal definition of "closer and closer," using limits, is just a generalization of this activity.)

3 Assignment

Recommended Assignment

- Questions 1–24
- Question 25 (extra credit)
- Reading Lesson 2-7
- Covering the Ideas 2-7

Additional Answers

5b.

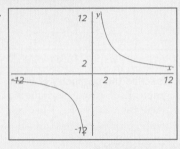

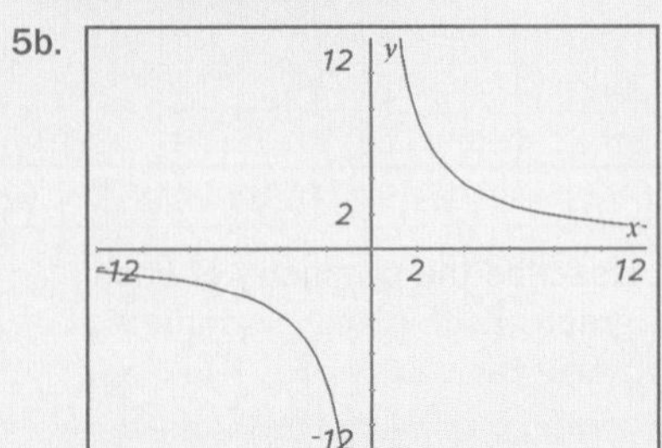

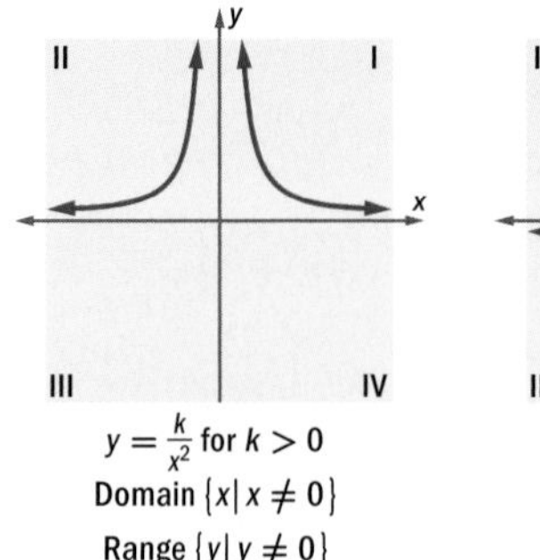

$y = \frac{k}{x^2}$ for $k > 0$
Domain $\{x \mid x \neq 0\}$
Range $\{y \mid y \neq 0\}$

$y = \frac{k}{x^2}$ for $k < 0$
Domain $\{x \mid x \neq 0\}$
Range $\{y \mid y < 0\}$

Notice that the graph of $y = \frac{k}{x^2}$ has the same vertical and horizontal asymptotes as the graph of $y = \frac{k}{x}$.

In general, asymptotes may be vertical, horizontal, or oblique, but not all graphs have asymptotes. For example, the parabola $y = kx^2$ does not have any asymptotes. When a graph has an asymptote, that asymptote is *not* part of the graph.

Questions

COVERING THE IDEAS

1. Why is 0 not in the domain of the functions with equations $y = \frac{k}{x}$ and $y = \frac{k}{x^2}$? It is not possible to divide by 0.
2. For what values of k is the range of the function $y = \frac{k}{x^2}$ the set $\{y \mid y < 0\}$? $k < 0$
3. Suppose $k \neq 0$. What shape is the graph of $y = \frac{k}{x}$? hyperbola

In 4 and 5, consider the function f with equation $f(x) = \frac{15}{x}$.

4. State the domain and range of f.
5. a. Evaluate $f(-10)$ and $f(15)$. $-\frac{3}{2}$; 1
   b. Graph f in the window $-12 \leq x \leq 12$ and $-12 \leq y \leq 12$ and sketch the graph. See margin.
6. Refer to the Condo Care Company situation and the graph of $t = \frac{48}{w}$ in this lesson. Why is the domain discrete?
7. Suppose $k \neq 0$. Is the graph of the equation symmetric to the y-axis?
   a. $y = \frac{k}{x}$ no
   b. $y = \frac{k}{x^2}$ yes
8. In which quadrants are the branches of $y = \frac{k}{x^2}$
   a. if k is positive? I, II
   b. if k is negative? III, IV

4. domain: $\{x \mid x \neq 0\}$; range: $\{y \mid y \neq 0\}$

6. You cannot have a fractional number of workers. (In some applications you could have a half-time or quarter-time worker.)

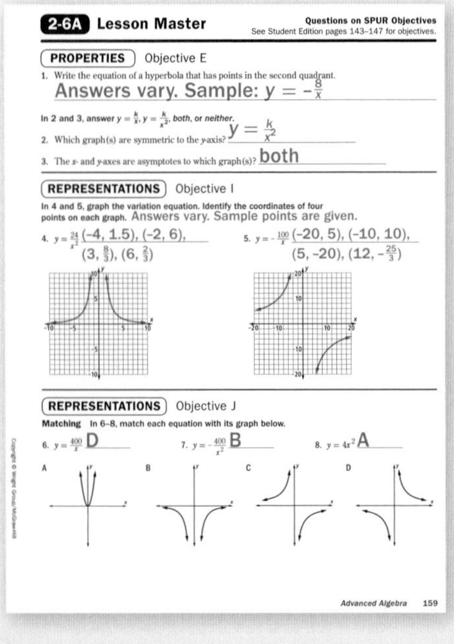
2-6A Lesson Master Questions on SPUR Objectives See Student Edition pages 143–147 for objectives.

PROPERTIES Objective E

1. Write the equation of a hyperbola that has points in the second quadrant. Answers vary. Sample: $y = -\frac{8}{x}$

In 2 and 3, answer $y = \frac{k}{x}$, $y = \frac{k}{x^2}$, both, or neither.

2. Which graph(s) are symmetric to the y-axis? $y = \frac{k}{x^2}$
3. The x- and y-axes are asymptotes to which graph(s)? both

REPRESENTATIONS Objective I

In 4 and 5, graph the variation equation. Identify the coordinates of four points on each graph. Answers vary. Sample points are given.

4. $y = \frac{24}{x^2}$ (-4, 1.5), (-2, 6), (3, $\frac{8}{3}$), (6, $\frac{2}{3}$)
5. $y = -\frac{100}{x}$ (-20, 5), (-10, 10), (5, -20), (12, $-\frac{25}{3}$)

REPRESENTATIONS Objective J

Matching In 6–8, match each equation with its graph below.

6. $y = \frac{400}{x^2}$ D
7. $y = -\frac{400}{x}$ B
8. $y = 4x^2$ A

A B C D

Advanced Algebra 159

Additional Answers

14b. Answers vary. Sample:

Weight	Distance from the Pivot
50	12
60	10
70	8.6
80	7.5
90	6.7
100	6
110	5.5
120	5
130	4.6
140	4.3

14c.

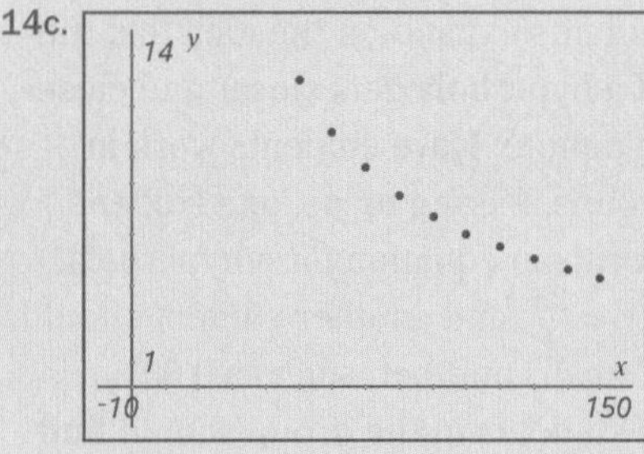

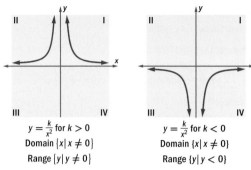

9. What happens to the y-coordinates of the graph of $y = \frac{21}{x}$ when x is positive and is getting closer and closer to 0?

10. Identify the asymptotes of the graph of $y = \frac{4}{x}$. $x = 0$, $y = 0$

9. The y-coordinates get larger and larger.

APPLYING THE MATHEMATICS

11. Match each equation with the proper graph.
    a. 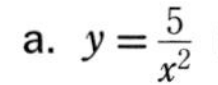 $y = \frac{5}{x^2}$ ii b. 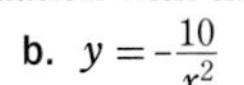 $y = -\frac{10}{x^2}$ iii c. $y = \frac{20}{x}$ i d. $y = -\frac{5}{x}$ iv

i. ii.

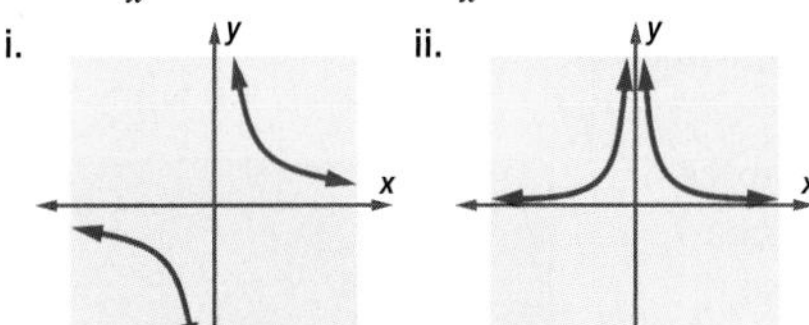

iii.

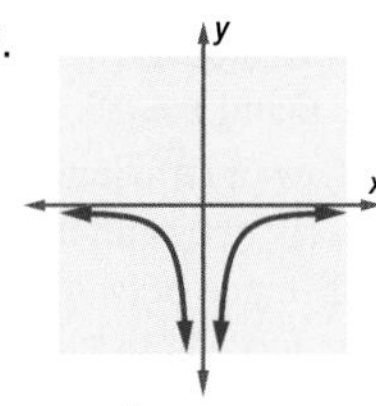

iv.

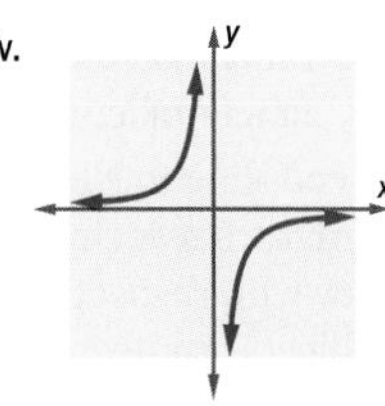

12. Compare and contrast the graphs of $y = -\frac{k}{x^2}$ and $y = \frac{k}{x^2}$ when $k = \frac{1}{10}$. They are reflections of each other over the x-axis.

13. *The Doorbell Rang*, by Pat Hutchins (1986), tells the story of 12 cookies to be divided among an increasing number of people. The story begins with 2 kids who want to share the cookies. Then another kid comes to the door and they must divide the cookies 3 ways, then 4, and so on.
    a. The table at the right shows some values of the function described in the story. Fill in the missing values.
    b. Write an equation for a function that contains the coordinate pairs in the table. Explain the meaning of your variables.
    c. Explain why this function has a discrete domain.

Number of Kids	Number of Cookies Each Kid Gets
1	12
2	6
3	? 4
4	3
5	$\frac{12}{5} = 2.4$
6	? 2
7	$\frac{12}{7} \approx 1.7$
8	? $\frac{12}{8} = 1.5$
9	$\frac{12}{9} \approx 1.3$
10	? $\frac{12}{10} = 1.2$

13b. $y = \frac{12}{x}$, x = number of kids, y = number of cookies each kid gets

13c. There cannot be a fractional number of kids.

14. Quentin is on a seesaw. He weighs 120 pounds and is sitting 5 feet from the pivot. Recall that the Law of the Lever is $d = \frac{k}{w}$, where d is distance from the pivot, w is weight, and k is a constant of variation. a. $k = 600$, $d = \frac{600}{w}$
    a. Find k and write a variation equation for this situation.
    b. Make a table of 10 different weights and their distances from the pivot that would balance Quentin. See margin.
    c. Plot your values from Part b. See margin.
    d. Is the domain for the context discrete? Explain why or why not. No; the weight of a person can take on fractional amounts.

Notes on the Questions

Questions 13, 14, and 16 These questions exhibit the ubiquity and importance of inverse variation relationships.

Question 14 Note that the domain for d is $0 < d < \frac{\ell}{2}$, where ℓ is the length of the seesaw. The plank for a typical seesaw might be between 8 and 16 feet long.

Question 15 In this question, as in all questions to this point, the constant of variation has been an integer. Ask: What kind of variation is described by the functions with equations $h(x) = \frac{1}{36x}$ and $j(x) = \frac{1}{36x^2}$? They are inverse and inverse-square variation, each with a constant of vari ation equal to $\frac{1}{36}$.

Additional Answers

15a.

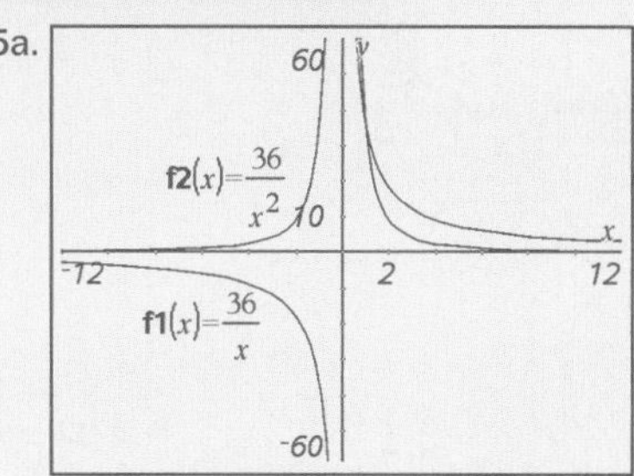

Answers vary. Both graphs have two branches, but the branches of the graph of f are in Quadrants I and III, whereas the branches of the graph of g are in Quadrants I and II.

15b. -6, -7; the average rate of change of g is more negative than the average rate of change of f.

15c. $-\frac{1}{2}$, $-\frac{1}{8}$; the average rate of change of g is less negative than the average rate of change of f.

Notes on the Questions

Question 16 A reasonable answer to Part b is "for all practical purposes."

Additional Answers

18. Neither; the graph of an inverse variation would be a curve (not a line), and the graph of a direct variation would pass through the origin.

15. Consider the functions f and g described by the equations $f(x) = \frac{36}{x}$ and $g(x) = \frac{36}{x^2}$. See margin.
    a. Use a graphing utility to graph both functions on the same axes, with the window $-12 \le x \le 12$ and $-60 \le y \le 60$. Describe some similarities and differences between the graphs.
    b. Find and compare the average rates of change of each function between $x = 1$ and $x = 6$.
    c. Find and compare the average rates of change of each function between $x = 6$ and $x = 12$.

16a. $9.2 \cdot 10^{-9}$ newtons

16b. No; as d goes to infinity, the force gets closer and closer to 0, but never actually becomes 0.

16. According to Newton's Law of Gravitation, the force of gravity between two objects obeys an inverse-square law with respect to the distance between the two objects. For example, the force of gravity between Earth and the Voyager 1 space probe launched in 1977 is approximately $F = \frac{1.56 \cdot 10^{12}}{d^2}$, where d is the distance between Earth and Voyager 1 in kilometers, and F is the force in newtons.
    a. In the summer of 2002, Voyager 1 was approximately $1.3 \cdot 10^{10}$ km from Earth. What was the force of gravity between Voyager 1 and Earth at that time?
    b. Will Voyager 1 ever completely escape Earth's gravity? Explain your answer.

The space probe Voyager 1

REVIEW

17. In the graph at the right, parabolas P_1 and P_2 are reflection images of each other over the x-axis. If parabola P_1 has equation $y = 3x^2$, what is an equation for parabola P_2? (Lesson 2-5) $y = -3x^2$

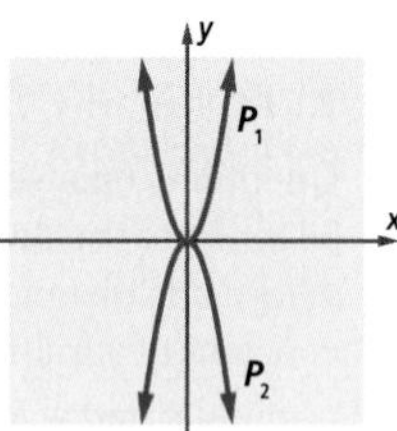

18. Does the line m graphed below at the right illustrate an example of direct variation, inverse variation, or neither? Justify your answer. (Lesson 2-4) See margin.

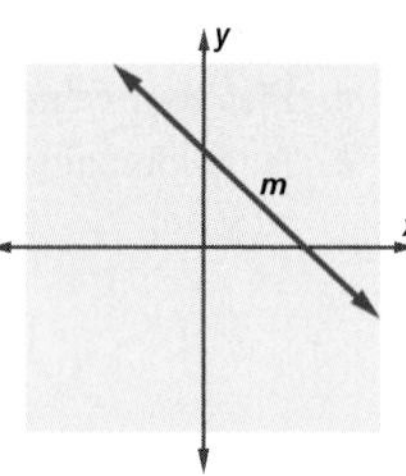

19. Dominique, a scuba diver 99 feet below the water's surface, inflates a balloon until it has a diameter of 6 inches. The air in the balloon expands as Dominique ascends. When Dominique reaches the surface, the balloon has a diameter of 9.5 inches. (Lesson 2-3)
    a. Write the ratio of the radius of the balloon at the surface to the radius 99 feet below the surface. $\frac{4.75}{3} \approx 1.58$
    b. The volume of the balloon at the surface is how many times the volume of the balloon at 99 feet? $1.58^3 \approx 3.94$
    c. Explain how your answer to Part a can be used to answer Part b. According to the Fundamental Theorem of Variation, the answer to Part b is the cube of the answer to Part a.

Multiple Choice In 20 and 21, which could be a formula for the *n*th term of the sequence? **(Lesson 1-8)**

20. 2, 4, 8, 16, 32, ... C
 A $t_n = 2n$ B $t_n = n^2$ C $t_n = 2^n$

21. 2, 9, 28, 65, 126, ... C
 A $t_n = 7n - 5$ B $t_n = 7n^2 - 2$ C $t_n = n^3 + 1$

22. Solve for x: $y = -\frac{1}{\pi}x$. **(Lesson 1-7)** $x = -\pi y$

23. Bob decided to bake a frozen pizza for dinner. It took 10 minutes to preheat the oven to 425° from room temperature of 75°. The pizza baked for 17 minutes, and then it took another 30 minutes for the oven to return to room temperature after Bob turned it off. **(Lessons 1-4, 1-2)**
 a. Identify the independent and dependent variables in this situation.
 b. Sketch a graph of the situation. Label the axes and explain the meaning of your variables. See margin.
 c. Identify the domain and range of the function mapping time onto the temperature of the oven. domain: 0 to 57; range: 75° to 425°

23a. independent variable: time; dependent variable: temperature

24. **Multiple Choice** The relationship between $\triangle ABC$ and $\triangle PRQ$, as shown below, is best described by which of the following? **(Previous Course)** B

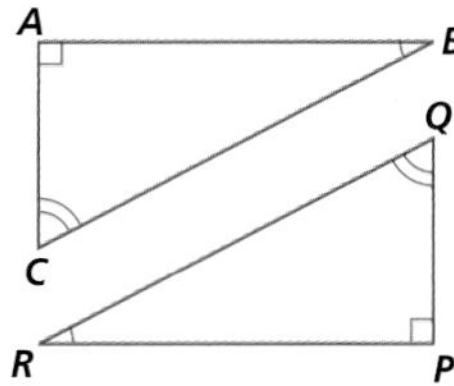

 A congruent
 B similar
 C both congruent and similar
 D neither congruent nor similar

EXPLORATION

25. Use a graphing utility to graph $y = \frac{10}{x^3}$, $y = \frac{10}{x^4}$, and $y = \frac{10}{x^5}$. What pattern do you notice? What generalization can you make about the value of n and the graph of $y = \frac{10}{x^n}$? Is the same generalization true for every function with equation $y = \frac{k}{x^n}$, $k \neq 0$? See margin.

QY ANSWERS

x-axis and y-axis

4 Wrap-Up

Ongoing Assessment

Ask students to describe the graphs of $y = \frac{-1}{x}$ and $y = \frac{1}{x^2}$, telling the number of branches for each, which quadrants the graphs are in, and the asymptotes (if any). The graph of $y = \frac{-1}{x}$ has two branches: It is in Quadrants II and IV and has the axes as asymptotes. The graph of $y = \frac{1}{x^2}$ has two branches: It is in Quadrants I and II and has the x-axis and the positive y-axis as asymptotes.

Administer Quiz 2 (or a quiz of your own) after students complete this lesson.

Project Update

Project 2, *Variation and Light,* on page 136 and Project 4, *Exploring a Connection between $y = \frac{1}{x}$ and the Altitudes of a Triangle,* on page 137 relate to the content of this lesson.

Additional Answers

23b.

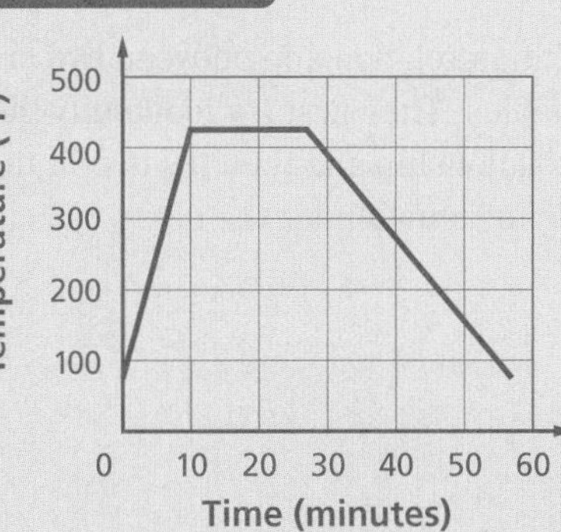

25. Answers vary. Sample:

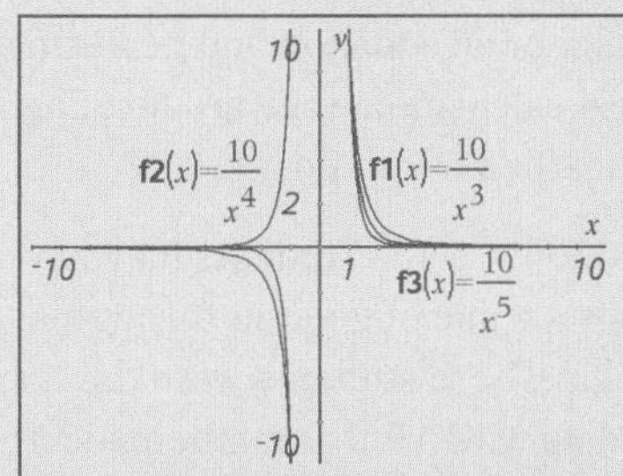

If n is even, the graph will be its own reflection across the y-axis; whereas if n is odd, it will not. Yes, this generalization is true for every function with equation $y = \frac{k}{x^n}$.

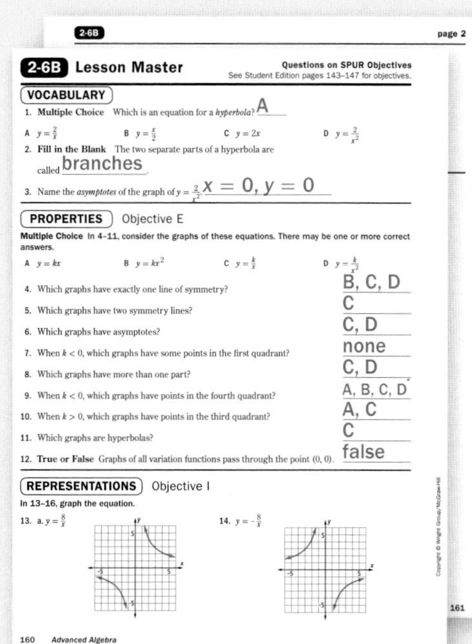

2-6B page 2

2-6B Lesson Master

Questions on SPUR Objectives
See Student Edition pages 143–147 for objectives.

VOCABULARY

1. **Multiple Choice** Which is an equation for a *hyperbola*? A
 A $y = \frac{2}{x}$ B $y = \frac{x}{2}$ C $y = 2x$ D $y = \frac{2}{x^2}$
2. **Fill in the Blank** The two separate parts of a hyperbola are called branches.
3. Name the *asymptotes* of the graph of $y = \frac{2}{x^2}$. $x = 0, y = 0$

PROPERTIES Objective E

Multiple Choice In 4–11, consider the graphs of these equations. There may be one or more correct answers.

A $y = kx$ B $y = kx^2$ C $y = \frac{k}{x}$ D $y = \frac{k}{x^2}$

4. Which graphs have exactly one line of symmetry? B, C, D
5. Which graphs have two symmetry lines? C
6. Which graphs have asymptotes? C, D
7. When $k < 0$, which graphs have some points in the first quadrant? none
8. Which graphs have more than one part? C, D
9. When $k < 0$, which graphs have points in the fourth quadrant? A, B, C, D
10. When $k > 0$, which graphs have points in the third quadrant? A, C
11. Which graphs are hyperbolas? C
12. **True or False** Graphs of all variation functions pass through the point (0, 0). false

REPRESENTATIONS Objective I

In 13–16, graph the equation.

13. a. $y = \frac{8}{x}$ 14. $y = -\frac{8}{x}$

Copyright © Wright Group/McGraw-Hill

160 *Advanced Algebra* 161

Lesson 2-7

GOAL

Find equations that describe data for direct or inverse variation; explore the idea that one place of origin for many math formulas is induction from actual data.

SPUR Objectives

H Fit an appropriate model to data.

Materials/Resources

- Lesson Masters 2-7A and 2-7B
- Resource Masters 31 and 32

HOMEWORK

Suggestions for Assignment

- Questions 1–22
- Question 23 (extra credit)
- Reading Lesson 2-8
- Covering the Ideas 2-8

Local Standards

1 Warm-Up

Caroline North measured how far a marble rolled down a ramp in 1 through 5 seconds. She obtained the following data:

Time (seconds)	Distance (inches)
1	0.3
2	1.2
3	2.6
4	4.9
5	7.6

Find an equation of variation relating time t and distance D. A graph suggests $D = kt^2$. Calculation from the first two points gives $k \approx 0.3$ in./sec^2. This checks very well with the other data points. So $D \approx 0.3t^2$.

Lesson 2-7 Fitting a Model to Data I

BIG IDEA If you determine from a particular set of data that y varies directly or inversely as x, you can graph the data to see what relationship is reasonable. Using that relationship, you can then substitute a known pair of values of x and y to obtain the constant k of variation, and compare what the variation equation predicts to the original data.

Mental Math

Emily is making a salad. The recipe calls for $5\frac{1}{2}$ cups of chopped lettuce. One head of lettuce yields about 3 cups of chopped lettuce.

a. How many heads of lettuce are needed for one recipe? 2

b. How many heads of lettuce does she need to double the recipe? 4

c. Heads of lettuce cost $2.53 each. How much will Emily spend on lettuce? $10.12

d. Emily can also buy 2-cup packages of chopped lettuce for $1.75 each. Would this be a better buy? no

Recall from Chapter 1 that a mathematical model for a real situation is a description of that situation using the language and concepts of mathematics. Models can be created from collected data or from mathematical properties. Using data to create a mathematical model that describes those data is called *fitting a model to data*.

A Model of Direct Variation

In 1638, the Italian scientist Galileo Galilei (1564–1642) published *Dialogues Concerning Two New Sciences*, in which he first proposed the Law of Free-Falling Objects. This law states that near the surface of Earth, all heavier-than-air objects dropped from the same height fall to Earth in the same amount of time, assuming no resistance on the objects. (Aristotle, 1900 years earlier, wrote that heavier objects fall faster, and people believed Aristotle.) Equipment for timing free-falling bodies with sufficient precision did not exist, so Galileo tested his theory and developed a model by rolling objects down an inclined plane.

Today, scientists have more precise measuring techniques. For example, scientists can use slow-motion film to determine the distance an object in free fall travels over different periods of time. The table below gives the distance d in meters that a ball travels in t seconds after it is dropped from the top of a cliff. The ordered pairs in the table are graphed at the right.

Time in Air t (sec)	1	1.5	2	2.5	3
Distance Fallen d (m)	4.9	11.0	19.6	30.6	44.1

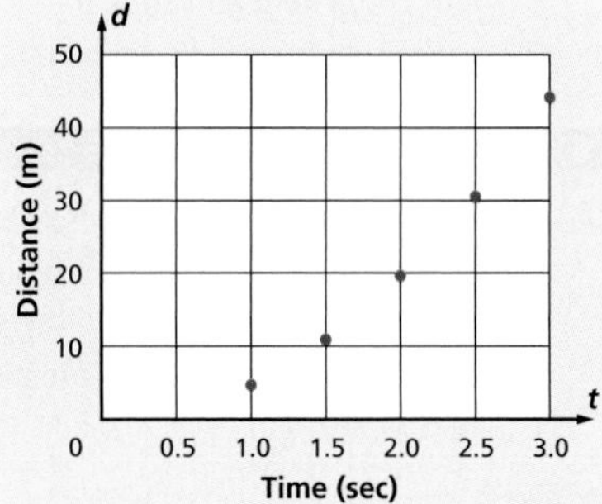

Background

Each time students translate a real situation into an algebraic equation and perform a numerical calculation, they are forming and using a mathematical model.

In past studies, some students may have tried to find a line of good fit through a scatterplot. These students were describing a set of data with a linear mathematical model. The mathematical models presented in this lesson are of a similar kind. Instead of looking specifically for a linear relationship, students learn to look for a variation relationship between two or more variables. They first try to identify the kind of relationship and then try to find the specific equation for the data.

Because the distance the ball travels depends on the elapsed time, distance is the dependent variable and is placed on the vertical axis. How is the distance traveled related to time? Notice that distance increases as more time elapses; this implies direct variation. However, the points do not all lie on a straight line. The points suggest a direct-variation model of the form $y = kx^2$.

GUIDED

Example 1

Find a variation equation to describe the free-falling object data on the previous page.

Solution The shape of the graph suggests the formula $d = kt^2$. Substitute one of the ordered pairs into this formula to find k. The easiest pair to use is (1, 4.9).

_?_ = k _?_ ^{2} 4.9; 1

k = _?_ $\frac{m}{sec^2}$ 4.9

So, a variation equation describing the situation is d = _?_ t^2. 4.9

Check See how close the values predicted by the equation are to the values observed.

Time in Air t (sec)	1	1.5	2	2.5	3
Observed Distance Fallen d (m)	4.9	11.0	19.6	30.6	44.1
Predicted Distance Fallen d (m)	? 4.9	? 11.0	? 19.6	? 30.6	? 44.1

QY1

After fitting a model to a set of data, you can use the model to predict other data points that were not in the original set. The model $d = 4.9t^2$ predicts that the distance traveled in 6.5 seconds would be

$$d = (4.9)(6.5)^2 = 207.025.$$

That is, the distance would be about 207 meters.

QY2

▸ QY1

If $k = 4.9$ m/sec^2 and $d = kt^2$, why is the unit for d meters?

▸ QY2

According to the model, approximately how far will an object fall in 8.25 seconds?

A Model of Inverse Variation

Anna Lyzer and her sister Jenna went to a playground to investigate the validity of the Law of the Lever. Anna sat at a fixed point on one side of the seesaw while nine of her friends took turns sitting on the other side. When the seesaw was in balance, Jenna measured each person's distance d from the pivot and recorded their weight w. The results are shown on the next page.

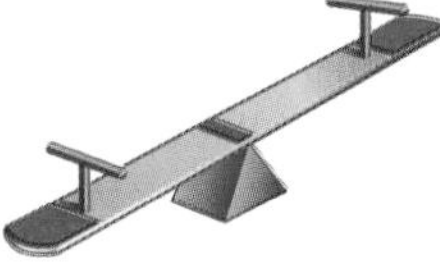

Notes on the Lesson

You may wish to guide students through this lesson page by page. The lesson begins with a famous historical example of mathematical modeling. Many people view Galileo's experiments as the beginning of the scientific method, whereby actual measurement displaced unmeasured theory as the barometer of validity for scientific principles. Example 1 uses data to construct a table of values for a direct-variation function. Pages 116 and 117 are devoted to one set of measurements using the Law of the Lever, using data like those students might collect. The Activity and Example 2 show students how to distinguish between inverse and inverse-square variation by testing the models.

An alternate approach to this lesson is to have students collect their own data, perhaps using a computer-based laboratory (CBL). The Projects at the end of the chapter also offer several opportunities for data collection.

Additional Example

Example 1 Find a variation equation to describe these data:

x	y
1	3.2
1.5	2.25
2	12.8
2.5	20
3	28.8

Solution A graph of the data will suggest the formula $y = kx^2$. Substitute one of the ordered pairs into the formula to find k. The easiest pair to use is (1, 3.2).

_?_ = k(_?_)^2 3.2; 1

k = _?_ 3.2

So, a variation equation describing the data is y = _?_ x^2. 3.2

2 Teaching

Notes on the Lesson

Show the class graphs of variation functions and ask for possible equations. For instance, here are some graphs you can show on the chalkboard or an overhead projector.

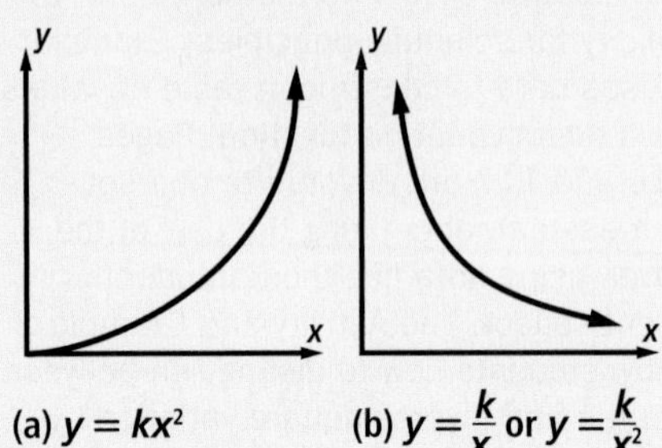

(a) $y = kx^2$ (b) $y = \frac{k}{x}$ or $y = \frac{k}{x^2}$

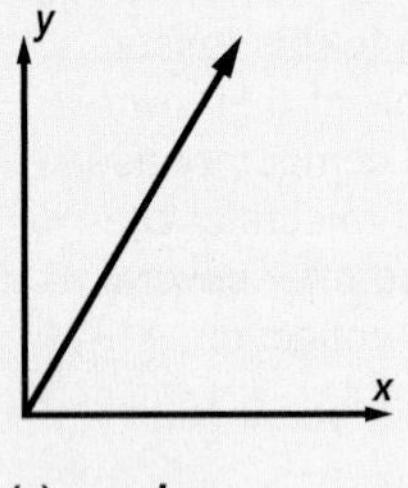

(c) $y = kx$

When talking about each mathematical model in the text, discuss which variable is independent and which is dependent. In some situations the choices are obvious; for example, the length of time it takes to drive a certain distance without stopping depends on the speed of the car, so speed is the independent variable, and time is the dependent variable. However, when a scientist measures skid marks to determine how fast a car was going, then skid distance becomes the independent variable and speed the dependent variable.

In other cases, the choice may be completely arbitrary. In the equation $ab = 12$, unless there is some distinction made between the variables, it is just as reasonable to refer to b as the dependent variable as to refer to it as the independent variable. However, it is commonly accepted in mathematics that, in a graph, the variable shown on the horizontal axis is considered to be the independent variable, and the variable shown on the vertical axis is considered to be the dependent variable.

The shape of the graph shows that distance decreased as weight increased and suggests an inverse variation. You have seen graphs like this from two possible models: $d = \frac{k}{w^2}$ and $d = \frac{k}{w}$. The Law of the Lever says that $d = \frac{k}{w}$ is the more appropriate model, but how can the data tell us that? This Activity shows one way.

w (lb)	d (yd)
70	1.7
80	1.5
85	1.4
100	1.2
109	1.1
133	0.9
140	0.9
170	0.7
206	0.6

Distance (yd) vs. Weight (lb)

Step 2: No; only $w = 85$ lb has the same value, but the other points do not fit very well.

Step 4: The values are not exactly the same, but they are closer than the first equation.

Step 5: Yes; the values that the second equation gives are much closer to the experimental results.

Activity

Step 1 First test $d = \frac{k}{w^2}$. To find k, select the point $(w, d) = (85, 1.4)$. Use the k-value you find to write an equation to model the situation. $k = 10{,}115$; $d = \frac{10{,}115}{w^2}$

Step 2 Use a spreadsheet. Enter the weights from the table above in the first column. Enter your variation equation from Step 1 at the top of the second column to generate a table of values. Compare the generated table to the values that Anna and Jenna observed. Do the values of d predicted by your model fit the observed data?

	A w	B d1	C	D	E
•		=10115/w^2			
1	70.	2.06429			
2	80.	1.58047			
3	85.	1.4			
4	100.	1.0115			
5	109.	.851359			
6	133.	.571824			

A1 70

Step 3 Now test $d = \frac{k}{w}$. Use the same point $(w, d) = (85, 1.4)$ that you used in Step 1. Find k and write an equation to model this situation. $k = 119$; $d = \frac{119}{w}$

Step 4 Enter your variation equation from Step 3 at the top of the third column to generate a table of values. Compare the values predicted by this equation to the observed values that Anna and Jenna found.

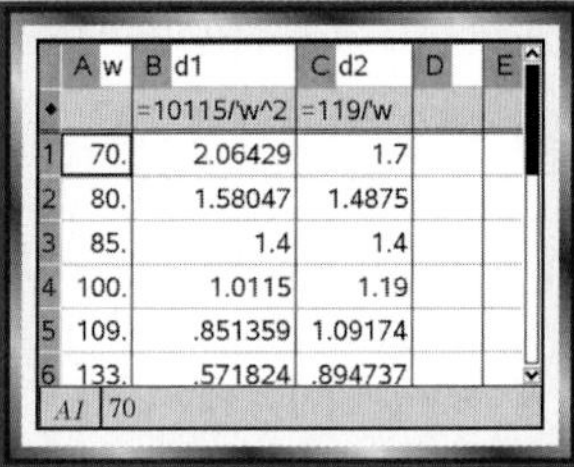

	A w	B d1	C d2	D	E
•		=10115/w^2	=119/w		
1	70.	2.06429	1.7		
2	80.	1.58047	1.4875		
3	85.	1.4	1.4		
4	100.	1.0115	1.19		
5	109.	.851359	1.09174		
6	133.	.571824	.894737		

A1 70

Step 5 Do your findings confirm that $d = \frac{k}{w}$ is the better model? Why or why not?

Another way to approach this problem is to use the Fundamental Theorem of Variation.

Accommodating the Learner

As preparation for this lesson, ask students to find the values of y_1, y_2, and y_3 for each x value in this table, graph each set of points, and draw a smooth line or curve through them.

x	$y_1 = 2x$	$y_2 = \frac{2}{x}$	$y_3 = \frac{2}{x^2}$
0.5	? 1	? 4	? 8
1	? 2	? 2	? 2
2	? 4	? 1	? 0.5
3	? 6	? 0.67	? 0.22

Discuss with students how the shape of each graph is related to the form of the equation that models and/or generates the data. The graph of $y_1 = 2x$ is a line through the origin with slope 2; the graph of $y_2 = \frac{2}{x}$ is a branch of a hyperbola; the graph of $y_3 = \frac{2}{x^2}$ is a branch of an inverse-square variation.

Example 2

a. Use the Fundamental Theorem of Variation to determine an appropriate model that relates the weights and distances in Jenna's table of experimental values.

b. Predict the distance in yards that a person weighing 90 pounds must be from the pivot in order to balance Anna's weight.

Solution

a. When d varies inversely with the square of w, then if w is doubled, d is divided by 4. Find a pair of ordered pairs (w_1, d_1) and (w_2, d_2) where the ratio $\frac{w_2}{w_1}$ equals 2. One such pair of points is (85, 1.4) and (170, 0.7). Since $0.7 \neq \frac{1.4}{4}$, as the w-coordinate doubles, the d-coordinate is not divided by 4. Therefore, d does not vary inversely with the square of w. However, as the w-coordinate doubles, the d-coordinate is halved $(0.7 = \frac{1.4}{2})$. Therefore, the more appropriate model for these data is $d = \frac{k}{w}$. To find k, solve the formula for k and substitute an ordered pair into the equation.

$d = \frac{k}{w}$

$k = wd$ Multiply both sides by w.

$k = (85)(1.4) = 119$ Substitute the values of one ordered pair.

Using these two points, the data are modeled by

$d = \frac{119}{w}$.

b. If a person weighs 90 pounds, then $w = 90$. Using this model, $d = \frac{119}{90} \approx 1.32$ yards.

So, sitting about 4 feet from the pivot will balance Anna.

 QY3

> **QY3**
> If Hector weighs 160 pounds, how far from the pivot should he sit to balance Anna? Is this distance approximately half of the distance from the pivot that the person who weighed 80 pounds sat?

Questions

COVERING THE IDEAS

In 1–4, refer to the data about a free-falling object.

1. Describe in words the variation relationship between distance and time.
2. Use the model $d = 4.9t^2$ to predict the distance that a free-falling ball will fall in 4.5 seconds. 99.2 m
3. If a ball is dropped from a height of 500 meters, how many seconds will it take to reach the ground? (Ignore the effects of air resistance.) about 10.1 sec

Sky divers are not free-falling due to wind resistence.

1. After it is dropped from the top of a cliff, the distance d a ball has fallen varies directly as the square of the time t.

Additional Example

Example 2

a. Use the Fundamental Theorem of Variation to determine an appropriate model that relates x and y in this table.

x	y
60	2.5
65	2.31
72	2.08
75	2
83	1.81
91	1.65
99	1.52
107	1.4

$y = \frac{150}{x}$

b. Predict the value of x for $y = 100$. $x = 1.5$

Note-Taking Tips

Encourage students to describe in their notes the 5-step process (in the Activity) to test and confirm that a particular equation is a model for data. Students can use that process to confirm (or eliminate) an equation as a model for any data.

3 Assignment

Recommended Assignment

- Questions 1–22
- Question 23 (extra credit)
- Reading Lesson 2-8
- Covering the Ideas 2-8

Notes on the Questions

We suggest that all questions be discussed in order.

ENGLISH LEARNERS

Vocabulary Development

This lesson provides a natural opportunity to review the two senses of model: as a noun, *a model* is an equation that can generate a data set; as a verb, *to model* a data set is to find (and confirm) an equation that can generate a data set.

Accommodating the Learner

Have students work in pairs or small groups. Taking turns, one student should think of an equation of the form $y = \frac{k}{x}$ or $y = \frac{k}{x^2}$ and generate a set of 5 to 10 same-quadrant ordered pairs for the equation. Then other students in the group should use the data to identify and confirm an equation to model the data. After checking the model, the group should repeat the activity, with another student thinking of an equation and generating data.

Notes on the Questions

Questions 9–12 These are the most important questions in the set, for they ask students to identify a model to fit given data. Students are expected to be able to choose models from data in Lessons 2-8 and 2-9.

Additional Answers

5. Answers vary. Sample: Jenna's data show that when $w = 80$, $d = 1.5$, but the model gives $d = 1.58$.
7. 5.95 yd; no, this is too long for a seesaw to be safe
10b. The two variables are directly related because y increases as x increases, so (iii) and (iv) are not correct. The average rate of change between the points is not constant, so (i) is ruled out, leaving (ii).
10c. $L \approx 200$; for $s = 30$, $L \approx 50$. By the Fundamental Theorem of Variation, for $s = 60$, which is twice the first value, L will be $2^2 = 4$ times as large, or $4(50) = 200$.

2-7A Lesson Master — Questions on SPUR Objectives. See Student Edition pages 143–147 for objectives.

USES Objective H

1. A baseball coach uses a machine to send fly balls to outfielders. The speed of the balls leaving the machine and the distance the balls travel is given in the table below.

Speed (ft/sec)	40	50	60	70	80	90	100
Distance (ft)	49	77	111	151	197	249	308

a. Graph the data using an appropriate scale on the axes at the right.

b. Which equation seems to model the data best: $y = kx$, $y = kx^2$, $y = \frac{k}{x}$, or $y = \frac{k}{x^2}$? $y = kx^2$

c. Find the constant of variation for your model. $k \approx 0.031$

d. According to your model, how far will a ball travel if it leaves the machine at 75 ft/sec? ≈ 174 ft

2. For six days, Sarah recorded the time it took her to bike to school and her average speed. Her data are shown in the table below.

Speed (mi/hr)	6	8	10	12	14	16
Time (min)	20	15	12	10	8.5	7.5

a. Graph the data using an appropriate scale on the axes at the right.

b. Which equation seems to fit the data best: $y = kx$, $y = kx^2$, $y = \frac{k}{x}$, or $y = \frac{k}{x^2}$? $y = \frac{k}{x}$

c. Find the constant of variation for your model. $k = 120$

d. According to your model, how long will it take her to get to school if she bikes at 20 mi/hr? ≈ 6 min

162 *Advanced Algebra*

4. Suppose a second ball is three times as heavy as the ball in Question 3. Compare the times it will take the balls to hit the ground.

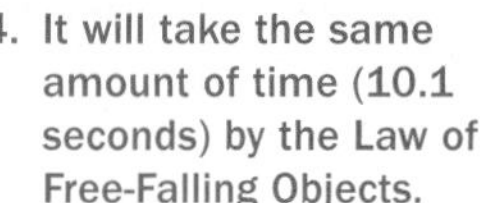

4. It will take the same amount of time (10.1 seconds) by the Law of Free-Falling Objects.

6. about 0.7 yard

In 5–7 refer to the Activity.

5. Use one of the data points in Jenna's table to show that $d = \frac{k}{w^2}$ is not a good model for the data. See margin.
6. Use the better model to predict the distance that a 180 lb person must be from the pivot in order to balance the seesaw with Anna.
7. How far from the pivot should a 20 lb baby sit to balance Anna? Does this seem possible in this situation? See margin.

APPLYING THE MATHEMATICS

8. Consider the equation $d = 4.9t^2$ where d is measured in meters and t is measured in seconds.
   a. Find the rate of change between the following pairs of points:
      (1, 4.9) and (1.5, 11.0) 12.2
      (1.5, 11.0) and (2, 19.6) 17.2
      (2, 19.6) and (2.5, 30.6) 22
   b. Is the rate of change a constant value? no
   c. For this model, the rate of change is measured in what units? meters per second

9. Malcolm is blowing up a balloon. Refer to the table and graph, which give the number n of breaths he has blown into the balloon and the volume V of the balloon in cubic inches.

n	2	4	6	8	10	12
V	28.6	57.3	85.9	114.5	143.2	171.8

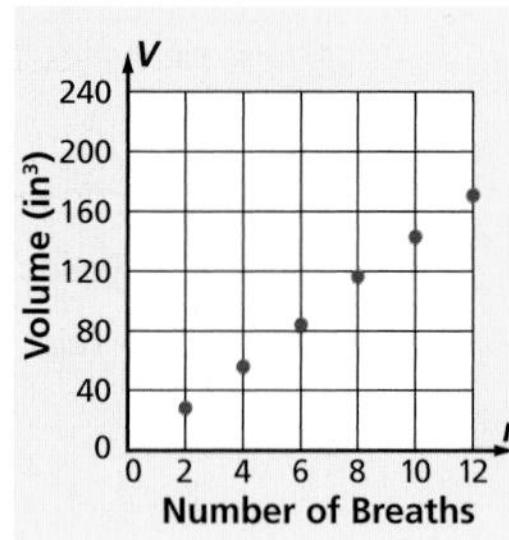

   a. **Multiple Choice** Which of the following equations is a good model for these data? i
      i. $V = kn$ ii. $V = kn^2$
      iii. $V = \frac{k}{n}$ iv. $V = \frac{k}{n^2}$
   b. Find the constant k for your model. $k = 14.3$
   c. Use your model to predict the value of V when n is 14. $V = 200.2$ in^3

10. a. **Multiple Choice** Which formula best models the data graphed at the right? ii
      i. $L = ks$ ii. $L = ks^2$
      iii. $L = \frac{k}{s}$ iv. $L = \frac{k}{s^2}$
   b. Justify your answer to Part a. See margin.
   c. Predict the value of L when $s = 60$. Use the Fundamental Theorem of Variation to explain your prediction. See margin.

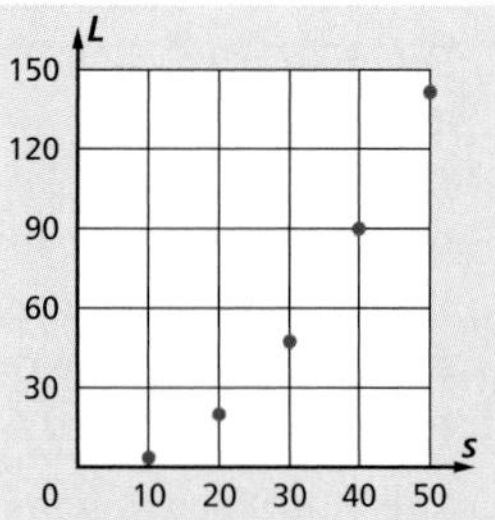

Extension

Ask students to explain the vertical and horizontal forces that can act on a wheelbarrow. Answers vary. Sample: At rest, the pivot is at one end (the wheel), and the weight of the wheelbarrow and its load provide a vertically downward force. When a person provides a vertically upward force by lifting the end of the handles, the wheelbarrow can be in vertical equilibrium. If the person then provides a small horizontal force, the wheelbarrow moves.

Then ask students to develop an equation to represent the "vertical equilibrium state" for a wheelbarrow. If D_1 is the distance from the pivot to weight W of the load, and D_2 is the distance from the pivot to the lifting force L applied to the handles, then $D_1W = D_2L$.

11. Refer to the table below and the graph at the right which show the intensity I of the sound, measured in decibels (dB), emitted from a 150-watt speaker at a distance d meters from the speaker.

d	1	2	3	4	5	6
I	11.9	3.0	1.3	0.75	0.48	0.33

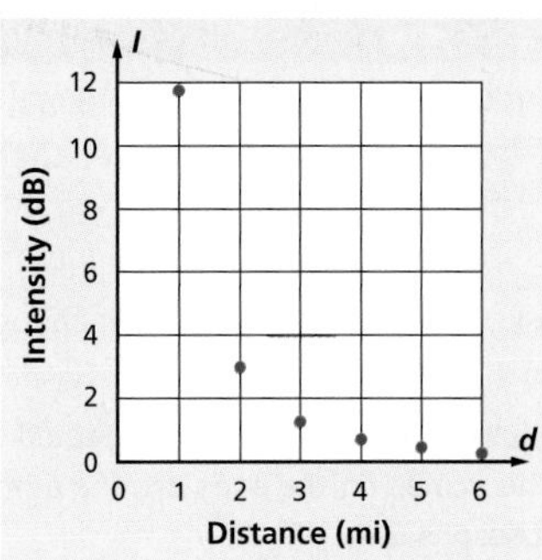

a. **Multiple Choice** Which of the following equations is a good model for these data? iv

i. $I = kd$ ii. $I = kd^2$

iii. $I = \frac{k}{d}$ iv. $I = \frac{k}{d^2}$

b. Find the constant k for your model. $k = 12$

c. Alex looked at the graph and predicted that when d is 8, I is 0.62. Do you agree with him? Why or why not?

d. Use your model to predict the value of I when d is 10. $I = 0.12$

11c. No; if this were true, I would have to increase with d, which is not what the data indicate.

12. The deeper a diver goes below sea level, the greater the water pressure on the diver. To model this relationship, pressure data (in pounds per square inch, or psi) was recorded at various depths (in feet). See margin.

Depth d (ft)	0	15	20	25	30	35
Pressure p (psi)	0	6.5	8.6	10.8	12.9	15

a. Draw a graph of these data points. Let the depth d in feet be the independent variable and the pressure p in pounds per square inch be the dependent variable.

b. Write a variation function to model these data. Use one data point to calculate k and check the model with other data points.

c. Use your model to predict the value of p when $d = 40$.

d. Depth below sea level is often measured in *atmospheres*. Each atmosphere in fresh water equals 34 feet of vertical distance. For each additional atmosphere below sea level, there is an increase of 14.7 pounds per square inch (psi) of pressure on a diver. Explain whether or not this information is consistent with the model you have found in Parts b and c.

Deep sea divers must wear special suits to combat the enormous underwater pressure.

Additional Answers

12a.

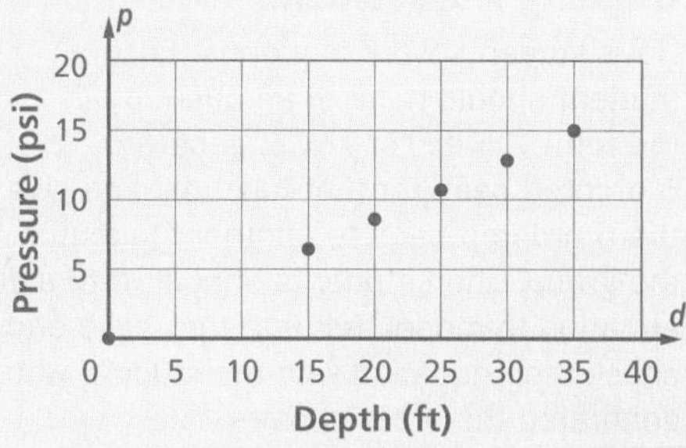

12b. $k = 0.43$, $p = 0.43d$;

Check: $12.9 = 0.43 \cdot 30$

12c. $p = 17.2$

12d. Yes; this makes sense with the model. When $d = 34$, $p = 0.43(34) \approx 14.7$.

4 Wrap-Up

Ongoing Assessment

Have students work in groups. Each student should think of an equation in the form $y = ax^2$ or $y = \frac{b}{x}$, generate 5 ordered pairs for that function, and give the 5 ordered pairs to another student in the group. Then students should write an equation to model the data they have and check their equation with the student who generated the ordered pairs. Answers vary. Check students' work.

Project Update

Project 5, *Galileo's Law of Free-Falling Objects,* on page 137 relates to the content of this lesson.

Additional Answers

13. Matt will need to sit 2.5 times as far from the pivot as Pat sits. Sample: Matt weighs 80 lb, Pat weighs 200 lb, and Pat is 3 ft from the pivot. Since $d = \frac{k}{w}$, $3 = \frac{k}{200}$ and $k = 600$. Then Matt's distance is $d = \frac{600}{80} = 7.5$, and $3 \cdot 2.5 = 7.5$.
19. The value of y is multiplied by $3^{23} = 94{,}143{,}178{,}827$.
20. (15): $\{x \mid x \text{ is a real number}\}$, $\{y \mid y \leq 0\}$; (16): $\{x \mid x \text{ is a real number}\}$, $\{y \mid y \text{ is a real number}\}$; (17): $\{x \mid x \neq 0\}$, $\{y \mid y > 0\}$; (18): $\{x \mid x \neq 0\}$, $\{y \mid y \neq 0\}$

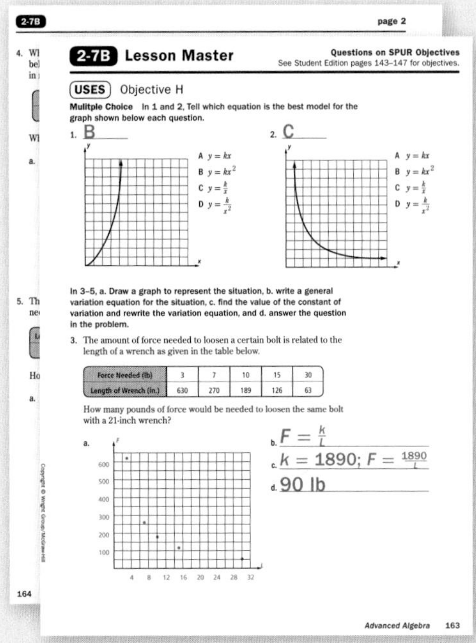

2-7B page 2

2-7B Lesson Master — Questions on SPUR Objectives. See Student Edition pages 143–147 for objectives.

USES Objective H

Mulitple Choice In 1 and 2, Tell which equation is the best model for the graph shown below each question.

1. B — A $y = kx$ B $y = kx^2$ C $y = \frac{k}{x}$ D $y = \frac{k}{x^2}$
2. C — A $y = kx$ B $y = kx^2$ C $y = \frac{k}{x}$ D $y = \frac{k}{x^2}$

In 3–5, a. Draw a graph to represent the situation, b. write a general variation equation for the situation, c. find the value of the constant of variation and rewrite the variation equation, and d. answer the question in the problem.

3. The amount of force needed to loosen a certain bolt is related to the length of a wrench as given in the table below.

Force Needed (lb)	3	7	10	15	30
Length of Wrench (in.)	630	270	189	126	63

How many pounds of force would be needed to loosen the same bolt with a 21-inch wrench?

a. [graph]
b. $F = \frac{k}{L}$
c. $k = 1890$; $F = \frac{1890}{L}$
d. 90 lb

Copyright © Wright Group/McGraw-Hill

164

Advanced Algebra 163

REVIEW

13. Pat weighs 2.5 times as much as her brother Matt. If they balance a seesaw, how do their distances from the pivot compare? Give sample weights and distances to support your answer. **(Lesson 2-6)** See margin.
14. Find the average rate of change between $x = 1$ and $x = 5$ for the function f with $f(x) = \frac{13}{x}$. **(Lesson 2-5)** -2.6

Multiple Choice In 15–18, match each graph to its equation. The scales on the axes are the same for all four graphs. (Lessons 2-4, 2-5, 2-6)

A $y = 2x$ B $y = \frac{2}{x}$ C $y = \frac{2}{x^2}$ D $y = -\frac{2}{x}$ E $y = -\frac{1}{2}x^2$

15. E

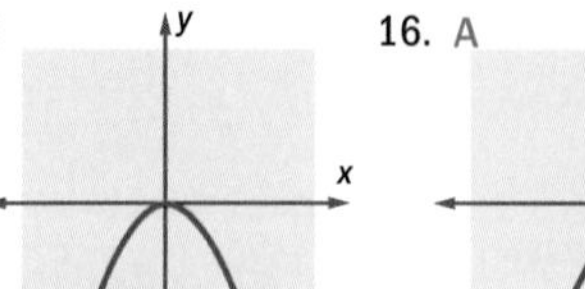

16. A

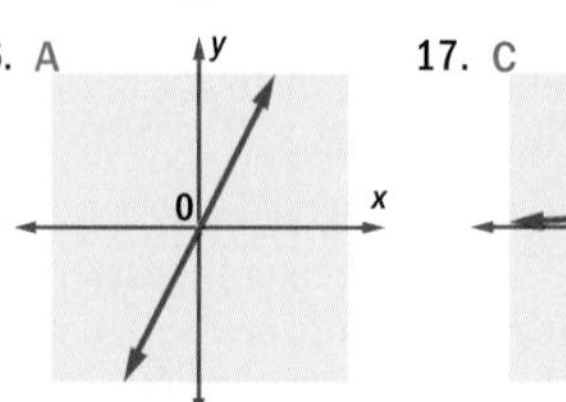

17. C

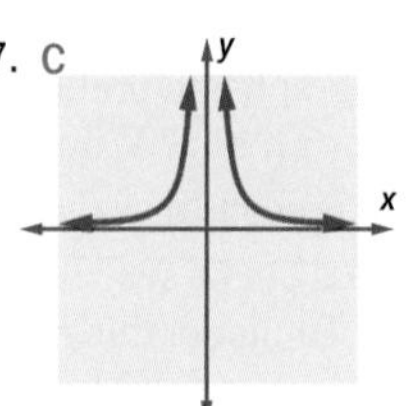

18. D

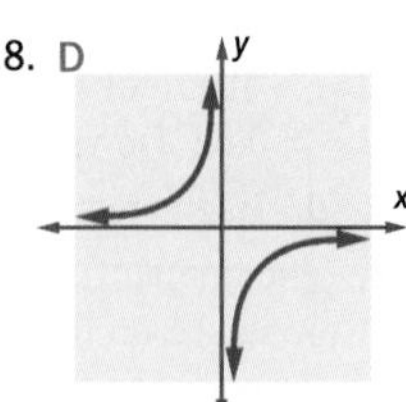

19. Suppose the value of x is tripled. How is the value of y changed if y is directly proportional to x^{23}? **(Lesson 2-3)** See margin.
20. Give the domain and range for each function graphed in Questions 15–18. **(Lesson 1-4, 2-1, 2-2)** See margin.
21. The table at the right provides data on the number of car sales in the U.S. from 1995 to 2004. **(Lessons 1-3, 1-5)**
    a. Let f be the function that maps the year y onto the number n of cars sold. Find $f(1999)$. $f(1999) = 8{,}698{,}000$
    b. For which year y is $f(y) = 8{,}104{,}000$? 2002
22. Suppose V is the volume of a circular cylinder in cubic inches and r is the radius of the cylinder in inches. Let $h = \frac{V}{\pi r^2}$. What is h, and in what unit is h measured? **(Previous Course)** height of the cylinder in inches

Year y	Car Sales $n = f(y)$ (thousands)
1995	8,635
1996	8,526
1997	8,272
1998	8,142
1999	8,698
2000	8,847
2001	8,423
2002	8,104
2003	7,610
2004	7,506

EXPLORATION

23. Research Galileo's Law of Free-Falling Objects. Find out how he was able to use the results of rolling objects down an inclined plane as the basis for his conclusions on free-falling objects. See margin.

QY ANSWERS

1. The units multiply. $\frac{\text{m}}{\text{sec}^2} \cdot \text{sec}^2 = \text{m}$.
2. about 333.5 meters
3. about 0.74 yard; Yes, this distance is about half.

Additional Answers

23. Answers vary. Sample: Galileo rolled objects of different masses down an incline and found that the distance the ball had traveled at any time depended on the square of the elapsed time at that moment. This made sense because the velocity of the object would increase with time. He noted that for objects of different masses, the rate of increase of the velocity was the same. He then hypothesized that this was also true for free-falling objects, and he was right.

Lesson

2-8 Fitting a Model to Data II

▶ **BIG IDEA** When a situation involves more than two variables that vary directly or inversely as each other, by pairing the dependent variable and each independent variable you can see how the variables fit into one *combined variation.*

So far in this chapter you have studied situations in which two quantities vary. In many real-world situations there are more than two variables. Consider the problem of determining the maximum weight that can be supported by a board.

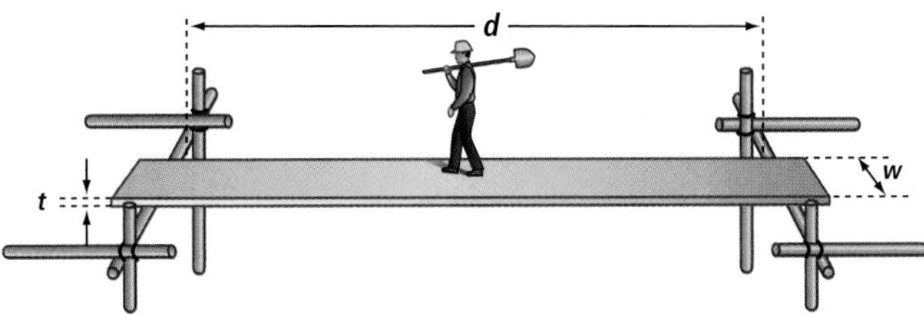

Three quantities that influence the maximum weight M that a board can hold are the board's width w, thickness t, and the distance d between supports. The goal is to find an equation relating w, t, d, and the dependent variable M.

In Lesson 2-7, you used a graph in two dimensions to determine equations relating two variables. You cannot use a single graph to determine the equation representing this situation because there are four variables to be considered. However, by keeping *all but one* independent variable constant, you can investigate separately the relationship between the dependent variable M and that independent variable.

To obtain equations that model these relationships, you can use the converse of the Fundamental Theorem of Variation.

Mental Math

Find the point of intersection of the two lines.

a. $x = 2$ and $y = 7$ (2, 7)

b. $x = 4$ and $y = 2x + 1.5$ (4, 9.5)

c. $3x + y = 18$ and $y = 3$ (5, 3)

Background

"Long" problems may discourage some students. People who make their living doing mathematics may spend days, weeks, or months working on a single problem—so some of the questions in this lesson really are not long. Also, computers have taken much of the tedium out of mathematical work. In certain situations, once the kind of variation represented in a graph has been identified, a computer can determine an equation for the best fitting line or curve.

This lesson looks at a relationship involving three independent variables—w, t, and d (width and thickness of the board and the distance between supports)—and a dependent variable M (the maximum amount of weight the board will support). To explore the relationships among these variables, we fix pairs of the independent variables and see the effect of the third on M. In Example 1, M varies directly

(continued on next page)

Lesson

2-8

GOAL

Continue modeling variation functions but now with more than one independent variable; prepare students for the ideas of combined and joint variation in Lesson 2-9.

SPUR Objectives

D Use the Fundamental Theorem of Variation.

H Fit an appropriate model to data.

Materials/Resources

- Lesson Masters 2-8A and 2-8B
- Resource Masters 1, 33–35

HOMEWORK

Suggestions for Assignment

- Questions 1–16
- Question 17 (extra credit)
- Reading Lesson 2-9
- Covering the Ideas 2-9

Local Standards

1 Warm-Up

1. How are walking speed s and distance walked d related? Distance varies directly as walking speed; that is, $d = k_1s$.
2. If the distance walked is kept constant, how are time t and speed s related to each other? Time varies inversely as speed; that is, $t = \frac{k_2}{s}$.
3. From Warm-Up Questions 1 and 2, how are walking speed, distance walked, and time walked related? $d = k_3st$; the value of k_3 depends on the units used.

2 Teaching

Notes on the Lesson

We recommend that you do not find the constants of variation in this lesson. (See Lesson 2-9.) We suggest discussing the reading in class and then reviewing the questions in order. The reading is important because the sample problem is carried over into the beginning of Lesson 2-9.

Remind students that they are already familiar with situations involving more than one independent variable. For instance, (1) the volume of a square pyramid depends on both the height of the pyramid and an edge of the base, and (2) the distance an airplane travels in a straight path depends on the speed of the airplane and its time in flight.

Additional Example

Example 1 Verify that P varies directly with q for these data.

P	1	2	3	4	5	6
q	4.5	9	13.6	17.9	22.5	27.1

Solution Assume $P = kq$. Select a data point from the table and use it to find k. *Note:* Answers vary depending on the specific data point selected. This solution uses (1, 4.5).

__?__ = k(__?__) 4.5; 1

__?__ = k 4.5

Use k to write a variation formula for P as a function of q.

__?__ = __?__ · __?__ P; 4.5; q

Use your formula to fill in values in the table predicted by this model.

P	q
1	__?__ 4.5
2	__?__ 9
3	__?__ 13.5
4	__?__ 18
5	__?__ 22.5
6	__?__ 27

Your results should be almost identical to the given data, so this verifies that P varies __?__ as __?__. directly; q

Converse of the Fundamental Theorem of Variation

a. If multiplying every x-value of a function by c results in multiplying the corresponding y-values by c^n, then y varies directly as the nth power of x, that is, $y = kx^n$.

b. If multiplying every x-value of a function by c results in dividing the corresponding y-values by c^n, then y varies inversely as the nth power of x, that is, $y = \frac{k}{x^n}$.

Below is an explanation of how to find a model for the board problem. The data are made up, but the idea is not.

Maximum Weight as a Function of Width

Perry worked on this problem and found the model by working with the variables two at a time. First, Perry held the two independent variables d and t constant. He did this by placing supports at the ends of 12-foot long, 1.5-inch thick boards of different widths. He measured how much weight a board of a given width could support before it broke. Perry obtained the following data.

Width of Board w (in.)	1	2	3	4	5	6
Observed Maximum Weight M (lb)	9	18	26	36	44	53

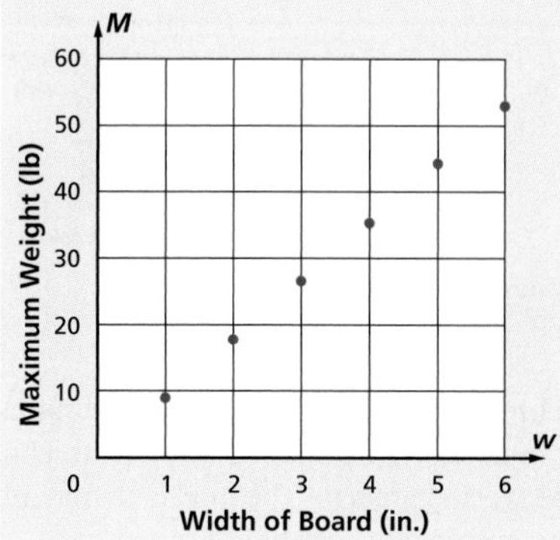

The graph shows how the maximum weight M depends on the width w of the board. Because the points seem to lie on a line through the origin, Perry concluded that M varies directly as w.

GUIDED

Example 1

Verify that M varies directly as w.

Solution Assume $M = kw$. Select a data point (__?__, __?__) from the table and use it to find k. Answers vary. Sample: 1; 9

__?__ = k __?__ 9; 1

__?__ = k 9

Use your k to write a variation formula for M as a function of w.

__?__ = __?__ · __?__ M; 9; w

Use your formula to fill in values in the table predicted by this model.

as w, so $M = kw$. Example 2 shows that M varies as the square of t, so $M = kwt^2$. Example 3 shows that M varies inversely as d, so $M = \frac{kwt^2}{d}$ or, showing the constant of variation as a coefficient, $M = \frac{k wt^2}{d}$.

Answers vary. Sample:

Width of Board w (in.)	1	2	3	4	5	6
Predicted Maximum Weight M (lb)	? 9	? 18	? 27	? 36	? 45	? 54

Your results should be almost identical to Perry's data, so this verifies that M varies __?__ as __?__. directly; w

Maximum Weight as a Function of Thickness

Perry then investigated the relationship between M and board thickness t. He held the distance d between supports constant at 12 feet, and the width w constant at 2 inches. He varied the thickness and measured the maximum weight that could be supported. The table below and graph at the right present his findings. On the graph, the points seem to lie on a parabola through the origin.

Thickness t (in.)	1	2	3	4	5	6
Predicted Maximum Weight M (lb)	8	32	72	128	200	288

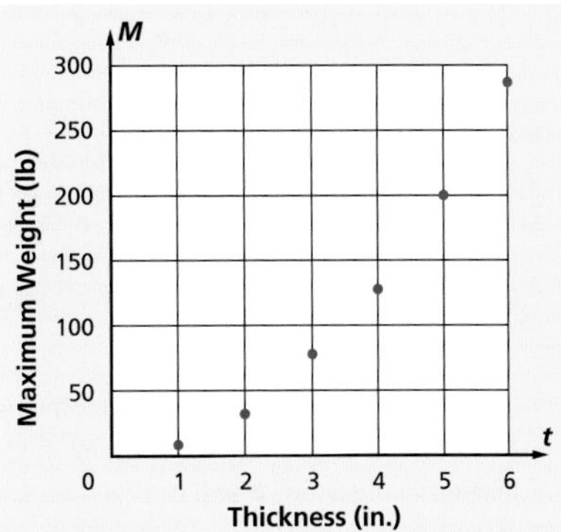

Example 2

Use the Converse of the Fundamental Theorem of Variation to determine how M varies with t and write a variation equation for the situation.

Solution Select two data points (t_1, M_1) and (t_2, M_2) from the table such that t_2 is *double* the value of t_1.

$(t_1, M_1) = (2, 32)$ and $(t_2, M_2) = (4, 128)$.

$\frac{M_2}{M_1} = \frac{128}{32} = 4$, so, as t doubles, M is multiplied by $4 = 2^2$.

Select two other data points (t_3, M_3) and (t_4, M_4) from the table such that t_4 is *triple* the value of t_3.

$(t_3, M_3) = (1, 8)$ and $(t_4, M_4) = (3, 72)$

$\frac{M_4}{M_3} = \frac{72}{8} = 9$, so, as t triples, M is multiplied by $9 = 3^2$.

So, M varies directly as the square of t.

 QY1

QY1

In Example 2, $M = kt^n$. What is the value of n? What is the value of k?

Note-Taking Tips

Encourage students to use subscripted variables in their notes. Example 2 shows an example where (t_n, m_n) represents the t and m values for data point n.

Additional Example

Example 2 Using the data given in this table, use the Converse of the Fundamental Theorem of Variation to determine how G varies with m and write a variation equation for the situation. What is the value of k?

G	m
1	5
2	20
3	45
4	80
5	125
6	180

Using (2, 20) and (4, 80), as G doubles, m is multiplied by $2^2 = 4$. Using (2, 20) and (6, 180), as G triples, m is multiplied by $3^2 = 9$. So m varies directly as the square of G; $m = 5G^2$; $k = 5$.

Accommodating the Learner

As an introduction to the Converse of the Fundamental Theorem of Variation, ask students to copy Parts a and b from the statement of the Fundamental Theorem of Variation in Lesson 2-3 (page 88) and label the hypothesis (the *if* statement) and the conclusion (the *then* statement) in each part of the theorem. Then ask students to confirm that the two parts of the theorem on page 122 are, in fact, converses of the statements from Lesson 2-3.

ENGLISH LEARNERS

Vocabulary Development

This lesson provides a natural opportunity to review the meaning of the *converse of a conditional statement*. Be sure students can state the converse for a conditional statement, identify statement-and-converse pairs, and understand that the converse of a theorem is not automatically a true statement.

Additional Example

Example 3 Using the data given in this table, use the Converse of the Fundamental Theorem of Variation to determine how R varies with s. Find the constant of variation k to verify the relationship between R and s.

R	s
1	350
2	175
3	117
4	88
5	70
6	58

Solution Select three data points from the table such that s_2 is double the value of s_1 and s_3 is triple the value of s_1: $(s_1, R_1) = (\underline{?}, \underline{?})$, $(s_2, R_2) = (\underline{?}, \underline{?})$, $(s_3, R_3) = (\underline{?}, \underline{?})$. (1, 350); (2, 175); (3, 117) $\frac{R_2}{R_1} = \underline{?}$, so as s doubles, R is divided by $\underline{?}$. $\frac{1}{2}$; 2 $\frac{R_3}{R_1} = \underline{?}$, so as s triples, R is divided by $\underline{?}$. $\frac{1}{3}$; 3 So r varies $\underline{?}$ as $\underline{?}$, and $R = \frac{k}{?}$.
inversely; s; s

Now select a data point from the table and use it to find k.

$\underline{?} = \underline{?}$, so $\underline{?} = k$ Answers vary. Sample: 350; $\frac{k}{1}$; 350

Use k to write a variation formula for R as a function of s: $\underline{?}$ $R = \frac{350}{s}$

Verify the relationship by filling in the values of R in this table:

R	s
1	? 350
2	? 175
3	? 116.7
4	? 87.5
5	? 70
6	? 58.3

Compare your results to the original data. Based on this comparison, you can confirm that R varies $\underline{?}$ as $\underline{?}$. inversely; s

Maximum Weight as a Function of Distance between Supports

Next, Perry investigated the relationship between M and d by holding t and w constant. He chose boards 1.5 inches thick and 2 inches wide and measured the maximum weight that boards of different lengths would hold. Perry obtained the following data. The graph shows how M depends on d. It is not immediately clear whether M varies inversely as d or inversely as d^2.

Distance d (ft)	1	2	3	4	5	6
Observed Maximum Weight M (lb)	212	106	71	53	42	35

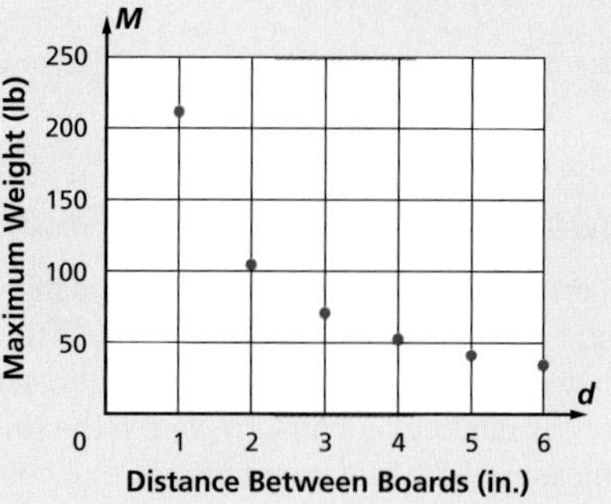

GUIDED

Example 3

Use the Converse of the Fundamental Theorem of Variation to determine how M varies with d. Then find the constant of variation k and use it to verify the relationship between M and d.

Solution Select three data points (d_1, M_1), (d_2, M_2), and (d_3, M_3) from the table such that d_2 is double the value of d_1 and d_3 is triple the value of d_1. Answers vary. Sample answers are given.

$(d_1, M_1) = (\underline{?}, \underline{?})$, $(d_2, M_2) = (\underline{?}, \underline{?})$, 1, 212; 2, 106
and $(d_3, M_3) = (\underline{?}, \underline{?})$ 3, 71

$\frac{M_2}{M_1} = \underline{?}$, so, as d doubles, M is divided by $\underline{?}$. $\frac{1}{2}$; 2

$\frac{M_3}{M_1} = \underline{?}$, so, as d triples, M is divided by $\underline{?}$. about $\frac{1}{3}$; 3

So, M varies $\underline{?}$ as $\underline{?}$, and $M = \frac{k}{?}$. inversely; d; d

Now select a data point from the table and use it to find k.

$\underline{?} = \frac{k}{?}$ 212;1

$\underline{?} = k$ 212

Use k to write a variation formula for M as a function of d:

$\underline{?}$. $M = \frac{212}{d}$

Accommodating the Learner

Tell students that a scientist noticed that the time T needed to heat water to a boil is affected by the amount A of water being heated, the initial temperature I of the water, and the elevation E (distance above sea level) of the laboratory. Ask students to describe a series of experiments to determine an equation relating A, I, E, and the dependent variable T. Answers vary. Check students' work. They should describe three experiments, each holding constant two of the variables A, I, and E and seeing how T varies with the third variable.

Verify the relationship by using your formula to fill in the values of M in the table below.

Distance d (ft)	1	2	3	4	5	6
Predicted Maximum Weight M (lb)	? 212	? 106	? 70.7	? 53	? 42.4	? 35.5

Compare your results to Perry's data. Based on this comparison, you can confirm that M varies __?__ as __?__. inversely; d

STOP QY2

▶ QY2

Why are there different values for k in Examples 1, 2, and 3?

Summarizing the Results with a Single Model

Perry summarized his findings as follows:

M varies directly as w and the square of t, while M varies inversely as d.

These relationships can be expressed in the single formula

$$M = \frac{kwt^2}{d},$$

where M is in pounds, w and t are in inches, d is in feet, and k is the constant of variation. Notice that the independent variables that have direct-variation relationships with M are in the numerator, and the independent variable that has an inverse-variation relationship with M is in the denominator. The formula tells you that the greater the width and the thickness of the board, and the shorter the distance between supports, the stronger the board will be. This situation is an example of *combined variation*. You will learn more about combined variation in the next lesson.

Questions

COVERING THE IDEAS

1. Which variables in the Examples are the independent variables? w, t, d
2. Why did it take three different tables to develop the single formula $M = \frac{kwt^2}{d}$? See margin.

Extension

Tell students that workers are painting the outside of a building. The variables are the length ℓ, the width w, and the height h of the building; the number n of workers; the number c of coats of paint; the size z of the paint brushes; and the time t needed to complete the paint job. Ask students how they could develop an equation to represent how the independent variables are related to the dependent variable t.

Answers vary. Sample: They would hold constant all but one of the dependent variables ℓ, w, h, c, n, and z and gather data to see the relationship between the remaining independent variable and t. An equation for all the variables is $t = k\frac{\ell whc}{nz}$.

3 Assignment

Recommended Assignment

- Questions 1–16
- Question 17 (extra credit)
- Reading Lesson 2-9
- Covering the Ideas 2-9

Notes on the Questions

Questions 1–9 These should be discussed in order.

Additional Answers

2. There were three independent variables, so we kept two of them constant in each table to determine the relationship between one independent variable and the dependent variable.

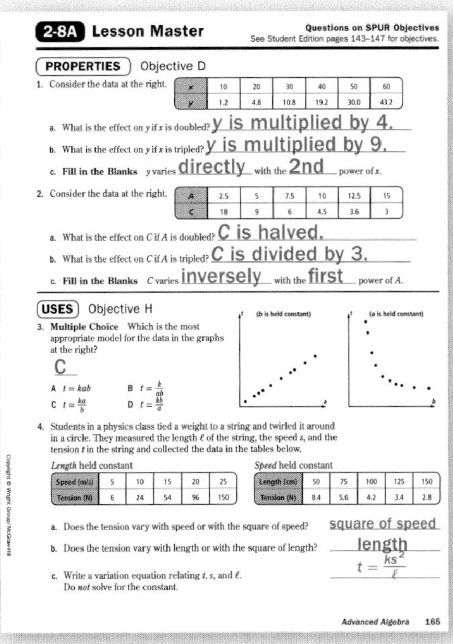
2-8A Lesson Master

Questions on SPUR Objectives See Student Edition pages 143–147 for objectives.

PROPERTIES Objective D

1. Consider the data at the right.

x	10	20	30	40	50	60
y	1.2	4.8	10.8	19.2	30.0	43.2

a. What is the effect on y if x is doubled? y is multiplied by 4.

b. What is the effect on y if x is tripled? y is multiplied by 9.

c. Fill in the Blanks y varies directly with the 2nd power of x.

2. Consider the data at the right.

A	2.5	5	7.5	10	12.5	15
C	18	9	6	4.5	3.6	3

a. What is the effect on C if A is doubled? C is halved.

b. What is the effect on C if A is tripled? C is divided by 3.

c. Fill in the Blanks C varies inversely with the first power of A.

USES Objective H

3. Multiple Choice Which is the most appropriate model for the data in the graphs at the right? C

A $t = kab$ B $t = \frac{k}{ab}$

C $t = \frac{ka}{b}$ D $t = \frac{kb}{a}$

(b is held constant) (a is held constant)

4. Students in a physics class tied a weight to a string and twirled it around in a circle. They measured the length ℓ of the string, the speed s, and the tension t in the string and collected the data in the tables below.

Length held constant

Speed (m/s)	5	10	15	20	25
Tension (N)	6	24	54	96	150

Speed held constant

Length (cm)	50	75	100	125	150
Tension (N)	8.4	5.6	4.2	3.4	2.8

a. Does the tension vary with speed or with the square of speed? square of speed

b. Does the tension vary with length or with the square of length? length

c. Write a variation equation relating t, s, and ℓ. Do *not* solve for the constant. $t = \frac{ks^2}{\ell}$

Advanced Algebra 165

Notes on the Questions

Questions 10 and 11 These are the heart of the question set. You may wish to discuss Question 10 on one day and Question 11 the next.

In 3–9, refer to the tables and graphs in this lesson.

3. What is the maximum weight supported by a board 12 ft long, 2 in. wide, and 2 in. thick? 32 lb
4. What is the maximum weight supported by a board 12 ft long, 6 in. wide, and 1.5 in. thick? 53 lb
5. What is the shape of the graph relating M and w when t and d are held constant? a straight line
6. Refer to the data for M as a function of t. Find an equation to model the data when $d = 12$ ft and $w = 2$ in. $M = 8t^2$
7. Use the Converse of the Fundamental Theorem of Variation to show that M does not vary inversely as d^2. When d doubles, M is divided by 2, not 4.
8. Suppose you run an experiment similar to the ones in the lesson and find that the maximum weight the board can hold is 50 pounds. Would you increase or decrease each of the following variables to increase the maximum weight the board could hold to 200 pounds?

   a. w increase b. t increase c. d decrease
9. If M varies directly as a variable in the formula $M = \frac{kwt^2}{d}$, is that variable in the numerator or denominator of the expression on the right side of the formula? numerator

APPLYING THE MATHEMATICS

10. **Multiple Choice** The two graphs below show the relationships between a dependent variable y and the independent variables x and z.

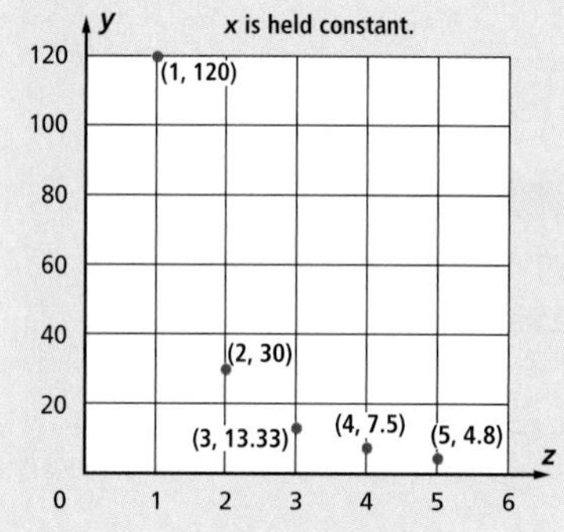

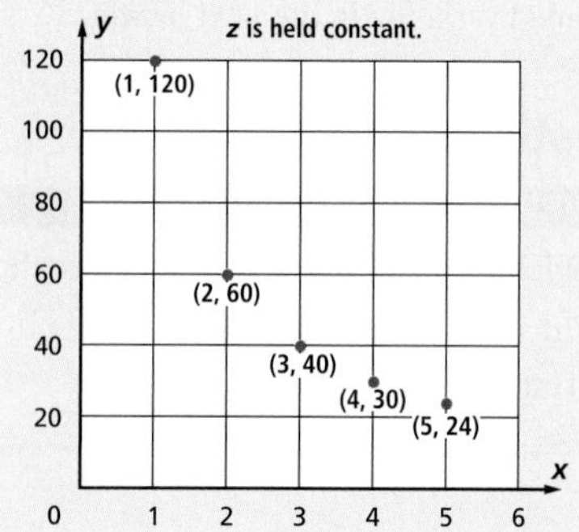

Which equation best models this situation? C

A $y = \frac{kx^2}{z^2}$ B $y = \frac{kx}{z}$ C $y = \frac{k}{xz^2}$ D $y = \frac{k}{x^2z}$

11. Carrie was trying to determine how the pressure P that is exerted on the floor by the heel of a shoe depends on the heel width h and the weight w of the person wearing the shoe. She started by measuring the pressure (in psi) exerted by several people of different weights wearing a shoe with a heel 3 inches wide.

a. A table and graph of these data points are shown, using P as the dependent variable. How does the pressure exerted on the floor appear to relate to a person's weight? Use the Converse of the Fundamental Theorem of Variation to test your conclusion for two ordered pairs in the table. See margin.

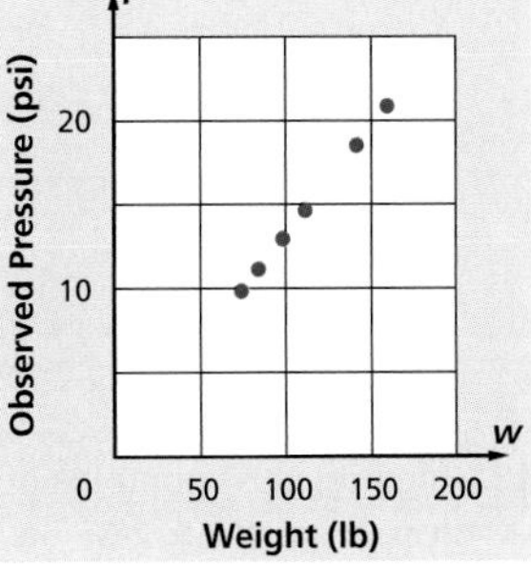

Weight w (lb)	75	85	99	112	142	160
Observed Pressure P (psi)	9.8	11.1	12.9	14.6	18.5	20.8

b. Carrie then had her sister Candice, who weighs 135 pounds, try on shoes with different heel widths h, and she measured the pressure exerted. The data are summarized in the table and graph below, again using P as the dependent variable. Use the Converse of the Fundamental Theorem of Variation to determine if P varies inversely as h or as h^2. P varies inversely as h^2.

Heel width h (in.)	1.25	1.5	1.75	2	2.25	2.5
Observed Pressure P (psi)	101.1	70.2	51.6	39.5	31.2	25.3

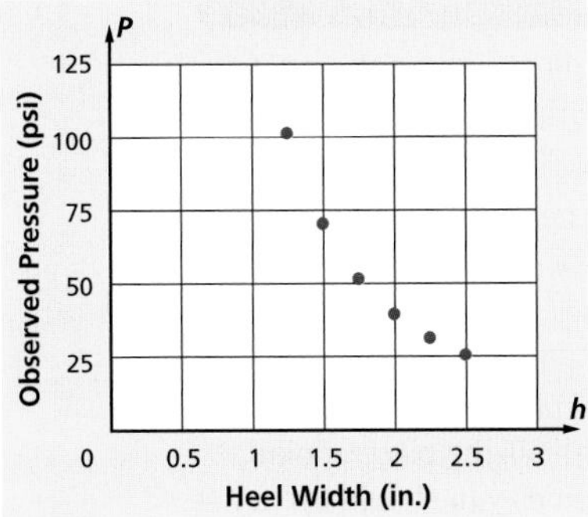

c. What amount of pressure would you expect to be exerted by Candice if she were wearing a 3-inch wide heel? Explain your reasoning. See margin.

d. Write an equation modeling the variation relationships between P, w, and h. Do not solve for k. $P = \frac{kw}{h^2}$

Additional Answers

11a. P varies directly as w. When w is multiplied by about $\frac{4}{3}$ to go from $w = 75$ to $w = 99$, P is multiplied by $\frac{12.9}{9.8} \approx \frac{4}{3}$.

11c. 17.6 psi; by the table in Part b, $P = 70.2$ when $w = 1.5$, so when w is doubled to 3, $P = \frac{70.2}{4} \approx 17.6$ by the Fundamental Theorem of Variation.

4 Wrap-Up

Ongoing Assessment

Ask students to explain how they can tell whether a set of data shows direct variation or inverse variation. Then ask them to explain how they can test whether a variation model fits a table of data. Answers vary. Sample: If data points lie on a line through the origin, the data show direct variation; if the data seem to lie on a branch of a hyperbola, they show inverse variation. To test a variation model, use it to generate ordered pairs (using the given domain values) and compare the resulting table to the given table of data.

Project Update

Project 3, *The Maximum Load of a Balsa Board,* and Project 6, *Average Rates of Change,* on page 137 relate to the content of this lesson.

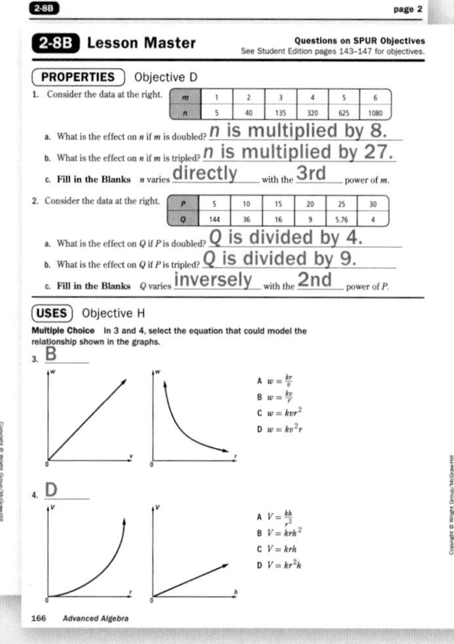

2-8B page 2

2-8B Lesson Master — **Questions on SPUR Objectives** See Student Edition pages 143–147 for objectives.

PROPERTIES Objective D

1. Consider the data at the right.

m	1	2	3	4	5	6
n	5	40	135	320	625	1080

a. What is the effect on n if m is doubled? n is multiplied by 8.

b. What is the effect on n if m is tripled? n is multiplied by 27.

c. **Fill in the Blanks** n varies directly with the 3rd power of m.

2. Consider the data at the right.

P	5	10	15	20	25	30
Q	144	36	16	9	5.76	4

a. What is the effect on Q if P is doubled? Q is divided by 4.

b. What is the effect on Q if P is tripled? Q is divided by 9.

c. **Fill in the Blanks** Q varies inversely with the 2nd power of P.

USES Objective H

Multiple Choice In 3 and 4, select the equation that could model the relationship shown in the graphs.

3. B

A $w = \frac{kr}{v}$
B $w = \frac{kv}{r}$
C $w = kvr^2$
D $w = kv^2r$

4. D

A $V = \frac{kh}{r^2}$
B $V = krh^2$
C $V = krh$
D $V = kr^2h$

166 *Advanced Algebra*

REVIEW

12. Consider $y = -\frac{7}{x^2}$ **(Lesson 2-6)**

a. What real number is excluded from the domain of x? 0

b. **Multiple Choice** Which could be the graph of the equation? C

A

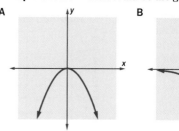

B

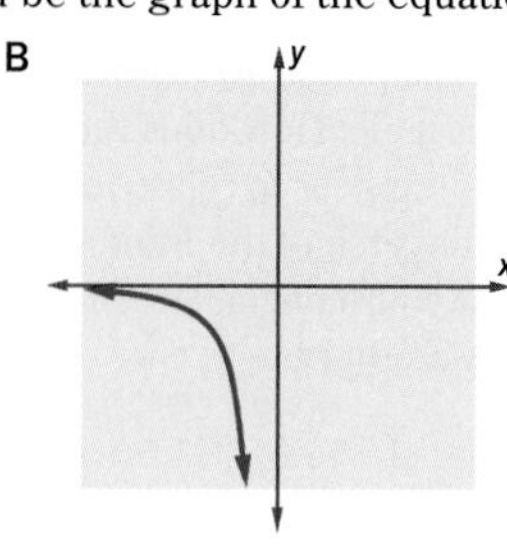

C

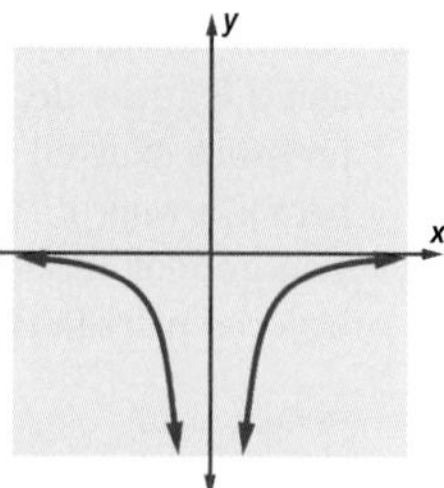

13. Identify all asymptotes of the graph of the equation. **(Lessons 2-4, 2-5, 2-6)** a. none; b. none; c. $x = 0$, $y = 0$; d. $x = 0$, $y = 0$

a. $y = \frac{7x}{4}$ b. $y = \pi x$ c. $y = -\frac{3}{x}$ d. $y = \frac{\frac{1}{2}}{x^2}$

14. **Fill in the Blanks** The graph of $y = \frac{5x}{3}$ is a ___?___ with slope ___?___. **(Lesson 2-4)** line; $\frac{5}{3}$

15. Suppose r varies inversely as the cube of t. If r is 8 when t is 4, find r when $t = 9$. **(Lesson 2-2)** $r = \frac{512}{729} \approx 0.7$

16. If you buy x granola bars at y cents per bar, what is the total cost? **(Lesson 1-1)** xy cents

EXPLORATION

17. The ability of a board to support a weight also depends on the type of wood. That is, the constant of variation k in the formula $M = \frac{kwt^2}{d}$ depends on the type of wood.

a. For a stronger kind of wood, is k larger or smaller? larger

b. Do some research to find out which wood is strongest: oak, balsa, or pine. Oak is the strongest.

c. Suppose you have a 10-foot piece of pine that is 1 inch thick and 6 inches wide. If you wanted to cut a piece of oak that could hold the same amount of weight as the piece of pine, what do you know about the dimensions you should use for the piece of oak?
The thickness and width could be smaller, but the length (distance between supports) could be longer.

QY ANSWERS

1. $n = 2$; $k = 8$

2. Examples 1, 2, and 3 all describe different relationships, and as such they have different values of k.

Lesson 2-9

Combined and Joint Variation

Vocabulary

combined variation
joint variation

▶ **BIG IDEA** The same methods used to solve variation problems involving two variables can be applied to variation problems involving more than two variables.

Combined Variation

At the beginning of this chapter, you read about how adjusting the number of teeth on the gears of a bicycle changes its speed. The speed S of a bicycle varies directly with the number of revolutions per minute (rpm) R that you turn the pedals and with the number F of teeth on the front gear. The speed also varies inversely with the number B of teeth on the back gear. This situation is modeled by the equation

$$S = \frac{kRF}{B}.$$

This equation is read "S varies directly as R and F and inversely as B." When both direct and inverse variations occur together in a situation, we say the situation is one of **combined variation**.

You saw another example of combined variation in Lesson 2-8, where the maximum weight M of a board varied directly with its width w and the square of its thickness t, and inversely with the distance d between its supports. This relationship was modeled by the equation

$$M = \frac{kwt^2}{d}.$$

 QY1

A combined-variation equation has two or more independent variables, and the independent variables can have any positive exponent. To find k in a combined-variation model, use the same strategy as in a variation problem with one independent variable:

- Find one instance that relates all the variables simultaneously.
- Substitute known values into the general variation equation.
- Solve for k.

Mental Math

Jeff is experimenting with a balance scale. He finds that 8 erasers balance 1 apple.

a. His calculator weighs 2.5 times as much as an apple. How many erasers does he need to balance his calculator? 20

b. A pair of scissors weighs the same as 2 erasers. How many pairs of scissors will balance the calculator? 10

c. There are two pairs of scissors on one side of the scale and the calculator on the other. How many erasers should he add to the pan with the scissors to balance the calculator? 16

▶ **QY1**

Write an equation that represents this statement: y varies directly as the square of x and inversely as z.

Lesson

2-9

GOAL

Continue the ideas from the previous lesson but find the constant of variation; review the process of solving variation problems.

SPUR Objectives

A Translate variation language into formulas and formulas into variation language.

B Solve variation problems.

G Solve real-world variation problems.

Materials/Resources

- Lesson Masters 2-9A and 2-9B
- Resource Masters 36 and 37

HOMEWORK

Suggestions for Assignment

- Questions 1–17
- Question 18 (extra credit)
- Self-Test

Local Standards

1 Warm-Up

Use the bicycle gear formula $S = \frac{kRF}{B}$. Consider three gear settings: (1) the front gear has 22 teeth, and the back gear has 30 teeth; (2) the front gear has 44 teeth, and the back gear has 30 teeth; (3) the front gear has 44 teeth, and the rear gear has 11 teeth.

1. The ratio $\frac{F}{B}$ is called the *gear ratio*. Which of the three settings has the highest gear ratio? setting 3
2. At the same number of pedal revolutions, which of these gear settings will cause a bicycle to travel the farthest? setting 3

(continued on next page)

Background

Example 1 To motivate and explain the formula $S = \frac{kRF}{B}$, ask students to consider a bicycle with 26-inch diameter wheels. Such a bicycle travels 26π inches in one revolution of its wheels. Now suppose a front gear has 22 teeth and a back gear has 30 teeth. For each pedal revolution, the back wheel revolves $\frac{22}{30}$ of the angle that the front wheel revolves, so the rear wheel travels $\frac{22}{30}(26\pi)$ inches, or about 60 inches, for each pedal revolution. The more teeth on the back gear, the slower the bicycle goes; the more teeth on the front gear, the faster the bicycle goes. The number $\frac{22}{30}$ is the *gear ratio*. If a bicycle has a front gear with 44 teeth and a back gear with 11 teeth, then the gear ratio is $\frac{44}{11}$ or 4 : 1, and if the bicycle has the same size tire, it goes $4 \cdot 26\pi$ inches, or about 327 inches, with each pedal revolution. Thus, a rider has to work much less to make the bicycle move. A rider might prefer a 4 : 1 gear ratio in climbing uphill (to make work easier) and a $\frac{22}{30}$ gear ratio in going downhill (to keep from going too fast).

(continued on next page)

3. **At the same number of pedal revolutions, compare how far a bicycle will travel at setting 1 than at setting 3.** The bicycle will travel $\frac{11}{60}$ as far using setting 1 rather than setting 3.
4. Explain why R is in the numerator of this formula. The number of pedal revolutions per minute is a rate, and distance varies directly to rate because circumference varies directly to the number of revolutions.

2 Teaching

Notes on the Lesson

This lesson is an appropriate summary for the chapter, combining the ideas of direct variation and inverse variation and including variables to the first and second powers.

Example 1 There is no substitute for bringing a bicycle into the classroom and showing the various gear ratios. If you are not familiar with this application, it is quite possible that one or more of the students in your class is.

Additional Example

Example 1 A bicyclist is pedaling at 85 revolutions per minute using a front gear with 39 teeth and a back gear with 13 teeth. At these settings, she is traveling 21 miles per hour. Describe how her speed would change if she decreased her pedaling to 60 revolutions per minute. $S = 15$; decreasing her rpm to 60 would decrease her speed by about 6 mph (from 21 mph to 15 mph).

Example 1

Mario is pedaling a bike at 80 revolutions per minute using a front gear with 35 teeth and a back gear with 15 teeth. At these settings, he is traveling 14.5 miles per hour. Describe how his speed would change if he increased his pedaling to 100 rpm.

Solution Use the combined variation equation $S = \frac{kRF}{B}$. Substitute $S = 14.5$, $R = 80$, $F = 35$, and $B = 15$ and solve for k.

$14.5 = \frac{k(80)(35)}{15}$

$14.5 \approx k(187)$

$0.078 \approx k$

So the variation formula for this situation is $S = \frac{0.078RF}{B}$.

To find Mario's new speed, substitute $R = 100$, $F = 35$, and $B = 15$ into your formula and solve for S.

$S = \frac{0.078(100)(35)}{15} \approx 18$

This means that by increasing his rpm to 100, Mario increases his speed by about 3.5 mph (from 14.5 mph to 18 mph).

Another Example of Combined Variation

Photographers are always looking for ways to make their pictures sharper. One way is to focus the lens at the *hyperfocal distance*. Focusing the lens at this distance will produce a photograph with the maximum number of objects in focus.

Photographers often use the hyperfocal distance when taking pictures of landscapes. The two images at the right were shot with the same camera at the same settings, except the one on the bottom was taken with the lens focused at the hyperfocal distance, giving the extra degree of sharpness.

Example 2 explores how the hyperfocal length H can be calculated using the focal length L of the camera lens in millimeters and the f-stop, or aperture, f. The *aperture* is a setting that tells you how wide the lens opening is on a camera. It is the ratio of the focal length to the diameter of the lens opening and so has no units.

In general, if the diameter of the wheels is 26 inches, the number of teeth on the front gear is F, and the number of teeth on the rear gear is B, then the gear ratio is $\frac{F}{B}$, and the distance traveled in one pedal revolution is $\frac{F}{B}(26\pi)$. If the number of pedal revolutions per minute is R, then in each minute the bicycle travels $\frac{RF}{B}(26\pi)$ inches. Thus the bicycle's speed is $S = (26\pi)\frac{RF}{B}\ \frac{\text{revolutions}}{\text{minute}}$, which is the formula $S = \frac{kRF}{B}$ with $k = 26\pi$. (Another formula, expressing the wheel's diameter as the variable d, is $S = \frac{kRFd}{B}$.)

An excellent Web site for more information is http://science.howstuffworks.com/bicycle4.htm.

Example 2

The hyperfocal length H in meters varies directly with the square of the focal length L in millimeters, and inversely with the selected aperture f.

a. **Write a general variation equation to model this situation.**

b. **Find the value and unit of k when the hyperfocal length H is 10.42 m when using a 50 mm lens (L) and the aperture f is set at 8.**

c. **Write a variation formula for the situation using your answer to Part b.**

d. **Find the hyperfocal length needed if you want to shoot with a 300 mm lens at an aperture setting of 2.8. Include the units in your calculations.**

Solution

a. Because the hyperfocal length varies directly with the square of the focal length of the lens, L^2 will be in the numerator of the expression on the right side of the formula. Because the hyperfocal length varies inversely with the aperture setting, f will be in the denominator of the expression.
A general equation is $H = \frac{kL^2}{f}$.

b. Use your formula from Part a with: $H = 10.42$ m, $L = 50$ mm, and $f = 8$. Include units when making substitutions. Here we show how to do it by hand and with a CAS.

By hand:

$10.42 \text{ m} = \frac{k(50 \text{ mm})^2}{8}$ Substitute the given values for H, L, and f.

$10.42 \text{ m} = \frac{2500 \text{ mm}^2 \cdot k}{8}$ Square 50 mm.

$83.36 \text{ m} = 2500 \text{ mm}^2 \cdot k$ Multiply both sides by 8.

$0.033 \frac{\text{m}}{\text{mm}^2} \approx k$ Divide both sides by 2500 mm^2.

With a CAS:

```
solve(10.42=k×50^2/8,k)
                {k=0.033344}
```

c. Substitute k into the equation from Part a.

$$H = \frac{0.033 L^2}{f}$$

d. Use the formula from Part c to calculate H when $L = 300$ mm and $f = 2.8$. Include the units when you substitute.

$$H = \frac{0.033 \frac{\text{m}}{\text{mm}^2}(300 \text{ mm})^2}{2.8}$$

$$H = \frac{0.033 \frac{\text{m}}{\text{mm}^2}(90{,}000 \text{ mm}^2)}{2.8}$$

$H \approx 1060.7$ m

The hyperfocal length is about 1,060 meters.

Accommodating the Learner ↑

Ask students to work through the steps of Example 1, this time including units with the values of S, R, F, and B. Ask them if the unit for k changes depending on whether S is measured in miles per hour or in kilometers per minute. In both cases, the unit for S is distance/revolution.

Accommodating the Learner ↓

Ask students to rewrite the equation $S = \frac{kRF}{B}$ as three equations, showing how S varies with R, F, and B. Ask students to use the constants k_R, k_F, and k_B for the three equations. $S = k_R R$; $S = k_F F$; $S = \frac{k_B}{B}$

Notes on the Lesson

Example 2 There is also no substitute for bringing a camera in and showing its various settings. Although it is difficult to get an entire class close enough to the camera to see the settings, it is easier to bring a camera into a class than a bicycle. You may wish to do the calculations without units first and then superimpose the unit analysis on the calculations. (The Accommodating the Learner Up activity on this page also deals with unit analysis.) Also, watch for students who mistakenly interpret millimeters as meters squared; you may need to remind them that 1000 millimeters = 1 meter.

Note-Taking Tips

When students use a formula to calculate the constant of variation or evaluate one of the variables, encourage them to annotate the process with a statement such as the one in the first sentence of the solution for Example 1. As always, this kind of annotation can help them explain their steps to others, re-create their thought process when they review their notes, and identify possible sources of error if they learn that their answer is incorrect.

Additional Example

Example 2 The hyperfocal length H in yards varies directly with the square of the focal length L in inches and inversely with the selected aperture f.

a. Write a general variation equation to model this situation. $H = \frac{kL^2}{f}$

b. Find the value and unit of k when the hyperfocal length of a 1.75-inch lens is 12 yards and the aperture is set at 9. $k \approx 35.3$ yd/in^2

c. Write a variation formula for the situation using your answer to Part b. $H = \frac{35.3L^2}{f}$

d. Find the hyperfocal length needed (in yards) if you want to shoot with a 12-inch lens at an aperture setting of 2.5. Include the units. $H \approx 2033$; the hyperfocal length is about 2033 yd.

Additional Example

Example 3 The volume of a solid with a circular base varies jointly as the height of the solid and the square of the radius of the base.

a. Write a general equation to model this situation.

b. If the volume of the solid is approximately 47.1 cubic inches when the radius is 3 inches and the height is 5 inches, find the value of k.

c. The value of $3k$ is approximately equal to what famous mathematical value? How can you express k in terms of that value?

d. Write a variation formula for the situation using your answer to Part c.

e. What well-known kind of solid figure could this be?

Solution

a. Let V be the volume of a solid, h be the height of the solid, and r be the radius of the base. A general equation is $V = k \cdot$ __?__. r^2h

b. Use your formula from Part a with $V = 47.1$, $h = 5$, and $r = 3$ to solve for k.

$47.1 = k \cdot$ (__?__)(__?__) 9; 5

$47.1 = k \cdot$ __?__ 45

__?__ $\approx k$ 1.046

c. The value of $3k$ is approximately equal to __?__, so k can be expressed as __?__. 3.14 or π; $\frac{1}{3}\pi$

d. Substitute k into your equation from Part a. So $V =$ __?__. $\frac{1}{3}\pi r^2h$

e. Based on the formula in Part d, this solid could be a(n) __?__. cone

Joint Variation

Sometimes one quantity varies directly as powers of two or more independent variables, but not inversely as any variable. This is called **joint variation**. The simplest joint-variation equation is

$$y = kxz,$$

where k is the constant of variation. The equation is read "y varies jointly as x and z" or "y varies directly as the product of x and z." Guided example 3 explores a joint-variation situation in geometry.

GUIDED

Example 3

The volume of a solid with a circular base varies jointly as the height of the solid and the square of the radius of the base.

a. Write a general equation to model this situation.

b. If the volume of the solid is approximately 75.4 cubic centimeters when the radius is 2 centimeters and the height is 6 centimeters, find the value of k.

c. The value of k is approximately equal to what famous mathematical value?

d. Write a variation formula using your answer to Part b.

e. What well-known kind of solid figure could this be?

Solution

a. Let V be the volume of the solid, h be the height of the solid, and r be the radius of the base.

A general equation is $V = k$ __?__. hr^2

b. Use your formula from Part a with $V = 75.4$, $h = 6$, and $r = 2$ to solve for k.

$75.4 = k$ __?__ __?__^{2} 6; 2

$75.4 = k$ __?__ 24

__?__ $\approx k$ 3.142

c. The value of k is approximately equal to __?__. π

d. Substitute k into your equation from Part a. So, $V =$ __?__. $3.142hr^2$ or πhr^2

e. Based on the formula in Part d, this solid could be a(n) __?__. cylinder

Many other geometry formulas can be interpreted as direct- or joint-variation equations.

STOP QY2

▶ QY2

Translate this statement into an equation: The area of a triangle varies jointly with the height and the base of the triangle. What is the constant of variation for this formula?

ENGLISH LEARNERS

Vocabulary Development

Many of the camera terms in Example 2 (hyperfocal, aperture, focal length) may be new to students. If any of your students are knowledgeable about cameras, you may want to ask them to lead a class discussion about cameras, both digital and nondigital.

As in combined variation, a joint-variation equation can have more than two independent variables, and the independent variables can have any positive exponent.

Questions

COVERING THE IDEAS

1. a. What is combined variation?
   b. How is joint variation different from combined variation?
2. Translate into a single formula: M varies directly as t and r^2 and inversely as d. $M = \frac{ktr^2}{d}$
3. Refer to Example 1. Suppose Mario slowed his pedaling to 75 rpm. What would his speed be? 13.7 mph
4. In Example 2, assume that a photographer calculated a hyperfocal length of 6.54 meters. If he used a lens with a focal length of 28 millimeters, at what aperture was the lens set? 3.96
5. Sonia calculated the volume of a cylindrical can of cat food with a radius of 1.5 inches and a height of 1.2 inches to be about 9.2 cubic inches.
   a. Use the equation $V = kr^2h$ to calculate the constant of variation k that she used. $k \approx 3.4$
   b. Did Sonia use the correct formula? How do you know? No; she used $k = 3.4$ instead of 3.14 or π.
6. Refer to Example 3. If the volume of the solid is 25.13 cm^3 with a radius of 2 cm, what is its height? 2 cm

1a. Combined variation is a situation in which both direct and inverse variation occur together.

1b. In joint variation a quantity varies directly as powers of two or more independent variables, but in combined variation there is both direct and inverse variation.

APPLYING THE MATHEMATICS

7. The formula $F = ma$ gives the force F on an object with mass m and acceleration a. a. F varies jointly as m and a.
   a. Rewrite the formula in words using the language of variation.
   b. What is the constant of variation? $k = 1$
8. The volume of a solid with a circular base varies jointly with the square of the base radius and the height. When the volume is 83.78 cm^3, the height is 5 cm and the base radius is 4 cm.
   a. Write a general equation to model this situation and find k. $V = khr^2$; $k \approx 1.05$
   b. k is a multiple of π. Write k in terms of π. $k = \frac{\pi}{3}$
   c. Write a variation formula for the volume of this solid in terms of π. $V = \frac{\pi hr^2}{3}$
   d. What kind of well-known solid is this? cone

3 Assignment

Recommended Assignment

- Questions 1–17
- Question 18 (extra credit)
- Self-Test

Extension

As an extension to Question 18, ask students to find the statement made by the Scarecrow in the movie *The Wizard of Oz* just after he receives a diploma. Ask students to provide one or more specific examples to tell whether the Scarecrow's statement is accurate.

The Scarecrow says, "The sum of the square roots of any two sides of an isosceles triangle is equal to the square root of the remaining side." The statement is not true. As an example, consider the isosceles triangle with sides 9, 9, and 4. For that triangle, the Scarecrow's statement translates to either $\sqrt{9} + \sqrt{9} = \sqrt{4}$ or $\sqrt{9} + \sqrt{4} = \sqrt{9}$, neither of which is a true equation.

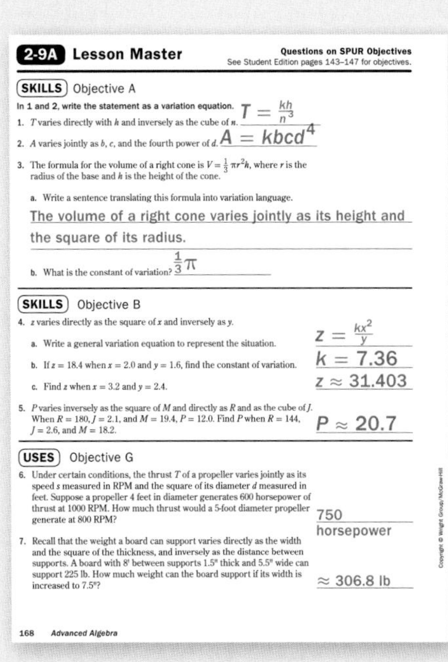

2-9A Lesson Master

Questions on SPUR Objectives
See Student Edition pages 143–147 for objectives.

SKILLS Objective A

In 1 and 2, write the statement as a variation equation.

1. T varies directly with h and inversely as the cube of n. $T = \frac{kh}{n^3}$
2. A varies jointly as b, c, and the fourth power of d. $A = kbcd^4$
3. The formula for the volume of a right cone is $V = \frac{1}{3}\pi r^2h$, where r is the radius of the base and h is the height of the cone.
   a. Write a sentence translating this formula into variation language.
   The volume of a right cone varies jointly as its height and the square of its radius.
   b. What is the constant of variation? $\frac{1}{3}\pi$

SKILLS Objective B

4. z varies directly as the square of x and inversely as y.
   a. Write a general variation equation to represent the situation. $z = \frac{kx^2}{y}$
   b. If $z = 18.4$ when $x = 2.0$ and $y = 1.6$, find the constant of variation. $k = 7.36$
   c. Find z when $x = 3.2$ and $y = 2.4$. $z \approx 31.403$
5. P varies inversely as the square of M and directly as R and as the cube of J. When $R = 180$, $J = 2.1$, and $M = 19.4$, $P = 12.0$. Find P when $R = 144$, $J = 2.6$, and $M = 18.2$. $P \approx 20.7$

USES Objective G

6. Under certain conditions, the thrust T of a propeller varies jointly as its speed s measured in RPM and the square of its diameter d measured in feet. Suppose a propeller 4 feet in diameter generates 600 horsepower of thrust at 1000 RPM. How much thrust would a 5-foot diameter propeller generate at 800 RPM? 750 horsepower
7. Recall that the weight a board can support varies directly as the width and the square of the thickness, and inversely as the distance between supports. A board with 8' between supports 1.5" thick and 5.5" wide can support 225 lb. How much weight can the board support if its width is increased to 7.5"? ≈ 306.8 lb

168 *Advanced Algebra*

Notes on the Questions

Question 11 This is the first example in which the variation is not in terms of a variable but in terms of a function of variables, namely the difference between the squares of radii. You will likely have to explain the language.

Additional Answers

12a.

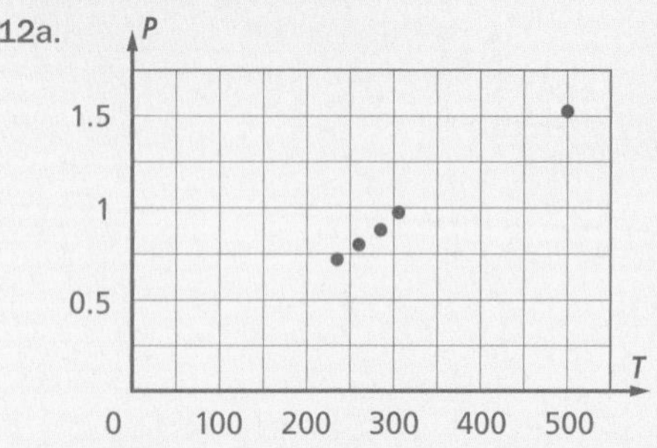

12c.

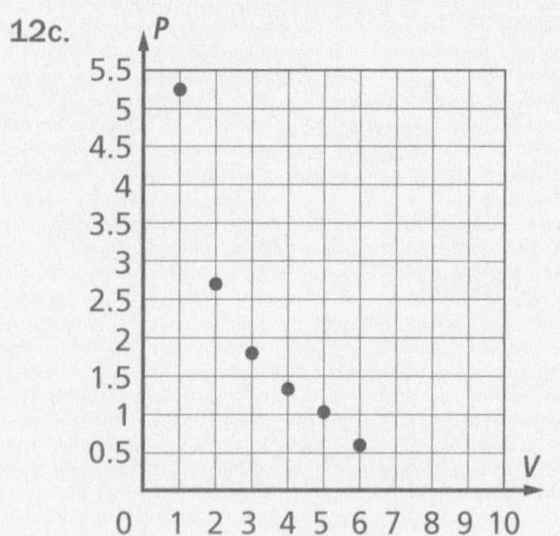

9. The volume of a certain solid varies jointly as its height, width, and length.
   a. Write a general equation to model this situation. $V = khwl$
   b. **Fill in the Blank** The answer to Part a suggests that this is a ___?___ solid. rectangular
   c. Based on your answer to Part b, find the value of k. $k = 1$

10. Suppose y varies directly as x and inversely as z. Describe how y changes when x and z are each tripled. Explain your answer.

10. y remains the same since $y = \frac{kx}{z}$ becomes $y = \frac{k3x}{3z} = \frac{kx}{z}$.

11. The cost C of polyvinyl chloride (PVC) piping in dollars varies jointly as the length L of the pipe and the difference between the squares of its outer and inner radii, $R_o^2 - R_i^2$. Suppose that a foot of PVC piping with an outer radius of 0.25 foot and an inner radius of 0.20 foot costs \$3.72. a. $C = kL(R_o^2 - R_i^2)$
   a. Using the given variables, write a joint variation equation.
   b. Find the constant of variation. $k = 165.33$
   c. Rewrite the variation equation using the constant from Part b.
   d. Find the cost of 10 feet of PVC piping with an outer radius of 0.5 foot and in inner radius of 0.48 foot. \$32.40
   e. Determine the unit of the constant of variation. dollars per cubic foot

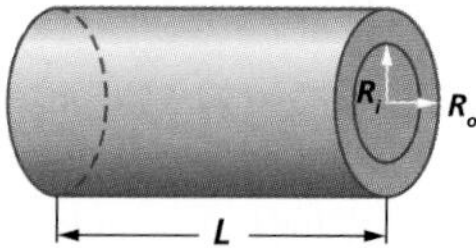

11c. $C = 165.33L(R_o^2 - R_i^2)$

REVIEW

12. The Ideal Gas Law in chemistry relates the pressure P (in atmospheres) exerted by a gas to the temperature T (in Kelvins) of the gas and volume V (in liters) of its container. Chantel obtained the following data using a 5-liter container in the lab. (Lessons 2-7, 2-8)

T (K)	235	260	285	305	500
P (atm)	0.7285	0.8060	0.8835	0.9455	1.55

   a. Graph the data points. See margin.
   b. How does P vary with T? P varies directly with T.
   c. With a temperature of 350 Kelvins, Chantel manipulated the volume of the container and obtained the following data. Graph these points on a different set of axes. See margin.

V (L)	1	2	3	4	5	6
P (atm)	5.425	2.713	1.808	1.356	1.085	0.603

   d. How does P vary with V? P varies inversely with V.
   e. Write an equation that relates P, T, and V. You do not need to find the constant of variation. $P = \frac{kT}{V}$

13. Let $g: x \rightarrow 3x^2$. **(Lesson 2-5)**
   a. Graph g over the domain $-2.5 \leq x \leq 2.5$. See margin.
   b. What is the name of the shape of this graph? parabola
   c. Find the average rate of change of g between $x = 1$ and $x = 2$. 9
   d. Would the answer to Part c be the same for any two values of x that differ by 1? Explain your answer.

14. If y varies directly as w^3, and $y = 25$ when $w = 5$, find the value of y when $w = 2$. **(Lesson 2-1)** $\frac{8}{5}$

15. One general equation for a combined variation is $y = k\frac{xz}{w}$. Solve for k in terms of the other variables. **(Lesson 1-7)** $k = \frac{wy}{xz}$

16. When Clara tried to solve the equation $\frac{1}{5}x + \frac{1}{7}x + 2 = 5$, her first step led to $7x + 5x + 70 = 175$. **(Lesson 1-6)**
   a. Explain what Clara did.
   b. Finish solving the equation. $x = \frac{35}{4}$

17. Given the function $f: x \rightarrow 4x^3 - 2x + 1$, find $f(\pi)$. **(Lesson 1-3)** 118.7

13d. No; the rate of change between x_1 and x_2 increases as the values of x_1 and x_2 increase.

16a. She multiplied by the least common multiple of the denominators, 35.

EXPLORATION

18. There are many instances of mathematics on TV shows. Watch a show in which mathematics plays a role and record any mathematics used on the show. Note whether the mathematics was used accurately and try to explain any mistakes.
Answers vary. Check students' work. Shows that use mathematics include *The Simpsons*, *Numb3rs*, *Deal or No Deal*, and *CSI*.

QY ANSWERS

1. $y = \frac{kx^2}{z}$
2. $A = kbh$. In this case, $k = \frac{1}{2}$.

Additional Answers

13a.

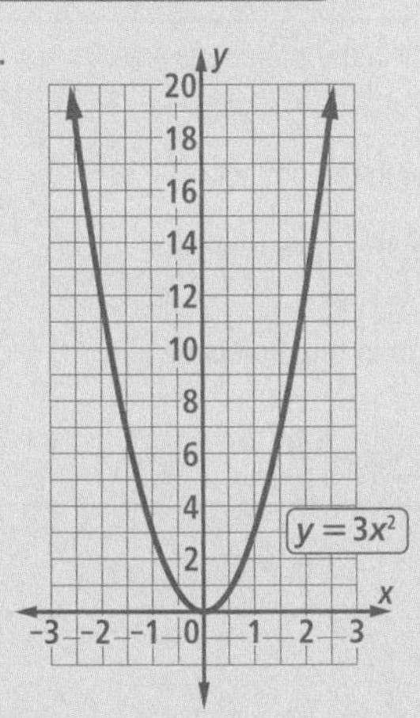

4 Wrap-Up

Ongoing Assessment

Ask students to write a variation equation for each situation.

1. B varies directly with C and the square of D and inversely with E. $B = \frac{kCD^2}{E}$
2. F varies directly with the square of G and the cube root of H and inversely with the square of J. $F = \frac{kG^2 \sqrt[3]{H}}{J^2}$

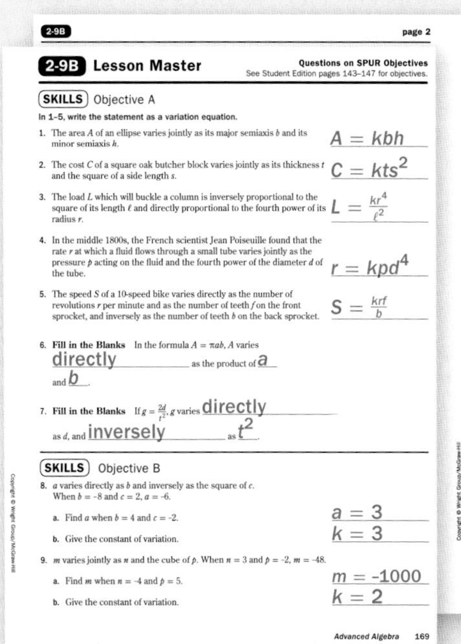

2-9B page 2

2-9B Lesson Master

Questions on SPUR Objectives
See Student Edition pages 143–147 for objectives.

SKILLS Objective A

In 1–5, write the statement as a variation equation.

1. The area A of an ellipse varies jointly as its major semiaxis b and its minor semiaxis h. $A = kbh$
2. The cost C of a square oak butcher block varies jointly as its thickness t and the square of a side length s. $C = kts^2$
3. The load L which will buckle a column is inversely proportional to the square of its length ℓ and directly proportional to the fourth power of its radius r. $L = \frac{kr^4}{\ell^2}$
4. In the middle 1800s, the French scientist Jean Poiseuille found that the rate r at which a fluid flows through a small tube varies jointly as the pressure p acting on the fluid and the fourth power of the diameter d of the tube. $r = kpd^4$
5. The speed S of a 10-speed bike varies directly as the number of revolutions r per minute and as the number of teeth f on the front sprocket, and inversely as the number of teeth b on the back sprocket. $S = \frac{krf}{b}$
6. **Fill in the Blanks** In the formula $A = \pi ab$, A varies directly as the product of a and b.
7. **Fill in the Blanks** If $g = \frac{2d}{t^2}$, g varies directly as d, and inversely as t^2.

SKILLS Objective B

8. a varies directly as b and inversely as the square of c. When $b = -8$ and $c = 2$, $a = -6$.
   a. Find a when $b = 4$ and $c = -2$. $a = 3$
   b. Give the constant of variation. $k = 3$
9. m varies jointly as n and the cube of p. When $n = 3$ and $p = -2$, $m = -48$.
   a. Find m when $n = -4$ and $p = 5$. $m = -1000$
   b. Give the constant of variation. $k = 2$

Advanced Algebra 169

Chapter 2

The projects relate to the content of the lessons of this chapter as follows:

Project	Lesson(s)
1	2-2
2	2-6
3	2-8
4	2-6
5	2-7
6	2-8

1 The Law of the Lever

As an extension to this project, ask students to rest a straight "string" of pennies, just touching each other at their edges, on one side of a lever, and balance that "string" with a "stack" of the same number of coins on the other side of the pivot. How far from the pivot is that stack? Can students make a conclusion about how a "string" of like objects is interpreted by a lever? The lever acts as though the "string" is a "stack" placed at the midpoint of the "string."

2 Variation and Light

You may want to emphasize the importance in this project for accurate measures of distances and diameters. Also, encourage students to keep the "outside light" as constant as possible when they take different measurements using a light meter.

Chapter 2 Projects

1 The Law of the Lever

Use a rigid ruler as a lever and a triangular object as a pivot. Place one penny on the ruler 6 inches from the pivot.

a. Stack two pennies on top of each other and place them on the ruler where they will balance the one penny on the other end. Record how far from the pivot the pennies are placed. Repeat the process for three pennies and four pennies. Does your experiment confirm the Law of the Lever?

b. Place a penny 4 inches from the pivot and then place a quarter so that it balances the penny. Repeat this process with a dime instead of a quarter. Use the Law of the Lever to determine how many times heavier a quarter is than a penny, and how many times heavier a penny is than a dime.

c. Use your findings in Part b to predict how far from the pivot a quarter should be placed to balance a dime 6 inches from the pivot. Test your prediction. How accurate was your prediction?

Archimedes wrote about the Law of the Lever in his work titled *On the Equilibrium of Planes.*

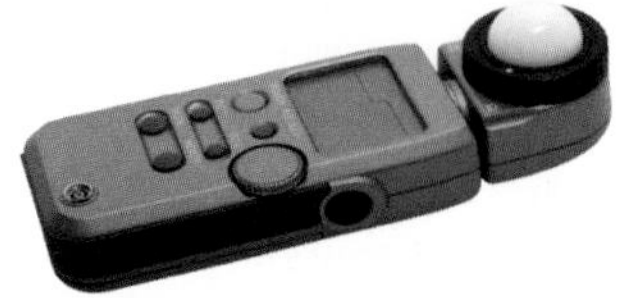

Photographers use light meters to help create the right light for a photo.

2 Variation and Light

Use a small, bright, pocket-sized flashlight and a sheet of printer paper. Put the paper on a desk in a dimly lit room and shine the light straight down on the paper from a sequence of increasing distances, for example, 1 inch, 2 inches, 4 inches, 7 inches, and so on, until the image becomes too dim to see.

a. At each distance, measure the diameter of the circular image produced by the beam of light. Create a table with the height h of the flashlight above the paper in the first column and the diameter d of the circular image in the second.

b. Graph your data from Part a.

c. Write a formula showing how the diameter of the image depends on the height of the flashlight. Does the diameter vary directly or inversely as h?

d. Borrow a light meter from a photographer or a science teacher. Repeat the process in Part a, but measure the intensity or brightness of the image at each height rather than the diameter of the image.

e. Theoretically, the intensity I of light varies inversely as the square of the height h of the flashlight above the image. How closely do your data fit this model?

Project Rubric

Advanced	Student correctly provides all of the details asked for in the project as well as additional correct independent conclusions.
Proficient	Student correctly provides all of the details asked for in the project.
Partially proficient	Student correctly provides some of the details asked for in the project or provides all details with some inaccuracies.
Not proficient	Student correctly provides few of the details asked for in the project or provides all details with many inaccuracies.
No attempt	Student makes little or no attempt to complete the project.

3 The Maximum Load of a Balsa Board

Refer to Perry's experiments in Lesson 2-8. Collect pieces of balsa wood of various lengths, widths, and thicknesses. Reconstruct the experiments regarding the maximum load M a board can hold. Find an equation relating d, w, t, and M for balsa wood.

4 Exploring a Connection between $y = \frac{1}{x}$ and the Altitudes of a Triangle

Use a DGS to graph the function $y = \frac{1}{x}$.

a. On one branch of the hyperbola, construct $\triangle ABC$ with its vertices on the hyperbola.

b. The *orthocenter* of a triangle is the intersection of the lines that contain the altitudes of the triangle. Construct M, the orthocenter of $\triangle ABC$.

c. Vary the location of the vertices of $\triangle ABC$ and observe how the location of M changes.

d. Give the coordinates of M and verify that it is located on the other branch of the hyperbola.

5 Galileo's Law of Free-Falling Objects

The Exploration in Lesson 2-7 asks you to find how Galileo used an inclined plane as the basis for his conclusions about free-falling objects. Recreate Galileo's experiment using a long board, a marble, and a stopwatch, or use a computer-based laboratory device. Write a report about your experiment. How close to the constant $k = 4.9 \text{ m/sec}^2$ did you come?

6 Average Rates of Change

On a CAS, define a function *arc* that has four inputs and computes the *average rate* of change between two given points.

a. Use *arc* to calculate the average rate of change for $y = 2x^2$ between each set of consecutive ordered pairs in a table of values where $x = -5, -4, -3, \ldots, 4, 5$. Repeat the calculations for $y = -2x^2$. Explain the connections between the average rates of change of each function and the graph of each function.

b. Repeat Part a using $y = 2x^3$ and $y = -2x^3$.

c. Repeat Part a using $y = \frac{1}{x}$.

d. Look up the term *concavity* and explain how it relates to the average rate of change you found in Parts a–c.

Galileo used an apparatus similar to this to test and develop the Law of Free-Falling Objects.

Notes

3 The Maximum Load of a Balsa Board

This project is recommended as a group activity. There are often irregularities in the density of balsa wood, so we suggest students cut several "identical" pieces for each set of d, w, and t values and enter the median of all the resulting M values into their data table for that set of d, w, and t values. All the students who select this project can pool their data to find those median M values.

4 Exploring a Connection between $y = \frac{1}{x}$ and the Altitudes of a Triangle

This project deals with the orthocenter of a triangle (the point of concurrency for the lines containing the altitudes of a triangle) and explores the property that if a triangle's vertices lie on one branch of a hyperbola, then the triangle's orthocenter lies on the other branch. A proof of the property involves writing and solving a system of equations. Writing the equations relies on the property (not yet studied in this course) that for any line with nonzero slope m, the slope of any line perpendicular to it is $-\frac{1}{m}$.

5 Galileo's Law of Free-Falling Objects

As a starting point for students who select this project, at each angle of their inclined plane, they should use marbles and other balls of various masses and determine whether the mass of the ball affects the time it takes a ball to roll down the inclined plane. If the ball is very light, such as a table tennis ball or beach ball, air resistance can influence the rolling time; otherwise, the time is independent of the mass of the ball.

6 Average Rates of Change

For student reports on this project, encourage them to take enough time describing the project to the class so all students understand what steps they took, what data they gathered, and how those data led to their conclusions.

Sample answers for projects are in the Solution Manual in the Electronic Teacher's Edition.

Chapter 2

Summary and Vocabulary

The Summary gives an overview of the entire chapter and provides an opportunity for students to consider the material as a whole. Thus, the Summary can be used to help students relate and unify the concepts presented in the chapter.

Vocabulary words and symbols are listed by lesson to provide a checklist of concepts that students must know. Emphasize to students that they should read the vocabulary list carefully before starting the Self-Test on pages 140–142. If students do not understand the meaning of a vocabulary word, they should refer back to the indicated lesson.

Theorems and Properties covered in the chapter are listed below the Summary with page references included to lead students back to the location in the chapter where the theorem or property is stated.

Chapter 2 Summary and Vocabulary

- The functions studied in this chapter are all based on direct and inverse variation. When $k \neq 0$ and $n > 0$, formulas of the form $y = kx^n$ define **direct-variation functions**, and those of the form $y = \frac{k}{x^n}$ define **inverse-variation functions**. Four special cases of direct and inverse variation commonly occur. The equation, graph, name of the curve, domain D, range R, asymptotes, and symmetries of each special case are summarized on the next page.

- In a formula where y is given in terms of x, it is logical to ask how changing x (the independent variable) affects the value of y (the dependent variable). In direct or inverse variation, when x is multiplied by a constant, the change in y is predicted by the **Fundamental Theorem of Variation**. If y varies directly as x^n, then when x is multiplied by c, y is multiplied by c^n. If y varies inversely as x^n, then when x is multiplied by c, y is divided by c^n. The converse of this theorem is also true.

- The rate of change $\frac{y_2 - y_1}{x_2 - x_1}$ between (x_1, y_1) and (x_2, y_2) is the **slope** of the line connecting the points. For graphs of equations of the form $y = kx$, the rate of change between any two points on the graph is the constant k. For nonlinear curves, the rate of change is not constant, but varies depending on which points are used to calculate it.

- Variation formulas may involve three or more variables, one dependent and the others independent. In a **joint variation**, all the independent variables are multiplied. If the independent variables are not all multiplied, the situation is a **combined variation**. Variation formulas can be derived from real data by examining two variables at a time and comparing their graphs with those given on the following page.

- There are many applications of direct, inverse, joint, and combined variation. They include perimeter, area, and volume formulas, the inverse-square laws of sound and gravity, a variety of relationships among physical quantities such as distance, time, force, and pressure, and costs that are related to these other measures.

Vocabulary

Lesson 2-1
varies directly as
directly proportional to
direct-variation equation
constant of variation
*direct-variation function

Lesson 2-2
*inverse-variation function
varies inversely as
inversely proportional to

Lesson 2-4
*rate of change, slope

Lesson 2-5
parabola
vertex of a parabola
reflection-symmetric
line of symmetry

Lesson 2-6
hyperbola
branches of a hyperbola
vertical asymptote
horizontal asymptote
discrete set
inverse-square curve

Lesson 2-9
combined variation
joint variation

Some **direct-variation functions**

$y = kx$

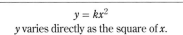

y varies directly as x.

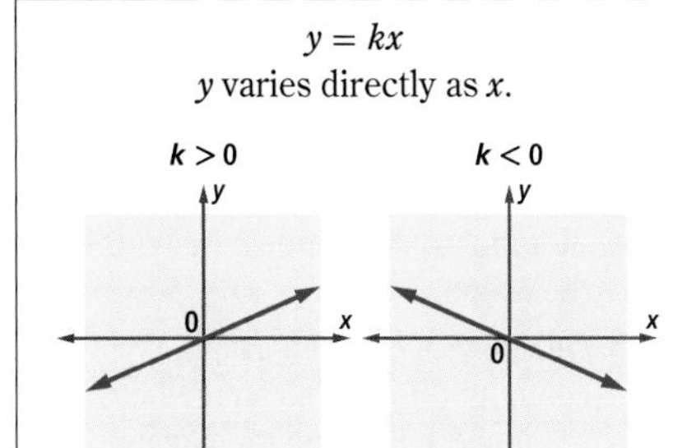

lines

$D = R =$ set of all real numbers

$y = kx^2$

y varies directly as the square of x.

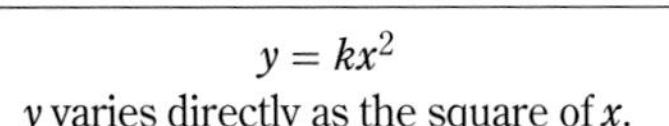
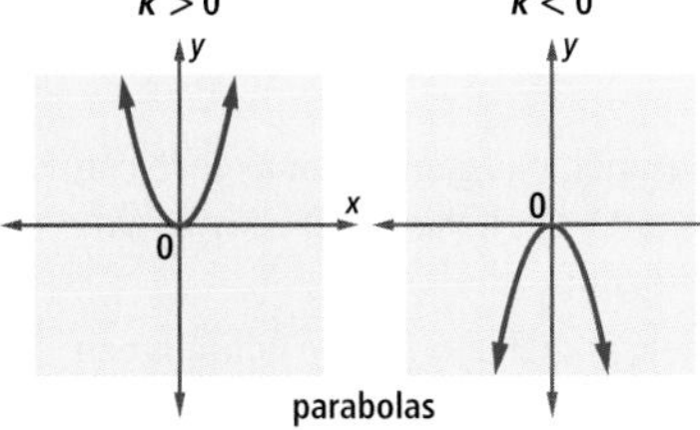

parabolas

$D =$ set of all reals $\quad D =$ set of all reals

$R = \{y|\ y \geq 0\} \quad R = \{y|\ y \leq 0\}$

reflection-symmetric to the y-axis

Some **inverse-variation functions**

$y = \frac{k}{x}$

y varies directly as x.

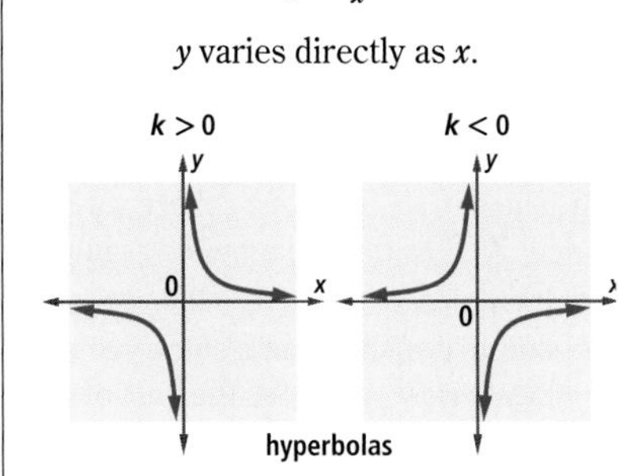

hyperbolas

$D = R = \{x|\ x \neq 0\}$

asymptotes: x-axis, y-axis

$y = \frac{k}{x^2}$

y varies inversely as the square of x

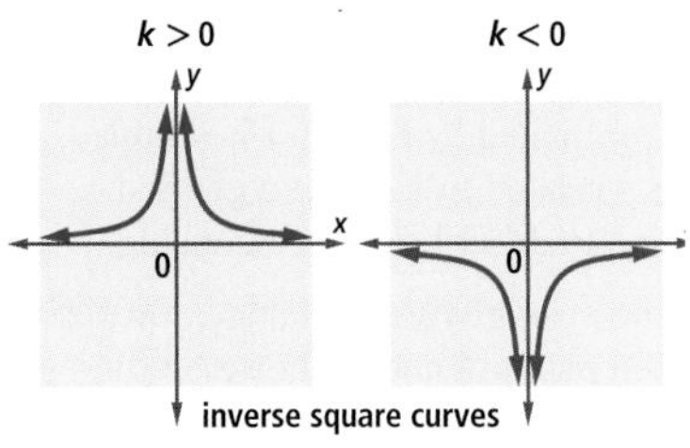

inverse square curves

$D = \{x|\ x \neq 0\} \quad D = \{x|\ x \neq 0\}$

$R = \{y|\ y > 0\} \quad R = \{y|\ y < 0\}$

asymptotes: x-axis, y-axis

reflection-symmetric to the y-axis

Theorems and Properties

Fundamental Theorem of Variation (p. 88)
Slope of $y = kx$ Throrem (p. 95)
Converse of the Fundamental Theorem of Variation (p. 122)

Summary and Vocabulary 139

Self-Test

For the development of mathematical competence, feedback and correction, along with the opportunity for practice, are necessary. The Self-Test provides the opportunity for feedback and correction; the Chapter Review provides additional opportunities for practice. We cannot overemphasize the importance of these end-of-chapter materials. It is at this point that the material gels for many students, allowing them to solidify skills and understanding. In general, student performance should improve after these pages.

Assign the Self-Test as a one-night assignment. Worked-out solutions for all questions are in the Selected Answers section of the student book. Encourage students to take the Self-Test honestly, grade themselves, and then be prepared to discuss the test in class.

Advise students to pay special attention to those Chapter Review questions (pages 143–147) that correspond to the questions they missed on the Self-Test.

Additional Answers

1. Direct variation means that n and ℓ increase together. n is the dependent variable and ℓ is the independent variable, so the equation is $n = k\ell$.
2. Direct variation means that w increases as d^4 increases, and inverse variation means that w decreases as L^2 increases. w is the dependent variable and d and L are the independent variables, so the equation is $w = \frac{kd^4}{L^2}$.
3. By the form of the equation, we know that s is the dependent variable, p is the independent variable, and k is the constant of variation. Because p^4 is in the denominator, this means that as p^4 increases, s decreases. So, to express this equation, we say that s varies inversely as p^4.
4. The equation described is $T = ks^3w^2$. Given $s = 2$ and $w = 1$, $T = 10$, thus $10 = k(2^3)(1^2)$ and $k = \frac{5}{4}$. Therefore, we can rewrite the equation as $T = \frac{5}{4}s^3w^2$. So for $s = 8$ and $w = \frac{1}{2}$, $T = \frac{5}{4}(8)^3\left(\frac{1}{2}\right)^2 = 160$.

Chapter 2 Self-Test

Take this test as you would take a test in class. Then use the Selected Answers section in the back of the book to check your work.

1–8. See margin.

In 1 and 2, translate the statement into a variation equation.

1. The number n of items that a store can display on a shelf varies directly as the length ℓ of the shelf.
2. The weight w that a bridge column can support varies directly as the fourth power of its diameter d and inversely as the square of its length L.
3. Write the variation equation $s = \frac{k}{p^4}$ in words.
4. If T varies directly as the third power of s and the second power of w, and if $T = 10$ when $s = 2$ and $w = 1$, find T when $s = 8$ and $w = \frac{1}{2}$.
5. For the variation equation $y = \frac{5}{x^2}$, how does the y-value change when an x-value is doubled? Give two specific ordered pairs (x, y) that support your conclusion.
6. If y is multiplied by 8 when x is doubled, how is y related to x? Write a general equation to describe the relationship.
7. Find the average rate of change of $y = x^2$ between points A and B shown on the graph.

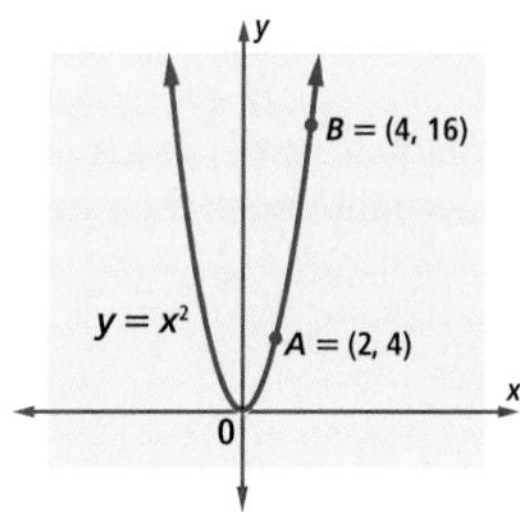

8. **True or False**
   a. All graphs of variation equations contain the origin.
   b. On a direct-variation graph, if you compute the rate of change between $x = 1$ and $x = 2$, and then again between $x = 2$ and $x = 3$, then you will get the same result.
9. a. **Fill in the Blanks** The graph of $y = kx^2$ is called a __?__ and opens upward if __?__. parabola; $k > 0$
   b. How does the graph of $y = kx^2$ change as k gets closer to 0? See margin.
10. Suppose f is a function with $f(d) = \frac{12}{d^2}$. What is the domain of f?
11. **Fill in the Blank** Complete each sentence with *inversely, directly,* or *neither inversely nor directly.* Explain your reasoning.
    a. The surface area of a sphere varies __?__ as the square of its radius.
    b. If you have exactly \$5,000 to invest, the number of shares of a stock you can buy varies __?__ as the cost of each share. 11–12. See margin.
12. a. Make a table of values for $y = -\frac{1}{2}x$. Include at least five pairs.
    b. Draw a graph of the equation in Part a.
    c. Find the slope of the graph in Part b.

10. $\{d \mid d \neq 0\}$. Since 0 cannot be in the denominator of a fraction, d^2 cannot equal 0, and, thus $d \neq 0$.

Additional Answers

5. From the equation, we can see that y varies inversely as x^2. Therefore, by the Fundamental Theorem of Variation, doubling the x-value divides the y-value by 4. For example, the points (1, 5) and $\left(2, \frac{5}{4}\right)$ satisfy the equation.
6. If y is multiplied by 8 when x is doubled, this implies that y and x are directly related. As the cube of 2 is 8, we see that y varies directly as the cube of x. A general equation to express this relationship is $y = kx^3$.
7. The average rate of change can be found by plugging the points into the formula $m = \frac{y_2 - y_1}{x_2 - x_1}$. Here we get $m = \frac{16 - 4}{4 - 2} = \frac{12}{2} = 6$.

8a. False; for inverse variation equations $y = \frac{k}{x^n}$, there is no value for y when $x = 0$.

8b. False; if y varies directly with x^n, where $n > 1$, the rate of change will not be constant.

9b. The opening of the parabola grows wider.

$\{d \mid d \neq 0\}$: Because 0 cannot be in the denominator of a fraction, d^2 cannot equal 0, and thus $d \neq 0$. d is defined for all other real numbers.

13. a. Use a graphing utility to sketch a graph of $y = \frac{4}{x}$. See margin.
b. Identify any asymptotes to the graph in Part a. $x = 0, y = 0$

14. a. **Multiple Choice** Which equation's graph looks the most like the graph below? 14–16. See margin.

A $y = 2x$ B $y = -\frac{2}{x}$

C $y = \frac{2}{x^2}$ D $y = -\frac{x}{2}$

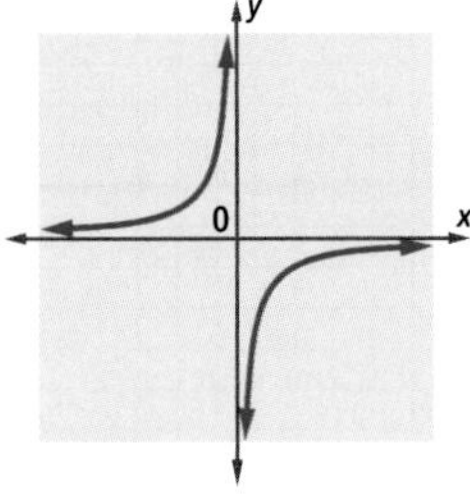

b. State the domain and range of your answer to Part a.

15. Bashir's family is buying a new car. After looking at several models they became interested in the relationship between a car's fuel economy F in miles per gallon (mpg) and its weight w in pounds. Bashir collected data in the table below.

Weight w (lb)	Fuel Economy F (mpg)
2,655	40
2,991	34
3,263	32
3,737	28
3,962	26
5,577	19

a. Graph the data points in the table.
b. Which variation equation is a better model for Bashir's data, $F = \frac{k}{w}$ or $F = \frac{k}{w^2}$? Justify your answer and find the constant of variation.
c. A family is thinking about buying a 5,900-pound sport-utility vehicle (SUV). Based on the model you found in Part b, what would you predict its fuel economy will be?
d. In you own words, explain what the model tells you about the relationship between fuel economy and vehicle weight.

16. Suppose that variables V, h, and g are related as illustrated in graphs I and II below. The points on graph I lie on a parabola. The points on graph II lie on a line through the origin. Write a single equation that represents the relationship among V, h, and g.

I

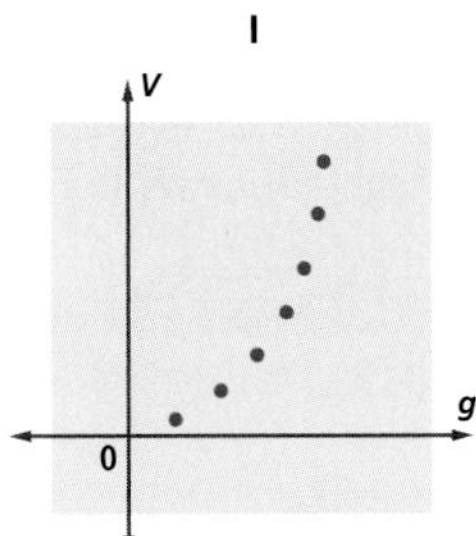

II

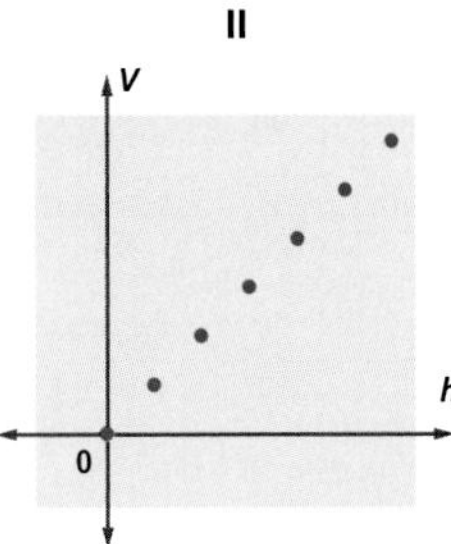

Additional Answers

11a. Directly; the volume of the sphere will increase as the radius increases.

11b. Inversely; the more expensive the stock, the fewer shares of stock you can buy.

12a. Answers vary. Sample:

x	y
0	0
1	-0.5
2	-1
3	-1.5
4	-2
5	-2.5

12b.

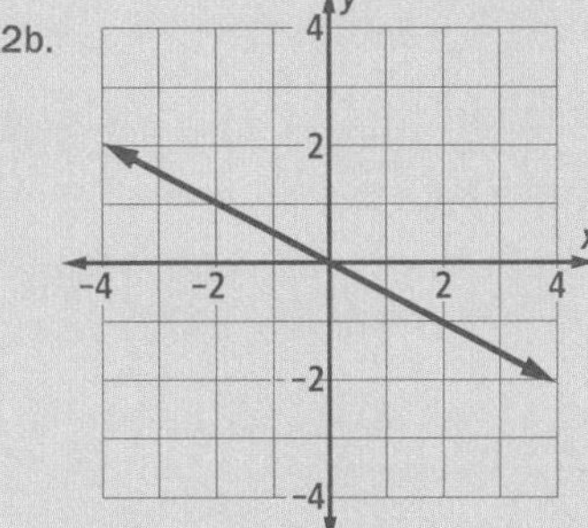

12c. We can use two points from the table to find the slope. Because the slope is constant, any two points will work. Therefore, $m = \frac{-2 - (-1)}{4 - 2} = -\frac{1}{2}$.

Chapter 2 Self-Test

Additional Answers

13a.

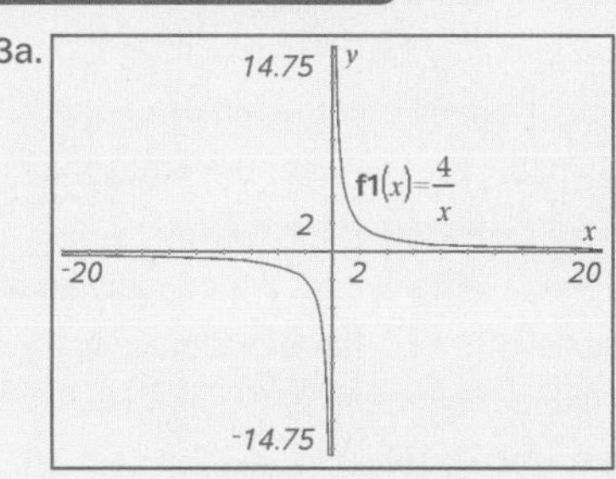

14a. B; the answer cannot be A or D because both of these graphs would have constant slope. The answer cannot be C because the y-values of this function must be positive, but the graph shown does not have this property.

14b. Because you cannot have 0 in the denominator, $x \neq 0$, but all other values of x are in the domain. Likewise $y \neq 0$, but all other values of y are in the range.

15a.

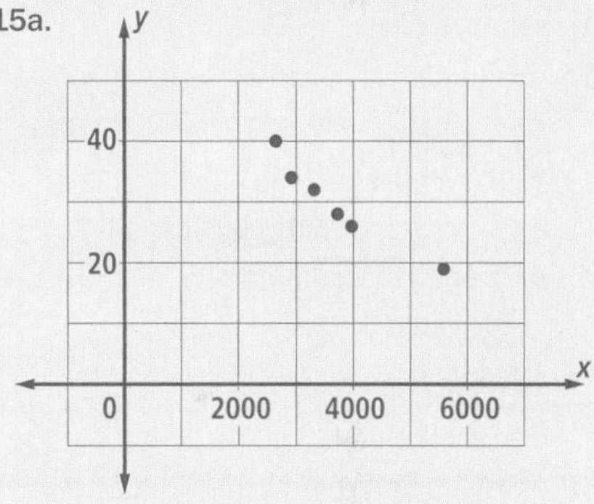

15b. $F = \frac{k}{w}$. As w doubles, F is halved. Find the constant of variation by plugging in a pair of values. Answers vary. Sample: $40 = \frac{k}{2655}$, $k = 106{,}200$.

15c. Plug in 5900 for the weight to find that according to the model, $F = \frac{106{,}200}{5900} = 18$ mpg.

15d. The model shows that as vehicle weight increases, fuel economy decreases.

16. V is the dependent variable, and because its graph with g is a parabola, it is related to g as follows: $V = kg^2$. Its graph with h is a line, so it is related to h as follows: $V = kh$. Because V varies jointly with g and h, we can combine these two equations into the general equation $V = kg^2h$.

17a. Because height is inversely proportional to the square of the radius by the Fundamental Theorem of Variation, as r doubles, h will be divided by 4. So when r increases from 5 cm to 10 cm, h will decrease from 10 cm to $\frac{10}{4} = 2.5$ cm.

Additional Answers

17b. In general, if two cylinders have the same volume and the radius of one is double the radius of the other, their heights are related in the ratio 1 : 4.

18a. If Paula is right, then the equation that fits is $m = kd^3$. Therefore, plugging in the given points, $k = \frac{6.0 \cdot 10^{24}}{(12{,}700)^3} = 2.9 \cdot 10^{12}$. Thus, the equation would be $m = 2.9 \cdot 10^{12}d^3$.

18b. The model from Part a predicts Jupiter's mass to be 1331 times the mass of Earth, because $11^3 = 1331$. Thus Jupiter's mass would be about $8.0 \cdot 10^{27}$ kg.

18c. Answers vary. Sample: Not all planets are made of the same materials. Jupiter is less dense than Earth; therefore, their masses cannot vary directly as their volumes alone.

19a. $d = kt$; the data appear to lie on a line, so d varies directly with time, not the square of time.

19b. Answers vary slightly, depending on the data point chosen. Sample: $41 = 30k$, $k = \frac{41}{30}$, and $d = \frac{41}{30}t$.

19c. Answers vary slightly. Sample: $d = \frac{41}{30}(180) = 246$ in.

19d. Answers vary slightly. Sample: 50 ft = 600 inches. $600 = \frac{41}{30}t$, $t \approx 439$. The water can run for 439 minutes, or 7 hours, 19 minutes.

17–19. See margin.

17. For a cylinder of fixed volume, the height is inversely proportional to the square of the radius.
    a. If a cylinder has height 10 cm and radius 5 cm, what is the height of another cylinder of equal volume and with a 10 cm radius?
    b. Generalize Part a. If two cylinders have the same volume, and the radius of one is double the radius of the other, what is the relationship between their heights?

18. Paula thinks the mass of a planet varies directly with the cube of its diameter.
    a. Assume Paula is correct. The diameter of Earth is approximately 12,700 km, and its mass is approximately 6.0×10^{24} kg. Compute the constant of variation, and write an equation to model the situation.
    b. The diameter of Jupiter is approximately 11 times that of Earth. What does the model from Part a predict Jupiter's mass to be?
    c. The mass of Jupiter is actually about 1.9×10^{27} kg. Why do you think this differs from the answer to Part b?

19. A cylindrical tank is being filled with water and the water depth is measured at 30-minute intervals. Below are a table and a graph showing the time passed t and the depth d of the water in the tank.

t (min)	30	60	90	120
d (in.)	41	80	122	162

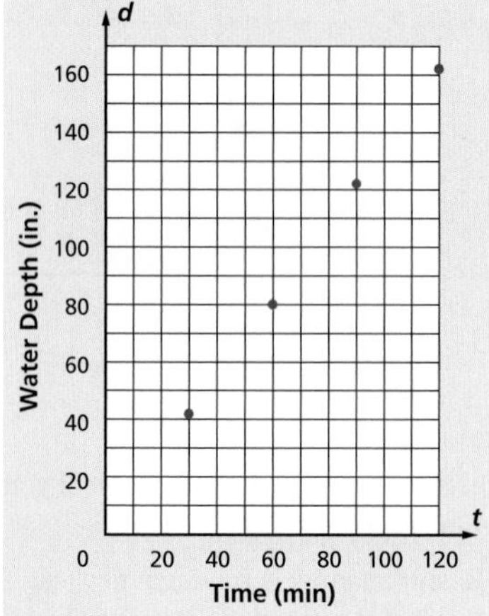

a. Which variation equation models this data better, $d = kt$ or $d = kt^2$? Justify your answer.
b. Find the constant of variation and write the variation equation.
c. Based on your model, what is the depth of the water after 3 hours?
d. If the tank is 50 feet tall, how long can the water run before the tank is full?

Chapter 2 Chapter Review

SKILLS
PROPERTIES
USES
REPRESENTATIONS

SKILLS Procedures used to get answers

OBJECTIVE A Translate variation language into formulas and formulas into variation language. (Lessons 2-1, 2-2, 2-9)

In 1–3, translate the sentence into a variation equation.

1. y varies directly as x. $y = kx$
2. d varies inversely as the square of t. $d = \frac{k}{t^2}$
3. z varies jointly as x and t. $z = kxt$
4. **Fill in the Blanks** In the equation $w = kyz$, where k is a constant, __?__ varies __?__ as __?__. w; jointly; y and z
5. **Fill in the Blanks** If $y = \frac{kx}{v^2}$, where k is a constant, then y varies __?__ as __?__, and varies __?__ as __?__. directly; x; inversely; the square of v

In 6–8, write each variation equation in words.

6. $y = kw^3$ y varies directly as the third power of w.
7. $y = \frac{k}{w^3}$ y varies inversely as the third power of w.
8. $y = \frac{kz}{w^3}$ y varies inversely as the third power of w and directly as z.

OBJECTIVE B Solve variation problems. (Lessons 2-1, 2-2, 2-9)

9. Suppose y varies directly as x. If $x = 3$, then $y = -21$. Find y when $x = -7$. $y = 49$
10. If y varies directly as the cube of x, and $y = \frac{3}{2}$ when $x = 3$, find y when $x = -6$. $y = -12$
11. Suppose y varies inversely as the square of x. When $x = 4$, $y = \frac{3}{4}$. Find y when $x = -6$. $y = \frac{1}{3}$
12. z varies directly as x and inversely as the cube of y. When $x = 12$ and $y = 2$, $z = 39$. Find z when $x = 7$ and $y = 3$. $z = 6.74074$

OBJECTIVE C Find slopes and rates of change. (Lessons 2-4, 2-5)

13. Find the slope of the line passing through (3, -12) and (10, 20). $\frac{32}{7}$
14. What is the slope of the line graphed below? $-\frac{4}{5}$

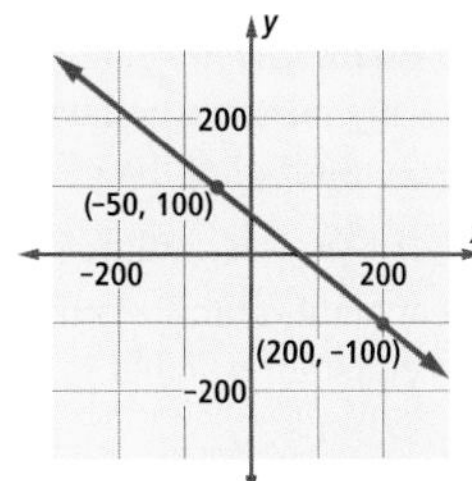

In 15 and 16, let $y = 2x^3$.

15. Find the average rate of change from $x = -2$ to $x = 0$. 8
16. Find the average rate of change from $x = 2$ to $x = 3$. 38

In 17 and 18, find the average rate of change from $x = 10$ to $x = 20$.

17. $y = \frac{5}{x}$ $-\frac{1}{40}$
18. $y = \frac{5}{x^2}$ $-\frac{3}{800}$

Chapter Review

The main objectives for the chapter are organized in the Chapter Review under the four types of understanding this book promotes: Skills, Properties, Uses, and Representations.

Whereas end-of-chapter material may be considered optional in some texts, in UCSMP *Advanced Algebra* we have selected these objectives and questions with the expectation that they will be covered. Students should be able to answer these questions with about 85% accuracy after studying the chapter.

You may assign these questions over a single night to help students prepare for a test the next day or you may assign the questions over a two-day period. If you work the questions over two days, we recommend assigning the evens for homework the first night so that students get feedback in class the next day, and then assigning the odds the night before the test because the answers are provided to the odd-numbered questions in the Selected Answers section at the back of the book.

It is effective to ask students which questions they still do not understand and use the day as a total class discussion of the material that the class finds most difficult.

Resources

- Assessment Resources: Chapter 2 Test Forms A–D; Chapter 2 Test, Cumulative Form

Technology Resources

Teacher's Assessment Assistant, Ch. 2
Electronic Teacher's Edition, Ch. 2

Additional Answers

25. y is multiplied by $\frac{a^n}{b^n}$.
26. y varies directly as the cube of x; $y = kx^3$.
34. Answers vary. Sample: Both functions do not have any points in Quadrants I and II. They are also both symmetric to the y-axis. However, $y = -2x^3$ is defined for $x = 0$ and $y = -\frac{2}{x^2}$ is not.

PROPERTIES Principles behind the mathematics

OBJECTIVE D Use the Fundamental Theorem of Variation. (Lessons 2-3, 2-8)

In 19–21, suppose x is tripled. Tell how the value of y changes under the given condition.

19. y varies directly as x. y is tripled.
20. y varies inversely as x^2. y is divided by 9.
21. y varies directly as x^n. y is multiplied by 3^n.
22. Suppose y varies inversely as x^2. How does y change if x is divided by 10? y is multiplied by 100.
23. **Fill in the Blank** If $y = \frac{k}{x^n}$, and x is multiplied by any nonzero constant c, then y is __?__. divided by c^n
24. **Fill in the Blank** If $y = \frac{k}{x^n}$, and x is divided by any nonzero constant c, then y is __?__. multiplied by c^n
25. Suppose $y = \frac{kx^n}{z^n}$, x is multiplied by nonzero constant a, and z is multiplied by a nonzero constant b. What is the effect on y? See margin.
26. Suppose that when x is divided by 3, y is divided by 27. How is x related to y? Express this relationship in words and in an equation. See margin.

OBJECTIVE E Identify the properties of variation functions. (Lessons 2-4, 2-5, 2-6)

27. **Fill in the Blank** The graph of the equation $y = kx^2$ is a __?__. parabola
28. **Fill in the Blanks** Graphs of all direct variation functions have the point (__?__, __?__) in common. (0, 0)

In 29–31, refer to the four equations below.

A $y = kx$ B $y = kx^2$

C $y = \frac{k}{x}$ D $y = \frac{k}{x^2}$

29. Which equations have graphs that are symmetric to the y-axis? B, D
30. The graph of which equation is a hyperbola? C
31. **True or False** When $k > 0$, all of the equations have points in Quadrant I. true
32. a. Identify the domain and range of $f(x) = \frac{k}{x^2}$ when $k < 0$. $\{x \mid x \neq 0\}$; $\{y \mid y < 0\}$
    b. What are the asymptotes of f if $f(x) = \frac{k}{x}$? x—axis, y—axis
33. For what domain values are the inverse and inverse-square variation functions undefined? $x = 0$
34. Write a short paragraph explaining how the functions $y = -2x^2$ and $y = -\frac{2}{x^2}$ are alike and how they are different. See margin.

USES Applications of mathematics in real-world situations

OBJECTIVE F Recognize variation situations. (Lessons 2-1, 2-2)

In 35–37, translate the sentence into a variation equation.

35. The number n of hamsters that can safely live in a square hamster cage is proportional to the square of the length ℓ of a side of the cage. $n = k\ell^2$
36. The length of time t required for an automobile to travel a given distance is inversely proportional to the velocity v at which it travels. $t = \frac{k}{v}$
37. The electromagnetic force F between two bodies with a given charge is inversely proportional to the square of the distance d between them. $F = \frac{k}{d^2}$
38. Translate Einstein's famous equation for the relationship between energy and mass, $E = mc^2$, into variation language. (E = energy, m = mass, c = the speed of light, which is a constant.) Energy varies directly as mass.

Fill in the Blank In 39–42, complete each sentence with *directly*, *inversely*, or *neither directly nor inversely*.

39. The number of people that can sit comfortably around a circular table varies __?__ with the radius of the table. directly

40. The volume of a circular cylinder of a given height varies __?__ as the square of the radius of its base. directly

41. The wall area that can be painted with a gallon of paint varies __?__ as the thickness of the applied paint. inversely

42. Your height above the ground while on a Ferris wheel varies __?__ as the number of minutes you have been riding it. neither directly nor inversely

OBJECTIVE G Solve real-world variation problems. (Lessons 2-1, 2-2, 2-9)

43–45. See margin.

43. One of Murphy's Laws says that the time t spent debating a budget item is inversely proportional to the number d of dollars involved. According to this law, if a committee spends 45 minutes debating a \$5,000 item, how much time will they spend debating a \$10,000,000 item?

44. Recall that the weight of an object is inversely proportional to the square of its distance from the center of Earth. If you weigh 115 pounds on the surface of Earth, how much would you weigh in space 50,000 miles from Earth's surface? (The radius of Earth is about 4,000 miles.)

45. Computer programmers are often concerned with the efficiency of the algorithms they create. Suppose you are analyzing large data sets and create an algorithm that requires a number of computations varying directly with n^4, where n is the number of data points to be analyzed. You first apply your algorithm to a test data set with 10,000 data points, and it takes the computer 5 seconds to perform the computations. If you then apply the algorithm to your real data set, which has 1,000,000 data points, how long would you expect the computation to take? (Assume the computer takes the same amount of time to do each computation.)

46. A credit card promotion offers a discount on all purchases made with the card. The discount is directly proportional to the size of the purchase. If you save \$1.35 on a \$20 purchase, how much will you save on a \$173 purchase? \$11.68

47. The force required to prevent a car from skidding on a flat curve varies directly as the weight of the car and the square of its speed, and inversely as the radius of the curve. It requires 290 lb of force to prevent a 2,200 lb car traveling at 35 mph from skidding on a curve of radius 520 ft. How much force is required to keep a 2,800 lb car traveling at 50 mph from skidding on a curve of radius 415 ft? ≈ 944.58 lb

48. An object is tied to a string and then twirled in a circular motion. The tension in the string varies directly as the square of the speed of the object and inversely as the length of the string. When the length of the string is 2 ft and the speed is 3 ft/sec, the tension on the string is 130 lb. If the string is shortened to 1.5 ft and the speed is increased to 3.4 ft/sec, find the tension on the string. ≈ 222.6 lb

Notes on the Questions

Question 43 All of Murphy's Laws can be found at http://www.murphys-laws.com/.

Additional Answers

43. only 0.0225 min, or about 1.35 sec
44. 0.631 lb
45. 500,000,000 sec, or about 16 yr

Additional Answers

49a.

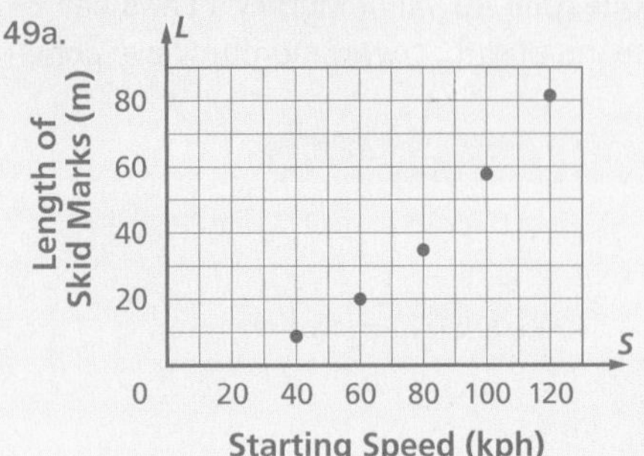

49b. $L = kS^2$

49c. $k = \frac{9}{1600}$; $L = \left(\frac{9}{1600}\right)S^2$

49d. $L \approx 126.6$ m

50a.

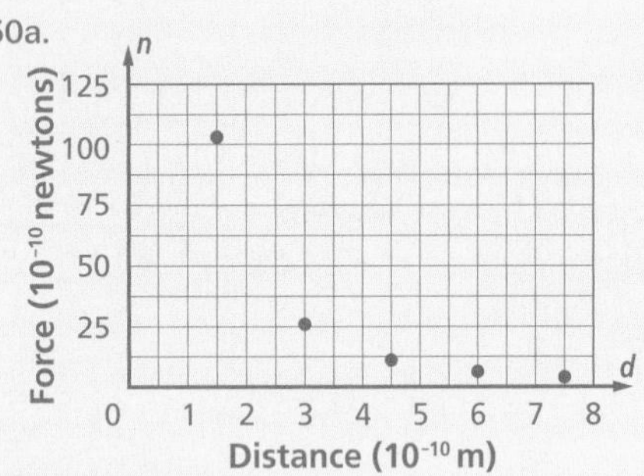

50b. $F = \frac{k}{d^2}$

50c. $k = 231.75$; $F = \frac{231.75}{d^2}$

50d. $2.3175 \cdot 10^{-8}$ N

51. $P = kdD$; because the points on both graphs lie on straight lines, P varies directly as D and also as d. Therefore, P varies jointly as D and d.

52a.

x	r
0	0
1	-0.333
2	-1.333
3	-3
4	-5.333
5	-8.333
6	12

OBJECTIVE H Fit an appropriate model to data. (Lessons 2-7, 2-8)

In 49 and 50, a situation and question are given.

a. Graph the given data.

b. Find a general variation equation to represent the situation.

c. Find the value of the constant of variation and use it to rewrite the variation equation.

d. Use your variation equation from Part c to answer the question. 49–50. See margin.

49. Officer Friendly measured the length L of car skid marks when the brakes were applied at different starting speeds S. He obtained the following data.

S (kph)	40	60	80	100	120
L (m)	9	20	36	56	81

How far would a car skid if the brakes were applied at 150 kph?

50. Two protons will repel each other with a force F that depends on the distance d between them. Some values of F are given in the following table. Note that d is measured in 10^{-10} meters, and F is measured in 10^{-10} newtons.

d	1.5	3	4.5	6	7.5
F	103	26	11	6	4

With what force will two protons repel each other if they are 1×10^{-10}m apart?

51. Jade performed an experiment to determine how the pressure P of a liquid on an object is related to the depth d of the object and the density D of the liquid. She obtained the graph on the left by keeping the depth constant and measuring the pressure on an object in solutions with different densities. She obtained the graph on the right by keeping the density constant and measuring the pressure on an object in solutions at various depths.

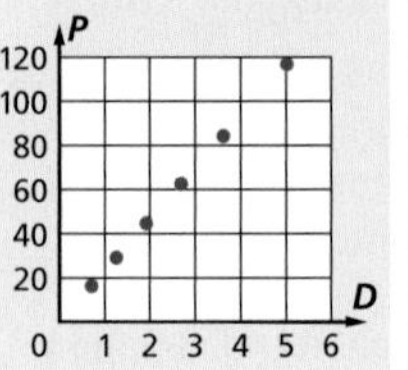

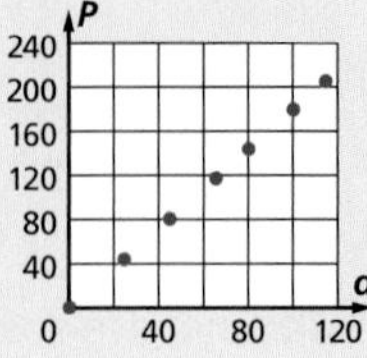

Write a general equation relating P, d, and D. Do not find the constant of variation. Explain your reasoning. See margin.

REPRESENTATIONS Pictures, graphs, or objects that illustrate concepts

OBJECTIVE I Graph variation equations. (Lessons 2-4, 2-5, 2-6) 52–53. See margin.

In 52 and 53, an equation is given.

a. Make a table of values.

b. Graph the equation for values of the independent variable from –3 to 3.

52. $r = -\frac{1}{3}x^2$

53. $p = \frac{2}{q^2}$

In 54 and 55, use graphing technology to graph the equation. 54–55. See margin.

54. $y = \frac{216}{x^3}$

55. $z = -\frac{4.85}{m}$

Additional Answers

52b.

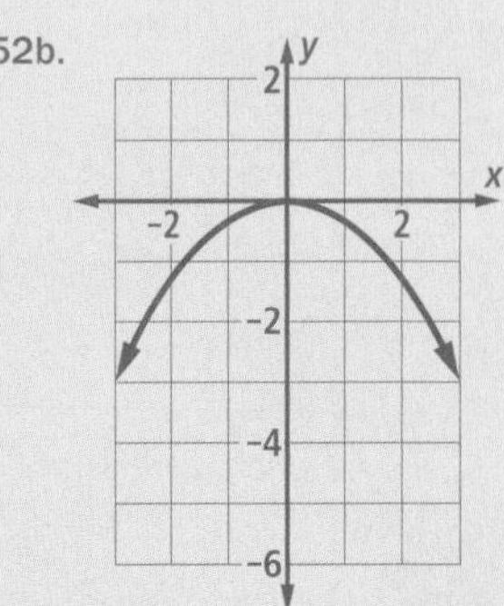

53a.

q	p
0	undef
1	2
2	5
3	0.222
4	0.125
5	0.8
6	0.056

56. Describe how the graph of $y = kx^2$ changes as k decreases from 1 to -1. See margin.

57. Describe how the graph of $y = -\frac{k}{x^2}$ changes as k increases from 1 to 100. See margin.

OBJECTIVE J Identify variation equations from graphs. (Lessons 2-4, 2-5, 2-6)

Multiple Choice In 58 and 59, select the equation whose graph is most like the one shown. Assume the scales on the axes are the same.

58. 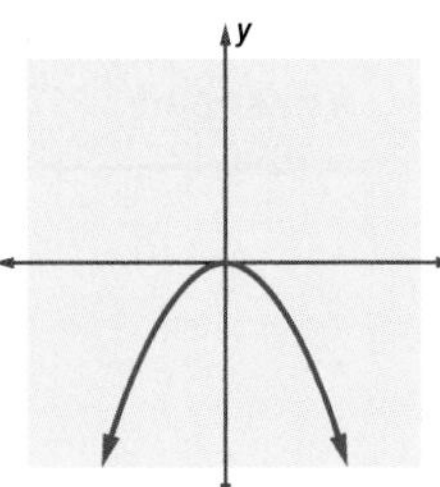

B

A $y = -x$ B $y = -x^2$

C $y = \frac{1}{x^2}$ D $y = x^2$

59. 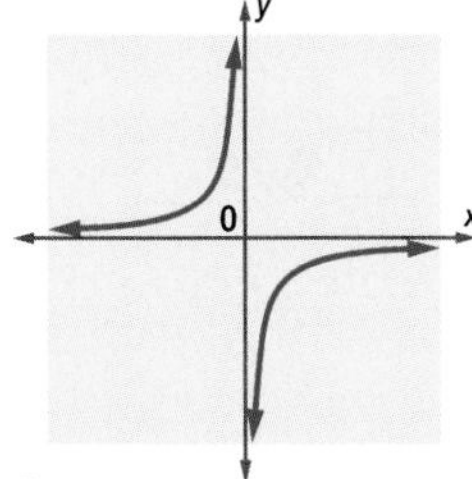

C

A $y = \frac{x^2}{8}$ B $y = \frac{8}{x}$

C $y = -\frac{8}{x}$ D $y = -\frac{8}{x^2}$

60. In the graph of $y = kx^2$, what type of number must k be? positive

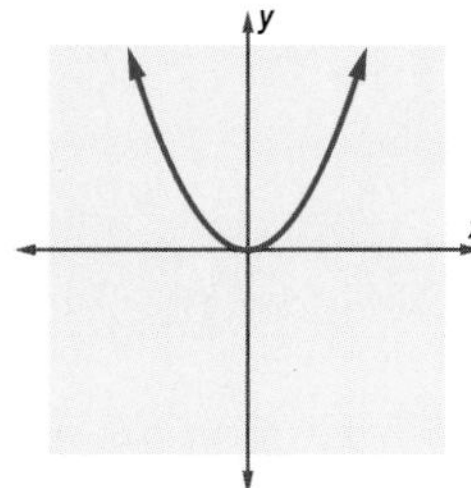

61. In the graph of $y = \frac{k}{x}$, what type of number must k be? negative

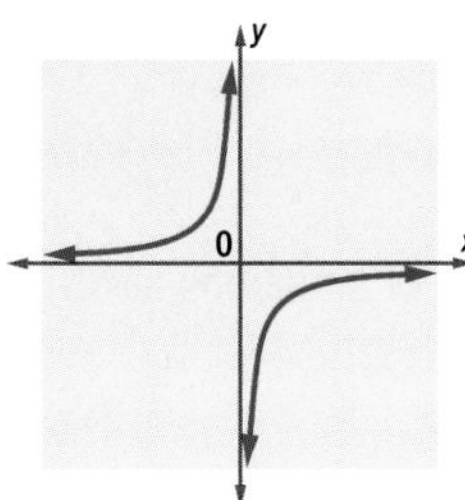

Assessment

Evaluation The *Assessment Resources* provide four forms of the Chapter 2 Test. Forms A and B present parallel versions of a short-answer format. Form C consists of four to six short-response questions that cover the SPUR objectives from Chapter 2. Form D offers performance assessment that covers a subset (or even just one) of the SPUR objectives for the chapter. The fifth type of test is a Chapter 2 Test, Cumulative Form. About 50% of this test covers Chapter 2, and the remaining 50% covers the previous chapter.

Feedback After students have taken the test for Chapter 2 and you have scored the results, return the tests to students for discussion. Class discussion on the questions that caused trouble for most students can be very effective in identifying and clarifying misunderstandings. You might want to have them note the items they missed and work either in groups or at home to correct them. It is important for students to receive feedback on every chapter test, and we recommend that students see and correct their mistakes before proceeding too far into the next chapter.

Suggestions for Assignment Assign Lesson 3-1 for homework the evening of the test. It gives students work to do after they have completed the test and keeps the class moving. If you do not do this, you may cover one less chapter over the course of the year.

Additional Answers

53b. 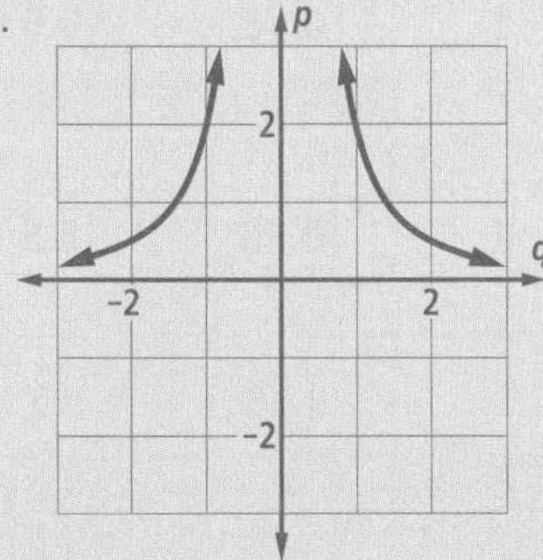

54. 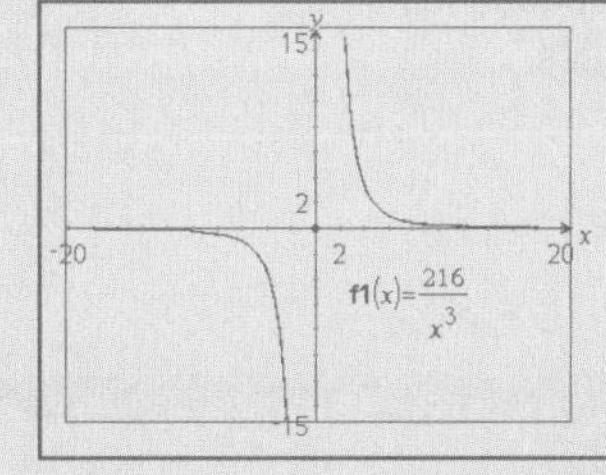

Additional Answers

55. 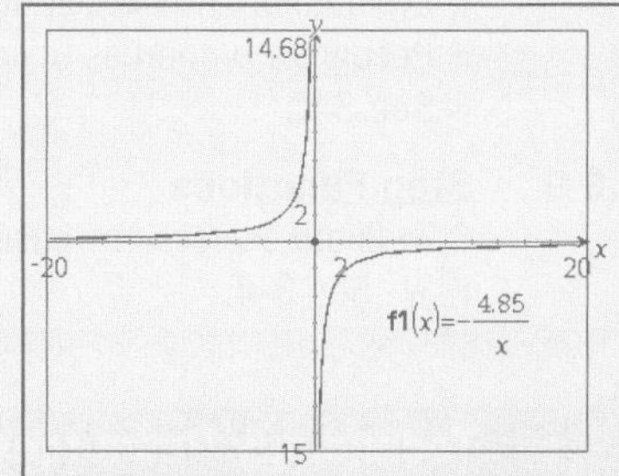

56. The graph opens upward, gradually flattens, and then opens downward.

57. The branches pull away from the y-axis.

Chapter 3

Linear Functions and Sequences

Chapter Overview

		Local Standards	Pacing (in days) Average	Advanced	Block
3-1	**Constant Change and the Graph of $y = mx + b$** **A** Determine the slope and intercepts of a line given its equation. **E** Recognize properties of linear functions. **G** Model constant-increase or constant-decrease situations or situations involving arithmetic sequences. **M** Graph or interpret graphs of linear equations.		1	0.75	0.5
3-2	**Linear Combinations and $Ax + By = C$** **E** Recognize properties of linear functions. **H** Model linear combination situations.		1	0.75	0.5
3-3	**The Graph of $Ax + By = C$** **A, E, M** See **3-1.**		1	0.75	0.5
	QUIZ 1		0.5	0.5	0.25
3-4	**Finding an Equation of a Line** **B** Find an equation of a line given two points on it or given a point on it and its slope. **I** In a real-world context, find an equation for a line containing two points. **K** Model situations leading to piecewise linear functions or to step functions. **N** Graph or interpret graphs of piecewise linear functions, step functions, or sequences.		1	0.75	0.5
3-5	**Fitting a Line to Data** **J** Fit lines to data.		1	0.75	0.5
3-6	**Recursive Formulas for Sequences** **D** Evaluate or find explicit or recursive formulas for sequences. **L** Model situations with recursive formulas.		1	0.75	0.5
	QUIZ 2		0.5	0.5	0.25
3-7	**Graphs of Sequences** **L** Model situations with recursive formulas. **N** See **3-4.**		1	0.75	0.5
3-8	**Formulas for Linear (Arithmetic) Sequences** **D** Evaluate or find explicit and recursive formulas for sequences. **F** Recognize properties of linear or arithmetic sequences. **G** See **3-1.**		1	0.75	0.5
3-9	**Step Functions** **C** Evaluate expressions based on step functions. **K, N** See **3-4.**		1	0.75	0.5
		Self-Test	1	0.75	0.5
		Chapter Review	2	1	0.5
		Test	1	1	0.5
		TOTAL	14	10.5	6.5

Technology Resources

Teacher's Assessment Assistant, Ch. 3

Electronic Teacher's Edition, Ch. 3

Differentiated Options  Universal Access

	Accommodating the Learner	Vocabulary Development	Ongoing Assessment	Materials
3-1	p. 152	p. 151	group, p. 156	
3-2	pp. 158, 159	p. 159	written, p. 162	
3-3	pp. 164, 165	p. 164	oral, p. 168	
3-4	pp. 170, 171	p. 171	oral, p. 175	
3-5	pp. 178–179	p. 177	written, p. 181	internet connection
3-6	pp. 183, 185	p. 184	group, p. 188	
3-7	pp. 190, 192	p. 191	written, p. 195	
3-8	pp. 198, 199	p. 197	oral, p. 202	
3-9	pp. 205, 206	p. 204	group, p. 209	

Objectives

Skills	Lessons	Self-Test Questions	Chapter Review Questions
A Determine the slope and intercepts of a line given its equation.	3-1, 3-3	2	1-6
B Find an equation of a line given two points on it or given a point on it and its slope.	3-4	4, 5	7-10
C Evaluate expressions based on step functions.	3-9	16b	11-13
D Evaluate or find explicit and recursive formulas for sequences.	3-6, 3-8	9a, 9b, 13	14-17
Properties			
E Recognize properties of linear functions.	3-1, 3-2, 3-3	3, 6	18-23
F Recognize properties of linear or arithmetic sequences.	3-8	9c	24-31
Uses			
G Model constant-increase or constant-decrease situations or situations involving arithmetic sequences.	3-1, 3-8	8	32, 33
H Model linear combination situations.	3-2	7	34, 35
I In a real-world context, find an equation for a line containing two points.	3-4	12	36, 37
J Fit lines to data.	3-5	18	38, 39
K Model situations leading to piecewise linear functions or to step functions.	3-4, 3-9	10, 15, 16a	40-44
L Model situations with recursive formulas.	3-6, 3-7	11	45, 46
Representations			
M Graph or interpret graphs of linear equations.	3-1, 3-3	1	47-53
N Graph or interpret graphs of piecewise linear functions, step functions, or sequences.	3-4, 3-7, 3-9	14, 17	54-58

Resource Masters Chapter 3

Resource Master 1, Graph Paper (page 2), can be used with Lessons 3-1 and 3-7. **Resource Master 2, Four Quadrant Graph Paper** (page 3), can be used with Lesson 3-9.

Resource Master 38 Lesson 3-1

Warm-Up

What is the slope and y-intercept of the line with equation $y = 0.07x + 24.9$?

Additional Example

1. A pool contains 85 gallons of water. Suppose a hose adds water to the pool at a rate of 7 gallons per minute. Write an equation for a function representing the amount of water in the pool t minutes after the hose is turned on. The pool can hold 1359 gallons of water.

Slopes of Lines

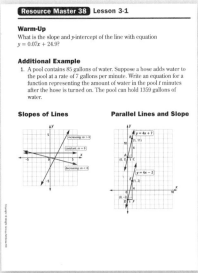

increasing: $m > 0$
constant: $m = 0$
decreasing: $m < 0$

Parallel Lines and Slope

$y = 4x + 7$
$y = 4x - 2$

Resource Master for Lesson 3-1

Resource Master 39 Lesson 3-1

Additional Example

2. A mudslide left 42 acre-feet of mud in a valley. The mud is being removed at the rate of 5 acre-feet per day.
   a. Write a linear equation to model this situation.
   b. When will all the mud be removed?
   c. What are the y-intercept and the slope of the line represented by the equation in Part a?
   d. Graph the line and indicate the point that indicates no mud.

Solution

a. Let $M(t)$ be the amount of mud in the valley after t days: $M(t) =$ ____ $-$ ____.
b. The mud will be gone when $M(t) = 0$. Solve ____ $= 0$ to find $t =$ ____. The mud will be gone after ____ days.
c. The y-intercept is the starting point; the slope is the rate of change. So in this situation, the y-intercept is ____, and the slope is ____.
d. Graph the line with y-intercept 42 and slope -5. The mud is gone when the line crosses the x-axis, at the point (8.4, 0).

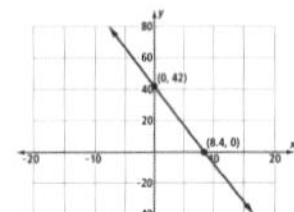

Resource Master for Lesson 3-1

Resource Master 40 Lesson 3-2

Warm-Up

Consider the following situation: Your car has a full tank of gas before the start of a driving trip. Your car gets 25 miles per gallon of gas while driving in the city and 32 miles per gallon on the highway. The gas tank holds 14 gallons. If the car is driven x miles in the city and runs out of gas after driving y miles on the highway, write an equation relating x, y, and the size of the tank. Check your answer with specific values of x and y.

Additional Examples

1. Give two different situations that could be modeled by the linear combination $4x + 8y = 48$. For each example, state whether the linear function is discrete or continuous and explain what the point (2, 5) represents.
   Solution
   a. You walk for x hours at 4 kilometers per hour and jog for y hours at 8 kilometers per hour, going a total of ____ kilometers. The point (2, 5) represents ____ hours of walking and ____ hours of jogging. You can walk and jog for any part of an hour; it does not make sense to restrict the domain. The function is ____.
   b. You buy x salads at ____ each and y sandwiches at ____ each. The total cost is ____. The point (2, 5) represents ____. You cannot buy part of a salad or sandwich. The function is ____.
2. Suppose you mix x liters of a 1.5 moles per liter solution of acid with y liters of a 6.5 moles per liter solution. The final mixture needs to contain 15 moles of acid.
   a. Write an equation that relates x, y, and the total number of moles of acid.
   b. How many liters of the 6.5 moles per liter solution must be added to 5 liters of the 1.5 moles per liter solution to get 15 moles of acid in the final mixture? Round to the nearest 0.01 liter.

Resource Master for Lesson 3-2

Resource Master 41 Lesson 3-3

Warm-Up

Graph each of the following equations on the same axes. What figure appears?

1. $3x + 8y = 20$
2. $3x - 8y = 20$
3. $-3x + 8y = 20$
4. $-3x - 8y = 20$

Additional Examples

1. Graph the equation $3x - 4y = 24$ using its x- and y-intercepts.
2. Graph $0x + y = -2$.
   a. Is the graph a line?
   b. Is the graph a function?
3. Find which equations below, if any, represent the same line.
   a. $2x - 4y = 12$
   b. $2x + 4y = -12$
   c. $2x + 4y = -16$
   d. $3x + 6y = -18$

   Solution Rewrite each line in slope-intercept form.
   a. $y =$ ____
   b. $y =$ ____
   c. $y =$ ____
   d. $y =$ ____
   Equations ____ and ____ are equivalent. Equations ____ and ____ are not equivalent to any other given equations.

Resource Master for Lesson 3-3

Resource Master 42 Lesson 3-4

Warm-Up

In 1–4, find an equation for the line through (0, 0) and the given point.

1. (5, 9)
2. (-17, 106)
3. $\left(\frac{2}{37}, 3\frac{1}{7}\right)$
4. (b, a)

Additional Examples

1. A spring is 23 inches long and has a 3-pound weight attached. Its length increases 3 inches with each additional pound of weight added. This is a constant-increase situation. Write a formula relating spring length L and weight w. Then graph the equation.
2. Find an equation of the line q through (6, 4) and (15, -2).
   Solution
   Compute the slope of line q: $m =$ ____.
   Because you know two points on the line and neither of them is the y-intercept, use one of the points in the point-slope form: $y -$ ____ $=$ ____$(x -$ ____$)$.
   This is one equation for line q. Now solve for y to put the equation in slope-intercept form, which is ____.
3. Write a piecewise linear function for a graph that goes from (0, 0) to (50, 40), then from (50, 40) to (60, 60), and then from (60, 60) to (100, 60). Use (p, q) as the variables.

Resource Master for Lesson 3-4

Resource Master 43 Lesson 3-4

Piecewise Linear Functions and Graphs

Distance from Home (mi)
Time (min)

Resource Master for Lesson 3-4

Resource Master 44 Lesson 3-5

Warm-Up

Consider these data of the ages of U.S. presidents at their deaths: {67, 90, 83, 85, 73, 80, 78, 79, 68, 71, 53, 65, 74, 64, 77, 56, 66, 63, 70, 49, 57, 71, 67, 58, 60, 72, 67, 57, 60, 90, 63, 88, 78, 46, 64, 81, 93}.
Find the median and the first and third quartiles of the data set.

Activity 1, Step 1

Number of Squares (n)	Score (s)

Resource Master for Lesson 3-5

Resource Master 45 Lesson 3-6

Warm-Up

1. Consider the sequence C of the positive integer powers of 3: 3, 9, 27, 81, ...
   a. Give an explicit formula for C_n.
   b. Describe how each term after the first is related to the term before it.
2. Consider the sequence B of negative integer powers of 3: $\frac{1}{3}, \frac{1}{9}, \frac{1}{27}, \frac{1}{81}, \ldots$.
   a. Give an explicit formula for B_n.
   b. Describe how each term after the first is related to the term before it.

Additional Example

1. Verify that the recursive definition
$\begin{cases} L_1 = 97 \\ L_2 = \text{previous term} - 23, \text{ for integers } n \geq 2 \end{cases}$
generates the first four terms of the sequence 97, 74, 51, 28, 5, -18, -41, ...

Solution The first term is given: $L_1 = 97$. According to the second line of the definition, L_2 = previous term − 23 = ____ − 23 = ____. To find L_3, use the definition again: L_3 = previous term − 23 = ____ − 23 = ____. Finally, L_4 = previous term − 23 = ____ − ____ = ____. The first four terms are 97, ____, ____, and ____, which checks according to what was calculated .

Resource Master for Lesson 3-6

Resource Master 46 Lesson 3-6

Additional Examples

2. Consider the sequence B = 850, 775, 700, ... Write a recursive definition for the sequence B.

   Solution The first line of the definition gives the initial term. So the first line is B_1 = ____.
   The second line relates each term to the previous term. So, the second line is $B_{n+1} = B_n -$ ____, for integers $n \geq$ ____. Thus, the recursive definition is ____.
3. A sequence C is 324, 108, 36, 12, 4.
   a. Use words to write a recursive definition of this sequence.
   b. Write a recursive formula for this sequence.
4. Use a spreadsheet to generate the first seven terms of the sequence
$\begin{cases} L_1 = 97 \\ L_n = L_{n-1} - 23, \text{ for integers } n \geq 2 \end{cases}$
5. Use a spreadsheet to generate the five terms of the sequence 324, 108, 36, 12, and 4.

   Solution The first term is 324. Each term after the first is found by dividing the previous term by 3. Enter 324 in cell ____. Enter ____ in cell A2. To see the five terms of this sequence in your spreadsheet, copy cell ____ and then paste it into cells ____ through ____. The five terms of the sequence are ____, ____, ____, ____, and ____.

Resource Master for Lesson 3-6

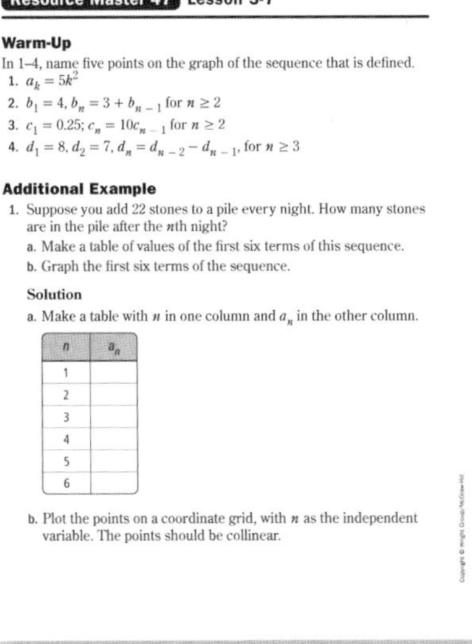

Resource Master 47 Lesson 3-7

Warm-Up

In 1–4, name five points on the graph of the sequence that is defined.

1. $a_k = 5k^2$
2. $b_1 = 4, b_n = 3 + b_{n-1}$ for $n \geq 2$
3. $c_1 = 0.25; c_n = 10c_{n-1}$ for $n \geq 2$
4. $d_1 = 8, d_2 = 7, d_n = d_{n-2} - d_{n-1}$, for $n \geq 3$

Additional Example

1. Suppose you add 22 stones to a pile every night. How many stones are in the pile after the nth night?
   a. Make a table of values of the first six terms of this sequence.
   b. Graph the first six terms of the sequence.

   Solution

   a. Make a table with n in one column and a_n in the other column.

n	a_n
1	
2	
3	
4	
5	
6	

   b. Plot the points on a coordinate grid, with n as the independent variable. The points should be collinear.

Resource Master for Lesson 3-7

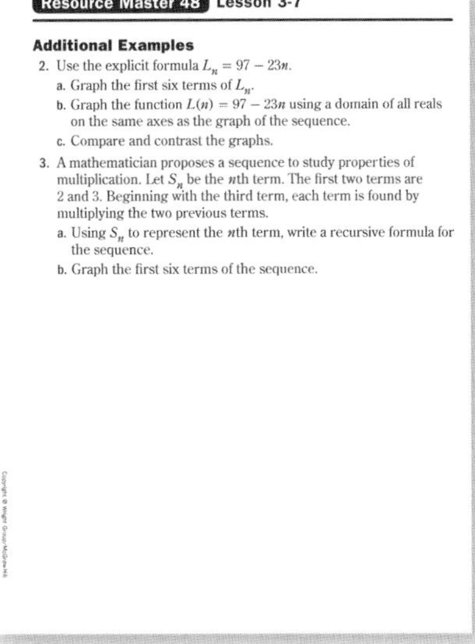

Resource Master 48 Lesson 3-7

Additional Examples

2. Use the explicit formula $L_n = 97 - 23n$.
   a. Graph the first six terms of L_n.
   b. Graph the function $L(n) = 97 - 23n$ using a domain of all reals on the same axes as the graph of the sequence.
   c. Compare and contrast the graphs.
3. A mathematician proposes a sequence to study properties of multiplication. Let S_n be the nth term. The first two terms are 2 and 3. Beginning with the third term, each term is found by multiplying the two previous terms.
   a. Using S_n to represent the nth term, write a recursive formula for the sequence.
   b. Graph the first six terms of the sequence.

Resource Master for Lesson 3-7

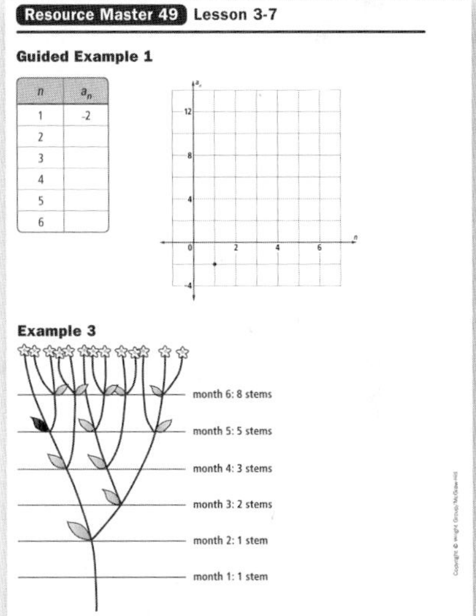

Resource Master 49 Lesson 3-7

Guided Example 1

n	a_n
1	-2
2	
3	
4	
5	
6	

Example 3

Resource Master for Lesson 3-7

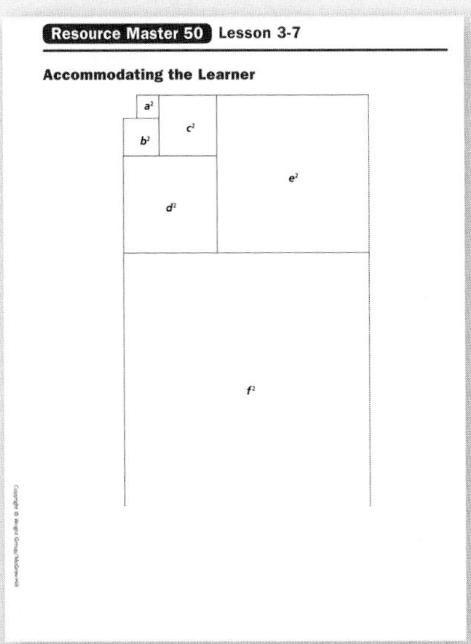

Resource Master 50 Lesson 3-7

Accommodating the Learner

Resource Master for Lesson 3-7

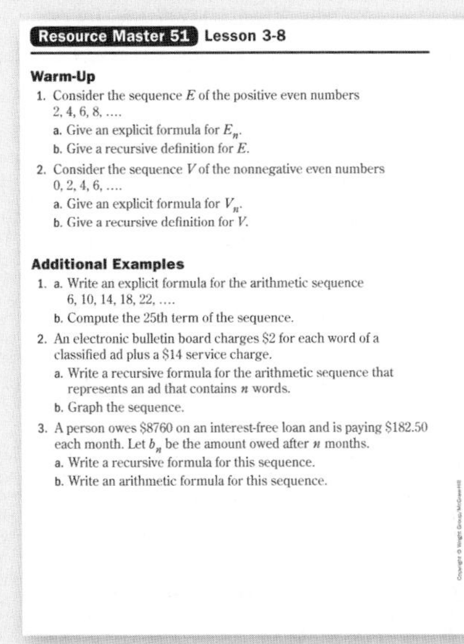

Resource Master 51 Lesson 3-8

Warm-Up

1. Consider the sequence E of the positive even numbers 2, 4, 6, 8, ...
   a. Give an explicit formula for E_n.
   b. Give a recursive definition for E.
2. Consider the sequence V of the nonnegative even numbers 0, 2, 4, 6, ...
   a. Give an explicit formula for V_n.
   b. Give a recursive definition for V.

Additional Examples

1. a. Write an explicit formula for the arithmetic sequence 6, 10, 14, 18, 22, ...
   b. Compute the 25th term of the sequence.
2. An electronic bulletin board charges \$2 for each word of a classified ad plus a \$14 service charge.
   a. Write a recursive formula for the arithmetic sequence that represents an ad that contains n words.
   b. Graph the sequence.
3. A person owes \$8760 on an interest-free loan and is paying \$182.50 each month. Let b_n be the amount owed after n months.
   a. Write a recursive formula for this sequence.
   b. Write an arithmetic formula for this sequence.

Resource Master for Lesson 3-8

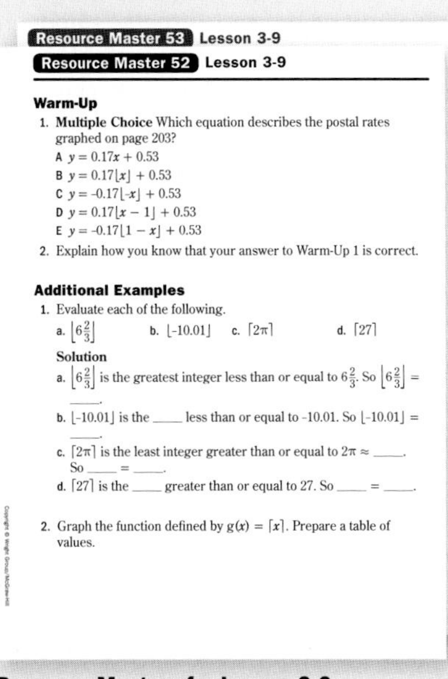

Resource Master 53 Lesson 3-9

Resource Master 52 Lesson 3-9

Warm-Up

1. **Multiple Choice** Which equation describes the postal rates graphed on page 203?
   A $y = 0.17x + 0.53$
   B $y = 0.17\lfloor x \rfloor + 0.53$
   C $y = -0.17\lfloor -x \rfloor + 0.53$
   D $y = 0.17\lfloor x - 1 \rfloor + 0.53$
   E $y = -0.17\lfloor 1 - x \rfloor + 0.53$
2. Explain how you know that your answer to Warm-Up 1 is correct.

Additional Examples

1. Evaluate each of the following.
   a. $\lfloor 6\frac{2}{3} \rfloor$ b. $\lfloor -10.01 \rfloor$ c. $\lceil 2\pi \rceil$ d. $\lceil 27 \rceil$

   Solution

   a. $\lfloor 6\frac{2}{3} \rfloor$ is the greatest integer less than or equal to $6\frac{2}{3}$. So $\lfloor 6\frac{2}{3} \rfloor$ = ____.
   b. $\lfloor -10.01 \rfloor$ is the ____ less than or equal to -10.01. So $\lfloor -10.01 \rfloor$ = ____.
   c. $\lceil 2\pi \rceil$ is the least integer greater than or equal to $2\pi \approx$ ____. So ____ = ____.
   d. $\lceil 27 \rceil$ is the ____ greater than or equal to 27. So ____ = ____.
2. Graph the function defined by $g(x) = \lceil x \rceil$. Prepare a table of values.

Resource Masters for Lesson 3-9

Chapter 3

Pacing

The amount of time you spend on this chapter may vary greatly, depending on the backgrounds of your students. For students with strong backgrounds, much of Lessons 3-1 through 3-5 should be review, and you may wish to cover these five lessons in 2 or 3 days. The rest of the chapter might take 5 to 7 days, for a total of perhaps 2 weeks. For other students, each lesson in this chapter is designed to be covered in 1 day. At the end of the chapter, you should plan to spend 1 day to review the Self-Test, 1 to 2 days for the Chapter Review, and 1 day for a test. You may wish to spend a day on projects and possibly a day is needed for quizzes. This chapter should therefore take 12 to 15 days. We strongly recommend that you not spend more than 16 days on this chapter.

Overview

Chapter 3 introduces situations that lead to linear relations and connects these relations to linear equations of the forms $y = kx$, $y = mx + b$, and $Ax + By = C$. This chapter is critical to the themes of graphing and applications that appear in subsequent chapters. Although many students will remember some of these concepts from their earlier studies in algebra and geometry, there is enough new material to make the lessons in this chapter interesting and worthwhile.

Chapter 3

Linear Functions and Sequences

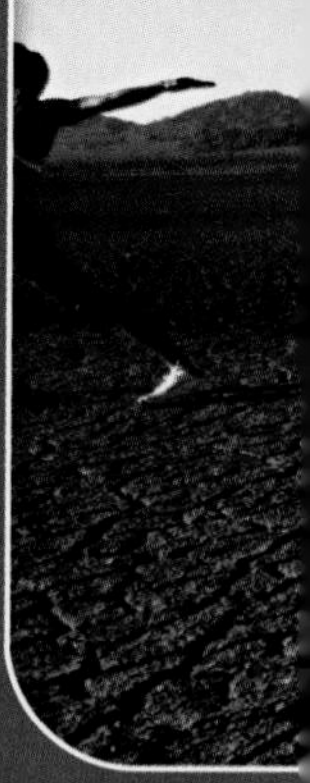

Contents

In Chapter 2, you studied direct variation situations modeled by functions with equations of the form $y = kx$, or $f(x) = kx$. f is a linear function whose graph contains (0, 0).

A linear function is a set of ordered pairs (x, y) in which $y = mx + b$, where m and b are constants. Many situations can be modeled mathematically using linear functions. For example, your body mass index (BMI) is a measure of body fat based on height and weight. The table on the next page shows some data about the average BMI for males of different ages. The graph shows that the data appear to be linear. In fact, if y is the average BMI of a person of age x, then $y \approx 0.07x + 24.9$.

148

Chapter 3 Overview

Chapter 3 has three themes, the first of which connects linear equations and their applications. Lesson 3-1 explains how constant-increase and -decrease situations lead to the slope-intercept form of a line and its graph. Lessons 3-2 and 3-3 explain how linear-combination situations lead to equations in standard form. Lesson 3-3 shows how to use intercepts to graph equations in standard form and also deals with equations for vertical lines.

The second theme is the relationship between lines, geometry, and statistics. Lesson 3-4 explains how to go from a graph, or from two points, to an equation and introduces piecewise linear graphs. Lesson 3-5 explores how to fit a line to more than two points. The last lesson of the chapter, Lesson 3-9, continues this theme with step functions, which are special piecewise linear graphs.

Age	BMI
25	26.6
35	27.5
45	28.4
55	28.7

Source: Centers for Disease Control and Prevention (CDC)

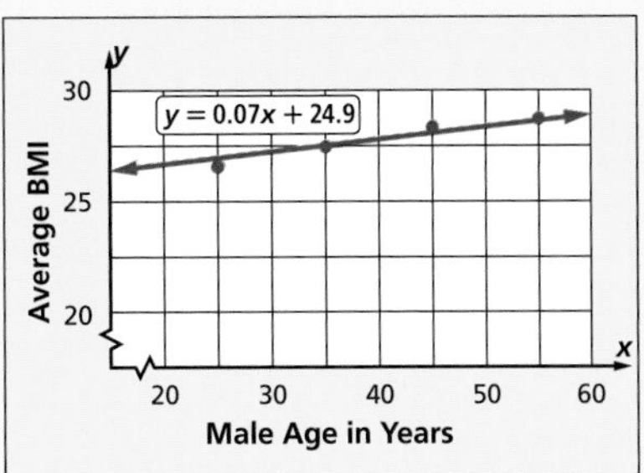

In this chapter, you will create linear models of real-world situations and in so doing, you will learn about relationships between lines, geometry, and statistics.

This chapter also extends the study of sequences you began in Chapter 1. Sequences with formulas of the form $a_n = mn + b$, where m and b are constants, model linear situations of constant rates of change and are examples of linear functions.

149

The third theme is that of sequences. Lessons 3-6 and 3-7 discuss recursive and explicit formulas for sequences. Lesson 3-8 connects the ideas of functions and sequences by dealing with arithmetic sequences as special types of linear functions.

Using Pages 148–149

As a Warm-Up, you might ask students to determine how far off each data point is from the corresponding point on the line $y = 0.09x + 22.5$. From left to right, the points are 0.05 too low, 0.15 too high, 0.35 too high, and 0.05 too low.

You also might ask students if they know the slope and y-intercept of the line with equation $y = 0.07x + 24.9$. slope, 0.07; y-intercept, 24.9 What does the slope mean? As a person ages 1 year, the average body mass index goes up 0.07.

The graph on this page relates to Lesson 3-5. Students might notice that the four data points are not collinear. In fact, it looks like a parabolic curve might fit them quite well. If there were some evidence that the BMI should ultimately be less for an older person, then the parabola might be a good model. In fact, this is a major message for students to learn. We can find functions that fit data, but it is preferable to have some theoretical basis for the degree of the formula (linear, quadratic, exponential, and so on) that is selected.

Chapter 3 Projects

At the end of each chapter, you will find projects related to the chapter. At this time you might want to have students look over the projects on pages 210 and 211. You might want to have students tentatively select a project on which to work. Then, as students read and progress through the chapter, they can finalize their project choices.

Sometimes students might work alone. At other times, you might let them collaborate with classmates for a presentation and discussion. We recommend that you allow for diversity and encourage students to use their imaginations when presenting their projects. As students work on projects throughout the year, they should see many uses of mathematics in the real world.

Lesson

3-1

GOAL

Show how the slope-intercept form of linear functions arises naturally from situations of constant increase or decrease; review graphing lines using slope and *y*-intercept.

SPUR Objectives

The SPUR Objectives for all of Chapter 3 are found in the Chapter Review on pages 215–219.

A Determine the slope and intercepts of a line given its equation.

E Recognize properties of linear functions.

G Model constant-increase or constant-decrease situations.

M Graph or interpret graphs of linear equations.

Materials/Resources

- Lesson Masters 3-1A and 3-1B
- Resource Masters 1, 38, and 39

HOMEWORK

Suggestions for Assignment

- Questions 1–27
- Question 28 (extra credit)
- Reading Lesson 3-2
- Covering the Ideas 3-2

Local Standards

1 Warm-Up

The Chapter 3 Opener (pages 148 and 149) suggests asking students if they know the slope and *y*-intercept of the line with equation $y = 0.07x + 24.9$. This can serve as a Warm-Up for Lesson 3-1.

Lesson 3-1 Constant Change and the Graph of $y = mx + b$

Vocabulary

y-intercept
linear function
slope-intercept form
x-intercept

BIG IDEA If *y* changes by a constant amount *m* as *x* increases by 1, then $y = mx + b$ for all (x, y) and the graph of the points (x, y) is a line with slope *m* and *y*-intercept *b*.

Constant-Increase and Constant-Decrease Situations

In many real-world situations, there is an initial condition and a constant increase or decrease applied to that condition. This type of situation can be modeled by a linear equation.

Example 1

Noah usually waits until he has only 1 gallon of gas left in his car before filling up. Suppose the gas pump pumps at a rate of 6 gallons per minute. Write an equation for a function representing the amount of gas in Noah's tank *x* minutes after he starts pumping gas. The tank holds 17.5 gallons when full.

Reighard's gas station, established in 1909, claims to be the oldest gas station in the United States.

Solution Let $A(x)$ be the amount of gas in Noah's tank *x* minutes after he starts pumping. The function will have the form

$A(x) =$ (amount in tank at start) + (amount added).

The amount in the tank at the start is 1 gallon. Every minute, 6 gallons are added, so after *x* minutes, 6*x* gallons have been added. The function with equation

$$A(x) = 1 + 6x$$

or

$$A(x) = 6x + 1$$

gives the amount of gas in his tank after *x* minutes.

A graph of the function *A* in Example 1 is shown on the next page.

Mental Math

a. Rafael graduated high school in May 2007 at the age of 18. How old will he be in October 2020? 31 or 32

b. Rafael's birthday is August 19. How old was he in November 2005? 17

c. Rafael's sister Bianca is 2 years and 8 months younger than he is. How old was Bianca in November 2005? 14

Background

Throughout UCSMP *Advanced Algebra,* mathematics is connected to the real world. This chapter connects linear equations to real-world situations in two contexts: *constant increase or decrease,* studied here, and *linear combination,* introduced in Lesson 3-2.

Constant-increase and constant-decrease situations lead naturally to equations of the form $y = mx + b$ because *m* and *b* have simple interpretations: *m* is the amount of increase or decrease per unit change of *x*, and *b* is the initial value. Another kind of constant change will be studied in Chapter 8, where students will encounter situations of constant growth or decay. The difference there is that the initial value is continually multiplied by (rather than increased or decreased by) the same number.

This lesson is centered on two examples. Example 1 shows how to obtain a linear equation from a constant-increase situation. This leads naturally into the ideas of slope

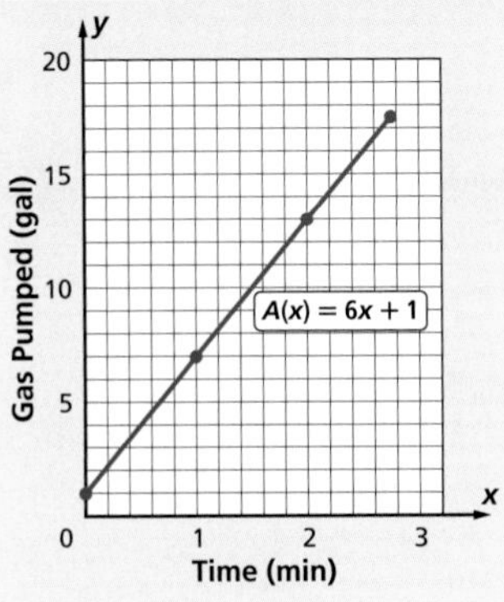

 QY1

> **QY1**
> In Example 1, how long will it take to fill up Noah's gas tank?

Outside the context of Noah's gas tank, $y = 6x + 1$ is an equation describing a function whose domain and range are each the set of real numbers. The graph of the equation is the line containing the segment graphed above.

The y-value of the point where a graph crosses the y-axis is called its **y-intercept**. The graph of $y = 6x + 1$ crosses the y-axis at the point $(0, 1)$, so its y-intercept is 1. The y-intercept is the initial condition, or starting point, of the situation modeled by the graph; in Noah's case it is 1 gallon.

The slope of this line is the rate of change, 6 gallons per minute. You can verify this by finding the slope between two points on the graph, for example $(0, 1)$ and $(2.75, 17.5)$.

$$\frac{y_2 - y_1}{x_2 - x_1} = \frac{(17.5 - 1)\text{gallons}}{(2.75 - 0)\text{minutes}} = \frac{16.5 \text{ gallons}}{2.75 \text{ minutes}} = 6\ \frac{\text{gallons}}{\text{minute}}$$

Notice that the unit of the slope matches the unit of the constant change.

Slope-Intercept Form

A function whose graph is a line or a part of a line is called a **linear function**. In general, a linear function is a function that can be represented by an equation in the form $y = mx + b$. The form $y = mx + b$, or $f(x) = mx + b$, is called the **slope-intercept form** of a linear equation. Although the letter b is commonly used for the y-intercept, and the letter m commonly represents the slope, any other letters could be used in their place. Example 2 illustrates how the slope and y-intercept can be used to graph a line.

and intercept, which should be a review for all students. Example 2 does the same for a constant-decrease situation.

Once slope has been established, students review the connection between parallel lines and slope. Most students encountered slope in their first year of algebra, but some students may not fully understand the idea.

ENGLISH LEARNERS

Vocabulary Development

Refer students to the phrase *an initial condition and a constant increase or decrease* near the beginning of the lesson. Ask them how that statement represents the slope-intercept form or the graph of a linear equation. The constant increase or decrease is the slope; the initial condition is the y-intercept.

2 Teaching

Notes on the Lesson

Use the graph on page 149 to initiate a discussion about the characteristics of a constant-increase or constant-decrease situation. Here are some other situations that could be used for class discussion:

- A salesperson receives a base salary of \$2,000 per month plus 3% of the value of sales made.
- A student buys a used car for \$900. Each year the student spends \$450 on repair bills.
- The rental fee on an intermediate-size car is \$39 per day and \$0.40 per mile.
- Myron Cash has \$2,500,000 under his mattress. He spends it at the rate of \$65,000 per year.

Ask: Why are virtually all models accurate over a limited domain only? Answers vary.

Additional Example

Example 1 A pool contains 85 gallons of water. Suppose a hose adds water to the pool at a rate of 7 gallons per minute. Write an equation for a function representing the amount of water in the pool t minutes after the hose is turned on. The pool can hold 1359 gallons of water. $P(t) = 85 + 7t$, where $P(t)$ is the number of gallons of water in the pool after t minutes.

Note-Taking Tips

Whenever students write a function such as $A(x) = 6x + 1$ (from Example 1), encourage them to add an explanation such as "$A(x)$ represents the number of gallons in a gas tank after x minutes of pumping gas." This will help them remember or explain their notes.

Notes on the Lesson

Example 2 You might ask students to explain why substitutions for *t* greater than 3.25 are not reasonable. The tank is empty, so there is no more water to drain. Ask: Why is the initial value of the constant increase or constant decrease important? It is the point from which the particular increase or decrease is computed. Explain that this value is the *y*-intercept of the graph for a linear increase or decrease. Similarly, the constant rate of change is the slope of the line.

Additional Example

Example 2 A mudslide left 42 acre-feet of mud in a valley. The mud is being removed at the rate of 5 acre-feet per day.

a. Write a linear equation to model this situation.

b. When will all the mud be removed?

c. What are the *y*-intercept and the slope of the line represented by the equation in Part a?

d. Graph the line and indicate the point that indicates no mud.

Solution

a. Let $M(t)$ be the amount of mud in the valley after *t* days: $M(t) =$ __?__ – __?__. 42; 5t

b. The mud will be gone when $M(t) = 0$. Solve __?__ $= 0$ to find $t =$ __?__. The mud will be gone after __?__ days. 42 – 5t; 8.4; 8.4

c. The *y*-intercept is the starting point; the slope is the rate of change. So in this situation, the *y*-intercept is __?__, and the slope is __?__. 42; -5

d. Graph the line with *y*-intercept 42 and slope -5. The mud is gone when the line crosses the *x*-axis, at the point (8.4, 0).

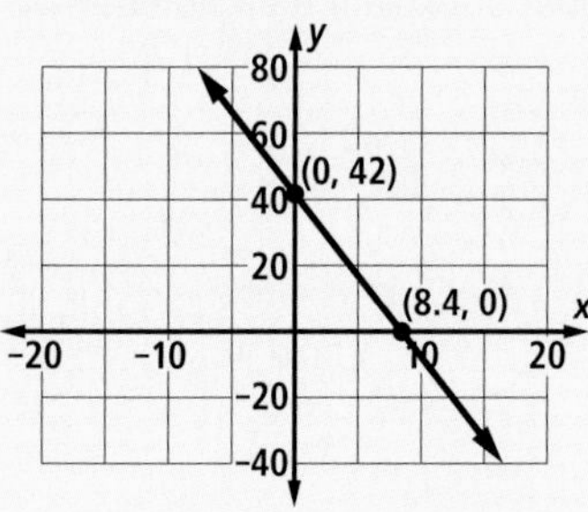

GUIDED

Example 2

A pond with about 26 acre-feet of water needs to be drained for repairs to its levy. Engineers determine that 8 acre-feet of water can be safely drained per day.

a. Write a linear equation to model this situation.

b. In how many days will the pond be empty?

c. What are the *y*-intercept and the slope of the line represented by your equation in Part a?

d. Graph the line and indicate the point where the reservoir is empty.

Solution

a. Let $M(t)$ be the amount of water in the pond after *t* days.
$M(t) =$ __?__ – __?__

b. The pond will be empty when $M(t) = 0$.
Solve __?__ $= 0$ to find $t =$ __?__.
The reservoir will be empty after __?__ days.

c. The *y*-intercept is the starting point; the slope is the rate of change. So in this situation, the *y*-intercept is __?__ and the slope is __?__.

d. To graph this line, first locate the *y*-intercept 26, which corresponds to a full pond when $t = 0$. Use the slope to locate another point. A slope of $-8 = \frac{-8}{1}$ means that every horizontal change of 1 unit to the right corresponds to a vertical change of 8 units down. This gives the new point $(0 + 1, 26 - 8) = (1, 18)$. Plot (1, 18) and draw the line. Label it $M(t) = -8t + 26$. The pond is empty at the point where the line crosses the *x*-axis, at the point (3.25, 0).

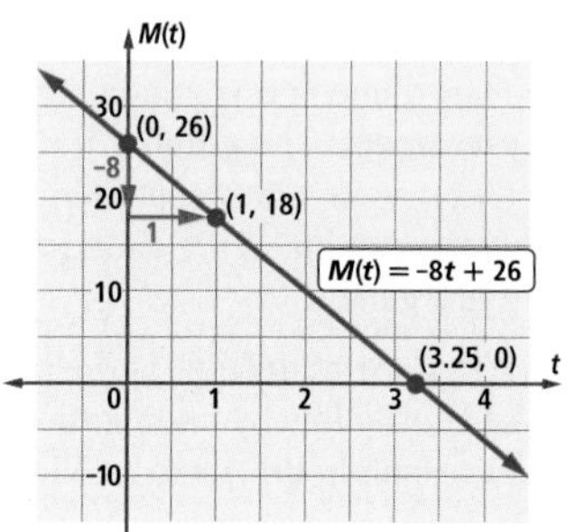

The *x*-value of the point where a line crosses the *x*-axis is called the **x-intercept** of the line. Because the line in Example 2 intersects the *x*-axis at (3.25, 0), 3.25 is the *x*-intercept of the line.

In constant-increase situations, such as Example 1, as the value of *x* increases, so does the value of *y*. The slope of the line is positive. The graph slants up to the right and the function is said to be *increasing*.

In constant-decrease situations, such as Example 2, as the value of *x* increases, the value of *y* decreases. The slope of the line is negative. The graph slants down to the right and the function is said to be *decreasing*.

Accommodating the Learner ↑

Have students look again at Example 2. Ask them to tell why the model requires a restricted domain to properly model the situation. Also, ask them to explain how to adjust the model. Once the pond is empty, no more water may be drained. The domain should be restricted to $\{x \mid 0 \le x \le 3.25\}$.

Accommodating the Learner ↓

Ask students to verify the statement that parallel lines have equal slope by drawing several pairs of parallel lines in a coordinate plane, selecting two convenient points on each line (such as the *x*- and *y*-intercepts), and calculating and comparing slopes. Answers vary. Check students' work.

When the slope $m = 0$, the graph does not rise or fall; the function is *constant*. A line with a slope of 0 is horizontal. Vertical lines do not represent functions and have an undefined slope.

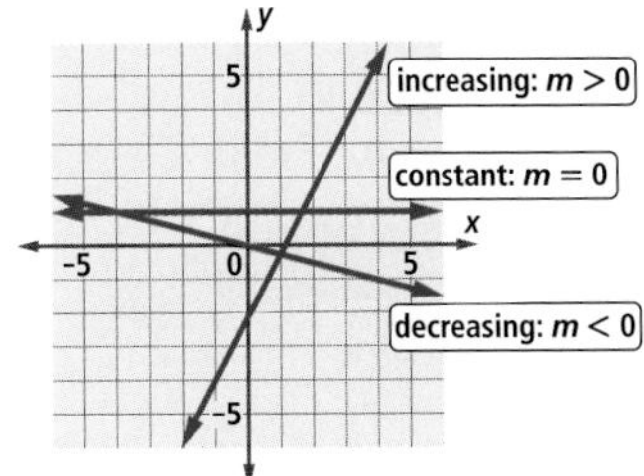

 QY2

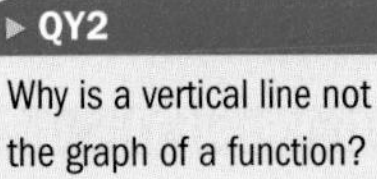

QY2
Why is a vertical line not the graph of a function?

Parallel Lines and Slope

Consider the graphs of $y = 4x + 7$ and $y = 4x - 2$ at the right. Both lines have slope 4; on each line, as you move 1 unit to the right, the line rises 4 units. In the figure, right triangles $\triangle ABC$ and $\triangle DEF$ are congruent by the SAS Congruence Theorem. So $\angle CAB \cong \angle FDE$, and these lines form congruent corresponding angles with the *y*-axis at *A* and *D*. Consequently, $\overleftrightarrow{AB}$ and $\overleftrightarrow{DE}$ are parallel.

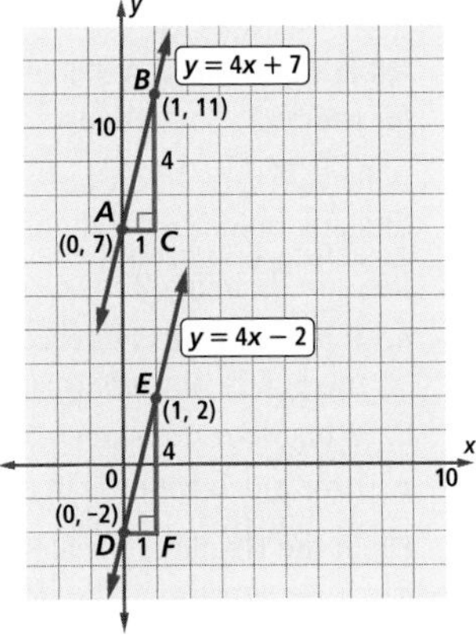

This argument can be repeated with any two lines that have the same slope. We also say that a line is parallel to itself. Thus, we can conclude the following:

If two lines have the same slope, then they are parallel.

The converse of this statement is: If two lines are parallel, then they have the same slope. This can be proved for all nonvertical lines as follows. Suppose lines *s* and *t* are parallel and not vertical, as shown at the right. Let m_1 be the slope of *s*, and m_2 be the slope of *t*. We want to show that $m_1 = m_2$. Draw line ℓ with equation $x = 1$. Note that ℓ is a transversal to the parallel lines. Draw horizontal segments from the *y*-intercepts of lines *s* and *t* to line ℓ as shown, forming right angles at *C* and *F*. Then m_1 = slope of $s = \frac{AC}{BC} = \frac{AC}{1} = AC$, and m_2 = slope of $t = \frac{DF}{EF} = \frac{DF}{1} = DF$. Recall from geometry that corresponding angles formed by parallel lines and a transversal are congruent. So $\angle ABC \cong \angle DEF$. Note also that $AC = DF$, so $\overline{AC} \cong \overline{DF}$. Since $\angle BCA \cong \angle EFD$, $\triangle ABC$ and $\triangle DEF$ are congruent by the AAS Congruence Theorem, and $BC = EF$. Because $m_1 = BC$ and $m_2 = EF$, the slopes are equal.

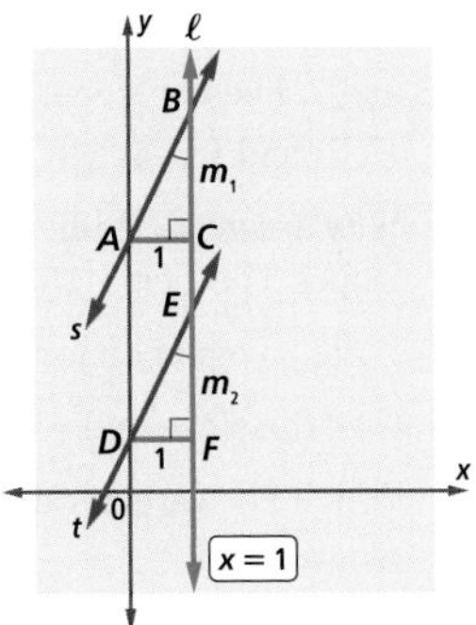

Notes on the Lesson

Point out to students that the graph of $y = mx + b$ is the image of the graph of the direct variation $y = mx$ under a translation *b* units up. This idea will be applied in later chapters to raise or lower the graph of a linear equation, usually writing that equation in the form $y - b = mx$.

Parallel lines and slope Proofs for the two theorems concerning parallel lines may be difficult for some students. Encourage them to read this material slowly, locating in the diagram each line, angle, and triangle as it is referenced. You may wish to go through the proof that equal slopes imply parallel lines, highlighting the SAS Congruence Theorem. Students may appreciate seeing that an idea they learned in one mathematics course is useful in another course. The proof of the converse, that parallel lines imply equal slopes, uses the AAS Congruence Theorem.

Extension

Ask students to write the equations of any two nonhorizontal or nonvertical parallel lines through two points $(0, y_1)$ and $(0, y_2)$, such as (0, 3) and (0, 5). Then ask them to find the equation of another line, parallel to the other two, through $(0, y_1 + y_2)$; in this example, it would be (0, 8). Ask students to consider the points of intersection of the three lines with any vertical line. What is true about those three points? The three points have the same *x*-coordinate, and the third *y*-coordinate is the sum of the other two *y*-coordinates.

3 Assignment

Recommended Assignment

- Questions 1–27
- Question 28 (extra credit)
- Reading Lesson 3-2
- Covering the Ideas 3-2

Notes on the Questions

Question 2 Generalize the result. A line with a slope of k means a vertical change of k units for every horizontal change of one unit.

Question 4 This is an important question. Students must be able to interpret equations and graphs in a real-world context.

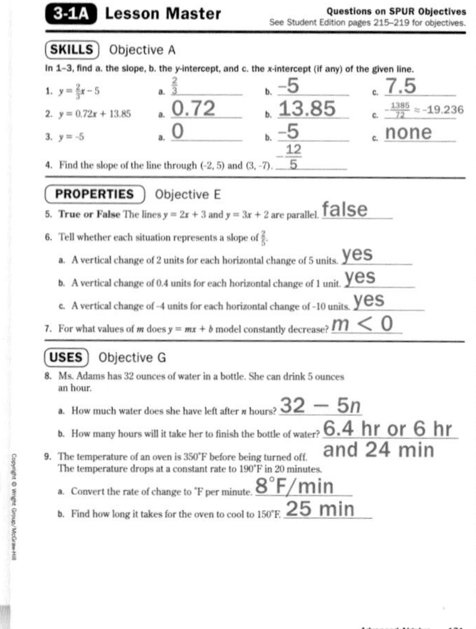

3-1A page 2

3-1A Lesson Master — Questions on SPUR Objectives. See Student Edition pages 215–219 for objectives.

SKILLS Objective A

In 1–3, find a. the slope, b. the y-intercept, and c. the x-intercept (if any) of the given line.

1. $y = \frac{2}{3}x - 5$ a. $\frac{2}{3}$ b. -5 c. 7.5
2. $y = 0.72x + 13.85$ a. 0.72 b. 13.85 c. $-\frac{1385}{72} \approx -19.236$
3. $y = -5$ a. 0 b. -5 c. none
4. Find the slope of the line through (-2, 5) and (3, -7). $-\frac{12}{5}$

PROPERTIES Objective E

5. **True or False** The lines $y = 2x + 3$ and $y = 3x + 2$ are parallel. false
6. Tell whether each situation represents a slope of $\frac{2}{5}$.
   a. A vertical change of 2 units for each horizontal change of 5 units. yes
   b. A vertical change of 0.4 units for each horizontal change of 1 unit. yes
   c. A vertical change of -4 units for each horizontal change of -10 units. yes
7. For what values of m does $y = mx + b$ model constantly decrease? $m < 0$

USES Objective G

8. Ms. Adams has 32 ounces of water in a bottle. She can drink 5 ounces an hour.
   a. How much water does she have left after n hours? $32 - 5n$
   b. How many hours will it take her to finish the bottle of water? 6.4 hr or 6 hr and 24 min
9. The temperature of an oven is 350°F before being turned off. The temperature drops at a constant rate to 190°F in 20 minutes.
   a. Convert the rate of change to °F per minute. 8°F/min
   b. Find how long it takes for the oven to cool to 150°F. 25 min

Advanced Algebra 171

Consequently, we have shown that the following is true:

If two non-vertical lines are parallel, then they have the same slope.

Because the original statement and its converse above are both true, you can combine them into one biconditional (if and only if) statement that is important enough to be labeled as a theorem.

Parallel Lines and Slope Theorem

Two non-vertical lines are parallel if and only if they have the same slope.

Questions

COVERING THE IDEAS

1. **Fill in the Blanks** In the equation $y = mx + b$, the slope is __?__ and the y-intercept is __?__. m; b
2. **Fill in the Blanks** A slope of 3 means a __?__ change of 3 units for every __?__ change of one unit. vertical; horizontal
3. Refer to Example 1. Suppose a car has 4 gallons in its tank and the tank holds 14.5 gallons. How long will it take to fill the tank? 1 minute 45 seconds
4. Refer to Example 2.
   a. What does the y-intercept mean in the context of draining the pond? the original volume of water in the pond
   b. What does the slope mean in this context?
   c. How much water is in the pond at the end of the second day? 10 acre-feet
5. **Fill in the Blanks** In real-world constant-increase or constant-decrease situations, the initial condition can be represented by the __?__, and the constant change can be represented by the __?__.

4b. the rate at which water can be safely drained

5. y-intercept; slope

In 6 and 7, find the slope of the line containing the points.

6. (7, 2) and (5, -4) 3
7. (32, 14) and (-8, -6) $\frac{1}{2}$
8. Why are vertical lines excluded from the Parallel Lines and Slopes Theorem? They have undefined slopes.
9. Write an equation for the line with y-intercept of -3 and slope of $\frac{2}{3}$. $y = \frac{2}{3}x - 3$
10. Give the slope and y-intercept of $y = 5 - 2x$. slope = -2; y-intercept = 5
11. Which lines are parallel? (There may be more than one pair.) a, c, and e; d and b
    a. $y = 2x - 7$
    b. $y = -3x + 4$
    c. $2x - y = 7$
    d. $y = 12 - 3x$
    e. $-4x + 2y = 12$

APPLYING THE MATHEMATICS

12. A stack of Sunday newspapers sits on a skid 3" off the ground. Each newspaper is $1\frac{3}{4}$" thick.
    a. How high is the stack if there are n newspapers in it? $3 + 1.75n$ inches
    b. If the top of the stack is 3' high, about how many newspapers are in the stack? about 19 newspapers

13. The Clear-Bell Cell phone company has a plan that costs customers \$29.99 for a monthly service fee plus 3¢ per minute used.
    a. Write a linear equation to model this situation.
    b. Identify the slope and the y-intercept. Interpret the slope and y-intercept in the context of this problem.
    c. If Polly talks for 136 minutes, how much would her cell phone bill be (excluding taxes)? \$34.07

13a. $y = 0.03x + 29.99$

13b. 0.03; 29.99; The slope is the constant rate per minute, the y-intercept is the initial condition, the monthly service fee.

14. The function slope$(a,b,c,d) = \frac{(d-b)}{(c-a)}$ calculates the slope of the line connecting two points. To use this function, define slope on a CAS, with the coordinates of the points (a, b) and (c, d) as arguments. Use the function to find the slope of the line through
    a. (2, -3) and (5, 3). 2
    b. (4.2, 8.3) and (-3.4, 5.01). ≈ 0.432895

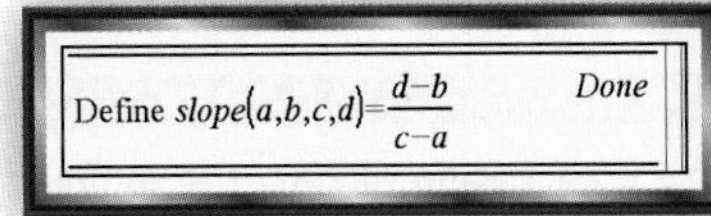

15. Find the slope of a line with y-intercept 4 that contains the point (2, 6). 1

In 16 and 17, use graph paper to draw an accurate graph of these lines.

16. $y = -\frac{2}{3}x + 4$
17. $y = 5$ 16 and 17. See margin.

18. The line with equation $y = \frac{5}{2}x + 4$ is graphed at the right.
    a. What is its slope? $\frac{5}{2}$
    b. Find the average rate of change between (0, 4) and (4, 14) to verify your answer to Part a. $\frac{14-4}{4-0} = \frac{5}{2}$
    c. What is the y-intercept? 4
    d. Is the point (-4, 3) on the line? Explain how you know. No; if you plug $x = -4$ into the equation, you get $y = -6$.

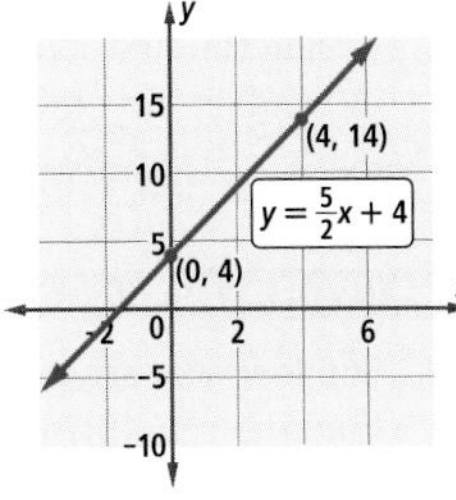

Notes on the Questions

Question 14 There does not have to be a line to have a slope. Two points are all that is needed. In calculus, one often is finding slopes of curves in which no subset is a line.

Question 17 Because $y = 0x + 5$, this equation is in slope-intercept form.

Additional Answers

16.

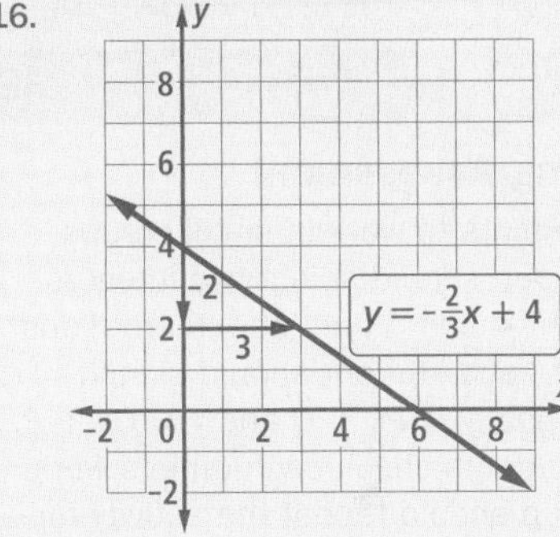

17.

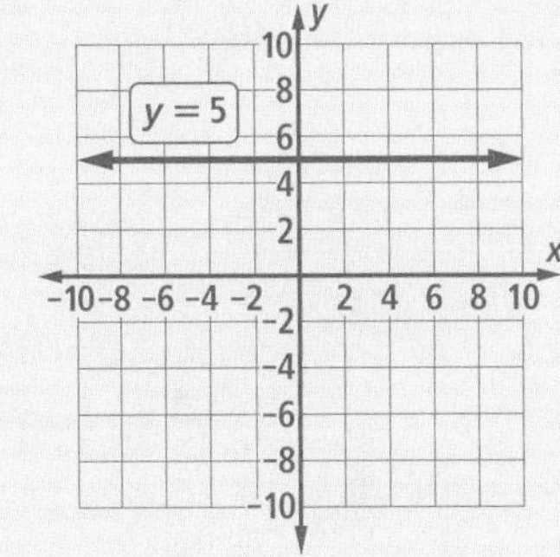

Notes on the Questions

Question 26 This situation leads to a linear sequence of the type that will be discussed in more detail in Lessons 3-6 to 3-8.

Question 28 You might add to the degree of difficulty by asking that the costs be calculated in the currency of the destination that was picked. Then ask for a second line that gives the cost in dollars.

4 Wrap-Up

Ongoing Assessment

Ask students to work in small groups. Each group should select two integers between -4 and 4 and label them P and Q. Then each student should sketch two graphs, $y = Px + Q$ and $y = Qx + P$. After students check each other's work, the group should repeat the activity for another pair of P and Q values. Answers vary. Check students' work.

Additional Answers

20b.

x	$f(x) = \frac{10}{3}x$
0	0
1	3.33333
2	6.66667
3	10
4	13.33333

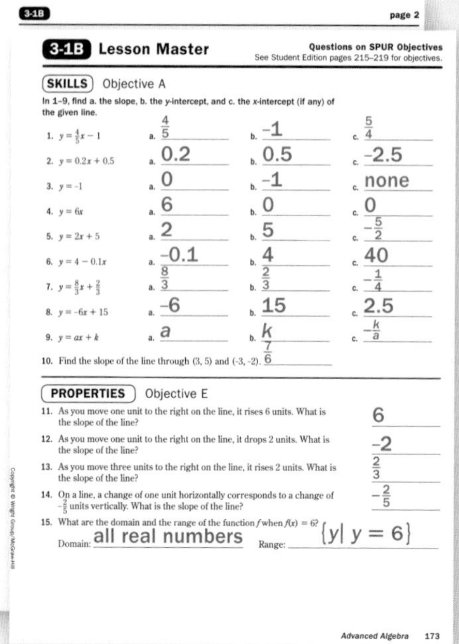

3-1B page 2

3-1B Lesson Master — Questions on SPUR Objectives. See Student Edition pages 215–219 for objectives.

SKILLS Objective A

In 1–9, find a. the slope, b. the y-intercept, and c. the x-intercept (if any) of the given line.

	a.	b.	c.
1. $y = \frac{4}{5}x - 1$	$\frac{4}{5}$	-1	$\frac{5}{4}$
2. $y = 0.2x + 0.5$	0.2	0.5	-2.5
3. $y = -1$	0	-1	none
4. $y = 6x$	6	0	0
5. $y = 2x + 5$	2	5	$-\frac{5}{2}$
6. $y = 4 - 0.1x$	-0.1	4	40
7. $y = \frac{8}{3}x + \frac{2}{3}$	$\frac{8}{3}$	$\frac{2}{3}$	$-\frac{1}{4}$
8. $y = -6x + 15$	-6	15	2.5
9. $y = ax + k$	a	k	$-\frac{k}{a}$

10. Find the slope of the line through (3, 5) and (-3, -2). $\frac{7}{6}$

PROPERTIES Objective E

11. As you move one unit to the right on the line, it rises 6 units. What is the slope of the line? 6
12. As you move one unit to the right on the line, it drops 2 units. What is the slope of the line? -2
13. As you move three units to the right on the line, it rises 2 units. What is the slope of the line? $\frac{2}{3}$
14. On a line, a change of one unit horizontally corresponds to a change of $-\frac{2}{5}$ units vertically. What is the slope of the line? $-\frac{2}{5}$
15. What are the domain and the range of the function f when $f(x) = 6$?
Domain: all real numbers Range: $\{y \mid y = 6\}$

Advanced Algebra 173

19. Stephanie is a taxi driver. She rents her taxi for \$300/week. She feels she can take in \$120/day in fares. Let D be the number of days she drives her taxi in a week and T be the total earnings she expects after subtracting the rental charge.
    a. Identify four ordered pairs (D, T).
    b. Write an equation that gives T as a function of D. $T = 120D - 300$
    c. What is the most she can earn in a year at this rate? \$28, 080

19a. Answers vary. Sample: (1, -180), (4, 180), (5, 300), (7, 540)

20. Suppose a varies directly as b, and that a is 10 when b is 3.
    a. Find the constant of variation and write an equation describing the variation. $k = \frac{10}{3}$, $a = \frac{10}{3}b$
    b. Make a table of values and graph the equation. See margin.
    c. Write the variation equation in slope-intercept form and identify the slope and y-intercept. $a = \frac{10}{3}b + 0$; $\frac{10}{3}$; 0
    d. Which type of variation does this represent: constant increase or constant decrease? constant increase

REVIEW

In 21–24, decide whether the variables in the equation exemplify direct, inverse, combined, or joint variation. (Lessons 2-1, 2-2, 2-9)

21. $ab = 5c$ joint
22. $x = y$ direct
23. $m = \frac{61g}{hz}$ combined
24. $2 = pr$ inverse
25. Consider the table of data at the right, which relates the number p of snowplows out on city streets to the number c of car crashes during a snowy day. **(Lesson 2-7)**
    a. Does c vary directly or inversely as a power of p? inversely
    b. Based on your answer to Part a , either $c = kp^n$ or $c = \frac{k}{p^n}$. Find n for the appropriate relation. $n = 1$

Plows p	Crashes c
1	50
2	25
3	16
4	12
5	10
6	7

26. Create the first five rows of a table for $y = \frac{3}{5}x$ with a start value of -10 and an increment of 5. **(Lesson 1-5)** See margin.
27. Solve $\frac{1}{3}y + 2x = 16$ for y. **(Lesson 1-7)** $y = 48 - 6x$

EXPLORATION

28. Suppose you are going on vacation outside the United States. Find the roundtrip airfare from your local airport to this destination. Estimate your daily expenses for hotel and food. Use the information to write a function that gives the cost of a trip to stay for d days. Is this function a linear function?
Answers vary. Sample: The roundtrip airfare from Chicago, Illinois to Cairo, Egypt is about \$1200. A person might spend about \$75 per day on hotel and food. The budget can be expressed by the linear function $C = 75d + 1200$.

QY ANSWERS

1. 2.75 min, or 2 min 45 sec
2. Two points on a vertical line have different second coordinates but the same first coordinate. So, these lines violate the definition of a function.

Additional Answers

20b.

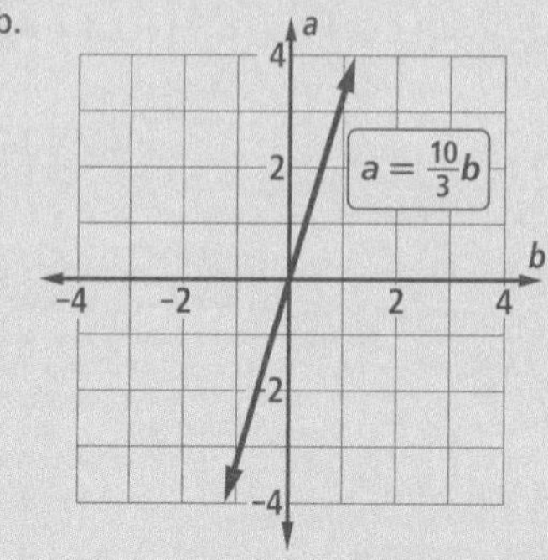

26.

x	$y = \frac{3}{5}x$
-10	-6
-5	-3
0	0
5	3
10	6

Lesson 3-2 Linear Combinations and $Ax + By = C$

Vocabulary

linear combination

standard form

▶ **BIG IDEA** When the sum of multiples of x and y is a constant, then $Ax + By = C$ for all (x, y).

Mental Math

Solve for x.

a. $|x| < 12$ $-12 < x < 12$

b. $|2x| < 12$ $-6 < x < 6$

c. $|2x - 4| < 12$ $-4 < x < 8$

d. $|2x - 4| \geq 12$ $x \leq -4$ or $x \geq 8$

The form $y = mx + b$ is convenient for graphing lines because the y-intercept and slope are obvious, but you have also seen many equations for lines in different forms. For example, in the rectangle with length ℓ, width w, and perimeter 20 inches, $20 = 2\ell + 2w$. This is a linear equation, and the expression $2\ell + 2w$ is called a *linear combination* of ℓ and w.

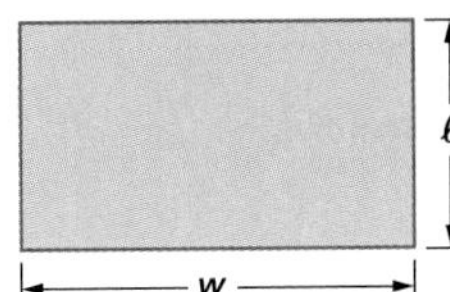

A **linear combination** is an expression in which all variables are raised to the first power and are not multiplied or divided by each other. Linear combinations may have 2, 3, 4, or more variables.

Activity

At Harry's Hamburger Hovel, hamburgers cost \$2.50 and hot dogs cost \$2. Suppose you have \$30 to spend for hamburgers and hot dogs for a family gathering.

Step 1 Write an equation relating the number b of hamburgers and the number d of hot dogs you can purchase to spend all the money. $2.5b + 2d = 30$

Step 2 Solve the equation in Step 1 for d. $d = 15 - 1.25b$

Step 3 Graph the equation in Step 2 without taking the real-world context into account. See graph on next page.

Step 4 Identify all points on the graph that correspond to a possible combination of hamburgers and hot dogs you can buy. (0, 15), (4, 10), (8, 5), (12, 0)

Background

Just as constant-increase or constant-decrease situations lead to linear equations in slope-intercept form, linear combinations lead to equations in the standard form, $Ax + By = C$.

It is possible (and quite common) to have linear combinations with more than two variables. The graph of $Ax + By + Cz = D$, an equation with three variables, is a plane.

If there are more than three variables, the graph is called a *hyperplane*. Although it is difficult to show the properties of a hyperplane in 2 or even in 3 dimensions, those properties can be developed, presented, and explored algebraically.

Lesson 3-2

GOAL

Translate linear combination situations to equations of the form $Ax + By = C$.

SPUR Objectives

E Recognize properties of linear functions.

H Model linear combination situations.

Materials/Resources

- Lesson Masters 3-2A and 3-2B
- Resource Master 40

HOMEWORK

Suggestions for Assignment

- Questions 1–16
- Question 17 (extra credit)
- Reading Lesson 3-3
- Covering the Ideas 3-3

Local Standards

1 Warm-Up

Consider the following situation: Your car has a full tank of gas before the start of a driving trip. Your car gets 25 miles per gallon of gas while driving in the city and 32 miles per gallon on the highway. The gas tank holds 14 gallons. If the car is driven x miles in the city and runs out of gas after driving y miles on the highway, write an equation relating x, y, and the size of the tank. Check your answer with specific values of x and y. **The car uses $\frac{1}{32}$ of a gallon for each mile in the country, so an equation is $\frac{x}{32} + \frac{y}{32} = 14$.** (This is a difficult question. The equation many would think of, $25x + 32y = 14$, is not correct. Have students check this using units: $\left(25 \frac{\text{miles}}{\text{gallon}}\right)(x \text{ miles})$. The reciprocal rates must be used to get an answer in gallons: $\left(\frac{1 \text{ gallon}}{25 \text{ miles}}\right)(x \text{ miles})$ gives the number of gallons used in the city.)

2 Teaching

Notes on the Lesson

Note the variety of contexts students will encounter in this lesson: shopping (Activity and Example 1b), chemistry (Example 2), distance-rate-time (Example 1a and Questions 4 and 10), and business (Question 11). Linear combinations are ubiquitous in real-world situations.

Activity Point out that when there is no context, then students should assume that the independent variable can take on any real number value that has meaning in the algebraic expression.

Additional Example

Example 1 Give two different situations that could be modeled by the linear combination $4x + 8y = 48$. For each example, state whether the linear function is discrete or continuous and explain what the point (2, 5) represents.

Solution

a. You walk for x hours at 4 kilometers per hour and jog for y hours at 8 kilometers per hour, going a total of _?_ kilometers. The point (2, 5) represents _?_ hours of walking and _?_ hours of jogging. You can walk and jog for any part of an hour; it does not make sense to restrict the domain. The function is _?_. 48; 2; 5; continuous

b. You buy x salads at _?_ each and y sandwiches at _?_ each. The total cost is _?_. The point (2, 5) represents _?_. You cannot buy part of a salad or a sandwich. The function is _?_. $4; $8; $48; 2 salads and 5 sandwiches; discrete

In Step 3 of the Activity you should have found that the graph of the equation is a line. This function is a *continuous* function whose domain and range are the set of real numbers. However, the entire line, as shown at the left below, is not an appropriate graph of this situation because counts of hamburgers and hot dogs are whole numbers. The linear function in this situation is *discrete; x* and *y* must be nonnegative integers. At the right below is a graph of the four ordered pairs of nonnegative integers that satisfy the equation.

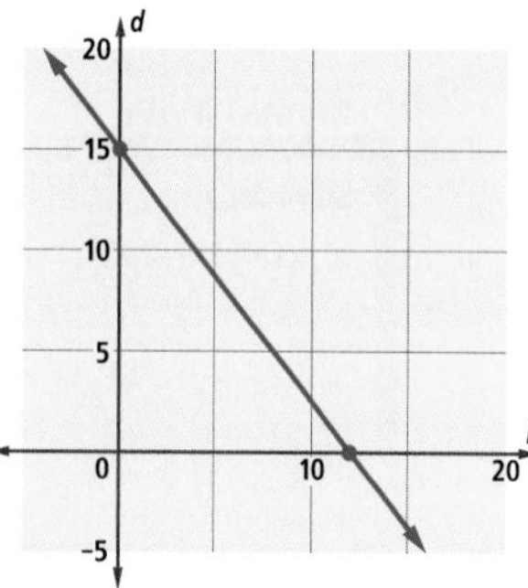

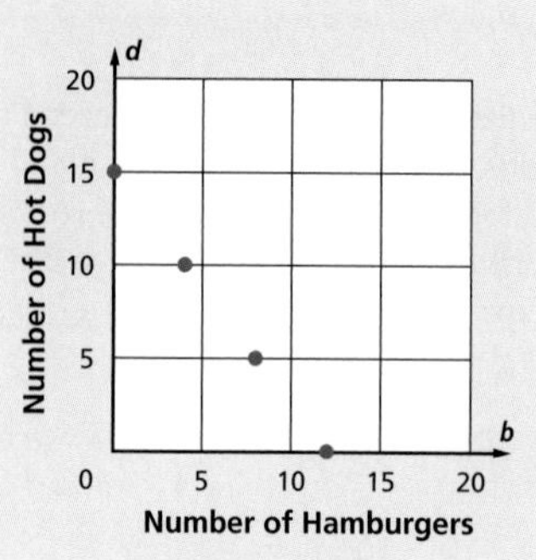

STOP QY

GUIDED

Example 1

Give two different situations that could be modeled by the linear combination equation $6x + 3y = 30$. For each situation, state whether the linear function is discrete or continuous, and explain what the point (3, 4) represents.

Solution Each situation should specify what the numbers and variables in the equations represent. Here are two possible solutions.

a. You jog for x hours at 6 miles per hour and walk for y hours at 3 miles per hour, going a total of _?_ miles. The point (3, 4) represents _?_ hours of jogging and _?_ hours of walking. 30; 3; 4

You can jog and walk for any part of an hour; it does not make sense to restrict the domain to whole numbers, so the function is _?_. continuous

b. You buy x adult tickets at _?_ each and y child tickets at _?_ each. The total cost is _?_. The point (3, 4) represents _?_. $6; $3; $30; buying 3 adult tickets and 4 child tickets

You cannot buy part of a ticket. The function is _?_. discrete

▸ QY

Give the domain and range of the discrete function graphed above at the right.

Accommodating the Learner

Refer students to the Activity, in which they found integer values of x and y that satisfied the equation $2.5b + 2d = 30$. Ask them how they could find integer values of x and y that satisfy $4x + 6y = 96$. How about $Ax + By = C$? Solve $4x + 6y = 96$ for y: $y = \left(\frac{-2}{3}\right)x - 16$. By selecting multiples of 3 for the x-values, the result will be ordered pairs such as (-3, -14), (0, -16), and (3, -18). For $Ax + By = C$, $y = \left(\frac{-A}{B}\right)x - \frac{C}{B}$. So if C is a multiple of B, then by taking multiples of B as x-values, the y-values will be integers.

The equation $6x + 3y = 30$ is in the form $Ax + By = C$, with $A = 6$, $B = 3$, and $C = 30$. When A and B are not both zero, the equation $Ax + By = C$ is called the **standard form** of an equation for a line.

Linear equations commonly occur in chemistry. For example, chemists describe the concentration of a solution in terms of the number of moles of the substance per liter (mol/L). One mole of a substance is approximately 6.02×10^{23} molecules. So, for example, 2 liters of a solution of 5 mol/L hydrochloric acid contains 2 L • 5 mol/L = 10 moles, or about 6.02×10^{24} molecules, of hydrochloric acid. Although a well-equipped lab usually stocks solutions in various concentrations, a chemist often has to mix his or her own solution at a particular concentration by combining other stock solutions. Pharmacists, painters, and others who deal with mixtures use the same mathematics.

Example 2

Suppose a chemist wants to mix *x* liters of a 2.5 mol/L solution of acid with *y* liters of a 7.25 mol/L solution to obtain a mixture with 10 moles of acid.

a. Write an equation that relates *x*, *y*, and the total number of moles of acid.

b. How many liters of the 7.25 mol/L solution must be added to 1.3 liters of the 2.5 mol/L solution to get 10 moles of acid in the final mixture? Answer to the nearest 0.1 liter.

Solution

a. To find the number of moles of acid in each solution, multiply the concentration by the quantity.

(L)(mol//L) = moles, so

x liters of 2.5 mol/L solution contain 2.5x moles of acid.

y liters of 7.25 mol/L solution contain 7.25y moles of acid.

So, an equation representing the situation is $2.5x + 7.25y = 10$.

b. Think: I want to know y when $x = 1.3$. On one CAS this translates to

```
solve(2.5x + 7.25y = 10,y)|x = 1.3.
```

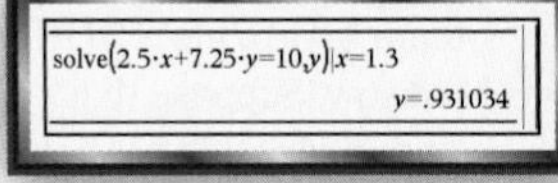

This CAS gives $y \approx 0.9$. So, you need to add approximately 0.9 liter of the 7.25 mol/liter solution.

Check 1 Substitute 1.3 for x and 0.9 for y in the original equation. $2.5(1.3) + 7.25(0.9) = 9.775$, which is close but not exactly equal because of rounding. It checks.

Check 2 Solve by hand. Substitute 1.3 for x. Then $2.5 \cdot 1.3 + 7.25y = 10$, so $7.25y = 6.75$. Then $y = \frac{6.75}{7.25} = \frac{27}{29} \approx 0.931$. It checks.

Accommodating the Learner

Ask students to verify that (1, 9) and (5, 3) satisfy the equation $3x + 2y = 21$. Then ask them to verify that the point halfway between (1, 9) and (5, 3) also satisfies the equation. $3(1) + 2(9) = 21$; $3(5) + 2(3) = 21$; the midpoint is (3, 6), and $3(3) + 2(6) = 21$.

ENGLISH LEARNERS

Vocabulary Development

Some students may recall that the term *combination* refers to the number of ways that objects can be arranged (if order does not matter). Tell students that this is another situation (such as *inverse* for conditional statements, multiplication, or trigonometric functions) where a single math term has different meanings in different contexts.

Notes on the Lesson

Example 2 The key to finding an equation relating x and y is to determine how many moles of acid are in x liters of the 2.5 moles per liter solution and how many moles of acid are in y liters of the 7.25 moles per liter solution. The equation represents the statement that the sum of the two quantities of acid is 10. If the exact mode is used, the equation in slope-intercept form is $y = -\frac{10}{29}x + \frac{40}{29}$, so messy decimals can be avoided.

Additional Example

Example 2 Suppose you mix x liters of a 1.5 moles per liter solution of acid with y liters of a 6.5 moles per liter solution. The final mixture needs to contain 15 moles of acid.

a. Write an equation that relates x, y, and the total number of moles of acid. $1.5x + 6.5y = 15$

b. How many liters of the 6.5 moles per liter solution must be added to 5 liters of the 1.5 moles per liter solution to get 15 moles of acid in the final mixture? Round to the nearest 0.01 liter. 1.15 L

Note-Taking Tips

When students record the definition of *standard form* in their notes, they should expand on the condition that A and B are not both zero. For example, they could indicate what an equation looks like if $A = 0$ or if $B = 0$, including what the graph of such an equation looks like. An example is as follows: If $A = 0$, then the equation has the form $By = C$, and the graph is a horizontal line.

3 Assignment

Recommended Assignment

- Questions 1–16
- Question 17 (extra credit)
- Reading Lesson 3-3
- Covering the Ideas 3-3

Notes on the Questions

Question 7 Although this question is directly patterned on Example 2, some students still may have difficulty with it. It is best to discuss the parts one by one. Remind students to be careful when choosing scales for their graphs. Work through the solution of the equation in Part e because some students may still have trouble with decimal coefficients in equations.

Questions

COVERING THE IDEAS

1. a. **Fill in the Blank** The expression $15P + 12L$ is called a __?__ of P and L. linear combination
   b. Give a situation that could be modeled by the equation $15P + 12L = 600$.
2. **Multiple Choice** Which of the following is not a linear combination of x and y? C
   A $x + y$ B $y - x$ C $4 \cdot x + x \cdot y$ D $x \cdot 2 + y \cdot -8$
3. At a vegetable market, Farmer Bob sells T tomatoes at \$0.50 each, S squash at \$0.75 each, and K bunches of kale at \$1.25 each. Write a linear combination to express the total amount of money he takes in. $0.5T + 0.75S + 1.25K$

1b. Answers vary. Sample: Biking 600 miles, with P hours at 15 mph and L hours at 12 mph

In 4 and 5, a situation is given.
a. Write a linear combination equation describing the situation.
b. Determine whether the situation is discrete or continuous.

4. Ayani is planning a trip across Europe. He will travel b km by bus and t km by train over a 5,000 km route.
5. Jewel is planning a trip across the United States. She wants to visit 12 cities along the way, taking a bus to b cities and taking a train to t cities.
6. Refer to Example 2.
   a. **Fill in the Blanks** The point (0.8, 1.1) is an approximate solution to the equation $2.5x + 7.25y = 10$. This solution means that you used about __?__ liters of 2.5 mol/L solution, about __?__ liters of 7.25 mol/L solution, with a total of about __?__ moles of acid.
   b. What is the domain of the relation $2.5x + 7.25y = 10$ in this situation? $\{x \mid 0 \le x \le 4\}$
   c. Find the y-intercept of the graph. What combination does it represent?
7. Sodium hydroxide, NaOH, is a common compound used in chemistry. Suppose that x liters of a solution that is 5.2 mol/L sodium hydroxide are combined with y liters of a solution that is 7.8 mol/L sodium hydroxide. In Parts a–c, write an expression for the number of moles of NaOH in
   a. the 5.2 mol/L solution. $5.2x$
   b. the 7.8 mol/L solution. $7.8y$
   c. the two solutions combined. $5.2x + 7.8y$

4a. $b + t = 5000$
4b. continuous
5a. $b + t = 12$
5b. discrete
6a. 0.8; 1.1; 10
6c. 1.38; 0 liters of 2.5 mol/L solution and 1.38 liters of 7.25 mol/L solution

Extension

Ask students to speak with a chemistry teacher or with students enrolled in a chemistry course to learn more about moles. Ask them to present their information to the class.

3-2A Lesson Master

Questions on SPUR Objectives
See Student Edition pages 215–219 for objectives.

PROPERTIES Objective E

1. Determine whether each expression is a linear combination.
   a. $3x + 4y$ yes b. $8.3k - 9.2j$ yes
   c. $2x^2 - 3x$ no d. $6a + 5b - 2c$ yes

In 2 and 3, a. write a linear combination representing the total cost, and b. determine whether the situation described is *discrete* or *continuous*.

2. Apples cost \$0.75 each and bananas cost \$0.45 each.
   a. $0.75A + 0.45B$ b. discrete
3. Apples cost \$1.29 per pound and bananas cost \$0.79 per pound.
   a. $1.29A + 0.79B$ b. continuous

USES Objective H

4. At a party store, helium balloons cost 79¢ each and a box of favors costs \$11.95. You have \$40 to spend and you need two boxes of favors. How many balloons can you buy? There is no sales tax. 20
5. A chemist has solutions of hydrochloric acid in two different concentrations. One solution has 10 moles per liter; the other has 2.5 moles per liter. She mixes x liters of the first solution and y liters of the second solution.
   a. How many moles of acid are in x liters of the first solution? $10x$
   b. How many moles of acid are in y liters of the second solution? $2.5y$
   c. How many moles of acid are in the mixture? $10x + 2.5y$
   d. The chemist wants to have 6 moles of acid in the final mixture. She uses 1 liter of the second solution. How many liters of the first solution should she use? 0.35 L
6. Describe a situation leading to the equation $3x + 5y = 45$.
   Answers vary. Sample: Children's tickets cost \$3 and adult tickets cost \$5. You have \$45 to spend.

Advanced Algebra 175

d. If Tyra wants 3.6 moles of NaOH in the final mixture, what equation relates x, y, and the 3.6 total moles of NaOH? $5.2x + 7.8y = 3.6$

e. How many liters of the 7.8 mol/L solution must be added to 0.4 liter of the 5.2 mol/L solution to get 3.6 moles of NaOH in the final mixture? approximately 0.19 L

APPLYING THE MATHEMATICS

8. Refer to the Activity. Suppose that you have \$40 to spend on hamburgers and hot dogs.
   a. In standard form, write a new equation relating the costs of hamburgers and hot dogs. $2.5b + 2d = 40$
   b. Graph your equation on your graphing utility. Set the window to $\{x \mid 0 \le x \le 16\}$ and $\{y \mid 0 \le y \le 20\}$. Sketch the graph. See margin.
   c. Make a table showing all the possible combinations of hamburgers and hot dogs that you could purchase for exactly \$40. See margin.

9. A charity makes and sells piñatas as a fundraiser. Large piñatas cost \$25 and small piñatas cost \$15. Let L be the number of large piñatas and S be the number of small piñatas that are sold.
   a. What kinds of numbers make sense for S and L in this context? nonnegative integers
   b. How much money will the charity take in if 4 large piñatas and 6 small piñatas are sold? \$190
   c. If the charity takes in a total of \$225, write an equation relating S, L, and the amount of money taken in. $25L + 15S = 225$
   d. Graph the equation from Part c. Use L as the independent variable. See margin.
   e. Make a discrete graph of the solution set appropriate to this situation. See margin.
   f. Give all possible pairs (L, S) of large and small piñatas the charity could have sold to earn \$225. (0, 15), (3, 10), (6, 5), (9, 0)

A traditional piñata is usually made of paper and is filled with toys or sweets.

10. Driving from the city to visit a friend in the country, suppose a person drives at an average speed of 15 miles per hour on city streets and 40 miles per hour on the highway. Suppose the person spends C hours on city streets and H hours driving on the highway, and the friend lives 60 miles away.
    a. Write an equation relating C, H, and the total distance. $15C + 40H = 60$
    b. If the person spent 2 hours driving on city streets, how many minutes did the person spend on the highway? 45 minutes

Notes on the Questions

Question 9 When graphing the equation, some students will ignore that the graph is discrete, not continuous.

Additional Answers

8b.

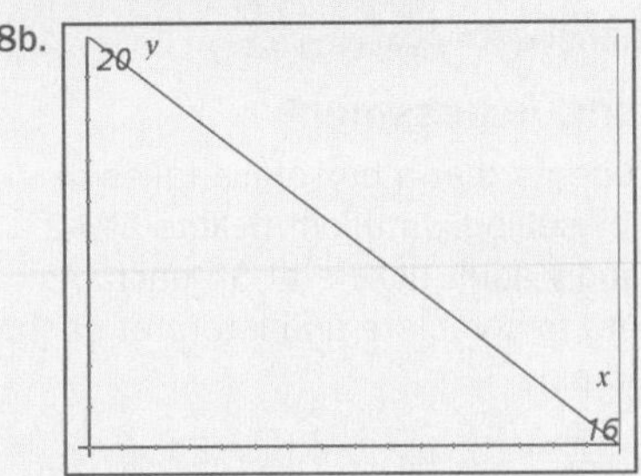

8c.

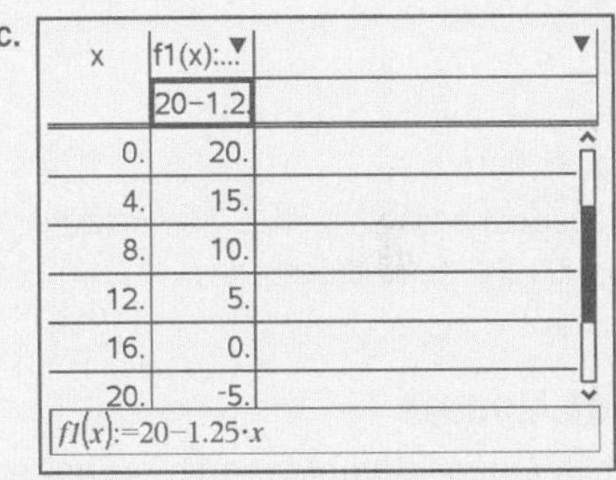

x	f1(x):=
	20−1.2
0.	20.
4.	15.
8.	10.
12.	5.
16.	0.
20.	-5.

f1(x):=20−1.25·x

9d.

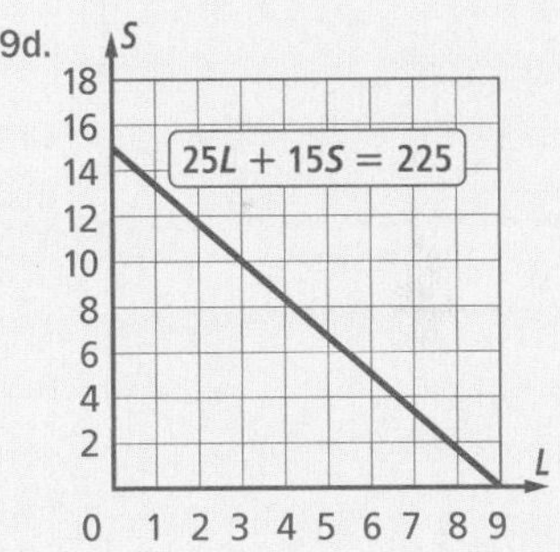

9e.

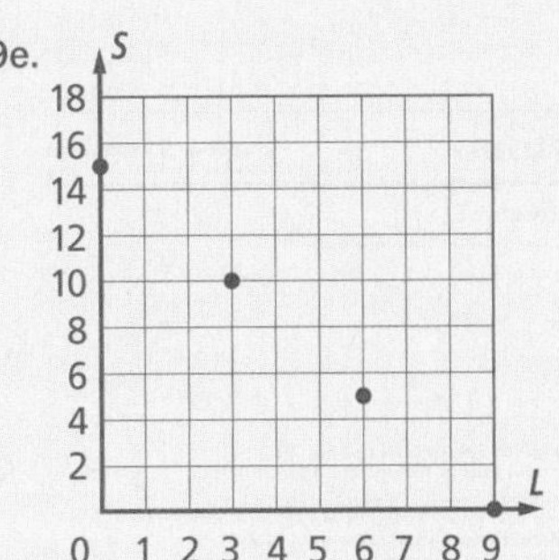

Notes on the Questions

Question 15b Encourage students to avoid a phrase such as "*n* times less"; a better phrase would be "$\frac{1}{n}$ times as much."

4 Wrap-Up

Ongoing Assessment

Tell students that a box office takes in \$150 by selling *x* student tickets at \$2 each and *y* adult tickets at \$6 each. Ask students to complete and interpret each ordered pair.

a. (0, __?__) (0, 25); the box office sells 0 student tickets and 25 adult tickets.

b. (__?__, 0) (75, 0); the box office sells 75 student tickets and 0 adult tickets.

c. (15, __?__) (15, 20); the box office sells 15 student tickets and 20 adult tickets.

Project Update

Project 3, *Linear Combinations*, on page 211 relates to the content of this lesson.

3-2B page 2

3-2B Lesson Master

Questions on SPUR Objectives
See Student Edition pages 215–219 for objectives.

PROPERTIES Objective E

1. Determine whether each expression is a linear combination.

a. $5x + 4y$ yes
b. $5.3k - 9.2j$ yes
c. $7x^2 - x$ no
d. $8r + 5s - 3t$ yes
e. $9x + 15z$ yes
f. $2x - 5y$ yes
g. $3x - 2xy - 16$ no
h. $a - c(3 - c)$ no
i. $5x + 3\sqrt{4}\,y$ yes
j. $5.3k - 0.2j$ yes
k. $7x - \sqrt{x}$ no
l. $8r + 5s - 3t$ yes

In 2–5, a. write a linear combination representing the total, and b. determine whether the situation described is *discrete* or *continuous*.

2. In football, touchdowns are worth 6 points, extra points are worth 1 point, and field goals are worth 3 points. Suppose the Manatee Cougars score *T* touchdowns, *P* extra points, and *F* field goals. Write an expression that gives the total number of points scored.
a. $6T + P + 3F$ b. discrete

3. Ivan bought *P* pounds of peaches at 79¢ a pound and *G* pounds of grapes at \$1.99 a pound. Write an expression that gives the amount Ivan paid for the peaches and the grapes.
a. $0.79P + 1.99G$ b. continuous

4. A chemist mixed *A* ounces of a 30% chlorine solution with *B* ounces of 40% chlorine solution. The final mixture contained 18 ounces of chlorine. Write an expression to model this situation.
a. $0.3A + 0.4B$ b. continuous

5. Alex bought *P* flats of petunias at \$12.99 each and *B* flats of begonias at \$8.99 each. Write an expression that gives the amount Alex spent.
a. $12.99P + 8.99B$ b. discrete

6. Describe a situation leading to the equation $0.4x + 0.6y = 24$.
Answers vary. Sample: A chemist mixes *x* ounces of a solution that is 40% acid with *y* ounces of a solution that is 60% acid. The final solution contains 24 ounces of acid.

176 *Advanced Algebra*

11. How many pounds of cashews at \$3.29/lb should be mixed with peanuts at \$1.79/lb to create a mixture of 5 pounds of nuts worth \$2.29/lb? $\frac{5}{3}$ lb

REVIEW

12. **Multiple Choice** Which of the following could be an equation of the graph at the right? **(Lesson 3-1)** E

A $y = \frac{2}{3}x + 1$ B $y = \frac{3}{2}x - 1$ C $y = 3x - 2$
D $y = x + \frac{2}{3}$ E $y = \frac{3}{2}x + \frac{5}{2}$

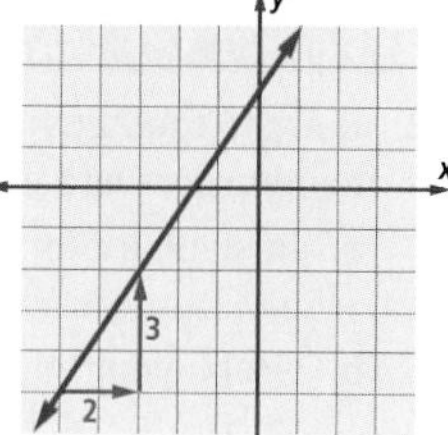

13. If *t* varies jointly with *s* and *r*, and *r* varies directly with *m*, show that *t* varies jointly with *s* and *m*. **(Lesson 2-9)**

14. Consider the points (3, 1), (-4, 4.5), and (5, 0). Determine if they lie on a line. If so, state the slope of the line; if not, explain why not. **(Lesson 2-4)** Yes; the slope is $-\frac{1}{2}$.

13. $t = ksr$ and $r = pm$, where *k* and *p* are constants. So then by substitution, $t = kpsm$. Let $a = kp$. Then *a* is a constant and $t = asm$, so *t* varies jointly with *s* and *m*.

15. Michelangelo's *David*, a statue in Florence, Italy, is 17 feet high and made out of marble. Over the years, many replicas have been made of this statue. The weight *w* of a marble replica varies directly as the cube of the replica's height *h*. **(Lesson 2-1)**

a. Write an equation modeling this situation. $w = kh^3$

b. **Fill in the Blank** The weight of a 12" marble replica would be __?__ the weight of the original statue. $\frac{1}{4913}$

16. Graph $y = \sqrt{x^2 - 4}$ on a calculator. **(Lesson 1-4)**

a. Does this graph appear to be a graph of a function? yes

b. What is the domain? $\{x \mid x \le -2 \text{ or } x \ge 2\}$

c. What is the range? $\{y \mid y \ge 0\}$

EXPLORATION

17. In many schools, a student's grade point average is calculated using linear combinations. Some schools give 4 points for each A, 3 points for each B, 2 points for each C, and 1 point for each D. Suppose a person gets 7 As, 3 Bs and 2 Cs.

a. Calculate this person's total number of points. 41

b. Divide your answer in Part a by the total number of classes to get the grade point average. ≈ 3.42

c. Calculate your own grade point average for last year using this method. Answers vary.

QY ANSWER

The domain is {0, 4, 8, 12} and the range is {0, 5, 10, 15}.

Lesson 3-3 The Graph of $Ax + By = C$

▶ **BIG IDEA** If a linear combination of two variables x and y is a constant, then the graph of all the points (x, y) is a line.

Recall the equation $2.5x + 2y = 30$ from the previous lesson. This equation represents allowable \$30 purchases of x hamburgers at \$2.50 each and y hot dogs at \$2.00 each from Harry's Hamburger Hovel. Because you do not buy fractions of sandwiches, both x and y are nonnegative integers. So a graph of the solution is a set of discrete points. However, if you allow x and y to be any real numbers, then the graph of $2.5x + 2y = 30$ is shown at the right.

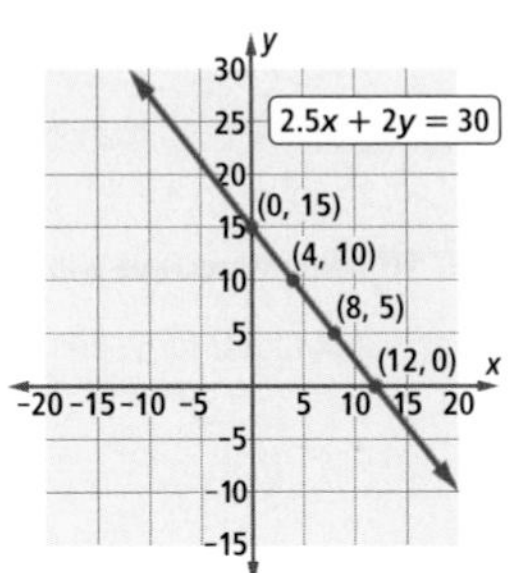

The equation $2.5x + 2y = 30$ is of the form $Ax + By = C$, with $A = 2.5$, $B = 2$, and $C = 30$. When A and B are not both zero, the graph of $Ax + By = C$ is always a line.

Standard Form of an Equation of a Line Theorem

The graph of $Ax + By = C$, where A and B are not both zero, is a line.

Proof There are two cases to consider: (1) if $B = 0$ and (2) if $B \neq 0$.

(1) If $B = 0$, then $A \neq 0$, and the equation is simply $Ax = C$. Multiply both sides by $\frac{1}{A}$ to obtain the equivalent equation $x = \frac{C}{A}$. The graph of this equation is a vertical line.

(2) If $B \neq 0$, then solve the given equation for y:

$Ax + By = C$	Given
$By = -Ax + C$	Add $-Ax$ to both sides.
$y = -\frac{A}{B}x + \frac{C}{B}$	Divide both sides by B.

Mental Math

Give a general variation equation based on the description.

a. The cost c of painting the interior of a house varies directly as the number n of rooms to be painted. $c = kn$

b. The amount p of paint needed for a wall varies jointly as the length ℓ and height h of the wall. $p = k\ell w$

c. The time t it will take to paint varies inversely as the number n of painters hired. $t = \frac{k}{n}$

d. The time d needed for the paint to dry varies directly as the thickness t of the paint applied and inversely as the square of the amount a of air circulation in the room. $d = \frac{kt}{a^2}$

Lesson 3-3

GOAL

Graph situations in which the expression $Ax + By$ is a constant; review the graphs of $Ax + By = C$, $x = a$, and $y = b$; use intercepts to graph.

SPUR Objectives

A Determine the slope and intercepts of a line given its equation.

E Recognize properties of linear functions.

M Graph or interpret graphs of linear equations.

Materials/Resources

- Lesson Masters 3-3A and 3-3B
- Resource Master 41
- Quiz 1

HOMEWORK

Suggestions for Assignment

- Questions 1–21
- Question 22 (extra credit)
- Reading Lesson 3-4
- Covering the Ideas 3-4

Local Standards

Background

The focus of this lesson, graphing from standard form and slope-intercept form, should be a review for most students. An advantage of the standard form for linear equations, $Ax + By = C$, is that *all* lines in the plane can be put into this form. In contrast, vertical lines (as in Example 2) cannot be put into slope-intercept form.

Example 3 Of all the equations of the form $Ax + By = C$, two are most frequently used. (1) If A, B, and C are rational, then $kAx + kBy = kC$, where kA, kB, and kC are integers with no common factors, and kA is positive. (2) When the denominators of an equation are the x- and y-intercepts, then the equation is $\frac{x}{\frac{C}{A}} + \frac{y}{\frac{C}{B}} = 1$ and is known as *intercept form*. In this example, Equation (2) is in the unique form in which the coefficients are integers with no common factors and the coefficient of x is positive. In intercept form, the equation of that line is $\frac{x}{3} + \frac{y}{8} = 1$.

1 Warm-Up

Graph each of the following equations on the same axes. What figure appears?

1. $3x + 8y = 20$
2. $3x - 8y = 20$
3. $-3x + 8y = 20$
4. $-3x - 8y = 20$

The graphs of these four equations form a kite with the vertices $(6\frac{2}{3}, 0)$, $(0, 2.5)$, $(-6\frac{2}{3}, 0)$, and $(0, -2.5)$.

Notes on the Lesson

Example 1 Encourage students to determine the *x*- and *y*-intercepts *mentally* whenever possible. Explain that when an equation is in the standard form of $Ax + By = C$ and when either or both values *A* and *B* evenly divide *C*, then intercepts can be found quickly. (Question 6 reflects this situation.) Because substituting 0 for *x* has the effect of eliminating the *x*-term, have students cover the *x*-term and mentally solve the resulting equation for *y*, thus obtaining the *y*-intercept. Likewise, covering the *y*-term and mentally solving for *x* produces the *x*-intercept.

Additional Example

Example 1 Graph the equation $3x - 4y = 24$ using its *x*- and *y*-intercepts.

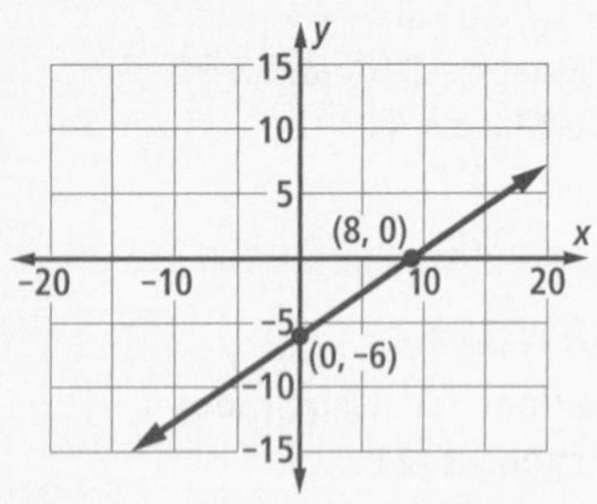

Stress to students that the method of graphing by using two intercepts is very useful with graphs that require large scales, such as $5x + 3y = 4500$. The *x*-intercept is 900, and the *y*-intercept is 1500. These values suggest to scale the axes by at least 100, if not 200. Using the slope-intercept method with a slope of $-\frac{5}{3}$ is cumbersome. Larger scales appear frequently in applications in this book.

In the general discussion of $Ax + By = C$, you may wish to discuss the one situation not covered in this lesson—when $A = B = 0$. There are two possibilities. When $C = 0$, the solution set is the entire coordinate plane. When $C \neq 0$, the solution set is the null set—{Ø}. Because neither situation is a line, these situations are usually avoided by requiring that *A* and *B* cannot both be zero ($A^2 + B^2 \neq 0$).

Note-Taking Tips

Have students compare the steps they take to graph a line for an equation in standard form and in slope-intercept form.

STOP QY1

▸ **QY1**

When $B \neq 0$, what are the slope and *y*-intercept of the line with equation $Ax + By = C$?

Graphing a Line Using Intercepts

Because the form $Ax + By = C$ can describe any line, it is called the *standard form of an equation for a line.* Although, if $B \neq 0$, you could rewrite such an equation in slope-intercept form in order to make a graph, it is often much quicker to graph such equations by hand using *x*- and *y*-intercepts. If *A*, *B*, and *C* are all nonzero, the line with equation $Ax + By = C$ has distinct *x*- and *y*-intercepts, so the intercepts can be used to graph the line.

Example 1

Graph the equation $-5x + 2y = 10$ using its *x*- and *y*-intercepts.

Solution To find the *x*-intercept, substitute 0 for *y*, and solve for *x*.

$-5x + 2(0) = 10$

$x = -2$

The x-intercept is -2.

To find the *y*-intercept, substitute 0 for *x*, and solve for *y*.

$-5(0) + 2y = 10$

$y = 5$

The y-intercept is 5.

Plot (-2, 0) and (0, 5) and draw the line containing them, as shown at the right.

Check Find a third ordered pair that satisfies $-5x + 2y = 10$. For example, when $x = 2$, $-10 + 2y = 10$, so $2y = 20$ and $y = 10$. Thus, (2, 10) should be on the graph. Is it? Yes. It checks.

This technique does not work when *A*, *B*, or *C* is zero. If $A = 0$, the slope is $-\frac{0}{B} = 0$. The line is horizontal, and so there is no *x*-intercept. If $B = 0$, the slope of the line is $-\frac{A}{0}$, which is undefined. The line is vertical, and so there is no *y*-intercept.

▸ **QY2**

Why can you not use the *x*- and *y*-intercepts to graph $Ax + By = C$ when $C = 0$?

STOP QY2

Accommodating the Learner

Ask students to describe how to write equations for a line given the intercepts (*a*, 0) and (0, *b*). Then have them write the equations in slope-intercept form and standard form. The slope is $-\frac{b}{a}$, and the *y*-intercept is *b*, so the slope-intercept form is $y = -\frac{b}{a}x + b$. The standard form is $bx + ay = ab$.

ENGLISH LEARNERS

Vocabulary Development

The beginning of the proof of the Equation of a Line Theorem includes the comment that "there are two cases to consider." Help students understand that the list of "cases" must include all possibilities, and no situation can fit into more than one case. For this theorem, the cases $B = 0$ and $B \neq 0$ include all possible values of *B*, and a number *B* cannot be both equal to zero and not equal to zero.

Example 2

Graph $x + 0y = 3$.

a. Is this the graph of a line?

b. Is this the graph of a function?

Solution

a. The equation simplifies to $x = 3$. The value of x is always 3, regardless of the value of y. The graph is a vertical line.

b. Create a table of values.

x	y
3	-5
3	0
3	2

It is not the graph of a function because more than one ordered pair has the same x-coordinate.

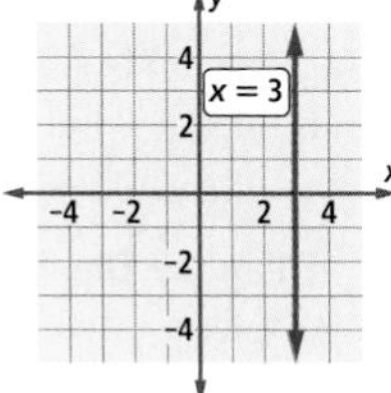

Equivalent Equations for Lines

One drawback of the standard form is that the same line can have many different, but equivalent, equations in standard form. Recall that multiplying both sides of an equation by a nonzero real number yields an equivalent equation. Since lines have a unique equation in slope-intercept form, you can test equations for equivalence by putting them in slope-intercept form.

GUIDED

Example 3

Find which equations below, if any, represent the same line.

(1) $4x + 1.5y = 12$ (2) $8x + 3y = 24$

(3) $8x + 3y = 12$ (4) $16x + 6y = 12$

Solution 1 Rewrite each line in slope-intercept form.

(1) y = __?__ (2) y = __?__ $-\frac{8}{3}x + 8$; $-\frac{8}{3}x + 8$

(3) y = __?__ (4) y = __?__ $-\frac{8}{3}x + 4$; $-\frac{8}{3}x + 2$

Equations __?__ are equivalent. Equations __?__ are not equivalent to any other given equations. (1) and (2); (3) and (4)

Solution 2 If I multiply both sides of Equation __?__ by 2, Equation __?__ results. So Equations __?__ and __?__ are equivalent. Since the right side of three of the given equations is 12, no other equations are equivalent. (1); (2); (1); (2)

Additional Examples

Example 2 Graph $0x + y = -2$.

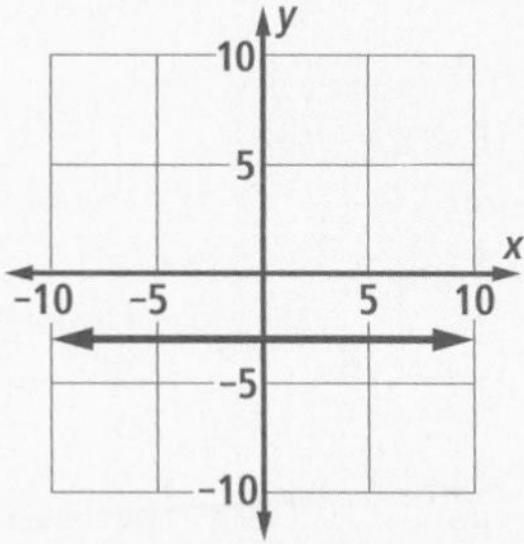

a. Is the graph a line? yes

b. Is the graph a function? yes

Example 3 Which equations, if any, represent the same line?

a. $2x - 4y = 12$

b. $2x + 4y = -12$

c. $2x + 4y = -16$

d. $3x + 6y = -18$

Solution Rewrite each line in slope-intercept form.

a. y = __?__ $\frac{1}{2}x - 3$

b. y = __?__ $-\frac{1}{2}x - 3$

c. y = __?__ $-\frac{1}{2}x - 4$

d. y = __?__ $-\frac{1}{2}x - 3$

Equations __?__ and __?__ are equivalent. Equations __?__ and __?__ are not equivalent to the other given equations. b; d; a; c

Accommodating the Learner

Ask students to express the ordered pairs that represent the intercepts of the line whose equation is $Ax + By = C$.

$\left(0, \frac{C}{B}\right), \left(\frac{C}{A}, 0\right)$

3 Assignment

Recommended Assignment

- Questions 1–21
- Question 22 (extra credit)
- Reading Lesson 3-4
- Covering the Ideas 3-4

Additional Answers

5c.

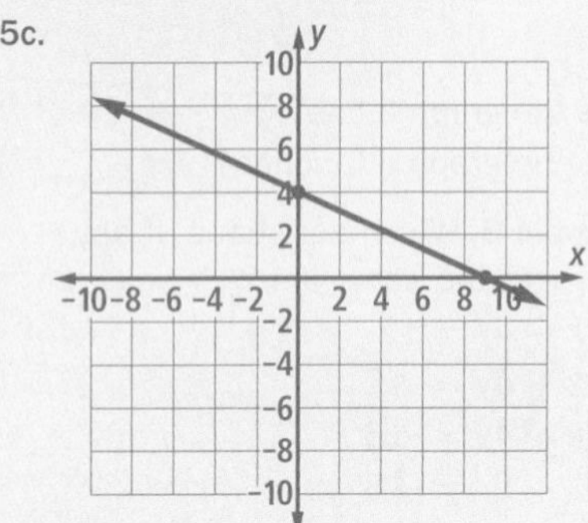

6c.

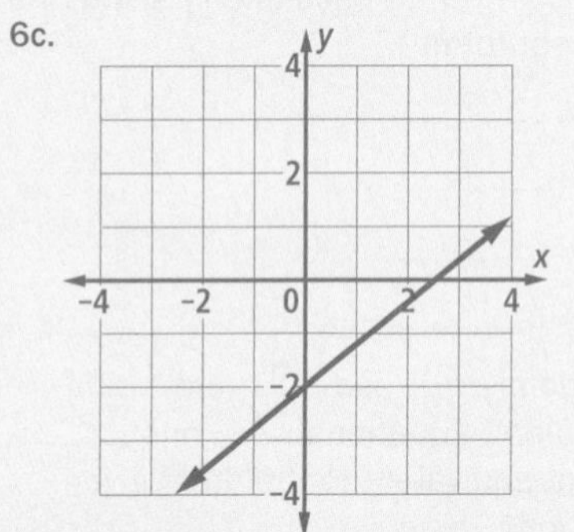

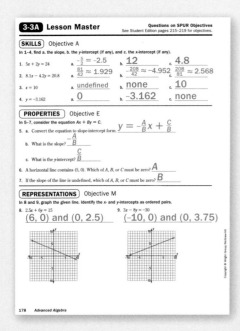

3-3A Lesson Master — **Questions on SPUR Objectives** See Student Edition pages 215–219 for objectives.

SKILLS Objective A

In 1–4, find a. the slope, b. the y-intercept (if any), and c. the x-intercept (if any).

1. $5x + 2y = 24$ a. $-\frac{5}{2} = -2.5$ b. 12 c. 4.8
2. $8.1x - 4.2y = 20.8$ a. $\frac{81}{42} \approx 1.929$ b. $-\frac{208}{42} \approx -4.952$ c. $\frac{208}{81} \approx 2.568$
3. $x = 10$ a. undefined b. none c. 10
4. $y = -3.162$ a. 0 b. -3.162 c. none

PROPERTIES Objective E

In 5–7, consider the equation $Ax + By = C$.

5. a. Convert the equation to slope-intercept form. $y = -\frac{A}{B}x + \frac{C}{B}$
   b. What is the slope? $-\frac{A}{B}$
   c. What is the y-intercept? $\frac{C}{B}$
6. A horizontal line contains (5, 0). Which of A, B, or C must be zero? A
7. If the slope of the line is undefined, which of A, B, or C must be zero? B

REPRESENTATIONS Objective M

In 8 and 9, graph the given line. Identify the x- and y-intercepts as ordered pairs.

8. $2.5x + 6y = 15$ (6, 0) and (0, 2.5)
9. $3x - 8y = -30$ (-10, 0) and (-10, 3.75)

178 Advanced Algebra

Equations (2), (3), and (4) from Example 3 represent lines with the same slope but different y-intercepts. This suggests that the graphs of $Ax + By = C$ and $Ax + By = D$ are distinct parallel lines when $C \neq D$.

Questions

COVERING THE IDEAS

1. a. **Fill in the Blank** If A and B are not both 0, the graph of $Ax + By = C$ is a __?__. line
   b. If $A \neq 0$ but $B = 0$, what kind of line is the graph? vertical
   c. If $B \neq 0$ but $A = 0$, what kind of line is the graph? horizontal
2. **Fill in the Blank** $Ax + By = C$ is in the __?__ of an equation of a line. standard form
3. What is true about the slope of a vertical line? It is undefined.
4. **True or False** Every line in standard form can be graphed by drawing the line containing its x- and y-intercepts. false

In 5 and 6, an equation for a line is given.

a. Find its x-intercept.

b. Find its y-intercept.

c. Graph the line using your answers to Parts a and b.

5. $4x + 9y = 36$
6. $4x - 5y = 10$
7. Consider $Ax + By = C$.
   a. Find the x-intercept of the line. What happens when $A = 0$?
   b. Find the y-intercept of the line. What happens when $B = 0$?

5a. 9; 6b. 4;
5c. See margin.
6a. 2.5; 7b. -2;
6c. See margin.
7a. $\frac{C}{A}$; there is no x-intercept.
7b $\frac{C}{B}$; there is no y-intercept.

APPLYING THE MATHEMATICS

8. Write an equation in standard form for the line graphed at the right. $7x + 3y = -21$

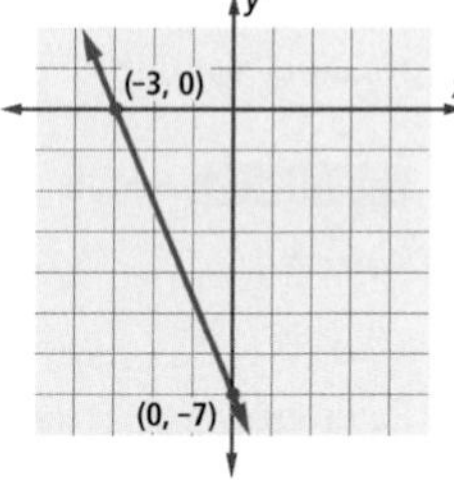

9. Find the value of C such that the point (4, -1) lies on the graph of $10x - 2y = C$. 42
10. Delaney's Deli makes ham and cheese sandwiches and turkey sandwiches. Each ham and cheese sandwich uses $\frac{1}{8}$ lb of cheese, while each turkey sandwich uses no cheese. Let x be the number of ham and cheese sandwiches the deli prepares. Let y be the number of turkey sandwiches the deli prepares.
    a. Write an equation stating that the total amount of cheese the deli uses is 5 lb. $\frac{1}{8}x = 5$
    b. Graph your equation from Part a. See margin.

Additional Answers

10b.

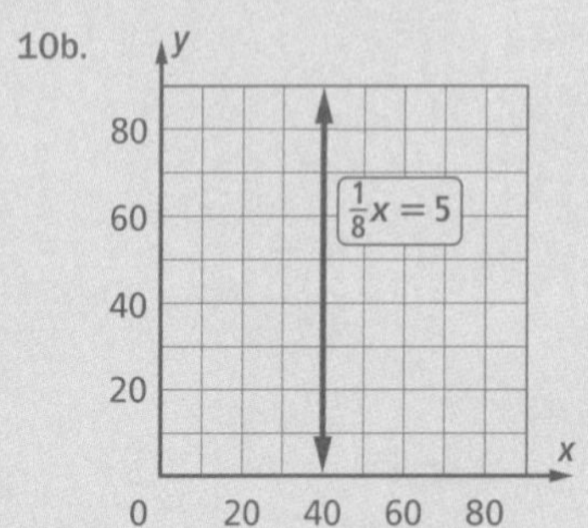

11. a. Graph the line with equation $0x + 4y = 14$. See margin.
    b. Find two ordered pairs satisfying the equation.
    c. Compute the slope of the line through the two points. 0

11b. Answers vary. Sample: (0, 3.5), (5, 3.5)

In 12 and 13, find an equation for a line in standard form with the given properties.

12. *y*-intercept -3 and slope 2 $-2x + y = -3$
13. no *y*-intercept and passes through the point (17, 29.93) $x = 17$
14. Mallory combines *n* liters of a solution that is 3 mol/L chlorine with *y* liters of a solution that is 5 mol/L chlorine. She ends up with a mixture that contains 2 moles of chlorine.
    a. Write an equation relating *n*, *y*, and the total amount of chlorine in the mixture. $3n + 5y = 2$
    b. Graph the equation you obtained in Part a by finding the *n*- and *y*-intercepts. Consider *n* to be the independent variable. See margin.
    c. Use your graph to find about how many liters of the 5 mol/L solution Mallory must add to 0.4 liter of the 3 mol/L solution to get the final mixture. 0.16 L
15. Consider the graphs of $Ax + By = C$ and $Ax + By = D$ if *A* and *B* are not both zero and $C \neq D$. a. $y = -\frac{A}{B}x + \frac{C}{B}$; $y = -\frac{A}{B}x + \frac{D}{B}$
    a. Rewrite each equation in slope-intercept form.
    b. What is the relationship between the slopes of the lines? What does that tell you about the lines?
    c. What is the relationship between the *y*-intercepts of the lines? What does that tell you about the lines?
    d. Write the conclusions of Parts b and c as one if-then statement.
    e. Use the if-then statement from Part d to give the equations of several lines parallel to $16x - 13y = 11$.
16. Use a CAS **expand** command to show that multiplying the equation $Ax + By = C$ by a nonzero number *k* yields another equation in standard form. Why must this new equation describe the same line as the original?

15b. The slopes are equal, so the lines are parallel or are the same line.

15c. The intercepts are different, so the lines cannot be the same line and are thus parallel.

15d. If equations for two lines are written in standard form with the same coefficients of *x* and *y* but different right sides, then the lines are unique and parallel.

15e. Answers vary. Sample: $16x - 13y = 15$, $16x - 13y = 20$

16. The lines are the same since the slopes and the intercepts will be the same, as the *k* will cancel itself out.

REVIEW

17. At a library book sale, paperbacks are being sold for \$0.50 each and hardcover books are \$1. If you want to buy *P* paperbacks and *H* hardcover books, write a linear combination that expresses the amount you will have to pay. (Lesson 3-2) $0.50P + H$

Notes on the Questions

Question 15 This question should definitely be discussed in some detail, as its result is one students should know: The graphs are parallel lines.

Additional Answers

11a.

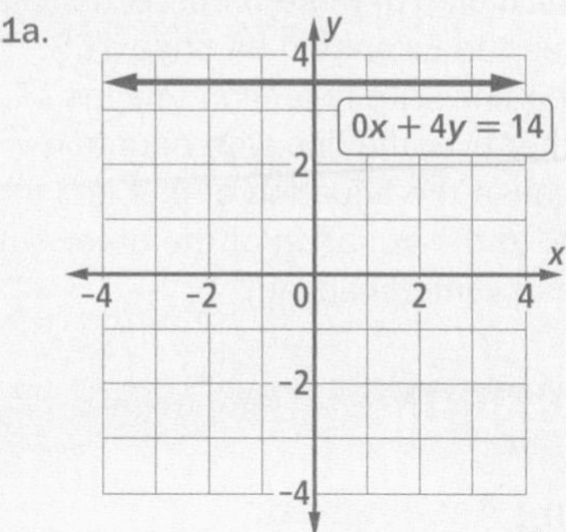

14b.

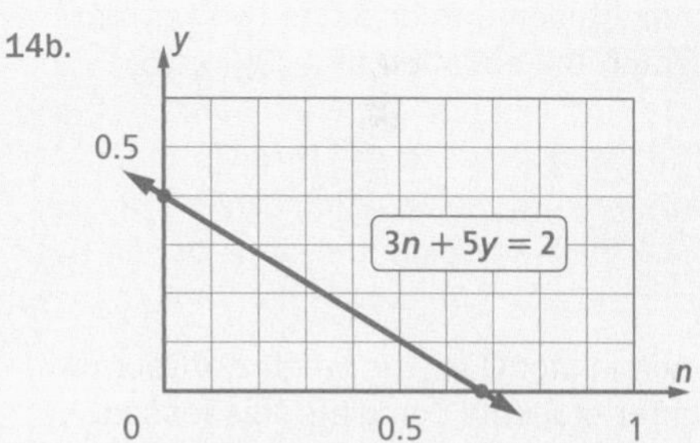

3-3

Notes on the Questions

Question 18 By using reciprocal rates, one can calculate that the car gets about 28.6 miles per gallon in the city and about 37 miles per gallon on the highway.

Question 22 If the second equation were $Bx - Ay = C$, then the lines would be perpendicular. (For more on perpendicular lines, see the Extension on page 168.) The given lines are reflection images of each other over the line with equation $y = x$ because the equation of one is identical to the equation of the other but with x and y interchanged.

4 Wrap-Up

Ongoing Assessment

Ask students to describe two ways to graph the equation $5x - 3y = 15$.
(1) Find and plot the intercepts (3, 0) and (0, -5) and draw a line through them.
(2) Rewrite the equation as $y = \frac{5}{3}x - 5$, use the y-intercept and slope to plot two points, and then draw a line though them.

Administer Quiz 1 (or a quiz of your own) after students complete this lesson.

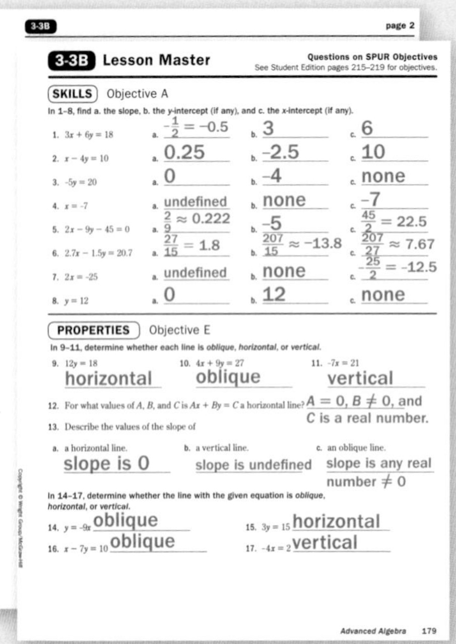

3-3B page 2

3-3B Lesson Master

Questions on SPUR Objectives
See Student Edition pages 215–219 for objectives.

SKILLS Objective A

In 1–8, find a. the slope, b. the *y*-intercept (if any), and c. the *x*-intercept (if any).

	a.	b.	c.
1. $3x + 6y = 18$	$-\frac{1}{2} = -0.5$	3	6
2. $x - 4y = 10$	0.25	-2.5	10
3. $-5y = 20$	0	-4	none
4. $x = -7$	undefined	none	-7
5. $2x - 9y - 45 = 0$	$\frac{2}{9} \approx 0.222$	-5	$\frac{45}{2} = 22.5$
6. $2.7x - 1.5y = 20.7$	$\frac{27}{15} = 1.8$	$\frac{207}{15} \approx -13.8$	$\frac{207}{27} \approx 7.67$
7. $2x = -25$	undefined	none	$-\frac{25}{2} = -12.5$
8. $y = 12$	0	12	none

PROPERTIES Objective E

In 9–11, determine whether each line is *oblique*, *horizontal*, or *vertical*.

9. $12y = 18$ horizontal
10. $4x + 9y = 27$ oblique
11. $-7x = 21$ vertical

12. For what values of A, B, and C is $Ax + By = C$ a horizontal line? $A = 0, B \neq 0$, and C is a real number.

13. Describe the values of the slope of
a. a horizontal line. slope is 0
b. a vertical line. slope is undefined
c. an oblique line. slope is any real number $\neq 0$

In 14–17, determine whether the line with the given equation is *oblique*, *horizontal*, or *vertical*.

14. $y = -9x$ oblique
15. $3y = 15$ horizontal
16. $x - 7y = 10$ oblique
17. $-4x = 2$ vertical

Advanced Algebra 179

18. Suppose your car uses 0.035 gallon of gas to travel 1 mile in the city and 0.027 gallon of gas to travel 1 mile on the highway. **(Lesson 3-2)**
    a. Write a linear combination to express the number of gallons of gas you would use to travel C miles in the city and H miles on the highway. $0.035C + 0.027H$
    b. If your car has 14 gallons of gas, how many city miles can you drive without refilling if you also make a 200-mile highway trip? about 246 miles

19. A car starts out 400 miles from St. Louis and drives directly toward St. Louis at 60 mph. **(Lesson 3-1)**
    a. Find an equation for the distance d from St. Louis as a function of time t in hours from the start of the trip. $400 - 60t = d$
    b. Does the equation in Part a describe a constant-increase or a constant-decrease situation? constant decrease

20. The sum S of the measures of the interior angles of a convex polygon varies directly as $n - 2$, where n is the number of sides of the polygon. **(Lesson 2-1, Previous Course)**
    a. Find the constant of variation. 180
    b. Graph the function. See margin.

21. The independent variable of a function is given. State a reasonable domain for the function. **(Lesson 1-4)**
    a. h = number of hours worked in a day
    b. d = distance traveled away from home while on vacation
    c. t = temperature in Indianapolis, Indiana, in February

Gateway Arch in St. Louis is the tallest national monument in the United States. The shape of the arch is known as a *catenary curve*.

21a. Answers vary. Sample: $\{h \mid 0 \leq h \leq 16\}$
21b. $\{d \mid 0 < d\}$.
21c. $\{t \mid -20 \leq t \leq 50\}$.

EXPLORATION

22. Consider the lines $Ax + By = C$ and $Bx + Ay = C$. Explore the connections between slopes and intercepts of these lines.
The slopes are reciprocals of each other, and the x-intercept of one line is the y-intercept of the other.

QY ANSWERS

1. The slope is $-\frac{A}{B}$, and the y-intercept is $\frac{C}{B}$.
2. When $C = 0$, the x- and y-intercepts are both zero. The line passes through the origin, and the x- and y-intercepts are not distinct.

Additional Answers

20b.

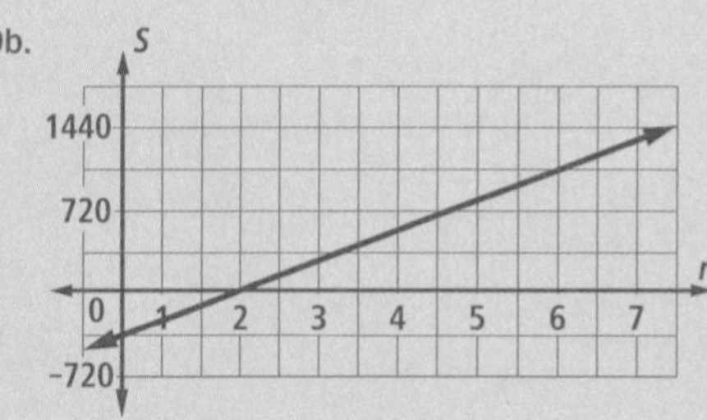

Extension

As an extension to Question 22, ask students to explore the connections between the lines $Ax + By = C$ and $Bx - Ay = D$. The lines, which have slopes $-\frac{A}{B}$ and $\frac{B}{A}$, are perpendicular to each other.

Lesson 3-4 Finding an Equation of a Line

Vocabulary

point-slope form

piecewise linear function

▸ **BIG IDEA** Postulates and theorems of geometry about lines tell when exactly one line is determined from given information. An equation of that line can often be determined algebraically.

In geometry you learned that *there is exactly one line through a given point parallel to a given line.* Since nonvertical lines are parallel if and only if they have the same slope, this means that there is exactly one line through a given point with a given slope. Using algebra you can determine the equation of this line.

Mental Math

Suppose you pull a chip from a bag. What is the probability of choosing a blue chip if

a. there are 8 blue chips and 4 red chips? $\frac{2}{3}$

b. there are 3 blue chips, 7 red chips, and 1 white chip? $\frac{3}{11}$

c. there are b blue chips, r red chips, and w white chips? $\frac{b}{b+r+w}$

Finding a Linear Equation

Example 1

In a physics experiment, a spring is 11 centimeters long with a 13-gram weight attached. Its length increases 0.5 centimeter with each additional gram of weight. This is a constant-increase situation up to the spring's elastic limit. Write a formula relating spring length L and weight W. Then graph the equation.

Solution The slope is $0.5\frac{\text{cm}}{\text{gram}}$. Because the unit for slope is centimeters per gram, length is the dependent variable and weight is the independent variable. The point (13, 11) is on the line. Substitute these values into the slope formula.

$$\frac{L-11}{W-13}=0.5$$

To put this equation in slope-intercept form, multiply both sides by $W - 13$.

$$L - 11 = 0.5(W - 13)$$

Then solve for L.

$$L - 11 = 0.5W - 6.5$$
$$L = 0.5W + 4.5$$

Now you know the y-intercept of this line as well as the point (13, 11). Use this information to graph the equation, as shown at the right.

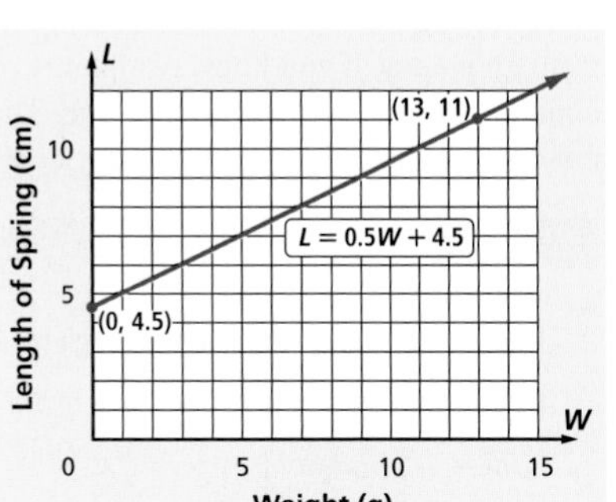

Lesson 3-4

GOAL

Connect the different forms of an equation of a line; introduce and explore piecewise linear functions.

SPUR Objectives

B Find an equation of a line given two points on it or given a point on it and its slope.

I In a real-world context, find an equation for a line containing two points.

K Model situations leading to piecewise linear functions.

N Graph and interpret graphs of piecewise linear functions.

Materials/Resources

- Lesson Masters 3-4A and 3-4B
- Resource Masters 42 and 43

HOMEWORK

Suggestions for Assignment

- Questions 1–22
- Question 23 (extra credit)
- Reading Lesson 3-5
- Covering the Ideas 3-5

Local Standards

1 Warm-Up

In 1–4, find an equation for the line through (0, 0) and the given point.
Answers vary.

1. (5, 9) Sample: $9x = 5y$
2. (-17, 106) Sample: $106x + 17y = 0$
3. $\left(\frac{2}{37}, 3\frac{1}{7}\right)$ Sample: $22 \cdot 37x - 2 \cdot 7y = 0$
4. (b, a) Sample: $y = \frac{a}{b}x$

Background

Although many students will be familiar with finding an equation for a line through two points, either from their first course in algebra or from their geometry course, for most students this review will be helpful.

In geometry, students learn that exactly one line can be drawn in the following situations: (1) through two points (this is usually a postulate); (2) through a point parallel to a given line (this is often Playfair's Parallel Postulate); and (3) through a point perpendicular to a given line (this is usually a theorem). This lesson shows students how to determine algebraic equations of lines for the first two situations. In Chapter 4, after talking about slopes of perpendicular lines, students will explore the third situation.

In all these cases, the problem is reduced to finding an equation for a line through a given point with a given slope. We have used (x_1, y_1) to name the given point. We

(continued on next page)

3 Assignment

Notes on the Lesson

Finding a linear equation Stress the phrase *"an" equation for the line through two points*, not *"the" equation ....* Lines have many equations. If one asks for an equation of a particular form (such as "slope-intercept" or "linear combination with positive coefficient of x and no common factors of the integer coefficients"), then the answer is a single equation; without such restrictions, many equations are often possible.

Additional Example

Example 1 A spring is 23 inches long and has a 3-pound weight attached. Its length increases 3 inches with each additional pound of weight added. This is a constant-increase situation. Write a formula relating the spring length L and the weight w. Then graph the equation. $L = 3w + 14$;

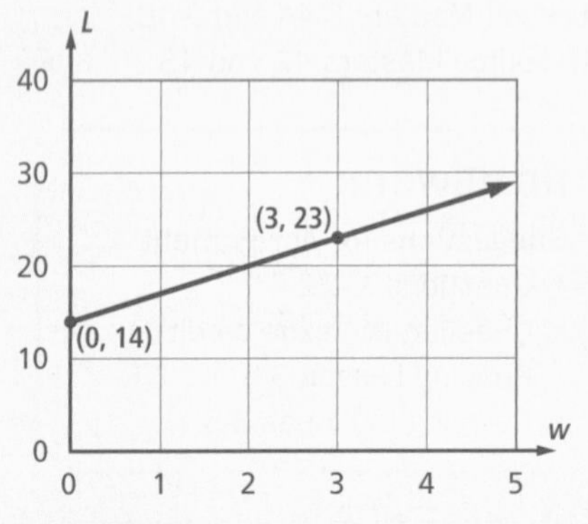

Finding an equation of a line through two points Some books discuss "the two-point form" for an equation of a line through (x_1, y_1) and (x_2, y_2): $\frac{y_2 - y_1}{x_2 - x_1} = \frac{y - y_1}{x - x_1}$. Although this form is certainly useful, we do not introduce it as a separate form because the left side is easily seen as the slope.

Example 2 Go through this example carefully. Some students have difficulty with the idea that (x, y) is any point on the line, for they are so accustomed to finding particular values of x and y. Many students have learned to use the slope-intercept form $y = mx + b$ to find the line through a given point with a given slope. They may want to use this form only. Stress the ease and quickness of using the point-slope equation. Questions 6 and 8 are designed to help you make this point.

STOP QY1

> **QY1**
> What does the y-intercept in the equation $L = 0.5W + 4.5$ represent in Example 1?

Point-Slope Form of a Line

Each of the equations $L = 0.5W + 4.5$ and $L - 11 = 0.5(W - 13)$ describes the situation of Example 1. The slope-intercept form is useful for computing values of L quickly if you know values of W. The form $L - 11 = 0.5(W - 13)$ shows the slope and a specific point on the graph, and it can be used to determine the slope-intercept form.

Point-Slope Theorem

If a line contains the point (x_1, y_1) and has slope m, then it has the equation $y - y_1 = m(x - x_1)$.

Proof Let ℓ be the line with slope m containing (x_1, y_1). If (x, y) is any other point on ℓ, then using the definition of slope,

$$m = \frac{y - y_1}{x - x_1}.$$

Multiplying both sides by $x - x_1$ gives

$$y - y_1 = m(x - x_1).$$

This is the desired equation of the line.

The equation $y - y_1 = m(x - x_1)$ is called a **point-slope form** of an equation for a line. Solving for y in the point-slope form of a line gives a form that combines aspects of the slope-intercept and point-slope forms.

$$y = m(x - x_1) + y_1$$

Finding an Equation of a Line through Two Points

Two points determine a line. You use this idea every time you draw a line through two points with a straightedge. It is another postulate from geometry. If you know two points on a line, you can find its equation by first computing its slope. Then use either point in the point-slope form $y - y_1 = m(x - x_1)$ or $y = m(x - x_1) + y_1$.

GUIDED

Example 2

Find an equation of the line p through (4, 7) and (6, -2).

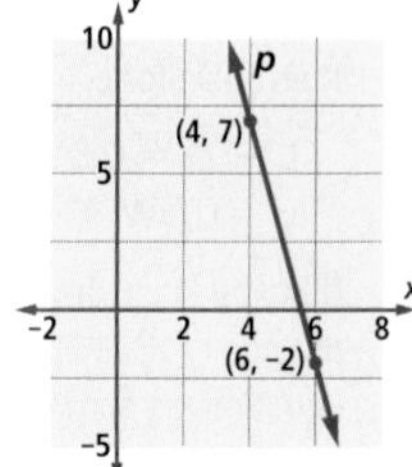

Solution First, compute the slope of the line p.

$m = \underline{\ ?\ }$ $-\frac{9}{2}$

could have used (h, k), which are the letters used in the Graph Translation Theorem in Chapter 6, but they are not traditional in this context. However, a translation idea helps to explain this theorem: The line through (x_1, y_1) with slope m is the image of $y = mx$ under a translation x_1 units horizontally and y_1 units vertically.

Accommodating the Learner

Ask students to go through the steps of Example 2 a second time, this time using the "other" given ordered pair. Ask students to show that both versions of the equation, $y - 7 = -\frac{9}{2}(x - 4)$ and $y - (-2) = -\frac{9}{2}(x - 6)$, give the same slope-intercept equation. Each point-slope form leads to $y = -\frac{9}{2}x + 25$.

Second, because you know two points on the line and neither of them is the y-intercept, use one of the points in the point-slope form.

$y - \underline{\ ?\ } = \underline{\ ?\ }(x - \underline{\ ?\ })$ 7; $-\frac{9}{2}$; 4

This is one equation for the line p. In slope-intercept form, this equation is ___?___. $y = -\frac{9}{2}x + 25$

 QY2

> **QY2**
>
> Check your solution to Example 2 by finding an equation of the line using the point you did not use before and putting the equation in slope-intercept form.

Piecewise Linear Functions and Graphs

In Chapter 1 you saw the graph at the right of Frank's bicycle trip to Chuck's house. You focused on the domain and range of the whole trip and on function representations for different parts of the trip. For instance, at time $t = 60$ minutes, Frank was about 6 miles from home, so $d = f(60) = 6$.

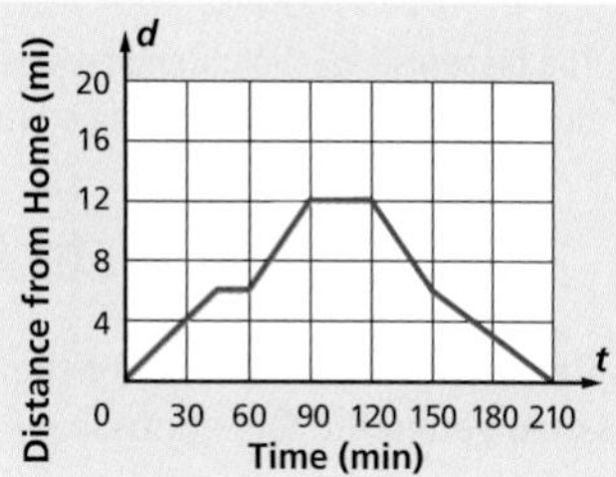

Because this graph does not have a constant rate of change over its domain $\{t|\ 0 \le t \le 210\}$, it cannot be represented by a single linear equation. But you can write an equation for each segment of the graph that does have a constant rate of change. Because the graph is described in pieces, the graph and the function are called **piecewise linear**. The graph is the union of several segments. Each segment can be described by a linear function that has a restricted domain indicating where the segment starts and stops.

Writing a function for a piecewise linear graph requires writing the equation of each line segment.

Example 3

Write a piecewise linear function for the first two segments of Frank's bicycle trip as described in the graph above. Estimate the values of segment endpoints where necessary.

Solution **First piece:** This segment appears to begin when $t = 0$ and end when $t = 45$. The ordered pairs represented by the endpoints are (0, 0) and about (45, 6). Write an equation for the line through these two points.

Find the slope: $m = \frac{6 - 0}{45 - 0} = \frac{6}{45} = \frac{2}{15}$.

Because (0, 0) is on the line, 0 is the d-intercept. So use the slope-intercept form of a line to get

$d = \frac{2}{15}t + 0$ or $d = \frac{2}{15}t$.

(continued on next page)

3-4

Additional Example

Example 2 Find an equation of the line q through (6, 4) and (15, -2).

Solution Compute the slope of line q: $m = \underline{\ ?\ }$. $\frac{4 - (-2)}{6 - 15} = \frac{6}{-9} = -\frac{2}{3}$

Because you know two points on the line and neither of them is the y-intercept, use one of the points in the point-slope form: $y - \underline{\ ?\ } = \underline{\ ?\ }(x - \underline{\ ?\ })$.
Answers vary. Sample: 4; $-\frac{2}{3}$; 6

This is one equation for line q. Now solve for y to put the equation in slope-intercept form, which is ___?___.
$y = -\frac{2}{3}x + 8$

Notes on the Lesson

Piecewise linear functions and graphs Piecewise linear functions model situations in which the rate of change is constant for intervals but not for the entire situation. A piecewise linear graph can be used to describe a situation or event only if the situation/event is represented by various segments, with each segment having a constant rate of change. And each segment of the graph must be a portion of a line.

Piecewise functions are very common in applications. They provide a new and interesting way to provide practice in interpreting graphs for independent and dependent variables and rates of change.

At first, students may find the task of determining equations for a piecewise linear graph difficult. Encourage students to use a classic problem-solving strategy—*divide a difficult problem into simpler parts and then solve each part.* Have them use the endpoints of each segment to calculate the slope of that segment; then they can use either endpoint and the point-slope form to find the equation of that segment. If the section is a ray, they should use the endpoint and any other point on the ray to determine the slope. Using the endpoints of segments or rays stresses the domain limitations for each equation.

Accommodating the Learner

Ask students to write an equation of the line through (x_1, y_1) and (x_2, y_2) in point-slope, slope-intercept, and standard forms.

$y - y_1 = \frac{y_2 - y_1}{x_2 - x_1}(x - x_1)$;

$y = \frac{y_2 - y_1}{x_2 - x_1}x - \left(\frac{y_2 - y_1}{x_2 - x_1}x_1 - y_1\right)$;

$(y_2 - y_1)x - (x_2 - x_1)y = (y_2 - y_1)x_1 - (x_2 - x_1)y_1$

ENGLISH LEARNERS
Vocabulary Development

The paragraph above Example 2 begins with the sentence "Two points determine a line." When you discuss that sentence with students, help them understand that part of the meaning of *determine* is that the number of lines through the two points is just one; part of *determine a line* means that the line is unique.

Notes on the Lesson

Example 3 Remind students that when they are asked for the equations of a piecewise linear graph, they must list the domain for each equation.

Additional Example

Example 3 Write a piecewise linear function for a graph that goes from (0, 0) to (50, 40), then from (50, 40) to (60, 60), and then from (60, 60) to (100, 60). Use (p, q) as the variables.

$$q = \begin{cases} \frac{4}{5}p, \text{ for } 0 \le p \le 50 \\ 2p - 60, \text{ for } 50 < p \le 60 \\ 60, \text{ for } 60 < p \le 100 \end{cases}$$

Activity You can define piecewise functions on a TI-89 using restricted domains ("such that") or using the "when(" command.

Note-Taking Tips

When students write and describe the point-slope form of a linear equation, encourage them to also write and describe the slope-intercept form. Students should be able to see how each form uses the slope and a particular point.

Since this equation describes only the part of the situation for t-values from 0 through 45, write

$$d = \frac{2}{15}t \text{ for } 0 \le t \le 45.$$

Second piece: This appears to be a constant function where $d = 6$ between $t = 45$ and $t = 60$. So,

$$d = 6 \text{ for } 45 < t \le 60.$$

In the second piece, we have a choice whether to include the value 45 in the domain. This is because (45, 6) is already included in the first piece and it is not necessary to repeat it.

The piecewise function: Combine the functions for the two pieces and their domains into one formula using a brace.

$$d = f(t) = \begin{cases} \frac{2}{15}t & \text{for } 0 \le t \le 45 \\ 6 & \text{for } 45 < t \le 60 \end{cases}$$

Writing a piecewise formula for the last four segments of the trip is left to you in the Questions.

The piecewise formula can be used to determine Frank's distance from home at any time, even if the distance cannot be easily determined from the graph. For instance, to determine how far Frank was from home after 20 minutes, use the first equation because $t = 20$ is in the domain $0 \le t \le 45$. So, when $t = 20$, $d = f(20) = \frac{2}{15}(20) \approx 2.67$ miles.

QY3

QY3 How far from home was Frank after 55 minutes?

If you know the formula for a piecewise function, a CAS or graphing utility can be used to graph it.

Activity

Step 1 Open a graphing utility and clear any functions that have been entered. Find out how to enter a piecewise function. On the CAS pictured at the right, a template is used to enter a piecewise function.

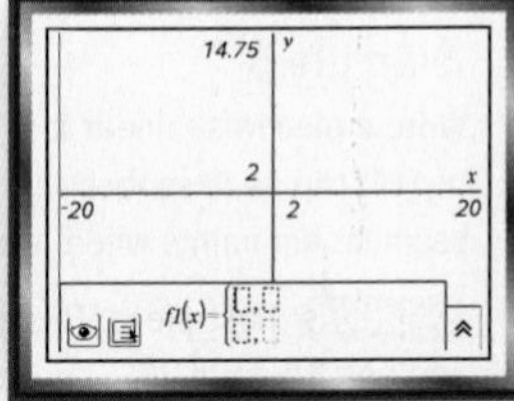

Step 2 Enter the piecewise formula you found in Example 3. Include the domain restrictions for each line of the formula.

Step 3 Graph the function. Adjust your window as necessary to see the whole graph.

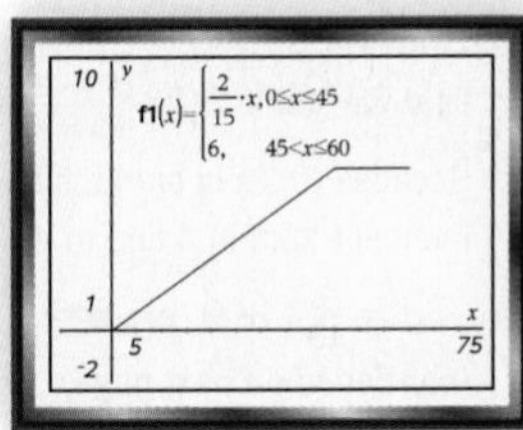

Step 4 Compare your graph to the first part of the graph found in this lesson. Do they look the same?

Extension

For Example 3, ask students to explain what is happening in the piecewise-linear graph between (90, 12) and (120, 12). The distance is not changing, so Frank is not moving. (Another possibility is that he is moving on an arc of a circle with Chuck's house at the center of that circle; then the distance between Frank and Chuck's house is not changing.) Then ask students if a piecewise-linear graph of distance and time can have any vertical segments. No; a vertical segment would mean that the distance changed without any change of time, which is physically impossible.

Questions

COVERING THE IDEAS

1. How many points determine a line? 2
2. Name a point on the line $L = 0.5W + 4.5$ other than the two used in Example 1. Answers vary. Sample: (2, 5.5)
3. **True or False** You can determine the equation of a line knowing only its slope. false
4. **Fill in the Blank** The point-slope form of the equation for a line with slope m and passing through point (x_1, y_1) is __?__.
5. Give a strategy for finding an equation for a line when you know two points on the line.
6. A line passes through the points $\left(\frac{1}{3}, \frac{2}{5}\right)$ and $\left(\frac{7}{3}, \frac{9}{10}\right)$.
   a. Compute the slope of the line. $\frac{1}{4}$
   b. Use $\left(\frac{1}{3}, \frac{2}{5}\right)$ and the slope to determine an equation of the line.
   c. Check that $\left(\frac{7}{3}, \frac{9}{10}\right)$ satisfies the equation.

In 7 and 8, write an equation for the line with the given information.

7. slope 6 and y-intercept $\sqrt{3}$ $y = 6x + \sqrt{3}$
8. slope $-\frac{3}{2}$ and passing through (-4, 1)
9. Find an equation in point-slope form for the line graphed at the right.
10. Refer to Example 3.
    a. Write the equations describing the last four segments of Frank's bicycle trip. See margin.
    b. How far from home was Frank after 132 minutes? 9.6 miles
    c. Graph the whole piecewise function on a CAS. See margin.

4. $y - y_1 = m(x - x_1)$

5. Compute the slope and then use either point in the point slope form $y - y_1 = m(x - x_1)$.

6b. $y = \frac{1}{4}\left(x - \frac{1}{3}\right) + \frac{2}{5}$

6c. $\frac{9}{10} = \frac{1}{4}\left(\frac{7}{3} - \frac{1}{3}\right) + \frac{2}{5}$
$= \frac{1}{2} + \frac{2}{5}$

8. $y = -\frac{3}{2}(x + 4) + 1$
$= -\frac{3}{2}x - 5$

9. $y + 3 = \frac{12}{7}(x + 2)$

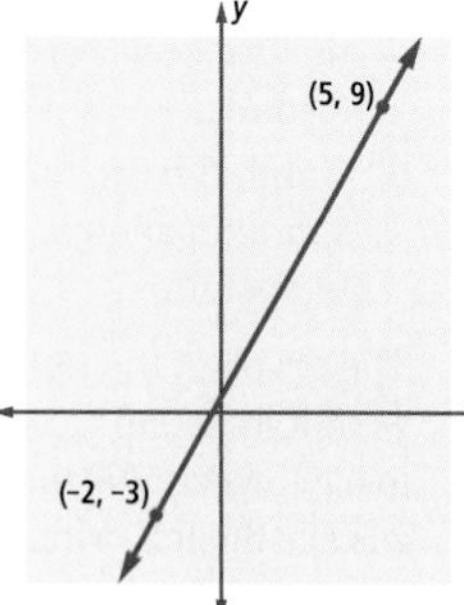

APPLYING THE MATHEMATICS

11. A club will be charged \$247.50 for printing 150 t-shirts and \$501.25 for printing 325 t-shirts. Let c be the cost of printing s shirts.
    a. Write c as a linear function of s. $c = 1.45s + 30$
    b. How much will it cost to print 0 t-shirts? (This is the set-up cost.) \$30
    c. How much will it cost to print 100 t-shirts? \$175
12. Find an equation for the line through (5, 3) and parallel to $y = \frac{4}{7}x - 12$. $y = \frac{4}{7}x + \frac{1}{7}$

3 Assignment

Recommended Assignment

- Questions 1–22
- Question 23 (extra credit)
- Reading Lesson 3-5
- Covering the Ideas 3-5

Notes on the Questions

Question 6 You might ask if this line contains any lattice points—points in which both coordinates are integers. No; an equation for the line is $4y = x + \frac{19}{15}$. If x and y are integers, they cannot both satisfy the equation.

Questions 11 and 14 These questions involve finding an equation for the line through two points.

Additional Answers

10a. $d = f(t) \begin{cases} \frac{1}{5}t - 6, \text{ for } 60 < t \leq 90 \\ 12, \text{ for } 90 < t \leq 120 \\ -\frac{1}{5}t + 36, \text{ for } 120 < t \leq 150 \\ -\frac{1}{10}t + 21, \text{ for } 150 < t \leq 210 \end{cases}$

10c.

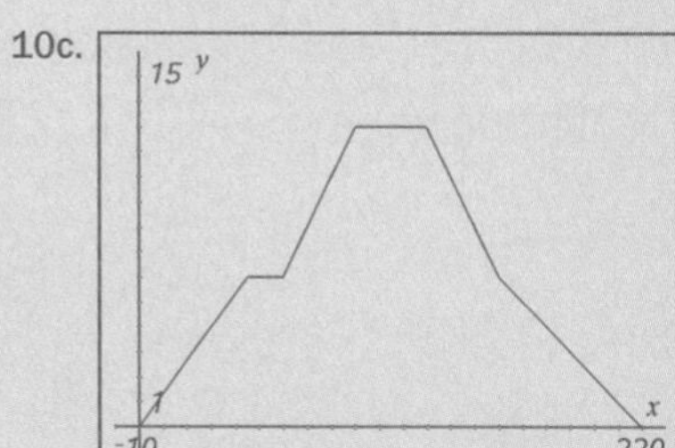

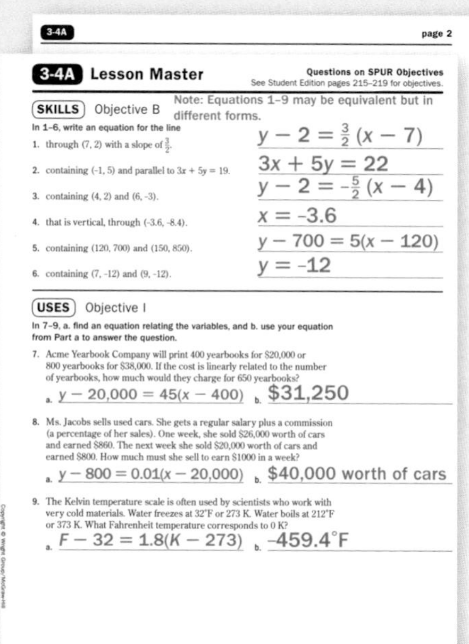

3-4A page 2

3-4A Lesson Master

Questions on SPUR Objectives
See Student Edition pages 215–219 for objectives.

SKILLS Objective B

Note: Equations 1–9 may be equivalent but in different forms.

In 1–6, write an equation for the line

1. through (7, 2) with a slope of $\frac{3}{2}$. $y - 2 = \frac{3}{2}(x - 7)$
2. containing (-1, 5) and parallel to $3x + 5y = 19$. $3x + 5y = 22$
3. containing (4, 2) and (6, -3). $y - 2 = -\frac{5}{2}(x - 4)$
4. that is vertical, through (-3.6, -8.4). $x = -3.6$
5. containing (120, 700) and (150, 850). $y - 700 = 5(x - 120)$
6. containing (7, -12) and (9, -12). $y = -12$

USES Objective I

In 7–9, a. find an equation relating the variables, and b. use your equation from Part a to answer the question.

7. Acme Yearbook Company will print 400 yearbooks for \$20,000 or 800 yearbooks for \$38,000. If the cost is linearly related to the number of yearbooks, how much would they charge for 650 yearbooks?
   a. $y - 20{,}000 = 45(x - 400)$ b. \$31,250
8. Ms. Jacobs sells used cars. She gets a regular salary plus a commission (a percentage of her sales). One week, she sold \$26,000 worth of cars and earned \$860. The next week she sold \$20,000 worth of cars and earned \$800. How much must she sell to earn \$1000 in a week?
   a. $y - 800 = 0.01(x - 20{,}000)$ b. \$40,000 worth of cars
9. The Kelvin temperature scale is often used by scientists who work with very cold materials. Water freezes at 32°F or 273 K. Water boils at 212°F or 373 K. What Fahrenheit temperature corresponds to 0 K?
   a. $F - 32 = 1.8(K - 273)$ b. −459.4°F

Advanced Algebra 181

Notes on the Questions

Question 16 We are assuming that time on Narnia is directly proportional to time on Earth.

13. Refer to the `slope` function defined in Question 14 of Lesson 3-1.
    a. Use `slope` to find the slope of the line through $P = (17.3, 2.4)$ and $Q = (43.9, 22.6)$. 0.759398
    b. Define a new function `ptslope` that will find the equation of a line with slope m and passing through the point (a, b) in point-slope form. A sample from one CAS is shown at the right.

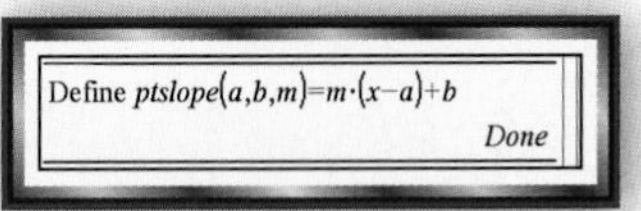

    c. Use `ptslope` to find an equation of $\overleftrightarrow{PQ}$ from Part a. Use $a = 17.3$, $b = 2.4$, and the slope you found in Part a as m.
    d. You can define one function, call it `line2pt(a,b,c,d)`, that combines the calculations of `slope` and `ptslope`. Define this function on a CAS.

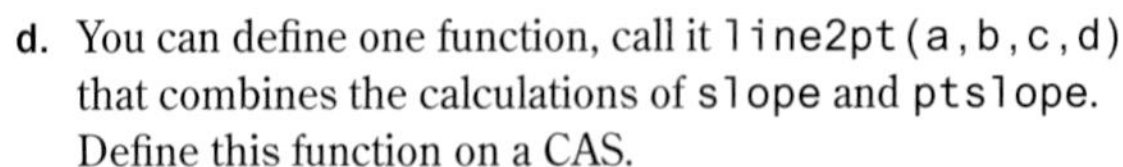

    e. Input the coordinates of points P and Q into `line2pt`. Are your results the same as in Part c? yes
14. An approximate conversion from degrees C on the Celsius scale to degrees F on the Fahrenheit scale is $F \approx 2C + 32$.
    a. Use the facts that $32°F = 0°C$, $100°C = 212°F$, and that the two scales are related linearly to write a more accurate formula. $F = 1.8C + 32$
    b. Graph the two formulas to determine when the approximation is within 3° of the actual Fahrenheit temperature.
15. The graph at the right represents the average weight in pounds of a child from age 3 months to age 5 years (60 months). Use the graph to answer the following questions.
    a. Write a piecewise linear function for this situation. See margin.
    b. What is the average weight of a 30-month-old child? 29.5 pounds

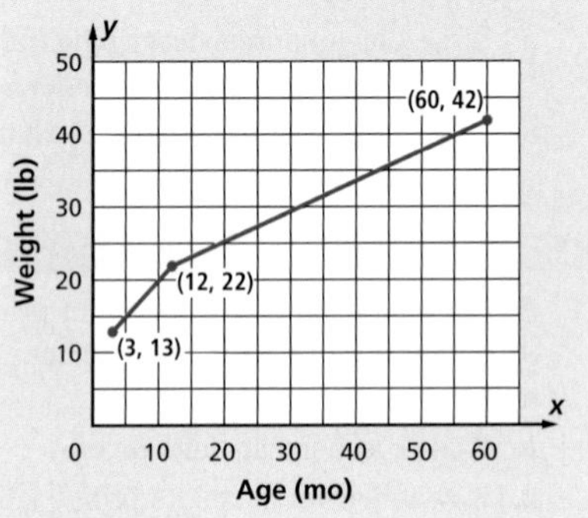

16. In the book, *The Lion, the Witch, and the Wardrobe* (C.S. Lewis, 1961), a group of children find a portal to the world of Narnia where time passes at a different rate than on Earth. The children are in Narnia for 15 years while only 5 minutes pass on Earth. Peter, the oldest child in the group, is 13 when he enters Narnia. Write a linear equation that shows Peter's age n in Narnia for each minute m that passes on Earth. $n = 3m + 13$

13b. Define ptslope$(a,b,m) = m \cdot (x - a) + b$

13c. $y = 0.759398x - 10.7376$

13d. Define line2pt(a,b,c,d) = ptslope$(a,b,$slope$(a,b,c,d))$

14b. The approximation is within 3 degrees between -15 and 15 degrees Celsius.

Additional Answers

15a. $w = f(x) = \begin{cases} x + 10, \text{ for } 3 \le x \le 12 \\ \frac{5}{12}x + 17, \text{ for } 12 < x \le 60 \end{cases}$

REVIEW

17. **Fill in the Blanks** The equation $Ax + By = C$ describes a line with an undefined slope whenever A is __?__ and B is __?__. **(Lesson 3-3)** not 0; 0

18. Write an equation of the line with x-intercept -2 and y-intercept 4 in standard form. **(Lesson 3-3)** $2x - y = -4$

19. **Multiple Choice** Which of the following is not a linear combination? **(Lesson 3-2)** D

 A $4a + (-3)b$ B $12x + 12y + 12z$ C $T - F$
 D $7A + 3C^2$ E $e + e + e + 3f$

20. Makayla finds that the amount she studies varies inversely as the number of phone calls she receives. One day she studied 3.5 chapters with 3 phone calls. How many chapters can she study if she gets 5 phone calls? **(Lesson 2-2)** 2.1 chapters

21. Consider the sequence r whose first 7 terms are -5, 3, 1700, −65.4, 0.354, 29, and -1327. **(Lesson 1-8)**
 a. What is r_3? $r_3 = 1700$
 b. Write the sentence $r_7 = -1327$ in words as you would read it.

22. The following table of values shows the height of Azra's dog for certain numbers of months after she bought him. **(Lesson 1-5)**

Month	0	1	2	3	4	5	6
Height (in.)	10	14	16	19	22	23	24

 a. Graph the values in the table on the coordinate axes, with time on the horizontal axis and height on the vertical axis.
 b. Azra thinks the domain of her function is all positive real numbers between 0 and 6, but her brother Marquis thinks it is only the whole numbers from 0 to 6. Who is right and why?

EXPLORATION

23. In 1912, the Olympic record for the men's 100-meter dash was 10.8 seconds. In 1996 it was 9.84 seconds. Assume a linear relationship between the year and the record time.
 a. According to the information given, determine a linear equation to model the given data. $y - 10.8 = -0.0114(x - 1912)$
 b. Using your model, compute the predicted world record in 2006. 9.7284 seconds
 c. A new world record of 9.76 seconds for the 100-meter dash was set in 2006. Compare your predicted record with the actual 2006 value.

21b. r sub seven equals negative one thousand three hundred twenty-seven.

22a. See margin.

22b. Answers vary. Sample: Azra is right because she could measure her dog's height after only part of a month.

23c. The model predicted a faster time than the actual record by about 0.0316 second.

QY ANSWERS

1. 4.5 cm, the length of the spring with no weights attached
2. Answers vary. Sample: $y + 2 = -4.5(x - 6)$. In slope-intercept form: $y = -4.5x + 25$.
3. 6 miles

Notes on the Questions

Question 23 This question leads naturally into the next lesson. You might have an interested student (perhaps a member of the track team) briefly research the evolution of the world record in the 100 meters.

4 Wrap-Up

Ongoing Assessment

Ask students to describe how to find an equation of a line given two points on the line if neither point is the *y*-intercept. Answers vary. Sample: Using the two points, find the slope. Then using one of the points and the slope, use the point-slope formula $y - y_1 = m(x - x_1)$ to write an equation of the line.

Project Update

Project 2, *Penalties for Speeding,* on page 210 relates to the content of this lesson.

Additional Answers

22a.

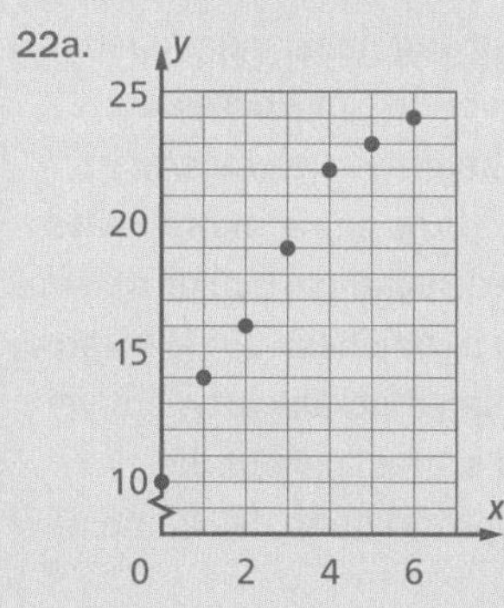

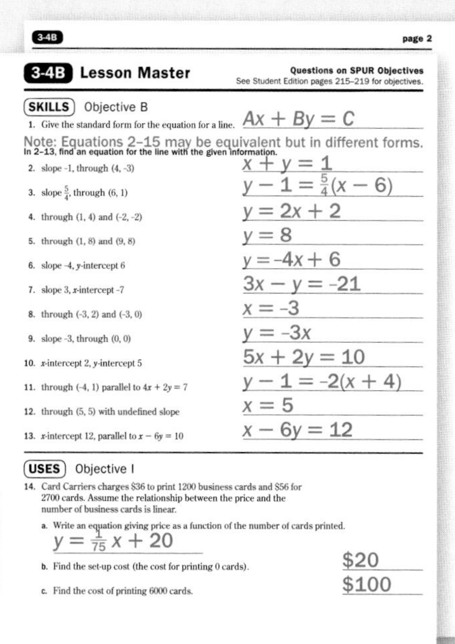

3-4B page 2

3-4B Lesson Master Questions on SPUR Objectives — See Student Edition pages 215–219 for objectives.

SKILLS Objective B

1. Give the standard form for the equation for a line. $Ax + By = C$

Note: Equations 2–15 may be equivalent but in different forms.
In 2–13, find an equation for the line with the given information.

2. slope -1, through (4, -3) $x + y = 1$
3. slope $\frac{5}{4}$, through (6, 1) $y - 1 = \frac{5}{4}(x - 6)$
4. through (1, 4) and (-2, -2) $y = 2x + 2$
5. through (1, 8) and (9, 8) $y = 8$
6. slope -4, y-intercept 6 $y = -4x + 6$
7. slope 3, x-intercept -7 $3x - y = -21$
8. through (-3, 2) and (-3, 0) $x = -3$
9. slope -3, through (0, 0) $y = -3x$
10. x-intercept 2, y-intercept 5 $5x + 2y = 10$
11. through (-4, 1) parallel to $4x + 2y = 7$ $y - 1 = -2(x + 4)$
12. through (5, 5) with undefined slope $x = 5$
13. x-intercept 12, parallel to $x - 6y = 10$ $x - 6y = 12$

USES Objective I

14. Card Carriers charges \$36 to print 1200 business cards and \$56 for 2700 cards. Assume the relationship between the price and the number of business cards is linear.
 a. Write an equation giving price as a function of the number of cards printed. $y = \frac{1}{75}x + 20$
 b. Find the set-up cost (the cost for printing 0 cards). \$20
 c. Find the cost of printing 6000 cards. \$100

Advanced Algebra 183

Lesson 3-5

GOAL

Explore two methods for modeling a set of points with a line: eyeballing and calculating the line of best fit.

SPUR Objectives

J Fit lines to data.

Materials/Resources

- Lesson Masters 3-5A and 3-5B
- Resource Master 44
- Internet connection

HOMEWORK

Suggestions for Assignment

- Questions 1–15
- Question 16 (extra credit)
- Reading Lesson 3-6
- Covering the Ideas 3-6

Local Standards

1 Warm-Up

Consider these data of the ages of U.S. presidents at their deaths: {67, 90, 83, 85, 73, 80, 78, 79, 68, 71, 53, 65, 74, 64, 77, 56, 66, 63, 70, 49, 57, 71, 67, 58, 60, 72, 67, 57, 60, 90, 63, 88, 78, 46, 64, 81, 93}. Find the median and the first and third quartiles of the data set. median, 68; 1st quartile, 61.5; 3rd quartile, 78.5

Lesson 3-5 Fitting a Line to Data

Vocabulary

linear regression
line of best fit, least-squares line, regression line
deviation

BIG IDEA When data are almost on a line, it is often helpful to approximate the data by a line that minimizes the sum of the squares of the distances from the data points to the corresponding points on the line.

Mental Math

Find the slope of the line.

a. $y = 2.5x + 7$ 2.5

b. $y = 14$ 0

c. $y - 0.2 = 0.144(x - 0.4)$ 0.144

d. $16x + 20y = 45$ -0.8

Square Grabber, which may be provided by your teacher, is a fun game with simple rules. You control a black square. Your job is to capture the other black squares by touching them while avoiding the red squares.

Play the game once. At the end of the game you are told the number of squares you captured and are given a score.

You can write the numbers as an ordered pair (number of squares, score). If you play many times and generate many ordered pairs, you can graph the ordered pairs and use the graph to find a model for the relationship between the number of squares you capture and your score. Is this a simple linear relationship?

Activity 1

MATERIALS internet connection

Step 1 Play Square Grabber 15 times. Record the number of squares you capture and your score for each game in a table like the one below. See margin.

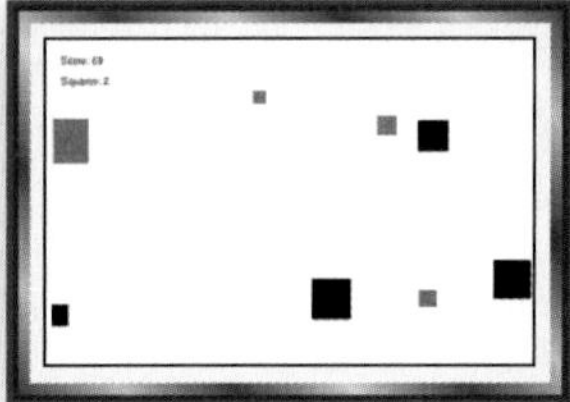

Number of Squares (n)	Score (s)
43	855
23	461
12	235

Step 2 Graph your data. Let n = number of squares and s = score. Use n as the independent variable and s as the dependent variable. Does it appear that a line could be a good model for your data? See margin.

Background

At least five kinds of situations lead to data that lie on or near a line: (1) The variables are precisely linearly related, as with many of the situations in the preceding lessons. (2) Although the variables are *in theory* linearly related, like the amount of weight placed on a spring and its length, *in practice* measurement error or other effects prevent the data from exactly fitting a line. (3) A situation like that in Activity 2, in which we expect the variables to be related and are not surprised to see a strong linear relationship. (4) Two variables increase or decrease together (e.g., the heights of elementary school students and how much mathematics they know), but there is no particular reason for the relationship to be linear. (5) We know the variables are related nonlinearly, but we are looking at such a small part of the domain that it is appropriate to use a linear model for the data.

Step 3 Eyeball a line that comes close to modeling all of the points in your data set. Draw it on your graph. See margin.

Step 4 Estimate the coordinates of any two points on your line. (They do not have to be actual data points.) Find an equation for the line through these points.

Step 5 Your equation from Step 4 can be used to estimate your score based on the number of squares you captured. Use your model to estimate your score for capturing 100 squares.

Step 4. Answers vary. Sample: (200, 4000), (300, 6000). In this case the equation is $y = 20x$.

Step 5. Answers vary. Sample: Using the equation in the previous step would give a score of 2000.

The Regression Line

In Activity 1, you approximated a *line of best fit* for your data by eye. How can you tell which line fits the data the *best*? If you passed your graph of ordered pairs around the room and asked each of your classmates to find a *line of best fit*, you might get as many different lines as you have classmates.

To solve this problem, statisticians have developed a method called **linear regression** that uses all the data points to find the line. A line found by using regression is what people call the **line of best fit**. It is also called the **least-squares line**, or simply the **regression line**. You will learn how regression works in a later course. For now, to find the line of best fit, use a statistics application. For details on how your application works, check the manual or ask your teacher.

Activity 2

Navy divers who remain underwater for long periods of time cannot come quickly back to the surface due to the high pressure under the water. They must make what are known as *decompression stops* on the way up. If divers skip this procedure they risk a serious medical condition known as *the bends*. The U.S. Navy has created tables that allow divers to know when and for how long they should stop on the way to the surface. The table below gives the decompression time needed (including ascent time) based on how many minutes were spent at a given depth. The points in the table are graphed at the right. Calculate the regression line for the decompression data.

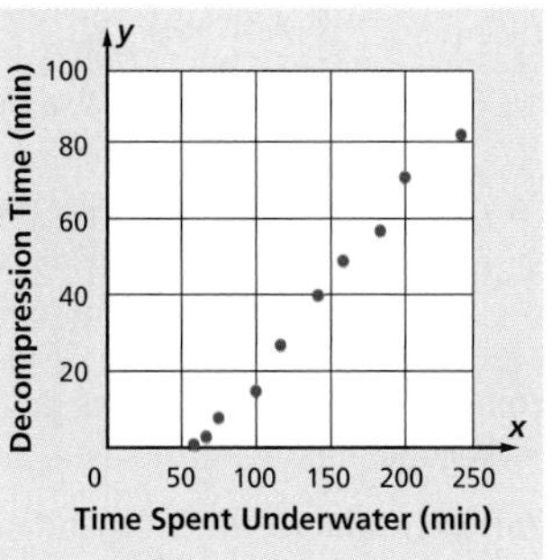

Time Spent at a Maximum Depth of 60 feet (min)	60	70	80	100	120	140	160	180	200	240
Decompression Time Needed (min)	1	3	8	15	27	40	49	57	71	82

(continued on next page)

2 Teaching

Notes on the Lesson

It is useful to have "nice" data sets for this lesson. A good data set for students has two variables that are expected to increase or decrease with each other and have 10 to 20 data points. *Hint:* If you (or a student) can enter large data sets into a worksheet or a computer or graphics calculator prior to class discussion, you will not have to spend class time on this task.

You might point out a nontrivial difference between eyeballing and finding the line of best fit. When we "eyeball," we tend to think of the distance between points and lines using the shortest distance—the perpendicular distance between each point and the line. The line of best fit uses the *vertical* distance between a point and the line because the goal is to minimize prediction errors. Specifically, the line of best fit minimizes the sum of the squares of the vertical distances between the data points and the line. Consequently, if the variables are reversed, most people's eyeballed line would not change, but the line of best fit does change.

Applets visually showing the squares of the deviations and calculating least squares can be found on the Internet. One such Web site is http://www.ies.co.jp/math/java/misc/least_sq/least_sq.html.

Note-Taking Tips

Encourage students to write, in their own words, a description of how to use their CAS to calculate a regression line. That can help them save time when they need to calculate other regression lines.

The lesson begins with the game *Square Grabber,* which is on the UCSMP Web site. Activity 2 fits the "line of best fit" to data. This is the first lesson that refers to CAS spreadsheets and regression tools. You may want to spend some time having students see how these features work with their technology.

ENGLISH LEARNERS
Vocabulary Development

Students should be able to use their own words to describe the terms *line of best fit* and *deviation.*

Notes on the Lesson

Activity 2 You might want to point out that Navy scuba diving is quite different from recreational scuba diving. Because Navy divers tend to spend longer amounts of time at lower depths than recreational divers, these data would look quite different for recreational dives.

Step 1 Enter the data into columns in your statistics or spreadsheet application. Name the first column *timespent* and the second column *decomptime* to indicate which is the independent and which is the dependent variable.

	A timespent	B decomptime	C
1	60	1	
2	70	3	
3	80	8	
4	100	15	
5	120	27	
6	140	40	
A1	60		

Step 2 Create a scatterplot of the data. You may be prompted to choose one column to use for the independent variable data and choose one column to use for the dependent variable data.

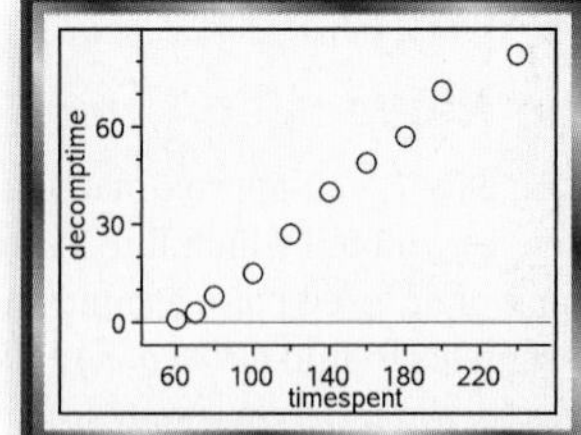

Step 3 If possible, add a movable line to your scatterplot. Adjust the position of the line to eyeball a line of best fit. Record the equation of your movable line. Also record the predicted values when $x = 80$ and when $x = 220$. Answers vary. Sample: $y = 0.4829x - 29.90$

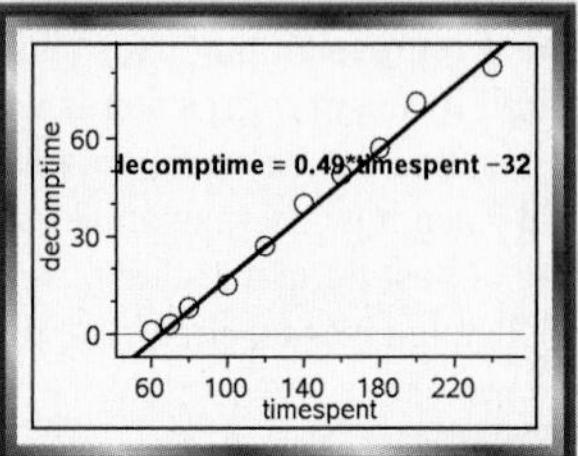

Step 4 Remove your movable line. Choose to show a linear regression line. The application will graph the regression line on the same axes as the data. Record the equation of the regression line. How does your movable line compare to the regression line? Answers vary. Sample: It is very close to the regression line.

Step 5 Compare your movable line's predictions to those of the regression line. When $x = 220$, by how much do the predicted values differ from each other? When $x = 80$, by how much does the predicted value differ from the value in the table? See margin.

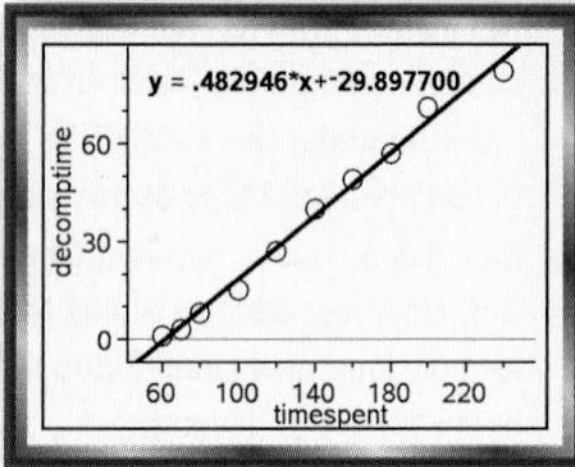

You can see from the graphs that the regression line is a reasonable model for the data.

For each value of the independent variable, the difference between the actual value of the dependent variable and the value predicted by the model is called the **deviation**. The line of best fit has the following property: *The sum of the squares of the deviations of its predicted values from the actual values is the least among all possible lines that could model the data.* This is why it is called the least-squares line.

Accommodating the Learner

Show students the table at the right, telling them that columns A and F contain actual data and columns B and D contain predicted values based on two possible lines of best fit for the data. Ask students to explain how the values in columns C and E were obtained. Why is one of the two predicted equations a better line of fit than the other?

[The answer is on the next page.]

A	B*	C	D**	E	F
x	y_1	$(y - y_a)^2$	y_2	$(y - y_a)^2$	y_a
0	1.3	0	1.5	0.04	1.3
1	3.8	0.04	3.9	0.01	4.0
2	6.3	0.01	6.3	0.01	6.4
3	8.8	0.04	8.7	0.01	8.6
4	11.3	0.01	11.1	0.09	11.4
		0.10		0.16	

*Prediction 1: $y_1 = 2.5x + 1.3$
**Prediction 2: $y_2 = 2.4x + 1.5$

Questions

COVERING THE IDEAS

In 1–3, refer to Activity 1.

1. A student playing Square Grabber recorded a data point of (48, 985). What does this ordered pair mean in this context?
2. a. Find the regression line for the data you collected in Activity 1.
   b. Pick two values of x to compare how well the regression line predicts y-values compared to the line you eyeballed.
3. A person found $y = 19.0x + 35$ to be an equation for the line of best fit for Activity 1.
   a. What is the slope of the line? 19
   b. What does the slope mean in this situation?
   c. What is the y-intercept of the line? 35
   d. What does the y-intercept mean in this situation?
   e. Does the x-intercept have a practical meaning in this case? no
4. Refer to Activity 2. If a diver spent 130 minutes at a maximum depth of 60 feet, estimate his decompression time using the regression line. about 32.88 min

1. The student captured 48 squares, for a score of 985 points.

2a. Answers vary. Sample: The regression method produced $y = 19.96x - 2.053$.

2b. Answers vary.

3b. 19 points are scored for every square captured.

3d. The player starts with 35 points.

APPLYING THE MATHEMATICS

5. a. Use regression to find an equation of the line through the points (1, 4) and (-2, 8). $y = -\frac{4}{3}x + \frac{16}{3}$
   b. Verify your equation in Part a by finding the slope of the line and using the Point-Slope Theorem. $y = -\frac{4}{3}x + \frac{16}{3}$
6. The table below gives the total payroll for the Chicago Cubs from 1998 to 2006.

Year	2006	2005	2004	2003	2002	2001	2000	1999	1998
Payroll (millions of dollars)	94.4	87.0	90.6	79.9	75.7	64.5	62.1	55.4	49.4

Source: http://content.usatoday.com/sports/baseball/salaries/teamresults.aspx?team=17

   a. Draw a scatterplot and eyeball a line of best fit to the data.
   b. Which data point has the greatest deviation from your line?
   c. Find an equation for the regression line for the data.
   d. Which data point has the greatest deviation from the regression line?
   e. Use the regression line and your line to predict the 2007 Chicago Cubs payroll. about 102.5 million dollars
   f. Which gives the closer prediction to the actual value of 99.7 million dollars, your eyeballed line or the regression line?

6a. See margin.

6b. Answers vary. Sample: (2004, 90.6)

6c. $y \approx 5.787x - 11{,}512$

6d. (2004, 90.6)

6f. Answers vary. Sample: the regression line

3 Assignment

Recommended Assignment

- Questions 1–15
- Question 16 (extra credit)
- Reading Lesson 3-6
- Covering the Ideas 3-6

Notes on the Questions

Question 5 This question shows that when a line of best fit is done with only two points, the result (expectedly) is a line through the two points. For a data set with more points that lie on a line, you might try the relationship between the number n of sides of a convex polygon and the sum S of the measures of its interior angles. Some ordered pairs (n, S) are as follows: (3, 180), (4, 360), (6, 720), and (10, 1440). As expected, the line of best fit for such data is the formula that relates them, $S = 180n - 360$. This idea is also the focus for the Accommodating the Learner Down activity on this page.

Question 6 In theory, we might expect payroll to be related to inflation and thus better fit by an exponential function rather than a linear function.

Columns B and D have data calculated from two prediction equations. Columns C and E have the squares of the deviations between the predicted and actual values and the sum of those squared deviations. That sum is less for the equation $y = 2.5x + 1.3$ than for the equation $y = 2.4x + 1.5$, so $y = 2.5x + 1.3$ is a better line of fit than $y = 2.4x + 1.5$.

Accommodating the Learner

Have students use a CAS to calculate a regression line for data that lie exactly on a line, such as $y = 4x + 1$. They could use data such as (1, 5), (2, 9), (3, 13), (4, 17), (5, 21)) and a regression line for data that lie "close to" such a line, for example, (1, 5.1), (2, 8.9), (3, 13.2), (4, 16.9), (5, 20.9). Ask students to compare each regression line to the graph of the equation $y = 4x + 1$.

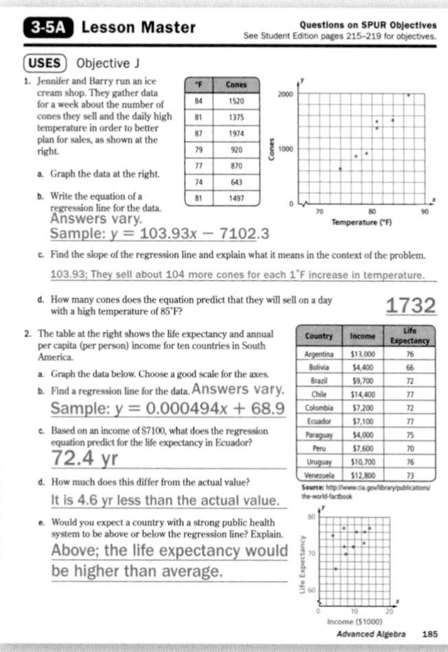

3-5A Lesson Master
Questions on SPUR Objectives
See Student Edition pages 215–219 for objectives.
USES Objective J
1. Jennifer and Barry run an ice cream shop. They gather data for a week about the number of cones they sell and the daily high temperature in order to better plan for sales, as shown at the right.
a. Graph the data at the right.
b. Write the equation of a regression line for the data. Answers vary. Sample: y = 103.93x − 7102.3
c. Find the slope of the regression line and explain what it means in the context of the problem.
103.93; They sell about 104 more cones for each 1°F increase in temperature.
d. How many cones does the equation predict that they will sell on a day with a high temperature of 85°F? 1732
2. The table at the right shows the life expectancy and annual per capita (per person) income for ten countries in South America.
a. Graph the data below. Choose a good scale for the axes.
b. Find a regression line for the data. Answers vary. Sample: y = 0.000494x + 68.9
c. Based on an income of $7100, what does the regression equation predict for the life expectancy in Ecuador? 72.4 yr
d. How much does this differ from the actual value? It is 4.6 yr less than the actual value.
e. Would you expect a country with a strong public health system to be above or below the regression line? Explain. Above; the life expectancy would be higher than average.
Advanced Algebra 185

Notes on the Questions

Question 8 The content of foods is a good type of data for fitting by a line because we expect a linear relationship between the amount of food and the amount of a particular vitamin, mineral, or other substance.

Additional Answers

Activity 1, Step 1. Answers vary. Sample:

Number of Squares	Score
240	5083
45	859
12	366
165	3115
174	3407
216	4257
165	3269
69	1409
225	4612
209	4097
225	4524
315	6340
210	4388
248	4807
150	2794

Step 2. Answers vary. Sample:

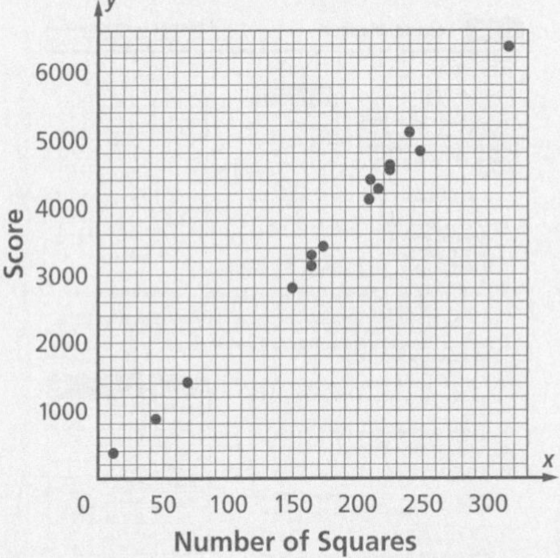

Yes; the data points appear to have a linear pattern.

7. Recall the data at the right from the beginning of the chapter on the average body mass index b for a male of age a. Verify that $b = 0.07a + 24.9$ is an equation for the line of best fit to the data. See margin.

Age	BMI
25	26.6
35	27.5
45	28.4
55	28.7

8. The table below shows nutritional information on various items from a fast-food menu. Included for each item are the number of calories and the fat content. A scatterplot of the data is shown.

Item	Calories	Fat Content (g)
chicken pieces	250	15
Asian salad	300	10
cheeseburger	300	12
fish fillet	380	18
chicken sandwich	360	16
large French fries	570	30
big hamburger	460	24
big cheeseburger	510	28
big breakfast	720	46

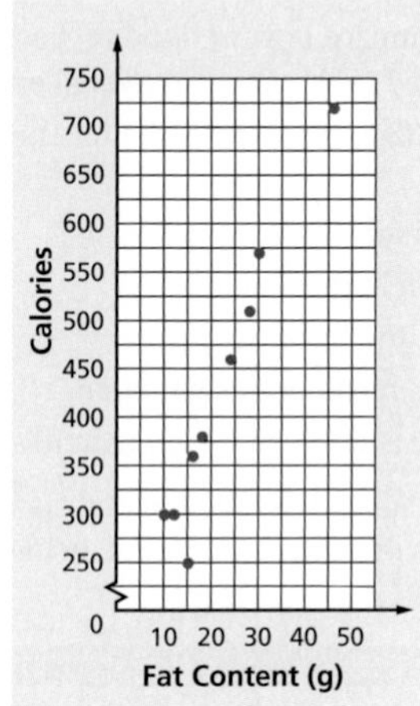

a. Describe the general relationship between calories and fat content.

b. What are the independent and dependent variables?

c. Find an equation of the regression line for this data set.

d. What is the slope of the regression line, and what does it mean in the context of the problem? What is the unit for the slope?

e. What is the y-intercept of the regression line, and what does it mean in context of the problem? Is the value practical in this situation?

f. A salad with chicken is not on this menu. It contains 320 calories. Use the regression line to estimate the number of grams of fat in the salad. 13.84g

9. Add a large vanilla milkshake with 740 calories and 18 grams of fat to the menu in Question 8. Recalculate the regression line.

8a. Generally, the greater amount of fat, the greater the number of calories.

8b. The dependent variable is calories; the independent variable is fat.

8c. $y = 13.04x + 139.50$

8d. 13.04; the increase in calories for every gram of fat; The unit is calories per gram of fat.

8e. 139.50; the number of calories that do not come from fat; It is not practical since in reality this value differs item by item.

9. $y = 11.74x + 204.3$

Additional Answers

Step 3. Answers vary. Sample:

y
6000
5000
4000
3000
2000
1000
Score
0
50 100 150 200 250 300
x
Number of Squares

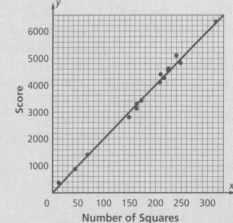

Activity 2, Step 5. Answers vary. Sample: At $x = 20$, the predictions differ by 0.01242. When $x = 80$, the prediction from the movable line differs from the value in the table by ≈ 0.73, and the prediction from the regression line differs from the value in the table by ≈ 0.74.

REVIEW

10. a. Find an equation for the line that passes through the points (2, 5) and $\left(-\frac{4}{3}, 9\right)$. $y = -1.2x + 7.4$
    b. Graph the line from Part a. **(Lesson 3-4)** See margin.

11. a. Write an equation of a line with slope $-\frac{5}{2}$ and y-intercept 3.
    b. Write an equation of a line parallel to the line in Part a that passes through the point (-1, -2). **(Lessons 3-4, 3-1)**

11a. $y = -\frac{5}{3}x + 3$
11b. $y = -\frac{5}{3}x - \frac{9}{2}$

12. Consider the formula for the volume of a sphere, $V = \frac{4}{3}\pi r^3$. If the radius of a sphere is divided by three, how many times smaller is the volume of the resulting sphere? **(Lesson 2-3)** 27 times

13. Consider the sequence $H_n = (-1)^n(n + 5)$, for integers $n \geq 1$. **(Lesson 1-8)**
    a. Write the first four terms. -6, 7, -8, 9
    b. Without explicitly calculating, is the 25th term positive or negative? negative

14. Jayla's cake company charged $25 per cake, and each week she paid $50 for supplies and the upkeep of her equipment. She found that $I = 25c - 50$ is an explicit formula for her income I based on the number c of cakes that she sold. **(Lesson 1-5)**
    a. Use a graphing utility to generate a table showing the number of cakes sold and Jayla's income.
    b. Graph the first six data values from your table on coordinate axes. 14a–b. See the Additional Answers Section at the back of the book.

The world's most expensive chocolate cake was decorated with diamonds and sold for over $8.3 million.

15. Given that $b: x \rightarrow \frac{3x + 5}{7 - 8x}$ evaluate **(Lesson 1-3)**
    a. $b(2)$.
    b. $b(0)$. $\frac{5}{7}$
    c. $b(a)$. $\frac{3a + 5}{7 - 8a}$
    d. $b(-2) + b(-4)$. $-\frac{200}{897} \approx -0.22$

15a. $-\frac{11}{9}$

EXPLORATION

16. When you calculate a regression equation, some calculators and software include an extra statistic r called *correlation* along with the slope and intercept. Find out what correlation means and what it tells you about the regression line. Go back and examine r for the data sets in Questions 6–8 and see if you can interpret its value in the context of the problems.
    Answers vary. Sample: The correlation coefficient r measures how well the linear model corresponds to the data; the closer the value is to 1, the better the line fits. In the case of Questions 8 and 9, for example, the introduction of the milkshake into the data caused r to decrease from 0.972, a strong positive correlation, to 0.725, a weak positive correlation.

Notes on the Questions

Additional Answers can be found in the back of the book.

4 Wrap-Up

Ongoing Assessment

Write a set of data points on a sheet of paper. On a second sheet, write the same data points and draw a regression line for the data. Distribute copies of the first sheet to students and ask them to estimate and draw the line of best fit for the data. Discuss student responses, comparing them to the second sheet. Answers vary. Check students' work.

Project Update

Project 1, *Residual Squares*, on page 210 and Project 5, *Time Series Data*, on page 211 relate to the content of this lesson.

Additional Answers

7.

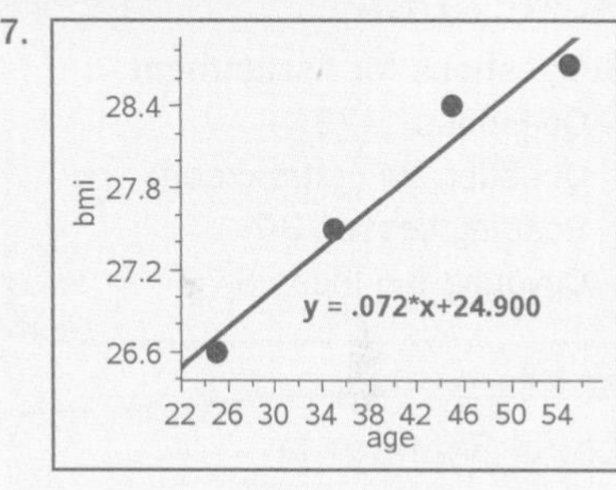

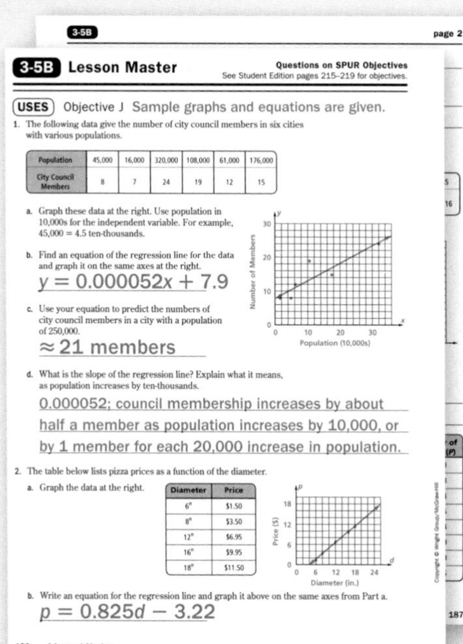

3-5B Lesson Master — page 2

Questions on SPUR Objectives
See Student Edition pages 215–219 for objectives.

USES Objective J Sample graphs and equations are given.

1. The following data give the number of city council members in six cities with various populations.

Population	45,000	16,000	320,000	108,000	61,000	176,000
City Council Members	8	7	24	19	12	15

a. Graph these data at the right. Use population in 10,000s for the independent variable. For example, 45,000 = 4.5 ten-thousands.

b. Find an equation of the regression line for the data and graph it on the same axes at the right.
$y = 0.000052x + 7.9$

c. Use your equation to predict the numbers of city council members in a city with a population of 250,000.
≈ 21 members

d. What is the slope of the regression line? Explain what it means, as population increases by ten-thousands.
0.000052; council membership increases by about half a member as population increases by 10,000, or by 1 member for each 20,000 increase in population.

2. The table below lists pizza prices as a function of the diameter.

a. Graph the data at the right.

Diameter	Price
6"	$1.50
8"	$3.50
12"	$6.95
16"	$9.95
18"	$11.50

b. Write an equation for the regression line and graph it above on the same axes from Part a.
$p = 0.825d - 3.22$

186 Advanced Algebra

Extension

Ask students to investigate the meaning of "quadratic regression." How does it compare to linear regression? Quadratic regression uses a parabola, rather than a line, as the shape of a "line" of best fit. This procedure uses a similar technique to find a quadratic equation that minimizes the sum of the squares of the deviations between predicted values and actual values.

Additional Answers

6. a.

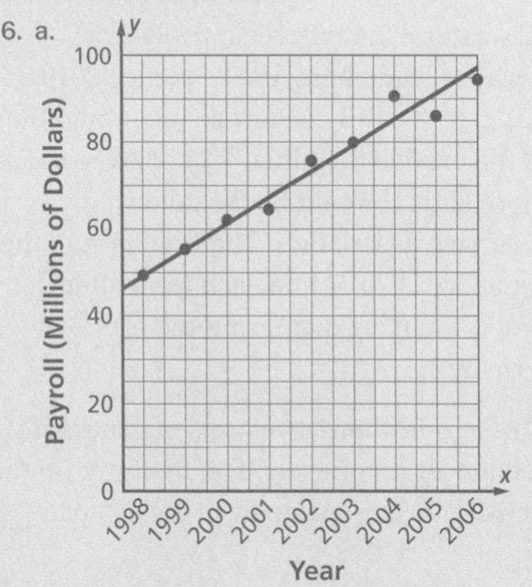

Lesson

3-6

GOAL

Introduce recursive formulas; introduce the term *explicit formulas* for linear functions studied at the beginning of the course.

SPUR Objectives

D Evaluate or find recursive formulas for sequences.

L Model situations with recursive formulas.

Materials/Resources

- Lesson Masters 3-6A and 3-6B
- Resource Masters 45 and 46
- Quiz 2

HOMEWORK

Suggestions for Assignment

- Questions 1–23
- Question 24 (extra credit)
- Reading Lesson 3-7
- Covering the Ideas 3-7

Local Standards

1 Warm-Up

1. Consider the sequence C of the positive integer powers of 3: 3, 9, 27, 81, ...
   a. Give an explicit formula for C_n. $C_n = 3^n$
   b. Describe how each term after the first is related to the term before it. $C_1 = 3$; C_n is 3 times the previous term, for $n \geq 2$.
2. Consider the sequence B of the negative integer powers of 3: $\frac{1}{3}, \frac{1}{9}, \frac{1}{27}, \frac{1}{81}, \ldots$.
   a. Give an explicit formula for B_n. $B_n = 3^{-n}$
   b. Describe how each term after the first is related to the term before it. $B_1 = \frac{1}{3}$; B_n is $\frac{1}{3}$ times the previous term, for $n \geq 2$.

Lesson

3-6 Recursive Formulas for Sequences

Vocabulary

recursive formula

recursive definition

BIG IDEA Some sequences can be defined by giving their first terms and indicating how later terms are related to each other.

Recall from Chapter 1 that a *sequence* is a function whose domain is the set of natural numbers or a subset of the natural numbers less than a given number. If you know an *explicit formula* for a sequence, then you can write the terms of a sequence rather quickly.

Consider a freight train consisting of one engine and a series of identical boxcars. The engine is 72 feet long and each boxcar is 41 feet long. So the length of a train with n boxcars is defined by the explicit formula $L_n = 72 + 41n$. The first four terms of the sequence are:

$L_1 = 72 + 41 \cdot 1 = 113$ 

$L_2 = 72 + 41 \cdot 2 = 154$

$L_3 = 72 + 41 \cdot 3 = 195$

$L_4 = 72 + 41 \cdot 4 = 236$

We say the formula $L_n = 72 + 41n$ ***generates*** the sequence 113, 154, 195, 236, ...

STOP QY1

Mental Math

Consider the sequence $t_n = \frac{n^2}{2} + 7$.

a. Find t_7. 31.5

b. Find t_{100}. 5007

c. Find $t_{12} - t_{10}$. 22

d. What is the domain of the sequence? the set of positive integers

QY1

Generate the first five terms of a sequence S when $S_n = 34 - 12(n - 1)$.

Generating Sequences Using a Calculator

You can use a calculator to generate sequences.

Activity

Use a calculator to generate the sequence of freight train lengths.

Step 1 Store the first value of this sequence, 113. When we enter 113 and press ENTER, this calculator stores it in the variable ans.

Step 2 Add 41 to ans, and repeatedly press ENTER. The first five terms of the sequence are shown at the right. To find additional terms, continue pressing ENTER.

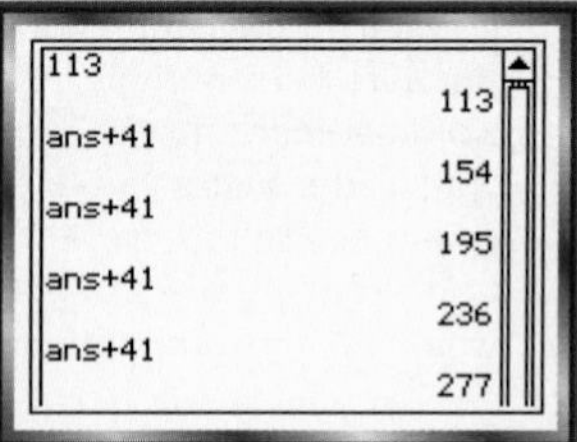

Background

It is natural to think recursively. For instance, in defining the sequence 2010, 2011, 2012, 2013, ..., few people would think of the explicit definition $Y_n = 2009 + n$. Far more natural would be the following recursive description: The first term of the sequence is 2010, and each term after the first is found by increasing the previous term by 1.

This lesson shows two ways of generating sequences recursively. The first way (in the Activity) is by repeatedly pressing some sort of operation key. The second way, beginning with Example 1, generates and/or uses a recursive definition.

What is a recursive formula? On page 183, note the use of the left-hand, one-sided brace. Students may remember that this brace is used with a system of equations. In that use, the brace has the same meaning it has here, namely, the word *and* connects all the statements collected by the brace.

 QY2

Any sequence of numbers that is defined by adding, subtracting, multiplying, or dividing by a constant can be generated on your calculator using the approach of the Activity.

▸ QY2

In the Activity, if you pressed ENTER 35 times, what term of the sequence would appear?

What Is a Recursive Formula?

Notice that no explicit formula was used to generate the sequence in the Activity. Instead, each term of the sequence was derived from the preceding one. For instance, to find the 6th term of the sequence, you add 41 to the preceding term (the 5th term, 271). This process generates the sequence *recursively.*

Definition of Recursive Formula

A **recursive formula** or **recursive definition** for a sequence is a set of statements that

a. indicates the first term (or first few terms) of the sequence, and

b. tells how the next term is calculated from the previous term or terms.

Consider the sequence $L = 113, 154, 195, 236, \dots$ of lengths of a train with n boxcars. You can write this sequence recursively as

$$\begin{cases} L_1 = 113 \\ L_n = \text{previous term} + 41, \text{ for integers } n \geq 2. \end{cases}$$

The brace { indicates that both lines are needed for the recursive definition. You should be able to read and evaluate recursive definitions.

GUIDED

Example 1

Verify that the recursive definition of L above generates the first four terms of the sequence.

Solution The first term is given,

$L_1 = 113.$

According to the second line of the definition,

$L_2 = \text{previous term} + 41 = \underline{\ ?\ } + 41 = \underline{\ ?\ }$. 113; 154

To find L_3, use the definition again.

$L_3 = \text{previous term} + 41 = \underline{\ ?\ } + 41 = \underline{\ ?\ }$. 154; 195

(continued on next page)

2 Teaching

Notes on the Lesson

Although the vocabulary and symbolism for recursion may be new to most students, the concept is not. Students naturally describe sequences recursively, saying, for example, that "the sequence grows by adding 5," and it is likely that they have been doing this since the early primary grades.

The sequence that opens this lesson, of the length of a train with n cars, runs through the lesson. It appears again and is graphed in Lesson 3-7.

What is a recursive formula? Emphasize that recursive formulas have two parts: (1) a starting point and (2) a rule for finding the nth term from one or more previous terms.

Additional Example

Example 1 Verify that the recursive definition

$$\begin{cases} L_1 = 97 \\ L_2 = \text{previous term} - 23 \end{cases}$$

for integers $n \geq 2$ generates the first four terms of the sequence 97, 74, 51, 28, 5, -18, -41, ...

Solution The first term is given, $L_1 = 97$. According to the second line of the definition, $L_2 = \text{previous term} - 23 = \underline{\ ?\ } - 23 = \underline{\ ?\ }$. 97; 74 To find L_3, use the definition again: $L_3 = \text{previous term} - 23 = \underline{\ ?\ } - 23 = \underline{\ ?\ }$. 74; 51 Finally, $L_4 = \text{previous term} - 23 = \underline{\ ?\ } - \underline{\ ?\ } = \underline{\ ?\ }$. 51; 23; 28 The first four terms are 97, __?__, __?__, and __?__, which checks with what was calculated previously. 74; 51; 28

The entire lesson can be done without a sophisticated calculator—or even without a calculator at all. However, students who have such a calculator available while reading will find it easier to understand the ideas.

Accommodating the Learner

Ask students to generate values of $f(n) = n^2$ for $n = 1, 2, 3, \dots$. 1, 4, 9, 16, ... Then ask them to find the difference between $f(n + 1)$ and $f(n)$. $f(n + 1) - f(n) = (n + 1)^2 - n^2 = 2n + 1$ Finally, ask students to use the difference between successive squares of integers to write a recursive formula for $f(n)$.

$$\begin{cases} S_1 = 1 \\ S_n = S_{n-1} + 2(n - 1) + 1, \text{ for } n \geq 2 \end{cases}$$

Note-Taking Tips

When students record recursive definitions in their notes, encourage them to label the two lines as "first term" or "initial value" and "recursive rule" or "relationship."

Notes on the Lesson

Notation for recursive formulas In Example 1, we use the phrase *previous term* rather than a variable. This is meant as an interim step to using the subscripted variable a_{n-1}. The recursive definition that defines a_{n+1} in terms of a_n, rather than a_n in terms of a_{n-1}, is very common, and students should be able to deal with both forms. Question 5 and the Vocabulary Development on page 184 ask students to relate the two forms.

Additional Examples

Example 2 Consider the sequence $B = 850, 775, 700, \ldots$. Write a recursive definition for the sequence B.

Solution The first line of the definition gives the initial term. So the first line is $B_1 = \underline{\ ?\ }$. 850 The second line relates each term to the previous term. So, the second line is $B_{n+1} = B_n - \underline{\ ?\ }$, for integers $n \geq \underline{\ ?\ }$. 75; 1 Thus, the recursive definition is $\underline{\ ?\ }$.

$$\begin{cases} B_1 = 850 \\ B_{n+1} = B_n - 75, \text{ for integers } n \geq 1 \end{cases}$$

Example 3 A sequence C is 324, 108, 36, 12, 4.

a. Write a recursive definition of this sequence. The first term is 324. Each term after the first is found by dividing the previous term by 3.

b. Write a recursive formula for this sequence.

$$\begin{cases} C_1 = 324 \\ C_n = \frac{1}{3}C_{n-1}, \text{ for integers } n = \{2, 3, 4, 5\} \end{cases}$$

$L_4 = \text{previous term} + 41 = \underline{\ ?\ } + 41 = \underline{\ ?\ }$. 195; 236

The first four terms are 113, $\underline{\ ?\ }$, $\underline{\ ?\ }$, $\underline{\ ?\ }$, which checks according to what was calculated before. 154; 195; 236

Notation for Recursive Formulas

In Example 1, the sequence is described using the symbol L and the symbol L_n denotes term number n. The term that precedes term n is term number $(n - 1)$, and the term that follows term n is term number $(n + 1)$. So the symbol L_{n-1} can be used in place of the words *previous term*. Thus the sequence of Example 1 can be defined as follows:

$$\begin{cases} L_1 = 113 \\ L_n = L_{n-1} + 41, \text{ for integers } n \geq 2 \end{cases}$$

Or, if you prefer, you could let L_n be the previous term and L_{n+1} be the next term. In this case, the definition would be

$$\begin{cases} L_1 = 113 \\ L_{n+1} = L_n + 41, \text{ for integers } n \geq 1. \end{cases}$$

A recursive definition always includes at least two lines. One or more lines define the initial values of the sequence, and another line defines the relationship between consecutive terms.

GUIDED

Example 2

Consider the sequence $A = 10{,}000; 9600; 9200; \ldots$ of dollar amounts left on a car loan if \$400 is repaid each month. Write a recursive definition for the sequence A_n.

Solution The first line of the definition gives the initial term. So, the first line is

$A_1 = \underline{\ ?\ }$. 10,000

The second line relates each term to the previous term. So, the second line is $A_{n+1} = A_n - \underline{\ ?\ }$, for integers $n \geq \underline{\ ?\ }$. 400; 1

If you can describe a sequence in words, then you can use that description to write a recursive formula for the sequence.

Example 3

The NCAA Women's Basketball Tournament originally consists of 64 teams, which are paired in single-elimination contests. At the end of each round of play, the number of teams proceeding to the next round is half the previous number.

ENGLISH LEARNERS

Vocabulary Development

For any recursive formula, an important part is the index for the variable n in the last line. Discuss the difference in the index variable for the two formulas on page 184:

$$\begin{cases} L_1 = 113 \\ L_n = L_{n-1} + 41, \text{ for integers } n \geq 2 \end{cases}$$

and

$$\begin{cases} L_1 = 113 \\ L_{n+1} = L_n + 41, \text{ for } n \geq 1 \end{cases}.$$

Be sure students understand that in both definitions, the first term that is described by the last line of the definition is L_2.

The sequence 64, 32, 16, 8, 4, 2 gives the number of teams in the tournament at the beginning of round n.

a. Use words to write a recursive definition of this sequence.

b. Write a recursive formula for this sequence.

Solution

a. Identify the first term and the rule for generating all following terms. The first term is 64. Each term after the first is found by dividing the previous term by 2.

b. Choose a name for the sequence. We call it b_n. Then write the recursive formula. Note that there are only six terms.

$$\begin{cases} b_1 = 64 \\ b_n = \frac{1}{2}b_{n-1}, \text{ for integers } n = \{2, 3, 4, 5, 6\} \end{cases}$$

The Tennessee Lady Vols defeated Rutgers in the 2007 NCAA Women's Championship game.

CAUTION: The first term of the sequence in Example 3 is 64, the term written in the first line of the recursive definition. Although 32 is the first term given by the rule for b_n in the solution, it is the second term of the sequence. Remember, b_n represents the nth term in this definition, and the formula for b_n is only defined for $n = \{2, 3, 4, 5, 6\}$.

Recursive Definitions and Spreadsheets

A spreadsheet is another efficient tool for generating a sequence from its recursive definition.

Example 4

Use a spreadsheet to generate the first five terms of the sequence

$$\begin{cases} L_1 = 113 \\ L_n = L_{n-1} + 41, \text{ for integers } n \geq 2. \end{cases}$$

Solution Enter 113 in cell A1.

Then in A2, enter =A1+41.

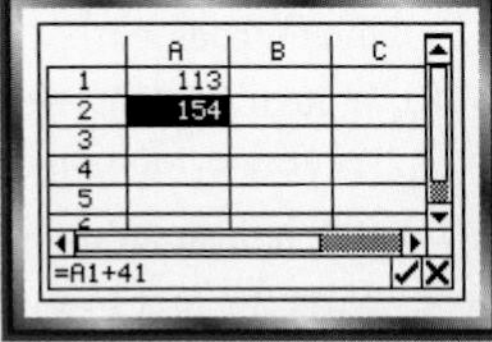

	A	B	C
1	113		
2	154		
3			
4			
5			

=A1+41

Each cell after A2 can be defined as the value in the previous cell + 41. A shortcut to do this is to copy cell A2 and paste it into cells A3–A5. For example, after the paste, the screen at right shows that the formula in A5 has been updated to refer to cell A4. You could also use the fill down function on the spreadsheet instead of copying and pasting.

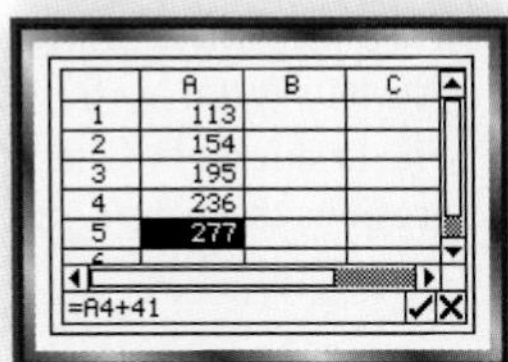

	A	B	C
1	113		
2	154		
3	195		
4	236		
5	277		

=A4+41

So the value in cell A5 = L_5 = 277.

The first five terms are 113, 154, 195, 236, and 277.

Additional Example

Example 4 Use a spreadsheet to generate the first seven terms of the sequence

$$\begin{cases} L_1 = 97 \\ L_n = L_{n-1} - 23, \text{ for integers } n \geq 2 \end{cases}.$$

97; 74; 51; 28; 5; -18; -41

Accommodating the Learner

Ask students to write recursive formulas for the sequences I = 1, 2, 3, 4, ..., E = 2, 4, 6, 8, ..., and T = 1, 10, 100, 1000, ...

$$\begin{cases} I_1 = 1 \\ I_n = I_{n-1} + 1, \text{ for } n \geq 2 \end{cases};$$

$$\begin{cases} E_1 = 2 \\ E_n = S_{n-1} + 2, \text{ for } n \geq 2 \end{cases}; \text{ and}$$

$$\begin{cases} T_1 = 1 \\ T_n = 10T_{n-1}, \text{ for } n \geq 2 \end{cases}$$

Additional Example

Example 5 Use a spreadsheet to generate the five terms of the sequence 324, 108, 36, 12, and 4.

Solution The first term is 324. Each term after the first is found by dividing the previous term by 3. Enter 324 in cell __?__. Enter __?__ in cell A2. To see the five terms of this sequence in your spreadsheet, copy cell __?__ and then paste it into cells __?__ through __?__. The five terms of the sequence are __?__, __?__, __?__, __?__, and __?__. A1; = (1/3)A1; A2; A3; A5; 324, 108, 36, 12, and 4

3 Assignment

Recommended Assignment

- Questions 1–23
- Question 24 (extra credit)
- Reading Lesson 3-7
- Covering the Ideas 3-7

Notes on the Questions

We suggest discussing Questions 1–12 in order.

3-6A Lesson Master

Questions on SPUR Objectives
See Student Edition pages 215–219 for objectives.

VOCABULARY

In 1–3, refer to the box at the right where a recursive definition for a sequence is given in both words and algebraic notation. Identify the part of the algebraic definition that corresponds to each phrase.

> **The first term of a sequence is 12. From the second term on, each term is seven more than the previous term.**
>
> $\begin{cases} t_1 = 12 \\ t_n = t_{n-1} + 7 \text{ for integers } n \geq 2 \end{cases}$

1. "The first term" t_1
2. "the previous term" t_{n-1}
3. "From the second term on" for integers $n \geq 2$

SKILLS Objective D

In 4 and 5, write the first five terms of the sequence.

4. $\begin{cases} d_1 = 36 \\ d_n = \frac{d_{n-1}}{3} \text{ for integers } n \geq 2 \end{cases}$ 36, 12, 4, $\frac{4}{3}$, $\frac{4}{9}$
5. $\begin{cases} t_1 = 1 \\ t_{n+1} = (t_n)^2 + 1 \text{ for integers } n \geq 1 \end{cases}$ 1, 2, 5, 26, 677
6. Write a recursive formula for a sequence with first term -3 where each term is one less than the previous term. Answers vary. Sample: $\begin{cases} t_1 = -3 \\ t_n = t_{n-1} - 1 \text{ for integers } n \geq 2 \end{cases}$
7. Write a recursive formula for a sequence with first term 200 where each term is four-fifths of the previous term. Answers vary. Sample: $\begin{cases} s_1 = 200 \\ s_{n+1} = \frac{4}{5} s_n \text{ for integers } n \geq 1 \end{cases}$

USES Objective L

8. You buy eight bags of candy for a party. Each bag has 60 pieces. Unfortunately, your little sister eats eight pieces each day. Write a recursive formula for the number of pieces of candy you have left on day n. Answers vary. Sample: $\begin{cases} c_1 = 480 \\ c_n = c_{n-1} - 8 \text{ for integers } n \geq 2 \end{cases}$
9. Allison opens a bank account with $500. Every year, she receives 2% interest on the account, then adds another $100. A recursive formula for her account balance at the beginning of year n is given at the right. Find her balance at the beginning of year four. $\begin{cases} t_1 = 500 \\ t_n = 1.02t_{n-1} + 100 \text{ for integers } n \geq 2 \end{cases}$ $836.64

188 *Advanced Algebra*

GUIDED

Example 5

Use a spreadsheet to generate the six terms of the sequence in Example 3.

Solution Enter 64 in cell __?__. A1

Enter __?__ in cell A2. $=\frac{A1}{2}$

To see the six terms of this sequence in your spreadsheet, copy cell __?__ and then paste it into cells __?__ through __?__. A2; A3; A6

The six terms of the sequence are __?__, __?__, __?__, __?__, __?__, and __?__. 64; 32; 16; 8; 4; 2

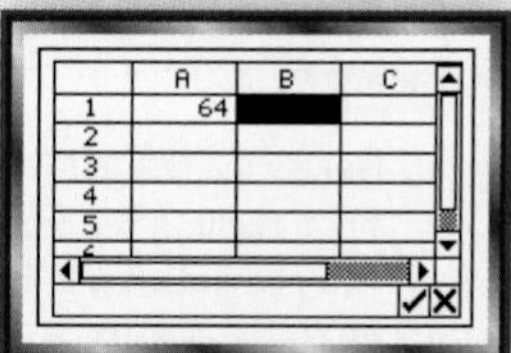

Questions

COVERING THE IDEAS

In 1 and 2, refer to the Activity.

1. What is the meaning of ans on the CAS? the answer of the last input
2. How long is the freight train with 12 boxcars? 564 feet
3. What is a recursive definition for a sequence?
4. Suppose t_n denotes the nth term of a sequence.
   a. What does t_{n-1} denote? b. What does t_{n-2} denote?
   c. What does t_{n+1} denote?

3. a set of statements that indicate the first (or first few) terms and tell how the next term is calculated from the previous term or terms

4a. the term before the nth term

4b. the term 2 before the nth term

4c. the term after the nth term

In 5 and 6, refer to Example 3.

5. Rewrite the recursive formula if b_n is the previous term instead of the next term. See margin.
6. Suppose that the NCAA Women's Basketball Tournament is expanded to include 128 teams.
   a. How many terms are now in the sequence describing the tournament? 7
   b. Write a recursive formula for this sequence using recursive notation. See margin.

In 7 and 8, a description of a sequence is given.

a. Write the first five terms of the sequence.

b. Write the recursive formula.

7. The first term is -2; each term after the first is 8 more than the previous term. a. -2, 6, 14, 22, 30 b. See margin.
8. The first term is 4; each term after the first is $-\frac{1}{4}$ times the previous term. a. 4, -1, $\frac{1}{4}$, $-\frac{1}{16}$, $\frac{1}{64}$ b. See margin.

Extension

Ask students to generate several terms in this sequence:

$$\begin{cases} P_1 = 1 \\ P_n = \dfrac{1}{\frac{1}{P_{n-1}} + 2}, \text{ for } n \geq 2 \end{cases}$$

Then ask them to calculate $4(P_1 - P_2 + P_3 - P_4 + \ldots)$. Can they guess what well-known value they are generating?

The first five terms are $P_1 = 1$, $P_2 = \frac{1}{\frac{1}{1} + 2} = \frac{1}{3}$, $P_3 = \frac{1}{\frac{1}{\frac{1}{3}} + 2} = \frac{1}{5}$, $P_4 = \frac{1}{\frac{1}{\frac{1}{5}} + 2} = \frac{1}{7}$, $P_5 = \frac{1}{\frac{1}{\frac{1}{7}} + 2} = \frac{1}{9}$.

For the first five terms, the sum is $4\left(1 - \frac{1}{3} + \frac{1}{5} - \frac{1}{7} + \frac{1}{9}\right) \approx 4(0.83492) = 3.33968$. The sequence is based on the Leibniz series for π: $\frac{\pi}{4} = 1 - \frac{1}{3} + \frac{1}{5} - \frac{1}{7} + \ldots$. This sequence takes a long time

9. Explain in your own words why a recursive formula must have at least two parts.

10. Consider the sequence that begins -19, -26, -33, -40, … .
   a. What is the first term? -19
   b. **Fill in the Blank** From the second term on, each term is ___?___ the previous term. 7 less than
   c. Write a recursive formula for the sequence. See margin.

11. Consider the decreasing sequence of negative even integers, beginning with -2, -4, -6, … . Write a recursive definition for this sequence if t_{n+1} is the next term in the second line. See margin.

12. Generate the first eight terms of the sequence below by hand or using a spreadsheet. 12, 27, 57, 117, 237, 477, 957, 1917
$$\begin{cases} S_1 = 12 \\ S_n = 2S_{n-1} + 3, \text{ for integers } n \geq 2 \end{cases}$$

9. Answers vary. Sample: If the formula did not have two parts, you would be missing either the initial condition or the instructions for how to calculate the following terms.

APPLYING THE MATHEMATICS

13. In an auditorium with 25 rows, the first row has 8 seats and each succeeding row has 2 more seats than the row in front of it.
   a. Write a recursive formula for a sequence that gives the number S_n of seats in row n. See margin.
   b. Find the number of seats in the 14th row. 34 seats

14. You are given a penny on the first day of September. On each subsequent day you are given twice as many as the previous day.
   a. Write a recursive formula to represent how much you will receive on the nth day of September. See margin.
   b. How much money will you receive on September 30? about $5.37 million

15. Let S be a sequence. Is the set of ordered pairs of the form (n, S_n) a function? Why or why not?

15. Yes; for each n there is a unique S_n.

16. The table at the right gives the cost per book of printing 100 or more books, based on the number of color pages in the book.
   a. Describe in words the sequence that gives the cost per book for books with n color pages. See margin.
   b. Write a recursive formula for the sequence that gives the cost per book for books with n color pages. See margin.

Number of Color Pages	Cost ($)
1	5.55
2	5.70
3	5.85
4	6.00
5	6.15
6	6.30
7	6.45
8	6.60

17. Consider the sequence 6.42, 3.69, 0.96, -1.77, -4.5, … .
   a. Write a description of this sequence in words. See margin.
   b. Write a recursive definition of this sequence. See margin.
   c. Find the eighth term of the sequence. -12.69

to approach π (the value through $-\frac{1}{47}$ is 0.774986, and 4 times that value is 3.0999). Still, once students know that $4(P_1 - P_2 + P_3 - P_4 + \ldots)$ approaches π, some of them may want to see how close they can get to π.

Notes on the Questions

Question 16 In the recursive formula, the first term is the cost per book of including one color page in a print run, and the recursive formula tells the cost of printing additional color pages. Definitely discuss this example because a refinement of this formula, involving postage and nonintegral weight values, is presented in Lesson 3-9.

Additional Answers

5. $\begin{cases} b_1 = 64 \\ b_{n+1} = \frac{1}{2}b_n, \text{ for integers } n = \{1, 2, 3, 4, 5\} \end{cases}$

6b. $\begin{cases} b_1 = 128 \\ b_n = \frac{1}{2}b_{n-1}, \text{ for integers } n = \{2, 3, 4, 5, 6, 7\} \end{cases}$

7b. $\begin{cases} a_1 = -2 \\ a_n = a_{n-1} + 8, \text{ for } n \geq 2 \end{cases}$

8b. $\begin{cases} a_1 = 4 \\ a_n = -\frac{1}{4}a_{n-1}, \text{ for } n \geq 2 \end{cases}$

10c. $\begin{cases} a_1 = -19 \\ a_n = a_{n-1} - 7, \text{ for } n \geq 2 \end{cases}$

11. $\begin{cases} t_1 = -2 \\ t_{n+1} = t_n - 2, \text{ for } n \geq 1 \end{cases}$

13a. $\begin{cases} S_1 = 8 \\ S_n = S_{n-1} + 2, \text{ for } 2 \leq n \leq 25 \end{cases}$

14a. $\begin{cases} a_1 = 1 \\ a_{n+1} = 2a_n, \text{ for } n \geq 1 \end{cases}$

16a. The initial term of the sequence is 0.70, and each subsequent term in the sequence is 0.17 more than the previous term.

16b. $\begin{cases} a_1 = 0.70 \\ a_n = a_{n-1} + 0.17, \text{ for } n \geq 2 \end{cases}$

17a. The initial term of the sequence is 6.42, and each subsequent term in the sequence is 2.73 less than the previous term.

17b. $\begin{cases} a_1 = 6.42 \\ a_n - a_{n-1} - 2.73, \text{ for } n \geq 2 \end{cases}$

4 Wrap-Up

Ongoing Assessment

Have students work in small groups. Each group should select integers *P* and *Q* and use them to write a specific recursive formula of the form $\begin{cases} A_1 = P \\ A_n = A_{n-1} + Q, \text{ for integers } n \geq 2 \end{cases}$. Then each member of the group should use the recursive definition to generate the first 5 values of A. Answers vary. Check students' work.

Administer Quiz 2 (or a quiz of your own) after students complete this lesson.

Additional Answers

18a. $\begin{cases} a_1 = 1 \\ a_n = n + a_{n-1}, \text{ for } n \geq 2 \end{cases}$

18b. Use two columns. Enter 1 in A1 and 1 in B1. In A2, enter =A1+1, and in B2 enter =B1+A2. Then drag the formulas down, and B12 will give the answer.

19. Yes; there appears to be a linear relationship between attendance and payroll.

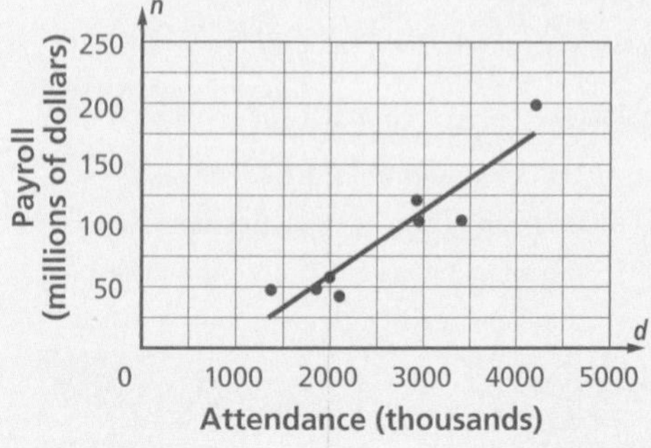

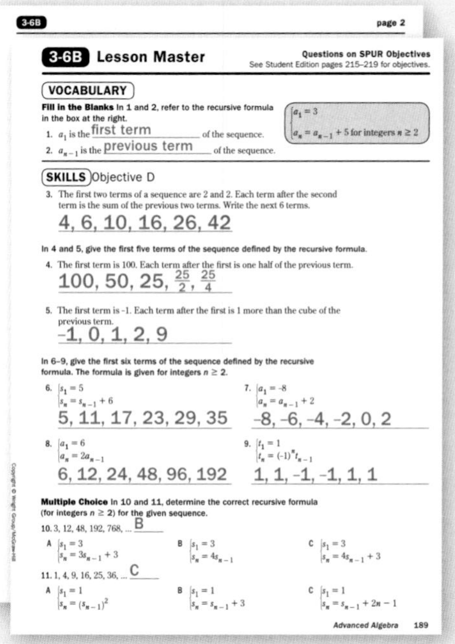

3-6B page 2

3-6B Lesson Master

Questions on SPUR Objectives
See Student Edition pages 215–219 for objectives.

VOCABULARY

Fill in the Blanks In 1 and 2, refer to the recursive formula in the box at the right.

$\begin{cases} a_1 = 3 \\ a_n = a_{n-1} + 5 \text{ for integers } n \geq 2 \end{cases}$

1. a_1 is the first term of the sequence.
2. a_{n-1} is the previous term of the sequence.

SKILLS Objective D

3. The first two terms of a sequence are 2 and 2. Each term after the second term is the sum of the previous two terms. Write the next 6 terms.
4, 6, 10, 16, 26, 42

In 4 and 5, give the first five terms of the sequence defined by the recursive formula.

4. The first term is 100. Each term after the first is one half of the previous term.
100, 50, 25, $\frac{25}{2}$, $\frac{25}{4}$

5. The first term is -1. Each term after the first is 1 more than the cube of the previous term.
–1, 0, 1, 2, 9

In 6–9, give the first six terms of the sequence defined by the recursive formula. The formula is given for integers $n \geq 2$.

6. $\begin{cases} s_1 = 5 \\ s_n = s_{n-1} + 6 \end{cases}$
5, 11, 17, 23, 29, 35

7. $\begin{cases} a_1 = -8 \\ a_n = a_{n-1} + 2 \end{cases}$
–8, –6, –4, –2, 0, 2

8. $\begin{cases} a_1 = 6 \\ a_n = 2a_{n-1} \end{cases}$
6, 12, 24, 48, 96, 192

9. $\begin{cases} t_1 = 1 \\ t_n = (-1)^n t_{n-1} \end{cases}$
1, 1, –1, –1, 1, 1

Multiple Choice In 10 and 11, determine the correct recursive formula (for integers $n \geq 2$) for the given sequence.

10. 3, 12, 48, 192, 768, ... B

A $\begin{cases} s_1 = 3 \\ s_n = 3s_{n-1} + 3 \end{cases}$
B $\begin{cases} s_1 = 3 \\ s_n = 4s_{n-1} \end{cases}$
C $\begin{cases} s_1 = 3 \\ s_n = 4s_{n-1} + 3 \end{cases}$

11. 1, 4, 9, 16, 25, 36, ... C

A $\begin{cases} s_1 = 1 \\ s_n = (s_{n-1})^2 \end{cases}$
B $\begin{cases} s_1 = 1 \\ s_n = s_{n-1} + 3 \end{cases}$
C $\begin{cases} s_1 = 1 \\ s_n = s_{n-1} + 2n - 1 \end{cases}$

Advanced Algebra 189

18. The first term of a sequence is 1. Suppose each term after that is the sum of its term number and the previous term.
    a. Write a recursive definition for this sequence. See margin.
    b. Explain how you would use a spreadsheet to generate this sequence through term 12. See margin.
    c. What is the 12th term? 78

REVIEW

19. The table at the right gives the total attendance and payroll of some of the Major League Baseball teams in 2006. Make a scatterplot of the data and find the line of best fit. Does there appear to be a linear relationship between attendance and payroll? **(Lesson 3-5)** See margin.

Team	Attendance (thousands)	Payroll (millions of dollars)
Yankees	4200	198.6
Angels	3406	103.6
White Sox	2957	102.8
Red Sox	2930	120.1
Rockies	2105	41.1
Indians	1998	56.8
Pirates	1861	46.8
Royals	1372	47.3

20. **True or False** The line of best fit for a set of collinear points is the line through those points. **(Lesson 3-5)** true

21. Suppose a store sells custom-made baseball caps with a graduated pricing scheme. The first 10 caps cost \$14 each, the next 10 cost \$12 each, and each cap after the 20th costs \$10. **(Lesson 3-4)**
    a. Draw a graph showing how the total cost *C* in dollars relates to the number of caps *n* that you order. See margin.
    b. Express the relation between *C* and *n* as a piecewise function with linear pieces. See margin.

22. A formula for the area of a trapezoid with height *h* and bases b_1 and b_2 is $A = \frac{1}{2}h(b_1 + b_2)$. Solve this formula for *h*. **(Lesson 1-7)**

22. $h = \frac{2A}{b_1 + b_2}$

23. When you drop an object, its distance fallen in feet is modeled by $d(t) = 4.9t^2$, where *t* is time in seconds. **(Lesson 1-3)**
    a. What does the sentence $d(3) = 44.1$ mean in English?
    b. Does the sentence $d(-1) = 4.9$ have meaning? Why or why not?

23a. After 3 seconds, the object has fallen 44.1 feet.

23b. No; the object cannot fall for a negative amount of time.

EXPLORATION

24. There is an expression *two steps forward, one step back*.
    a. Write a recursive definition for the sequence of stopping points on a path following these directions. Let the *n*th term of the sequence be your position after you have followed these directions *n* times.
    b. What does the phrase mean? 24a–b. See the Additional Answers section at the back of the book.

QY ANSWERS

1. 34, 22, 10, –2, –14
2. the 36th term of the sequence, 1548

Additional Answers

21a.

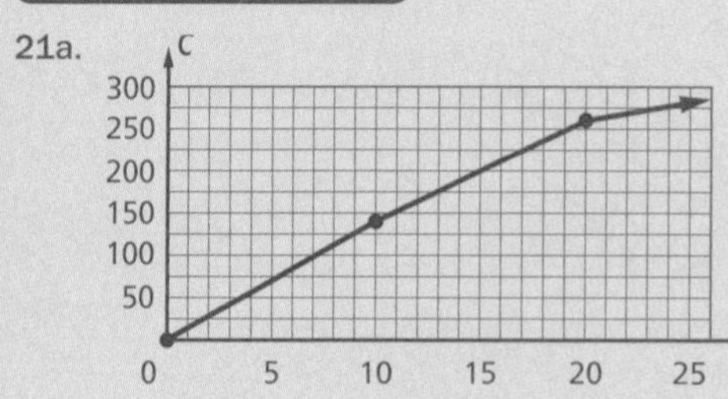

21b. $C = \begin{cases} 14n, \text{ for } 0 \leq n \leq 10 \\ 12n + 20, \text{ for } 10 < n \leq 20 \\ 10n + 60, \text{ for } 20 < n \end{cases}$

Additional Answers can be found in the back of the book.

Lesson 3-7 Graphs of Sequences

Vocabulary

Fibonacci sequence

BIG IDEA Sequences are graphed like other functions. The major differences are that the graph of a sequence is discrete and you can obtain some values of sequences using a recursive definition.

Mental Math

a. What is 30% of 70x? 21x

b. What is 70% of 30x? 21x

c. What is 75% of $8x - 24y$? $6x - 18y$

As you saw in Lesson 1-8 and in the last lesson, sequences can be described in two ways:

- An *explicit formula* gives an expression for the nth term of a sequence in terms of n. An example is $a_n = 4n - 6$.
- A *recursive formula* gives a first term or first few terms and an expression for the nth term of a sequence in terms of previous terms. An example is

$$\begin{cases} a_1 = -2 \\ a_n = a_{n-1} + 4, \text{ for } n > 1. \end{cases}$$

To graph a sequence, plot each ordered pair (n, a_n). You can generate the ordered pairs using a written description of a sequence, an explicit formula, or a recursive formula. The next three examples explore these possibilities.

GUIDED

Example 1

Consider the sequence with recursive formula $\begin{cases} a_1 = -2 \\ a_n = a_{n-1} + 4, \text{ for } n > 1. \end{cases}$

a. Make a table of values of the first six terms of this sequence.

b. Graph the first six terms of the sequence.

Solution

a. Make a table with n in one column and a_n in another column, as shown at the right. From the recursive definition, $a_1 = -2$ and each succeeding term is 4 larger than the previous term.

n	a_n
1	-2
2	? 2
3	? 6
4	? 10
5	? 14
6	? 18

(continued on next page)

Background

A sequence of real numbers can be considered as the range values for a function with the natural numbers as its domain. Thus, a sequence is a function and can be graphed. Students already know how to graph data points, so in this relatively easy lesson, the only new idea may be using a calculator to form a discrete rather than a continuous graph. This can be done by graphing a list (many students may be familiar with this feature of a calculator), by putting the calculator into sequence mode (as in Example 2, which is likely new to students), or by using a spreadsheet (as in Example 3).

Graphing a sequence using a recursive formula The Fibonacci sequence in Example 3 has been related to the numbers of seeds, flowers, petals, and designs in pinecones, fruit, and vegetables. It is the first sequence in the book in which the last line of the recursive formula refers to more than one previous term.

Lesson 3-7

GOAL

Graph a sequence, given either an explicit or recursive formula for it.

SPUR Objectives

L Model situations with recursive formulas.

N Graph or interpret graphs of sequences.

Materials/Resources

- Lesson Masters 3-7A and 3-7B
- Resource Masters 1 and 47–50

HOMEWORK

Suggestions for Assignment

- Questions 1–16
- Question 17 (extra credit)
- Reading Lesson 3-8
- Covering the Ideas 3-8

Local Standards

1 Warm-Up

In 1–4, name five points on the graph of the sequence that is defined. Answers vary.

1. $ak = 5k^2$ Sample: (1, 5), (2, 20), (3, 45), (4, 80), (5, 125)
2. $b_1 = 4$, $b_n = 3 + b_{n-1}$, for $n \geq 2$ Sample: (1, 4), (2, 7), (3, 10), (4, 13), (5, 16)
3. $c_1 = 0.25$; $c_n = 10c_{n-1}$, for $n \geq 2$ Sample: (1, 0.25), (2, 2.5), (3, 25), (4, 250), (5, 2500)
4. $d_1 = 8$, $d_2 = 7$, $d_n = d_{n-2} - d_{n-1}$, for $n \geq 3$ Sample: (1, 8), (2, 7), (3, 1), (4, 6), (5, -5)

2 Teaching

Notes on the Lesson

This lesson is explored and explained through its examples, and you might wish to go through the lesson, taking the examples in order and working through them. Example 1 is straightforward. The purpose of Example 2 is to show how to use a calculator to graph a sequence. Example 3 shows how to use a spreadsheet to generate the terms of a recursively defined sequence. From that table, a graph can be made. You may want to graph the Fibonacci sequence. It will look very much like the graph of a discrete exponential function because F_n is the integer closest to $\frac{1}{\sqrt{5}}\left(\frac{\sqrt{5}+1}{2}\right)^n$.

The different ways of graphing sequences are provided so that you can use whatever technology is available to you. Students do not need to be proficient in all these ways of graphing a sequence. Proficiency in one method is desired.

Additional Example

Example 1 Suppose you add 22 stones to a pile every night. How many stones are in the pile after the nth night?

a. Make a table of values of the first six terms of this sequence.

b. Graph the first six terms of the sequence.

Solution

a. Prepare a table with n in one column and a_n in the other column.

n	a_n	n	a_n
1	?	4	?
2	?	5	?
3	?	6	?

22; 44; 66; 88; 110; 132

b. Plot the points on a coordinate grid, with n as the independent variable. The points should be collinear.

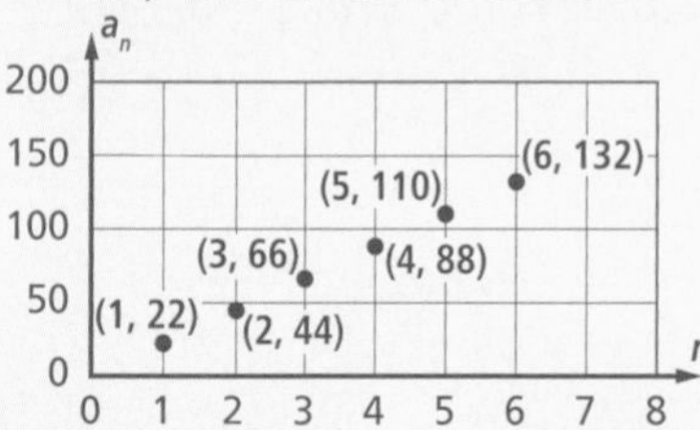

b. Plot the points from your table on a coordinate grid, with n as the independent variable. The points should be collinear. (The graph at the right is not complete.)

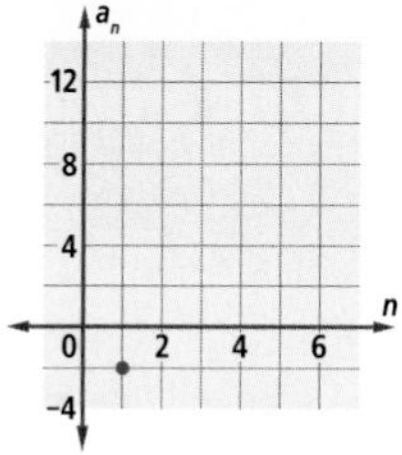

In Example 1, you could calculate each term of the sequence by hand. Using a spreadsheet, you can automatically generate the terms of a sequence if you know an explicit or recursive formula for it. Example 2 shows how to do this, and also points out an important difference between the graph of a line and the graph of a sequence.

Example 2

Recall the explicit formula for the sequence of lengths L_n of a train with n boxcars from Lesson 3-6, $L_n = 72 + 41n$.

a. Graph the first six terms of L_n using the explicit formula.

b. Graph the function $L(n) = 72 + 41n$ using a domain of the set of all reals on the same axes as the graph of the sequence.

c. Compare and contrast the graphs.

Solution

a. Enter the index values 1 through 6 into column A of a spreadsheet. Then use the explicit formula to generate values for the train-length sequence. On one calculator, we do this by entering the formula at the top of column B, as shown at the right. On other machines, you might do this by using the fill function.

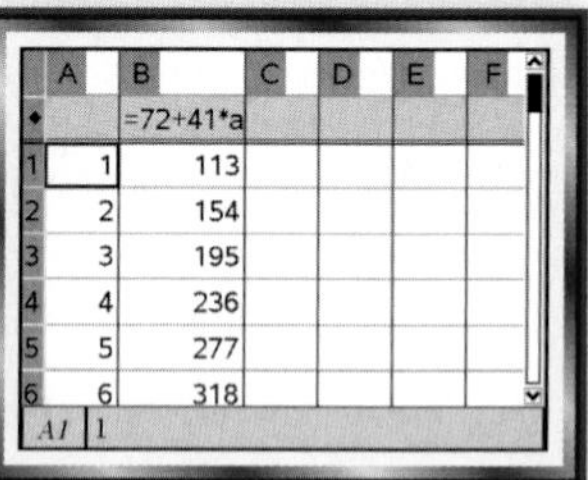

	A	B	C	D	E	F
•		=72+41*a				
1	1	113				
2	2	154				
3	3	195				
4	4	236				
5	5	277				
6	6	318				

A1 1

Create a scatterplot of the sequence, as shown below.

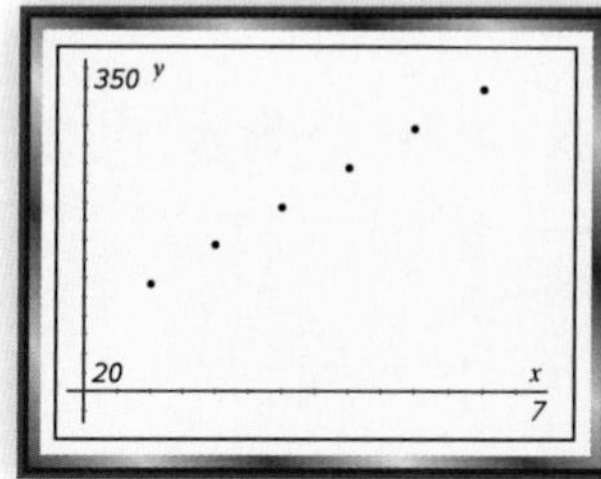

b. Graph $L(n) = 72 + 41n$ on your plot from Part a, as shown at the right.

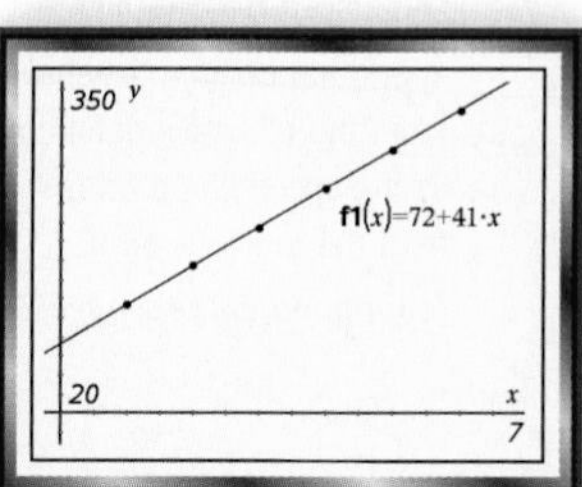

Accommodating the Learner

Show students the diagram at the right, which represents a sequence that starts with two squares with area a^2 and b^2. Then each "next" square has sides that are the sum of the sides of the two previous squares.

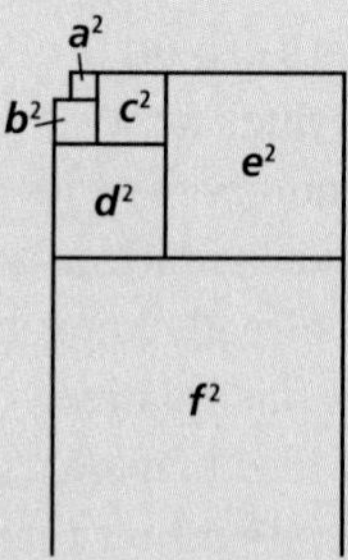

a. What are the lengths of the sides for the first two squares? What is the length of the side of squares 3, 4, and 5? a; b; $a + b$; $a + 2b$; $2a + 3b$

b. Find the lengths of the sides of squares 6 through 10. $3a + 5b$; $5a + 8b$; $8a + 13b$; $13a + 21b$; $21a + 34b$

c. Write a recursive definition for the function that is represented.

$$\begin{cases} E_1 = a \\ E_2 = b \\ E_n = E_{n-1} + E_{n-2}, \text{ for } n \geq 3 \end{cases}$$

c. Notice the similarities and differences between the two graphs.

Both graphs have the same constant rate of change of 41 feet per car. The difference is that the line graph is continuous, while the sequence graph is discrete.

Graphing a Sequence Using a Recursive Formula

Sometimes, it is easier to write a recursive formula for a sequence than an explicit formula. Example 3 illustrates such a situation. It also shows how spreadsheets can be used to generate terms and graph a recursively defined sequence.

Example 3

The sneezewort plant (also called sneezeweed or *Achillea ptarmica*) starts as a single stem. After two months of growth, the stem sends off a shoot that becomes a new stem, and produces a new shoot every month thereafter. The new shoots must mature for two months before they are strong enough to produce shoots of their own.

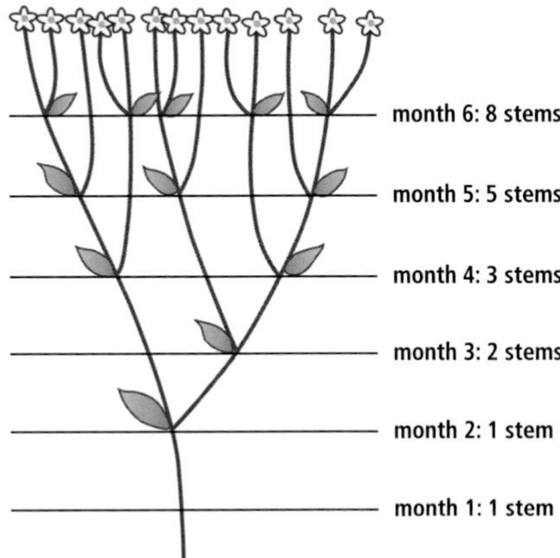

Let F_n be the number of stems in month n. The first two terms are equal to 1. Beginning with the third term, each term is found by adding the previous two terms.

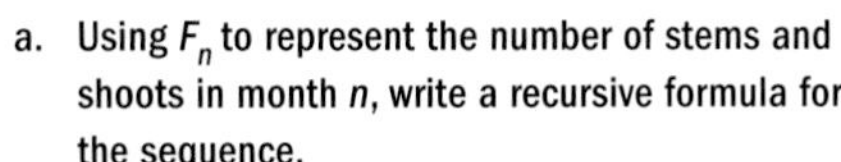

a. Using F_n to represent the number of stems and shoots in month n, write a recursive formula for the sequence.

b. Graph the first ten terms of the sequence.

Solution

a. After the first two terms, each term of the sequence is calculated by adding the previous two terms. As you know, when F_n is the nth term, then the previous $(n - 1)$st term is F_{n-1}. Similarly, the term preceding F_{n-1} is the $(n - 2)$nd term, or F_{n-2}. So a recursive definition is

$$\begin{cases} F_1 = 1 \\ F_2 = 1 \\ F_n = F_{n-1} + F_{n-2}, \text{ for } n \geq 3. \end{cases}$$

(continued on next page)

ENGLISH LEARNERS
Vocabulary Development

Help students understand that the same sequence can be defined by an *explicit formula* and by a *recursive formula*. Students should be able to explain and give examples of each kind of formula.

Additional Examples

Example 2 Use the explicit formula $L_n = 97 - 23n$.

a. Graph the first six terms of L_n.

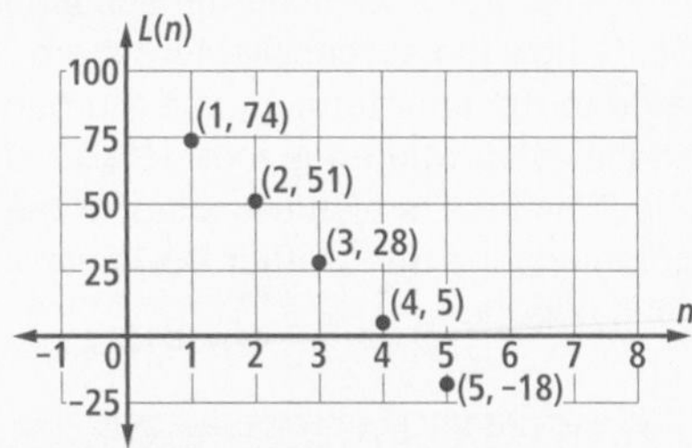

b. Graph the function $L(n) = 97 - 23n$ using a domain of all reals.

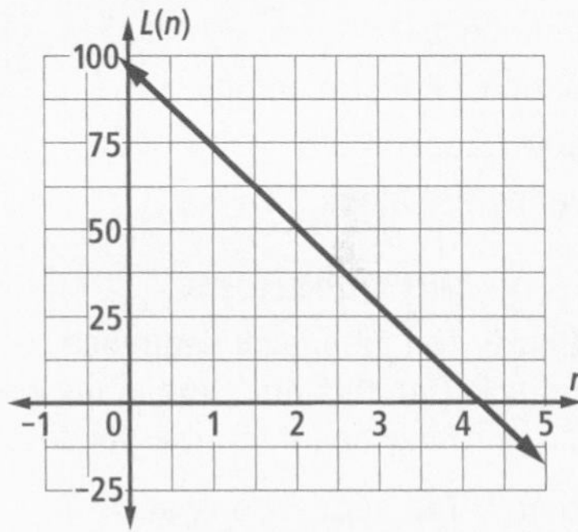

c. Compare and contrast the graphs. Both graphs have a constant rate of change of –23 and a *y*-intercept of 97. The difference is that the line graph is continuous, while the sequence graph is discrete.

Example 3 A mathematician proposes a sequence to study properties of multiplication. Let S_n be the nth term. The first two terms are 2 and 3. Beginning with the third term, each term is found by multiplying the two previous terms.

a. Write a recursive formula for the sequence.

$$\begin{cases} S_1 = 2 \\ S_2 = 3 \\ S_n = S_{n-1} \cdot S_{n-2}, \text{ for } n \geq 3 \end{cases}$$

b. Graph the first six terms of the sequence.

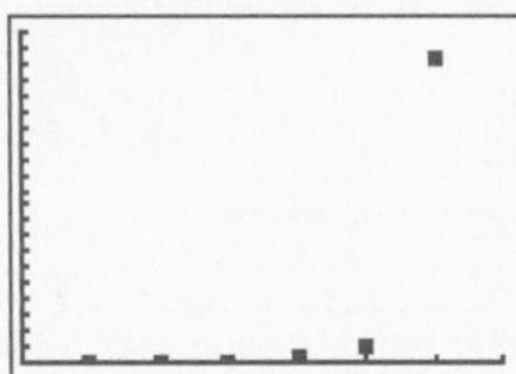

Note-Taking Tips

In Example 3, discuss with students the subscripts in the third line of the recursive formula. Encourage students to always check two features of the last line of a recursive formula: the subscripts indicate how the successive terms are related to the prior term(s), and the rule for *n* indicates where the index starts and stops. This idea is also the focus of the Accommodating the Learner Down activity on this page.

3 Assignment

Recommended Assignment

- Questions 1–16
- Question 17 (extra credit)
- Reading Lesson 3-8
- Covering the Ideas 3-8

Notes on the Questions

Question 5 The Fibonacci sequence grows quickly, so this question is not as difficult as it may seem at first glance.

Question 7 The sequence is an exponential sequence.

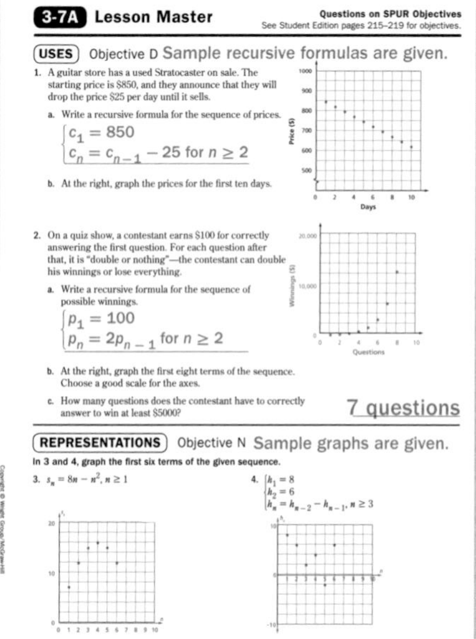

3-7A Lesson Master — Questions on SPUR Objectives. See Student Edition pages 215–219 for objectives.

USES Objective D Sample recursive formulas are given.

1. A guitar store has a used Stratocaster on sale. The starting price is \$850, and they announce that they will drop the price \$25 per day until it sells.
   a. Write a recursive formula for the sequence of prices.
   $\begin{cases} c_1 = 850 \\ c_n = c_{n-1} - 25 \text{ for } n \geq 2 \end{cases}$
   b. At the right, graph the prices for the first ten days.

2. On a quiz show, a contestant earns \$100 for correctly answering the first question. For each question after that, it is "double or nothing"—the contestant can double his winnings or lose everything.
   a. Write a recursive formula for the sequence of possible winnings.
   $\begin{cases} p_1 = 100 \\ p_n = 2p_{n-1} \text{ for } n \geq 2 \end{cases}$
   b. At the right, graph the first eight terms of the sequence. Choose a good scale for the axes.
   c. How many questions does the contestant have to correctly answer to win at least \$5000? 7 questions

REPRESENTATIONS Objective N Sample graphs are given.

In 3 and 4, graph the first six terms of the given sequence.

3. $s_n = 8n - n^2, n \geq 1$

4. $\begin{cases} h_1 = 8 \\ h_2 = 6 \\ h_n = h_{n-2} - h_{n-1}, n \geq 3 \end{cases}$

Advanced Algebra 191

Alternatively, you could write

$$\begin{cases} F_1 = 1 \\ F_2 = 1 \\ F_{n+1} = F_n + F_{n-1}, \text{ for } n \geq 1. \end{cases}$$

b. Use a spreadsheet. Enter the index numbers 1 through 10 into column A. The terms of the sequence will be in column B.

The recursive definition from Part a says that $F_1 = F_2 = 1$. So enter 1 in each cell B1 and B2.

Each of the terms F_3 through F_{10} is defined as the sum of the two previous terms. So, each cell from B3 through B10 needs to be defined as the sum of the previous two cells. Enter =B1+B2 in cell B3, as shown at the right. Then copy and paste this formula into cells B4 through B10 to generate the rest of the desired terms of the sequence. When this is done, 55 should appear in cell B10, as shown below at the left.

	A	B	C	D	E	F
1	1	1				
2	2	1				
3	3	2				
4	4					
5	5					
6	6					

B3 =b1+b2

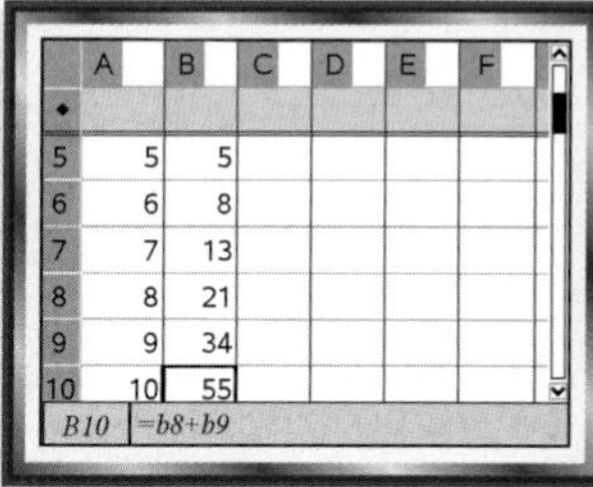

	A	B	C	D	E	F
5	5	5				
6	6	8				
7	7	13				
8	8	21				
9	9	34				
10	10	55				

B10 =b8+b9

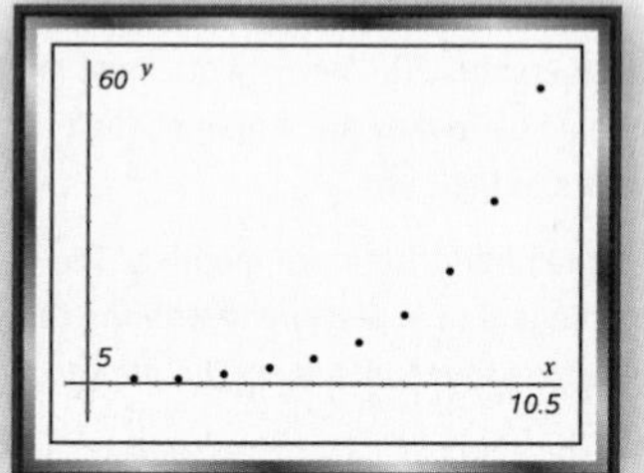

Create a scatter plot of the sequence, as shown above at the right.

The sequence in Example 3 is called the **Fibonacci** (pronounced "Fee-boh-NOTCH-ee") **sequence**. It is named after Leonardo of Pisa, a 12th century mathematician who wrote under the name Fibonacci. The Fibonacci numbers arise in a wide variety of contexts, and are so mathematically rich that there is an entire publication, the *Fibonacci Quarterly*, devoted to the mathematics arising from them.

QY

You may also have noticed that the points on the graphs in Examples 1 and 2 are collinear, but the points on the graph in Example 3 are not. This is because in the sequences in Examples 1 and 2, there is a constant difference between terms, but in the Fibonacci sequence, the difference between terms is not constant. The sequences in Examples 1 and 2 are examples of *arithmetic sequences*. You will learn more about arithmetic sequences in the next lesson.

▶ QY

In the sequence *F* of Example 3, find F_{11}.

Accommodating the Learner

Give students recursive definitions such as

$$\begin{cases} A_1 = 5 \\ A_n = A_{n-1} + 7, \text{ for } n \geq 2 \end{cases}$$

and

$$\begin{cases} B_1 = 10 \\ B_2 = 5 \\ B_{n+2} = B_n + B_{n+1}, \text{ for } n \geq 1 \end{cases}.$$

Ask them to rewrite the two definitions so the last line for sequence *A* defines A_{n+1} and the last line for sequence *B* defines B_n.

$$\begin{cases} A_1 = 5 \\ A_{n+1} = A_n + 7, \text{ for } n \geq 1 \end{cases};$$

$$\begin{cases} B_1 = 10 \\ B_2 = 5 \\ B_n = B_{n-1} + B_{n-2}, \text{ for } n \geq 3 \end{cases}$$

Questions

COVERING THE IDEAS

1. Refer to Example 1.
   a. What is a_{10}? 34
   b. Write a recursive rule for a_{n+1}. See margin.
2. Refer to Example 2. See margin.
   a. Write the recursive formula for L_n.
   b. Explain why it does not make sense to let n be any real number.
3. **Multiple Choice** Which formula below gives the sequence graphed at the right? D

   A $s_n = n^2$

   B $\begin{cases} s_1 = 1 \\ s_n = s_{n-1} + 1, n > 1 \end{cases}$

   C $\begin{cases} s_1 = 40 \\ s_n = s_{n-1} - 3, n > 1 \end{cases}$

   D $\begin{cases} s_1 = 4 \\ s_n = s_{n-1} + 3, n > 1 \end{cases}$

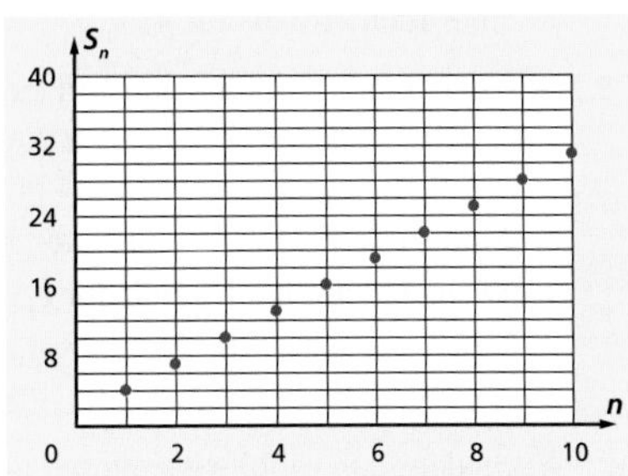

4. Give one reason why you might choose to model a situation with a recursively defined sequence rather than an explicitly defined one.

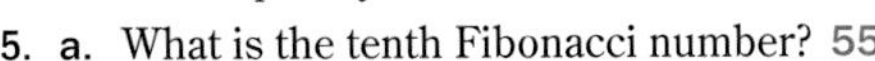

5. a. What is the tenth Fibonacci number? 55
   b. How many 3-digit Fibonacci numbers are there? 5
   c. How many 5-digit Fibonacci numbers are there? 5

4. Answers vary. Sample: It might be easier to describe how the terms are related to each other than to describe how to calculate them explicitly.

APPLYING THE MATHEMATICS

6. a. Graph the first ten terms of the sequence whose explicit formula is $s_n = n^2$. See margin.
   b. On the same axes, graph the first ten terms of the sequence whose recursive formula is
   $\begin{cases} r_1 = 1 \\ r_n = r_{n-1} + 2n - 1, n > 1. \end{cases}$ See margin.
   c. What do the graphs suggest about the sequence of numbers 1, 4, 9, 16, ...? The sequence of numbers can be represented by either formula.
7. Forrest, a crime scene investigator, is called to investigate a missing person's case. On entering the person's apartment, he discovers hundreds of bugs crawling around. Suppose that the number of bugs increases by 20% every day the apartment is left unoccupied, and that on the first day the apartment was left unoccupied, there were about 10 bugs.
   a. Write a recursive definition that describes the sequence giving the number b_n of bugs on day n. See margin.
   b. Graph the first 20 terms of the sequence you found in Part a. See margin.
   c. A detailed census determines that there are 450 bugs in the apartment. For how long has the apartment been unoccupied? 22 days

Additional Answers

1b. $\begin{cases} a_1 = -2 \\ a_{n+1} = a_n + 4_3, \text{ for } n \geq 1 \end{cases}$

2a. $\begin{cases} L_1 = 113 \\ L_n = L_{n-1} + 41, \text{ for } n \geq 2 \end{cases}$

2b. n represents the number of cars in a train, so it does not make sense to talk about a noninteger number of cars.

6a.

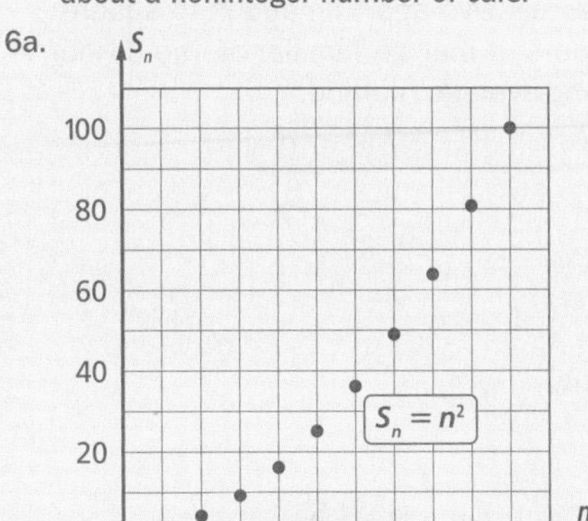

6b.

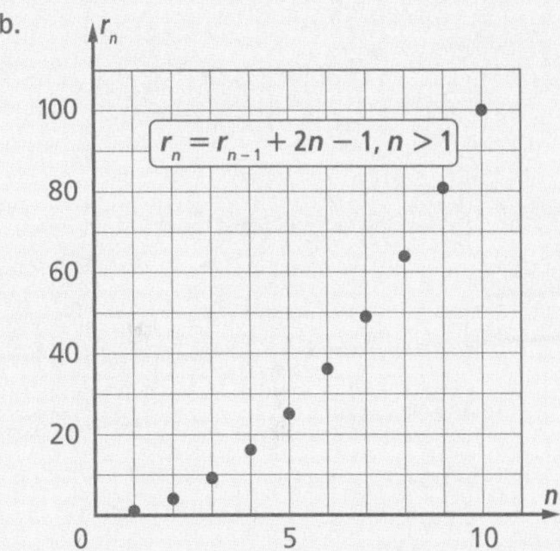

7a. $\begin{cases} b_1 = 10 \\ b_{n+1} = 1.2b_n, \text{ for } n \geq 1 \end{cases}$

7b.

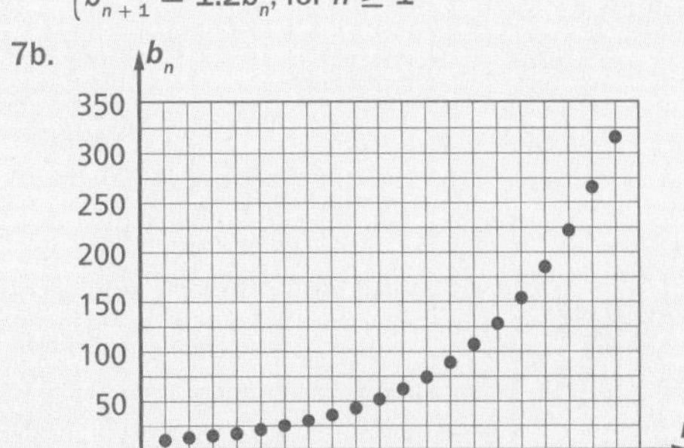

Extension

Ask students to explore the difference between recursive functions of the forms $\begin{cases} A_1 = a \\ A_n = A_{n-1} + b, \text{ for } n \geq 2 \end{cases}$ and $\begin{cases} G_1 = c \\ G_n = dG_{n-1}, \text{ for } n \geq 2 \end{cases}$. Ask them to write specific recursive formulas of each kind and try to generate an explicit function from their recursive ones. Answers vary. Sample: An example of sequence A is $\begin{cases} A_1 = 5 \\ A_n = A_{n-1} + 3, \text{ for } n \geq 2 \end{cases}$, which generates the sequence 5, 8, 11, 14, ...; that sequence can be represented by the explicit function $A(n) = 3n + 2$. An example of sequence G is $\begin{cases} G_1 = 3 \\ G_n = 2G_{n-1}, \text{ for } n \geq 2 \end{cases}$, which generates the sequence 3, 6, 12, 24, ...; that sequence can be represented by the explicit formula $G(n) = 3 \cdot 2^{n-1}$. (**Note:** Students will learn more about the two types of sequences, called **arithmetic sequences** and **geometric sequences,** respectively, in Lesson 3-8 [arithmetic], and in Lesson 7-5 [geometric].)

Notes on the Questions

Question 10 This sequence is a logistic sequence and is often used to describe populations and other quantities that have an upper limit. Historically, it was with rabbits that the Fibonacci sequence was first defined.

Question 11 This sequence represents successive approximations to square roots; it may be familiar as the divide-and-average method.

Additional Answers

8b. $\begin{cases} b_1 = 1 \\ b_2 = 1 \\ b_3 = 2 \\ b_n = b_{n-1} + b_{n-2} + b_{n-3}, \text{ for } n \geq 4 \end{cases}$

9a.

n	b_n
1	$500
2	$575
3	$650
4	$725
5	$800
6	$875

9b. $\begin{cases} b_1 = 500 \\ b_n = b_{n-1} + 75, \text{ for } n \geq 2 \end{cases}$

9c.

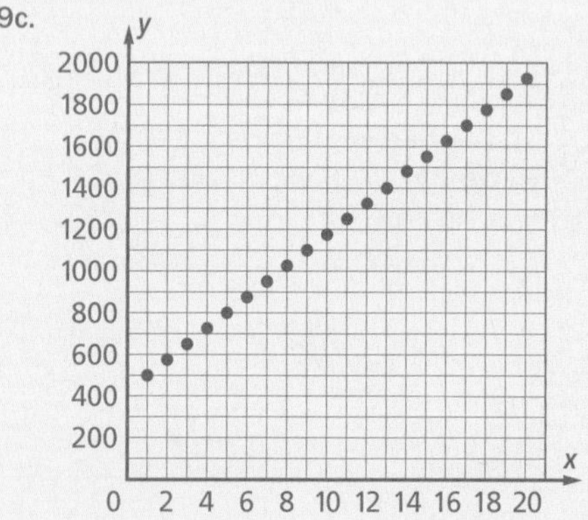

9d. Yes; all the points lie on the line $y = 500 + 75n$ because Kamilah saves the same amount every week.

10a.

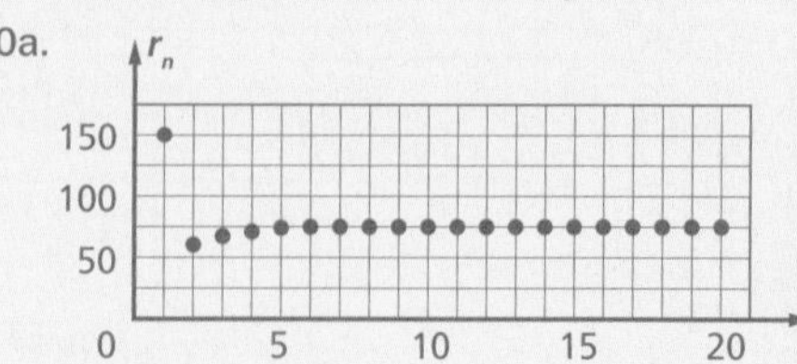

8. The *tribonacci* numbers R_n are defined as follows:
   (1) The first three tribonacci numbers are 1, 1, and 2.
   (2) Each later tribonacci number is the sum of the *three* preceding numbers.
   a. Using the rule, the fourth tribonacci number is $1 + 1 + 2 = 4$. Compute the fifth, sixth, and seventh tribonacci numbers. 7, 13, 24
   b. Give a recursive formula for the tribonacci numbers. See margin.
   c. Use a spreadsheet to find the 17th tribonacci number greater than 1000. 29,249,425

9. Kamilah gets a part-time job and saves $75 each week. At the start of the summer, her bank account has a balance of $500. Let b_n be the balance at the start of week n (so $b_1 = \$500$). See margin.
   a. Make a table of values of b_n for $n = 1, 2, \ldots, 6$.
   b. Write a recursive formula for b_n.
   c. Make a graph of the first 20 values of b_n.
   d. Are the points on the graph collinear? Justify your answer.

10. A population of rabbits is counted annually; the number of rabbits in year n is r_n. The values of r_n can be modeled by a recursively defined sequence:
$$\begin{cases} r_1 = 150 \\ r_{n+1} = 0.008r_n(200 - r_n), \text{ for } n \geq 1. \end{cases}$$
   a. Graph the first 20 terms of this sequence. See margin.
   b. In the long term, what happens to the population of rabbits? Does it increase, decrease, stabilize at a particular value, or follow some other pattern you can describe?
   c. Try graphing the sequence with several different values of r_1, for $2 \leq r_1 < 200$. How does the starting value affect the long-term population? See margin.

The largest litter of rabbits on record is 24. This occured in 1978 and 1999.

10b. The population of rabbits stabilizes at 75.

11. a. Graph the first ten terms of the sequence given by the recursive formula $a_n = \frac{1}{2}\left(a_{n-1} + \frac{9}{a_{n-1}}\right)$, $n > 1$, with $a_1 = 20$.
   b. Describe any patterns you see in the graph in words. For example, do the terms get larger or smaller? Do they appear to get closer to a particular number?
   c. Repeat Parts a and b using the recursive formula $a_1 = 20$, $a_n = \frac{1}{2}\left(a_{n-1} + \frac{25}{a_{n-1}}\right)$. How do your answers change? See margin.

11b. The numbers get smaller and closer to 3.

REVIEW

12. Write the first five terms of the sequence defined by
$$\begin{cases} b_1 = 2 \\ b_{n+1} = 2b_n + 1, \text{ for integers } n \geq 1. \end{cases}$$
(Lesson 3-6) 2, 5, 11, 23, 47

Additional Answers

10c. Answers vary. Sample: The population of rabbits stabilizes at 75 regardless of the starting value.

11a.

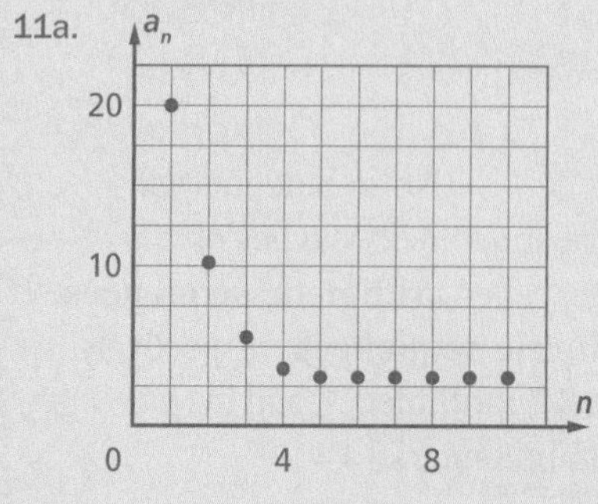

11c.

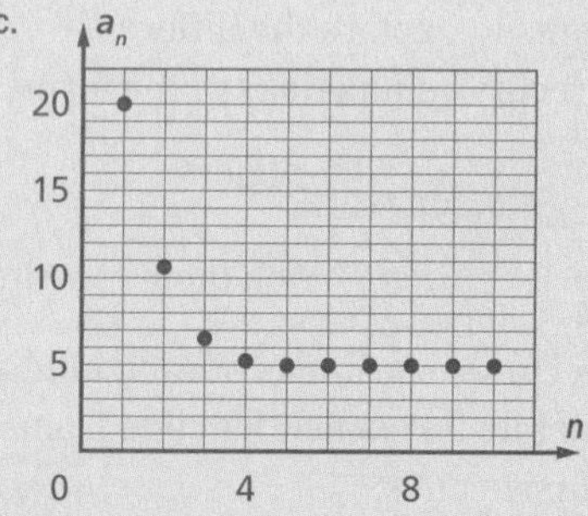

The numbers get smaller and closer to 5. The only change in the answer between the two formulas is in the numbers that the sequences approached.

13. Consider the sequence that begins 81, 27, 9, 3, … . **(Lesson 3-6)**
    a. **Fill in the Blank** From the second term on, each term is ___?___ the previous term. one third of
    b. Write a recursive formula for this sequence. See margin.
    c. Compute the next four terms in the sequence. $1, \frac{1}{3}, \frac{1}{9}, \frac{1}{27}$

14. The table at the right lists body lengths and weights for several humpback whales. Compute the regression line for these data and use it to estimate the weight of a humpback whale that is 12 meters long. **(Lesson 3-5)** $y \approx 6.16x - 53.55$; about 20.4 metric tons

Length (meters)	Weight (metric tons)
12.5	23
13.4	30
13.5	29
14.5	36
13.0	27
14.0	32

15. **Multiple Choice** Which of the following equations describes a line that does not have an x-intercept? **(Lesson 3-3)** E
    A $4x + 3y = 0$ B $2x - 2y = 1$ C $0x + 0y = 3$
    D $-3x + 0y = 0$ E $0x + 2y = -6$

16. Two perpendicular lines $\overleftrightarrow{AB}$ and $\overleftrightarrow{AC}$ have been drawn and their slopes measured. If the slope of $\overleftrightarrow{AB}$ is r, then the slope s of $\overleftrightarrow{AC}$ is a function of r. The point (r, s) is plotted as the lines rotate. **(Lesson 2-7)**
    a. Use the graph to determine whether there is a direct or inverse variation relationship between r and s. inverse variation
    b. Ana used the table function of her calculator to generate the table of s and r values at the right. Based on her data, determine an equation relating r and s. $s = -\frac{1}{r}$

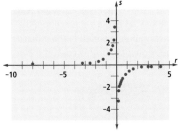

Slope $\overleftrightarrow{AB}$; r	Slope $\overleftrightarrow{AC}$; s
4.11	-0.24
3.30	-0.30
3.05	-0.33
2.35	-0.42
1.76	-0.57
1.40	-0.71
1.17	-0.86
0.99	-1.01
0.86	-1.16
0.77	-1.29
0.70	-1.44
0.63	-1.58
0.58	-1.72
0.53	-1.87
-18.08	0.06

EXPLORATION

17. The Fibonacci numbers have many arithmetic properties. Label the Fibonacci numbers $F_1 = 1$, $F_2 = 1$, $F_3 = 2$, and so on. Use a list of the first 15 Fibonacci numbers to explore each of the following.
    a. Let s_n be the sum of the first n Fibonacci numbers. That is, $s_1 = F_1$, $s_2 = F_1 + F_2$, $s_3 = F_1 + F_2 + F_3$, etc. Make a table of values of s_n for $n = 1, 2, \dots, 14$. See margin.
    b. Find a pattern in your table that allows you to quickly compute F_n from a list of Fibonacci numbers. $s_n = F_{n+2} - 1$
    c. Do some research and find some other arithmetical properties of the Fibonacci numbers. See margin.

QY ANSWER

$F_{11} = 89$

Notes on the Questions

Question 17c Many hundreds of properties of the Fibonacci sequence terms are known.

4 Wrap-Up

Ongoing Assessment

Show students a recursive formula such as $\begin{cases} b_1 = -5 \\ b_n = b_{n-1} + 3, \text{ for } n > 1 \end{cases}$. Ask students to find the ordered pairs (n, b_n) for $n = 1$ to 5. Then ask students to plot the ordered pairs and describe the slope and y-intercept of the line that contains the ordered pairs. The graph consists of the ordered pairs (1, -5), (2, -2), (3, 1), (4, 4), and (5, 7). The line through those points has slope 3 and y-intercept -8.

Additional Answers

13b. $\begin{cases} b_1 = 81 \\ b_n = \frac{1}{3}b_{n-1}, \text{ for } n \geq 2 \end{cases}$

17a.

n	s_n	n	s_n
1	1	8	54
2	2	9	88
3	4	10	143
4	7	11	232
5	12	12	376
6	20	13	609
7	33	14	986

17c. Answers vary. Sample: If we let t_n be the sum of the squares of the first n Fibonacci numbers, then a table for t_n is as follows:

n	t_n	n	t_n
1	1	8	714
2	2	9	1870
3	6	10	4895
4	15	11	12,816
5	40	12	33,552
6	104	13	87,841
7	273	14	229,970

An equation for t_n is $t_n = F_n \cdot F_{n+1}$.

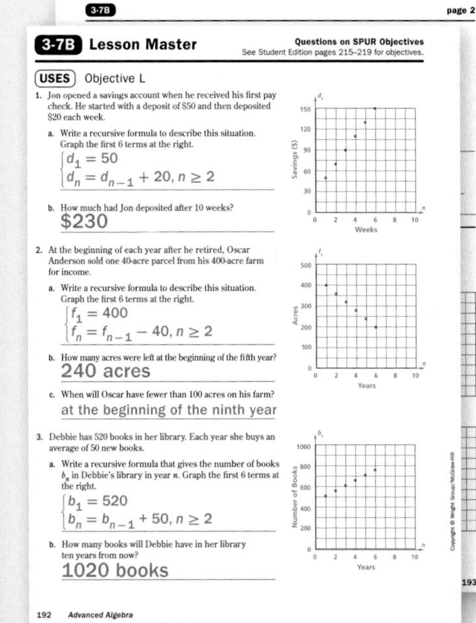
3-7B page 2

3-7B Lesson Master Questions on SPUR Objectives
See Student Edition pages 215–219 for objectives.

USES Objective L

1. Jon opened a savings account when he received his first pay check. He started with a deposit of $50 and then deposited $20 each week.
   a. Write a recursive formula to describe this situation. Graph the first 6 terms at the right.
   $\begin{cases} d_1 = 50 \\ d_n = d_{n-1} + 20, n \geq 2 \end{cases}$
   b. How much had Jon deposited after 10 weeks?
   $230
2. At the beginning of each year after he retired, Oscar Anderson sold one 40-acre parcel from his 400-acre farm for income.
   a. Write a recursive formula to describe this situation. Graph the first 6 terms at the right.
   $\begin{cases} f_1 = 400 \\ f_n = f_{n-1} - 40, n \geq 2 \end{cases}$
   b. How many acres were left at the beginning of the fifth year?
   240 acres
   c. When will Oscar have fewer than 100 acres on his farm?
   at the beginning of the ninth year
3. Debbie has 520 books in her library. Each year she buys an average of 50 new books.
   a. Write a recursive formula that gives the number of books b_n in Debbie's library in year n. Graph the first 6 terms at the right.
   $\begin{cases} b_1 = 520 \\ b_n = b_{n-1} + 50, n \geq 2 \end{cases}$
   b. How many books will Debbie have in her library ten years from now?
   1020 books

192 Advanced Algebra 193

Lesson

3-8

GOAL

Discuss explicit and recursive formulas for linear sequences.

SPUR Objectives

D Evaluate or find explicit and recursive formulas for sequences.

F Recognize properties of linear (arithmetic) sequences.

G Model situations involving arithmetic sequences.

Materials/Resources

- Lesson Masters 3-8A and 3-8B
- Resource Master 51

HOMEWORK

Suggestions for Assignment

- Questions 1–23
- Question 24 (extra credit)
- Reading Lesson 3-9
- Covering the Ideas 3-9

Local Standards

1 Warm-Up

1. Consider the sequence E of the positive even numbers 2, 4, 6, 8, ...
   a. Give an explicit formula for E_n. $E_n = 2n$
   b. Give a recursive definition for E. $E_1 = 2$; $E_n = E_{n-1} + 2$, for $n \geq 2$
2. Consider the sequence V of the nonnegative even numbers 0, 2, 4, 6, ...
   a. Give an explicit formula for V_n. $V_n = 2(n - 1)$
   b. Give a recursive definition for V. $V_1 = 0$; $V_n = V_{n-1} + 2$, for $n \geq 2$

Lesson 3-8

Formulas for Linear (Arithmetic) Sequences

Vocabulary

linear sequence, arithmetic sequence

▸ **BIG IDEA** As with other linear functions, two points on the graph of a *sequence*, or one point on the graph and its constant difference, are enough to determine an explicit formula.

Mental Math

Tell whether the graph of the function is a line, a parabola, a hyperbola, or none of these.

a. $f(x) = 6x^2$ parabola

b. $g(x) = -2x$ line

c. $h(x) = -\frac{3}{x^2}$ none of these

d. $j(x) = \frac{17}{x}$ hyperbola

Demetrius is adding water to a fish tank one gallon at a time. The tank weighs 32 pounds when empty and each gallon of water weighs 8.33 pounds. Let $W(g) = 32 + 8.33g$ represent the weight of the tank after g gallons of water are added. Notice that this equation is in slope-intercept form with a slope of 8.33 and a y-intercept of 32. The increase of 8.33 pounds after each gallon is added is the *constant difference* between terms of the sequence. In this case, the constant difference is a constant increase.

A sequence with a *constant difference* between successive terms is called a **linear** or **arithmetic sequence**. (Here the word *arithmetic* is used as an adjective; it is pronounced a-rith-MEH-tik.) Because there is a constant difference between successive terms, a linear sequence is a linear function with the domain of a sequence.

Developing an Explicit Formula for an Arithmetic Sequence

As you learned in Lesson 1-8, an explicit formula for a sequence can be developed by examining the pattern in a table.

Example 1

a. Write an explicit formula for the arithmetic sequence 4, 7, 10, 13, ...

b. Compute the 30th term of the sequence.

Background

The phrases *arithmetic sequence, arithmetic progression,* and *linear sequence* are synonyms. Each refers to a sequence in which consecutive terms differ by a constant d. The synonym, *arithmetic progression,* seems to be losing popularity. *Linear sequence* is the most descriptive of the three. (A corresponding list of names for sequences with a constant ratio occurs in Chapter 7: *geometric sequence, geometric progression,* and *exponential sequence.*)

A linear sequence is a linear function. The linear function $f(x) = mx + b$, with the domain as real numbers, contains the sequence $f_n = mn + b$. A recursive formula for this sequence is $f_1 = m + b, f_n = f_{n-1} + m$, for $n \geq 2$. Thus, the slope of the function is the constant difference between terms of the sequence. If we work backward using the recursive formula to find f_0, we see that $f_0 = b$, the y-intercept.

Solution

a. To develop an explicit formula, use the constant difference to write each term after the first. Consider the pattern in the table at the right. Notice that in term n, the number of 3s added to the initial term is 1 less than n. So, an explicit formula for the sequence is

$a_n = 4 + (n - 1) \cdot 3.$

$a_n = 3n + 1$

b. a_{30} is the 30th term of the sequence. Substitute 30 for n.

$a_{30} = 3(30) + 1$

$a_{30} = 91$

n = number of term	term = a_n
1	4
2	$4 + 1 \cdot 3 = 7$
3	$4 + 2 \cdot 3 = 10$
4	$4 + 3 \cdot 3 = 13$
5	$4 + 4 \cdot 3 = 16$
⋮	⋮
n	$4 + (n - 1) \cdot 3 = a_n$

Because the sequence in Example 1 is a function, it can be written as a set of ordered pairs: {(1, 4), (2, 7), (3, 10), ... }. These points lie on a line with slope, or constant increase, of 3. Substitute this slope and the point (1, 4) in the point-slope form of the equation of a line.

$y - 4 = 3(x - 1)$

$a_n - 4 = 3(n - 1)$ Substitute.

$a_n = 4 + 3(n - 1) = 3n + 1$ Solve for a_n.

This is the formula found in Part a of Example 1. This suggests the following theorem.

nth Term of an Arithmetic Sequence Theorem

The nth term a_n of an arithmetic (linear) sequence with first term a_1 and constant difference d is given by the explicit formula $a_n = a_1 + (n - 1)d$.

Proof Each ordered pair of the arithmetic sequence is of the form $(x, y) = (n, a_n)$. The first ordered pair is $(x_1, y_1) = (1, a_1)$. Because arithmetic sequences represent constant-increase or constant-decrease situations, a graph of the sequence consists of points that lie on a line. The slope of the line is the constant difference d. Substitute these values into the point-slope form of a linear equation.

$y - y_1 = m(x - x_1)$ Point-slope form

$a_n - a_1 = d(n - 1)$ Substitute.

$a_n = a_1 + (n - 1)d$ Solve for a_n.

 QY

▸ QY

Use the theorem to find an explicit formula for the sequence 6, 10, 14, 18, ...

A line is determined by one point and its slope. Therefore, if you know one term of the sequence and the common difference, you can determine an explicit formula for the sequence. If you know the first two terms of the sequence, you can determine a recursive formula for the sequence.

ENGLISH LEARNERS

Vocabulary Development

Emphasize the statement, from the third paragraph, that an *arithmetic sequence* is a sequence with a *constant difference* between successive terms. Students may be interested to know that a later topic (in Chapter 7) will introduce another type of sequence, such as 1, 2, 4, 8, ... or 243, 81, 27, 9, 3, ..., which has a *constant ratio* for successive terms; that type of sequence is called a *geometric sequence.*

2 Teaching

Notes on the Lesson

One starting place for this lesson is the characterization that a recursive formula for a sequence has two parts: a statement of the first term and a formula to generate the rest of the sequence. For a linear sequence, the first term is the y-intercept of the linear function, and the number added to each term to get the next term is the slope of the function.

It is often helpful to have students translate a recursive formula into words. For the arithmetic sequence $a_1 = -5$, $a_n = a_{n-1} + 3$, the translation is, "The first term is -5. To get the nth term in the sequence, add 3 to the previous term." A translation of the general formula is, "The first term is a_1; all other terms of the sequence are found by adding d to the previous term."

Additional Example

Example 1

a. Write an explicit formula for the arithmetic sequence 6, 10, 14, 18, 22, ... $a_n = 4n + 2$

b. Compute the 25th term of the sequence. $a_{25} = 102$

Note-Taking Tips

Encourage students to record the difference between notations such as $P(n) = 15n$, used in the second paragraph of the lesson, and $a_n = 3n + 1$, used in the solution to Example 1. Students should realize that the function notation emphasizes the general relationship between the input and output variables, while the subscript notation emphasizes the specific value of a_n, the nth term.

Notes on the Lesson

This lesson presents arithmetic sequences in several ways: in pictures (beginning of the lesson), by a list (Example 1), by formula (solution to Example 1), in words (Examples 2 and 3), by a graph (solution to Example 2), and by a command for technology (last paragraph of the lesson). Students understand this lesson if they can move from any one of these presentations to any other.

Additional Examples

Example 2 An electronic bulletin board charges $2 for each word of a classified ad plus a $14 service charge.

a. Write a recursive formula for the arithmetic sequence that represents an ad that contains n words.

$$\begin{cases} c_1 = 16 \\ c_n = c_{n-1} + 2, \text{ for integers } n \geq 2 \end{cases}$$

b. Graph the sequence.

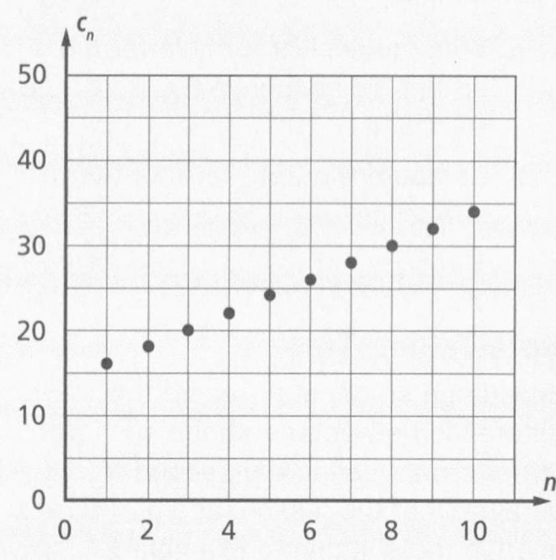

Recursive Notation for Arithmetic Sequences

A recursive formula for the arithmetic sequence in Example 1 is

$$\begin{cases} a_1 = 4 \\ a_n = a_{n-1} + 3, \text{ for integers } n \geq 2. \end{cases}$$

The second line of this formula can be rewritten as

$$a_n - a_{n-1} = 3.$$

This shows the constant difference between term n and term $(n - 1)$. The constant difference 3 is the slope between the points $(n - 1, a_{n-1})$ and (n, a_n).

More generally, suppose a sequence is defined recursively as

$$\begin{cases} a_1 \\ a_n = a_{n-1} + d, \text{ for integers } n \geq 2. \end{cases}$$

When $n \geq 2$, we can rewrite the second line as $a_n - a_{n-1} = d$. This means that the difference between consecutive terms is the constant d. By definition, the sequence is arithmetic. This proves the following theorem.

Constant-Difference Sequence Theorem

The sequence defined by the recursive formula

$$\begin{cases} a_1 \\ a_n = a_{n-1} + d, \text{ for integers } n \geq 2 \end{cases}$$

is the arithmetic sequence with first term a_1 and constant difference d.

Example 2

A cell-phone company charges 25¢ per minute for overseas calls along with a 30¢ service charge.

a. **Write a recursive formula for the arithmetic sequence that represents the cost of a call lasting n minutes.**

b. **Graph the sequence.**

Solution

a. When the call begins you are immediately charged 55¢ (25¢ for your first minute plus the 30¢ service charge). Then you pay 25¢ for each additional minute that the call lasts, so the difference between successive terms is $d = 25$. A recursive formula for this arithmetic sequence is

$$\begin{cases} a_1 = 55 \\ a_n = a_{n-1} + 25, \text{ for integers } n \geq 2. \end{cases}$$

Accommodating the Learner

Show students an explicit formula (1) $a_n = a_1 + nd$ and a recursive formula

(2) $\begin{cases} b_1 \\ b_n = b_{n-1} + c, \text{ for integers } n \geq 1 \end{cases}$.

Ask them to write the first 5 terms of each sequence and then write a recursive formula for (1) and an explicit formula for (2).

a_1; $a_1 + d$; $a_1 + 2d$; $a_1 + 3d$; $a_1 + 4d$;

$\begin{cases} a_1 \\ a_n = a_{n-1} + d, \text{ for integers } n \geq 2; \end{cases}$

b_1; $b_1 + c$; $b_1 + 2c$; $b_1 + 3c$; $b_1 + 4c$; $b_n = b_1 + (n - 1)c$

b. You can graph arithmetic sequences using the methods you used in Lesson 3-7. The graph of the first ten values of the sequence is shown at the right.

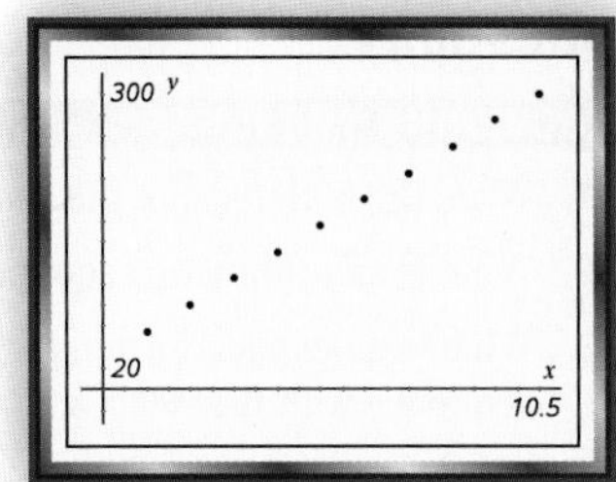

You should be able to translate from a recursive formula to an explicit formula for an arithmetic sequence, and vice versa. To go from recursive to explicit form you can use the theorems on the previous two pages. Use the second theorem to find a_1 and d and then substitute the values into the first theorem. To go from explicit to recursive form, you can use the explicit formula to find a_1, and substitute the known values of a_1 and d into the recursive pattern for an arithmetic sequence.

Example 3

Some car dealers offer interest-free loans, provided that you pay back the amount borrowed by a certain date. Suppose a car that costs \$14,736 requires monthly payments of \$245.60. Let a_n be the amount you still owe after n months.

a. Write a recursive formula for this sequence.

b. Write an explicit formula for this sequence.

Solution

a. After 1 month you owe \$14,736 − \$245.60 = \$14,490.40, so $a_1 = 14{,}490.40$. Each month you pay \$245.60, so the difference between successive terms is $d = -245.60$. A recursive formula for this sequence is

$$\begin{cases} a_1 = 14{,}490.40 \\ a_n = a_{n-1} - 245.60, \text{ for integers } n \geq 2. \end{cases}$$

b. You know that $a_1 = 14{,}490.40$ and $d = -245.60$.

So, $a_n = 14{,}490.40 + (n-1)(-245.60)$

$a_n = -245.60n + 14{,}736$

where n = the number of payments and a_n = the current balance owed.

Many calculators have a sequence command seq that lets you generate the terms of a sequence if you know its explicit form. At the right is how one calculator generates the first four terms of the sequence in Example 3. The "x,1,4" tells the machine to start at $x = 1$ and end at $x = 4$.

Additional Examples

Example 3 A person owes \$8760 on an interest-free loan and is paying \$182.50 each month. Let b_n be the amount owed after n months.

a. Write a recursive formula for this sequence.
$$\begin{cases} b_1 = 8577.50 \\ b_n = b_{n-1} - 182.50, \text{ for integers } n \geq 2 \end{cases}$$

b. Write an arithmetic formula for this sequence. $b_n = -182.5n + 8760$

Accommodating the Learner

Ask students to look at the Constant Difference Sequence Theorem on page 198, which states $\begin{cases} a_1 \\ a_n = a_{n-1} + d, \text{ for } n \geq 2 \end{cases}$ is the arithmetic sequence with first term a_1 and constant difference d. Ask students to identify the slope and y-intercept of the line that contains all the ordered pairs (n, a_n) for that arithmetic sequence. The points lie on the line $y = dx + (a_1 - d)$, so the slope is d and the y-intercept is $a_1 - d$.

3 Assignment

Recommended Assignment

- Questions 1–23
- Question 24 (extra credit)
- Reading Lesson 3-9
- Covering the Ideas 3-9

Notes on the Questions

Question 12 The sequence of triangular numbers is a *quadratic sequence*—that is, a sequence that can be modeled by a quadratic function. The differences between consecutive terms of a quadratic sequence form a linear sequence. Question 19 is a related question.

Additional Answers

5b. $\begin{cases} a_1 = 12 \\ a_n = a_{n-1} + 4, \text{ for integers } n \geq 2 \end{cases}$

7. $\begin{cases} a_1 = 1.3 \\ a_n = a_{n-1} + 0.3, \text{ for integers } n \geq 2 \end{cases}$

9a. $\begin{cases} t_{-1} = 12 \\ t_{-n} = t_{n-1} + 7, \text{ for integers } n \geq 2 \end{cases}$

11. $\begin{cases} a_1 = -70 \\ a_{n+1} = a_n + 22.5, \text{ for integers } n \geq 1 \end{cases}$

3-8A Lesson Master — Questions on SPUR Objectives. See Student Edition pages 215–219 for objectives.

SKILLS Objective D — Sample recursive formulas are given.

In question 1 give a. recursive and b. explicit formulas for the arithmetic sequence described.

1. first term -12, constant difference 2
   a. $\begin{cases} a_1 = -12 \\ a_{n+1} = a_n + 2, n \geq 1 \end{cases}$ b. $a_n = -12 + 2(n - 1)$

PROPERTIES Objective F

In 2 and 3, determine whether the numbers could be the terms of an arithmetic sequence.

2. 14, 12, 11, 10 no
3. -9, -7.5, -6, -4.5 yes

In 4 and 5, determine whether the formula describes an arithmetic sequence.

4. $t_n = 8 - 2.4n$ yes
5. $\begin{cases} r_1 = 3 \\ r_n = 2r_{n-1}, n \geq 2 \end{cases}$ no

6. If the fourth term of an arithmetic sequence is 9 and the seventh term is 30, find the first term. -12

USES Objective G

7. A family bought 42 boxes of macaroni and cheese when it was on sale. The kids eat three boxes per week. Write sequence formulas for the number of boxes left at the beginning of week n.
   a. Recursive: $\begin{cases} b_1 = 42 \\ b_n = b_{n-1} - 3, n \geq 2 \end{cases}$ b. Explicit: $b_n = 42 - 3(n - 1)$
   c. Find the first four terms in the sequence. 42, 39, 36, 33
   d. Find the number of boxes left at the beginning of week 12. 9 boxes

8. Airlines work on the assumption that passengers weigh an average of 190 pounds. A regional jet weighs 25,900 pounds with only one person (the pilot) aboard. Write recursive and explicit sequences for the weight of the aircraft with n people aboard.
   a. Recursive: $\begin{cases} j_1 = 25{,}900 \\ j_{n+1} = j_n + 190, n \geq 1 \end{cases}$ b. Explicit: $j_n = 25{,}900 + 190(n - 1)$
   c. Find the weight of the plane fully loaded with a crew of 3 and 51 passengers. 35,970 lb

194 *Advanced Algebra*

Questions

COVERING THE IDEAS

1. Write the 50th term of the sequence from Example 1. 151
2. What is an arithmetic sequence? 2. An arithmetic sequence is a sequence with a constant difference between successive terms.
3. What is an explicit formula for the nth term of an arithmetic sequence with first term a_1 and constant difference d? $a_n = a_1 + (n - 1)d$
4. What is the connection between the slope of a linear function and the constant difference of an arithmetic sequence? 4. They are equal (when dealing with positive integers).
5. Consider the arithmetic sequence 12, 16, 20, 24, 28, … .
   a. Write an explicit formula for the nth term of the sequence. 5a. $a_n = 12 + (n - 1)4$
   b. Write a recursive definition of the sequence. See margin.
   c. Calculate the 47th term of this sequence. 196

In 6 and 7, refer to Example 2.

6. What term of the sequence gives the cost of a 20-minute overseas phone call? the 20th term
7. Rewrite the formula if the service charge is $1.00 and the cost per minute is 30¢. See margin.
8. An arithmetic sequence has an initial term of -127 and a constant difference of 42.
   a. Write an explicit formula for the sequence. $a_n = -127 + (n - 1)42$
   b. Use the `seq` command on a calculator to find the first seven terms. 8b. -127, -85, -43, -1, 41, 83, 125
9. Suppose $t_n = 12 + 7(n - 1)$. a. See margin.
   a. Write a recursive formula for the arithmetic sequence t.
   b. Compute t_{77}. 544
10. Consider the sequence $\begin{cases} a_1 = 10.5 \\ a_n = a_{n-1} + 4.3, \text{ for integers } n \geq 2. \end{cases}$
    a. Write its first three terms. 10.5, 14.8, 19.1
    b. Write an explicit formula for the sequence. $a_n = 10.5 + (n - 1)4.3$
11. Write a recursive formula for the linear sequence -70, -47.5, -25, -2.5, … . See margin.

APPLYING THE MATHEMATICS

12. In Chapter 1, the sequence of triangular numbers was described by the explicit formula $t(n) = \frac{n(n+1)}{2}$. Is this an example of an arithmetic sequence? Why or why not? 12. No; there is not a constant difference between terms.

Extension

As an extension to Question 19, ask students to find the first 8 "pentagonal numbers." 1, 5, 12, 22, 35, 51, 70, 92 Then ask students to verify that the formulas $P(n) = \frac{n(3n - 1)}{2}$ and $\begin{cases} P_1 = 1 \\ P_n = P_{n-1} + 3n - 2, \text{ for } n \geq 2 \end{cases}$ generate the first 8 pentagonal numbers. As an extra activity, ask students to illustrate and describe the pentagonal numbers.

Pentagonal numbers are numbers of dots that start with 1 dot, then 5 dots that form a pentagon, and then adding dots so each outside edge of the pentagon has 3 dots, 4 dots, and so on.

13. At the right is a graph of the first five terms of an arithmetic sequence. Write an explicit formula for the sequence.

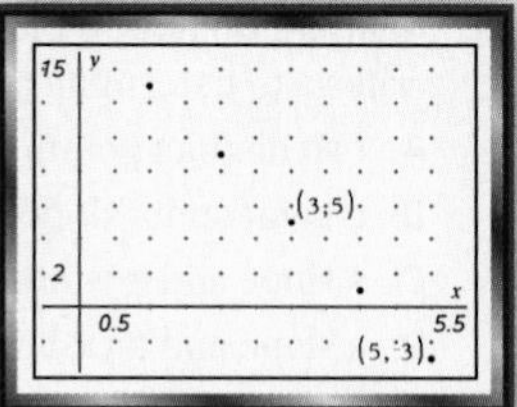

13. $a_n = 13 - 4(n - 1)$

14. A formula for the sum of the measures of the interior angles of a convex polygon is $S_n = 180(n - 2)$ for $n \geq 3$, where n is the number of sides of the polygon.
   a. Evaluate S_n for $n = 3, 4, 5, 6, 7$. 180, 360, 540, 720, 900
   b. Explain why the results of Part a represent the terms of an arithmetic sequence.
   c. Find a recursive formula for S_n. See margin.

14b. There is a constant difference (180) between each of the terms.

In 15 and 16, a local radio station holds a weekly contest to give away a cash prize. The announcer calls a number and if the person who answers guesses the correct amount of money in the pot, he or she wins the money. If the person misses, $25 is added to the money pot.

15. On the 12th call, a contestant won $675. How much was in the pot at the beginning? $400

16. Suppose the pot starts with $140. On what call could the winner receive $1,115? on the 40th call

17. A 16 ounce jar candle is advertised to burn an average of 110 hours. Suppose that the candle burns at a constant rate.
   a. Write the first three terms of the sequence that shows how many ounces of the candle remain after each hour it burns. 15.85, 15.71, 15.56
   b. Write the explicit formula for r_n, the number of ounces of the candle left after n hours of burning.
   $r_n = 15.85 - 0.14545(n - 1)$, or $r_n = 16 - 0.14545n$

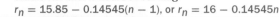

REVIEW

18. Graph the first eight terms of the sequence $r_n = \frac{n^3}{n!}$. Describe how the value of r_n changes as n increases. Recall that $n! = n \cdot (n - 1) \cdot (n - 2) \cdot \ldots \cdot 3 \cdot 2 \cdot 1$. (Lesson 3-7) See margin.

19. Verify that the explicit formula for the nth triangular number $T_n = \frac{n(n+1)}{2}$ satisfies the recursive formula
$$\begin{cases} T_1 = 1 \\ T_n = T_{n-1} + n. \end{cases}$$
(Lessons 3-6, 1-8) See margin.

20. Write the first twelve terms of the sequence defined by
$$\begin{cases} p_1 = 1 \\ p_2 = -1 \\ p_n = p_{n-1} \cdot p_{n-2}, \text{ for integers } n \geq 3. \end{cases}$$
(Lesson 3-6) 1, -1, -1, 1, -1, -1, 1, -1, -1, 1, -1, -1

Notes on the Questions

Question 20 Because this sequence uses the previous two terms to generate its next term, once it is seen that the fourth and fifth terms equal the first and second terms, respectively, then it is known that the sequence repeats itself every third term. You might ask students to give the first 12 terms of the sequence defined by $p_1 = 1$, $p_2 = 1$, and $p_n = (-1)^n(p_{n-1})(p_{n-2})$. 1, 1, -1, -1, 1, 1, -1, -1, 1, 1, -1, -1; the sequence repeats every fourth term.

Additional Answers

14c. $\begin{cases} S_3 = 180 \\ S_n = S_{n-1} + 180, \text{ for integers } n \geq 4 \end{cases}$

18.

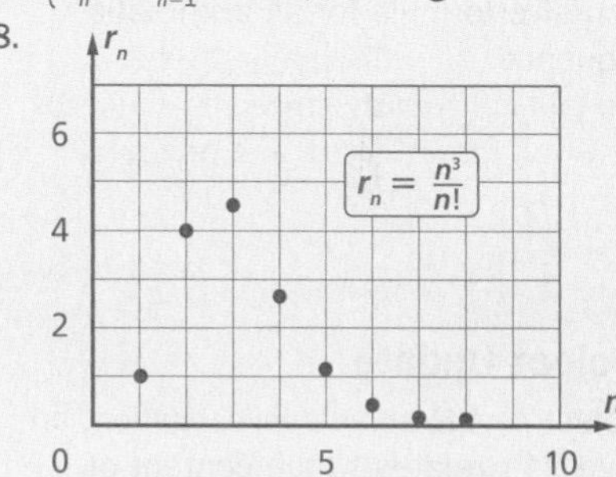

r_n increases, reaches a maximum, and then approaches 0 as n increases.

19. $T_1 = \frac{1(1+1)}{2} = 1$

$T_2 = \frac{2(2+1)}{2} = 3 = 1 + 2$

$T_3 = \frac{3(3+1)}{2} = 6 = 3 + 3$

Notes on the Questions

Question 24 The problem that historically generated the idea of the hailstone numbers is called the Collatz or $3n + 1$ problem. The Collatz problem asks if the sequence always has the number 1 in it as a term, regardless of the value of its first term a_1. This conjecture has been shown to be valid for all $a_n \leq 3 \cdot 2^{53}$ (this includes all numbers with fewer than 170 digits), but it has not been proved for all a_n.

4 Wrap-Up

Ongoing Assessment

Ask students to explain how to write a recursive formula for an arithmetic sequence. Identify the first term a_1 and use two consecutive terms to find the common difference d. The recursive formula is

$$\begin{cases} a_1 \\ a_n = a_{n-1} + d, \text{ for integers } n \geq 2 \end{cases}.$$

Project Update

Project 4, *A Graphical Investigation*, on page 211 relates to the content of this lesson.

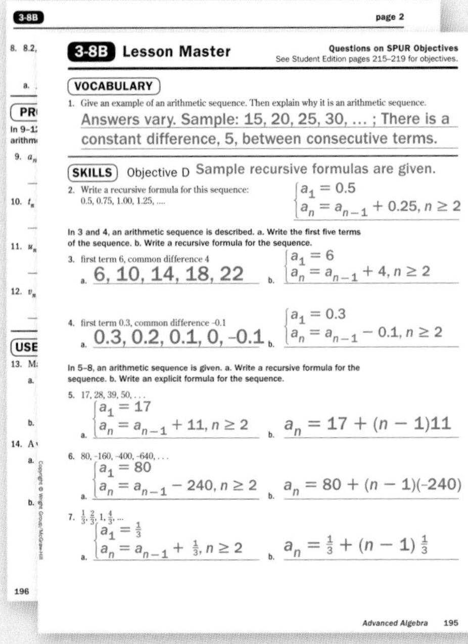

3-8B page 2

3-8B Lesson Master

Questions on SPUR Objectives
See Student Edition pages 215–219 for objectives.

VOCABULARY

1. Give an example of an arithmetic sequence. Then explain why it is an arithmetic sequence.
Answers vary. Sample: 15, 20, 25, 30, … ; There is a constant difference, 5, between consecutive terms.

SKILLS Objective D Sample recursive formulas are given.

2. Write a recursive formula for this sequence: 0.5, 0.75, 1.00, 1.25, ….
$\begin{cases} a_1 = 0.5 \\ a_n = a_{n-1} + 0.25, n \geq 2 \end{cases}$

In 3 and 4, an arithmetic sequence is described. a. Write the first five terms of the sequence. b. Write a recursive formula for the sequence.

3. first term 6, common difference 4
a. 6, 10, 14, 18, 22
b. $\begin{cases} a_1 = 6 \\ a_n = a_{n-1} + 4, n \geq 2 \end{cases}$

4. first term 0.3, common difference -0.1
a. 0.3, 0.2, 0.1, 0, -0.1
b. $\begin{cases} a_1 = 0.3 \\ a_n = a_{n-1} - 0.1, n \geq 2 \end{cases}$

In 5–8, an arithmetic sequence is given. a. Write a recursive formula for the sequence. b. Write an explicit formula for the sequence.

5. 17, 28, 39, 50, . . .
a. $\begin{cases} a_1 = 17 \\ a_n = a_{n-1} + 11, n \geq 2 \end{cases}$
b. $a_n = 17 + (n - 1)11$

6. 80, -160, -400, -640, . . .
a. $\begin{cases} a_1 = 80 \\ a_n = a_{n-1} - 240, n \geq 2 \end{cases}$
b. $a_n = 80 + (n - 1)(-240)$

7. $\frac{1}{3}, \frac{2}{3}, 1, \frac{4}{3}, \ldots$
a. $\begin{cases} a_1 = \frac{1}{3} \\ a_n = a_{n-1} + \frac{1}{3}, n \geq 2 \end{cases}$
b. $a_n = \frac{1}{3} + (n - 1)\frac{1}{3}$

196

Advanced Algebra 195

21. **Multiple Choice** Which of the following are *not* sufficient criteria to determine a (unique) line? **(Lesson 3-4)** E
   A two distinct points
   B a point and a slope
   C a slope and a y-intercept
   D a slope and an x-intercept
   E All of the above uniquely determine a line.

22. Suppose you have two solutions of oxalic acid, one at 0.1 mol/L, the other 0.5 mol/L. **(Lessons 3-2)**
   a. If you mix A liters of the first solution with B liters of the second, what will be the concentration of the resulting solution? $\frac{0.1A + 0.5B}{A + B}$ mol/L
   b. How many liters of the 0.5 mol/L solution must be added to 4 liters of the 0.1 mol/L solution to get 1 mole of acid in the final mixture? 1.2 L

23. Suppose y varies directly as x, and $y = -24$ when $x = 48$. **(Lesson 2-4, 2-1)**
   a. Find the constant of variation k. $k = -\frac{1}{2}$
   b. How is k represented on the graph of the function? k is the slope of the line.

EXPLORATION

24. The following recursively defined sequence generates numbers known as ***hailstone numbers***.

$$\begin{cases} a_1 \text{ is any positive integer.} \\ \text{For } n > 1, \text{ If } a_{n-1} \text{ is even, } a_n = \frac{a_{n-1}}{2}. \\ \qquad\qquad \text{If } a_{n-1} \text{ is odd, } a_n = 3a_{n-1} + 1. \end{cases}$$

For example, if $a_1 = 46$, then $a_2 = 23$, $a_3 = 70$, $a_4 = 35$, $a_5 = 106\ldots$.
   a. Explore this sequence rule for at least five different values of a_1. Continue generating terms until you can predict what will happen in the long run. See margin.
   b. Look up hailstone numbers on the Internet to find out how they got their name and what is known about them. Briefly describe what you find. See margin.

Hailstones rise and fall within clouds, growing larger and larger until they are so heavy they fall out of the cloud.

QY ANSWER

$a_n = 6 + (n - 1) \cdot 4 = 4n + 2$

Additional Answers

24a. Answers vary. Sample: 7, 22, 11, 34, 17, 52, 26, 13, 40, 20, 10, 5, 16, 8, 4, 2, 1, 4, 2, 1; in the long run, the sequence will reach 1 and then repeat 4, 2, 1 infinitely.

24b. Answers vary. Sample: Hailstone numbers got their name because the sequence rises and falls just like a hailstone in a cloud.

Lesson 3-9 Step Functions

Vocabulary

step function
floor symbol ⌊ ⌋
ceiling symbol ⌈ ⌉
floor function, greatest-integer function, rounding-down function, int function
ceiling function, rounding-up function

BIG IDEA *Step functions* have applications in many situations that involve rounding.

In 2007, the U.S. postage rate for first class flats (certain large envelopes) was $0.70 for the first ounce plus $0.17 for each additional ounce or part of an ounce. First-class mail rates for flats up to 13 ounces are given in the table below. Notice that the phrase "up to and including the given weight" means that the weight is *rounded up* to the nearest ounce. For instance, an envelope weighing 4.4 ounces is charged at the 5-ounce rate.

Mental Math

Each sequence below is either arithmetic or consists of consecutive powers of a number. Give the next two terms in the sequence.

a. 2, 4, 6, 8, ... 10, 12
b. 23, 17, 11, 5, ... -1, -7
c. 1, -1, 1, -1, ... 1, -1

2007 First-Class Mail Rates for Flats*

Weight (oz)	Rate (dollars)	Weight (oz)	Rate (dollars)
1	0.70	8	1.89
2	0.87	9	2.06
3	1.04	10	2.23
4	1.21	11	2.40
5	1.38	12	2.57
6	1.55	13	2.74
7	1.72		

*Rate is for a flat up to and including the given weight.

The graph at the right shows the cost of mailing a first-class flat for weights up to 13 ounces. Because the cost is rounded up, the left end of each segment is not included on the graph and the right end of each segment is included. Because no single weight has two costs, this graph pictures a function.

The domain is the set of possible weights of a flat in ounces between 0 and 13 ounces, and the range is the set of costs {$0.70, $0.87, $1.04, … , $2.74}.

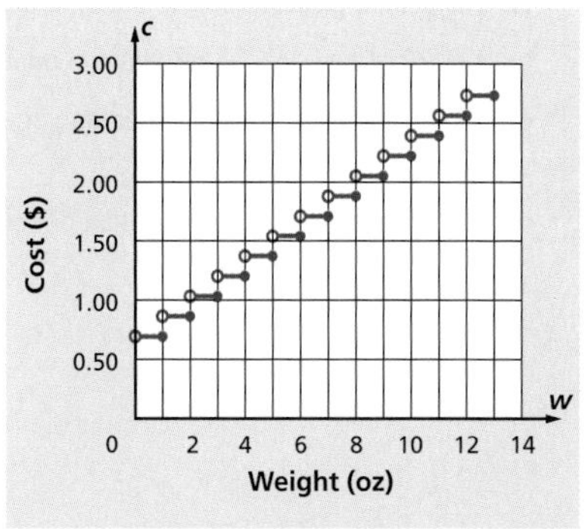

Lesson 3-9

GOAL

Introduce and explore the important class of functions called step functions.

SPUR Objectives

C Evaluate expressions based on step functions.

K Model situations leading to step functions.

N Graph or interpret graphs of step functions.

Materials/Resources

- Lesson Masters 3-9A and 3-9B
- Resource Masters 2, 52, and 53

HOMEWORK

Suggestions for Assignment

- Questions 1–21
- Question 22 (extra credit)
- Self-Test

Local Standards

1 Warm-Up

1. **Multiple choice** Which equation describes the postal rates graphed on page 203?
   A $y = 0.17x + 0.53$
   B $y = 0.17\lfloor x \rfloor + 0.53$
   C $y = -0.17\lfloor -x \rfloor + 0.53$
   D $y = 0.17\lfloor x - 1 \rfloor + 0.53$
   E $y = -0.17\lfloor 1 - x \rfloor + 0.53$
   C
2. Explain how you know that your answer to Warm-Up Question 1 is correct. Answers vary but should include that $\lceil x \rceil = -\lfloor -x \rfloor$ (see the Background on this page).

Background

Step functions abound in real-world applications; they are appropriate whenever rounding or truncating takes place. One measure of the importance of step functions is reflected in the number of names they have acquired. The function with equation $y = \lfloor x \rfloor$ is called the *rounding-down function*, the *floor function*, or the *greatest-integer function*. On computers and calculators, this function is usually denoted by int, INT, or intg. The function with equation $y = \lceil x \rceil$ is called the *rounding-up function* or the *ceiling function*. Some calculators do not have a preprogrammed command for the ceiling function. On those calculators, you can round x up to the nearest integer by using $y = -\lfloor -x \rfloor$.

There are four major activities to emphasize in this lesson: (1) calculating the values of a greatest integer function, (2) translating real situations into greatest-integer-function language, (3) graphing greatest-integer functions, and (4) learning to use (and/or find) the function on the technology you have.

(continued on next page)

2 Teaching

Notes on the Lesson

Many situations in students' lives can be described by step functions. Any rounding can be described by using the greatest-integer symbol, as discussed in the Accommodating the Learner Up activity and the Extension in this lesson (see pages 205 and 207).

Some students get confused when rounding a number that already looks rounded. For instance, to round 100 up to the nearest 10, they might answer "110." Check that students are not making this mistake.

Students are expected to be able to evaluate and make graphs of functions whose formulas are given in terms of the greatest-integer function. Encourage students to begin by working with specific arguments for the independent variable and point out that these arguments must include noninteger values. Alternatively, students can begin with integer values to get a feel for some of the values of the function and then substitute noninteger values between.

Caution: On some calculators, INT does not refer to the greatest-integer function but to the integer part of a decimal. On these calculators, INT(-5.9) = -5, whereas for the greatest-integer function INT(-5.9) = -6. In this text, INT always stands for the greatest-integer function.

The mail-rates function is not a linear function, but it is a piecewise linear function. Because its graph looks like a series of steps, it is called a **step function**. Each step is part of a horizontal line. Two step functions commonly used are the *floor function* and the *ceiling function*.

The Floor and Ceiling Functions

The **floor symbol** $\lfloor\ \rfloor$ and the **ceiling symbol** $\lceil\ \rceil$ are defined as follows.

Definition of Greatest Integer/Least Integer

$\lfloor x \rfloor$ = the greatest integer less than or equal to x, and

$\lceil x \rceil$ = the least integer greater than or equal to x.

The **floor function** is the function f with $f(x) = \lfloor x \rfloor$, for all real numbers x. It is also called the **greatest-integer function**, or the **rounding-down function**. On some calculators and in some computer languages it is called the **int function**. Another notation you may see for the floor function is $f(x) = [\![x]\!]$.

The **ceiling function** is the function f with $f(x) = \lceil x \rceil$, for all real numbers x. It is also called the **rounding-up function**.

 QY1

> **QY1**
> What names does your calculator use for the floor and ceiling functions?

GUIDED

Example 1

Evaluate each of the following.

a. $\left\lfloor 5\frac{7}{8} \right\rfloor$ b. $\lfloor -4.2 \rfloor$ c. $\lceil \pi \rceil$ d. $\lceil 13 \rceil$

Solution

a. $\left\lfloor 5\frac{7}{8} \right\rfloor$ is the greatest integer less than or equal to $5\frac{7}{8}$. So, $\left\lfloor 5\frac{7}{8} \right\rfloor$ = __?__. 5

b. $\lfloor -4.2 \rfloor$ is the __?__ less than or equal to -4.2. So, $\lfloor -4.2 \rfloor$ = __?__. greatest integer; -5

c. $\lceil \pi \rceil$ is the least integer greater than or equal to $\pi \approx$ __?__. So, $\lceil$ __?__ $\rceil$ = __?__ 3.1416; π; 4

d. $\lceil 13 \rceil$ is the __?__ greater than or equal to 13. So, $\lceil$ __?__ $\rceil$ = __?__. smallest integer; 13; 13

When you use function-plotting software or graphing calculators to demonstrate step functions, check ahead of time to see if the technology correctly handles the points of discontinuity. Some utilities produce misleading graphs that show vertical segments, called "risers," that connect two vertically aligned endpoints of consecutive horizontal segments.

ENGLISH LEARNERS

Vocabulary Development

Many students have initial difficulty with the phrases *greatest integer less than* $\lfloor\ \rfloor$ and *least integer greater than* $\lceil\ \rceil$. A number line can help students visualize these phrases. Have students graph on a number line:

a. $\lfloor \pi \rfloor$, the greatest integer less than π.

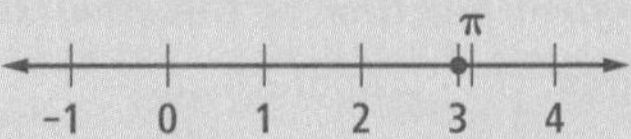

b. $\lceil \sqrt{5} \rceil$, the least integer greater than $\sqrt{5}$.

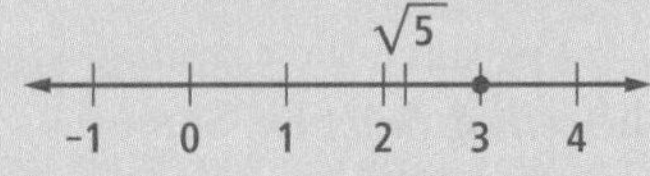

The Graph of the Floor Function

One way to sketch the graph of a step function is to make a table of values so you can see the pattern.

Example 2

Graph the function f defined by $f(x) = \lfloor x \rfloor$.

Solution Make a table of values. For all x greater than or equal to 0 but less than 1, the greatest integer less than or equal to x is 0. For all x greater than or equal to 1 but less than 2, the greatest integer less than or equal to x is 1. In a similar manner, you can get the other values in the table below. The graph is at the right below.

x	$f(x) = \lfloor x \rfloor$
$-3 \le x < -2$	-3
$-2 \le x < -1$	-2
$-1 \le x < 0$	-1
$0 \le x < 1$	0
$1 \le x < 2$	1
$2 \le x < 3$	2
$3 \le x < 4$	3

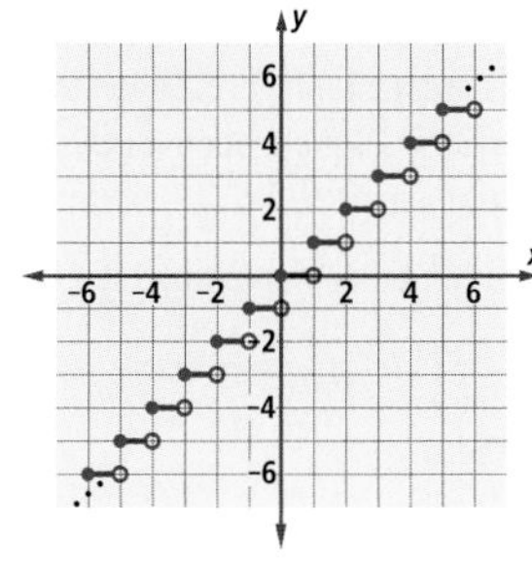

In the graph in Example 2, the open circles at (1, 0), (2, 1), (3, 2), and so on, indicate that these points do not lie on the graph of $f(x) = \lfloor x \rfloor$. At these points, the function value jumps to the next step. The solid circles indicate that the points (1, 1), (2, 2), (3, 3), and so forth, do lie on the graph. Notice that the domain of the greatest-integer function is the set of real numbers, but the range is the set of integers.

If your graphing utility has the `int`, or floor function, it will graph the greatest-integer function for you. The graph from one graphing utility is shown at the right. By default, some graphing utilities connect successive pixels, so they may join successive steps. This makes it appear as if the graph does not represent a function. On these graphing utilities, you can get the correct graph by switching from connected mode to dot mode.

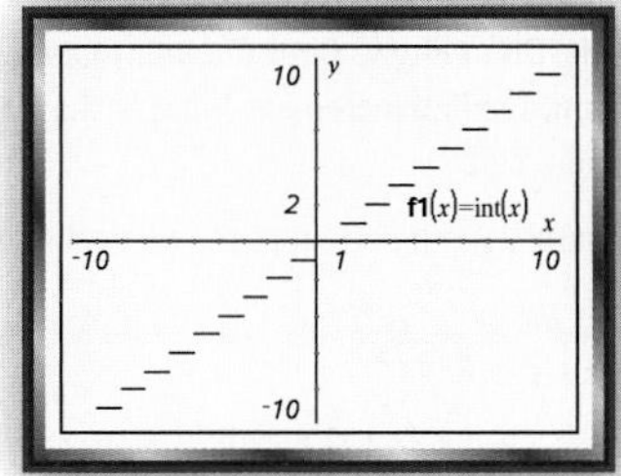

Accommodating the Learner

Ask students to describe how to round a decimal to a given place value. Answers vary. Sample: Round up if the digit just to the right of the given place value is ≥ 5; round down (actually, truncate) if that digit is < 5. Then ask students to explain how they can use the greatest-integer function to write an expression for a decimal rounded to the nearest whole number. The expression $\lfloor D + 0.5 \rfloor$ rounds a decimal value D to the nearest whole number. For example, if $D = 27.832$, then $D + 0.5 = 28.332$ and $\lfloor D + 0.5 \rfloor = \lfloor 28.332 \rfloor = 28$.

Additional Examples

Example 1 Evaluate each of the following.

a. $\left\lfloor 6\frac{2}{3} \right\rfloor$

b. $\lfloor -10.01 \rfloor$

c. $\lceil 2\pi \rceil$

d. $\lceil 27 \rceil$

Solution

a. $\left\lfloor 6\frac{2}{3} \right\rfloor$ is the greatest integer less than or equal to $6\frac{2}{3}$. So $\left\lfloor 6\frac{2}{3} \right\rfloor$ = __?__. 6

b. $\lfloor -10.01 \rfloor$ is the __?__ less than or equal to -10.01. So $\lfloor -10.01 \rfloor$ = __?__. greatest integer; -11

c. $\lceil 2\pi \rceil$ is the least integer greater than or equal to $2\pi \approx$ __?__. So __?__ = __?__. 6.283; $\lceil 2\pi \rceil$; 7

d. $\lceil 27 \rceil$ is the __?__ greater than or equal to 27. So __?__ = __?__. least integer; $\lceil 27 \rceil$; 27

Example 2 Graph the function defined by $g(x) = \lceil x \rceil$. Prepare a table of values.

x	$g(x) = \lceil x \rceil$
$-3 < x \le -2$	-2
$-2 < x \le -1$	-1
$-1 < x \le 0$	0
$0 < x \le 1$	1
$1 < x \le 2$	2

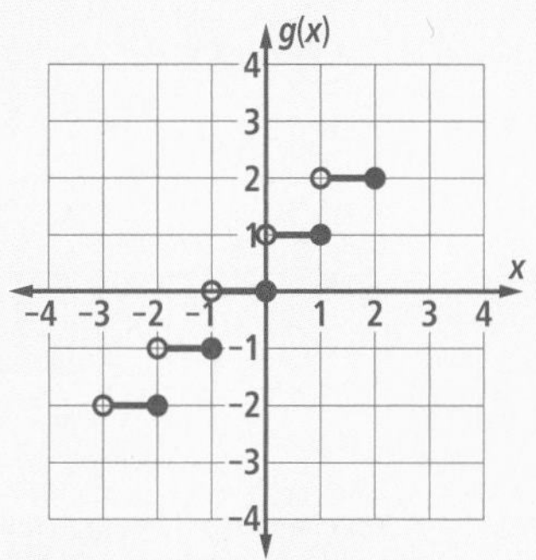

Note-Taking Tips

Floor function, greatest-integer function, and rounding-down function are synonyms for the same process. Have students describe that process in their notes and then identify which of the terms they think best identifies the process.

Additional Examples

Example 3 Suppose a taxi rate is an initial fee of \$3 plus \$0.60 for each full quarter-mile traveled.

a. Write a formula for $T(m)$, the charge for a trip of m miles.
$T(m) = 3 + 0.6\lfloor 4m \rfloor$

b. What is the charge for a 2.9-mile taxi ride? \$9.60

Example 4 An errand-running service charges \$38 per hour, billing for a full hour when any part of an hour is used. What is the charge for running errands for 2 hours, 45 minutes?

Solution The time is rounded up to the nearest hour, so use the ceiling function: $38 \cdot \left\lceil 2\frac{45}{60} \right\rceil = 38 \cdot$ __?__ = __?__. The company charges __?__ for the errands.
3; \$114; \$114

Applications of Step Functions

The floor or ceiling function is appropriate when function values must be integers and other formulas would give noninteger values.

Example 3

In March 2008, New York City taxi rates were an initial fee of \$2.50 plus \$0.40 for each full $\frac{1}{5}$-mile traveled.

a. Write a formula for $T(m)$, the charge for a trip of m miles.

b. What is the charge for an 8.75-mile trip in a New York City taxi?

The taxi to resident ratio in New York City is 1:149.

Solution

a. Because there are 5 one-fifths of a mile in each mile, multiply the miles by 5 to determine the number of $\frac{1}{5}$-miles traveled. This number, $5m$, may not be a whole number, so use the greatest-integer function to change it to an integer before multiplying by \$0.40. An equation for this function is $T(m) = 2.50 + 0.40\lfloor 5m \rfloor$.

b. The charge for a trip of 8.75 miles can be computed by substituting $m = 8.75$ into the formula for $T(m)$.

$$\begin{aligned} T(m) &= \$2.50 + \$0.40\lfloor 5 \cdot 8.75 \rfloor \\ &= \$2.50 + \$0.40\lfloor 43.75 \rfloor \\ &= \$2.50 + \$0.40 \cdot 43 \\ &= \$19.70 \end{aligned}$$

 QY2

▶ **QY2**
What is the charge for a 15.3-mile trip in a NYC taxi?

GUIDED

Example 4

Users of pre-paid calling cards are billed in 1-minute increments. This means that customers are billed for a full minute when any part of a minute is used. If the Call-Me-Often Phone Card Company charges \$0.03 per minute with a 1-minute billing increment, what is the charge for a 5-minute, 40-second phone call?

Solution Call-Me-Often's charge is rounded up to the nearest minute, so use a ceiling function.

$0.03\left\lceil 5\frac{40}{60} \right\rceil = 0.03($__?__$) =$ __?__ 6; 0.18

Call-Me-Often charges __?__ cents for the call. 18

Accommodating the Learner

Ask students to compare the rounding-up function and the rounding-down function for negative and positive numbers. For example, ask students to discuss results such as these:

$\lfloor 8.7 \rfloor = 8$, while $\lfloor -8.7 \rfloor = -9$

$\lceil 5.3 \rceil = 6$, while $\lceil -5.3 \rceil = -5$

Some students may find it easier to use the terms *floor function* and *ceiling function.*

- floor(8.7) = $\lfloor 8.7 \rfloor = 8$ and floor(-8.7) = $\lfloor -8.7 \rfloor = -9$; each is the integer to the left of the given number.
- ceiling(5.3) = $\lceil 5.3 \rceil = 6$ and ceiling(–5.3) = $\lceil -5.3 \rceil = -5$; each is the integer to the right of the given number.

Questions

COVERING THE IDEAS

In 1 and 2, refer to the postage example at the beginning of this lesson.

1. What is the cost to mail a letter weighing 4.3 ounces? $1.38
2. What is the domain of the function? $0 < x \le 13$
3. In your own words, write the meaning of $\lceil x \rceil$. Why do you think it is also called the ceiling function?

In 4–7, evaluate.

4. $\left\lfloor 4\frac{3}{4} \right\rfloor$ 4
5. $\lfloor 4\pi \rfloor$ 12
6. $\lfloor -5.87 \rfloor$ −6
7. $\lceil 7 - 0.5 \rceil$ 7

8. a. **Fill in the Blanks** The function f defined by $f(x) = \lfloor x \rfloor$ is called the ___?___ or ___?___ function.
   b. The range of $f: x \to \lfloor x \rfloor$ is ___?___. the set of all integers
   c. Why are there open circles at (1, 0), (2, 1), (3, 2), and so on in the graph of f?
9. Give the domain and range of the function.
   a. $f(x) = \lceil x \rceil$
   b. the function in Example 3
10. Refer to Example 4. A 2-minute billing increment charges for parts of minutes as if they were the next even minute (for example, a 3-minute call is billed for 4 minutes). If Call-Me-Often Phone Card Company charges \$0.03 per minute with a 2-minute billing increment, what does an 18-minute, 10-second phone call cost? \$0.60

APPLYING THE MATHEMATICS

11. Let $r(x) = \lfloor x + 0.5 \rfloor$.
    a. Find $r(1.2)$. 1
    b. Find $r(1.7)$. 2
    c. What kind of rounding does r do?

In 12 and 13, an auditorium used for a high school graduation has 750 seats available for its g graduates.

12. **Multiple Choice** If the tickets are divided evenly among the graduates, which of the following represents the number of tickets each graduate may have? B

    A $\left\lceil \frac{750}{g} \right\rceil$ B $\left\lfloor \frac{750}{g} \right\rfloor$ C $\left\lceil \frac{g}{750} \right\rceil$ D $\left\lfloor \frac{g}{750} \right\rfloor$

3. Answers vary. Sample: $\lceil x \rceil$ means the smallest integer greater than or equal to x. It is called the ceiling function because the ceiling of a room is the *smallest* (or *next up*) level of the building that is above that room.

8a. Answers vary. Samples: floor, greatest-integer, rounding-down, int

8c. There are open circles at those values because those points do not lie on the graph. At those points the function value jumps to the next step.

9a. domain: set of all real numbers; range: set of all integers

9b. domain: set of all positive real numbers; range: {2.50, 2.90, 3.30, ...}

11c. r rounds to the greatest integer less than or equal to $x + 0.5$.

Extension

Refer to the Accommodating the Learner Up activity on page 205, which asks students to use the greatest-integer function to round a value to the nearest whole number. Ask students how they can use the greatest-integer function to extend that problem to round a given value to *any* decimal place. To round a number D, such as $D = 27.6836$, to the nearest hundredth, multiply D by 100 (getting 2768.36), add 0.5 (getting 2768.86), apply the greatest-integer function ($\lfloor 2768.86 \rfloor = 2768$), and finally divide by 100 (getting 27.68). In general, to round a decimal D to the nearest 10^{-n}-th, calculate $\frac{\lfloor 10^n \cdot D + 0.5 \rfloor}{10^n}$. To round to a place value greater than units, such as 10, 100, or, in general, 10^n, calculate $\left\lfloor \frac{D}{10^n} + 0.5 \right\rfloor \cdot 10^n$.

3-9

3 Assignment

Recommended Assignment

- Questions 1–21
- Question 22 (extra credit)
- Self-Test

Notes on the Questions

Question 12 This question shows that the answer to an integer division problem (one in which the quotient and remainder are integers) can be described using the greatest-integer function symbol. This is an important idea that should be discussed.

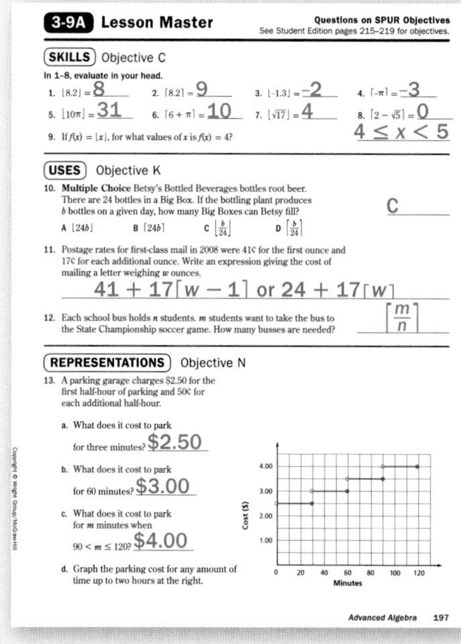

3-9A Lesson Master

Questions on SPUR Objectives
See Student Edition pages 215–219 for objectives.

SKILLS Objective C

In 1–8, evaluate in your head.

1. $\lfloor 8.2 \rfloor$ = 8
2. $\lceil 8.2 \rceil$ = 9
3. $\lfloor -1.3 \rfloor$ = −2
4. $\lceil -\pi \rceil$ = −3
5. $\lfloor 10\pi \rfloor$ = 31
6. $\lceil 6 + \pi \rceil$ = 10
7. $\lfloor \sqrt{17} \rfloor$ = 4
8. $\lceil 2 - \sqrt{5} \rceil$ = 0
9. If $f(x) = \lfloor x \rfloor$, for what values of x is $f(x) = 4$? $4 \le x < 5$

USES Objective K

10. **Multiple Choice** Betsy's Bottled Beverages bottles root beer. There are 24 bottles in a Big Box. If the bottling plant produces b bottles on a given day, how many Big Boxes can Betsy fill? C

    A $\lfloor 24b \rfloor$ B $\lceil 24b \rceil$ C $\left\lfloor \frac{b}{24} \right\rfloor$ D $\left\lceil \frac{b}{24} \right\rceil$
11. Postage rates for first-class mail in 2008 were 41¢ for the first ounce and 17¢ for each additional ounce. Write an expression giving the cost of mailing a letter weighing w ounces. $41 + 17\lceil w - 1 \rceil$ or $24 + 17\lceil w \rceil$
12. Each school bus holds n students. m students want to take the bus to the State Championship soccer game. How many busses are needed? $\left\lceil \frac{m}{n} \right\rceil$

REPRESENTATIONS Objective N

13. A parking garage charges \$2.50 for the first half-hour of parking and 50¢ for each additional half-hour.
    a. What does it cost to park for three minutes? \$2.50
    b. What does it cost to park for 60 minutes? \$3.00
    c. What does it cost to park for m minutes when $90 < m \le 120$? \$4.00
    d. Graph the parking cost for any amount of time up to two hours at the right.

Advanced Algebra 197

Notes on the Questions

Question 17 This question illustrates one of the more amazing applications of any function and almost always generates an interesting discussion. Make certain that students enter the entire number for the year instead of just the last two digits. Most parts of the formula are relatively easily explained: y is added because there is one more day in a normal year than an even number of weeks; $\lfloor \frac{y}{4} \rfloor$ accounts for leap years; $\lfloor \frac{y}{100} \rfloor$ is subtracted because the century years are not leap years unless they are divisible by 4. That last condition explains why $\lfloor \frac{y}{400} \rfloor$ is added. The d at the beginning and the 2 at the end make the formula begin at the right place. Only the terms involving m cannot be directly explained. They are found by trial and error and account for the different numbers of days in the months.

Additional Answers

16. $b(m) = \begin{cases} 500, \text{ for } 5000 \le m < 25{,}000 \\ 1000, \text{ for } 25{,}000 \le m < 40{,}000 \\ 2000, \text{ for } 40{,}000 \le m \end{cases}$

13. Write an expression for the number of tickets left over, if any, after each graduate gets his or her tickets. $750 - g\lfloor \frac{750}{g} \rfloor$

14. A used-car salesperson is paid $350 per week plus a commission of $100 for each $1500 in sales during the week.
   a. Find the salesperson's salary during a week in which he or she had $3500 in sales. $550
   b. When the person has d dollars in sales, write an equation that gives the weekly earnings E. $E = 350 + 100 \cdot \lfloor \frac{d}{1500} \rfloor$
   c. Is it possible for the salesperson to earn exactly $1000 a week? Why or why not?

14c. No; He can only earn $350 + 100n$ for integers n, so he could earn $950 or $1050.

15. The table at the right shows the typical fees charged by the postal service for its COD (collect on delivery) service as a function of the amount of money to be collected from the recipient (as of 2008).
   a. Can these data be modeled by a step function? yes
   b. **Fill in the Blank** Complete the following piecewise definition of a function that gives the COD fee $F(a)$ (in dollars) as a function of the amount a (in dollars) to be collected.

$$F(a) = \begin{cases} 5.10, \text{ if } a \le 50 \\ \underline{\ ?\ }, \text{ if } 50 < a \le 1000 \end{cases}$$ $5.10 + 1.15\lceil \frac{a}{100} \rceil$

Amount Collected from Recipient (dollars)	COD Fee (dollars)
0.01 to $50.00	5.10
50.01 to 100.00	6.25
100.01 to 200.00	7.40
200.01 to 300.00	8.55
300.01 to 400.00	9.70
400.01 to 500.00	10.85
500.01 to 600.00	12.00
600.01 to 700.00	13.15
700.01 to 800.00	14.30
800.01 to 900.00	15.45
900.01 to 1000.00	16.60

16. The Fine Furniture Factory pays employees a bonus based on their monthly sales. For sales of $5,000 up to $25,000 the bonus is $500. For sales of $25,000 up to $40,000, the bonus is $1,000. For sales of $40,000 or more, the bonus is $2,000. Write a piecewise linear function to give the bonus b for monthly sales m. See margin.

17. The formula $W = d + 2m + \lfloor \frac{3(m+1)}{5} \rfloor + y + \lfloor \frac{y}{4} \rfloor - \lfloor \frac{y}{100} \rfloor + \lfloor \frac{y}{400} \rfloor + 2$ gives the day of the week based on our current calendar where d = the day of the month of the given date; m = the number of the month in the year with January and February regarded as the 13th and 14th months of the previous year; that is, 2/22/90 is 14/22/89. The other months are numbered 3 to 12 as usual; and y = the year as a 4-digit number. Once W is computed, divide by 7 and the remainder is the day of the week, with Saturday = 0, Sunday = 1, ..., Friday = 6. Enter the formula into a spreadsheet to answer the questions.
   a. On what day of the week were you born? Answers vary. Sample: Monday
   b. On what day of the week was the Declaration of Independence adopted? Thursday
   c. On what day of the week was January 1, 2001, the first day of the current millennium? Monday

REVIEW

18. **Multiple Choice** Which of the following is *not* an arithmetic sequence? (Lesson 3-8) C

A $a_n = 3 - 7n$

B $b_n = n + n$

C $\begin{cases} c_1 = 1 \\ c_2 = 5 \\ c_n = c_{n-1} + c_{n-2}, \text{ for } n \geq 3 \end{cases}$

D $\begin{cases} d_1 = 1 \\ d_2 = 5 \\ d_n = d_{n-1} + 4, \text{ for } n \geq 3 \end{cases}$

E $\begin{cases} e_1 = -6 \\ e_n = e_{n-1} + 4, \text{ for } n \geq 2 \end{cases}$

19. Consider the arithmetic sequence $\sqrt{2}, \sqrt{2} + 2\sqrt{3}, \sqrt{2} + 4\sqrt{3}, \sqrt{2} + 6\sqrt{3}, \ldots$. (Lesson 3-8)
    a. Write a recursive definition of the sequence. See margin.
    b. Write an explicit formula for the *n*th term of the sequence.
    c. Find the 101st term of the sequence.

20. The table at the right shows the number of voters (in thousands) that voted in each of the presidential elections in the United States from 1980 to 2004. (Lesson 3-5)
    a. Find an equation for the regression line for these data.
    b. According to the answer in Part a, what would be the predicted voter turnout in 2008?
    c. What is the slope of the line you found in Part a? Name a real-life factor that may influence this slope.

21. A line passes through the points (2, 2) and (0, -3). (Lesson 3-4)
    a. Find an equation for this line in point-slope form using the point (2, 2). $y - 2 = 2.5(x - 2)$
    b. Find an equation for this line in point-slope form using the point (0, -3). $y + 3 = 2.5x$
    c. Verify that your equations from Parts a and b are equivalent. $y = 2.5(x - 2) + 2 = 2.5x - 5 + 2 = 2.5x - 3$

EXPLORATION

22. a. Solve the equation $\left\lfloor \frac{x}{2} \right\rfloor = \frac{x}{2}$. $x = 2m$, for some integer m
    b. Generalize Part a to solve $\left\lfloor \frac{x}{n} \right\rfloor = \frac{x}{n}$. $x = nm$, for some integer m

19b. $a_n = \sqrt{2} + 2\sqrt{3}(n - 1)$

19c. $\sqrt{2} + 200\sqrt{3}$

Year	Voters (thousands)
1980	86,515
1984	92,652
1988	91,594
1992	104,405
1996	96,456
2000	105,586
2004	122,294

20a. $y \approx 1232.74x - 2{,}355{,}691$

20b. about 119,653 thousand

20c. $\approx 1232.74 \frac{\text{thousand voters}}{\text{year}}$ Answers vary. Sample: population growth or a change in minimum voting age

QY ANSWERS

1. Answers vary. Sample: floor(x); ceiling(x)
2. $32.90

Notes on the Questions

Question 22 Students are often surprised at the solutions to these sentences. They provide a way to describe some common sets of numbers that is quite different from the usual way involving multiples.

4 Wrap-Up

Ongoing Assessment

Have students work in groups of three or more. Taking turns, one student selects the rounding-up function or the rounding-down function, a second student selects a positive or negative decimal value, and all the students in the group find the selected function of the selected number. Then students check each other's work and repeat the activity.
Answers vary. Check students' work.

Additional Answers

19a. $\begin{cases} a_1 = \sqrt{2} \\ a_n = a_{n-1} + 2\sqrt{3}, \text{ for } n \geq 2 \end{cases}$

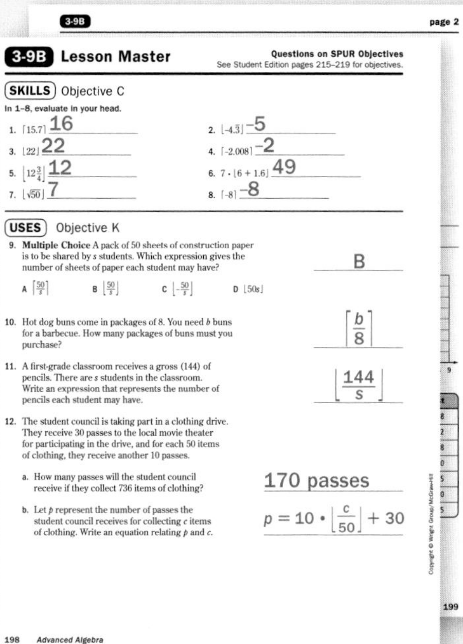

3-9B page 2

3-9B Lesson Master

Questions on SPUR Objectives
See Student Edition pages 215–219 for objectives.

SKILLS Objective C

In 1–8, evaluate in your head.

1. $\lceil 15.7 \rceil$ 16
2. $\lfloor -4.\overline{3} \rfloor$ −5
3. $\lfloor 22 \rfloor$ 22
4. $\lceil -2.008 \rceil$ −2
5. $\lfloor 12\frac{3}{4} \rfloor$ 12
6. $7 \cdot \lfloor 6 + 1.6 \rfloor$ 49
7. $\lfloor \sqrt{50} \rfloor$ 7
8. $\lceil -8 \rceil$ −8

USES Objective K

9. **Multiple Choice** A pack of 50 sheets of construction paper is to be shared by *s* students. Which expression gives the number of sheets of paper each student may have? B

A $\left\lceil \frac{50}{s} \right\rceil$ B $\left\lfloor \frac{50}{s} \right\rfloor$ C $\left\lfloor -\frac{50}{s} \right\rfloor$ D $\lfloor 50s \rfloor$

10. Hot dog buns come in packages of 8. You need *b* buns for a barbecue. How many packages of buns must you purchase? $\left\lceil \frac{b}{8} \right\rceil$

11. A first-grade classroom receives a gross (144) of pencils. There are *s* students in the classroom. Write an expression that represents the number of pencils each student may have. $\left\lfloor \frac{144}{s} \right\rfloor$

12. The student council is taking part in a clothing drive. They receive 30 passes to the local movie theater for participating in the drive, and for each 50 items of clothing, they receive another 10 passes.
    a. How many passes will the student council receive if they collect 736 items of clothing? 170 passes
    b. Let *p* represent the number of passes the student council receives for collecting *c* items of clothing. Write an equation relating *p* and *c*. $p = 10 \cdot \left\lfloor \frac{c}{50} \right\rfloor + 30$

198 *Advanced Algebra*

199

Chapter 3

The projects relate to the content of the lessons of this chapter as follows:

Project	Lesson(s)
1	3-5
2	3-4
3	3-2
4	3-8
5	3-5

1 Residual Squares

Ask students to find an Internet site that calculates a regression line from a given set of ordered pairs. Does the regression line agree with the line that minimizes the sum of squares as shown on the CAS?

2 Penalties for Speeding

As an extension of this project, ask students if their state or province includes "points" with speeding tickets. After what number of points does a driver lose his or her license?

Chapter 3 Projects

1 Residual Squares

A CAS can be used to illustrate why the line of best fit is sometimes called the *least squares line.*

a. The decompression-time data from Lesson 3-5 are given in the table below. Use a graphing utility to create a scatterplot of the data. Add a movable line and adjust it until you think it is the line of best fit. Record the equation of your line.

Time Spent at a Maximum Depth of 60 Feet (min)	Decompression Time Needed (min)
60	1
70	3
80	8
100	15
120	27
140	40
160	49
180	57
200	71
240	82

b. Show the residual squares on your plot. Some graphing utilities will show the sum of the squares on the screen. Continue to adjust your line until you think you have minimized the sum of the squares. Record the equation of this adjusted line.

c. Remove your movable line and add a regression line to the plot. Record the equation of the regression line. Compare it to your equations from Parts a and b. Were you able to make a closer estimate to the regression line by using the residual squares?

2 Penalties for Speeding

States in the United States have speed limits for motor vehicles traveling on public roadways. States use point systems to penalize drivers who speed and to identify repeat offenders. In general, the number of points you receive is a function of the amount that your speed exceeds the legal speed limit. In some states these functions are linear functions; in other states they are piecewise linear.

a. Find out what the point penalties are for speeding (in a car or a truck) in your state. Describe the point-penalty function using a table and a graph. What are the domain and range of this function? Does this function belong to any of the categories of functions you have studied in this course? If so, what kind of function is it? If possible, find an equation for the point-penalty function.

b. Find a state that has a different set of point penalties for speeding than your state. Describe those fines with a table, graph, and equation. Describe some ways the two point-penalty functions are alike and the ways they are different.

Project Rubric

Advanced	Student correctly provides all of the details asked for in the project as well as additional correct independent conclusions.
Proficient	Student correctly provides all of the details asked for in the project.
Partially proficient	Student correctly provides some of the details asked for in the project or provides all details with some inaccuracies.
Not proficient	Student correctly provides few of the details asked for in the project or provides all details with many inaccuracies.
No attempt	Student makes little or no attempt to complete the project.

3 Linear Combinations

In the sport of Rugby, different point values are awarded for various actions. A *try* is worth 5 points and allows for a follow-up kick through two uprights worth an additional 2 points (called *converting a try*, or a *conversion*). Teams may also attempt to drop kick the ball through the uprights without having scored a try. A successful drop kick (a *dropped goal*) is worth 3 points. So a Rugby team may score 3, 5, 6, etc., points, but cannot score 1, 2, 4, etc., points.

a. What is the largest number of points that a Rugby team cannot score? Explain how you got your answer. (*Hint:* The number of conversions must always be equal to or less than the number of tries.)

b. Imagine you are creating your own sport with its own scoring system. A team achieves x points for scoring with their hands, and y points for scoring with their feet. If x and y have no common factors, what is the greatest number of points a team cannot score? Explain how you got your answer.

4 A Graphical Investigation

Graphs of equations of the form $Ax + By = C$, where A, B, and C are consecutive terms in an arithmetic sequence, have something in common.

a. Graph five equations of this type, such as the following:

$$x + 2y = 3$$
$$3x + 5y = 7$$
$$8x + 6y = 4$$
$$-2x - 3y = -4$$
$$3x - y = -5.$$

b. Make a conjecture based on these five graphs.

c. Test your conjecture with a few more graphs.

d. Use the definitions or theorems about arithmetic sequences to verify your conjecture.

5 Time Series Data

When the value of a dependent variable changes over time, like daily temperatures and world population, the data are called *time-series data*.

a. Find an example of time-series data in which the dependent variable appears to vary linearly with time. Make a scatterplot of the data.

b. Use a computer or calculator to find a line of best fit and draw it on the graph with the scatterplot.

c. According to your model, what will the value of the variable be in the year 2025, 2075, 3000, and 3050? Do your predictions seem reasonable? Why or why not?

Notes

3 Linear Combinations

As an extension, ask students to consider the greatest number of points not possible if there are three methods of scoring, each awarding different numbers of points.

4 A Graphical Investigation

Encourage students to include descriptions of which arithmetic sequence is represented by the consecutive terms, how they tested their conjectures, and how they verified any conjectures. Such notes can help them describe their projects to others.

5 Time Series Data

As an extension, ask students to find time-series data that repeat over a year, such as temperature data or data on retail sales. Ask students to explain how they could compare several years of that kind of data.

Sample answers for projects are in the Solution Manual in the Electronic Teacher's Edition.

Chapter 3

Summary and Vocabulary

The Summary gives an overview of the entire chapter and provides an opportunity for students to consider the material as a whole. Thus, the Summary can be used to help students relate and unify the concepts presented in the chapter.

Vocabulary words and symbols are listed by lesson to provide a checklist of concepts that students must know. Emphasize to students that they should read the vocabulary list carefully before starting the Self-Test on pages 213–214. If students do not understand the meaning of a vocabulary word, they should refer back to the indicated lesson.

Theorems and Properties covered in the chapter are listed below the Summary with page references included to lead students back to the location in the chapter where the theorem or property is stated.

Chapter 3 Summary and Vocabulary

- A **linear equation** is one that is equivalent to an equation of the form $Ax + By = C$, where A and B are not both zero. The graph of every linear equation is a line. If the line is not vertical, then its equation represents a linear function and can be put into the **slope-intercept form** $y = mx + b$, where m is its slope and b is its ***y*-intercept**. Horizontal lines have slope 0 and equations of the form $y = b$. Slope is not defined for vertical lines, which have equations of the form $x = a$. In these last three forms, m, b, and a can be any real numbers.
- If the slope m and one point (x_1, y_1) on a line are known, then an equation for the line is $y - y_1 = m(x - x_1)$, or $y = m(x - x_1) + y_1$.
- In many real-world situations, a set of data points is roughly linear. In such cases, a regression or least squares line, **the line of best fit**, can be used to describe the data and make predictions.
- Linear equations can model two basic kinds of real-world situations: constant increase or decrease, and **linear combinations**. The graph of a constant-increase or constant-decrease situation is a line, with the slope of the line representing the constant change and the y-intercept representing the initial condition.
- Sequences with a constant difference between terms are called **linear** or **arithmetic sequences**. If a_n is the nth term of an arithmetic sequence with constant difference d, then the sequence can be described explicitly as $a_n = a_1 + (n - 1)d$, for integers $n \geq 1$, or recursively as $\begin{cases} a_1 \\ a_n = a_{n-1} + d \end{cases}$, for integers $n \geq 2$.
- A function whose graph is the union of segments or rays is called **piecewise linear**. **Step functions** are instances of piecewise linear functions. Step functions represent situations in which rates are constant for a while but change to a different constant rate at known points.

Theorems

Parallel Lines and Slope Theorem (p. 158)
Standard Form of an Equation of a Line Theorem (p. 167)
Point-Slope Theorem (p. 174)
*n*th Term of an Arithmetic Sequence Theorem (p. 201)
Constant-Difference Sequence Theorem (p. 202)

Vocabulary

Lesson 3-1
y-intercept
*linear function
*slope-intercept form
x-intercept

Lesson 3-2
*linear combination
*standard form

Lesson 3-4
*point-slope form
piecewise linear

Lesson 3-5
linear regression
least-squares line, regression line, line of best fit
deviation

Lesson 3-6
*recursive formula
recursive definition

Lesson 3-7
Fibonacci sequence

Lesson 3-8
linear sequence, *arithmetic sequence

Lesson 3-9
*step function
floor symbol $\lfloor\ \rfloor$
ceiling symbol $\lceil\ \rceil$
*floor function, greatest-integer function, rounding-down function, int function
ceiling function, rounding-up function

Chapter 3 Self-Test

Take this test as you would take a test in class. Then use the Selected Answers section in the back of the book to check your work.

1–13. See margin.

1. Graph the line with equation $y = \frac{1}{2}x - 3$.

2. Consider the line with equation $5x - 3y = 10$.
   a. What is its slope?
   b. What are its *x*- and *y*-intercepts?

3. If $m < 0$, does the equation $y = mx + b$ model a constant-increase or a constant-decrease situation?

4. Write an equation for the line graphed below.

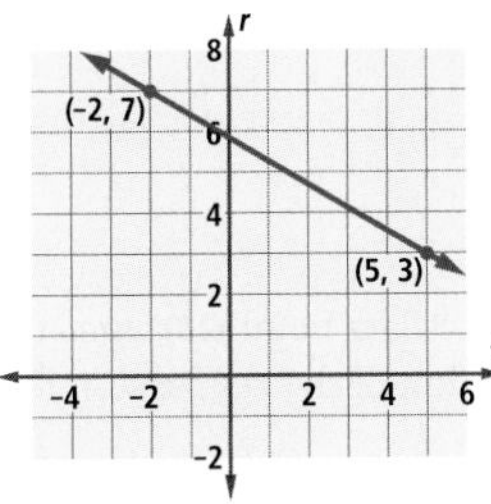

5. Write an equation for the line parallel to $y = -\frac{2}{3}x - 7$ that contains (-6, 3).

6. a. Slope is undefined for which type of line?
   b. Which type of line has a slope of zero?

7. A restaurant sells hot dogs for $2.25 and tacos for $3.75. Write an expression that gives the amount of money the restaurant takes in by selling *H* hot dogs and *T* tacos.

8. A crane lowers a 500-pound load from the top of a 310-foot tall building at the rate of 20 feet per minute. Write a formula for the height *h* of the load above the ground after *t* seconds.

9. Consider the sequence defined by $a_n = 50 - 3(n - 1)$.
   a. Is this an explicit or recursive formula for the sequence? Explain your answer.
   b. Write the sequence's first five terms.
   c. Is the sequence arithmetic? Explain your answer.

10. A cell-phone plan costs $23.50 a month for the first 200 minutes of calls, plus 8 cents per minute for all calls after that.
    a. In July, Michelle's calls total 453 minutes. How much will she be charged?
    b. Write an equation for the piecewise linear function that gives the monthly cost *C* in terms of the minutes *m* spent on the phone.

11. The Lucas sequence *L* begins with the terms 1 and 3. After that, each term is the sum of the two preceding terms. The first six Lucas numbers are 1, 3, 4, 7, 11, and 18.
    a. Write the next four Lucas numbers.
    b. Let L_n be the *n*th Lucas number. Write a recursive formula for the Lucas sequence *L*.

12. Temperature *F* in degrees Fahrenheit and temperature *K* in kelvins are related by a linear equation. Two pairs of corresponding temperatures are 32°F = 273.2 kelvins and 90°F = 305.4 kelvins. Write a linear equation relating *F* and *K*, and solve for *K*.

13. Write an explicit formula for the arithmetic sequence -25, -45, -65, -85, ...

Additional Answers

1.

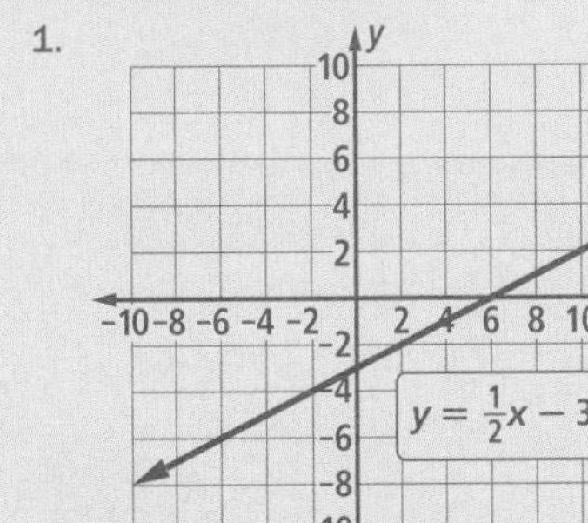

2a. $\frac{5}{3}$, because $-3y = 10 - 5x$, $y = -\frac{10}{3} + \frac{5}{3}x$

2b. *x*-intercept: 2, *y*-intercept: $-\frac{10}{3}$; $5x - 3(0) = 10$, $x = 2$; $5(0) - 3y = 10$, $y = -\frac{10}{3}$

3. constant decrease; as the *x*-value increases, the *y*-value decreases.

4. $m = \frac{7-3}{-2-5} = -\frac{4}{7}$, so an equation in point-slope form is $y - 7 = -\frac{4}{7}(x + 2)$.

5. The line will have the same slope, $-\frac{2}{3}$. Use point-slope form: $y - 3 = -\frac{2}{3}(x + 6)$.

Chapter 3 Self-Test

Self-Test

For the development of mathematical competence, feedback and correction, along with the opportunity for practice, are necessary. The Self-Test provides the opportunity for feedback and correction; the Chapter Review provides additional opportunities for practice. We cannot overemphasize the importance of these end-of-chapter materials. It is at this point that the material gels for many students, allowing them to solidify skills and understanding. In general, student performance should improve after these pages.

Assign the Self-Test as a one-night assignment. Worked-out solutions for all questions are in the Selected Answers section of the student book. Encourage students to take the Self-Test honestly, grade themselves, and then be prepared to discuss the test in class.

Advise students to pay special attention to those Chapter Review questions (pages 215–219) that correspond to the questions they missed on the Self-Test.

Additional Answers

6a. vertical lines, division by zero is undefined

6b. horizontal lines, there is no vertical change

7. *H* hot dogs cost 2.25*H*, and *T* tacos cost 3.75*T*, so the total amount is $2.25H + 3.75T$

8. The constant change is $-\frac{1}{3}$, and the initial condition is 310; $h = 310 - \frac{1}{3}t$

9a. Explicit; you can find the value of a_n directly by plugging in the value of *n*.

9b. $a_1 = 50 - 3(1 - 1) = 50$
$a_2 = 50 - 3(2 - 1) = 47$
$a_3 = 50 - 3(3 - 1) = 44$
$a_4 = 50 - 3(4 - 1) = 41$
$a_5 = 50 - 3(5 - 1) = 38$

9c. Yes; there is a constant difference of 3 between consecutive terms.

10a. $C = 23.50 + 0.8(m - 200)$
$C = 23.50 + 0.8(453 - 200)$
$C = \$43.74$

10b. $C = \begin{cases} 23.50, & 0 \le m \le 200 \\ 23.50 + 0.08(m - 200), & m > 200 \end{cases}$

Chapter 3 Self-Test

Additional Answers

11a. 29, 47, 76, 123 because 11 + 18 = 29, 18 + 29 = 47, 29 + 47 = 76, and 47 + 76 = 123

11b. $\begin{cases} L_1 = 1 \\ L_2 = 3 \\ L_{n+2} = L_n + L_{n+1}, \text{ for } n \geq 1 \end{cases}$

12. $m = \frac{305.4 - 273.2}{90 - 32} = \frac{32.2}{58} = 0.56$

$K - 273.2 = 0.56(F - 32)$

$K - 273.2 = 0.56F - 17.9$

$K = 0.56F + 255.3$

13. $a_n = -25 - 20(n - 1)$ because -20 is the common difference between terms, and -25 is the initial term.

14. B; each piece has a steeper slant than the previous one.

15.

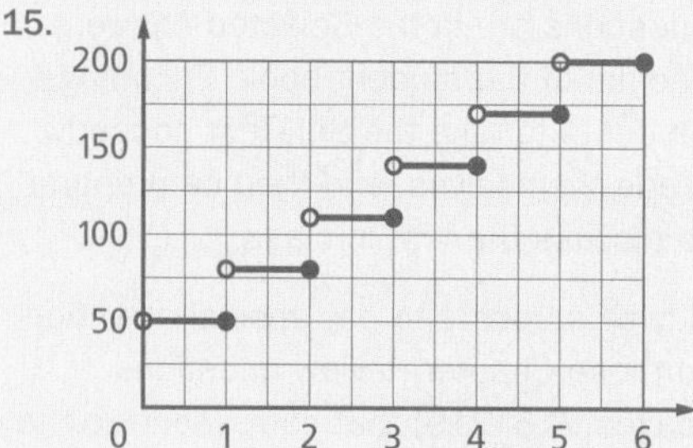

17.

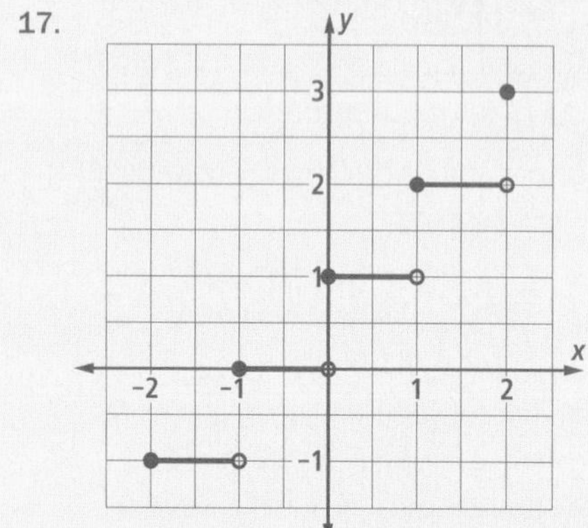

14. **Multiple Choice** Which graph most closely describes a piecewise function where each piece has a slope greater than the previous piece? Explain your response. (The scales on all four sets of axes are the same.) 14–15. See margin.

A

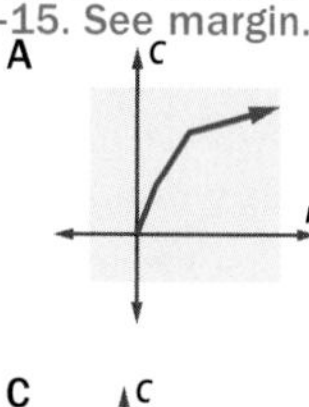

B

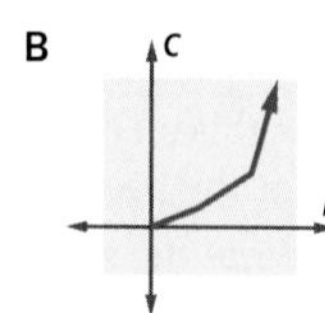

C

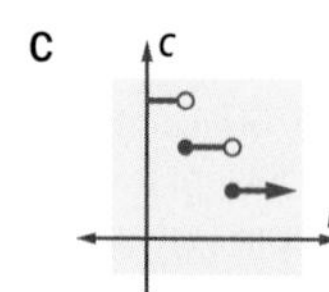

D

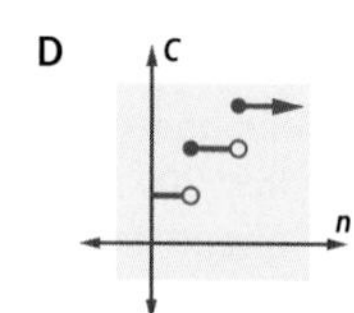

15. Suppose the U.S. Postal Service sought to set the price of mailing a letter weighing 1 ounce or less at 50¢, with each additional ounce or part of an ounce costing an extra 30¢. Graph the function that maps weight w (in ounces) of a letter onto the cost c (in cents) to mail the letter.

16. a. **Multiple Choice** Which equation describes the function in Question 15? D

A $c = 50 - 30\lceil 1 - w \rceil$

B $c = 50 + 30\lceil 1 - w \rceil$

C $c = 50 - 30\lceil w - 1 \rceil$

D $c = 50 + 30\lceil w - 1 \rceil$

b. Find the cost of mailing a 3.2-ounce letter. $c = 0.50 + 0.30\lceil 3.2 - 1 \rceil = \$1.40$

17. Sketch a graph of $y = \lfloor x \rfloor + 1$ for $-2 \leq x \leq 2$. 17–18. See margin.

18. The table and the scatterplot below give the life expectancy in the U.S. at selected ages in 2003.

Age	Expected Years of Life
0	77.4
10	68.1
20	58.4
30	48.9
40	39.5
50	30.5
60	22.2
70	14.8
80	8.9
90	4.8
100	2.5

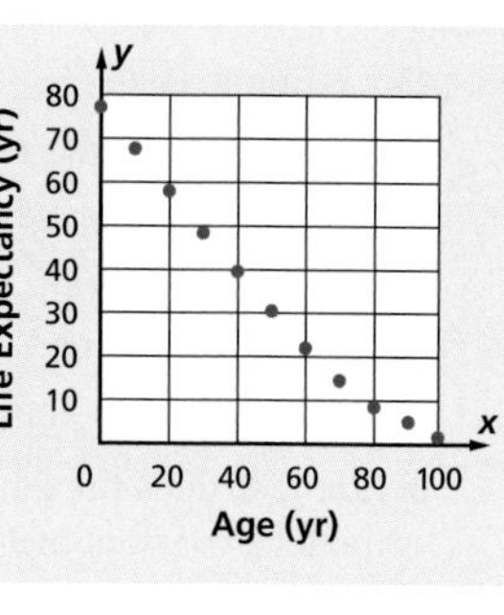

Source: Centers for Disease Control and Prevention

a. Using the data points for ages 0 to 80, find an equation of the regression line.

b. Using your answer to Part a, estimate the life expectancy of someone who is currently 42.

c. Which data point is farthest vertically from the regression line? What does this mean in context?

d. Why is it unreasonable to use a linear model for ages over 80?

Additional Answers

18a. $y \approx -0.875x + 75.9$

18b. $y \approx -0.875(42) + 75.9 \approx 39.2$

18c. (80, 8.9); it means that the regression line gives a less accurate prediction for an 80-year-old.

18d. Answers vary. Sample: People who are ages 80–100 have many more health factors affecting their life expectancy than people who are younger.

Chapter 3 Chapter Review

SKILLS
PROPERTIES
USES
REPRESENTATIONS

SKILLS Procedures used to get answers

OBJECTIVE A Determine the slope and intercepts of a line given its equation. (Lessons 3-1, 3-3)

In 1–6, an equation for a line is given.

a. Give its slope.
b. Give its x-intercept.
c. Give its y-intercept.

1. a. 3 b. 4 c. -12
2. a. $\frac{5}{4}$ b. $-\frac{6}{5}$ c. $\frac{3}{2}$

1. $y = 3x - 12$
2. $4y = 6 + 5x$
3. $y = -17$ See margin.
4. $x = 8$ See margin.
5. $300x - 250y = -100$ a. $\frac{6}{5}$ b. $-\frac{1}{3}$ c. $\frac{2}{5}$
6. $x + y = 1.46$ a. -1 b. 1.46 c. 1.46

OBJECTIVE B Find an equation of a line given two points on it or given a point on it and its slope. (Lesson 3-4)

In 7–10, find an equation of the line satisfying the given conditions.

7. The line has a slope of $\frac{2}{5}$ and contains (-5, 10). $y - 10 = \frac{2}{5}(x + 5)$
8. The line contains the point (8, 2) and goes through the origin. $y = \frac{1}{4}x$
9. The line contains the points (-3, 4) and (5, -4). $y = -(x + 3) + 4$, or $y = -x + 1$
10. The line is parallel to $y = 6x - 1$ and contains the point (7, 1). $y = 6(x - 7) + 1$, or $y = 6x - 41$

OBJECTIVE C Evaluate expressions based on step functions. (Lesson 3-9)

In 11–13, evaluate the expression.

11. a. $\lfloor 13.5 \rfloor$ 13 b. $\lceil -13.5 \rceil$ -13
12. a. $\lfloor x - 0.4 \rfloor$ when $x = 3.6$ 3
    b. $\lceil x + 0.4 \rceil$ when $x = 3.6$ 4
13. $4\lfloor 2n + 1.4 \rfloor$ when $n = 0.4$ 8

OBJECTIVE D Evaluate or find explicit and recursive formulas for sequences. (Lessons 3-6, 3-8)

In 14 and 15, an arithmetic (linear) sequence is given. For the sequence:

a. find an explicit formula.
b. write a recursive formula.
c. find the fourth through the eighth terms.

14. -2, 1, 4, ...
15. 37, 16, -5, ...

14.–17. See margin.

16. Write a recursive definition of the sequence whose *n*th term is $a_n = -4n + 15$.
17. Use this recursively-defined sequence.
$$\begin{cases} a_1 = -\frac{2}{3} \\ a_n = a_{n-1} + \frac{1}{4} \text{ for integers } n \geq 2 \end{cases}$$
    a. Write an explicit formula for the *n*th term of this sequence.
    b. Generate the first five terms.

PROPERTIES Principles behind the mathematics

OBJECTIVE E Recognize properties of linear functions. (Lessons 3-1, 3-2, 3-3)

18. **Multiple Choice** Which of the following does *not* mean a line has a slope of $-\frac{2}{3}$? C
    A It has a vertical change of $\frac{2}{3}$ unit for a horizontal change of -1 unit.
    B It has the equation $y = -\frac{2}{3}x + 5$.
    C It has the equation $2x - 3y = 7$.
    D It is parallel to the line with equation $2x + 3y = 7$.

Additional Answers

3a. 0
3b. no x-intercept
3c. -17
4a. undefined
4b. 8
4c. no y-intercept
14a. $a_n = -2 + (n - 1)3 = 3n - 5$, for integers $n \geq 1$
14b. $\begin{cases} a_1 = -2 \\ a_n = a_{n-1} + 3, \text{ for integers } n \geq 2 \end{cases}$
14c. 7, 10, 13, 16, 19
15a. $a_n = 37 + (n - 1)(-21) = -21n + 58$, for integers $n \geq 1$
15b. $\begin{cases} a_1 = 37 \\ a_n = a_{n-1} - 21, \text{ for integers } n \geq 2 \end{cases}$
15c. -26, -47, -68, -89, -110
16. $\begin{cases} a_1 = 11 \\ a_n = a_{n-1} - 4, \text{ for integers } n \geq 2 \end{cases}$
17a. $a_n = \frac{-11}{12} + \frac{n}{4}$, for integers $n \geq 1$
17b. $-\frac{2}{1}, -\frac{5}{12}, -\frac{1}{6}, \frac{1}{12}, \frac{1}{3}$

Chapter Review

The main objectives for the chapter are organized in the Chapter Review under the four types of understanding this book promotes: Skills, Properties, Uses, and Representations.

Whereas end-of-chapter material may be considered optional in some texts, in UCSMP *Advanced Algebra* we have selected these objectives and questions with the expectation that they will be covered. Students should be able to answer these questions with about 85% accuracy after studying the chapter.

You may assign these questions over a single night to help students prepare for a test the next day or you may assign the questions over a two-day period. If you work the questions over two days, we recommend assigning the evens for homework the first night so that students get feedback in class the next day, and then assigning the odds the night before the test because the answers are provided to the odd-numbered questions in the Selected Answers section at the back of the book.

It is effective to ask students which questions they still do not understand and use the day as a total class discussion of the material that the class finds most difficult.

Resources

- Assessment Resources: Chapter 3 Test Forms A–D; Chapter 3 Test, Cumulative Form; Comprehensive Test, Chapters 1–3

Technology Resources

Teacher's Assessment Assistant, Ch. 3
Electronic Teacher's Edition, Ch. 3

Additional Answers

20. Vertical lines are not functions; thus the equation does not represent a function for $B = 0$.

24. a sequence with a constant difference between terms

19. **True or False** Two lines in a plane are parallel if they have equal slopes. true

20. Consider $Ax + By = C$. For what values of A and B does this equation not represent a function? Explain your response. See margin.

21. What is the x-intercept of $y = mx + b$? $-\frac{b}{m}$

22. **Multiple Choice** Three points A, B, and C are on a line with B between A and C and $AB = 3(BC)$. The slope determined by B and C C
    - A is 3 times the slope determined by A and B.
    - B is $\frac{1}{3}$ the slope determined by A and B.
    - C equals the slope determined by A and B.
    - D None of the above is true.

23. Suppose a line has slope $-\frac{3}{4}$. Then if (x, y) is a point on the line, name another point on the line. Answers vary. Sample: $(x + 4, y - 3)$

OBJECTIVE F Recognize properties of linear or arithmetic sequences. (Lesson 3-8)

24. What is a linear sequence? See margin.

25. Describe the graph of an arithmetic sequence. It is a set of collinear points.

In 26 and 27, tell whether the numbers could be the first four terms of an arithmetic sequence.

26. -4, -6, -8, -10 yes

27. 3, 4, 6, 9 no

In 28 and 29, does the formula generate an arithmetic sequence?

28. $\begin{cases} a_1 = 3 \\ a_n = \frac{1}{2}a_{n-1} - 1, \text{ for integers } n \geq 2 \end{cases}$ no

29. $\begin{cases} a_1 = 3 \\ a_{n+1} = a_n - 5, \text{ for integers } n \geq 1 \end{cases}$ yes

30. Find the nth term of a linear sequence whose 1st term is 11 and whose constant difference is -4. $a_n = -4n + 15$ for integers $n \geq 1$

31. If the 10th term of an arithmetic sequence is 8 and the 20th term is 16, what is the first term? 0.8

USES Applications of mathematics in real-world situations

OBJECTIVE G Model constant-increase or constant-decrease situations or situations involving arithmetic sequences. (Lessons 3-1, 3-8)

32. A truck weighs 2000 kg when empty. It is loaded with crates of oranges weighing 17 kg each. a. $w = 17c + 2000$
    a. Write an equation relating the total weight w and the number c of crates.
    b. Find the weight when there are 112 crates in the truck. $w = 3904$ kg

33. On his way to work, Rusty drives over a nail that punctures his tire. The tire begins to lose pressure at about 2 pounds per square inch (psi) per hour.
    a. If Rusty's tire had 44 psi of pressure before the puncture, write an equation to show how much pressure p the tire has after t hours. $p = 44 - 2t$
    b. In order to drive safely, the tire must have at least 26 psi of pressure. How long can Rusty wait to replace his tire? 9 hours

OBJECTIVE H Model linear combination situations. (Lesson 3-2)

34. A crate contains grapefruits and oranges. On average, an orange weighs 0.3 pound and a grapefruit weighs 1.1 pounds. The contents of the crate weigh a total of 30 pounds. Let x be the number of oranges and let y be the number of grapefruits.
    a. Write an equation to model this situation. $30 = 0.3x + 1.1y$
    b. If there are 15 grapefruits in the crate, how many oranges are there? 45

35. A chemist combines A liters of a solution that is 2.5 moles/liter bromic acid with B liters of a solution that is 6.25 moles/liter bromic acid.

a. Write an expression for how many liters of solution there are altogether. $A + B$

b. How many moles of bromic acid are there altogether? $2.5A + 6.25B$

c. The chemist preparing the solution needs a total of 0.75 mole of bromic acid in a solution. Write an equation that describes this situation. $0.75 = 2.5A + 6.25B$

d. List three ordered pairs that are realistic solutions to the equation in Part c. Answers vary. Sample: (0.3, 0), (0, 0.12), (0.25, 0.02)

OBJECTIVE I In a real-world context, find an equation for a line containing two points. (Lesson 3-4)

36. On a trip abroad, Salena buys 7000 Indian rupees for 150 U.S. dollars, and then buys 11,200 Indian rupees for 250 U.S. dollars.

a. Assume a linear relationship exists between the number of Indian rupees and the cost in U.S. dollars. Write an equation representing the relationship. $R = 42D + 700$

b. How much will it cost to buy 20,000 Indian rupees? $459.52

37. Gerald finds that it takes 30 ml of a standard solution to neutralize 12 ml of a solution of unknown concentration. If he starts with 20 ml of the unknown solution, it takes 50 ml of standard solution to neutralize it. Assuming a linear relationship exists between the amount of unknown solution and the amount of standard solution required to neutralize it, how much unknown solution can be neutralized with 175 ml of standard solution? 70 ml

OBJECTIVE J Fit lines to data. (Lesson 3-5)

38. The display below shows the number of tons of sulfur dioxide, a major form of air pollution, in the United States from 1990 to 2002. An equation of the regression line is $y = -652.51x + 23{,}846$, with $x = 1$ in 1990.

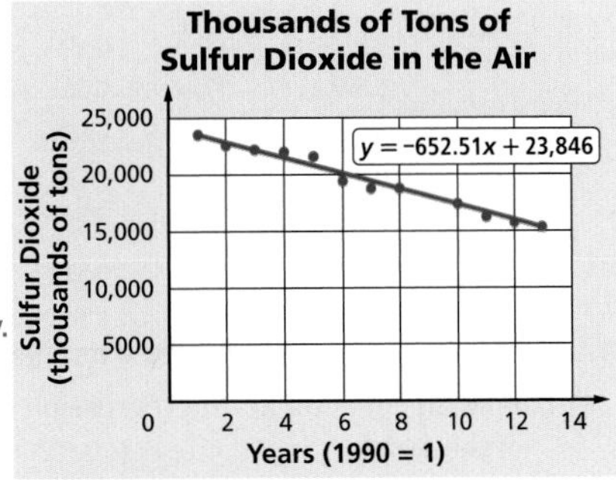

a. What value does the regression equation predict for 1998 (year 9)? 17,973.41 thousand tons

b. The actual value for 1998 is 18,944. What is the difference between the value predicted by the regression equation and the actual value? 971 thousand tons

c. What is the percent decrease from 1990 (23,760,000 tons) to 2002 (15,353,000 tons)? 35.4% decrease

d. If this linear trend continued, what would have been the approximate number of tons of sulfur dioxide in the air in 2006? about 12,753 thousand tons

Additional Answers

39a.

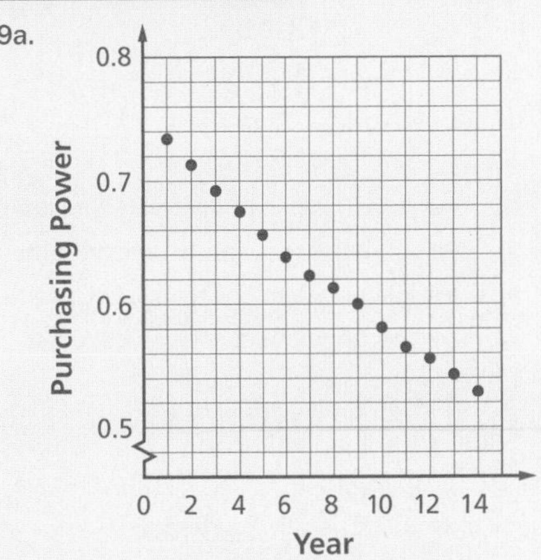

39c. Yes; the decrease in the purchasing power is relatively stable from year to year.

41. $\begin{cases} C = 0.99d, \text{ for } d \le 20 \\ 19.80 + 0.89(d - 20), \text{ for } d > 20 \end{cases}$

Additional Answers

43c. $d = \begin{cases} 3t, \text{ for } t \leq 0.5 \\ 1.5, \text{ for } 0.5 < t \leq 6.5 \\ -3t + 21, \text{ for } 6.5 < t \leq 6.75 \\ 0.75, \text{ for } 6.75 < t \leq 7.5 \\ -3t + 23.25, \text{ for } 7.5 < t \leq 7.75 \end{cases}$

43d. Her speed walking home was the same. We can use the graph to calculate the rate of change of d with respect to t to see this. In both cases she walked at 3 mph.

44. $\begin{cases} c = 39.99, \text{ for } 0 \leq t \leq 450 \\ 39.99 + 0.45\lceil t - 450 \rceil, \text{ for } t > 450 \end{cases}$

45a. $\begin{cases} a_1 = 2300 \\ a_n = a_{n-1} - 26, \text{ for integers } n \geq 1 \end{cases}$

45b. $a_n = 2326 - 26n$ for integers $n \geq 1$

45c. Yes; she will have 246 nuts left at the end of the winter.

46a. $\begin{cases} a_1 = 10 \\ a_{n+1} = 2a_n, \text{ for integers } n \geq 1 \end{cases}$

47.

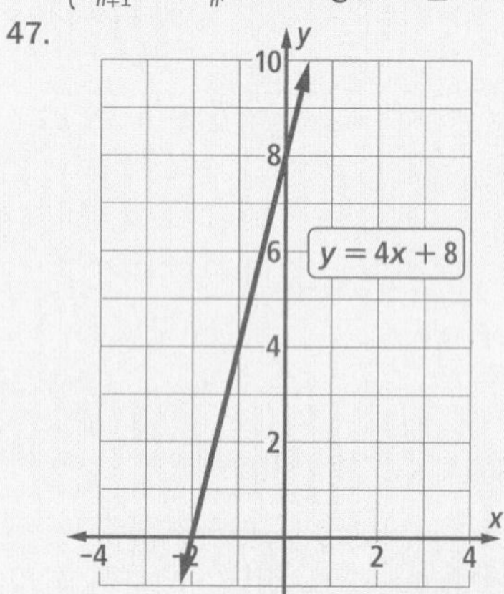

48.

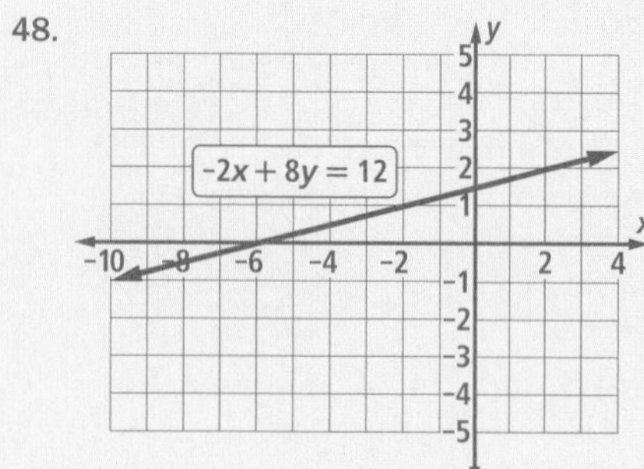

49.

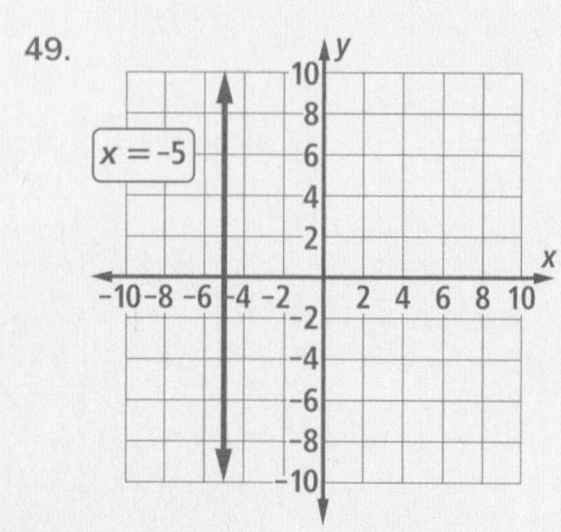

39. The table below gives a measure of the purchasing power of the U.S. dollar from 1991 to 2004. Here year 1 = 1991 and year 14 = 2004.

Year	Purchasing Power	Year	Purchasing Power
1	0.734	8	0.613
2	0.713	9	0.600
3	0.692	10	0.581
4	0.675	11	0.565
5	0.656	12	0.556
6	0.638	13	0.543
7	0.623	14	0.529

a. Make a scatterplot of these data. See margin.

b. Find an equation for the regression line of these data. $y \approx -0.016x + 0.790$

c. Does it appear that a linear equation would be a good model for these data? Explain why or why not. See margin.

OBJECTIVE K Model situations leading to piecewise linear functions or to step functions. (Lessons 3-4, 3-9)

In 40 and 41, an online music service charges 99¢ for each of the first 20 music downloads and then 89¢ for each additional download.

40. Find the total cost for a user who completes

a. 15 downloads. \$14.85

b. 27 downloads. \$26.03

41. Describe the situation with a function mapping the number d of downloads onto the total cost C. See margin.

42. **Multiple Choice** Suppose a salesperson earns a \$50 bonus for each \$1000 in sales that he or she makes. What is a rule for the function that relates sales s to the amount b of bonus? A

A $b = 50 \cdot \left\lfloor \frac{s}{1000} \right\rfloor$

B $b = \left\lfloor \frac{50s}{1000} \right\rfloor$

C $b = 50 + \left\lfloor \frac{s}{1000} \right\rfloor$

D $b = 50 + \left\lfloor \frac{1000}{s} \right\rfloor$

43. The graph below shows Imani's trip directly from home to school. After attending school all day she went to her friend's house where they did their math homework. Then she returned to her house.

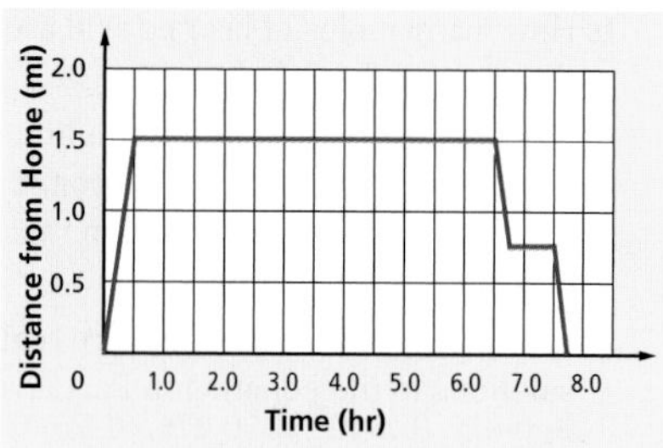

a. At what rate did she walk to school? 3 mph

b. At what rate did she walk to her friend's house? 3 mph

c. Write a piecewise linear function for this graph. 44c and 44d. See margin.

d. Was her speed walking home the same, faster, or slower than her speed walking to school? Explain how you know.

44. A cell-phone plan charges \$39.99 for the first 450 minutes plus \$0.45 for each additional minute or part of a minute. Write an equation to model this situation. See margin.

OBJECTIVE L Model situations with recursive formulas. (Lessons 3-6, 3-7)

45. On the first day of winter, Charo Chipmunk has a pile of 2300 nuts. Each day, she eats 26 nuts. Let a_n be the number of nuts in her pile on day n. See margin.

a. Write a recursive formula for a_n.

b. Write an explicit formula for a_n.

c. The winter typically lasts 80 days. Will Charo's supply of nuts last her through the winter?

Additional Answers

50.

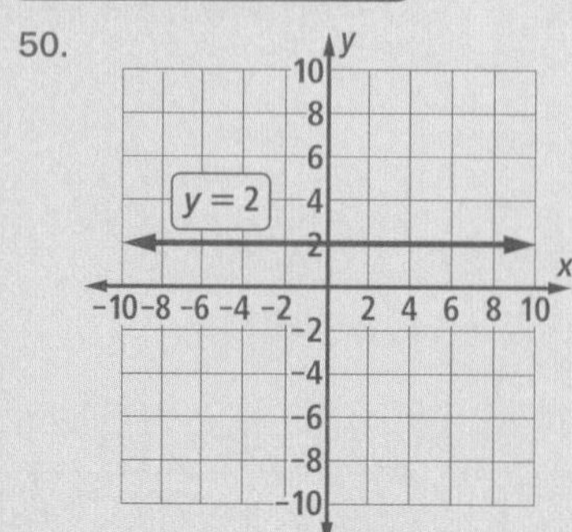

54a.

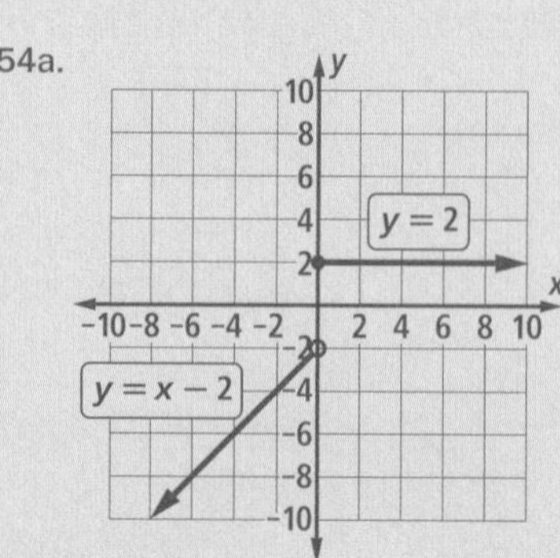

54b. Domain: set of all real numbers; Range: $\{y \mid y < -2 \text{ or } y = 2\}$

55b. Domain: set of all real numbers; range: set of all integers

46. Martin raises emus. The number a_n of emus on Martin's farm in year n is given by the table below.

n	1	2	3	4
a_n	10	20	40	80

a. Assume the doubling pattern in the table continues. Write a recursive formula for a_n. See margin.

b. How many emus should he expect to have in year 10? 5120

REPRESENTATIONS Pictures, graphs, or objects that illustrate concepts

OBJECTIVE M Graph or interpret graphs of linear equations. (Lessons 3-1, 3-3)

47. Graph the line with slope 4 and y-intercept 8. 47–50. See margin.

48. Graph the line $-2x + 8y = 12$ using its intercepts.

49. Graph $x = -5$ in the coordinate plane.

50. Graph $y = 2$ in the coordinate plane.

In 51 and 52, tell whether the slope of the line is positive, negative, zero, or undefined.

51. 52.

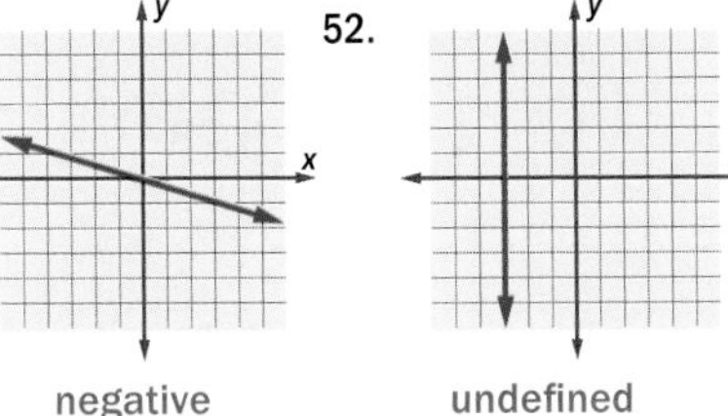

negative undefined

53. What is an equation of the line graphed below? Answers vary. Sample: $y = -\frac{1}{3}x - 1$

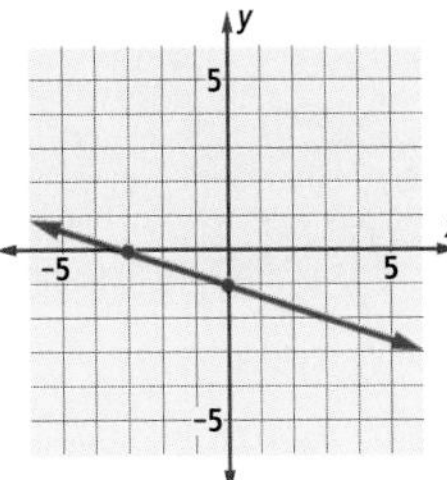

OBJECTIVE N Graph or interpret graphs of piecewise linear functions, step functions, or sequences. (Lessons 3-4, 3-7, 3-9)

54. Consider the function f, where

$$f(x) = \begin{cases} x - 2, \text{ for } x < 0 \\ 2, \text{ for } x \geq 0 \end{cases}.$$ 54–58. See margin.

a. Draw a graph of $y = f(x)$.

b. Find the domain and range of f.

55. a. Graph the function h, where $h(x) = 3 + \lfloor x \rfloor$.

b. Give the domain and range of h.

56. A personal trainer earns a bonus of \$150 for every 2 pounds of weight a client loses. Draw a graph of the bonuses as a function of the number of pounds lost.

57. A graph of the first five terms of an arithmetic sequence is shown at the right. Write an explicit formula for the sequence.

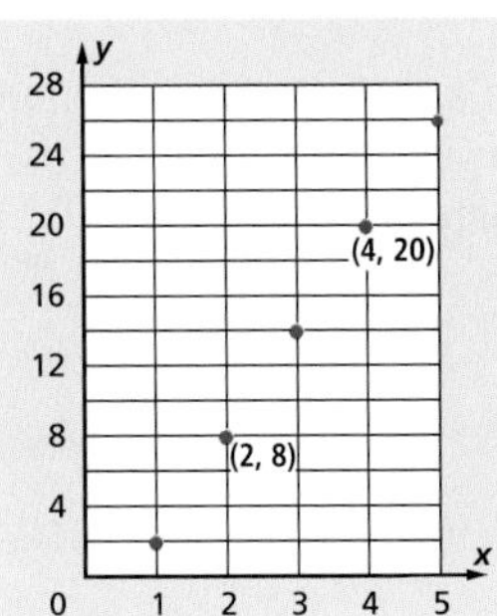

58. Graph this sequence.

$$\begin{cases} a_1 = -5 \\ a_n = a_{n-1} + 3.5, \text{ for integers } n \geq 2 \end{cases}$$

Assessment

Evaluation The *Assessment Resources* provide four forms of the Chapter 3 Test. Forms A and B present parallel versions of a short-answer format. Form C consists of four to six short-response questions that cover the SPUR objectives from Chapter 3. Form D offers performance assessment that covers a subset (or even just one) of the SPUR objectives for the chapter. The fifth type of test is a Chapter 3 Test, Cumulative Form. About 50% of this test covers Chapter 3, and the remaining 50% covers the previous chapters evenly.

Feedback After students have taken the test for Chapter 3 and you have scored the results, return the tests to students for discussion. Class discussion on the questions that caused trouble for most students can be very effective in identifying and clarifying misunderstandings. You might want to have them note the items they missed and work either in groups or at home to correct them. It is important for students to receive feedback on every chapter test, and we recommend that students see and correct their mistakes before proceeding too far into the next chapter.

Suggestions for Assignment Assign Lesson 4-1 for homework the evening of the test. It gives students work to do after they have completed the test and keeps the class moving. If you do not do this, you may cover one less chapter over the course of the year.

Additional Answers

55a.

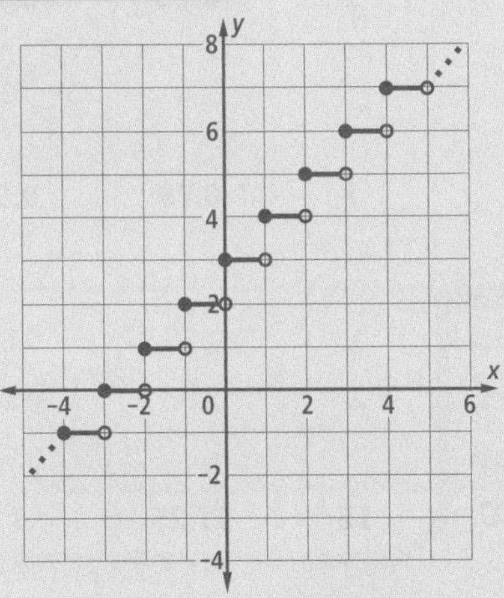

56.

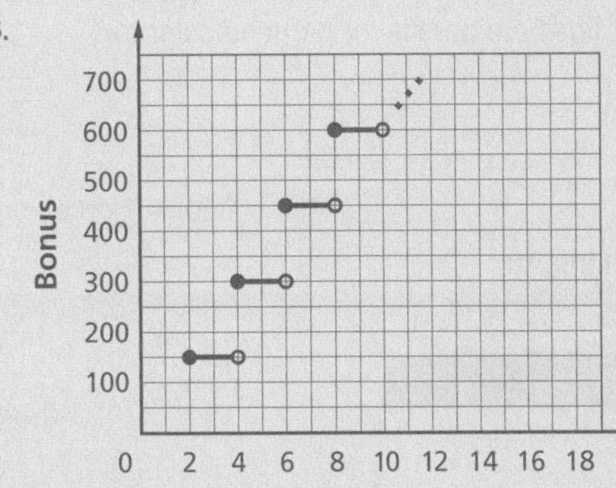

57. $a_n = 6n - 4$

58.

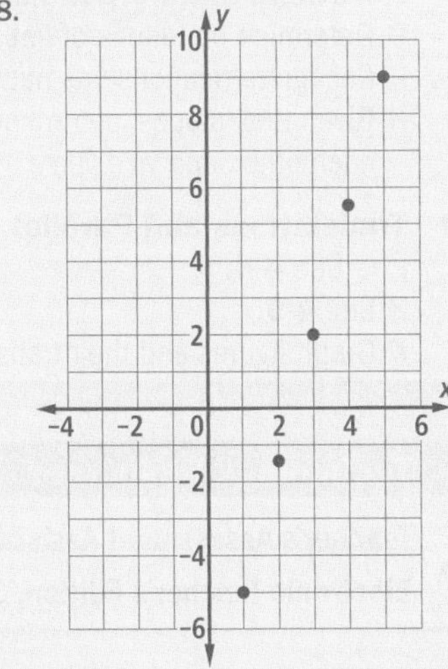

Chapter

4 Matrices

Chapter Overview

		Local Standards	Pacing (in days) Average	Advanced	Block
4-1	**Storing Data in Matrices** **A** Write matrices for points and polygons. **I** Use matrices to store data.		1	0.75	0.5
4-2	**Matrix Addition** **B** Add, subtract, and find scalar multiples of matrices. **E** Recognize properties of matrix operations. **J** Use matrix addition, matrix multiplication, and scalar multiplication to solve real-world problems.		1	0.75	0.5
4-3	**Matrix Multiplication** **C** Multiply matrices. **E, J** See **4-2.**		1	0.75	0.5
	QUIZ 1		0.5	0.5	0.25
4-4	**Matrices for Size Changes** **F** Recognize relationships between figures and their transformation images. **G** Relate transformations to matrices, and vice versa. **K** Graph figures and their transformation images.		1	0.75	0.5
4-5	**Matrices for Scale Changes** **F, G, K** See **4-4.**		1	0.75	0.5
4-6	**Matrices for Reflections** **F, G, K** See **4-4.**		1	0.75	0.5
4-7	**Transformations and Matrices** **E** Recognize properties of matrix operations. **G, K** See **4-4.**		1	0.75	0.5
	QUIZ 2		0.5	0.5	0.25
4-8	**Matrices for Rotations** **F, G, K** See **4-4.**		1	0.75	0.5
4-9	**Rotations and Perpendicular Lines** **D** Determine equations of lines perpendicular to given lines. **F** Recognize relationships between figures and their transformation images. **H** Given their slopes, determine whether lines are parallel or perpendicular to each other, and vice versa.		1	0.75	0.5
4-10	**Translations and Parallel Lines** **F, G** See **4-4.** **H** See **4-9.** **K** Graph figures and their transformation images.		1	0.75	0.5
		Self-Test	1	0.75	0.5
		Chapter Review	2	1	0.5
		Test	1	1	0.5
		TOTAL	15	11.25	7

Technology Resources

Teacher's Assessment Assistant, Ch. 4

Electronic Teacher's Edition, Ch. 4

Differentiated Options  Universal Access

	Accommodating the Learner	Vocabulary Development	Ongoing Assessment	Materials
4-1	pp. 223, 224	p. 224	group, p. 227	matrix polygon application
4-2	pp. 229, 230	p. 229	written, p. 234	CAS
4-3	pp. 236, 237	p. 238	oral, p. 241	CAS or graphing calculator
4-4	pp. 244, 245	p. 244	group, p. 248	graph paper, ruler
4-5	pp. 250, 252	p. 251	group, p. 254	CAS or graphing calculator
4-6	pp. 257, 258	p. 259	oral, p. 261	matrix polygon application
4-7	pp. 264, 265	p. 265	group, p. 268	matrix polygon application
4-8	pp. 271, 272	p. 270	oral, p. 273	tracing paper, protractor
4-9	pp. 276, 278	p. 276	group, p. 279	matrix polygon application
4-10	pp. 283, 284	p. 282	written, p. 285	

Objectives

	Lessons	Self-Test Questions	Chapter Review Questions
Skills			
A Write matrices for points and polygons.	4-1	1	1-2
B Add, subtract, and find scalar multiples of matrices.	4-2	6, 15	3-8
C Multiply matrices.	4-3	4	9-14
D Determine equations of lines perpendicular to given lines.	4-9	9, 23	15-18
Properties			
E Recognize properties of matrix operations	4-2, 4-3, 4-7	3, 5, 7	19-25
F Recognize relationships between figures and their transformation images.	4-4, 4-5, 4-6, 4-8, 4-9, 4-10	11, 20, 21, 22	26-31
G Relate transformations to matrices, and vice versa.	4-4, 4-5, 4-6, 4-7, 4-8, 4-10	10, 15, 16, 17, 19	32-43
H Given their slopes, determine whether lines are parallel or perpendicular to each other, and vice versa.	4-9, 4-10	8	44-48
Uses			
I Use matrices to store data.	4-1	2	49-52
J Use matrix addition, matrix multiplication, and scalar multiplication to solve real-world problems.	4-2, 4-3	13, 14	53-56
Representations			
K Graph figures and their transformation images.	4-4, 4-5, 4-6, 4-7, 4-8, 4-10	11, 12, 18	57-61

Resource Masters Chapter 4

Resource Master 1, Graph Paper (page 2), can be used with Lesson 4-1, 4-4, 4-5, 4-6, 4-7, 4-8, and 4-10.

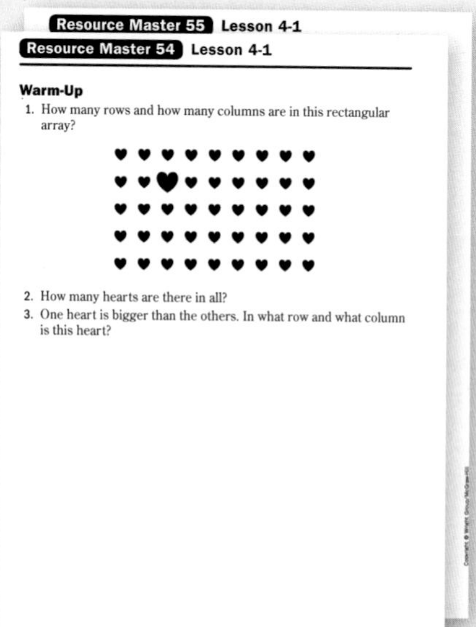

Resource Master 55 Lesson 4-1

Resource Master 54 Lesson 4-1

Warm-Up

1. How many rows and how many columns are in this rectangular array?
2. How many hearts are there in all?
3. One heart is bigger than the others. In what row and what column is this heart?

Resource Masters for Lesson 4-1

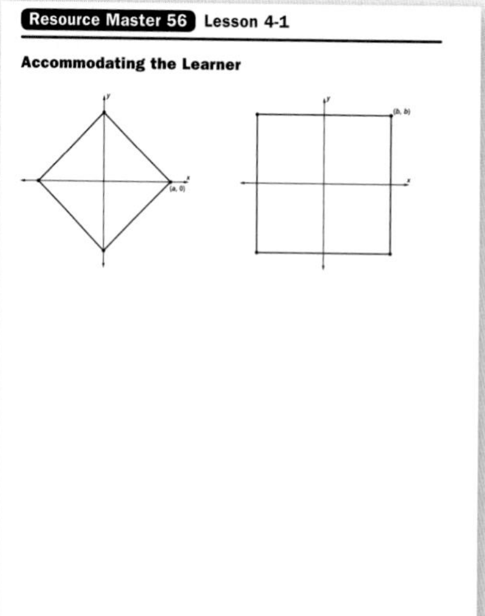

Resource Master 56 Lesson 4-1

Accommodating the Learner

Resource Master for Lesson 4-1

Resource Master 58 Lesson 4-2

Resource Master 57 Lesson 4-2

Warm-Up

Matrices O and N below show the amount of money (in dollars) a household spent in two consecutive months on three utilities.

Oct. electricity, water, gas $\begin{bmatrix} 82 \\ 22 \\ 14 \end{bmatrix} = O$ Nov. electricity, water, gas $\begin{bmatrix} 64 \\ 22 \\ 25 \end{bmatrix} = N$

1. What matrix represents the total expenses for electricity, water, and gas for the two consecutive months?
2. Suppose there is a 5% increase in these costs this year from last year. What would be the costs for utilities in October of this year?

Resource Masters for Lesson 4-2

Resource Master 60 Lesson 4-3

Resource Master 59 Lesson 4-3

Warm-Up

An ounce of ground beef has about 60 calories, a French fry has about 11 calories, and an ounce of yogurt has about 40 calories.

1. If you eat a quarter pound of beef, 20 French fries, and 4 ounces of yogurt, how many calories have you consumed?
2. Write the calculation of Warm-Up 1 as a matrix multiplication.

Additional Examples

1. Use the data on page 235 to write a single expression giving the total price for pizzas at the Pizza Shop for the volleyball team and evaluate it.
2. Let $P = \begin{bmatrix} 5 & -2 \\ 3 & 1 \end{bmatrix}$ and $Q = \begin{bmatrix} 2 & 0 & -3 \\ 4 & 1 & 5 \end{bmatrix}$. Find the product PQ by hand.

Solution P has ______ rows, and Q has ______ columns. So the matrix PQ will have ______ entries.

Use the algorithm for row-by-column multiplication to fill in the missing entries.

$PQ = \begin{bmatrix} 5 \cdot 2 + (-2) \cdot 4 & 5 \cdot 0 + \_\_\_ & \_\_\_ \\ 3 \cdot 2 + 1 \cdot 4 & \_\_\_ + 1 \cdot 1 & \_\_\_ \end{bmatrix}$

$= \begin{bmatrix} 2 & \_\_\_ & \_\_\_ \\ 10 & \_\_\_ & \_\_\_ \end{bmatrix}$

Resource Masters for Lesson 4-3

Resource Master 62 Lesson 4-4

Resource Master 61 Lesson 4-4

Warm-Up

In 1–3, find each product.

1. $\begin{bmatrix} 14 & 0 \\ 0 & 14 \end{bmatrix} \begin{bmatrix} x \\ y \end{bmatrix}$
2. $\begin{bmatrix} -0.5 & 0 \\ 0 & -0.5 \end{bmatrix} \begin{bmatrix} 1 & 5 & 8 \\ 2 & 7 & -2 \end{bmatrix}$
3. $\begin{bmatrix} m & 0 \\ 0 & m \end{bmatrix} \begin{bmatrix} n & 0 \\ 0 & n \end{bmatrix}$

Additional Example

1.

a. What is the magnitude of the size change that maps the preimage $\triangle TRI$ to its image $\triangle T'R'I'$?

b. Write the size change using mapping notation.

Resource Masters for Lesson 4-4

Resource Master 64 Lesson 4-5

Resource Master 63 Lesson 4-5

Warm-Up

In 1–4, use a graph labeled for $-15 \le x \le 15$ and $-15 \le y \le 15$.

1. The points (5, 0), (4, 3), (3, 4), and (0, 5) all lie on the circle with center ______ and radius ______.
2. Find five more points on this circle.
3. Find the images of all nine points under the transformation with matrix $\begin{bmatrix} 2 & 0 \\ 0 & 3 \end{bmatrix}$.
4. Describe the image.
5. Show that the distance between (5, 0) and (4, 3) is not equal to the distance between the images of these points under the transformation of Warm-Up Question 3.

Additional Examples

1. Using the same triangle as Guided Example 1, find its image under $S_{3,1.5}$.

Solution $S_{3,1.5}(x, y) = ($______x, ______$y)$, so multiply all the x-coordinates of the preimage by ______ and all the y-coordinates of the preimage by ______.

A': $S_{3,1.5}(0, 4) = (0, 6)$
B': $S_{3,1.5}(5, 6) = ($______, ______$)$
C': $S_{3,1.5}(6, 0) = ($______, ______$)$

So the image of $\triangle ABC$ is $\triangle A'B'C'$ with the vertex coordinates above.

2. Consider the quadrilateral $PQRT$ with $P = (-3, 6)$, $Q = (0, 9)$, $R = (8, 2)$, and $T = (-5, -3)$. Find its image under $S_{5,3}$.

Resource Masters for Lesson 4-5

Resource Master 66 Lesson 4-6

Resource Master 65 Lesson 4-6

Warm-Up

Graph the quadrilateral determined by the points $Q = (3, 1)$, $U = (3, -5)$, $A = (6, 4)$, and $D = (6, 7)$. Find the image of $QUAD$ under these transformations:

1. r_x
2. r_y
3. $r_{y=x}$

Additional Examples

1. If $P = (2, 5)$, $Q = (4, 7)$, and $R = (9, 1)$, find the image of $\triangle PQR$ under r_y.
2. Use the Matrix Basis Theorem to verify the 2×2 matrices for a. r_y and b. r_x.

   Solution Find the images of (1, 0) and (0, 1) for each reflection.

   a. $r_y(1, 0) = (\_\_\_, \_\_\_)$, $r_y(0, 1) = (\_\_\_, \_\_\_)$, so the matrix for r_y is $\begin{bmatrix} \_\_\_ & \_\_\_ \\ \_\_\_ & \_\_\_ \end{bmatrix}$.

   b. $r_x(1, 0) = (\_\_\_, \_\_\_)$, $r_x(0, 1) = (\_\_\_, \_\_\_)$, so the matrix for r_x is $\begin{bmatrix} \_\_\_ & \_\_\_ \\ \_\_\_ & \_\_\_ \end{bmatrix}$.

Resource Masters for Lesson 4-6

Resource Master 67 Lesson 4-7

Warm-Up

In 1–4, find the image of the point (100, 36) under each transformation.

1. reflection over the x-axis
2. the composite of a reflection over the x-axis followed by a reflection over the line $y = x$
3. the composite of a reflection over the y-axis followed by a reflection over the line $y = x$
4. the composite of S_3 followed by S_4

Additional Example

Refer to the Example on page 265. Suppose three points on the original golf club are $P = (4, 0)$, $G = (4, -7)$, and $A = (5, -7)$. Use matrix multiplication to find the image of PGA under R_{-90}.

Resource Master for Lesson 4-7

Resource Master 69 Lesson 4-8

Resource Master 68 Lesson 4-8

Warm-Up

Adjacent pairs of compass directions N, E, S, and W are bisected by the directions NE, SE, SW, and NW, and adjacent pairs of those eight directions are bisected by eight others, clockwise from north: NNE, ENE, ESE, SSE, SSW, WSW, WNW, and NNW.

1. Draw a figure with these 16 directions radiating from a single point.
2. If NNE is rotated 90° clockwise, what direction results?
3. If SSE is rotated 90° counterclockwise, what direction results?
4. Suppose you rotate N to NE. How many rotations of this magnitude would it take to rotate N to SW?
5. Suppose you rotate NW to WSW. What is the magnitude of that rotation?

Resource Masters for Lesson 4-8

Resource Master 70 Lesson 4-9

Warm-Up

1. Rotate the triangle represented by the matrix $\begin{bmatrix} 2 & 11 & 11 \\ 5 & 5 & -7 \end{bmatrix}$ by -90° about the origin.
2. By using the Pythagorean Distance Formula or some other means, demonstrate that your image is indeed the rotation image of the original triangle under a rotation of -90°.

Additional Example

Line p contains (-2, 7) and is perpendicular to line q, whose equation is $y = \frac{4}{7}x - 8$. Find an equation for line p.

Solution The slope of line q is ______. So by the Perpendicular Lines and Slopes Theorem, the slope of line p is ______. Because line p contains (-2, 7), an equation for line p in point-slope form is ______.

Resource Master for Lesson 4-9

Resource Master 72 Lesson 4-10

Resource Master 71 Lesson 4-10

Warm-Up

1. Graph the polygon whose consecutive vertices are $\begin{bmatrix} 3 & 5 & 2 & -8 & -8 & 0 & 1 \\ -2 & 2 & 5 & 1 & -3 & -4 & -4 \end{bmatrix}$. Add the matrix $\begin{bmatrix} -2 & -2 & -2 & -2 & -2 & -2 & -2 \\ -3 & -3 & -3 & -3 & -3 & -3 & -3 \end{bmatrix}$ to the polygon matrix and graph the polygon whose image results.
2. How are the two polygons in Warm-Up 1 related?

Resource Masters for Lesson 4-10

Resource Master 73 Lesson 4-10

Guided Example 1

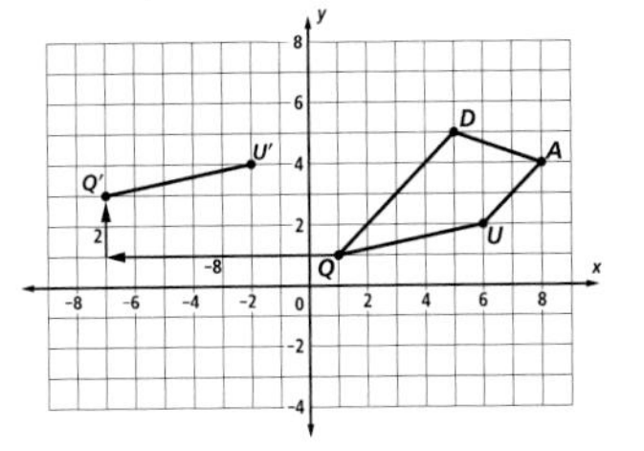

Accommodating the Learner

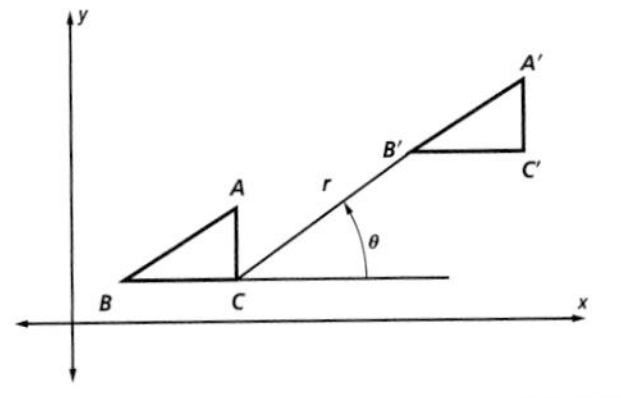

Resource Master for Lesson 4-10

Chapter 4

Pacing

Each lesson in this chapter is designed to be covered in 1 day, but Lessons 4-1 and 4-6 may take less time. At the end of the chapter, you should plan to spend 1 day to review the Self-Test, 1 to 2 days for the Chapter Review, and 1 day for a test. You may wish to spend a day on projects and possibly a day is needed for quizzes. This chapter should therefore take 12 to 16 days. We strongly advise you not to spend more than 17 days on this chapter.

Overview

One way to introduce matrices is to have students discuss situations in which they need to store and manipulate data. Many real-world problems seem complex because they require manipulation of large quantities of data, sometimes with tens of thousands of variables, and matrices are almost always involved in storing and manipulating such data. The chart on page 220 is a small part of such a large matrix. It includes the seven largest countries in the world, as measured by land area. (The next three are Argentina, Kazakhstan, and Sudan, each with an area of over 2.5 million square kilometers.)

Besides storing and manipulating data, another use of matrices is to describe geometric *transformations*. Transformations provide one of the many ties between geometry and algebra; here, the geometric properties are congruence and similarity. Be sure that students do not "glide" over this content; transformations are used in later chapters to show how the graphs of functions and relations are related to each other.

Occasionally in this chapter, words or letters appear above rows or to the left of columns. Be sure students understand that these labels are for explanation and description only; they are not considered part of the matrix.

Chapter 4 Matrices

Contents

A *matrix* is a rectangular arrangement of objects or numbers, often used to store data. We use brackets [ ] to identify a matrix. In the matrix below, the numbers give information about the largest seven countries in land area. The titles of the rows and columns are not part of the matrix.

Country	Land Area (km^2)	Water Area (km^2)	Highest Point (m)	Lowest Point (m)
Russia	16,995,800	79,400	5633	–28
China	9,326,410	270,550	8850	154
USA	9,161,923	664,707	6198	–86
Canada	9,093,507	891,163	5959	0
Brazil	8,456,510	55,455	3014	0
Australia	7,617,930	68,920	2229	–15
India	2,973,190	314,400	8598	0

Source: www.cia.gov/cia/publications/factbook

Chapter 4 Overview

The content of Chapter 4 will be new to most students. With the importance of matrices in business practices, computer applications, and linear algebra, all students need to be familiar with this content. We present matrices early in this book so that we can use the language of matrices later to study systems of equations. Matrices also provide an opportunity to review the properties of real numbers; for some students, it is only with the study of matrices that they understand and appreciate the associative and commutative properties of multiplication of real numbers.

This chapter has three main goals: (1) to introduce matrices for later work in this course; (2) to study how to use matrices as a tool for storing data and solving problems; and (3) to use matrices to revisit the geometric topics of reflections, rotations, translations, size changes, and scale changes. These topics will be used in later chapters to study trigonometry and quadratic relations.

Matrices can also describe geometric transformations. In the graph at the right, *PENTA* has been reflected over the *x*-axis, and then translated left by 3 units and down by 5 units. The vertices of *PENTA* may be described by the matrix below the graph. You will learn that the coordinates of the image *P′E′N′T′A′* can be found through matrix operations.

In this chapter you will study various matrix operations, and learn how those operations can be applied to geometric transformations and real-life situations.

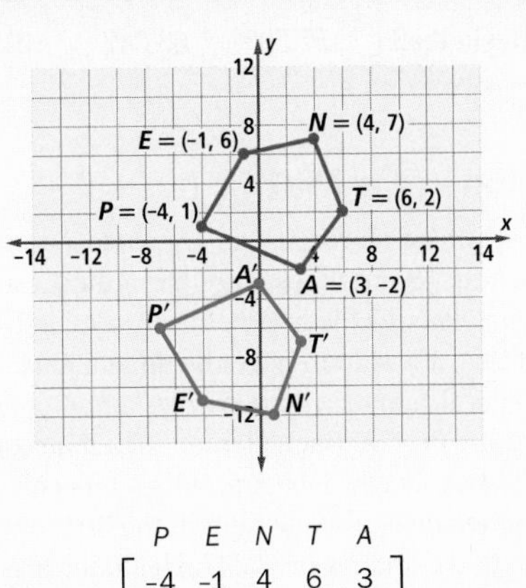

$$\begin{matrix} P & E & N & T & A \end{matrix}$$
$$\begin{bmatrix} -4 & -1 & 4 & 6 & 3 \\ 1 & 6 & 7 & 2 & -2 \end{bmatrix}$$

221

Lessons 4-1 to 4-3 introduce students to the vocabulary and notation for matrices, their use in storing data, and the definitions of matrix addition and matrix multiplication. Lessons 4-4 through 4-8 discuss how matrices can be used to represent transformations, first for size and scale changes (Lessons 4-4 and 4-5) and then for reflections and rotations (Lessons 4-6, 4-7, and 4-8); these lessons also explore the question of preserving (or not preserving) various properties under such transformations. Lesson 4-9 builds on the previous lessons to explore the relationship between slopes of perpendicular lines. Finally, Lesson 4-10 returns to matrix addition (introduced in Lesson 4-2) and studies its application to translations.

Using Pages 220–221

Some pre-algebra and first-year algebra texts mention matrices, including UCSMP *Algebra*. Matrices are also studied in some computer programming courses. Spreadsheets deal with matrices. And many graphing calculators have the ability to store and manipulate data in matrix form. Probe your class to determine whether any students are familiar with matrices for one of these or other reasons. Though this chapter is designed for students who have never seen matrices before, and in the past has proved not to be difficult, experienced students may be able to help others.

Enough information is given about the transformation that maps *PENTA* onto *P′E′N′T′A′* to determine a representation for the transformation. One way to represent the statement that *PENTA* was reflected over the *x*-axis is that each point (x, y) is transformed to $(x, -y)$. Also, the translation "left by 3 units and down by 5 units" can be represented by the statement that each point (x, y) is transformed to $(x - 3, y - 5)$. The composite of these transformations maps (x, y) onto $(x - 3, 5 - y)$. You might ask students if they can determine that transformation on their own; alternately, you can ask them to verify that rule for all vertices of the polygon.

Chapter 4 Projects

At the end of each chapter, you will find projects related to the chapter. At this time you might want to have students look over the projects on pages 286 and 287. You might want to have students tentatively select a project on which to work. Then, as students read and progress through the chapter, they can finalize their project choices.

Sometimes students might work alone. At other times, you might let them collaborate with classmates for a presentation and discussion. We recommend that you allow for diversity and encourage students to use their imaginations when presenting their projects. As students work on projects throughout the year, they should see many uses of mathematics in the real world.

Lesson

4-1

GOAL

Introduce the basic vocabulary of matrices—rows, columns, dimensions, equal matrices, and point matrix—and establish the groundwork for the rest of the chapter.

SPUR Objectives

The SPUR Objectives for all of Chapter 4 are found in the Chapter Review on pages 293–297.

A Write matrices for points and polygons.

I Use matrices to store data.

Materials/Resources

- Lesson Masters 4-1A and 4-1B
- Resource Masters 1 and 54–56
- Matrix polygon application

HOMEWORK

Suggestions for Assignment

- Questions 1–22
- Question 23 (extra credit)
- Reading Lesson 4-2
- Covering the Ideas 4-2

Local Standards

1 Warm-Up

1. How many rows and how many columns are in this rectangular array? 5 rows, 9 columns

2. How many hearts are there in all? 45
3. One heart is bigger than the others. In what row and what column is this heart? second row, third column

Lesson

4-1 Storing Data in Matrices

Vocabulary

matrix
element
dimensions
equal matrices
point matrix

BIG IDEA A variety of types of data, from numerical information to coordinates of points, can be stored in *matrices*.

A rectangular arrangement of objects or numbers is called a **matrix**. The plural of *matrix* is *matrices*. Each object in a matrix is called an **element** of the matrix. Matrices are useful for storing data of all kinds.

For example, the median salaries of collegiate head coaches for three different sports, based on the highest degree an institution grants, are shown in the matrix below. Entries are in dollars.

	column 1 ↓ Doctoral	column 2 ↓ Master's	column 3 ↓ Bachelor's	column 4 ↓ Associate's
row 1 → Football	185,000	72,070	62,499	31,314
row 2 → Baseball	72,975	46,654	41,105	44,799
row 3 → Basketball	157,500	63,347	51,092	45,982

Source: *Chronicle of Higher Education*, March 2006

Mental Math

Find an equation for a line satisfying the conditions.

a. slope 4 and y-intercept 2.5 $y = 4x + 2.5$

b. undefined slope and passing through (–7, 2) $x = -7$

c. slope $\frac{1}{3}$ and passing through $(0, \frac{9}{10})$ $y = \frac{1}{3}x + \frac{9}{10}$

d. passing through (17, 12) and (0.4, 12) $y = 12$

Dimensions of a Matrix

The elements of the above matrix are enclosed by large square brackets. (Sometimes large parentheses are used in place of brackets.) This matrix has 3 *rows* and 4 *columns*. Because of this, it is said to have the **dimensions** 3 by 4, written 3×4. In general, a matrix with m rows and n columns has dimensions $m \times n$. Each element of a matrix is identified first by its row location, then by its column location. For example, the element in the 3rd row and 2nd column of this matrix is 63,347. Headings are placed outside the matrix, like the sports and degrees above.

	A doct...	B mas...	C bac...	D asso...
•				
1	185000	72070	62499	31314
2	72975	46654	41105	44799
3	157500	63347	51092	45982
4				
5				
6				

B3 63347

A rectangular block of cells in a spreadsheet also constitutes a matrix. Spreadsheets use the reverse order for identifying an element—column first (a letter) and row second (a number). Like matrices, spreadsheets can have headings to identify their row(s) and column(s).

Background

To signify that an array is a matrix, we use brackets. Some texts use large parentheses. Make sure students realize that the titles or descriptions of the rows and columns are not part of the matrix.

Activity If a geometric figure is determined by a set of n points, then it can be represented by a $2 \times n$ matrix. Thus, the first three columns of the matrix that represents polygon $ABCDE$ could also represent three points that determine an angle, the vertices of a triangle, any other triple of points.

Typically, the material in this lesson is fairly easy and interesting for most students. It is often possible to cover this lesson on the day after the Chapter 3 Test.

Many calculators let you enter and manipulate matrices. Use the Guided Example to see how to enter a matrix into a CAS and to store a matrix as a variable.

GUIDED

Example

According to the *Statistical Abstract of the United States*, in 1980, approximately 3.5 million males and 1.9 million females participated in high school athletic programs. Ten years later, 3.4 million males and 1.9 million females participated. In 2000, 3.9 million males and 2.8 million females participated.

a. Store the high school athletic participation information in a matrix *M*.

b. What are the dimensions of the matrix?

c. Enter the matrix from Part a into a CAS and store it as a variable.

Solution

a. You can write either of the two matrices below. Matrix *M*1 has the years as rows, and matrix *M*2 has the years as columns. Either matrix is an acceptable way to store the data.

	Males	Females
Matrix $M1$: 1980	?	?
1990	?	?
2000	?	?

3.5; 1.9
3.4; 1.9
3.9; 2.8

	1980	1990	2000
Matrix $M2$: Males	?	?	?
Females	?	?	?

First row: 3.5; 3.4; 3.9;
Second row: 1.9; 1.9; 2.8

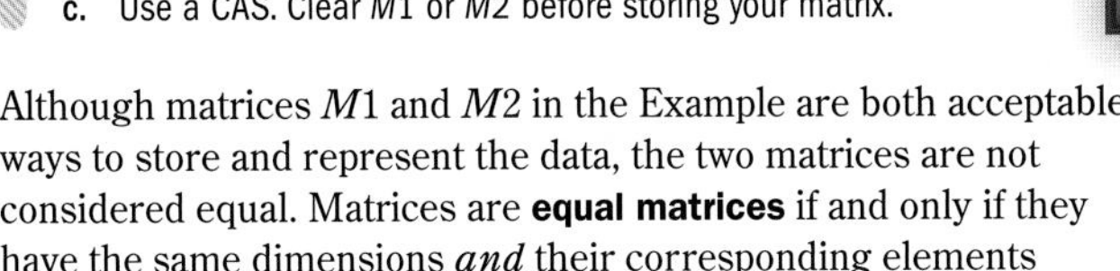

b. Matrix *M*1 has _?_ rows and _?_ columns. 3; 2
The dimensions of M1 are _?_. 3×2
Matrix *M*2 has _?_ rows and _?_ columns. 2; 3
The dimensions of M2 are _?_. 2×3

c. Use a CAS. Clear *M*1 or *M*2 before storing your matrix.

Although matrices $M1$ and $M2$ in the Example are both acceptable ways to store and represent the data, the two matrices are not considered equal. Matrices are **equal matrices** if and only if they have the same dimensions *and* their corresponding elements are equal.

Accommodating the Learner

Show students the two squares at the right, each with one labeled vertex. Ask students to find the other three vertices for each square and write the four vertices as a 2×4 matrix.

$\begin{bmatrix} a & 0 & -a & 0 \\ 0 & a & 0 & -a \end{bmatrix}$; $\begin{bmatrix} b & -b & -b & b \\ b & b & -b & -b \end{bmatrix}$

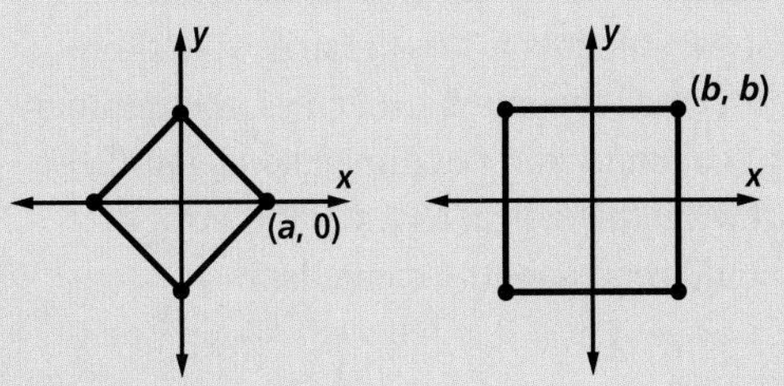

2 Teaching

Notes on the Lesson

It is important that students always distinguish between the dimensions of a matrix (the number of rows and columns) and the values of the elements. To help students use the terms *row* and *column* for matrices (because in everyday language, items aligned vertically can be described as being "in a row"), point out that the vertically aligned entries are in a *column*, so *row* refers only to the horizontally aligned entries.

Example Emphasize that one result of the definition of matrix equality is that two matrices *cannot be equal* if they do not have the same dimensions. Thus, while matrix *M*1 and matrix *M*2 are both acceptable ways to store the same data, they are not equal matrices.

Activity Students need to become comfortable rather quickly with representing a plane figure in matrix form. This skill is essential for the study of transformations, which begins in Lesson 4-4. Note that matrices for geometric figures show ordered pairs aligned vertically, so such a matrix always has the dimensions $2 \times n$, where n is the number of points represented by the matrix. Stress that a $2 \times n$ matrix can stand for other things as well, for instance, n pieces of information on two people. Students should be able to use the context of a problem to tell when a $2 \times n$ matrix represents a geometric figure.

Note-Taking Tips

Ask students to make up their own memory device to remember that $m \times n$ lists rows first and columns second. One simple memory device is that *row* and *one* have the same number of letters, as do *column* and *second*.

Additional Example

Example A cell phone company offers a family plan and an individual plan. Five years ago, the company had about 6 million family plan members and 9.4 million individual plan members. Three years ago, there were 11.5 million family plan members and 8.8 million individual plan members. There were 13.6 million family plan members and 10.2 million individual plan members last year.

a. Store the membership information in a matrix *M*.

b. What are the dimensions of the matrix?

c. Enter the matrix from Part a into a CAS and store it as a variable.

Solution

a. Matrix *M*1 has "years ago" as rows, and matrix *M*2 has "years ago" as columns. Either matrix is an acceptable way to store the data.

Matrix *M*1:

	family	individual
5 years ago	?	?
3 years ago	?	?
1 year ago	?	?

Matrix *M*2:

	5 years ago	3 years ago	1 year ago
family	?	?	?
individual	?	?	?

$$M1 = \begin{bmatrix} 6.0 & 9.4 \\ 11.5 & 8.8 \\ 13.6 & 10.2 \end{bmatrix};$$

$$M2 = \begin{bmatrix} 6 & 11.5 & 13.6 \\ 9.4 & 8.8 & 10.2 \end{bmatrix}$$

b. Matrix *M*1 has __?__ rows and __?__ columns. The dimensions of *M*1 are __?__. 3; 2; 3×2 Matrix *M*2 has __?__ rows and __?__ columns. The dimensions of *M*2 are __?__. 2; 3; 2×3

c. Clear *M*1 and *M*2 from memory before storing your matrix on a CAS.

```
DelVar m1                                  Done
DelVar m2                                  Done
[6.   9.4 ]              [6.   9.4 ]
[11.5 8.8 ] → m1         [11.5 8.8 ]
[13.6 10.2]              [13.6 10.2]
```


Matrices and Geometry

Points and polygons can also be represented by matrices.

The ordered pair (x, y) is generally represented by the matrix $\begin{bmatrix} x \\ y \end{bmatrix}$.

This 2×1 matrix is called a **point matrix**. Notice that the element in the first row is the x-coordinate and the element in the second row is the y-coordinate. For instance, the point $(5, -1)$ is represented by the matrix $\begin{bmatrix} 5 \\ -1 \end{bmatrix}$.

Similarly, polygons can be written as matrices. Each column of the matrix contains the coordinates of a vertex of the polygon in the order in which the polygon is named. The Activity illustrates this.

Activity Activity: See margin.

MATERIALS matrix polygon application

Step 1 Pentagon *ABCDE* with vertices $A = (3, -5)$, $B = (6, -1)$, $C = (4, 5)$, $D = (-2.5, 4)$, and $E = (-5, -0.75)$, is shown at the right. Write a matrix representing the coordinates of the vertices of the pentagon, starting with point *A*.

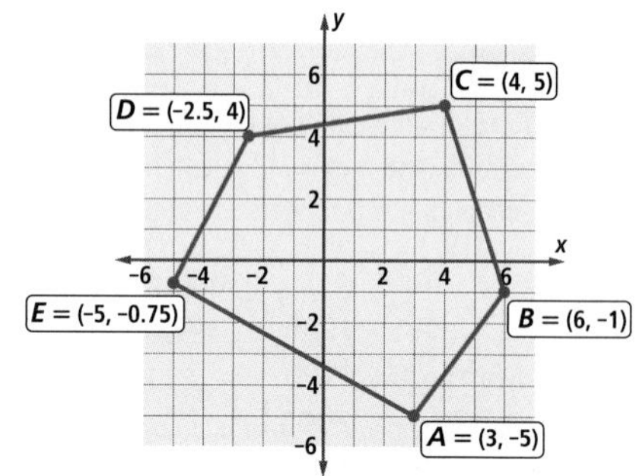

Step 2 Write two other matrices representing the pentagon. (*Hint:* Start with a different vertex.)

Step 3 Verify that your matrices from Step 2 are correct by plotting the pentagon each matrix describes. Each picture should be the same as pentagon *ABCDE*. You can do this by using a matrix polygon application supplied by your teacher.

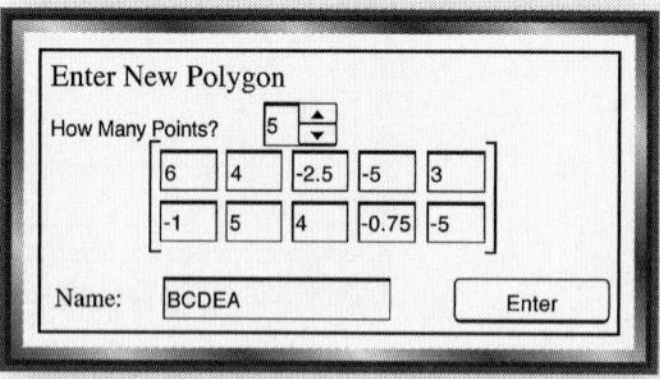

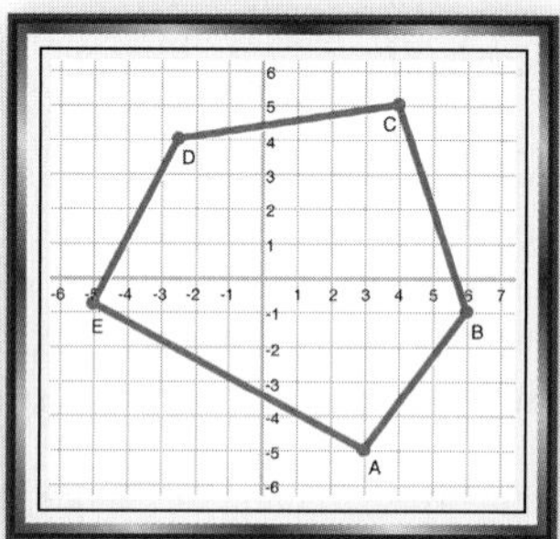

Step 4 Plot $\begin{array}{c} \begin{matrix} B & A & C & D & E \end{matrix} \\ \begin{bmatrix} 6 & 3 & 4 & -2.5 & -5 \\ -1 & -5 & 5 & 4 & -0.75 \end{bmatrix} \end{array}$.

Explain why *BACDE* does not describe a pentagon.

 QY

QY

Are the four matrices in the Activity equal? Explain your answer.

Accommodating the Learner

Show students a 3×4 matrix. Ask them to (1) tell the number of rows, the number of columns, and the dimensions and (2) to rewrite the matrix as a 4×3 matrix that could represent the same data.

(1) 3, 4, 3×4; (2) Answers vary. Check students' work.

ENGLISH LEARNERS

Vocabulary Development

Be sure students can distinguish between a 1×2 matrix, an ordered pair, and a point matrix. For example, students should be able to describe $\begin{bmatrix} 5 & 1 \end{bmatrix}$ as a 1×2 matrix, (5, 1) as an ordered pair, and $\begin{bmatrix} 5 \\ 1 \end{bmatrix}$ as a 2×1 matrix (also called a point matrix) that can represent the ordered pair (5, 1).

Questions

COVERING THE IDEAS

1. What is a matrix? A matrix is a rectangular arrangement of objects.

In 2–4, refer to the matrix regarding coaching salaries at the beginning of the lesson.

2. a. What is the element in row 2, column 3? 41,105
   b. What does this element represent?
3. Write instructions that someone could use to enter the matrix on your CAS.
4. What would be the dimensions of the matrix if *highest degrees* were rows, and *sports* were columns? 4×3
5. Refer to the Example. In 1985, there were 3,344,275 males and 1,807,121 females participating in high school athletic programs. Construct a 2×4 matrix that incorporates this new information with the old. See margin.

2b. the median salary in dollars of the head coach of a collegiate baseball team at an institution whose highest degree granted is a Bachelor's

3. Answers vary. Sample: Find the matrix command and enter the dimensions.

6. In the fall of 2008, mathematics classes at a local community college had a total enrollment of 2850, compared to 2241 in the fall of 2007. Additionally, English classes had total enrollments of 2620 and 2051, biology classes had enrollments of 1160 and 1572, and psychology classes had enrollments of 740 and 784, all respectively.
   a. Arrange the data into a matrix on a CAS or graphing calculator, representing years as rows. a–b. See margin.
   b. Now arrange the data into a matrix representing years as columns.

Many colleges campuses have inner courtyards called quadrangles.

7. a. Write the ordered pair (x, y) as a matrix. $\begin{bmatrix} x \\ y \end{bmatrix}$
   b. What is this matrix called? a point matrix
8. **Multiple Choice** Which matrix represents the point $(15\sqrt{2}, -7.3)$? D

   A $\begin{bmatrix} 15\sqrt{2} & -7.3 \end{bmatrix}$ B $\begin{bmatrix} -7.3 & 15\sqrt{2} \end{bmatrix}$

   C $\begin{bmatrix} -7.3 \\ 15\sqrt{2} \end{bmatrix}$ D $\begin{bmatrix} 15\sqrt{2} \\ -7.3 \end{bmatrix}$

9. Write $\triangle ABC$ at the right as a matrix.

   $\begin{matrix} A & B & C \end{matrix}$
   $\begin{bmatrix} -3 & 5 & -2 \\ 4 & 1 & -2 \end{bmatrix}$

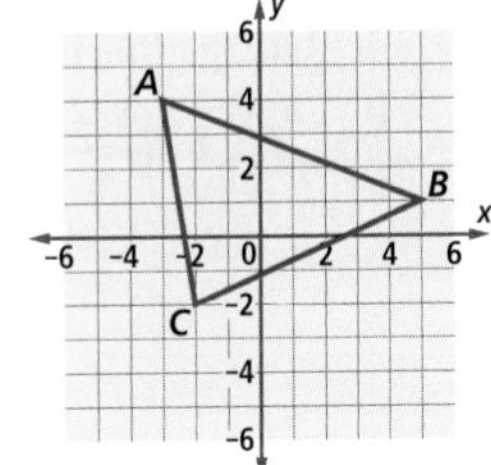

3 Assignment

Recommended Assignment

- Questions 1–22
- Question 23 (extra credit)
- Reading Lesson 4-2
- Covering the Ideas 4-2

Notes on the Questions

Question 9 Just as in dealing with congruence and similarity in geometry, the order of points is important when representing a polygon with a matrix, because the vertices will be labled and connected in the order they appear. You might ask students how they can write $\triangle ACB$ as a matrix. switch the second and third columns

Additional Answers

Activity

Step 1: Answers vary. Sample:

$$\begin{bmatrix} 3 & 6 & 4 & -2.5 & -5 \\ -5 & -1 & 5 & 4 & -0.75 \end{bmatrix}$$

Step 2: Answers vary. Sample:

$$\begin{bmatrix} 6 & 4 & -2.5 & -5 & 3 \\ -1 & 5 & 4 & -0.75 & -5 \end{bmatrix} \text{ and }$$

$$\begin{bmatrix} -2.5 & -5 & 3 & 6 & 4 \\ 4 & -0.75 & -5 & -1 & 5 \end{bmatrix}$$

Step 4:

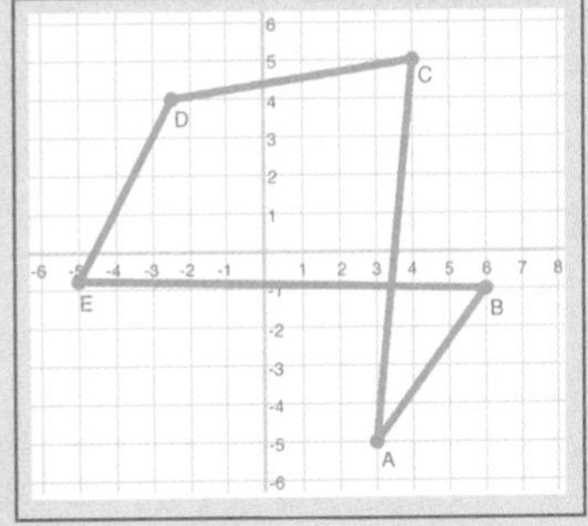

BACDE is not a polygon because $\overline{AC}$ intersects $\overline{BE}$.

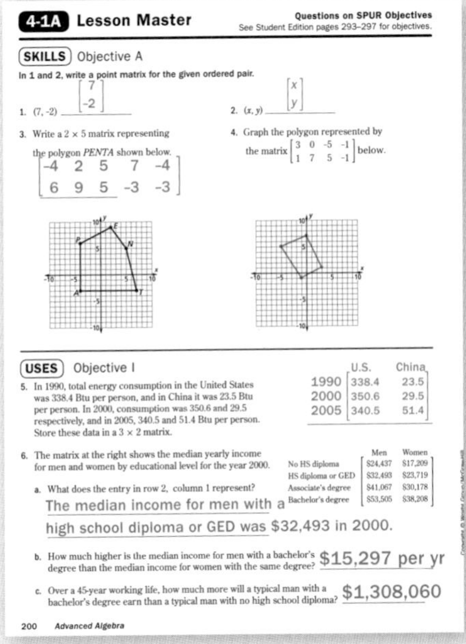

4-1A Lesson Master

Questions on SPUR Objectives
See Student Edition pages 293–297 for objectives.

SKILLS Objective A

In 1 and 2, write a point matrix for the given ordered pair.

1. (7, -2) $\begin{bmatrix} 7 \\ -2 \end{bmatrix}$
2. (x, y) $\begin{bmatrix} x \\ y \end{bmatrix}$
3. Write a 2×5 matrix representing the polygon *PENTA* shown below. $\begin{bmatrix} -4 & 2 & 5 & 7 & -4 \\ 6 & 9 & 5 & -3 & -3 \end{bmatrix}$
4. Graph the polygon represented by the matrix $\begin{bmatrix} 3 & 0 & -5 & -1 \\ 1 & 7 & 5 & -1 \end{bmatrix}$ below.

USES Objective I

5. In 1990, total energy consumption in the United States was 338.4 Btu per person, and in China it was 23.5 Btu per person. In 2000, consumption was 350.6 and 29.5 respectively, and in 2005, 340.5 and 51.4 Btu per person. Store these data in a 3×2 matrix.

	U.S.	China
1990	338.4	23.5
2000	350.6	29.5
2005	340.5	51.4

6. The matrix at the right shows the median yearly income for men and women by educational level for the year 2000.

	Men	Women
No HS diploma	$24,437	$17,209
HS diploma or GED	$32,493	$23,719
Associate's degree	$41,067	$30,178
Bachelor's degree	$53,505	$38,208

   a. What does the entry in row 2, column 1 represent? The median income for men with a high school diploma or GED was $32,493 in 2000.
   b. How much higher is the median income for men with a bachelor's degree than the median income for women with the same degree? $15,297 per yr
   c. Over a 45-year working life, how much more will a typical man with a bachelor's degree earn than a typical man with no high school diploma? $1,308,060

200 *Advanced Algebra*

Notes on the Questions

Questions 12 and 13 Ask students how they are using the definition of matrix equality when they are answering these questions.

Additional Answers

5.

	1980	1985	1990	2000
Males	3.5	3.3	3.4	3.9
Females	1.9	1.8	1.9	2.8

6a. Answers vary. Sample:

$\begin{bmatrix} 2850 & 2620 & 1160 & 740 \\ 2241 & 2051 & 1572 & 784 \end{bmatrix} \rightarrow m1$

$\begin{bmatrix} 2850 & 2620 & 1160 & 740 \\ 2241 & 2051 & 1572 & 784 \end{bmatrix}$

6b. Answers vary. Sample:

$\begin{bmatrix} 2850 & 2241 \\ 2620 & 2051 \\ 1160 & 1572 \\ 740 & 784 \end{bmatrix} \rightarrow m2$ $\begin{bmatrix} 2850 & 2241 \\ 2620 & 2051 \\ 1160 & 1572 \\ 740 & 784 \end{bmatrix}$

10a.

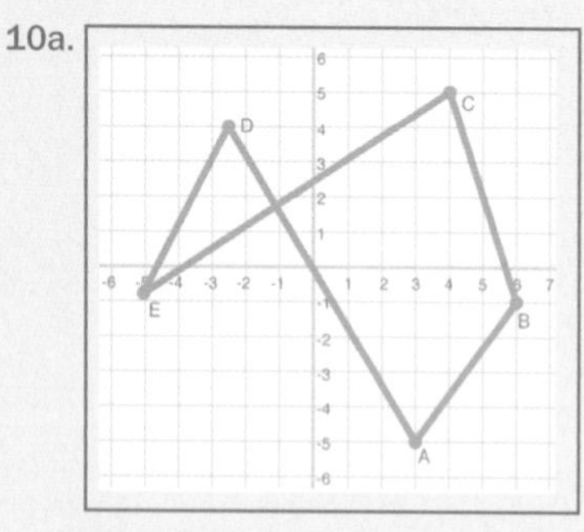

The points are connected in a different order.

15a.

	A	E	I	O	U
English	0.08	0.13	0.07	0.08	0.03
SCRABBLE	0.09	0.12	0.09	0.08	0.04

10. Refer to the Activity.
    a. The matrix at the right uses the same points as the Activity. Use a matrix polygon application to draw (or plot by hand) and connect the points in the matrix. Use the same window as in the Activity. Why is the picture different from pentagon *ABCDE*? See margin.

    $$\begin{matrix} A & B & C & E & D \end{matrix}$$
    $$\begin{bmatrix} 3 & 6 & 4 & -5 & -2.5 \\ -5 & -1 & 5 & -0.75 & 4 \end{bmatrix}$$

    b. How many matrices can represent the pentagon *ABCDE*? 10
11. The matrix at the right gives the numbers of professional degrees earned in 2000 in four professions, separated by gender.
    a. What are the dimensions of this matrix? 4 × 2
    b. What does the sum of the elements in row 3 represent?
    c. What does the sum of the elements in column 2 represent?

	Males	Females
Medicine	8,759	6,527
Dentistry	2,546	1,704
Law	20,640	17,512
Theology	4,339	1,790

APPLYING THE MATHEMATICS

Many colleges graduations use different colored tassels or sashes to denote individual majors.

12. **Fill in the Blanks** If $\begin{bmatrix} -6 & 4.3 \\ \frac{1}{2} & w \end{bmatrix} = \begin{bmatrix} -6 & r \\ \frac{1}{2} & 0.9 \end{bmatrix}$, then $w =$ _?_ and $r =$ _?_. 0.9; 4.3
13. **Fill in the Blanks** If $\begin{bmatrix} 2a - 3 \\ h + 0.4 \end{bmatrix} = \begin{bmatrix} -9 \\ \frac{1}{2} \end{bmatrix}$, then $a =$ _?_ and $h =$ _?_. -3; 0.1
14. Recall on your CAS the matrix $M1$ from the Guided Example. If $M1 = \begin{bmatrix} x & y \\ z - 1 & y \\ 3w & 2.8 \end{bmatrix}$, find w, x, y, and z. $x = 3.5$; $y = 1.9$; $w = 1.3$; $z = 4.4$
15. In the English language, the vowels A, E, I, O, and U show up with frequencies among all letters of about 8%, 13%, 7%, 8%, and 3%, respectively. In the board game SCRABBLE®, these letters show up with frequencies 9%, 12%, 9%, 8%, and 4%, respectively.
    a. Arrange this information into a 2 × 5 matrix. See margin.
    b. Explain how to enter this matrix into a CAS.

11b. the number of law degrees earned in 2000

11c. the total number of professional degress in Medicine, Dentistry, Law, and Theology earned by women in 2000

15b. Answers vary. Sample: Go to the matrix prompt, and then specify the 2 × 5 dimensions and enter the elements in their appropriate location.

Extension

Questions 12 and 13 use the property that if $\begin{bmatrix} a & b \\ c & d \end{bmatrix} = \begin{bmatrix} e & f \\ g & h \end{bmatrix}$, then corresponding elements are equal ($a = e$, $b = f$, and so on). Ask students to write the equation $\begin{bmatrix} 2x + 3y \\ x - 2y \end{bmatrix} = \begin{bmatrix} -5 \\ 8 \end{bmatrix}$ as a system of linear equations. Then ask them to find the solution to the system. $2x + 3y = -5$, $x - 2y = 8$; $(x, y) = (2, -3)$

16. The endpoints of $\overline{PA}$ on line m are given by the matrix $\begin{bmatrix} \frac{1}{2} & 2 \\ \frac{17}{2} & 13 \end{bmatrix}$.

The endpoints of $\overline{LN}$ on line n are defined by the matrix $\begin{bmatrix} 4 & -1 \\ 8 & -7 \end{bmatrix}$.

Prove that lines m and n are parallel.

17. Use a matrix polygon application to draw (or plot by hand) the octagon $\begin{bmatrix} 0 & 1 & 5 & 1 & 0 & -1 & -5 & -1 \\ 5 & 1 & 0 & -1 & -5 & -1 & 0 & 1 \end{bmatrix}$. Sketch a picture of the output, and explain if the polygon is convex or nonconvex. See margin.

REVIEW

18. Evaluate the following expressions. **(Lesson 3-9)**
   a. $r\lceil\pi\rceil - r\lfloor\pi\rfloor$ r b. $n\lceil 10\rceil - n\lfloor 10\rfloor$ 0 c. $\lceil -\frac{1}{2}\rceil$ 0
   d. $\lfloor -3.6\rfloor - \lfloor -3\rfloor$ -1 e. $\lfloor 56.63\rfloor - \lfloor -56.9\rfloor$ 113
   f. $\lceil 5\rceil - \lceil 5.02\rceil$ -1 g. $\lfloor -4.5\rfloor + \lfloor 9.7\rfloor$ 4
19. Shelby put $50 on her public transportation card. For every bus or train ride she takes, $2 is deducted from her total. Express the total left on her card as an explicit formula of an arithmetic sequence dependent on the number of train or bus rides taken. **(Lesson 3-8)** $a_n = 50 - 2n$
20. **Fill in the Blank** $Ax + By = C$ is the __?__ form of an equation for a line. **(Lesson 3-2)** standard
21. If the volume of cube A is 27 times the volume of cube B, how do the lengths of their edges compare? **(Lesson 2-3)**
22. a. What does the Commutative Property of Addition say?
   b. Is subtraction commutative? If so, explain. If not, give a counterexample. **(Previous Course)**

EXPLORATION

23. What is a dot-matrix printer? How is it related to the matrices discussed in this lesson?
   Answers vary. Sample: A dot-matrix printer is a printer with a print head that prints by impact as it moves back and forth. It is related to matrices since any character or image printed is made up of an array of dots whose location has critical meaning, just as the location of a piece of data in a data matrix gives the data meaning.

16. The slope of $m = \frac{13 - \frac{17}{2}}{2 - \frac{1}{2}} = \frac{9}{3} = 3$, and the slope of $n = \frac{8-(-7)}{4-(-1)} = \frac{15}{5} = 3$. Nonvertical lines with equal slopes are parallel. So, by the Parallel Lines and Slope Theorem, m and n are parallel.

21. The lengths of the edges of A are 3 times as long as the lengths of the edges of B.

22a. For all real numbers a and b, $a + b = b + a$.

22b. Subtraction is not commutative. Answers vary. Sample: If $a = 3$ and $b = 5$, then $a - b = -2$ but $b - a = 2$, and $-2 \neq 2$.

QY ANSWER

No, corresponding elements are not equal.

Notes on the Questions

Question 22 This question reviews commutativity in advance of applying it to matrix operations in the next two lessons.

4 Wrap-Up

Ongoing Assessment

Have students work in groups. Each student in the group should draw a polygon (with vertices that have integer coordinates) on graph paper and write a matrix for the polygon. Students should exchange matrices, draw a polygon for the received matrix, and compare their polygon with the original polygon. Answers vary. Check students' work.

Project Update

Project 1, *History of Matrices,* on page 286 and Project 5, *Computer Graphics,* on page 287 relate to the content of this lesson.

Additional Answers

17.

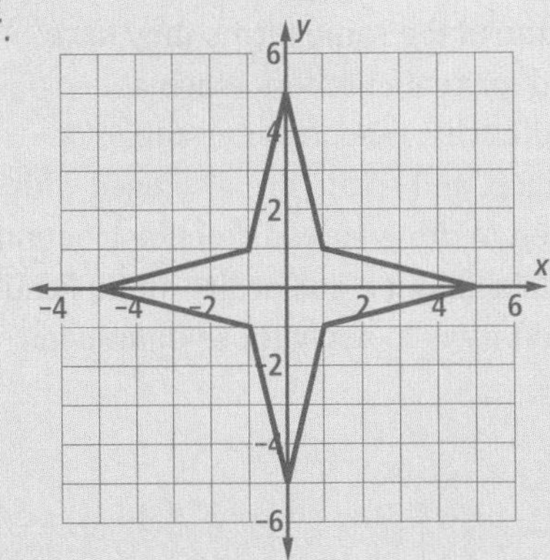

This is a nonconvex polygon.

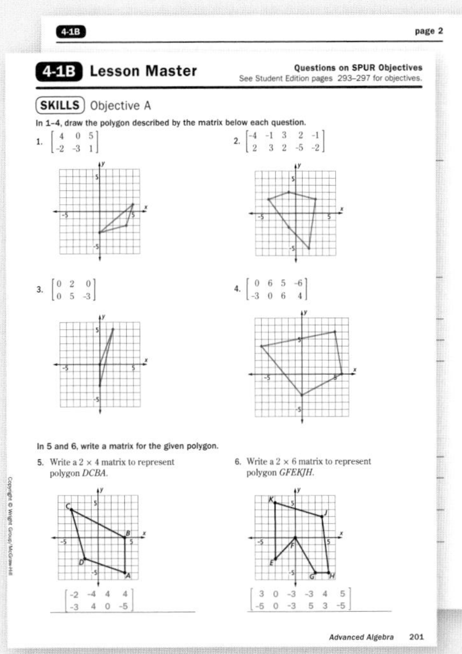

Lesson

4-2

GOAL

Introduce the operations of matrix addition, subtraction, and scalar multiplication.

SPUR Objectives

B Add, subtract, and find scalar multiples of matrices.

E Recognize properties of matrix operations.

J Use matrix addition and scalar multiplication to solve real-world problems.

Materials/Resources

- Lesson Masters 4-2A and 4-2B
- Resource Masters 57 and 58
- CAS

HOMEWORK

Suggestions for Assignment

- Questions 1–21
- Question 22 (extra credit)
- Reading Lesson 4-3
- Covering the Ideas 4-3

Local Standards

1 Warm-Up

Matrices *O* and *N* below show the amount of money (in dollars) a household spent in two consecutive months on three utilities.

$$\begin{array}{r}\text{Oct.}\\ \begin{array}{r}\text{electricity}\\ \text{water}\\ \text{gas}\end{array}\begin{bmatrix}82\\22\\14\end{bmatrix}=O\end{array} \qquad \begin{array}{r}\text{Nov.}\\ \begin{array}{r}\text{electricity}\\ \text{water}\\ \text{gas}\end{array}\begin{bmatrix}64\\22\\25\end{bmatrix}=N\end{array}$$

1. What matrix represents the total expenses for electricity, water, and gas for the two consecutive months? $\begin{bmatrix}146\\44\\39\end{bmatrix}$

Lesson

4-2 Matrix Addition

Vocabulary

matrix addition, sum of two matrices

scalar multiplication, scalar product

difference of two matrices

▸ **BIG IDEA** Matrices with the same dimensions can be added in a very natural way.

How Are Matrices Added?

There are many situations which require adding the information stored in matrices. For instance, suppose matrix *C* represents the current inventory of cars at Rusty's Car Dealership.

$$\begin{array}{c}\text{Current Inventory}\\ \begin{array}{r}\\ \text{Turbo}\\ \text{Cruiser}\\ \text{Clunker}\\ \text{Vacationer}\end{array}\begin{array}{c}\begin{array}{ccccc}\text{Red}&\text{Blue}&\text{White}&\text{Silver}&\text{Tan}\end{array}\\ \begin{bmatrix}12&10&7&8&2\\14&12&7&12&7\\17&8&2&\textcircled{12}&5\\15&4&14&13&3\end{bmatrix}\end{array}=C\end{array}$$

A new shipment of cars arrives and the numbers stored in matrix *D* are the quantities of the new cars received by Rusty.

$$\begin{array}{c}\text{Deliveries}\\ \begin{array}{r}\\ \text{Turbo}\\ \text{Cruiser}\\ \text{Clunker}\\ \text{Vacationer}\end{array}\begin{array}{c}\begin{array}{ccccc}\text{Red}&\text{Blue}&\text{White}&\text{Silver}&\text{Tan}\end{array}\\ \begin{bmatrix}6&2&3&5&1\\7&4&2&10&2\\4&7&1&\textcircled{8}&1\\3&3&5&9&1\end{bmatrix}\end{array}=D\end{array}$$

The current total inventory is found by adding matrices *C* and *D*. This **matrix addition** is performed according to the following rule.

Definition of Matrix Addition

If two matrices *A* and *B* have the same dimensions, their **sum** $A + B$ is the matrix in which each element is the sum of the corresponding elements in *A* and *B*.

Add corresponding elements of *C* and *D* to find the elements of $C + D$. One set of corresponding elements is circled in the two matrices on this page and the matrix at the top of the following page: $12 + 8 = 20$.

Mental Math

At the movies, a bag of popcorn costs $4.50, a soda costs $3.25, and a package of candy costs $3.00.

a. How much do one bag of popcorn and two sodas cost? $11.00

b. How much do two sodas and two packages of candy cost? $12.50

c. How much do one bag of popcorn, one soda, and one package of candy cost? $10.75

d. How much do *p* bags of popcorn, *s* sodas, and *c* packages of candy cost? $4.5p + 3.25s + 3c$

Custom paint jobs such as the one above can give cars a unique look.

Background

For most students, this is another rather simple lesson. All three matrix operations—addition, subtraction, and scalar multiplication—follow conventions that students would expect.

The addition of matrices and the scalar multiplication of a matrix are fundamental operations in linear algebra. Students will see later (Lesson 4-10) that matrix addition can represent a translation; they should realize here that these operations are analogous to operations with real numbers, and some of the same terms they have learned for real numbers (such as commutativity, associativity, sum, difference, and so on) are also used with matrices. Writing spreadsheet instructions for matrix addition and scalar multiplication are good ways to apply those definitions.

New Inventory

	Red	Blue	White	Silver	Tan
Turbo	18	12	10	13	3
Cruiser	21	16	9	22	9
Clunker	21	15	3	(20)	6
Vacationer	18	7	19	22	4

$= C + D$

Since matrix addition involves adding corresponding elements, only matrices with the same dimensions can be added. As the car dealership example shows, the sum matrix will have the same dimensions as the matrices that were added.

Because addition of real numbers is commutative, *addition of matrices is commutative.* Thus, if two matrices A and B can be added, then $A + B = B + A$. Also, *addition of matrices is associative*, meaning that for all matrices A, B, and C with the same dimensions, $(A + B) + C = A + (B + C)$.

Scalar Multiplication

Matrix addition is related to a special multiplication involving matrices called *scalar multiplication.*

Activity

MATERIALS CAS

Step 1 Enter the matrix $\begin{bmatrix} a & b & c \\ d & e & f \end{bmatrix}$ into your CAS and store it as *M*1. Steps 2–8: See margin.

Step 2 Add the matrix from Step 1 to itself and write down the result. You should see a display similar to the one at the right.

$\begin{bmatrix} a & b & c \\ d & e & f \end{bmatrix} \to m1$ $\quad \begin{bmatrix} a & b & c \\ d & e & f \end{bmatrix}$

$m1+m1 \quad \begin{bmatrix} 2\cdot a & 2\cdot b & 2\cdot c \\ 2\cdot d & 2\cdot e & 2\cdot f \end{bmatrix}$

Step 3 Add the result from Step 2 to the original matrix in Step 1 and write down the result.

Step 4 If you add the result from Step 3 to the matrix in Step 1, what result do you expect? Why?

Step 5 Clear your screen and enter $2 * \begin{bmatrix} a & b & c \\ d & e & f \end{bmatrix}$ and write down the result.

Step 6 Enter $3 * \begin{bmatrix} a & b & c \\ d & e & f \end{bmatrix}$ and write down the result.

Step 7 If you enter $4 * \begin{bmatrix} a & b & c \\ d & e & f \end{bmatrix}$, what result do you expect? Why?

Step 8: Is there a connection between your responses to Step 4 and Step 7? If so, what is it?

Accommodating the Learner

Tell students that any matrix with 0 as every element is called a *zero matrix*. Then tell students to write an $m \times n$ matrix A and find a matrix B so that $A + B$ is a zero matrix. Answers vary. Sample: If $A = \begin{bmatrix} 5 & -3 & 2 \\ -1 & 4 & 7 \end{bmatrix}$ and $B = \begin{bmatrix} -5 & 3 & -2 \\ 1 & -4 & -7 \end{bmatrix}$, then $A + B = \begin{bmatrix} 0 & 0 & 0 \\ 0 & 0 & 0 \end{bmatrix}$.

ENGLISH LEARNERS

Vocabulary Development

For the scalar product kA, where k is a real number and A is a matrix, students should understand that kA represents a matrix, and that matrix has the same dimensions as matrix A.

2. Suppose there is a 5% increase in these costs this year from last year. What would be the costs for utilities in October of this year?

$\begin{bmatrix} 86.10 \\ 23.10 \\ 14.70 \end{bmatrix}$

(*Note:* Warm-Up Question 1 illustrates matrix addition; Warm-Up Question 2 represents multiplying the original October matrix by the scalar 1.05.)

2 Teaching

Notes on the Lesson

Matrix addition usually comes naturally to students. Stress that to perform matrix addition or subtraction, the two matrices *must* have the same dimensions. Students should easily see that matrix addition is commutative. This result is very easy to prove for matrices of any given size. Consider the 2×2 matrices $M = \begin{bmatrix} a & b \\ c & d \end{bmatrix}$ and $N = \begin{bmatrix} e & f \\ g & h \end{bmatrix}$, where all the elements of the matrices are real numbers. Then $M + N = \begin{bmatrix} a+e & b+f \\ c+g & d+h \end{bmatrix}$ (definition of matrix addition) $= \begin{bmatrix} e+a & f+b \\ g+c & h+d \end{bmatrix}$ (commutativity of real number addition) $= N + M$ (definition of matrix addition).

Similarly, if $P = \begin{bmatrix} j & k \\ l & m \end{bmatrix}$, you can use the associativity of real number addition to deduce that $(M + N) + P = M + (N + P)$. These properties may seem obvious here, but students will see in Lesson 4-3 that matrix multiplication is not necessarily commutative.

Note-Taking Tips

Call students' attention to the statement on page 229 that "only matrices with the same dimensions can be added." Encourage students to make a note to themselves about the dimensions of matrices before adding ("Both matrices are 2×5, so they can be added."). This attention to dimensions will become more important when students consider pairs of matrices to be multiplied.

Additional Example

Example 1 Find the scalar product $8\begin{bmatrix} 4.2 & \frac{3}{2} \\ -6.4 & 2 \end{bmatrix}$. $\begin{bmatrix} 33.6 & 12 \\ -51.2 & 16 \end{bmatrix}$

Additional Answers

Activity

Step 2: $\begin{bmatrix} 2a & 2b & 2c \\ 2d & 2e & 2f \end{bmatrix}$

Step 3: $\begin{bmatrix} 3a & 3b & 3c \\ 3d & 3e & 3f \end{bmatrix}$

Step 4: $\begin{bmatrix} 4a & 4b & 4c \\ 4d & 4e & 4f \end{bmatrix}$; The coefficients seem to be increasing by 1 each time I add the original matrix.

Step 5: $\begin{bmatrix} 2a & 2b & 2c \\ 2d & 2e & 2f \end{bmatrix}$

Step 6: $\begin{bmatrix} 3a & 3b & 3c \\ 3d & 3e & 3f \end{bmatrix}$

Step 7: $\begin{bmatrix} 4a & 4b & 4c \\ 4d & 4e & 4f \end{bmatrix}$; Again, the coefficients seem to be increasing by 1.

Step 8: Answers vary. Sample: Yes; Steps 4 and 7 show that the result of adding a matrix to itself a certain number of times is the same as multiplying the original matrix by the number of times you added it.

With real numbers, you can use multiplication as shorthand for repeated addition. For instance, $a + a + a$ can be written as $3 \cdot a$ or $3a$. The Activity gives evidence that this rule also holds true for matrices. Repeated matrix addition gives rise to an operation called **scalar multiplication**.

Definition of Scalar Multiplication

The **scalar product** of a real number k and a matrix A is the matrix kA in which each element is k times the corresponding element in A.

Example 1

Find the scalar product $6\begin{bmatrix} -2.3 & 8 \\ 7.1 & \frac{1}{2} \end{bmatrix}$.

Solution Multiply each element in the matrix by 6.

$$6\begin{bmatrix} -2.3 & 8 \\ 7.1 & \frac{1}{2} \end{bmatrix} = \begin{bmatrix} 6 \cdot -2.3 & 6 \cdot 8 \\ 6 \cdot 7.1 & 6 \cdot \frac{1}{2} \end{bmatrix} = \begin{bmatrix} -13.8 & 48 \\ 42.6 & 3 \end{bmatrix}$$

How Are Matrices Subtracted?

In the set of real numbers, subtraction has the following property: $a - b = a + -b = a + -1 \cdot b$. Matrices are subtracted in a similar manner:

$$A - B = A + (-1)B = A + (-B).$$

Definition of Matrix Subtraction

Given two matrices A and B with the same dimensions, their **difference** $A - B$ is the matrix in which each element is the difference of the corresponding elements in A and B.

Accommodating the Learner

Give students two $m \times n$ matrices such as $A = \begin{bmatrix} 1 & -3 & 5 \\ 2 & 0 & 8 \end{bmatrix}$ and $B = \begin{bmatrix} 4 & 7 & 9 \\ -3 & 4 & 2 \end{bmatrix}$. Ask them to find another $m \times n$ matrix C so that the sum of C and itself is equal to $A + B$. Ask students to explain their work.

Answers vary. Sample: $A + B = \begin{bmatrix} 5 & 4 & 14 \\ -1 & 4 & 10 \end{bmatrix}$.

I took half of each entry to get

$C = \begin{bmatrix} 2.5 & 2 & 7 \\ -0.5 & 2 & 5 \end{bmatrix}$, so $C + C = 2C\begin{bmatrix} 5 & 4 & 14 \\ -1 & 4 & 10 \end{bmatrix}$.

Example 2

The matrices $P1$ and $P2$ below represent the degrees earned by men and women in four professions during 2003 and 2004.

$$\begin{array}{l} \\ \text{Medicine} \\ \text{Dentistry} \\ \text{Law} \\ \text{Theology} \end{array} \overset{\begin{array}{cc} & 2003 \\ \text{Male} & \text{Female} \end{array}}{\begin{bmatrix} 8{,}221 & 6{,}813 \\ 2{,}653 & 1{,}691 \\ 19{,}916 & 19{,}151 \\ 3{,}499 & 1{,}852 \end{bmatrix}} = P1 \qquad \begin{array}{l} \\ \text{Medicine} \\ \text{Dentistry} \\ \text{Law} \\ \text{Theology} \end{array} \overset{\begin{array}{cc} & 2004 \\ \text{Male} & \text{Female} \end{array}}{\begin{bmatrix} 8{,}273 & 7{,}169 \\ 2{,}532 & 1{,}803 \\ 20{,}332 & 19{,}877 \\ 3{,}511 & 1{,}821 \end{bmatrix}} = P2$$

Source: U.S. Census Bureau

a. Create a new matrix that shows the change in the number of degrees awarded from 2003 to 2004, separated by gender.

b. Which group, male or female, had the greater total increase in degrees awarded?

Solution

a. The change by gender of degrees awarded can be found by creating $P2 - P1$. Store $P1$ and $P2$ on a CAS. Then subtract the matrices as shown at the right.

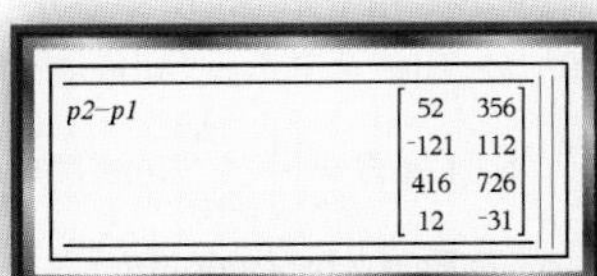

b. The sum of the elements in the first column in matrix $P2 - P1$ gives the overall change for males, and the sum of the elements in the second column gives the overall change for females.

Overall change for males: $52 + -121 + 416 + 12 = 359$

Overall change for females: $356 + 112 + 726 + -31 = 1163$

Females had the greater total increase in degrees awarded with 1163 more degrees in 2004 than 2003.

STOP QY

When more than one matrix operation appears in an expression, you should follow the same order of operations as with expressions involving real numbers. That is, you should perform scalar multiplication before addition or subtraction. You are asked to evaluate expressions with more than one matrix operation in Questions 4 and 5.

▶ QY

Check your answer to Part a of Example 2 by performing the subtraction of the first row by hand.

Questions

COVERING THE IDEAS

1. Can you add $\begin{bmatrix} 6 & -8 \end{bmatrix}$ to $\begin{bmatrix} 4 \\ 2 \end{bmatrix}$? Explain why or why not.

1. No; in order to add two matrices, they must have the same dimensions. The two matrices in question have different dimensions.

Additional Example

Example 2 The following two matrices give the numbers of gallons of gasoline (in thousands) sold at a busy gas station, organized by the type of gas and the type of vehicle. Matrices J and L represent the months of June and July, respectively.

$$\begin{array}{r} \\ \text{cars} \\ \text{trucks} \\ \text{SUVs} \end{array} \overset{\begin{array}{ccc} \text{Reg.} & \text{Prem.} & \text{Super} \end{array}}{\begin{bmatrix} 25.0 & 22.5 & 31.0 \\ 10.8 & 9.4 & 8.8 \\ 31.0 & 40.5 & 49.5 \end{bmatrix}} = J$$

$$\begin{array}{r} \\ \text{cars} \\ \text{trucks} \\ \text{SUVs} \end{array} \overset{\begin{array}{ccc} \text{Reg.} & \text{Prem.} & \text{Super} \end{array}}{\begin{bmatrix} 21.0 & 28.0 & 44.5 \\ 9.5 & 8.2 & 6.0 \\ 41.8 & 51.7 & 59.5 \end{bmatrix}} = L$$

a. Create a new matrix that shows the change in sales from June to July. $\begin{bmatrix} -4.0 & 5.5 & 13.5 \\ -1.3 & -1.2 & -2.8 \\ 10.8 & 11.2 & 10.0 \end{bmatrix}$

b. Which category had the greatest increase? Which category had the greatest decrease? super for cars; regular for cars

3 Assignment

Recommended Assignment

- Questions 1–21
- Question 22 (extra credit)
- Reading Lesson 4-3
- Covering the Ideas 4-3

Extension

Ask students to use any two 2×3 matrices A and B and any nonzero real number k to verify the distributive property for scalar multiplication and matrix addition: $k(A + B) = kA + kB$. Answers vary. Check students' work.

Notes on the Questions

Questions 10–12 When matrices represent real-world data, students should label the matrices so that the data are easily identifiable. These questions illustrate appropriate labeling.

Additional Answers

7. $\begin{bmatrix} 6 & 8 & 4 & 3 & 1 \\ 7 & 8 & 5 & 2 & 5 \\ 13 & 1 & 1 & 4 & 4 \\ 12 & 1 & 9 & 4 & 2 \end{bmatrix}$;

The matrix represents the cars at Rusty's Car Dealership that were not damaged by the hailstorm.

10a. $T = \begin{matrix} 9 & 10 & 11 & 12 \\ \end{matrix}$ $\begin{bmatrix} 683 & 659 & 635 & 612 \\ 682 & 665 & 642 & 618 \end{bmatrix}\begin{matrix} \text{boys} \\ \text{girls} \end{matrix}$ (columns 9, 10, 11, 12)

10b. $\begin{bmatrix} -135 & -133 & -133 & -132 \\ -156 & -145 & -138 & -132 \end{bmatrix}\begin{matrix} \text{boys} \\ \text{girls} \end{matrix}$ (columns 9, 10, 11, 12)

In 2–5, perform the indicated operations.

2. $\begin{bmatrix} -2 & 5 \\ 0 & -7 \end{bmatrix} + \begin{bmatrix} 1 & -3 \\ 8 & -2 \end{bmatrix}$

3. $\begin{bmatrix} 13 & -9 \\ -21 & 6 \end{bmatrix} - \begin{bmatrix} 8 & 6 \\ -15 & 3 \end{bmatrix}$

4. $2\begin{bmatrix} -1 & -3 \\ \frac{1}{2} & \frac{5}{2} \end{bmatrix} + \begin{bmatrix} 6 & -4 \\ 2 & 0 \end{bmatrix}$

5. $-3\begin{bmatrix} 0 & 1 \\ \frac{1}{2} & -2 \end{bmatrix} - 4\begin{bmatrix} \frac{1}{4} & 0 \\ \frac{3}{4} & -1 \end{bmatrix}$

In 6 and 7, refer to Rusty's car inventory matrices *C* and *D* at the beginning of this lesson.

6. Does $C + D = D + C$? Explain why or why not.
7. Suppose matrix D represents cars in the current inventory that were damaged in a hailstorm. Find $C - D$, and explain what it represents. See margin.
8. Refer to the matrix $P2 - P1$ from Example 2.
   a. For which profession was there the greatest change in the number of degrees awarded? law
   b. Is the change in Part a an increase or decrease? increase
9. a. **True or False** Subtraction of matrices is commutative. false
   b. Let $B = \begin{bmatrix} 1 & 4 \\ 7 & 10 \end{bmatrix}$ and $C = \begin{bmatrix} 2 & 5 \\ 8 & 11 \end{bmatrix}$. Support your answer to Part a by evaluating $B - C$ and $C - B$.

APPLYING THE MATHEMATICS

10. The matrices $N1$, $N2$, and $N3$ give the enrollments by gender and grade at North High School over a 3-year period, beginning with $N1$ and ending with $N3$. In each matrix, row 1 gives the number of boys and row 2 the number of girls. Columns 1 to 4 give the number of students in grades 9 through 12, respectively. a–b. See margin.

Grades (columns 9, 10, 11, 12)

$N1 = \begin{bmatrix} 289 & 282 & 276 & 270 \\ 299 & 288 & 276 & 264 \end{bmatrix}\begin{matrix} \text{boys} \\ \text{girls} \end{matrix}$

$N2 = \begin{bmatrix} 240 & 228 & 216 & 204 \\ 240 & 234 & 228 & 222 \end{bmatrix}\begin{matrix} \text{boys} \\ \text{girls} \end{matrix}$

$N3 = \begin{bmatrix} 154 & 149 & 143 & 138 \\ 143 & 143 & 138 & 132 \end{bmatrix}\begin{matrix} \text{boys} \\ \text{girls} \end{matrix}$

   a. Find matrix T that shows the total enrollment in each grade by gender over the 3-year time span.
   b. What was the change in enrollment for boys and girls in each grade from the first year to the last year?

2. $\begin{bmatrix} -1 & 2 \\ 8 & -9 \end{bmatrix}$
3. $\begin{bmatrix} 5 & -15 \\ -6 & 3 \end{bmatrix}$
4. $\begin{bmatrix} 4 & -10 \\ 3 & 5 \end{bmatrix}$
5. $\begin{bmatrix} -1 & -3 \\ -\frac{9}{2} & 10 \end{bmatrix}$
6. Yes; the addition of matrices is commutative.

9b. $B - C = \begin{bmatrix} -1 & -1 \\ -1 & -1 \end{bmatrix}$; $C - B = \begin{bmatrix} 1 & 1 \\ 1 & 1 \end{bmatrix}$

4-2A Lesson Master

Questions on SPUR Objectives
See Student Edition pages 293–297 for objectives.

SKILLS Objective B

In 1–4, perform the indicated operations.

1. $\begin{bmatrix} 8 \\ 5 \end{bmatrix} + \begin{bmatrix} 4 \\ -1 \end{bmatrix} = \begin{bmatrix} 12 \\ 4 \end{bmatrix}$
2. $[-3 \;\; 5 \;\; -1] - [5 \;\; 2 \;\; 0] = [-8 \;\; 3 \;\; -1]$
3. $2\begin{bmatrix} 7 & 8 \\ -3 & 5 \end{bmatrix} + \frac{1}{2}\begin{bmatrix} 4 & 2 \\ 5 & 0 \end{bmatrix} = \begin{bmatrix} 16 & 17 \\ -\frac{7}{2} & 10 \end{bmatrix}$
4. $\begin{bmatrix} a & b \\ c & d \end{bmatrix} + \begin{bmatrix} e & f \\ g & h \end{bmatrix} = \begin{bmatrix} a+e & b+f \\ c+g & d+h \end{bmatrix}$
5. Find a and b. $3\begin{bmatrix} 7 & 8 & -2 \\ -3 & 5 & 1 \end{bmatrix} - \begin{bmatrix} 4 & 2a & -9 \\ 5 & 0 & -1 \end{bmatrix} = \begin{bmatrix} 17 & 2 & 3 \\ -14 & 15 & b \end{bmatrix}$ $a = 11, b = 4$

PROPERTIES Objective E

6. Give the dimensions of a matrix that could be added to $\begin{bmatrix} 4 & 2 & -3 \\ -6 & 0 & 1 \end{bmatrix}$ 2×3
7. A 4×3 matrix is multiplied by the scalar 5. What are the dimensions of the resulting matrix? 4×3
8. Is matrix addition *associative*, *commutative*, *both*, or *neither*? both

USES Objective J

In 9 and 10, companies *A* and *B* merge. The total number of employees at each company before the merger is given in matrices *A* and *B* below.

A =

	Management	Administrative	Manufacturing
Full-time	12	15	7
Part-time	1	7	1

B =

	Management	Administrative	Manufacturing
Full-time	28	33	125
Part-time	3	5	9

9. Find the matrix $C = A + B$ and explain what C represents.

C =

	Management	Administrative	Manufacturing
Full-time	40	48	196
Part-time	4	12	20

C represents the total number of employees in the merged company, organized by department and schedule.

10. After the merger, the board of directors decides to reduce the workforce by 25%. Show the matrix arithmetic that will give the new employment totals.

$0.75\begin{bmatrix} 40 & 48 & 196 \\ 4 & 12 & 20 \end{bmatrix} = \begin{bmatrix} 30 & 36 & 147 \\ 3 & 9 & 15 \end{bmatrix}$ or

$\begin{bmatrix} 40 & 48 & 196 \\ 4 & 12 & 20 \end{bmatrix} - 0.25\begin{bmatrix} 40 & 48 & 196 \\ 4 & 12 & 20 \end{bmatrix} = \begin{bmatrix} 30 & 36 & 147 \\ 3 & 9 & 15 \end{bmatrix}$

Advanced Algebra 203

11. Some key results for four teams from the National Football League for the 2005 and 2006 regular season are given in the matrices below. W = number of wins, L = number of losses, PF = points scored for the team, and PA = points scored against the team.

2006

	W	L	PF	PA
New England	12	4	385	237
Pittsburgh	8	8	353	315
Indianapolis	12	4	427	360
Denver	9	7	319	305

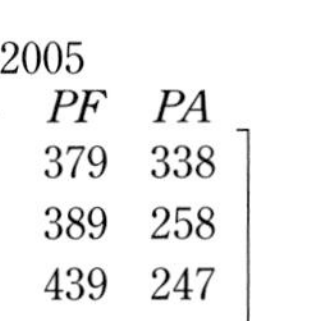

2005

	W	L	PF	PA
New England	10	6	379	338
Pittsburgh	11	5	389	258
Indianapolis	14	2	439	247
Denver	13	3	395	258

Source: www.NFL.com

a. Subtract the right matrix from the left matrix. Call the difference M. See margin.

b. What is the meaning of the 4th column of M?

c. Interpret each number in the 1st row of M. See margin.

11b. the difference in points scored against each team in 2006 from 2005

12. Pearl, a puzzle maker, constructs three types of animal puzzles for children in two different styles. Pearl's output last year is given in the matrix P below.

	Cat	Dog	Mouse
Wood	12	20	8
Cardboard	18	14	11

$= P$

a. Suppose Pearl wants to increase output by 25%. Write the matrix that represents the needed output. Round all decimals to the nearest whole number.

b. If your answer to Part a is the matrix kP, what is k? $k = 1.25$

The Pittsburgh Steelers celebrated their 2006 Super Bowl win.

12a. $\begin{bmatrix} 15 & 25 & 10 \\ 23 & 18 & 14 \end{bmatrix}$

13. Let $F = \begin{bmatrix} \frac{1}{3} & \frac{1}{6} \\ \frac{1}{9} & \frac{1}{12} \end{bmatrix}$. Let $G = \begin{bmatrix} 1 & \frac{1}{2} \\ \frac{1}{3} & \frac{1}{4} \end{bmatrix}$.

a. Solve $F = kG$ for k. $k = \frac{1}{3}$ b. Solve $G = \ell F$ for ℓ. $\ell = 3$

14. Is $D = \begin{bmatrix} 20 & 12 \\ 50 & 40 \end{bmatrix}$ a scalar multiple of $E = \begin{bmatrix} \frac{1}{3} & \frac{1}{5} \\ \frac{5}{6} & \frac{3}{2} \end{bmatrix}$? If so, identify the scalar k. If not, explain why not.

14. No; all of the elements in matrix D are not multiplied by the same scalar to produce the respective elements in matrix E.

In 15 and 16, solve for a, b, c and d.

15. $\begin{bmatrix} a & 18 \\ 54 & 35 \end{bmatrix} + \begin{bmatrix} 17 & b \\ c & d \end{bmatrix} = \begin{bmatrix} 21 & 81 \\ 25 & 30 \end{bmatrix}$ $a = 4, b = 63, c = -29, d = -5$

16. $2\begin{bmatrix} a & b \\ 14 & 4 \end{bmatrix} - 7\begin{bmatrix} 3 & -1 \\ c & -2.5 \end{bmatrix} = \begin{bmatrix} \frac{1}{2} & 0 \\ 4 & d \end{bmatrix}$ $a = 10.75, b = -3.5, c = \frac{24}{7}, d = 25.5$

Notes on the Questions

Question 13 To find k, only one equation needs to be solved. However, students should confirm that the value of k works for the other three pairs of corresponding entries in the matrices.

Questions 15 and 16 Some teachers like to call this type of question "an instant quiz" because each question requires students to solve four equations.

Question 18 One purpose of this question is to illustrate that it is much more difficult to comprehend data when seeing it in a paragraph than when the same data are presented in a matrix.

Additional Answers can be found in the back of the book.

Additional Answers

11a. $M = \begin{bmatrix} 2 & -2 & 6 & -101 \\ -3 & 3 & -36 & 57 \\ -2 & 2 & -12 & 113 \\ -4 & 4 & -76 & 47 \end{bmatrix}$

11c. 2 means New England had 2 more wins in 2006 compared to 2005; –2 represents the 2 fewer losses New England had in 2006 compared to 2005; 6 represents how many more points New England scored in 2006 compared to 2005; –101 represents how many fewer points against New England were incurred in 2006 compared to 2005.

4 Wrap-Up

Ongoing Assessment

Show students the two matrices $A = \begin{bmatrix} 5 & -3 & 2 \\ -1 & 4 & 7 \end{bmatrix}$ and $B = \begin{bmatrix} 2 & 8 & 3 \\ 0 & -2 & 5 \end{bmatrix}$. Ask them to calculate $A + B$, $5B$, and $B - A$.

$A + B = \begin{bmatrix} 7 & 5 & 5 \\ -1 & 2 & 12 \end{bmatrix}$; $5B = \begin{bmatrix} 10 & 40 & 15 \\ 0 & -10 & 25 \end{bmatrix}$;

$B - A = \begin{bmatrix} -3 & 11 & 1 \\ 1 & -6 & -2 \end{bmatrix}$

Additional Answers

21b.

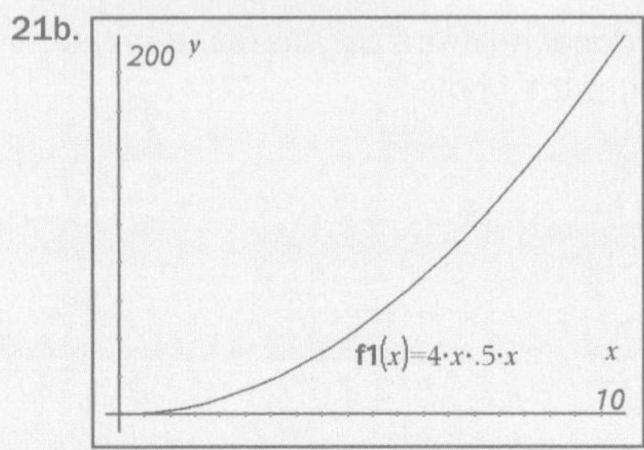

21e.

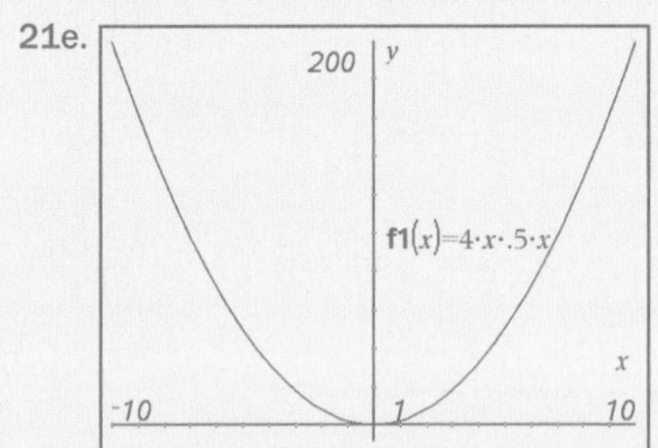

4-2B page 2

4-2B Lesson Master

Questions on SPUR Objectives
See Student Edition pages 293–297 for objectives.

SKILLS Objective B

In 1 and 2, perform the indicated operations.

1. $\begin{bmatrix} 1 & 4 & -6 \\ 2 & -3 & -3 \end{bmatrix} + \begin{bmatrix} 3 & 0 & 6 \\ 4 & -3 & 8 \end{bmatrix}$ $\begin{bmatrix} 4 & 4 & 0 \\ 6 & -6 & 5 \end{bmatrix}$

2. $\begin{bmatrix} 5 & 2 \\ 2 & -1 \\ 5 & 4 \end{bmatrix} - \begin{bmatrix} -2 & 2 \\ 0 & -1 \\ -5 & 7 \end{bmatrix}$ $\begin{bmatrix} 7 & 0 \\ 2 & 0 \\ 10 & -3 \end{bmatrix}$

In 3–8, let $A = \begin{bmatrix} -7 & 2 & 6 \\ 9 & 0 & -2 \\ -5 & 3 & 3 \end{bmatrix}$ and $B = \begin{bmatrix} 4 & -7 & -2 \\ 5 & 5 & 0 \\ -2 & 9 & 6 \end{bmatrix}$. Calculate

3. $3A$ $\begin{bmatrix} -21 & 6 & 18 \\ 27 & 0 & -6 \\ -15 & 9 & 9 \end{bmatrix}$

4. $-4B$ $\begin{bmatrix} -16 & 28 & 8 \\ -20 & -20 & 0 \\ 8 & -36 & -24 \end{bmatrix}$

5. $A + B$ $\begin{bmatrix} -3 & -5 & 4 \\ 14 & 5 & -2 \\ -7 & 12 & 9 \end{bmatrix}$

6. $2A + 3B$ $\begin{bmatrix} -2 & -17 & 6 \\ 33 & 15 & -4 \\ -16 & 33 & 24 \end{bmatrix}$

7. $B - A$ $\begin{bmatrix} 11 & -9 & -8 \\ -4 & 5 & 2 \\ 3 & 6 & 3 \end{bmatrix}$

8. $A - 5B$ $\begin{bmatrix} -27 & 37 & 16 \\ -16 & -25 & -2 \\ 5 & -42 & -27 \end{bmatrix}$

In 9–11, solve for *a* and *b*.

9. $\begin{bmatrix} 3 & a & -2 \\ -2 & 6 & 10 \end{bmatrix} + \begin{bmatrix} 3 & 8 & 0 \\ 1 & -1 & b \end{bmatrix} = \begin{bmatrix} 6 & 11 & -2 \\ -1 & 5 & 5 \end{bmatrix}$ $a =$ 3 $b =$ -5

10. $\begin{bmatrix} 6 & 8 & 0 \\ a & 7 & 13 \end{bmatrix} - \begin{bmatrix} 1 & b & 4 \\ 3 & 7 & 6 \end{bmatrix} = \begin{bmatrix} -5 & 11 & -4 \\ 0 & 0 & 7 \end{bmatrix}$ $a =$ 3 $b =$ -3

11. $4\begin{bmatrix} a & 7 \\ 5 & -4 \end{bmatrix} - 3\begin{bmatrix} 4 & b \\ 2 & 0 \end{bmatrix} = \begin{bmatrix} 14 & 31 \\ 14 & -16 \end{bmatrix}$ $a =$ 6.5 $b =$ -1

204 *Advanced Algebra*

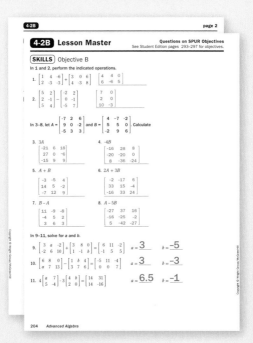

REVIEW

17. Write a matrix to represent the triangle with vertices at the origin, (0, 4), and (-1, 0). **(Lesson 4-1)**

17. $\begin{bmatrix} 0 & 0 & -1 \\ 0 & 4 & 0 \end{bmatrix}$

18. According to the 2000 United States Census, in 2000 there were 7,229,068 foreign-born and 46,365,310 native-born people living in the Northeast; 3,509,937 foreign-born and 60,882,839 native-born people living in the Midwest; 8,608,441 foreign-born and 91,628,379 native-born people living in the South; and 11,760,443 foreign-born and 51,437,489 native-born people living in the West. Write a matrix to store this information in millions, rounding each population to the nearest million. **(Lesson 4-1)**

18.

	foreign-born	native-born
Northeast	7	46
Midwest	4	61
South	9	92
West	12	51

19. Graph $f(x) = -\lfloor x \rfloor$ and $g(x) = \lfloor -x \rfloor$ separately. Explain the difference in the two graphs. **(Lesson 3-9)** See margin.

20. A plumber charges a fixed fee to come to your house, plus an hourly fee for the time spent on the repair job. Suppose the plumber comes to your house, works for an hour, and charges \$120. The next week the plumber has to return to finish the job and spends one and a half hours working, and charges \$160. Write a possible equation that describes how much the plumber charges based on hours of work. Use it to figure out the fixed fee. **(Lesson 3-4)**

20. Cost of plumber = $40 + 80x$; the plumber's fixed fee is \$40.

21. A rectangle has sides of length $4x$ and $0.5x$. **(Lesson 2-5)**
   a. Write an equation for the area of the rectangle as a function of the lengths of its sides. Area $= 4x \cdot 0.5x = 2x^2$
   b. Graph this equation in an appropriate window. See margin.
   c. What is the domain of the function you graphed? $\{x \mid x > 0\}$
   d. What is the domain of the function if the context is ignored? the set of real numbers
   e. Graph the function again over the domain in Part d. See margin.

4x

0.5x

EXPLORATION

22. The matrix $\begin{bmatrix} 1 & 3 \\ 2 & 4 \end{bmatrix}$ gives the endpoints of a line segment. a–c. See margin.
   a. Find the slope of the line containing the segment and graph it.
   b. Find the slope of the line through points $\begin{bmatrix} -2 & -4 \\ 1 & 3 \end{bmatrix}$ and graph it.
   c. Compare the two matrices. Then generalize Parts a and b.

QY ANSWER

[8273 7169] − [8221 6813] = [8273 − 8221 7169 − 6813] = [52 356] The subtraction checks.

Additional Answers

22a. $m = 1$

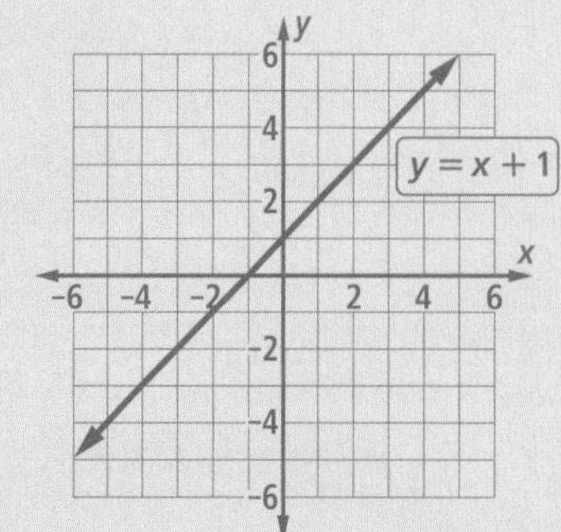

22b. $m = -1$

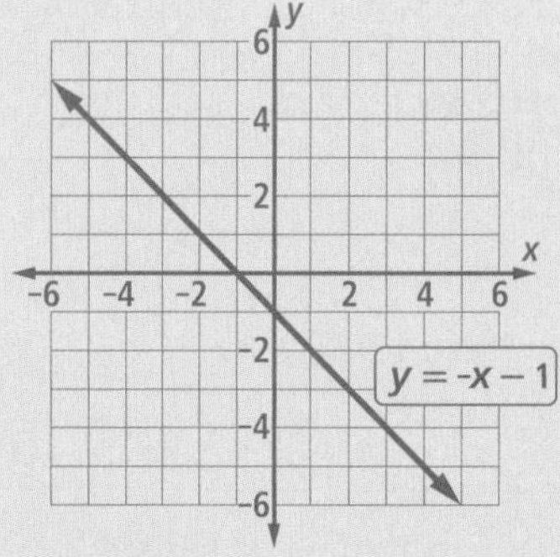

22c. Answers vary. Sample: Switching the values of the x- and y-coordinates and then making the new x-coordinate negative creates a line that is perpendicular to the original line.

Lesson 4-3 Matrix Multiplication

Vocabulary

row-by-column multiplication
matrix multiplication
matrix product

BIG IDEA Matrices with compatible dimensions can be multiplied using row-by-column multiplication.

If you want to buy four \$12 pizzas, you find the total cost by multiplying: $12\ \frac{\text{dollars}}{\text{pizza}} \cdot 4$ pizzas = \$48. But consider a more complicated situation: the Forensics Club (F), the Jazz Band (J), and the Volleyball team (V) are each holding pizza parties, are each ordering different quantities of cheese (C), mushroom (M), and "garbage" (G) pizzas (which have everything on them), and want to compare prices at two different pizzerias, Lorenzo's and Billy's.

These data have been organized into the two matrices below. One matrix contains the prices in dollars for each type of pizza at the two pizzerias, and the second matrix contains the number of each type of pizza ordered by each club.

Price per Pizza

	C	M	G
Lorenzo's Prices	12	15	20
Billy's Prices	11	17	18

Pizzas per Club

	F	J	V
Cheese	4	1	3
Mushroom	3	5	3
Garbage	2	3	3

 QY1

Mental Math

Estimate the tip to the nearest dime.

a. a 10% tip on a bill of \$24.95 \$2.50

b. a 15% tip on a bill of \$32.20 \$4.80

c. a 20% tip on a bill of \$73.83 \$14.80

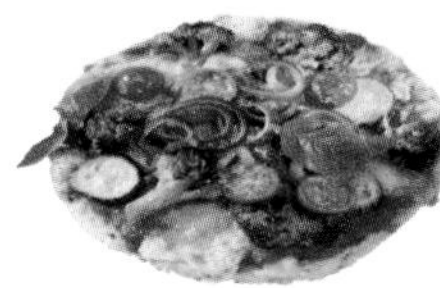

a "garbage" pizza of vegetables

QY1

a. What is the price of a cheese pizza at Lorenzo's?

b. How many mushroom pizzas has the Forensics Club ordered?

Example 1

Write a single expression giving the total price for pizzas at Lorenzo's for the Forensics Club and evaluate it.

Solution The prices at Lorenzo's are in the first row of the Price-per-Pizza matrix. The numbers of each kind of pizza ordered by the Forensics Club are in the first column of the Pizza-per-Club matrix.

Lorenzo's Prices per Pizza: $\begin{array}{c} \begin{matrix} C & M & G \end{matrix} \\ \begin{bmatrix} 12 & 15 & 20 \end{bmatrix} \end{array}$

Pizzas Ordered by the Forensics Club: $\begin{matrix} C \\ M \\ G \end{matrix} \begin{bmatrix} 4 \\ 3 \\ 2 \end{bmatrix}$

Total Price for the Forensics Club Order at Lorenzo's: $\$12 \cdot 4 + \$15 \cdot 3 + \$20 \cdot 2 = \$133$

Background

In a later lesson, students will see matrix multiplication as a way to keep track of coefficients in the composition of linear transformations (in fact, that use led to the operation we call matrix multiplication). There are four common elementary applications for matrix multiplication: (1) business situations, given in this lesson; (2) transformation applications, introduced in Lesson 4-4; (3) applications to systems, discussed in Chapter 5; and (4) applications to networks, a topic in UCSMP *Precalculus and Discrete Mathematics.*

We purposely delay the systems application—most commonly given first—because it does not show students anything they could not do before. The business applications are a nice surprise.

(continued on next page)

Lesson 4-3

GOAL

Multiply 2 × 2 matrices and apply matrix multiplication in various situations.

SPUR Objectives

C Multiply matrices.

E Recognize properties of matrix operations.

J Use matrix multiplication to solve real-world problems.

Materials/Resources

- Lesson Masters 4-3A and 4-3B
- Resource Masters 59 and 60
- Quiz 1
- CAS or graphing calculator

HOMEWORK

Suggestions for Assignment

- Questions 1–22
- Question 23 (extra credit)
- Reading Lesson 4-4
- Covering the Ideas 4-4

Local Standards

1 Warm-Up

An ounce of ground beef has about 60 calories, a French fry has about 11 calories, and an ounce of yogurt has about 40 calories.

1. If you eat a quarter pound of beef, 20 French fries, and 4 ounces of yogurt, how many calories have you consumed? 620
2. Write the calculation in Warm-Up Question 1 as a matrix multiplication.
$\begin{bmatrix} 60 & 11 & 40 \end{bmatrix} \cdot \begin{bmatrix} 4 \\ 20 \\ 4 \end{bmatrix} = [620]$

2 Teaching

Notes on the Lesson

We recommend the following four-step approach for teaching matrix multiplication.

1. Explain how to combine one row and one column.
2. Point out that matrices can be multiplied only when the number of columns of the left matrix equals the number of rows of the right matrix.
3. Show how to determine the dimensions of the product.
4. Find each element of the product matrix as the product of that element's row and column from the multiplied matrices.

Emphasize how the elements in a row are paired with the elements in a column.

When multiplying $\begin{bmatrix} a & b & c \end{bmatrix} \cdot \begin{bmatrix} d \\ e \\ f \end{bmatrix}$, students should see that every element in the row has a corresponding element in the column. In contrast, if students tried to multiply $\begin{bmatrix} a & b & c & g \end{bmatrix} \cdot \begin{bmatrix} d \\ e \\ f \end{bmatrix}$, they would not be able to do so because g has no corresponding element.

This kind of discussion helps to emphasize the importance of a dimensional check before multiplying matrices. To multiply matrices, the number of columns of the left matrix must equal the number of rows of the right matrix.

Additional Example

Example 1 Use the data on page 235 to write a single expression giving the total price for pizzas at the Pizza Shop for the volleyball team and evaluate it. $\$11 \cdot 3 + \$17 \cdot 3 + \$18 \cdot 3 = \$138$

Multiplying Two Matrices

The calculation $\$12 \cdot 4 + \$15 \cdot 3 + \$20 \cdot 2 = \$133$ in Example 1 illustrates an idea that is used to calculate the product of these matrices. The idea is called **row-by-column multiplication**. The solution to Example 1 is shown in matrix notation below. A row matrix is multiplied by a column matrix to get a 1×1 product matrix.

$$\begin{bmatrix} 12 & 15 & 20 \end{bmatrix} \cdot \begin{bmatrix} 4 \\ 3 \\ 2 \end{bmatrix} = [12 \cdot 4 + 15 \cdot 3 + 20 \cdot 2] = [133]$$

This process can be generalized into the algorithm below.

Algorithm for Row-by-Column Multiplication

Step 1 Multiply the first element in the row matrix by the first element in the column matrix. Multiply the second element in the row matrix by the second element in the column matrix. Continue multiplying the nth element in the row by the nth element in the column until you reach the end of the row and the column.

Step 2 Add the products in Step 1.

Notice that the row and the column have to have the same number of elements in order for this multiplication to work. Also, the row is on the left and the column is on the right.

The product $A \cdot B$ or AB of two matrices A and B is found by using the above algorithm to multiply each row of A times each column of B. For example, if matrix A has 2 rows and matrix B has 3 columns, then there are 6 ways to multiply a row by a column. The 6 products of these rows and columns are the 6 elements of the product matrix AB. The entry in row 2, column 3 of the product comes from multiplying row 2 of the first matrix by column 3 of the second matrix, as shown below.

$$\begin{bmatrix} 12 & 15 & 20 \\ 11 & 17 & 18 \end{bmatrix} \cdot \begin{bmatrix} 4 & 1 & 3 \\ 3 & 5 & 3 \\ 2 & 3 & 3 \end{bmatrix} = \begin{bmatrix} 133 & 147 & 141 \\ 131 & 150 & 138 \end{bmatrix}$$

If you multiply the Price-per-Pizza matrix by the Pizzas-per-Club matrix, you will get a product matrix for price per club. The calculator display at the right shows the product. This is not scalar multiplication; it is **matrix multiplication**.

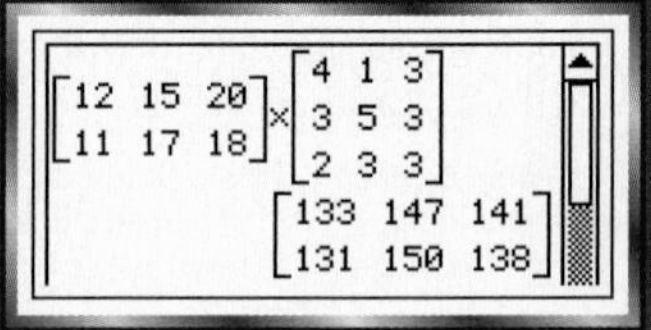

A common misconception is that matrix multiplication is difficult for students to learn. We believe, and students and their teachers support this belief, that after students calculate a few row-by-column terms, they will develop skill and comfort in multiplying matrices. That approach is given in this lesson and recommended in the Notes on the Lesson.

Accommodating the Learner

Tell students to select an $m \times n$ matrix A and two $n \times p$ matrices B and C. Ask them to use their matrices to answer these questions.

1. Can B and C be added? Explain. Yes, B and C have the same dimensions, so they can be added.
2. What are the products AB and AC? What is the value of the expression $A(B + C)$? Answers vary. Check students' work.
3. What property did you illustrate in Part b? the distributive property of matrix multiplication over matrix addition

 QY2

In the 2×3 product matrix, the rows represent the 2 pizzerias and the columns represent the 3 clubs as shown at the right.

	F	J	V
Lorenzo's Prices	133	147	141
Billy's Prices	131	150	138

Each element in this product matrix is the total price of a pizza order. For example, the Forensics Club would pay a total of $133 at Lorenzo's, and the Jazz Band would pay $150 at Billy's.

▶ QY2

Use your calculator to verify the matrix product on the previous page.

GUIDED

Example 2

Let $A = \begin{bmatrix} 1 & 3 \\ -2 & 4 \end{bmatrix}$ and $B = \begin{bmatrix} 0 & 5 & 2 \\ 3 & -1 & 4 \end{bmatrix}$. Find their product AB by hand.

Solution A has __?__ rows and B has __?__ columns. So the matrix AB will have __?__ entries. 2; 3; 6

Use the algorithm for row-by-column multiplication to fill in the missing entries below.

$$AB = \begin{bmatrix} 1 \cdot 0 + 3 \cdot 3 & 1 \cdot 5 + \underline{?} & \underline{?} \\ -2 \cdot 0 + 4 \cdot 3 & \underline{?} + 4 \cdot -1 & \underline{?} \end{bmatrix} = \begin{bmatrix} 9 & \underline{?} & \underline{?} \\ 12 & \underline{?} & \underline{?} \end{bmatrix}$$

$3 \cdot -1$; $1 \cdot 2 + 3 \cdot 4$; $-2 \cdot 5$; $-2 \cdot 2 + 4 \cdot 4$; 2; 14; -14; 12

In general, to multiply matrices A and B, find all possible products using rows from matrix A and columns from matrix B. This leads to the following definition.

Definition of Matrix Multiplication

If A is an $m \times n$ matrix and B is a $n \times q$ matrix, then the **matrix product** $A \cdot B$ (or AB) is an $m \times q$ matrix whose element in row r, column c is the product of row r of A and column c of B.

Caution! The product of two matrices A and B exists only when the *number of columns of A equals the number of rows of B*. So if A is $m \times n$, B must be $n \times q$ in order for AB to exist.

These matrices can be multiplied.

$$\begin{bmatrix} 4 & -1 \\ 6 & 2 \end{bmatrix} \begin{bmatrix} 3 & -2 & 7 \\ 5 & 3 & 0 \end{bmatrix} = \begin{bmatrix} 7 & -11 & 28 \\ 28 & -6 & 42 \end{bmatrix}$$

2×2 $\quad 2 \times 3$ $\quad 2 \times 3$

equal

dimensions of product

These matrices cannot be multiplied.

$$\begin{bmatrix} 3 & -2 & 7 \\ 5 & 3 & 0 \end{bmatrix} \begin{bmatrix} 4 & -1 \\ 6 & 2 \end{bmatrix}$$

2×3 $\quad 2 \times 2$

not equal

no product

Notes on the Lesson

Algorithm for row-by-column multiplication Students should now be ready to multiply matrices with more than one row or one column. Emphasize that the element in row m and column n of the product matrix is the result of pairing elements from row m in the left matrix with elements in column n in the right matrix. For instance, in Example 2, go to the product matrix AB. Pick one of its elements identified with a question mark. If that element is in the 1st row, 3rd column, then students should combine the 1st row of the left matrix and the 3rd column of the right matrix to get the value of the element.

Additional Example

Example 2 Let $P = \begin{bmatrix} 5 & -2 \\ 3 & 1 \end{bmatrix}$ and $Q = \begin{bmatrix} 2 & 0 & -3 \\ 4 & 1 & 5 \end{bmatrix}$. Find the product PQ by hand.

Solution P has __?__ rows, and Q has __?__ columns. So the matrix PQ will have __?__ entries. 2; 3; 6 Use the algorithm for row-by-column multiplication to fill in the missing entries.

$$PQ = \begin{bmatrix} 5 \cdot 2 + (-2) \cdot 4 & 5 \cdot 0 + \underline{?} & \underline{?} \\ 3 \cdot 2 + 1 \cdot 4 & \underline{?} + 1 \cdot 1 & \underline{?} \end{bmatrix}$$

$(-2) \cdot 1$; $5 \cdot (-3) + (-2) \cdot 5$; $3 \cdot 0$; $3 \cdot (-3) + 1 \cdot 5$

$$= \begin{bmatrix} 2 & \underline{?} & \underline{?} \\ 10 & \underline{?} & \underline{?} \end{bmatrix}$$ -2; 25 1; -4

Accommodating the Learner

Show students this matrix:

$$\begin{bmatrix} 2 \cdot 4 + 3 \cdot 2 + 5 \cdot 1 & 2 \cdot 3 + 3 \cdot 5 + 5 \cdot 7 \\ 1 \cdot 4 + 7 \cdot 2 + 2 \cdot 1 & 1 \cdot 3 + 7 \cdot 5 + 2 \cdot 7 \end{bmatrix}.$$

1. Ask them the following questions. Simplify the matrix. $\begin{bmatrix} 19 & 56 \\ 20 & 52 \end{bmatrix}$
2. What are the 2×3 matrix and the 3×2 matrix whose product is the given matrix?

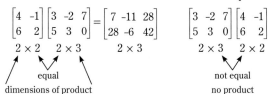

$$\begin{bmatrix} 2 & 3 & 5 \\ 1 & 7 & 2 \end{bmatrix} \begin{bmatrix} 4 & 3 \\ 2 & 5 \\ 1 & 7 \end{bmatrix}$$

Note-Taking Tips

Call students' attention to the statement, found below the box "Algorithm for Row-by-Column Multiplication," that "the row [on the left] and the column [on the right] have to have the same number of elements." Encourage students to make a note to themselves about the dimensions of matrices before multiplying ("The left matrix has __?__ rows and the right matrix has __?__ columns. If these numbers are equal, then the matrices can be multiplied.")

Notes on the Lesson

Activity The property illustrated that $(M1 \cdot M2) \cdot M3 = M1 \cdot (M2 \cdot M3)$ is the associative property of multiplication. It is a surprise to many students that an operation as complicated as matrix multiplication satisfies this property.

These two cases indicate that, in general, ***multiplication of matrices is not commutative.*** When both AB and BA exist, we can avoid confusion by saying "Multiply A on the left by B" to mean "find BA."

STOP **QY3**

▶ **QY3**

Can you multiply a 3 × 4 matrix on the right by a 4 × 2 matrix? If so, what would the dimensions of the product be? If not, why not?

When matrices arise from real situations, you often have several choices for ways of arranging your data. However, when you are multiplying two matrices, the number of columns of the first matrix must match the number of rows of the second matrix. In order to set up matrices for multiplication, think about the units involved: the *headings of the columns* of the left matrix must match the *headings of the rows* of the right matrix. That is how the matrices were set up in the opening example.

Multiplying More Than Two Matrices

The Activity below suggests that an important property of real-number multiplication extends to matrix multiplication.

Activity

MATERIALS CAS or graphing calculator

Step 1 Store these matrices in your calculator:

$M1 = \begin{bmatrix} 4 & 3 \end{bmatrix}$, $M2 = \begin{bmatrix} -2 & 4 & 1 \\ 3 & 6 & -5 \end{bmatrix}$, and $M3 = \begin{bmatrix} 6 \\ 11 \\ 2 \end{bmatrix}$.

Step 2 Calculate $(M1 \cdot M2) \cdot M3$. [358]

Step 3 Calculate $M1 \cdot (M2 \cdot M3)$. [358]

Step 4 Compare the results of Steps 2 and 3. What property holds true for matrices $M1$, $M2$, and $M3$?
The Associative Property of Multiplication

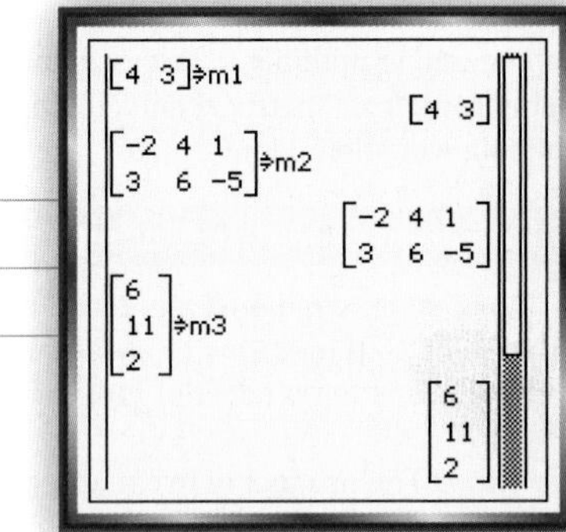

This property holds for all matrices. For any matrices A, B, and C, if the applicable products exist, $(A \cdot B) \cdot C = A \cdot (B \cdot C)$.

Matrix multiplication has many applications. In this course, you will use it to model linear combinations, to perform geometric transformations, and to solve systems of equations.

ENGLISH LEARNERS

Vocabulary Development

This lesson provides a natural opportunity to discuss the term *algorithm*. Help students understand that an algorithm is a clear set of step-by-step instructions for a mathematical calculation or procedure. You may want to review the long-division algorithm or ask students to look up and discuss the Euclidean Algorithm for finding the greatest common factor of two whole numbers.

Extension

The Extension in Lesson 4-1 (see page 226) asks students to show how $\begin{bmatrix} 2x + 3y \\ x - 2y \end{bmatrix} = \begin{bmatrix} -5 \\ 8 \end{bmatrix}$ represents a system of equations. Ask students to show that $\begin{bmatrix} 2 & 3 \\ 1 & -2 \end{bmatrix}\begin{bmatrix} x \\ y \end{bmatrix} = \begin{bmatrix} -5 \\ 8 \end{bmatrix}$ represents the same system of equations.

$\begin{bmatrix} 2 & 3 \\ 1 & -2 \end{bmatrix}\begin{bmatrix} x \\ y \end{bmatrix} = \begin{bmatrix} 2x + 3y \\ 1x - 2y \end{bmatrix}$;

so $\begin{bmatrix} 2x + 3y \\ x - 2y \end{bmatrix} = \begin{bmatrix} -5 \\ 8 \end{bmatrix}$ by the Transitive Property of Equality

Questions

COVERING THE IDEAS

In 1–3, refer to the Price-per-Pizza, Pizzas-per-Club, and Price-per-Club matrices at the beginning of this lesson.

1. How many mushroom pizzas did the Volleyball team order? 3
2. How many garbage pizzas were ordered by all the clubs together? 8
3. Write an expression to calculate the total cost for the Jazz Band's order from Billy's pizzeria. $\$11 \cdot 1 + \$17 \cdot 5 + \$18 \cdot 3 = \$150$

In 4 and 5, perform the multiplication.

4. $\begin{bmatrix} 3 & 5 \end{bmatrix} \cdot \begin{bmatrix} 1 \\ 0 \end{bmatrix}$ $[3]$

5. $\begin{bmatrix} 1 & 4 & -5 & 6 \end{bmatrix} \cdot \begin{bmatrix} 2 \\ -3 \\ 11 \\ 7 \end{bmatrix}$ $[-23]$

In 6 and 7, use the matrices $A = \begin{bmatrix} 5 & 1 \\ 6 & 2 \\ 3 & -1 \end{bmatrix}$ **and** $B = \begin{bmatrix} -4 \\ 4 \end{bmatrix}$.

6. a. **Fill in the Blanks** The product AB has __?__ row(s) and __?__ column(s). 3; 1

   b. **Fill in the Blanks** The element in the second row and first column of AB is __?__ • __?__ + __?__ • __?__. 6; -4; 2; 4

   c. Compute the product AB.

7. a. Is it possible to compute the product BA? Explain why or why not.

   b. What property of matrix multiplication does the answer to Part a illustrate?

8. Multiply the matrices at the right in two different ways to show that matrix multiplication is associative. See margin.

9. Multiply the matrices at the right in two different orders to show that matrix multiplication is not commutative. See margin.

10. Consider the matrices M and N below.

$$M = \begin{bmatrix} 11 & 12 & 13 & 14 & 15 \\ 21 & 22 & 23 & 24 & 25 \\ 31 & 32 & 33 & 34 & 35 \\ 41 & 42 & 43 & 44 & 45 \end{bmatrix}, N = \begin{bmatrix} 11 & 12 & 13 & 14 \\ 21 & 22 & 23 & 24 \\ 31 & 32 & 33 & 34 \\ 41 & 42 & 43 & 44 \end{bmatrix}$$

   a. Only one of the products MN and NM exists. Which is it? NM

   b. What are the dimensions of the product? 4×5

   c. Write an expression for the element in the third row, second column of the product. $31 \cdot 12 + 32 \cdot 22 + 33 \cdot 32 + 34 \cdot 42$

6c. $\begin{bmatrix} -16 \\ -16 \\ -16 \end{bmatrix}$

7a. No; the number of elements in a row of B is not the same as the number of elements in a column of A.

7b. Matrix multiplication is not commutative.

$\begin{bmatrix} 4 & 3 \\ -2 & 1 \end{bmatrix} \cdot \begin{bmatrix} \frac{1}{2} & 1 \\ -1 & 0 \end{bmatrix} \cdot \begin{bmatrix} 12 \\ 6 \end{bmatrix}$

$\begin{bmatrix} 4 & 6 \\ -1 & 8 \end{bmatrix} \begin{bmatrix} 7 & 3 \\ 5 & 1 \end{bmatrix}$

3 Assignment

Recommended Assignment

- Questions 1–22
- Question 23 (extra credit)
- Reading Lesson 4-4
- Covering the Ideas 4-4

Notes on the Questions

Question 4 In this case, the product $\begin{bmatrix} 1 \\ 0 \end{bmatrix} \cdot \begin{bmatrix} 3 & 5 \end{bmatrix}$ does exist, but that product is a 2×2 matrix. This points out that even when matrices can be multiplied in both orders, matrix multiplication is not commutative.

Question 5 When multiplying in "the other order," the result is a 4×4 matrix.

Question 8 This question illustrates a special case of the property in the Activity on page 238.

Question 9 Compare the two products in this question with Questions 4 and 5. Here we see that even when the dimensions of the product matrices are the same, matrix multiplication is not commutative.

Additional Answers

8. $\left(\begin{bmatrix} 4 & 3 \\ -2 & 1 \end{bmatrix} \cdot \begin{bmatrix} \frac{1}{2} & 1 \\ -1 & 0 \end{bmatrix}\right) \begin{bmatrix} 12 \\ 6 \end{bmatrix} =$

$\begin{bmatrix} -1 & 4 \\ -2 & -2 \end{bmatrix} \cdot \begin{bmatrix} 12 \\ 6 \end{bmatrix} = \begin{bmatrix} 12 \\ -36 \end{bmatrix}$;

$\begin{bmatrix} 4 & 3 \\ -2 & 1 \end{bmatrix} \left(\begin{bmatrix} \frac{1}{2} & 1 \\ -1 & 0 \end{bmatrix} \cdot \begin{bmatrix} 12 \\ 6 \end{bmatrix}\right) =$

$\begin{bmatrix} 4 & 3 \\ -2 & 1 \end{bmatrix} \cdot \begin{bmatrix} 12 \\ -12 \end{bmatrix} = \begin{bmatrix} 12 \\ -36 \end{bmatrix}$

9. $\begin{bmatrix} 4 & 6 \\ -1 & 8 \end{bmatrix} \cdot \begin{bmatrix} 7 & 3 \\ 5 & 1 \end{bmatrix} = \begin{bmatrix} 58 & 18 \\ 33 & 5 \end{bmatrix}$

$\begin{bmatrix} 7 & 3 \\ 5 & 1 \end{bmatrix} \cdot \begin{bmatrix} 4 & 6 \\ -1 & 8 \end{bmatrix} = \begin{bmatrix} 25 & 66 \\ 19 & 38 \end{bmatrix}$

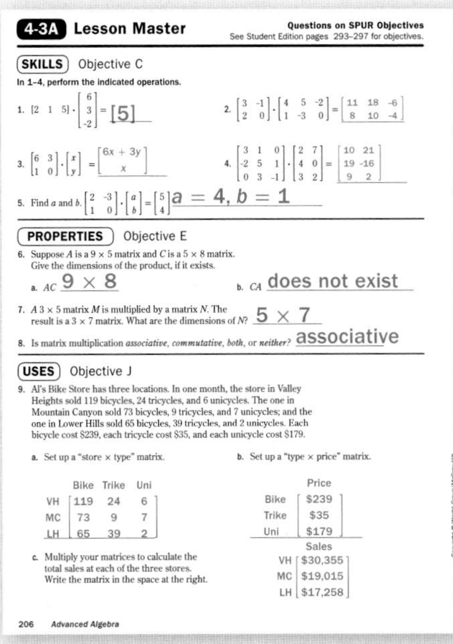

4-3A Lesson Master

Questions on SPUR Objectives
See Student Edition pages 293–297 for objectives.

SKILLS Objective C

In 1–4, perform the indicated operations.

1. $\begin{bmatrix} 2 & 1 & 5 \end{bmatrix} \cdot \begin{bmatrix} 6 \\ 3 \\ -2 \end{bmatrix} = [5]$

2. $\begin{bmatrix} 3 & -1 \\ 2 & 0 \end{bmatrix} \cdot \begin{bmatrix} 4 & 5 & -2 \\ 1 & -3 & 0 \end{bmatrix} = \begin{bmatrix} 11 & 18 & -6 \\ 8 & 10 & -4 \end{bmatrix}$

3. $\begin{bmatrix} 6 & 3 \\ 1 & 0 \end{bmatrix} \cdot \begin{bmatrix} x \\ y \end{bmatrix} = \begin{bmatrix} 6x + 3y \\ x \end{bmatrix}$

4. $\begin{bmatrix} 3 & 1 & 0 \\ -2 & 5 & 1 \\ 0 & 3 & -1 \end{bmatrix} \cdot \begin{bmatrix} 2 & 7 \\ 4 & 0 \\ 3 & 2 \end{bmatrix} = \begin{bmatrix} 10 & 21 \\ 19 & -16 \\ 9 & 2 \end{bmatrix}$

5. Find a and b. $\begin{bmatrix} 2 & -3 \\ 1 & 0 \end{bmatrix} \cdot \begin{bmatrix} a \\ b \end{bmatrix} = \begin{bmatrix} 5 \\ 4 \end{bmatrix}$ $a = 4, b = 1$

PROPERTIES Objective E

6. Suppose A is a 9×5 matrix and C is a 5×8 matrix. Give the dimensions of the product, if it exists.

   a. AC 9×8

   b. CA does not exist

7. A 3×5 matrix M is multiplied by a matrix N. The result is a 3×7 matrix. What are the dimensions of N? 5×7

8. Is matrix multiplication *associative, commutative, both,* or *neither?* associative

USES Objective J

9. Al's Bike Store has three locations. In one month, the store in Valley Heights sold 119 bicycles, 24 tricycles, and 6 unicycles. The one in Mountain Canyon sold 73 bicycles, 9 tricycles, and 7 unicycles; and the one in Lower Hills sold 65 bicycles, 39 tricycles, and 2 unicycles. Each bicycle cost $239, each tricycle cost $35, and each unicycle cost $179.

   a. Set up a "store × type" matrix.

	Bike	Trike	Uni
VH	119	24	6
MC	73	9	7
LH	65	39	2

   b. Set up a "type × price" matrix.

	Price
Bike	$239
Trike	$35
Uni	$179

   c. Multiply your matrices to calculate the total sales at each of the three stores. Write the matrix in the space at the right.

	Sales
VH	$30,355
MC	$19,015
LH	$17,258

206 *Advanced Algebra*

Notes on the Questions

Question 13 This is an important, conceptual question. The identity matrix (Part b) is an important matrix both in transformation applications in this chapter and later in solving systems. Be sure students notice (from Parts b and e) that multiplication of A by $\begin{bmatrix} k & 0 \\ 0 & k \end{bmatrix}$ results in the same product as multiplying by the scalar k.

Question 15 This question (and the Extension on page 238) helps set up the use of matrices to solve systems, which will be discussed in Chapter 5.

Additional Answers

11. $\begin{matrix} & \text{TTB} & \text{TB} & \text{BB} \end{matrix}$
$\begin{matrix} \text{Wt.} \\ \text{Vol.} \end{matrix}\begin{bmatrix} 1.5 & 5 & 12 \\ 1 & 1 & 0.6 \end{bmatrix} \cdot \begin{matrix} \text{TTB} \\ \text{TB} \\ \text{BB} \end{matrix}\overset{\text{Store 1} \quad \text{Store 2}}{\begin{bmatrix} 20 & 60 \\ 50 & 10 \\ 12 & 15 \end{bmatrix}} = \begin{matrix} \text{Wt.} \\ \text{Vol.} \end{matrix}\overset{\text{Store 1} \quad \text{Store 2}}{\begin{bmatrix} 424 & 320 \\ 77.2 & 19 \end{bmatrix}}$

13a. $\begin{bmatrix} x+y \\ x+y \end{bmatrix}$; A is moved to the right y units and up x units to B.

13b. $\begin{bmatrix} x \\ y \end{bmatrix}$; $B = A$

13c. $\begin{bmatrix} y \\ x \end{bmatrix}$; A's coordinates are switched to get B.

13d. $\begin{bmatrix} -y \\ x \end{bmatrix}$; the y-coordinate of A is changed to its opposite and then the coordinates are switched to get B.

13e. $\begin{bmatrix} 2x \\ 2y \end{bmatrix}$; A's coordinates are doubled to get B.

APPLYING THE MATHEMATICS

11. Lenora runs a small shipping company. One afternoon, she gets requests from two sporting-goods stores to transport shipments of sports equipment. Store 1 wants to transport 20 cases of table tennis balls (TTB), 50 cases of tennis balls (TB), and 12 bowling balls (BB). Store 2 wants to transport 60 cases of table tennis balls, 10 cases of tennis balls, and 15 bowling balls. One case of table tennis balls weighs 1.5 pounds, one case of tennis balls weighs 5 pounds, and one bowling ball weighs 12 pounds. In addition, each case of table tennis balls or tennis balls takes up 1 cubic foot of cargo space, but each bowling ball takes 0.6 cubic foot of space. Use matrix multiplication to find the total weight and cargo space required for each order. See margin.

Bowling balls are available in a wide variety of weights, patterns, and colors.

12. Refer to the pizza story in this lesson. According to the product matrix, is there any group that will save money by ordering their pizza at Lorenzo's? How much would the group save? the Jazz Band; $3

13. Consider the point matrix $A = \begin{bmatrix} x \\ y \end{bmatrix}$. Perform the indicated multiplication. Call the product B. Then describe the relationship between points A and B. a–e. See margin.
    a. $\begin{bmatrix} 1 & 1 \\ 1 & 1 \end{bmatrix} \cdot A$
    b. $\begin{bmatrix} 1 & 0 \\ 0 & 1 \end{bmatrix} \cdot A$
    c. $\begin{bmatrix} 0 & 1 \\ 1 & 0 \end{bmatrix} \cdot A$
    d. $\begin{bmatrix} 0 & -1 \\ 1 & 0 \end{bmatrix} \cdot A$
    e. $\begin{bmatrix} 2 & 0 \\ 0 & 2 \end{bmatrix} \cdot A$

14. You own the Sweet Cakes Bakery, which produces three sizes of muffins: mini, regular, and large. You are concerned with three main ingredients: flour, butter, and sugar. Matrix R shows the amount of each ingredient (in pounds) required per dozen of each muffin size. Matrix Q shows the average number of dozens of each muffin size sold on Mondays and Fridays.

$$\begin{matrix} \text{Flour} \\ \text{Butter} \\ \text{Sugar} \end{matrix}\overset{\text{Mini} \quad \text{Regular} \quad \text{Large}}{\begin{bmatrix} 0.3 & 0.5 & 0.8 \\ 0.1 & 0.2 & 0.3 \\ 0.1 & 0.2 & 0.3 \end{bmatrix}} = R \qquad \begin{matrix} \text{Mini} \\ \text{Regular} \\ \text{Large} \end{matrix}\overset{\text{Mon} \quad \text{Fri}}{\begin{bmatrix} 10 & 20 \\ 15 & 35 \\ 20 & 50 \end{bmatrix}} = Q$$

   a. What does the number in the third row, first column of Q represent in this situation?
   b. Compute RQ.
   c. What does the number in the second row, second column of RQ represent? the average amount of butter used on Fridays
   d. One Saturday, the weekly sugar shipment does not come in. There are 8 pounds of sugar on hand. How will that impact your preparations for Monday?

14a. the average number of dozens of large muffins sold on Mondays

14b. $\begin{bmatrix} 26.5 & 63.5 \\ 10 & 24 \\ 10 & 24 \end{bmatrix}$

14d. Answers vary. Sample: I wouldn't be able to make as many muffins as usual, because to do that, I need 10 lb of sugar. I would make muffins until I ran out of sugar, then I would apologize to my customers if I ran out of muffins and offer them a free muffin the next time they came in.

15. Suppose $\begin{bmatrix} 4 & 3 \\ 2 & x \end{bmatrix} \cdot \begin{bmatrix} y \\ 1 \end{bmatrix} = \begin{bmatrix} 23 \\ 13 \end{bmatrix}$. Find the value of x. $x = 3$

16. a. The matrix $I = \begin{bmatrix} 1 & 0 \\ 0 & 1 \end{bmatrix}$ is called the *2 × 2 identity matrix.*

If $A = \begin{bmatrix} 4 & 2 \\ -3 & 6 \end{bmatrix}$, compute IA and AI.

b. Why is I called the identity matrix? Multiplying a matrix by I does not change the matrix.

16a. $IA = AI = \begin{bmatrix} 4 & 2 \\ -3 & 6 \end{bmatrix}$

REVIEW

17. Compute $\begin{bmatrix} 6 & -4 \\ -1 & 20 \end{bmatrix} + 2\begin{bmatrix} -3 & 2 \\ \frac{1}{2} & -10 \end{bmatrix}$. **(Lesson 4-2)**

18. If $\begin{bmatrix} a & 3.3 & 5c \\ 7 & -2e & -9 \end{bmatrix} = k\begin{bmatrix} 9 & -11 & -8c \\ d & \frac{4}{9} & 5f \end{bmatrix}$, find a, c, d, e, f, and k. **(Lesson 4-2)**

17. $\begin{bmatrix} 0 & 0 \\ 0 & 0 \end{bmatrix}$

18. $a = -2.7$, $c = 0$, $d = -23\frac{1}{3}$, $e = \frac{1}{15}$, $f = 6$, $k = -0.3$

19. What are the dimensions of the matrix at the right? **(Lesson 4-1)** 4 × 3

$\begin{bmatrix} 4 & 0 & 0 \\ 0 & 2 & 0 \\ 0 & 0 & -1 \\ 1 & 0 & \pi \end{bmatrix}$

20. **Multiple Choice** Which formula best models the data in the table below? **(Lesson 2-7)** D

A $P = km$ B $P = km^2$ C $P = \frac{k}{m}$ D $P = \frac{k}{m^2}$

m	1	2	3	4	5	6
P	36	9	4	2.25	1.44	1

21. Let $K = (1, 3)$, $L = (-4, 3)$, $M = (-4, 8)$, and $N = (1, 8)$. **(Previous Course)**

a. What kind of figure is $KLMN$? square

b. Divide each coordinate of the vertices of $KLMN$ by 2 to find the coordinates of $K'L'M'N'$. $K' = (0.5, 1.5)$; $L' = (-2, 1.5)$; $M' = (-2, 4)$; $N' = (0.5, 4)$

c. What kind of figure is $K'L'M'N'$? How do you know?

21c. Square; it is a size-change image of $KLMN$, and size-change images are similar to their preimages.

22. Find the distance between each pair of points. **(Previous Course)**

a. (2, 4) and (8, 16) $6\sqrt{5}$

b. (1.2, 0.7) and (6.3, -3.75) $\sqrt{45.8125} \approx 6.77$

c. $\left(-\frac{3}{4}, \frac{2}{3}\right)$ and $\left(-\frac{4}{9}, \frac{1}{2}\right)$ $\frac{\sqrt{157}}{36} \approx 0.348$

EXPLORATION

23. Suppose the product of two 2 × 2 matrices A and B is $\begin{bmatrix} 0 & 0 \\ 0 & 0 \end{bmatrix}$, but neither matrix is $\begin{bmatrix} 0 & 0 \\ 0 & 0 \end{bmatrix}$. What is the largest number of nonzero elements possible in A and B in order for this to happen? 8

QY ANSWERS

1a. $12

1b. 3

2. Calculator display should be similar to the one shown on page 236.

3. Yes; the product would be a 3 × 2 matrix.

Notes on the Questions

Question 16 You might ask students to determine the identity matrix for a 3 × 3 matrix.

$\begin{bmatrix} 1 & 0 & 0 \\ 0 & 1 & 0 \\ 0 & 0 & 1 \end{bmatrix}$

Question 18 Although we would never consider the time spent solving equations as anything but an enjoyable activity, some teachers like to think of this exercise, in which a single question requires the solving of six equations, as "the teacher's revenge!"

4 Wrap-Up

Ongoing Assessment

Ask students to explain how to multiply a 2 × 2 matrix by a 2 × 3 matrix. Answers vary. Sample: The left matrix has 2 columns and the right matrix has 2 rows, so the product can be found. To find, say, the element in the 1st row, 3rd column of the product, find the row-by-column product using the elements in the 1st row of the left matrix and the elements in the 3rd column of the right matrix.

Administer Quiz 1 (or a quiz of your own) after students complete this lesson.

Project Update

Project 2, *Matrices and the Fibonacci Sequence*, and Project 4, *Transpose of a Matrix*, on page 286 and Project 6, *Predicting the Weather*, on page 287 relate to the content of this lesson.

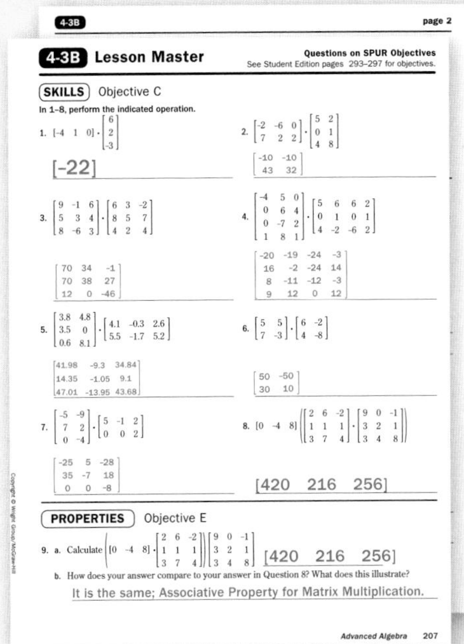

4-3B page 2

4-3B Lesson Master Questions on SPUR Objectives
See Student Edition pages 293–297 for objectives.

SKILLS Objective C

In 1–8, perform the indicated operation.

1. $[-4 \ \ 1 \ \ 0] \cdot \begin{bmatrix} 6 \\ 2 \\ -3 \end{bmatrix}$ $[-22]$

2. $\begin{bmatrix} -2 & -6 & 0 \\ 7 & 2 & 2 \end{bmatrix} \cdot \begin{bmatrix} 5 & 2 \\ 0 & 1 \\ 4 & 8 \end{bmatrix}$ $\begin{bmatrix} -10 & -10 \\ 43 & 32 \end{bmatrix}$

3. $\begin{bmatrix} 9 & -1 & 6 \\ 5 & 3 & 4 \\ 8 & -6 & 3 \end{bmatrix} \cdot \begin{bmatrix} 6 & 3 & -2 \\ 8 & 5 & 7 \\ 4 & 2 & 4 \end{bmatrix}$ $\begin{bmatrix} 70 & 34 & -1 \\ 70 & 38 & 27 \\ 12 & 0 & -46 \end{bmatrix}$

4. $\begin{bmatrix} -4 & 5 & 0 \\ 0 & 6 & 4 \\ 0 & -7 & 2 \\ 1 & 8 & 1 \end{bmatrix} \cdot \begin{bmatrix} 5 & 6 & 6 & 2 \\ 0 & 1 & 0 & 1 \\ 4 & -2 & -6 & 2 \end{bmatrix}$ $\begin{bmatrix} -20 & -19 & -24 & -3 \\ 16 & -2 & -24 & 14 \\ 8 & -11 & -12 & -3 \\ 9 & 12 & 0 & 12 \end{bmatrix}$

5. $\begin{bmatrix} 3.8 & 4.8 \\ 3.5 & 0 \\ 0.6 & 8.1 \end{bmatrix} \cdot \begin{bmatrix} 4.1 & -0.3 & 2.6 \\ 5.5 & -1.7 & 5.2 \end{bmatrix}$ $\begin{bmatrix} 41.98 & -9.3 & 34.84 \\ 14.35 & -1.05 & 9.1 \\ 47.01 & -13.95 & 43.68 \end{bmatrix}$

6. $\begin{bmatrix} 5 & 5 \\ 7 & -3 \end{bmatrix} \cdot \begin{bmatrix} 6 & -2 \\ 4 & -8 \end{bmatrix}$ $\begin{bmatrix} 50 & -50 \\ 30 & 10 \end{bmatrix}$

7. $\begin{bmatrix} -5 & -9 \\ 7 & 2 \\ 0 & -4 \end{bmatrix} \cdot \begin{bmatrix} 5 & -1 & 2 \\ 0 & 0 & 2 \end{bmatrix}$ $\begin{bmatrix} -25 & 5 & -28 \\ 35 & -7 & 18 \\ 0 & 0 & -8 \end{bmatrix}$

8. $[0 \ \ -4 \ \ 8]\left(\begin{bmatrix} 2 & 6 & -2 \\ 1 & 1 & 1 \\ 3 & 7 & 4 \end{bmatrix} \cdot \begin{bmatrix} 9 & 0 & -1 \\ 3 & 2 & 1 \\ 3 & 4 & 8 \end{bmatrix}\right)$ $[420 \ \ 216 \ \ 256]$

PROPERTIES Objective E

9. a. Calculate $\left([0 \ \ -4 \ \ 8] \cdot \begin{bmatrix} 2 & 6 & -2 \\ 1 & 1 & 1 \\ 3 & 7 & 4 \end{bmatrix}\right)\begin{bmatrix} 9 & 0 & -1 \\ 3 & 2 & 1 \\ 3 & 4 & 8 \end{bmatrix}$ $[420 \ \ 216 \ \ 256]$

b. How does your answer compare to your answer in Question 8? What does this illustrate?

It is the same; Associative Property for Matrix Multiplication.

Advanced Algebra 207

Lesson

4-4

GOAL

Begin a two-lesson exploration of the relationship between transformations and matrices, starting with size changes—the transformations that have the simplest matrices.

SPUR Objectives

F Recognize relationships between figures and their size-change images.

G Relate size changes to matrices, and vice versa.

K Graph figures and their size-change images.

Materials/Resources

- Lesson Masters 4-4A and 4-4B
- Resource Masters 1, 61, and 62
- Graph paper
- Ruler

HOMEWORK

Suggestions for Assignment

- Questions 1–21
- Question 22 (extra credit)
- Reading Lesson 4-5
- Covering the Ideas 4-5

Local Standards

1 Warm-Up

In 1–3, find each product.

1. $\begin{bmatrix} 14 & 0 \\ 0 & 14 \end{bmatrix}\begin{bmatrix} x \\ y \end{bmatrix}$ $\begin{bmatrix} 14x \\ 14y \end{bmatrix}$

2. $\begin{bmatrix} -0.5 & 0 \\ 0 & -0.5 \end{bmatrix}\begin{bmatrix} 1 & 5 & 8 \\ 2 & 7 & -2 \end{bmatrix}$ $\begin{bmatrix} -0.5 & -2.5 & -4 \\ -1 & -3.5 & 1 \end{bmatrix}$

3. $\begin{bmatrix} m & 0 \\ 0 & m \end{bmatrix}\begin{bmatrix} n & 0 \\ 0 & n \end{bmatrix}$ $\begin{bmatrix} mn & 0 \\ 0 & mn \end{bmatrix}$

Lesson

4-4 Matrices for Size Changes

Vocabulary

transformation
preimage
image
size change
center of a size change
magnitude of a size change
identity matrix
identity transformation
similar

BIG IDEA 2×2 matrices can represent geometric transformations.

In the next few lessons, you will see how matrices can represent a variety of geometric transformations. Recall from geometry that a **transformation** is a one-to-one correspondence between the points of a **preimage** and the points of an **image**. Consider the transformation S_k that maps (x, y) onto (kx, ky). If $k = 5$, the transformation images of a few points under S_5 are written as follows:

$$S_5(2, -3) = (10, -15);$$
$$S_5(-3, 0) = (-15, 0);$$
$$S_5(-2, -1.5) = (-10, -7.5);$$

and, in general, $S_5(x, y) = (5x, 5y)$.

Mental Math

True or False

a. All squares are rectangles. true

b. All rectangles are parallelograms. true

c. All integers are whole numbers. false

d. All whole numbers are integers. true

Definition of Size Change

For any $k \neq 0$, the transformation that maps (x, y) onto (kx, ky) is called the **size change** with **center** (0, 0) and **magnitude** k, and is denoted S_k.

From the definition, $S_k(x, y) = (ky, ky)$,
or $S_k: (x, y) \rightarrow (kx, ky)$.

These are read "Under the size change of magnitude k and center (0, 0), the image of (x, y) is (kx, ky)," or "The size change of magnitude k and center (0, 0) maps (x, y) onto (kx, ky)."

Example 1

a. What is the magnitude of the size change that maps the preimage $\triangle TRI$ onto its image $\triangle T'R'I'$ as shown at the right?

b. Write the size change using mapping notation.

Solution

a. Pick one coordinate pair on the preimage and compare it to the corresponding coordinate pair of the image.

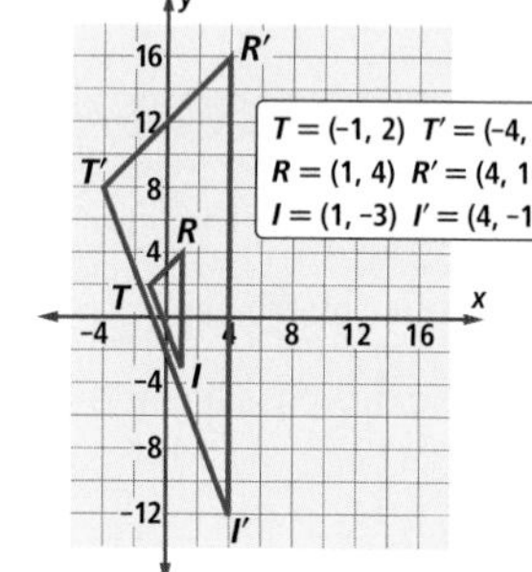

Background

We believe that any student who has had a geometry course has worked with ratios of similarity, so size changes should be familiar to most students. For students who have studied transformations, this lesson will provide a review and additional time to work with matrix multiplication.

A size change or size transformation is sometimes called a *dilatation* or *dilation*, an *expansion* or *contraction*, or a *homothety*. Students should note that in the notation S_k, S indicates a size change, and the subscript provides the magnitude of the size change.

$T = (-1, 2)$ and $T' = (-4, 8)$. The coordinates of T have been multiplied by 4. So the magnitude of the size change is 4.

b. This size change maps (x, y) onto $(4x, 4y)$.
$S_4: (x, y) \rightarrow (4x, 4y)$

Activity

MATERIALS graph paper, ruler

Work with a partner. See margin.

Step 1 You and your partner should each copy polygon *NUMER* shown at the right, then together write a matrix to represent it.

Step 2 One of you should multiply *NUMER* on the left by $\begin{bmatrix} 2 & 0 \\ 0 & 2 \end{bmatrix}$.

The other partner should multiply *NUMER* on the left by $\begin{bmatrix} \frac{1}{3} & 0 \\ 0 & \frac{1}{3} \end{bmatrix}$.

Each of you should draw the image polygon on your graph of *NUMER* and label it *N′U′M′E′R′*. Complete Steps 3–6 for your own graph.

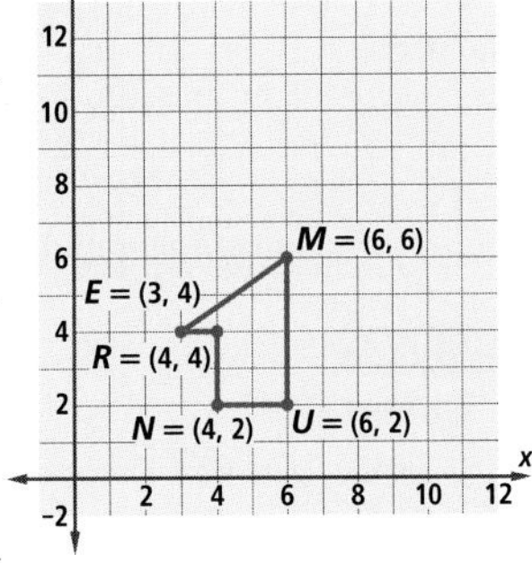

Step 3 How do the coordinates of *NUMER* compare to the coordinates of *N′U′M′E′R′*?

Step 4 Draw a ray from the origin (point *O*) through vertex *E* of *NUMER*. Then draw a ray from the origin through *E′*.

Step 5 Measure the distances *OE* and *OE′* and compare them. What is $\frac{OE'}{OE}$?

Step 6 Repeat Steps 4 and 5 for the other vertices of *NUMER* and *N′U′M′E′R′*.

Step 7 Discuss each other's results and generalize. If the matrix for *NUMER* is multiplied on the left by $\begin{bmatrix} k & 0 \\ 0 & k \end{bmatrix}$ to get polygon *N′U′M′E′R′*, where *k* is a real number, how do the vertices of the polygon *NUMER* compare to those of the polygon *N′U′M′E′R′*?

QY

▶ **QY**
How do the lengths of sides of the polygons *NUMER* and *N′U′M′E′R′* from Step 2 compare?

Using Matrices to Perform Size Changes

As the Activity illustrates, size change images can be found by multiplying matrices. When the matrix for the point (x, y) is multiplied on the left by $\begin{bmatrix} k & 0 \\ 0 & k \end{bmatrix}$, the matrix for the point (kx, ky) results.

2 Teaching

Notes on the Lesson

Many students will have seen size changes before, perhaps in as many as four courses before this one. They may have seen S_k as picturing multiplication by *k*, used S_k algebraically as the mapping $S_k(x, y) = (kx, ky)$, or seen S_k as a basic transformation in the study of similar figures. Those students will not need to draw figures and their images, but they do need to know that they can find images by multiplying matrices.

If your students have not previously studied size changes, encourage them to draw preimage and image figures. Have students calculate the lengths of sides to verify that the ratio of image length to preimage length is the magnitude of the size change. By measuring angles and slopes of segments, students can verify that these quantities are preserved under size changes.

After a size change, corresponding angle measurements are equal, and corresponding lengths are in the same ratio, so the preimage and image are similar. Thus, size changes are similarity transformations. The magnitude of the size transformation is the ratio of similitude.

In this lesson, the examples of size changes of magnitude *k* are limited to positive values for *k*. However, note that the definition of size change allows *k* to take on negative values. A size change of magnitude $-k$ is the composite of a size change of magnitude *k* and a rotation of 180°. (Question 17 and the Extension on page 245 further explore that idea.) Rotations are covered in Lesson 4-8.

Students should notice that the size change S_k can be applied to a figure represented by a matrix by multiplying every element of the matrix by *k*. Thus, multiplying a $2 \times n$ matrix by $\begin{bmatrix} k & 0 \\ 0 & k \end{bmatrix}$ has the same effect as multiplying that $2 \times n$ matrix by the scalar *k*.

Additional Answers

Activity

Step 1: $\begin{bmatrix} 4 & 6 & 6 & 3 & 4 \\ 2 & 2 & 6 & 4 & 4 \end{bmatrix}$

Step 2: $\begin{bmatrix} 2 & 0 \\ 0 & 2 \end{bmatrix}\begin{bmatrix} 4 & 6 & 6 & 3 & 4 \\ 2 & 2 & 6 & 4 & 4 \end{bmatrix} = \begin{bmatrix} 8 & 12 & 12 & 6 & 8 \\ 4 & 4 & 12 & 8 & 8 \end{bmatrix}$;

$\begin{bmatrix} \frac{1}{3} & 0 \\ 0 & \frac{1}{3} \end{bmatrix}\begin{bmatrix} 4 & 6 & 6 & 3 & 4 \\ 2 & 2 & 6 & 4 & 4 \end{bmatrix} = \begin{bmatrix} \frac{4}{3} & 2 & 2 & 1 & \frac{4}{3} \\ \frac{2}{3} & \frac{2}{3} & 2 & \frac{4}{3} & \frac{4}{3} \end{bmatrix}$

Step 3: The coordinates of *N′U′M′E′R′* are each $2 \left(\text{or } \frac{1}{3}\right)$ times the corresponding coordinates of the original *NUMER*.

Step 4: See the Additional Answers in the back of the book.

Step 5: $\frac{OE'}{OE} = 2 \left(\text{or } \frac{1}{3}\right)$

Step 6: $\frac{OR'}{OR} = 2 \left(\text{or } \frac{1}{3}\right)$; $\frac{ON'}{ON} = 2 \left(\text{or } \frac{1}{3}\right)$; $\frac{OM'}{OM} = 2 \left(\text{or } \frac{1}{3}\right)$; $\frac{OU'}{OU} = 2 \left(\text{or } \frac{1}{3}\right)$

Step 7: The vertices of *N′U′M′E′R′* are *k* times the vertices of the original *NUMER*.

Additional Examples

Example 1

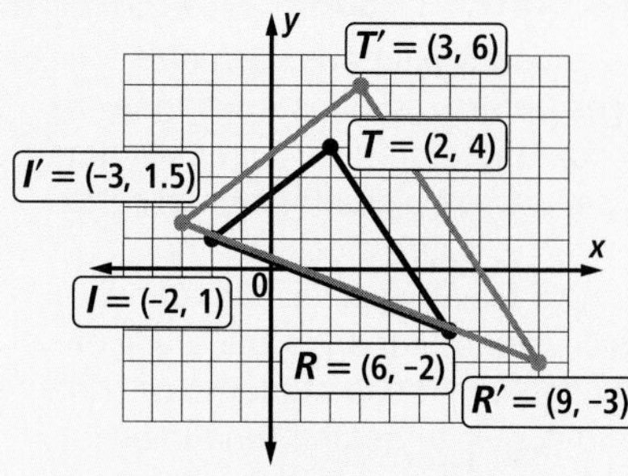

a. What is the magnitude of the size change that maps the preimage △*TRI* to its image △*T′R′I′*? 1.5

b. Write the size change using mapping notation. $S_{1.5}$: $(x, y) \to (1.5x, 1.5y)$

Example 2 Using the coordinates *T* = (2, 4), *R* = (6, -2), and *I* = (-2, 1) from Additional Example 1, perform the appropriate matrix multiplication to find the vertices of the image △*T′R′I′* from the vertices of the preimage △*TRI*.

Solution Write △*TRI* and $S_{1.5}$ in matrix form and multiply.

$$\overset{S_{1.5}}{\begin{bmatrix} \underline{1.5} & 0 \\ \underline{0} & 1.5 \end{bmatrix}} \overset{T \quad R \quad I}{\begin{bmatrix} \underline{2} & 6 & \underline{-2} \\ 4 & \underline{-2} & 1 \end{bmatrix}} = \overset{T' \quad R' \quad I'}{\begin{bmatrix} 3 & \underline{9} & -3 \\ \underline{6} & -3 & \underline{1.5} \end{bmatrix}}$$

So △*T′R′I′* has vertices *T′* = (3, __?__), *R′* = (__?__, -3), and *I′* = (-3, __?__). 6; 9; 1.5

Notes on the Lesson

Size changes and the multiplication of distance Question 6c applies the Pythagorean Distance formula. If your students have not seen this formula, then you may need to discuss how to calculate the distance between two points in the coordinate plane.

$$\begin{bmatrix} k & 0 \\ 0 & k \end{bmatrix}\begin{bmatrix} x \\ y \end{bmatrix} = \begin{bmatrix} kx + 0y \\ 0x + ky \end{bmatrix} = \begin{bmatrix} kx \\ ky \end{bmatrix}$$

This proves the following theorem.

Size Change Theorem

$\begin{bmatrix} k & 0 \\ 0 & k \end{bmatrix}$ is the matrix for S_k.

When $k = 1$, the **identity matrix** $\begin{bmatrix} 1 & 0 \\ 0 & 1 \end{bmatrix}$ maps each point $\begin{bmatrix} x \\ y \end{bmatrix}$ of a figure onto itself.

$$\begin{bmatrix} 1 & 0 \\ 0 & 1 \end{bmatrix}\begin{bmatrix} x \\ y \end{bmatrix} = \begin{bmatrix} 1 \cdot x + 0 \cdot y \\ 0 \cdot x + 1 \cdot y \end{bmatrix} = \begin{bmatrix} x \\ y \end{bmatrix}$$

This size change of magnitude 1 is called the **identity transformation**.

GUIDED

Example 2

Using the figure from Example 1, perform the appropriate matrix multiplication to find the vertices of the image △*T′R′I′* from the vertices of the preimage △*TRI*.

Solution Write △*TRI* and S_4 in matrix form and multiply.

$$\overset{S_4}{\begin{bmatrix} \underline{4?} & 0 \\ \underline{0?} & 4 \end{bmatrix}} \overset{T \quad R \quad I}{\begin{bmatrix} \underline{-1?} & 1 & \underline{1?} \\ 2 & \underline{4?} & -3 \end{bmatrix}} = \overset{T' \quad R' \quad I'}{\begin{bmatrix} -4 & \underline{4?} & 4 \\ \underline{8?} & 16 & \underline{-12?} \end{bmatrix}}$$

So △T′R′I′ has vertices T′ = (-4, __8?__), R′ = (__4?__, 16), and I′ = (4, -12).

Check Compare the vertices from the matrix with the graph of △*T′R′I′*. The coordinates are the same.

Size Changes and the Multiplication of Distance

Recall that the Pythagorean Theorem can be applied to calculate the distance between two points given their coordinates.

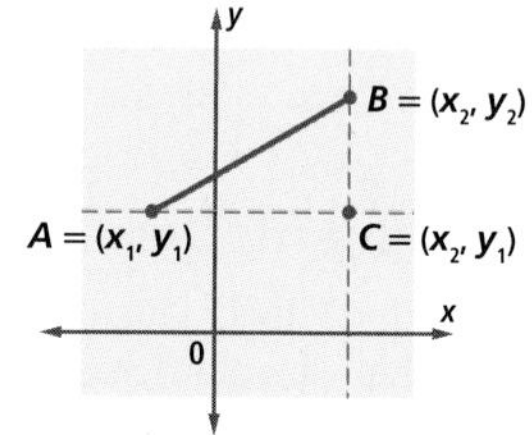

Suppose you wish to find the distance *AB* when $A = (x_1, y_1)$ and $B = (x_2, y_2)$. If you don't remember the general formula, let $C = (x_2, y_1)$ to create right triangle △*ABC*. In that triangle,

$$AB^2 = AC^2 + BC^2.$$

$\overline{AC}$ and $\overline{BC}$ lie on horizontal and vertical lines. So their lengths are like distances on a number line.

Accommodating the Learner

Ask students to plot the vertices of a △*ABC* and to select two positive values *k* and *j*. Ask students to find the vertices of △*A′B′C′*, the image of △*ABC* under a size change of magnitude *k*. Then ask them to find the vertices of △*A″B″C″*, the image of △*ABC* under a size change of magnitude *j*. Can they draw any conclusions about the composite of two size changes? The composite of two size changes of magnitudes *k* and *j* is a size change of magnitude *kj*.

ENGLISH LEARNERS

Vocabulary Development

Students should realize that while the different statements in the definition of size change have the same meaning, there should be slight differences when they are read aloud. The first statement can be read "The image of the ordered pair (*x*, *y*) under the size change S_k is the ordered pair (*kx*, *ky*)," while the second statement can be read "The size change S_k is a mapping that takes the ordered pair (*x*, *y*) to the ordered pair (*kx*, *ky*)."

$$AB^2 = |x_2 - x_1|^2 + |y_2 - y_1|^2$$

Take the square root of each side and you have the Pythagorean Distance Formula.

Pythagorean Distance Formula

If $A = (x_1, y_1)$ and $B = (x_2, y_2)$, then
$AB = \sqrt{|x_2 - x_1|^2 + |y_2 - y_1|^2}$.

So, for instance, in Example 1, where $T = (-1, 2)$ and $I = (1, -3)$, then

$TI = \sqrt{|1 - (-1)|^2 + |-3 - 2|^2}$ and $T'I' = \sqrt{|4 - (-4)|^2 + |-12 - 8|^2}$
$= \sqrt{2^2 + 5^2}$ $\quad = \sqrt{8^2 + 20^2}$
$= \sqrt{29}$ $\quad = \sqrt{464}$
$\quad = 4\sqrt{29}$.

This example illustrates that, in the size change S_k, the distance between images is $|k|$ times the distance between their preimages.

Similarity and Size Changes

Size changes are fundamental in the study of similarity. Recall from geometry that two figures are **similar** if and only if one is the image of the other under a composite of reflections and size changes. Composites of reflections, such as rotations, translations, and reflections themselves, preserve distance. So, if two figures are similar, as are $\triangle TRI$ and $\triangle T'R'I'$ in Example 1, distances in one are a constant multiple of distances in the other.

Example 3

Refer to triangles $\triangle TRI$ and $\triangle T'R'I'$ in Example 1. Calculate the following to verify that they are similar.

a. **The ratios of each pair of corresponding sides of the triangles**

b. **Measures of corresponding angles of the triangles**

Solution Plot both triangles in your dynamic geometry system (DGS). Use the DGS to show measures of the angles of the triangles and the ratios of the sides. Answers to Parts a and b are shown in the display at the right.

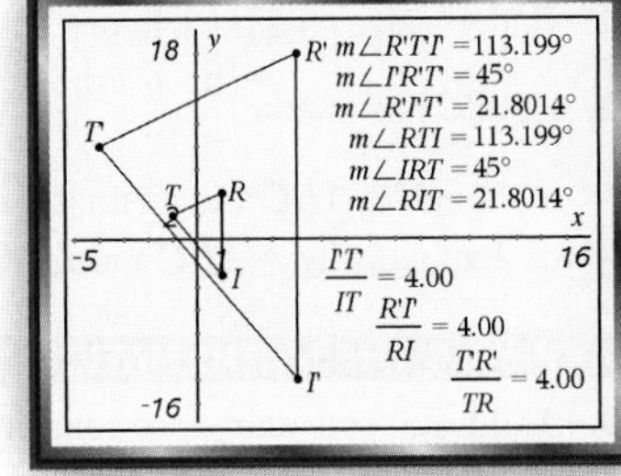

Based on these measures, the triangles appear to be similar. The ratios of sides are all equal to the magnitude of the size change, 4. The corresponding angles have equal measure.

Note-Taking Tips

This lesson introduces the notation S_k to indicate a size change. Encourage students to compare, in their notes, the notation $S_k(x, y) = (kx, ky)$ and the notation for scalar multiplication, $k\begin{bmatrix} a & b \\ c & d \end{bmatrix} = \begin{bmatrix} ka & kb \\ kc & kd \end{bmatrix}$. In both cases, the real number k is multiplied by each entry, whether in an ordered pair or in a matrix.

Additional Example

Example 3 Refer to $\triangle TRI$ and $\triangle T'R'I'$ from Additional Example 1, where $T = (2, 4)$, $R = (6, -2)$, $I = (-2, 1)$, $T' = (3, 6)$, $R' = (9, -3)$, and $I' = (-3, 1.5)$. Calculate the following to verify that the triangles are similar.

a. the ratios of each pair of corresponding sides of the triangles
$\frac{TR}{T'R'} = \frac{\sqrt{52}}{\sqrt{117}} = \frac{2}{3}$; $\frac{TI}{T'I'} = \frac{5}{\sqrt{56.25}} = \frac{2}{3}$; $\frac{RI}{R'I'} = \frac{\sqrt{73}}{\sqrt{164.25}} = \frac{2}{3}$

b. the measures of corresponding angles of the triangles
$m\angle T = m\angle T' \approx 106.4$; $m\angle R = m\angle R' \approx 34.1$; $m\angle I = m\angle I' \approx 39.4$

Accommodating the Learner

Ask students to complete the following steps:

a. Select two ordered pairs and calculate the distance between them.

b. Find the image of each point after a size change of magnitude 5 by using the matrix $\begin{bmatrix} 5 & 0 \\ 0 & 5 \end{bmatrix}$.

c. Find the distance between the images of the two original points.

Ask them how their values in Parts a and c compare. Answers vary. Check students' work. The value in Part c should be 5 times the value in Part a.

Extension

Ask students to compare a size change of magnitude k (for $k > 0$) with a size change of magnitude $-k$. How does a negative sign affect the image of a point? How does a negative sign affect the image of a figure?
Answers vary. Sample: Applying a size change of a negative magnitude $-k$ is the same as applying a size change of positive magnitude k, then rotating the point or figure 180° around the origin.

3 Assignment

Recommended Assignment

- Questions 1–21
- Question 22 (extra credit)
- Reading Lesson 4-5
- Covering the Ideas 4-5

Notes on the Questions

Question 4 In this context, "the size of a polygon" refers to linear dimensions.

Question 13 Students should understand that the scale model itself would not be changed, only a drawing of it would change. Technically, to change the model itself, we would need three dimensions, so the matrix would have the form $\begin{bmatrix} k & 0 & 0 \\ 0 & k & 0 \\ 0 & 0 & k \end{bmatrix}$.

Additional Answers

6a. $\begin{bmatrix} 3 & 5 & -2 & 0 \\ 7 & -9 & -8 & 4 \end{bmatrix}$

6b. $\begin{matrix} Q' & U' & A' & D' \end{matrix}$ $\begin{bmatrix} 18 & 30 & -12 & 0 \\ 42 & -54 & -48 & 24 \end{bmatrix}$

6c. $Q'U' = \sqrt{|30 - 18|^2 + |(-54) - 42|^2} = 12\sqrt{65} \approx 96.7$; $QU = \sqrt{|5 - 3|^2 + |-9 - 7|^2} = 2\sqrt{65} \approx 16.1$; $12\sqrt{65} = 6 \cdot 2\sqrt{65}$

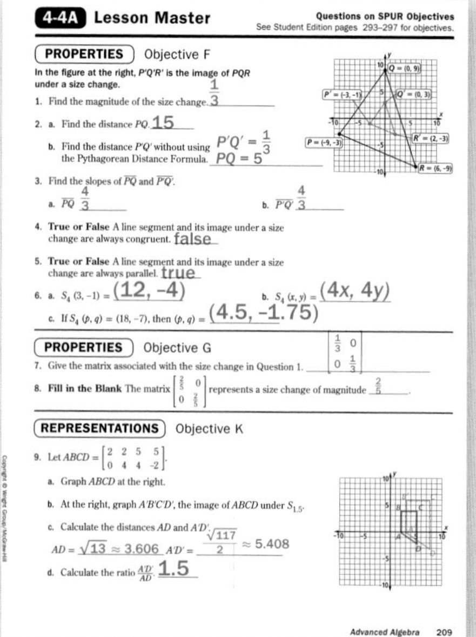

4-4A Lesson Master — Questions on SPUR Objectives. See Student Edition pages 293–297 for objectives.

PROPERTIES Objective F

In the figure at the right, $P'Q'R'$ is the image of PQR under a size change.

1. Find the magnitude of the size change. $\frac{1}{3}$
2. a. Find the distance PQ. 15
   b. Find the distance $P'Q'$ without using the Pythagorean Distance Formula. $P'Q' = \frac{1}{3}PQ = 5$
3. Find the slopes of $\overline{PQ}$ and $\overline{P'Q'}$.
   a. $\overline{PQ}$ $\frac{4}{3}$ b. $\overline{P'Q'}$ $\frac{4}{3}$
4. **True or False** A line segment and its image under a size change are always congruent. false
5. **True or False** A line segment and its image under a size change are always parallel. true
6. a. $S_4(3, -1) =$ (12, –4) b. $S_4(x, y) =$ (4x, 4y)
   c. If $S_4(p, q) = (18, -7)$, then $(p, q) =$ (4.5, –1.75)

PROPERTIES Objective G

7. Give the matrix associated with the size change in Question 1. $\begin{bmatrix} \frac{1}{3} & 0 \\ 0 & \frac{1}{3} \end{bmatrix}$
8. **Fill in the Blank** The matrix $\begin{bmatrix} \frac{2}{5} & 0 \\ 0 & \frac{2}{5} \end{bmatrix}$ represents a size change of magnitude $\frac{2}{5}$.

REPRESENTATIONS Objective K

9. Let $ABCD = \begin{bmatrix} 2 & 2 & 5 & 5 \\ 0 & 4 & 4 & -2 \end{bmatrix}$.
   a. Graph $ABCD$ at the right.
   b. At the right, graph $A'B'C'D'$, the image of $ABCD$ under $S_{1.5}$.
   c. Calculate the distances AD and $A'D'$. $AD = \sqrt{13} \approx 3.606$ $A'D' = \frac{\sqrt{117}}{2} \approx 5.408$
   d. Calculate the ratio $\frac{A'D'}{AD}$. 1.5

Questions

COVERING THE IDEAS

1. Refer to the Activity. How does $N'U'M'E'R'$ compare to $NUMER$ if the matrix $NUMER$ is multiplied by $\begin{bmatrix} k & 0 \\ 0 & k \end{bmatrix}$ and k is:
   a. 4? b. $\frac{1}{2}$? c. 1?

In 2 and 3, how is the expression read?

2. $S_6(3, -2) = (18, -12)$
3. $S_{1.2}: (4, 3.4) \rightarrow (4.8, 4.08)$
4. What matrix would you use to change the size of a polygon by a magnitude of $\frac{1}{5}$?
5. **Multiple Choice** If $S_k: (2, 5) \rightarrow \left(1, \frac{5}{2}\right)$, what is the value of k? C
   A 2 B 4 C $\frac{1}{2}$ D $\frac{1}{4}$
6. a. Write a matrix to describe the vertices of the quadrilateral $QUAD$ with coordinates $Q = (3, 7)$, $U = (5, -9)$, $A = (-2, -8)$, and $D = (0, 4)$. a–c. See margin.
   b. Give the coordinates of the vertices of $Q'U'A'D'$, the image of the quadrilateral $QUAD$ in Part a, under S_6.
   c. Verify that $Q'U' = 6 \cdot QU$.
7. Refer to Example 2. Write a size change matrix that transforms $\triangle T'R'I'$ back to $\triangle TRI$.
8. **True or False** To map a point onto itself, multiply the point matrix on the left by $\begin{bmatrix} 0 & 1 \\ 1 & 0 \end{bmatrix}$. false

In 9–11, answer *always, sometimes but not always,* or *never.*

9. Under a size change, an angle and its image are congruent. always
10. Under a size change, a segment and its image are congruent. sometimes but not always
11. Under a size change, a figure and its image are similar. always
12. $\triangle ABC$ has matrix $\begin{bmatrix} 3 & -9 & 6 \\ 8 & 12 & 4 \end{bmatrix}$. a–b. See margin.
    a. Graph $\triangle ABC$ and its image $\triangle A'B'C'$ under $S_{\frac{1}{3}}$.
    b. Explain why $\triangle ABC$ and $\triangle A'B'C'$ are similar.

APPLYING THE MATHEMATICS

13. A Chicago souvenir store sells an exact scale replica of the Sears Tower that is 7.5 inches tall. The actual Sears Tower is 1730 feet tall. What transformation matrix could be used to change the size of the scale model to the size of the actual tower? See margin.

The Sears Tower was built in 1970–73 at a cost of $250 million.

1a. $N'U'M'E'R'$ is similiar to $NUMER$, with sides four times as long.

1b. $N'U'M'E'R'$ is similiar to $NUMER$, with sides half as long.

1c. $N'U'M'E'R'$ is identical to $NUMER$.

2. Under the size change of magnitude 6 and center (0, 0), the image of (3, –2) is (18, –12).

3. The size change of magnitude 1.2 and center (0, 0) maps (4, 3.4) onto (4.8, 4.08).

4. $\begin{bmatrix} \frac{1}{5} & 0 \\ 0 & \frac{1}{5} \end{bmatrix}$

7. $\begin{bmatrix} \frac{1}{4} & 0 \\ 0 & \frac{1}{4} \end{bmatrix}$

Additional Answers

12a.

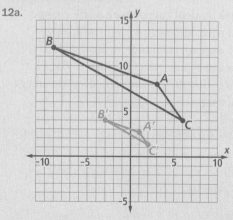

12b. Answers vary. Sample: The corresponding angles have equal measure, and the ratios of the sides are all equal to the magnitude of the size change, $\frac{1}{3}$.

13. $\begin{bmatrix} 2768 & 0 \\ 0 & 2768 \end{bmatrix}$

14. The Japanese fairy tale *Issunbōshi* (Suyeoka, Goodman, & Spicer, 1974), tells the story of a 2.5 cm tall boy named Issunbōshi who goes on a journey and eventually becomes a full-sized man.
    a. If the average height of a man is 170.2 cm, what size-change magnitude k is needed to transform Issunbōshi's height? 68.08
    b. Issunbōshi has a cricket for a pet. The average cricket length is 3.8 cm. If the length of the cricket were transformed by the same size change as Issunbōshi, how long would the cricket be? $\approx$ 258.7 cm

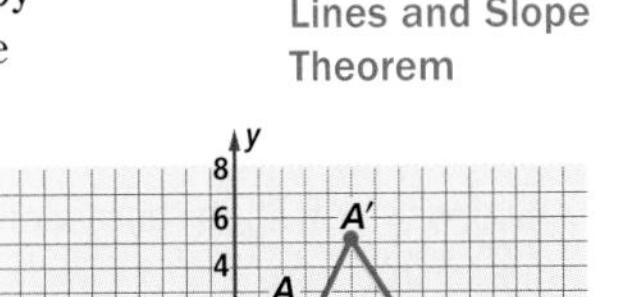

15d. yes, by the Parallel Lines and Slope Theorem

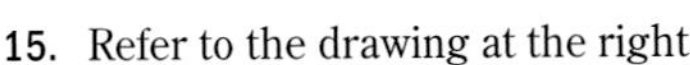

15. Refer to the drawing at the right.
    a. Find the matrix of the transformation mapping $ABCD$ onto $A'B'C'D'$. See margin.
    b. Find the slope of $\overleftrightarrow{BC}$. 1
    c. Find the slope of $\overleftrightarrow{B'C'}$. 1
    d. Is $\overleftrightarrow{BC}$ parallel to $\overleftrightarrow{B'C'}$? Why or why not?

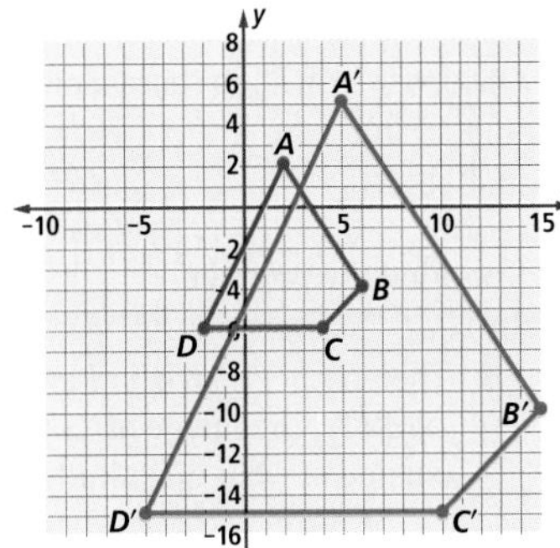

16. Define a function `pdf` (Pythagorean distance function) on a CAS with inputs `xa`, `ya`, `xb`, and `yb` that finds the Pythagorean Distance between any two ordered pairs (xa, ya) and (xb, yb). (We use these names because `x1`, `y1`, `x2` and `y2` are reserved names on many calculators.) Use `pdf` to check the lengths of TI and $T'I'$ in the lesson. See margin.

17. a. Refer to Example 1. Find the image $\triangle T^*R^*I^*$ of $\triangle TRI$ under a size change of magnitude -4. See margin.
    b. What are some differences between the image $\triangle T^*R^*I^*$ and the image $\triangle T'R'I'$? $\triangle T^*R^*I^*$ is the rotation image of $\triangle T'R'I'$ under a half turn.

REVIEW

18. **Multiple Choice** Refer to the matrices at the right. Which of the following matrix multiplications are defined? (There may be more than one correct answer.) (Lesson 4-3) C and F

    A AB B AC C BA
    D BC E CA F CB

$$A = \begin{bmatrix} 1 & 0 & 0 \\ 0 & 2 & 0 \\ 3 & 3 & -2 \end{bmatrix}$$

$$B = \begin{bmatrix} a & b & c \\ 8 & 8 & 8 \end{bmatrix}$$

$$C = \begin{bmatrix} 2 & 1 \\ 1 & 2 \end{bmatrix}$$

19. Let $Q = \begin{bmatrix} 1 \\ 1 \end{bmatrix}$. (Lessons 4-3, 4-1) 19, 20. See margin.
    a. Compute $\begin{bmatrix} 2 & 0 \\ 0 & 1 \end{bmatrix}Q$, $\begin{bmatrix} 4 & 0 \\ 0 & 1 \end{bmatrix}Q$, $\begin{bmatrix} 1 & 0 \\ 0 & 2 \end{bmatrix}Q$, and $\begin{bmatrix} 1 & 0 \\ 0 & 4 \end{bmatrix}Q$.
    b. Plot Q and the four answers to Part a as points in the plane.

20. Compute $\begin{bmatrix} a & b \\ c & d \end{bmatrix} + \begin{bmatrix} b & d \\ a & c \end{bmatrix} + \begin{bmatrix} d & c \\ b & a \end{bmatrix} + \begin{bmatrix} c & a \\ d & b \end{bmatrix}$. (Lesson 4-2)

Notes on the Questions

Question 17 Students who have never seen size changes of negative magnitude may be surprised at the relationship between the preimage and the image.

Question 19a Students may not realize that Q in each case stands for a matrix, and these expressions stand for four matrix products.

Question 20 The four matrices are rotation images of each other.

Additional Answers

17a.

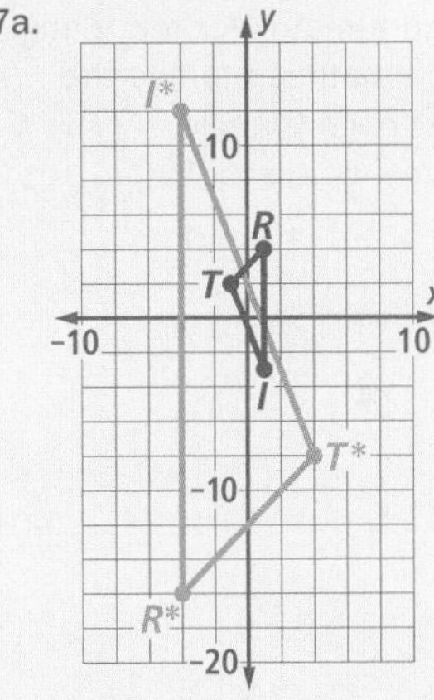

19a. $\begin{bmatrix} 2 \\ 1 \end{bmatrix}$; $\begin{bmatrix} 4 \\ 1 \end{bmatrix}$; $\begin{bmatrix} 1 \\ 2 \end{bmatrix}$; $\begin{bmatrix} 1 \\ 4 \end{bmatrix}$

19b.

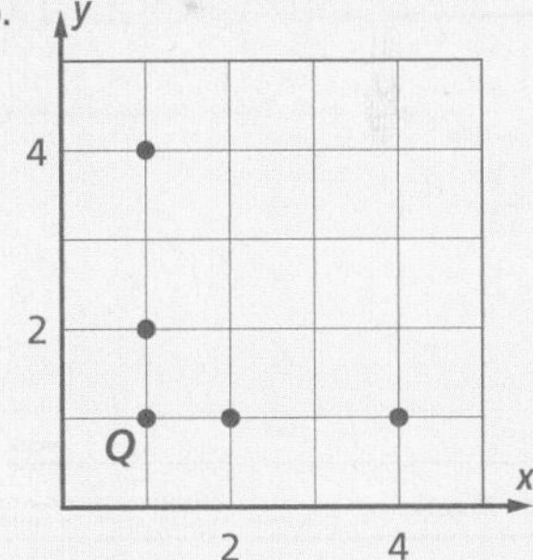

20. $\begin{bmatrix} a+b+d+c & b+d+c+a \\ c+a+b+d & d+c+a+b \end{bmatrix}$

Additional Answers

15a. $\begin{bmatrix} \frac{5}{2} & 0 \\ 0 & \frac{5}{2} \end{bmatrix}$

16.

Define pdf(xa,ya,xb,yb)=√((xb−xa)²+(y

Done

pdf(−1, 2, 1, −3) = $\sqrt{29}$;
pdf(−4, 8, 4, −12) = $4\sqrt{29}$;
the answer checks.

Notes on the Questions

Question 22 The matrix polygon applet on the UCSMP Web site can be used to investigate size changes in this question.

4 Wrap-Up

Ongoing Assessment

Have students work in small groups. In each group, one student should plot and label the vertices of a triangle, and another student should select a value of k for a size change S_k. Then all students in the group should write a matrix for the size change and a matrix for the triangle and multiply the matrices to find the vertices of the image triangle. Answers vary. Check students' work.

4-4B page 2

4-4B Lesson Master Questions on SPUR Objectives
See Student Edition pages 293–297 for objectives.

PROPERTIES Objective F

1. Suppose $C'D'E'F'$ is the image of quadrilateral $CDEF$ under a size change of magnitude k.
   a. How do the measures of $\angle D$ and $\angle D'$ compare? $m\angle D = m\angle D'$
   b. How do EF and $E'F'$ compare? $E'F' = k(EF)$
2. Under $S_{\frac{1}{4}}$, what is the image of each point?
   a. (8, -4) (2, –1)
   b. (3, 12) $(\frac{3}{4}, 3)$
   c. (0, -8) (0, –2)
   d. $(5, \frac{1}{2})$ $(\frac{5}{4}, \frac{1}{8})$

PROPERTIES Objective G

3. Give the matrix for each size transformation.
   a. S_8 $\begin{bmatrix} 8 & 0 \\ 0 & 8 \end{bmatrix}$
   b. $S_{\frac{4}{5}}$ $\begin{bmatrix} \frac{4}{5} & 0 \\ 0 & \frac{4}{5} \end{bmatrix}$
   c. $S_{0.75}$ $\begin{bmatrix} 0.75 & 0 \\ 0 & 0.75 \end{bmatrix}$
   d. S_k $\begin{bmatrix} k & 0 \\ 0 & k \end{bmatrix}$
4. What matrix is associated with the size transformation that maps (-12, 8) onto (–3, 2)? $\begin{bmatrix} \frac{1}{4} & 0 \\ 0 & \frac{1}{4} \end{bmatrix}$
5. What is the magnitude of the size transformation associated with $\begin{bmatrix} 6 & 0 \\ 0 & 6 \end{bmatrix}$? 6

Fill in the Blanks In 6 and 7, fill in the blanks to complete each statement.

6. The matrix $\begin{bmatrix} 7 & 0 \\ 0 & 7 \end{bmatrix}$ is associated with a size change with center (0, 0) and magnitude 7.
7. The matrix associated with a size change of magnitude 8 is $\begin{bmatrix} 8 & 0 \\ 0 & 8 \end{bmatrix}$.

210 Advanced Algebra

21. You know the volume of a rectangular solid is given by the formula $V = \ell wh$. (Lesson 2-9)
    a. Solve this equation for ℓ. $\ell = \frac{V}{wh}$
    b. **Fill in the Blanks** From Part a, ℓ varies directly as __?__ and inversely as __?__ and __?__. V; w; h
    c. If w is multiplied by 8, h is multiplied by 9, and V is multiplied by 20, by what is ℓ multiplied? $\frac{5}{18}$

EXPLORATION

22. Suppose $\triangle MIA$ is represented by the matrix $\begin{bmatrix} 4 & 8 & 10 \\ -2 & 5 & -3 \end{bmatrix}$.
    a. Find the product $\begin{bmatrix} \frac{1}{2} & 0 \\ 0 & \frac{1}{2} \end{bmatrix}\begin{bmatrix} 4 & 8 & 10 \\ -2 & 5 & -3 \end{bmatrix}$.
    b. The product matrix in Part b represents $\triangle M'I'A'$, the image of $\triangle MIA$ under a size change of what magnitude? Draw $\triangle MIA$ and $\triangle M'I'A'$. b–e. See margin.
    c. You can do Parts a and b by using a matrix polygon application. First input a matrix for $\triangle MIA$ and a matrix for a size change of a magnitude of your choosing. Then run the program for the product of those matrices.
    d. How are the lengths of the sides of $\triangle M'I'A'$ related to the lengths of the sides of $\triangle MIA$?
    e. How are the areas of $\triangle M'I'A'$ and $\triangle MIA$ related?

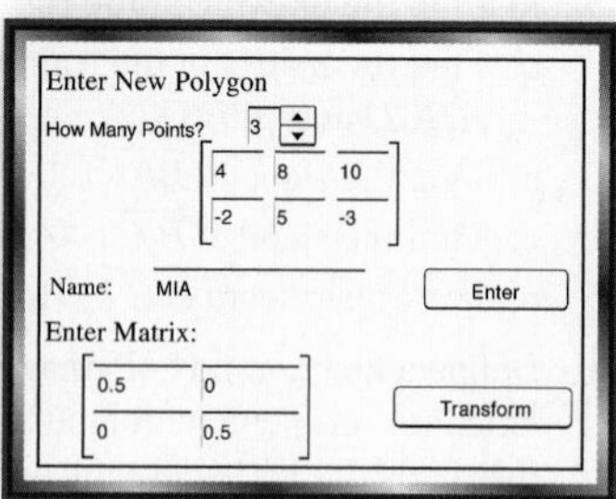

22a. $\begin{bmatrix} 2 & 4 & 5 \\ -1 & \frac{5}{2} & -\frac{3}{2} \end{bmatrix}$

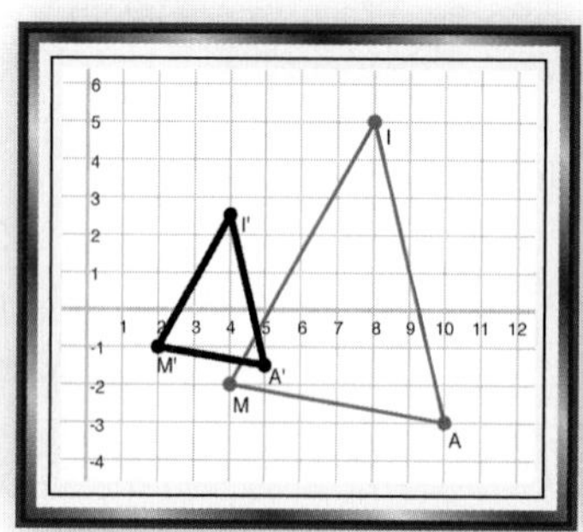

QY ANSWER

The lengths of sides of $N'U'M'E'R'$ are two times (or $\frac{1}{3}$ of) the lengths of corresponding sides of $NUMER$.

Additional Answers

22b. $\frac{1}{2}$;

22c. See diagrams in text.

22d. The length of the sides of $\triangle M'I'A'$ are half the length of the sides of $\triangle MIA$.

22e. The area of $\triangle M'I'A'$ is one-fourth of the area of $\triangle MIA$.

Lesson 4-5 Matrices for Scale Changes

Vocabulary

scale change
horizontal magnitude
vertical magnitude
stretch
shrink

BIG IDEA Matrices can represent scale changes.

Mental Math

Identify the quadrants in which the graph of the equation appears.

a. $y = 7x^2$ I and II

b. $y = -7x$ II and IV

c. $y = -\frac{7}{x^2}$ III and IV

d. $y = \frac{7}{x}$ I and III

What Is a Scale Change?

In the previous lesson you studied size changes, which are transformations in which the changes to the preimage have the same magnitude in both the horizontal and vertical directions. Sometimes it is more useful to apply a transformation in which the horizontal and vertical changes have *different* magnitudes.

For example, imagine that a friend hands you a rubber band and says there is a secret message written on it. The writing on the rubber band looks like the picture at the left below. If you apply a size change, and stretch the rubber band by the same amount in both directions, it looks like the picture in the center. It is still unreadable. However, if you stretch the rubber band more in the horizontal direction than the vertical direction, it looks like the picture at the right, and you can read the message.

I love Advanced Algebra!

Transformations that multiply coordinates by constants are called *scale changes.*

Definition of Scale Change

For any nonzero numbers a and b, the transformation that maps (x, y) onto (ax, by) is called the **scale change** with **horizontal magnitude** a and **vertical magnitude** b, and is denoted $S_{a,b}$.

$$S_{a,b}(x, y) = (ax, by) \text{ or}$$

$$S_{a,b} : (x, y) \rightarrow (ax, by)$$

When $|a| > 1$ (or $|b| > 1$), the scale change is a **stretch** in the horizontal (or vertical) direction. When $|a| < 1$ (or $|b| < 1$), the scale change is a **shrink** in the horizontal (or vertical) direction.

Souvenirs are often scale models of the actual things they represent.

Lesson 4-5

GOAL

Continue a two-lesson exploration of transformations and matrices by discussing scale changes, which are stretches and shrinks in both horizontal and vertical directions.

SPUR Objectives

F Recognize relationships between figures and their scale-change images.

G Relate scale changes to matrices, and vice versa.

K Graph figures and their scale-change images.

Materials/Resources

- Lesson Masters 4-5A and 4-5B
- Resource Masters 1, 63, and 64
- CAS or graphing calculator

HOMEWORK

Suggestions for Assignment

- Questions 1–21
- Question 22 (extra credit)
- Reading Lesson 4-6
- Covering the Ideas 4-6

Local Standards

1 Warm-Up

In 1–4, use a graph labeled for $-15 \le x \le 15$ and $-15 \le y \le 15$.

1. The points (5, 0), (4, 3), (3, 4), and (0, 5) all lie on the circle with center __?__ and radius __?__. (0, 0); 5
2. Find five more points on this circle. Answers vary. Sample: (–4, 3), (–3, 4), (–5, 0), (0, –5), (3, –4)
3. Find the images of all nine points under the transformation with matrix $\begin{bmatrix} 2 & 0 \\ 0 & 3 \end{bmatrix}$. In order from left to right: (10, 0), (8, 9), (6, 12), (0, 15), (–8, 9), (–6, 12), (–10, 0), (0, –15), (6, –12)

(continued on next page)

Background

Although this lesson's material will probably be new for all students, the subject should be relatively easy for most students.

Size changes, discussed in the previous lesson, stretch or shrink a figure by the same amount in both the horizontal and the vertical directions. In contrast, a scale change can affect the figure by a different amount in each direction. Therefore, two numbers are needed to describe a scale change.

Although we do not require magnitudes on either size changes or scale changes to be positive, our examples all have positive magnitudes. If one factor is negative, a reflection is performed; if both factors are negative, then a 180° rotation (the result of two reflections over perpendicular lines) is performed. Our reason for keeping the magnitudes positive is for simplicity only.

(continued on next page)

Like size changes, scale changes are functions because each point in the preimage maps to one and only one point in the image.

GUIDED

Example 1

Consider the triangle at the right. Find its image under $S_{4,0.5}$.

Solution $S_{4,0.5}(x, y) = (\underline{\ ?\ }x, \underline{\ ?\ }y)$, so multiply all *x*-coordinates of the preimage points by _?_ and all *y*-coordinates of the preimage points by _?_. Images of the vertices determine the image polygon. 4; 0.5; 4; 0.5

A': $S_{4,0.5}(0, 4) = (0, 2)$

B': $S_{4,0.5}(5, 6) = (\underline{\ ?\ }, \underline{\ ?\ })$ 20; 3

C': $S_{4,0.5}(6, 0) = (\underline{\ ?\ }, \underline{\ ?\ })$ 24; 0

The image of $\triangle ABC$ is $\triangle A'B'C'$ with the vertex coordinates above.

Check Check using the graph at the right. The image of every point should be 4 times as far from the *y*-axis and half as far from the *x*-axis as its preimage. For instance, the image $B' = (20, 3)$ is 4 times as far from the *y*-axis and half as far from the *x*-axis as its preimage $B = (5, 6)$.

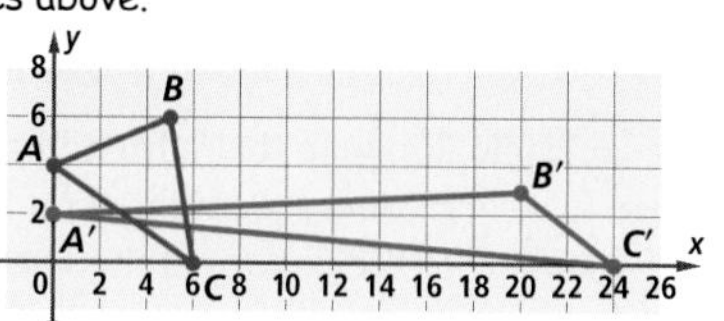

Example 1 demonstrates that scale changes might not multiply both vertical and horizontal distances by a constant amount, and so images are not necessarily similar to their preimages.

Matrices for Scale Changes

Because a size change is represented by a matrix, it is reasonable to expect that a scale change has a matrix.

Activity

Materials CAS or graphing calculator

Step 1 Sketch a graph of $\triangle ABC$ from Example 1. Write a matrix to represent $\triangle ABC$ and store the matrix as *M* on a CAS.

Step 2 Define a second matrix *S*1 on your CAS, with $S1 = \begin{bmatrix} 4 & 0 \\ 0 & 0.5 \end{bmatrix}$. Calculate $S1 \cdot M$, the matrix for $\triangle A'B'C'$.

Step 3 Sketch $\triangle A'B'C'$ on the same graph. Compare your graph to the graphs in Example 1. What transformation do you think matrix *S*1 represents?

Step 4 Define a third matrix $S2 = \begin{bmatrix} 1.2 & 0 \\ 0 & 3 \end{bmatrix}$. Calculate $S2 \cdot M$, the matrix for $\triangle A''B''C''$. Sketch $\triangle A''B''C''$ on the same graph.

Step 1. See first graph in Guided Example 1.

Step 2. $S1 \cdot M = \begin{bmatrix} 0 & 20 & 24 \\ 2 & 3 & 0 \end{bmatrix}$

Step 3. See second graph in Example 1. *S*1 represents the scale change $S_{4,0.5}$.

Step 4. See margin.

4. Describe the image. The points all lie on an ellipse that is symmetric to both the *x*-axis and *y*-axis.
5. Show that the distance between (5, 0) and (4, 3) is not equal to the distance between the images of these points under the transformation of Warm-Up Question 3. The distance between (5, 0) and (4, 3) is $\sqrt{10}$. The distance between (10, 0) and (8, 9) is $\sqrt{85}$.

2 Teaching

Notes on the Lesson

Scale changes can be found in fun house mirrors. (For examples that use the laws of physics, see http://www.learner.org/teacherslab/science/light/lawslight/funhouse/index.html.)

It is important that students understand that $S_{a,b} \neq S_{b,a}$. Have them graph the rectangle represented by the matrix $\begin{bmatrix} 2 & 5 & 5 & 2 \\ 0 & 0 & 6 & 6 \end{bmatrix}$. Ask them to sketch its image under $S_{3,4}$ and then under $S_{4,3}$. They will see that the transformations are not the same, and the ratios of the lengths of the sides and their images are not the same. Thus scale changes are not similarity transformations. However, the size-change transformations studied in Lesson 4-3 are special cases of scale change transformations. They are scale changes with equal horizontal and vertical magnitudes. This is obvious algebraically: If $a = b$, then $\begin{bmatrix} a & 0 \\ 0 & b \end{bmatrix}$ becomes $\begin{bmatrix} a & 0 \\ 0 & a \end{bmatrix}$, which is a matrix for a size change. But it may not be obvious that shrinking by the same amount in just two directions, horizontal and vertical, shrinks in all directions by that amount.

Stress that a positive magnitude that is less than 1 produces a shrink, and a magnitude that is greater than 1 produces a stretch. The magnitude 1 is an identity magnitude, producing neither a stretch nor a shrink.

Students will see scale changes again to map circles onto ellipses. In a later chapter, we use $S_{a,b}$ to provide an elegant description of getting the ellipse $\frac{x^2}{a^2} + \frac{y^2}{b^2} = 1$ from the equation of the unit circle, $x^2 + y^2 = 1$.

Accommodating the Learner 

Ask students to plot a nonsquare rectangle and then find a scale change that transforms the rectangle into a square. After students find such a scale change for a specific rectangle, ask them to find it for rectangles in general. Answers vary. Sample: If a rectangle in Quadrant I has opposite vertices (0, 0) and (*a*, *b*), then $S_{k, k \cdot \frac{a}{b}}$ takes the opposite vertices to (0, 0) and (*ak*, *ak*), so the image is a square.

Step 5 Compare the coordinates and graph of $\triangle ABC$ to the coordinates and graph of $\triangle A''B''C''$. What transformation do you think $S2$ represents?

Step 5. S2 represents the scale change $S_{1.2,3}$.

Step 6 Generalize your findings. Make a conjecture about the matrix for the scale change $S_{a,b}$.

Step 6. The matrix $\begin{bmatrix} a & 0 \\ 0 & b \end{bmatrix}$ represents the scale change $S_{a,b}$.

Algebra easily proves the results of the Activity. Suppose that $S_{a,b}$ has the matrix

$$\begin{bmatrix} e & f \\ g & h \end{bmatrix}$$

where $e, f, g,$ and h are real numbers. Because $S_{a,b}$ maps (x, y) onto (ax, by), we want to find $e, f, g,$ and h so that for all x and y,

$$\begin{bmatrix} e & f \\ g & h \end{bmatrix}\begin{bmatrix} x \\ y \end{bmatrix} = \begin{bmatrix} ax \\ by \end{bmatrix}.$$

By matrix multiplication, $\begin{bmatrix} ex + fy \\ gx + hy \end{bmatrix} = \begin{bmatrix} ax \\ by \end{bmatrix}.$

Thus for all x and y, $ex + fy = ax$, so $e = a$ and $f = 0$, and $gx + hy = by$, so $g = 0$ and $h = b$. We have proved the following theorem.

Scale Change Theorem

$\begin{bmatrix} a & 0 \\ 0 & b \end{bmatrix}$ is the matrix for $S_{a,b}$.

QY

QY

What is the matrix for $S_{7,4}$?

Example 2

Consider the quadrilateral $ABCD$ with $A = (-2, 5)$, $B = (0, 7)$, $C = (4, 1)$, and $D = (-4, -1)$. Find its image $A'B'C'D'$ under $S_{3,2}$.

Solution 1 Write $S_{3,2}$ and $ABCD$ in matrix form. Calculate the product by hand.

$$\overset{S_{3,2}}{\begin{bmatrix} 3 & 0 \\ 0 & 2 \end{bmatrix}}\overset{\begin{matrix} A & B & C & D \end{matrix}}{\begin{bmatrix} -2 & 0 & 4 & -4 \\ 5 & 7 & 1 & -1 \end{bmatrix}} = \overset{\begin{matrix} A' & B' & C' & D' \end{matrix}}{\begin{bmatrix} -6 & 0 & 12 & -12 \\ 10 & 14 & 2 & -2 \end{bmatrix}}$$

Solution 2 Use technology to do the calculations. Let m represent the transformation matrix and n represent quadrilateral $ABCD$.

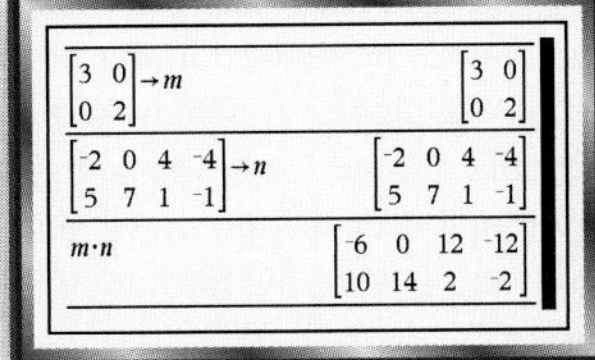

ENGLISH LEARNERS

Vocabulary Development

When you discuss the statement on page 252 (just before the Questions) that a size change is a special type of scale change, you may want to ask students about *two* special types of scale changes. Students should understand that the scale change $S_{k,k}$ is equivalent to a size change with magnitude k, so students should use the term *similar* to compare figures transformed by a size change to their preimages. Also, the scale change $S_{1,1}$ results in a figure with the same size and same shape as the preimage, so students should use the term *congruent* to describe figures related by such a change.

Additional Examples

Example 1 Using the same triangle as in Example 1, find its image under $S_{3,1.5}$.

Solution $S_{3,1.5}(x, y) = (\underline{\ ?\ }x, \underline{\ ?\ }y)$, so multiply all the x-coordinates of the preimage by $\underline{\ ?\ }$ and all the y-coordinates of the preimage by $\underline{\ ?\ }$. 3; 1.5; 3; 1.5

A': $S_{3,1.5}(0, 4) = (0, 6)$

B': $S_{3,1.5}(5, 6) = (\underline{\ ?\ }, \underline{\ ?\ })$ 15; 9

C': $S_{3,1.5}(6, 0) = (\underline{\ ?\ }, \underline{\ ?\ })$ 18; 0

So the image of $\triangle ABC$ is $\triangle A'B'C'$ with the vertex coordinates above.

Example 2 Consider the quadrilateral $PQRT$ with $P = (-3, 6)$, $Q = (0, 9)$, $R = (8, 2)$, and $T = (-5, -3)$. Find its image under $S_{5,3}$. $P' = (-15, 18)$, $Q' = (0, 27)$, $R' = (40, 6)$, and $T' = (-25, -9)$

Note-Taking Tips

As discussed following Example 2, encourage students to compare, in their notes, the notation $S_{a,b}$ for a scale change and S_k for a size change. Students should understand that a scale change in which the vertical and horizontal magnitudes are equal can be expressed as a size change.

Additional Answers

Activity

Step 4: $S2 \cdot M = \begin{bmatrix} 0 & 6 & 7.2 \\ 12 & 18 & 0 \end{bmatrix}$

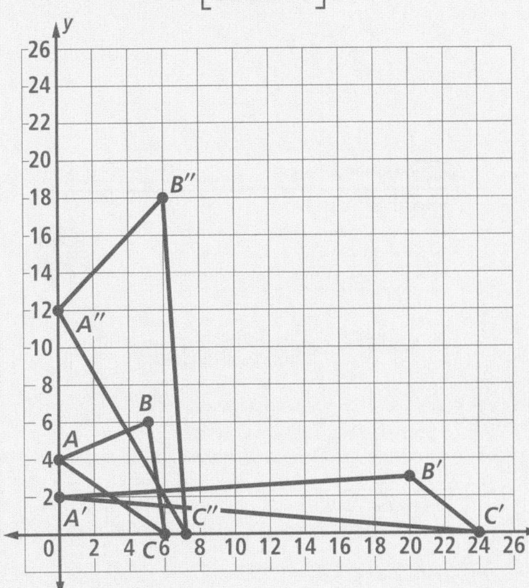

3 Assignment

Recommended Assignment

- Questions 1–21
- Question 22 (extra credit)
- Reading Lesson 4-6
- Covering the Ideas 4-6

Additional Answers

4a–b.

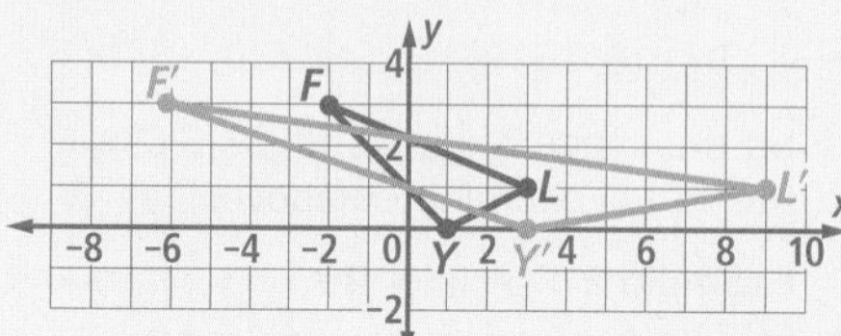

Notice that a scale change may or may not stretch or shrink by different factors in the horizontal and vertical directions. If the factors are the same in both directions, then the scale-change matrix has the form $\begin{bmatrix} k & 0 \\ 0 & k \end{bmatrix}$, and the transformation is just a size change.

Conversely, a size change with magnitude k is a scale change with horizontal magnitude k and vertical magnitude k. Thus *size changes are special types of scale changes*. In symbols, $S_k = S_{k,k}$.

Questions

COVERING THE IDEAS

1. **Fill in the Blank** $S_{0.8, \frac{4}{7}}: (x, y) \to$ ___?___ $(0.8x, \frac{4}{7}y)$
2. **Multiple Choice** Which of the following mappings gives a horizontal shrink and a vertical stretch? C

   A $S_{\frac{1}{5}, \frac{2}{3}}$ B $S_{9, 0.75}$ C $S_{0.36, 1.03}$ D $S_{5,5}$
3. a. What is the image of (3, 7.5) under $S_{4,2}$? (12, 15)
   b. Describe $S_{4,2}$ in words.
4. a. Draw $\triangle FLY$ with $F = (-2, 3)$, $L = (3, 1)$, and $Y = (1, 0)$.
   b. Draw its image $\triangle F'L'Y'$ under $S_{3,1}$. a–b. See margin.
   c. Which component changed, the horizontal or vertical? horizontal

In 5 and 6, refer to Example 2.

5. What are the coordinates of the image quadrilateral?
6. Find the image matrix of $ABCD$ under $S_{1,4}$.
7. **True or False** All scale changes produce images that are not similar to their preimages. false
8. Describe the scale change with a horizontal shrink of magnitude $\frac{1}{8}$ and a vertical stretch of magnitude 2
   a. in $f(x)$ notation. b. in mapping notation. c. as a matrix.
9. **Fill in the Blanks** The scale change $S_{8,8}$ can be thought of as the ___?___ change identified as ___?___. size; S_8

3b. $S_{4,2}$ stretches horizontally by a factor of 4 and stretches vertically by a factor of 2.

5. $A' = (-6, 10)$, $B' = (0, 14)$, $C' = (12, 2)$, $D' = (-12, -2)$

6. $\begin{bmatrix} -2 & 0 & 4 & -4 \\ 20 & 28 & 4 & -4 \end{bmatrix}$

8a. $S_{\frac{1}{8},2}(x, y) = \left(\frac{1}{8}x, 2y\right)$

8b. $S_{\frac{1}{8},2}: (x, y) \to \left(\frac{1}{8}x, 2y\right)$

8c. $\begin{bmatrix} \frac{1}{8} & 0 \\ 0 & 2 \end{bmatrix}$

APPLYING THE MATHEMATICS

In 10 and 11, consider this information. Pictures in word processors can usually be resized under both scale changes and size changes. When the picture is selected, a rectangle with small boxes (handles) appears around it, similar to the one at the right. Which of the handles A through H could you move, and how would you need to move it, to apply the given transformation to the preimage at the right?

A E B
H F
D G C

10. $S_{3, \frac{3}{4}}$ 11. $S_{1.6}$ 10–11. See margin.

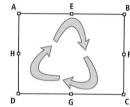

4-5A Lesson Master Questions on SPUR Objectives. See Student Edition pages 293–297 for objectives.

PROPERTIES Objective F

1. **Fill in the Blanks** Write *stretch* or *shrink*: The scale change $S_{\frac{1}{2},4}$ represents a horizontal shrink and a vertical stretch.
2. **Matching** The preimage of a stop sign is shown at the right. Match each scale change with the image of the sign under that scale change.
   a. $S_{\frac{1}{4},2}$ iii b. $S_{3,\frac{1}{2}}$ ii c. $S_{1,\frac{1}{16}}$ i
3. Give an example of a scale change that results in an image that Answers vary. Samples:
   a. is similar to its preimage. $S_{2,2}$ b. is not similar to its preimage. $S_{2,3}$
4. a. $S_{2,3}(4, -2) =$ (8, −6) b. $S_{2,3}(x, y) =$ (2x, 3y)
   c. If $S_{2,3}(p, q) = (14, -9)$, then $(p, q) =$ (7, −3)

PROPERTIES Objective G

5. Describe the scale change represented by $\begin{bmatrix} 4 & 0 \\ 0 & 1.5 \end{bmatrix}$. Horizontal stretch, magnitude 4, and vertical stretch, magnitude 1.5
6. Write the matrix for a scale change with horizontal magnitude 3 and vertical magnitude $\frac{3}{4}$. $\begin{bmatrix} 3 & 0 \\ 0 & \frac{3}{4} \end{bmatrix}$

REPRESENTATIONS Objective K

7. Let $QUAD = \begin{bmatrix} -3 & -3 & 4 & 6 \\ -2 & 4 & 5 & -2 \end{bmatrix}$.
   a. At the right, graph $QUAD$ and its image under $S_{1.5,0.5}$.
   b. Name a segment of $QUAD$ that is parallel to its image. QU or QD
   c. Name a segment of $QUAD$ that is *not* parallel to its image. AU or AD

212 Advanced Algebra

Accommodating the Learner

Tell students to graph a rectangle in Quadrant I so two opposite vertices are (0, 0) and (2, 8). Ask them to find (1) the side length of a square that has the same area as their rectangle and (2) a scale change that will transform their rectangle to that square. 1. 4 units; 2. $S_{2,\frac{1}{2}}$

Additional Answers

10. Answers vary. Sample: Move F right to make the image 3 times as wide, and move E down to make the image 0.75 times as small.
11. Answers vary. Sample: Move B to make both dimensions 1.6 times as long.

12. The transformation $S_{2,1.5}$ is applied to the rectangular fenced-in plot at the right. Coordinates are given for each vertex of the plot.

a. Find the perimeter P and area A of the pictured fenced-in plot. $P = 110$; $A = 666$

b. Find the coordinates of the vertices of the image of the plot. (6, 27), (80, 27), (6, 0), (80, 0)

c. Find the perimeter P and area A of the new image. $P = 202$; $A = 1998$

13. $\triangle BLT$ is represented by the matrix $\begin{bmatrix} 0 & 0 & 10 \\ 0 & 10 & 0 \end{bmatrix}$. a–c. See margin.

a. Graph the triangle. Classify $\triangle BLT$ as isosceles or scalene, and as acute, right, or obtuse.

b. Find the matrix for $\triangle B'L'T'$, the image of $\triangle BLT$ under the scale change represented by $\begin{bmatrix} 4 & 0 \\ 0 & 1.2 \end{bmatrix}$.

c. Graph $\triangle B'L'T'$. Would you classify $\triangle B'L'T'$ the same way as $\triangle BLT$? If not, what is different?

14. Prove or disprove the following: If $\overline{A'B'}$ is the image of $\overline{AB}$ under a scale change, then $\overline{AB} \parallel \overline{A'B'}$. See margin.

15. Consider the matrix equation below that maps $\triangle FOR$ onto $\triangle F'O'R'$.

$$\begin{bmatrix} 5 & 0 \\ 0 & 7 \end{bmatrix} \begin{bmatrix} a & b & c \\ d & e & f \end{bmatrix} = \begin{bmatrix} 25 & 5 & 20 \\ 14 & 28 & -7 \end{bmatrix}$$

a. What transformation is applied to $\triangle FOR$? $S_{5,7}$

b. Find the coordinates of the vertices of $\triangle FOR$.

c. Find $\frac{F'O'}{FO}$ and $\frac{O'R'}{OR}$. (*Hint:* Use the formula for distance between two points or a DGS.) $\frac{F'O'}{FO} \approx 5.5$; $\frac{O'R'}{OR} \approx 6.5$

d. Should the ratios in Part c be the same? Why or why not?

15b. $F = (5, 2)$, $O = (1, 4)$, $R = (4, -1)$

15d. No; the transformation given here is a scale change that is not a size change. The figure and its image are not similar triangles, so the ratios will not be the same.

REVIEW

16. Let $R = \begin{bmatrix} 5 & -1 & -1 & 5 \\ 3 & 3 & 6 & 5 \end{bmatrix}$. (Lesson 4-4) See margin.

a. What matrix will produce a size change of magnitude $\frac{2}{3}$ on R?

b. Multiply your matrix in Part a by R. Call your answer R'.

c. Is the rectangle whose vertices are given by R similar to the rectangle whose vertices are given by R'? Justify your answer.

Notes on the Questions

Question 14 The segments are parallel (allowing a line to be parallel to itself) if and only if the scale change is a size change, that is, if its vertical and horizontal magnitudes are equal.

Question 15 This question shows that, under this scale change, $\triangle FOR$ is not similar to $\triangle F'O'R'$.

Additional Answers

13a.

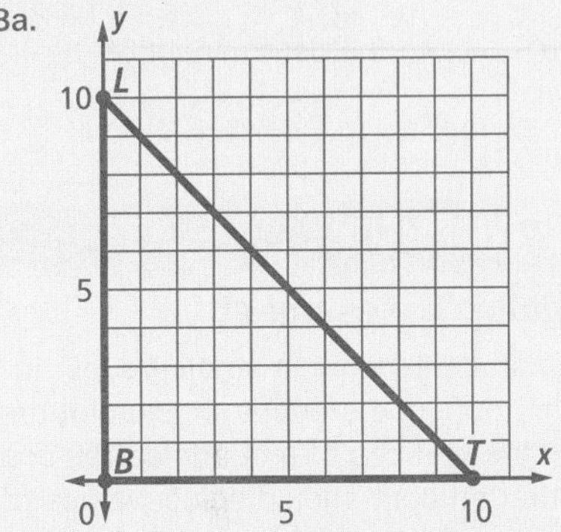

ΔBLT is an isosceles right triangle.

13b. $\Delta B'L'T' = \begin{bmatrix} 0 & 0 & 40 \\ 0 & 12 & 0 \end{bmatrix}$

13c.

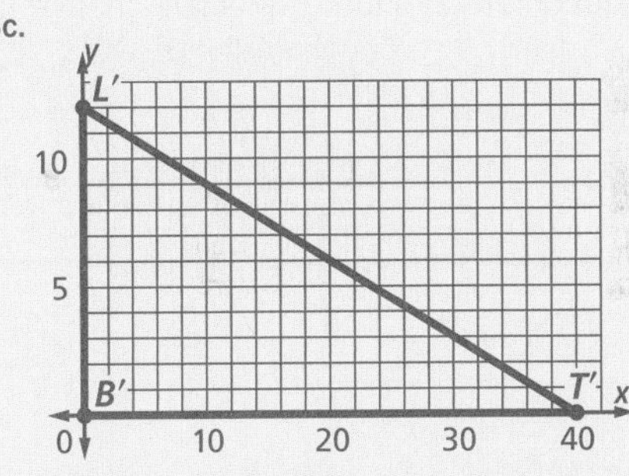

$\Delta B'L'T'$ is also a right triangle, but it is scalene, not isosceles.

14. Answers vary. Sample: A counterexample will disprove this claim. Let $A = (0, 0)$ and $B = (5, 2)$. If we apply $S_{2,7}$ to $\overline{AB}$, $A' = (0, 0)$ and $B' = (10, 14)$. The slope of $\overline{AB}$ is $\frac{2}{5}$, whereas the slope of $\overline{A'B'}$ is $\frac{7}{5}$. So, $\overline{AB}$ is not parallel to $\overline{A'B'}$.

16a. $\begin{bmatrix} \frac{2}{3} & 0 \\ 0 & \frac{2}{3} \end{bmatrix}$

16b. $R' = \begin{bmatrix} \frac{10}{3} & -\frac{2}{3} & -\frac{2}{3} & \frac{10}{3} \\ 2 & 2 & 4 & \frac{10}{3} \end{bmatrix}$

16c. Yes; all figures are similar to their size-change images.

Notes on the Questions

Question 22 Using the idea of the *determinant of a matrix,* if a matrix for a transformation has determinant *d,* then it multiplies the area of the preimage by $|d|$; in other words, the ratio of the area of any image to the area of its preimage is $|d|$. If $d > 0$, then the figure and its image have the same orientation. If $d \le 0$, then the figure and its image have opposite orientation. In the 2×2 case, the determinant of $\begin{bmatrix} a & b \\ c & d \end{bmatrix}$ is $ad - bc$, so the determinant of $\begin{bmatrix} a & 0 \\ 0 & b \end{bmatrix}$ is ab.

4 Wrap-Up

Ongoing Assessment

Have students work in small groups. In each group, one student should plot and label the vertices of a quadrilateral, and another student should select values of *a* and *b* for the scale change $S_{a,b}$. Then all students in the group should write matrices for the scale change and for the vertices and multiply the matrices to find the vertices of the image of the quadrilateral under that scale change. Answers vary. Check students' work.

4-5B Lesson Master — Questions on SPUR Objectives. See Student Edition pages 293–297 for objectives.

PROPERTIES Objective F

1. **True or False** A figure and its scale-change image are similar. false

In 2–7, $\triangle A'B'C'$ is the image of $\triangle ABC$ under a scale change $S_{0.5,4}$.

2. If $A = (4, -2)$, what are the coordinates of A'? (2, –8)
3. If $A' = (3, 12)$, what are the coordinates of A? (6, 3)
4. Is $\triangle ABC$ similar to $\triangle A'B'C'$? no
5. Is this scale change a size change? no
6. In which direction is $\triangle ABC$ stretched? vertically
7. In which direction is $\triangle ABC$ shrunk? horizontally

PROPERTIES Objective G

In 8–12, give the scale-change matrix corresponding to each given transformation.

8. a vertical shrink of $\frac{1}{2}$ and a horizontal stretch of 3 $\begin{bmatrix} 3 & 0 \\ 0 & \frac{1}{2} \end{bmatrix}$
9. $S_{2,9}$ $\begin{bmatrix} 2 & 0 \\ 0 & 9 \end{bmatrix}$
10. vertical stretch of 2 and a horizontal shrink of $\frac{2}{3}$ $\begin{bmatrix} \frac{2}{3} & 0 \\ 0 & 2 \end{bmatrix}$
11. $S_{5,2}$ $\begin{bmatrix} 5 & 0 \\ 0 & 2 \end{bmatrix}$
12. the transformation that maps $(3, -9)$ onto $(1.5, -3)$ $\begin{bmatrix} \frac{1}{2} & 0 \\ 0 & \frac{1}{3} \end{bmatrix}$

Advanced Algebra 213

17. **Fill in the Blanks** Let $T = \begin{bmatrix} 4 & 0 \\ 0 & 4 \end{bmatrix}$, and $V = \begin{bmatrix} \frac{1}{2} & 0 \\ 0 & \frac{1}{2} \end{bmatrix}$. (Lessons 4-4, 4-3)
   a. T is the matrix for a size change of magnitude __?__. 4
   b. V is the matrix for a size change of magnitude __?__. $\frac{1}{2}$
   c. Compute TV. TV is the matrix for a size change of magnitude __?__.

18. Let $P = \begin{bmatrix} 2 \\ 4 \end{bmatrix}$. (Lessons 4-3, 4-1, 2-7)
   a. Compute $\begin{bmatrix} \frac{1}{2} & 0 \\ 0 & \frac{1}{2} \end{bmatrix}P$, $\begin{bmatrix} 1 & 0 \\ 0 & 1 \end{bmatrix}P$, $\begin{bmatrix} 2 & 0 \\ 0 & 2 \end{bmatrix}P$, and $\begin{bmatrix} 4 & 0 \\ 0 & 4 \end{bmatrix}P$.
   b. If you consider all of your answers to Part a as representing points (x, y), what single direct-variation equation do x and y satisfy? $y = 2x$

19. **Fill in the Blank** The explicit formula for the nth term of an arithmetic sequence with first term a_1 and constant difference d is __?__. (Lesson 3-8) $a_n = a_1 + d(n - 1)$

20. Suppose a line goes through the points $(-4, -4)$ and $(2, 1)$. (Lesson 3-4) a. Answers vary. Sample: $y - 1 = \frac{5}{6}(x - 2)$; b. $a = \frac{31}{6}$
   a. Write an equation for this line in point-slope form.
   b. This line goes through a point $(7, a)$. What is the value of a?

21. a. Name three properties that are preserved under reflections.
   b. A reflection is a type of isometry. What is an isometry? Name two other types of isometries. (Previous Course)

17c. $\begin{bmatrix} 2 & 0 \\ 0 & 2 \end{bmatrix}$; 2

18a. $\begin{bmatrix} 1 \\ 2 \end{bmatrix}$; $\begin{bmatrix} 2 \\ 4 \end{bmatrix}$; $\begin{bmatrix} 4 \\ 8 \end{bmatrix}$; $\begin{bmatrix} 8 \\ 16 \end{bmatrix}$

21a. Answers vary. Sample: distance, angle measure, and collinearity

21b. An isometry is a transformation that preserves distance. Answers vary. Sample: rotation and translation

QY ANSWER

$\begin{bmatrix} 7 & 0 \\ 0 & 4 \end{bmatrix}$

EXPLORATION

a–c. See margin.

22. Let $ABCD$ be the square defined by the matrix $\begin{bmatrix} 0 & 2 & 2 & 0 \\ 0 & 0 & 2 & 2 \end{bmatrix}$.
   a. Transform $ABCD$ by multiplying its matrix on the left by each of the following matrices (and by some others of your own choice).
      i. $\begin{bmatrix} 3 & 0 \\ 0 & 4 \end{bmatrix}$ ii. $\begin{bmatrix} 3 & 0 \\ 0 & 1 \end{bmatrix}$
      iii. $\begin{bmatrix} 3 & 0 \\ 0 & 2 \end{bmatrix}$ iv. $\begin{bmatrix} 5 & 0 \\ 0 & 5 \end{bmatrix}$
   b. Find the area of each image. Enter your results in a table like the one shown at the right.
   c. What is the connection between the elements a and b of the scale-change matrix $\begin{bmatrix} a & 0 \\ 0 & b \end{bmatrix}$ and the effect the scale change has on area?

Transformation Matrix	Preimage Area	Image Area
$\begin{bmatrix} 3 & 0 \\ 0 & 4 \end{bmatrix}$	4 sq. units	? sq. units
$\begin{bmatrix} 3 & 0 \\ 0 & 1 \end{bmatrix}$	4 sq. units	? sq. units
$\begin{bmatrix} 3 & 0 \\ 0 & 2 \end{bmatrix}$	?	?
$\begin{bmatrix} 5 & 0 \\ 0 & 5 \end{bmatrix}$	?	?

Extension

Ask students to work with rectangles where two opposite vertices have coordinates $(0, 0)$ and (a, b), where $a > 0$, $b > 0$, and $a \neq b$. Ask them to find a scale change so that two opposite vertices of the image of that rectangle under the scale change are $(0, 0)$ and (b, a). The scale change is $S_{\frac{b}{a}, \frac{a}{b}}$.

Additional Answers

22a. i. $\begin{bmatrix} 0 & 6 & 6 & 0 \\ 0 & 0 & 8 & 8 \end{bmatrix}$ ii. $\begin{bmatrix} 0 & 6 & 6 & 0 \\ 0 & 0 & 2 & 2 \end{bmatrix}$

iii. $\begin{bmatrix} 0 & 6 & 6 & 0 \\ 0 & 0 & 4 & 4 \end{bmatrix}$ iv. $\begin{bmatrix} 0 & 10 & 10 & 0 \\ 0 & 0 & 10 & 10 \end{bmatrix}$

22b. 4 sq. units; 12 sq. units; 4 sq. units; 24 sq. units; 4 sq. units; 100 sq. units

22c. The scale change multiplies the area by *ab*.

Lesson 4-6 Matrices for Reflections

Vocabulary

reflection image of a point over a line

reflecting line, line of reflection

reflection

▸ **BIG IDEA** Matrices can represent reflections.

What Is a Reflection?

Recall from geometry that the **reflection image of a point *A* over a line *m*** is:

1. the point A, if A is on m;
2. the point A' such that m is the perpendicular bisector of $\overline{AA'}$, if A is not on m.

The line m is called the **reflecting line** or **line of reflection**.

A **reflection** is a transformation that maps a figure to its reflection image. The figure on the right is the *reflection image* of a drawing and the point A over the line m. This transformation is called r_m, and we write $A' = r_m(A)$.

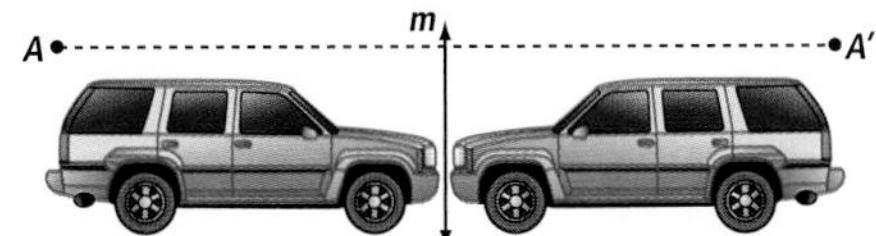

Mental Math

Use matrices *A*, *B*, and *C* below. Tell whether it is possible to calculate each of the following.

$A = \begin{bmatrix} 2 & 3 \\ -1 & 7 \end{bmatrix}$

$B = \begin{bmatrix} 4 & 0.5 \end{bmatrix}$

$C = \begin{bmatrix} 6 & 3 \\ 0 & -12 \end{bmatrix}$

a. $A + B$ no

b. AB no

c. BA yes

d. BC yes

Reflection over the *y*-axis

Suppose that $A = (x, y)$ and $B = (-x, y)$, as shown at the right. Notice that the slope of $\overline{AB}$, like the slope of the x-axis, is zero, which means that $\overline{AB}$ is parallel to the x-axis, and perpendicular to the y-axis. Also, because the y-coordinates are the same and the x-coordinates are opposites, the points are equidistant from the y-axis. So the y-axis is the perpendicular bisector of $\overline{AB}$. This means that $B = (-x, y)$ is the reflection image of $A = (x, y)$ over the y-axis. Reflection over the y-axis can be denoted $r_{y\text{-axis}}$ or r_y. In this book we use r_y.

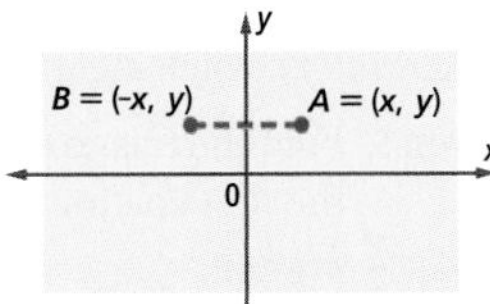

You can write

$$r_y: (x, y) \rightarrow (-x, y) \text{ or } r_y(x, y) = (-x, y).$$

Both are read "the reflection over the y-axis maps point (x, y) onto point $(-x, y)$."

Lesson 4-6

GOAL

Continue the process of finding matrices for common transformations: find matrices for reflections over the *x*-axis, the *y*-axis, and the line *y* = *x*; prove and apply a general procedure for remembering those matrices.

SPUR Objectives

F Recognize relationships between figures and their reflection images.

G Relate certain reflections to matrices, and vice versa.

K Graph figures and their reflection images.

Materials/Resources

- Lesson Masters 4-6A and 4-6B
- Resource Masters 1, 65, and 66
- Matrix polygon application

HOMEWORK

Suggestions for Assignment

- Questions 1–22
- Question 23 (extra credit)
- Reading Lesson 4-7
- Covering the Ideas 4-7

Local Standards

1 Warm-Up

Graph the quadrilateral determined by the points $Q = (3, 1)$, $U = (3, -5)$, $A = (6, 4)$, and $D = (6, 7)$. Find the image of $QUAD$ under these transformations:

1. $r_x\ r_x(QUAD)$ has vertices $(3, -1)$, $(3, 5)$, $(6, -4)$, and $(6, -7)$.
2. $r_y\ r_y(QUAD)$ has vertices $(-3, 1)$, $(-3, -5)$, $(-6, 4)$, and $(-6, 7)$.
3. $r_{y=x}\ r_{y=x}(QUAD)$ has vertices $(1, 3)$, $(-5, 3)$, $(4, 6)$, and $(7, 6)$.

Background

One reason that reflections are important transformations is that the preimage and image figures are congruent. The image looks "backward" because orientation is reversed. For example, refer to $\triangle JKL$ and $\triangle J'K'L'$ in Example 1. If you imagine walking from J to K to L to J, you will travel counterclockwise; the interior of the triangle will be on your left. For the corresponding walk on the image from J' to K' to L' to J', you will travel clockwise, with the interior of the triangle on your right.

Another reason reflections are important is their intimate connection with bilateral symmetry, which is so common in the real world and in mathematics. For this course, another significant reason is that the graphs of inverse functions are reflection images of each other over the line $y = x$. This topic is discussed in a later chapter.

(continued on next page)

2 Teaching

Notes on the Lesson

Students unfamiliar with reflection concepts will need to study this lesson carefully, but students generally have little trouble concluding that the reflection image of (x, y) over the y-axis is $(-x, y)$, over the x-axis is $(x, -y)$, and over the line $y = x$ is (y, x).

You may want to point out that when reflecting a point over the y-axis, the image point is the same distance above or below the x-axis as the preimage, so they share the same y-coordinate. Also, the image point is the same distance from the y-axis as the preimage, but on the opposite side of the y-axis, so the image and preimage have opposite x-coordinates. Similar arguments apply for reflection images over the x-axis.

For some students, it may be difficult at first to remember the matrix associated with each reflection. Notice that $r_y: (x, y) \rightarrow (-x, y)$ says that r_y changes the sign of the x-coordinate but does not affect the y-coordinate. Students who become facile at multiplying by 2×2 matrices will notice that multiplying on the left by $\begin{bmatrix} -1 & 0 \\ 0 & 1 \end{bmatrix}$ changes the sign of each element of the top row (of the right matrix) and does not change the elements in the bottom row. Similarly, multiplying on the left by r_x, $\begin{bmatrix} 1 & 0 \\ 0 & -1 \end{bmatrix}$, changes the sign of each element in the bottom row and does not change the elements in the top row. This provides a way for students to associate the matrix with the transformation. As another example, $\begin{bmatrix} 0 & 1 \\ 1 & 0 \end{bmatrix}$ switches the rows of the matrix being multiplied, and because $r_{y=x}$ switches the coordinates of each point, it is associated with $\begin{bmatrix} 0 & 1 \\ 1 & 0 \end{bmatrix}$.

Additional Example

Example 1 If $P = (2, 5)$, $Q = (4, 7)$, and $R = (9, 1)$, find the image of $\triangle PQR$ under r_y. $P' = (-2, 5)$, $Q' = (-4, 7)$, and $R' = (-9, 1)$

Notice that $\begin{bmatrix} -1 & 0 \\ 0 & 1 \end{bmatrix}\begin{bmatrix} x \\ y \end{bmatrix} = \begin{bmatrix} -1 \cdot x + 0 \cdot y \\ 0 \cdot x + 1 \cdot y \end{bmatrix} = \begin{bmatrix} -x \\ y \end{bmatrix}$.

This means that there is a matrix associated with r_y and proves the following theorem.

Matrix for r_y Theorem

$\begin{bmatrix} -1 & 0 \\ 0 & 1 \end{bmatrix}$ is the matrix for r_y.

Example 1

If $J = (1, 4)$, $K = (2, 4)$, and $L = (1, 7)$, find the image of $\triangle JKL$ under r_y.

Solution Represent r_y and $\triangle JKL$ as matrices and multiply.

$$\underset{r_y}{\begin{bmatrix} -1 & 0 \\ 0 & 1 \end{bmatrix}}\ \underset{\triangle JKL}{\begin{bmatrix} 1 & 2 & 1 \\ 4 & 4 & 7 \end{bmatrix}} = \underset{\triangle J'K'L'}{\begin{bmatrix} -1 & -2 & -1 \\ 4 & 4 & 7 \end{bmatrix}}$$

The image $\triangle J'K'L'$ has vertices $J' = (-1, 4)$, $K' = (-2, 4)$, and $L' = (-1, 7)$.

Check Use a DGS to plot $\triangle JKL$ and its image $\triangle J'K'L'$. The preimage and image are graphed at the right. It checks.

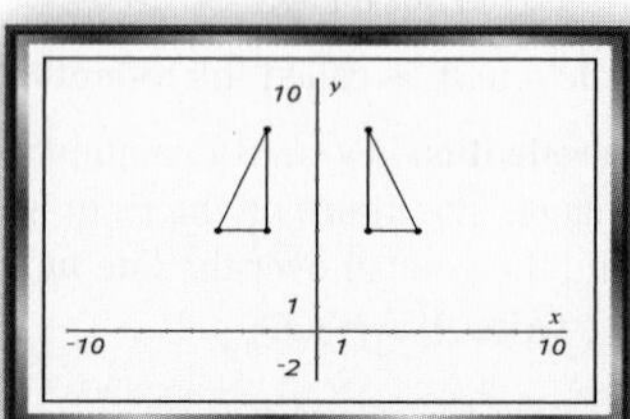

Remembering Transformation Matrices

You have now seen matrices for size changes, scale changes, and one reflection, r_y. You may wonder: Is there a way to generate a matrix for any transformation A so that I do not have to just memorize them? One method of generating transformation matrices that works for reflections, rotations, and scale changes is to use the following two-step algorithm.

Step 1 Find the image of (1, 0) under A and write the coordinates in the first column of the transformation matrix.

Step 2 Find the image of (0, 1) under A and write these coordinates in the second column.

For example, here is a way to remember the matrix for r_y, the reflection over the y-axis.

The image of (1, 0) under r_y is (-1, 0). → $\begin{bmatrix} -1 & 0 \\ 0 & 1 \end{bmatrix}$ ← The image of (0, 1) under r_y is (0, 1).

Multiplying by the 2×2 matrices in this lesson is easy. Still, it will take some effort for students to learn which matrix is associated with which reflection. It is for this reason that we give the Matrix Basis Theorem, which applies to any transformation that can be represented by a 2×2 matrix.

This general property is called the *Matrix Basis Theorem*.

Matrix Basis Theorem

Suppose A is a transformation represented by a 2×2 matrix. If $A : (1, 0) \rightarrow (x_1, y_1)$ and $A : (0, 1) \rightarrow (x_2, y_2)$, then A has the matrix $\begin{bmatrix} x_1 & x_2 \\ y_1 & y_2 \end{bmatrix}$.

Proof Let the 2×2 transformation matrix for A be $\begin{bmatrix} a & b \\ c & d \end{bmatrix}$, and suppose $A: (1, 0) \rightarrow (x_1, y_1)$ and $A: (0, 1) \rightarrow (x_2, y_2)$. Then

$$\begin{bmatrix} a & b \\ c & d \end{bmatrix}\begin{bmatrix} 1 & 0 \\ 0 & 1 \end{bmatrix} = \begin{bmatrix} x_1 & x_2 \\ y_1 & y_2 \end{bmatrix}.$$

Multiply the 2×2 matrices on the left side of the equation.

$$\begin{bmatrix} a \cdot 1 + b \cdot 0 & a \cdot 0 + b \cdot 1 \\ c \cdot 1 + d \cdot 0 & c \cdot 0 + d \cdot 1 \end{bmatrix} = \begin{bmatrix} x_1 & x_2 \\ y_1 & y_2 \end{bmatrix}$$

$$\begin{bmatrix} a & b \\ c & d \end{bmatrix} = \begin{bmatrix} x_1 & x_2 \\ y_1 & y_2 \end{bmatrix}$$

Thus, the matrix for the transformation A is $\begin{bmatrix} x_1 & x_2 \\ y_1 & y_2 \end{bmatrix}$.

Reflections over Other Lines

Other transformation matrices let you easily reflect polygons over lines other than the y-axis.

GUIDED

Example 2

Use the Matrix Basis Theorem to find the transformation matrix for $r_{y=x}$.

Solution Find the image of (1, 0) under $r_{y=x}$ and write its coordinates in the first column of the matrix for $r_{y=x}$.

$r_{y=x}(1, 0) = (\underline{\ ?\ }, \underline{\ ?\ })$ 0; 1

$\begin{bmatrix} \underline{0?} & \underline{\ ?\ } \\ \underline{1?} & \underline{\ ?\ } \end{bmatrix}$

Find the image of (0, 1) under $r_{y=x}$ and write its coordinates in the second column of the matrix for $r_{y=x}$.

$r_{y=x}(0, 1) = (\underline{\ ?\ }, \underline{\ ?\ })$ 1; 0

$\begin{bmatrix} \underline{0?} & \underline{1?} \\ \underline{1?} & \underline{0?} \end{bmatrix}$ is the matrix for $r_{y=x}$.

Accommodating the Learner

Ask students to find the images of several points over the line $x = 3$. Then ask them why they cannot use the Matrix Basis Theorem for such a reflection. Answers vary. Sample: The images of (1, 0) and (0, 1) are (5, 0) and (6, 1), and the matrix $\begin{bmatrix} 5 & 6 \\ 0 & 1 \end{bmatrix}$ *does not* generate points reflected over $x = 3$. An explanation is that reflection over $x = 3$ cannot be represented by a 2×2 matrix, and the Matrix Basis Theorem states that it applies only to transformations that can be represented by a 2×2 matrix. (See the Extension on page 259 for an additional analysis of reflections over vertical or horizontal lines.)

Notes on the Lesson

The Matrix Basis Theorem has a proof that is so short it does not seem like a proof! Consider the transformation with matrix $\begin{bmatrix} a & b \\ c & d \end{bmatrix}$. Apply this transformation to the segment with endpoints (1, 0) and (0, 1), that is, the segment with matrix $\begin{bmatrix} 1 & 0 \\ 0 & 1 \end{bmatrix}$. The result is the original matrix. Its left column is the image of (1, 0), and its right column is the image of (0, 1). So, if we wish to reconstruct the matrix from the images, we just reverse the process.

Additional Example

Example 2 Use the Matrix Basis Theorem to verify the 2×2 matrices for (**a**) r_y and (**b**) r_x.

Solution Find the images of (1, 0) and (0, 1) for each reflection.

a. $r_y(1, 0) = (\underline{\ ?\ }, \underline{\ ?\ })$, $r_y(0, 1) = (\underline{\ ?\ }, \underline{\ ?\ })$, so the matrix for r_y is $\underline{\ ?\ }$.

–1; 0; 0; 1; $\begin{bmatrix} -1 & 0 \\ 0 & 1 \end{bmatrix}$

b. $r_x(1, 0) = (\underline{\ ?\ }, \underline{\ ?\ })$, $r_x(0, 1) = (\underline{\ ?\ }, \underline{\ ?\ })$, so the matrix for r_x is $\underline{\ ?\ }$.

1; 0; 0; –1; $\begin{bmatrix} 1 & 0 \\ 0 & -1 \end{bmatrix}$

Note-Taking Tips

When students record a matrix multiplication in their notes, such as the one in Example 1, they should include a comment such as "the number of columns in the matrix for r_y is 2 and the number of rows in the matrix for the vertices is also 2, so the matrices can be multiplied." Encourage students to always check that two matrices can be multiplied before they begin the multiplication algorithm.

Additional Answers

Activity

Step 4: The corresponding points have the same *x*-coordinate and opposite *y*-coordinates; reflection over the *x*-axis.

Step 5: Corresponding points have *x*- and *y*-coordinates switched; reflection over the line $y = x$; corresponding points have *x*- and *y*-coordinates switched and each coordinate is multiplied by -1; reflection over the line $y = -x$.

Activity

MATERIALS matrix polygon application

Step 1 Familiarize yourself with how a matrix polygon application lets you draw and transform polygons.

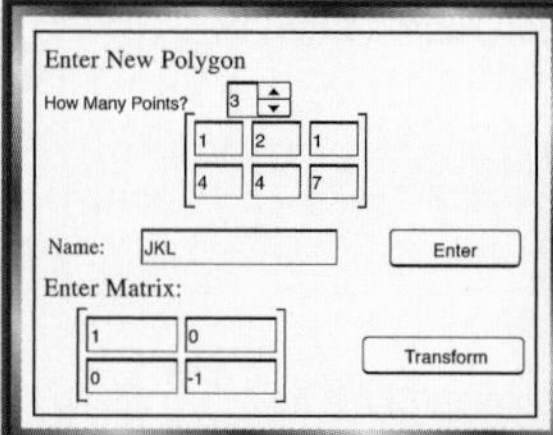

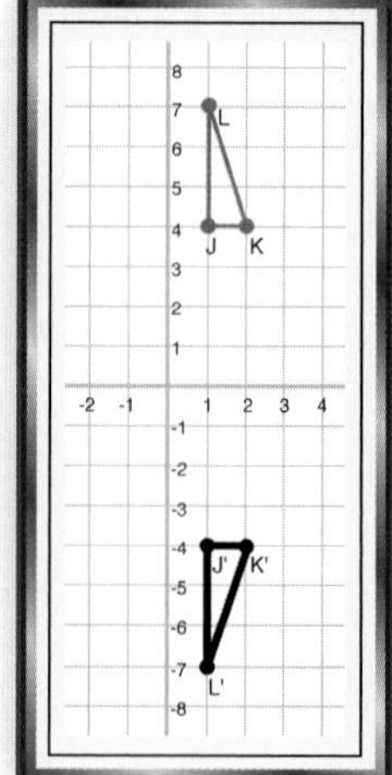

Step 2 Enter the matrix $\begin{bmatrix} 1 & 2 & 1 \\ 4 & 4 & 7 \end{bmatrix}$, which represents $\triangle JKL$.

Step 3 Enter the transformation matrix $T1 = \begin{bmatrix} 1 & 0 \\ 0 & -1 \end{bmatrix}$.

Step 4 Graph $\triangle J'K'L'$, the image of $\triangle JKL$ under the transformation represented by $T1$. How do the coordinates of corresponding points on $\triangle J'K'L'$ and $\triangle JKL$ compare? What transformation maps $\triangle JKL$ onto $\triangle J'K'L'$? If you are not sure, enter another polygon and transform it.

Step 5 Enter two more transformation matrices, $T2 = \begin{bmatrix} 0 & 1 \\ 1 & 0 \end{bmatrix}$ and $T3 = \begin{bmatrix} 0 & -1 \\ -1 & 0 \end{bmatrix}$.

Repeat Step 4, answering the same questions for each of these transformations. **Steps 4 and 5: See margin.**

The Activity verifies that matrix multiplication can be used to reflect $\triangle JKL$ over three lines: the *x*-axis, the line $y = x$, and the line $y = -x$. Graphs of the triangle and its images are shown below.

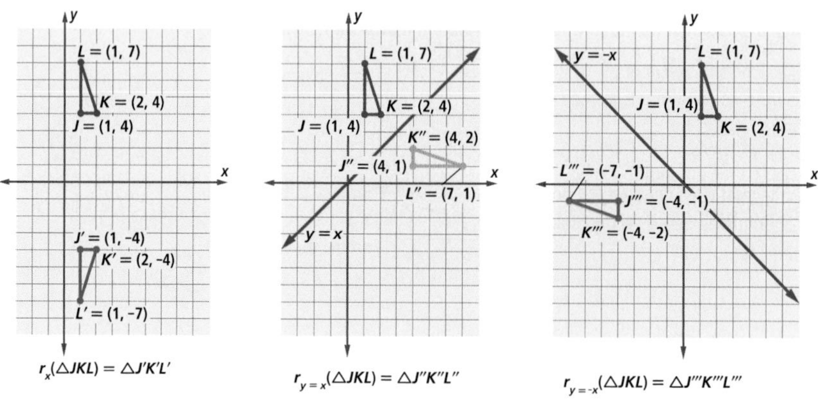

$r_x(\triangle JKL) = \triangle J'K'L'$ $r_{y=x}(\triangle JKL) = \triangle J''K''L''$ $r_{y=-x}(\triangle JKL) = \triangle J'''K'''L'''$

Accommodating the Learner

Ask students for the relationship, in terms of reflections, of the ordered pairs (5, 3) and (5, -3). **They are reflections of each other over the *x*-axis.** Ask them to use the matrix for r_x to show that each is the image of the other under r_x. **The matrix for r_x is $\begin{bmatrix} 1 & 0 \\ 0 & -1 \end{bmatrix}$, and $\begin{bmatrix} 1 & 0 \\ 0 & -1 \end{bmatrix}\begin{bmatrix} 5 & 5 \\ 3 & -3 \end{bmatrix} = \begin{bmatrix} 5 & 5 \\ -3 & 3 \end{bmatrix}$.** Then ask the same questions for (5, 3) and (-5, 3). **The points are reflection images of each other over the *y*-axis; $\begin{bmatrix} -1 & 0 \\ 0 & 1 \end{bmatrix}\begin{bmatrix} 5 & -5 \\ 3 & 3 \end{bmatrix} = \begin{bmatrix} -5 & 5 \\ 3 & 3 \end{bmatrix}$.**

In general, in mapping notation,

r_x: $(x, y) \to (x, -y)$, $r_{y=x}$: $(x, y) \to (y, x)$, and $r_{y=-x}$: $(x, y) \to (-y, -x)$.

It is easy to prove that the matrices for r_x, $r_{y=x}$, and $r_{y=-x}$ are as stated in the next theorem.

Matrices for r_x, $r_{y=x}$, and $r_{y=-x}$ Theorem

1. $\begin{bmatrix} 1 & 0 \\ 0 & -1 \end{bmatrix}$ is the matrix for r_x.
2. $\begin{bmatrix} 0 & 1 \\ 1 & 0 \end{bmatrix}$ is the matrix for $r_{y=x}$.
3. $\begin{bmatrix} 0 & -1 \\ -1 & 0 \end{bmatrix}$ is the matrix for $r_{y=-x}$.

Proof of 1

$$\begin{bmatrix} 1 & 0 \\ 0 & -1 \end{bmatrix}\begin{bmatrix} x \\ y \end{bmatrix} = \begin{bmatrix} 1 \cdot x + 0 \cdot y \\ 0 \cdot x + -1 \cdot y \end{bmatrix} = \begin{bmatrix} x \\ -y \end{bmatrix}$$

You are asked to prove 2 and 3 in Questions 14 and 15.

QY

You have seen that matrix multiplication can be used to perform geometric transformations such as size changes, scale changes, and reflections. It is important to note how reflections, size changes, and scale changes differ. All reflections preserve shape and size, so reflection images are always congruent to their preimages. All size-change images are similar to their preimages, but only S_1 and S_{-1} yield congruent images. In general, scale-change images are neither congruent nor similar to their preimages.

▶ QY

Let $A = (1, 3)$, $B = (4, 5)$, and $C = (-2, 6)$. Use matrix multiplication to find the image of $\triangle ABC$ under r_x.

Questions

COVERING THE IDEAS

1. Consider the photograph of a duck and its reflection image shown at the right. For the preimage, assume that the coordinates of the pixel at the tip of the bill are (-30, 150). What are the coordinates of the pixel at the tip of the bill of the image if the reflecting line is the x-axis? (-30, -150)
2. Sketch $\triangle DEF$ with $D = (0, 0)$, $E = (0, 3)$ and $F = (4, 0)$. Sketch its reflection image $\triangle D'E'F'$ over the y-axis on the same grid. See margin.

3 Assignment

Recommended Assignment

- Questions 1–22
- Question 23 (extra credit)
- Reading Lesson 4-7
- Covering the Ideas 4-7

Additional Answers

2.

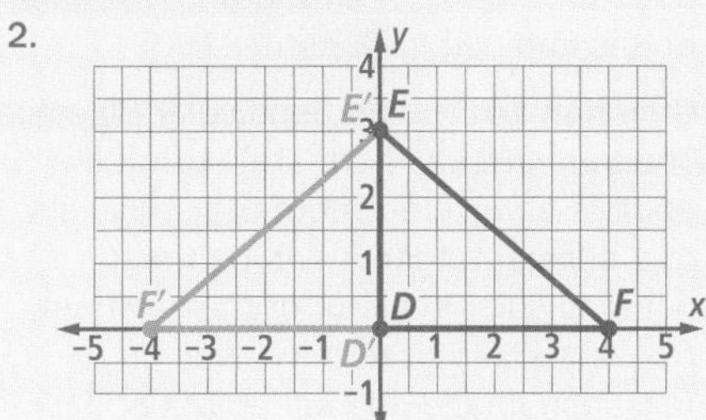

Extension

Discuss with students how the Accommodating the Learner Up activity on page 257 asked students to consider a reflection over a vertical line other than the y-axis. Ask students to find mappings that will let them describe the result of reflecting a point over the vertical line $x = a$ or over the horizontal line $y = b$.

$r_{x=a}(x, y) \to (2a - x, y)$;

$r_{y=b}(x, y) \to (x, 2b - y)$

ENGLISH LEARNERS
Vocabulary Development

The last paragraph on page 259 (just before the questions) contains the important terms *size change, scale change, reflection, preserve size, preserve shape, congruent,* and *similar.* Be sure students can describe and illustrate each term.

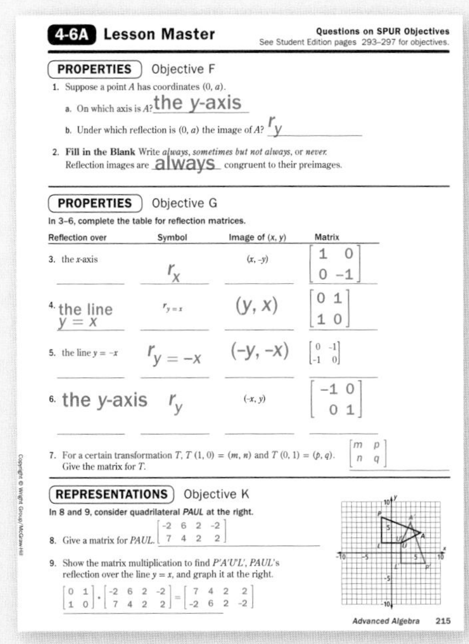

4-6A Lesson Master

Questions on SPUR Objectives
See Student Edition pages 293–297 for objectives.

PROPERTIES Objective F

1. Suppose a point A has coordinates $(0, a)$.
   a. On which axis is A? the y-axis
   b. Under which reflection is $(0, a)$ the image of A? r_y
2. **Fill in the Blank** Write *always, sometimes but not always,* or *never.* Reflection images are always congruent to their preimages.

PROPERTIES Objective G

In 3–6, complete the table for reflection matrices.

Reflection over	Symbol	Image of (x, y)	Matrix
3. the x-axis	r_x	$(x, -y)$	$\begin{bmatrix} 1 & 0 \\ 0 & -1 \end{bmatrix}$
4. the line $y = x$	$r_{y=x}$	(y, x)	$\begin{bmatrix} 0 & 1 \\ 1 & 0 \end{bmatrix}$
5. the line $y = -x$	$r_{y=-x}$	$(-y, -x)$	$\begin{bmatrix} 0 & -1 \\ -1 & 0 \end{bmatrix}$
6. the y-axis	r_y	$(-x, y)$	$\begin{bmatrix} -1 & 0 \\ 0 & 1 \end{bmatrix}$

7. For a certain transformation T, $T(1, 0) = (m, n)$ and $T(0, 1) = (p, q)$. Give the matrix for T. $\begin{bmatrix} m & p \\ n & q \end{bmatrix}$

REPRESENTATIONS Objective K

In 8 and 9, consider quadrilateral $PAUL$ at the right.

8. Give a matrix for $PAUL$. $\begin{bmatrix} -2 & 6 & 2 & -2 \\ 7 & 4 & 2 & 2 \end{bmatrix}$
9. Show the matrix multiplication to find $P'A'U'L'$, $PAUL$'s reflection over the line $y = x$, and graph it at the right.

$\begin{bmatrix} 0 & 1 \\ 1 & 0 \end{bmatrix} \cdot \begin{bmatrix} -2 & 6 & 2 & -2 \\ 7 & 4 & 2 & 2 \end{bmatrix} = \begin{bmatrix} 7 & 4 & 2 & 2 \\ -2 & 6 & 2 & -2 \end{bmatrix}$

Notes on the Questions

Questions 11 and 12 It should be clear to students who have studied transformations that figures are congruent to their reflection images and are similar (but not necessarily congruent) to their size-change images.

Question 14 A student may ask: How do we know that the image of (x, y) under $r_{y=x}$ is (y, x)? An elegant proof uses the Pythagorean Distance Formula and is outlined in Question 16.

Question 16 The Perpendicular Bisector Theorem invoked here states that if a point is equidistant from the endpoints of a segment, then it lies on the perpendicular bisector of the segment. Consequently, given the definition of reflection image, the endpoints of the segment will be reflection images of each other over the line of reflection.

3. **Fill in the Blank** Suppose that A' is the reflection image of A over m, and A' is not on line m. Then m is the perpendicular bisector of _?_. $\overline{AA'}$
4. What is the reflection image of a point C over a line m if C is on m? C
5. Write in symbols in two ways: "The reflection over the x-axis maps point (x, y) onto point $(x, -y)$." $r_x: (x, y) \rightarrow (x, -y)$; $r_x(x, y) = (x, -y)$
6. Translate "$r_{y=x}(x, y) = (y, x)$" into words.

Multiple Choice In 7–9, choose the matrix that corresponds to the given reflection.

A $\begin{bmatrix} 1 & 0 \\ 0 & -1 \end{bmatrix}$ B $\begin{bmatrix} -1 & 0 \\ 0 & 1 \end{bmatrix}$ C $\begin{bmatrix} -1 & 0 \\ 0 & -1 \end{bmatrix}$ D $\begin{bmatrix} 0 & 1 \\ 1 & 0 \end{bmatrix}$ E $\begin{bmatrix} 0 & -1 \\ -1 & 0 \end{bmatrix}$

7. $r_{y=x}$ D
8. r_x A
9. r_y B

10. a. Write a matrix for quadrilateral $RUTH$ shown at the right.
    b. Use matrix multiplication to draw $R'U'T'H'$, its reflection image over the line with equation $y = -x$. See margin.

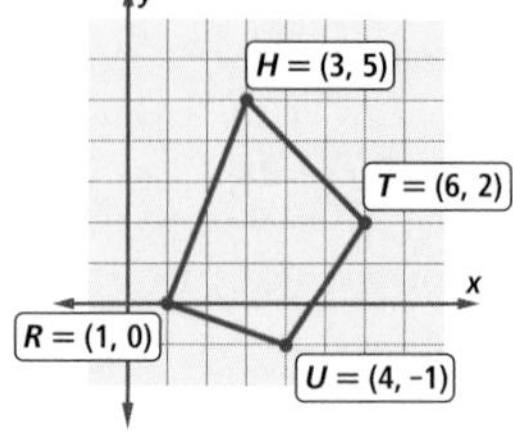

True or False In 11 and 12, if the statement is false, provide a counterexample.

11. Reflection images are always congruent to their preimages. true
12. Reflection images are always similar to their preimages. true
13. **Fill in the Blanks** The matrix equation $\begin{bmatrix} 0 & 1 \\ 1 & 0 \end{bmatrix}\begin{bmatrix} 4 \\ 6 \end{bmatrix} = \begin{bmatrix} 6 \\ 4 \end{bmatrix}$ shows that the reflection image of the point _?_ over the line with equation _?_ is the point _?_. (4, 6); $y = x$; (6, 4)

APPLYING THE MATHEMATICS

14, 15. See margin.

14. Prove that $\begin{bmatrix} 0 & 1 \\ 1 & 0 \end{bmatrix}$ is a matrix for the reflection over the line with equation $y = x$.
15. Prove that $\begin{bmatrix} 0 & -1 \\ -1 & 0 \end{bmatrix}$ is a matrix for the reflection over the line with equation $y = -x$.
16. Suppose $P = (x, y)$ and $Q = (y, x)$. Let $R = (a, a)$ be any point on the line with equation $y = x$.
    a. Verify that $PR = QR$. (*Hint:* Use the Pythagorean Distance Formula.)
    b. **Fill in the Blank** Therefore, the line with equation $y = x$ is the _?_ of $\overline{PQ}$. perpendicular bisector
    c. What does your answer to Part b mean in terms of reflections?

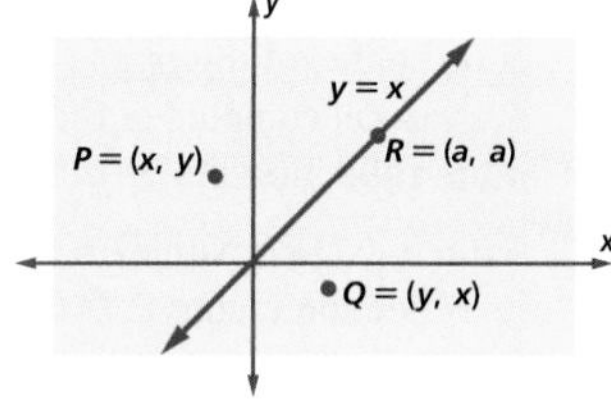

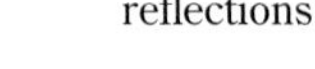

6. The reflection over the line with equation $y = x$ maps point (x, y) onto point (y, x).

10a. $\begin{bmatrix} 1 & 4 & 6 & 3 \\ 0 & -1 & 2 & 5 \end{bmatrix}$

16a. $QR = \sqrt{|y - a|^2 + |x - a|^2}$; $PR = \sqrt{|x - a|^2 + |y - a|^2}$

16c. Q is the image of P when P is reflected over the line with equation $y = x$.

Additional Answers

10b.

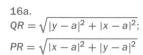

14. $\begin{bmatrix} 0 & 1 \\ 1 & 0 \end{bmatrix}\begin{bmatrix} x \\ y \end{bmatrix} = \begin{bmatrix} 0(x) + 1(y) \\ 1(x) + 0(y) \end{bmatrix} = \begin{bmatrix} y \\ x \end{bmatrix}$

15. $\begin{bmatrix} 0 & -1 \\ -1 & 0 \end{bmatrix}\begin{bmatrix} x \\ y \end{bmatrix} = \begin{bmatrix} 0(x) + -1(y) \\ -1(x) + 0(y) \end{bmatrix} = \begin{bmatrix} -y \\ -x \end{bmatrix}$

REVIEW

17. a. What is the image of (2, -3) under $S_{0.5,\,2}$? (1, -6)
    b. Write a matrix for $S_{0.5,\,2}$.
    c. Describe $S_{0.5,\,2}$ in words. **(Lesson 4-5)**

18. When does the scale change matrix $\begin{bmatrix} a & 0 \\ 0 & b \end{bmatrix}$ represent a size change? **(Lessons 4-5, 4-4)** when $a = b$

19. Let $P = \begin{bmatrix} -2 \\ 3 \end{bmatrix}$, and $Q = \begin{bmatrix} 4 \\ 4 \end{bmatrix}$. **(Lesson 4-4)**
    a. Compute the distance between P and Q. $\sqrt{|4+2|^2 + |4-3|^2} = \sqrt{37}$
    b. Compute the distance between P' and Q' if $P' = \begin{bmatrix} \frac{1}{2} & 0 \\ 0 & \frac{1}{2} \end{bmatrix} P$, and $Q' = \begin{bmatrix} \frac{1}{2} & 0 \\ 0 & \frac{1}{2} \end{bmatrix} Q$. $\sqrt{|2+1|^2 + \left|2-\frac{3}{2}\right|^2} = \frac{\sqrt{37}}{2}$
    c. Does the transformation given by the matrix $\begin{bmatrix} \frac{1}{2} & 0 \\ 0 & \frac{1}{2} \end{bmatrix}$ preserve distance? no

20. a. Write the first 6 terms of the sequence defined by
    $\begin{cases} c_1 = 1 \\ c_n = (-1)^n c_{n-1} - 3, \text{ for integers } n \geq 2 \end{cases}$. **(Lesson 3-6)**
    b. Rewrite the second line of this recursive definition if the previous term is called c_n. $c_{n+1} = (-1)^{n+1} c_n - 3$, for $n \geq 1$

21. The surface area A of a box with length ℓ, height h, and width w is given by the equation $A = 2\ell h + 2\ell w + 2hw$. **(Lesson 1-7)**
    a. Rewrite this equation if all edges are the same length, x. $A = 6x^2$
    b. Solve the equation in Part a for x. $x = \sqrt{\frac{A}{6}}$

22. On the television show *The Price is Right*, contestants spinning the Big Wheel have to make sure it turns at least one full revolution. Describe the range in degrees d that the Wheel must turn in order for the spin to count. **(Previous course)** $d \geq 360°$

EXPLORATION

23. a. Either by graphing manually, or by using a DGS, find the matrix for the reflection $r_{y=2x}$.
    b. To check this matrix, test at least five points. Make sure that at least two of the points are on the line of reflection.

17b. $\begin{bmatrix} 0.5 & 0 \\ 0 & 2 \end{bmatrix}$

17c. a scale change in which horizontal distances are halved and vertical distances are doubled

20a. $c_1 = 1$, $c_2 = -2$, $c_3 = -1$, $c_4 = -4$, $c_5 = 1$, $c_6 = -2$

23a. $\begin{bmatrix} 0 & \frac{1}{2} \\ 2 & 0 \end{bmatrix}$

23b. Answers vary. Sample:

(2, 4): $\begin{bmatrix} 0 & \frac{1}{2} \\ 2 & 0 \end{bmatrix}\begin{bmatrix} 2 \\ 4 \end{bmatrix} = \begin{bmatrix} 2 \\ 4 \end{bmatrix}$;

(1, 2): $\begin{bmatrix} 0 & \frac{1}{2} \\ 2 & 0 \end{bmatrix}\begin{bmatrix} 1 \\ 2 \end{bmatrix} = \begin{bmatrix} 1 \\ 2 \end{bmatrix}$;

(3, 4): $\begin{bmatrix} 0 & \frac{1}{2} \\ 2 & 0 \end{bmatrix}\begin{bmatrix} 3 \\ 4 \end{bmatrix} = \begin{bmatrix} 2 \\ 6 \end{bmatrix}$;

(12, 1): $\begin{bmatrix} 0 & \frac{1}{2} \\ 2 & 0 \end{bmatrix}\begin{bmatrix} 12 \\ 1 \end{bmatrix} = \begin{bmatrix} \frac{1}{2} \\ 24 \end{bmatrix}$;

(3, 8): $\begin{bmatrix} 0 & \frac{1}{2} \\ 2 & 0 \end{bmatrix}\begin{bmatrix} 3 \\ 8 \end{bmatrix} = \begin{bmatrix} 4 \\ 6 \end{bmatrix}$

QY ANSWER

$\begin{bmatrix} 1 & 0 \\ 0 & -1 \end{bmatrix}\begin{bmatrix} 1 & 4 & -2 \\ 3 & 5 & 6 \end{bmatrix} = \begin{bmatrix} 1 & 4 & -2 \\ -3 & -5 & -6 \end{bmatrix}$;

$A' = (1, -3)$, $B' = (4, -5)$, and $C' = (-2, -6)$

Notes on the Lesson

Question 21b The desired formula gives the length of an edge of a cube when the cube's surface area is known.

Question 23 With a grid, students can find the images of several key points by trial and error. For instance, it is reasonably easy to find the image of (3, 1) over this line. With two points (a, b) and (c, d) and their images (a', b') and (c', d'), it is possible to solve a matrix equation of the form $\begin{bmatrix} w & y \\ x & z \end{bmatrix}\begin{bmatrix} a & c \\ b & d \end{bmatrix} = \begin{bmatrix} a' & c' \\ b' & d' \end{bmatrix}$ for w, x, y, and z.

4 Wrap-Up

Ongoing Assessment

Ask students to explain how to reflect a point over the x-axis or over the y-axis. Then ask them to describe the matrices that represent r_x and r_y. Answers vary. Sample: To reflect over the x-axis, keep the x-coordinate and use the opposite of the y-coordinate, or $r_x(x, y) = (x, -y)$. To reflect over the y-axis, use the opposite of the x-coordinate and keep the y-coordinate, or $r_y(x, y) = (-x, y)$. The matrices are $r_x = \begin{bmatrix} 1 & 0 \\ 0 & -1 \end{bmatrix}$ and $r_y = \begin{bmatrix} -1 & 0 \\ 0 & 1 \end{bmatrix}$.

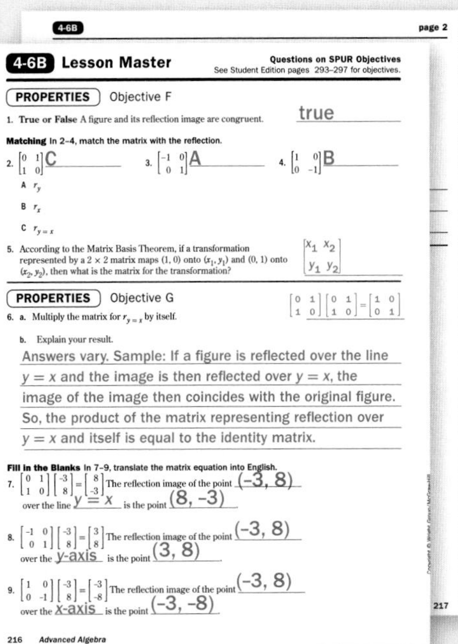

4-6B page 2

4-6B Lesson Master — Questions on SPUR Objectives. See Student Edition pages 293–297 for objectives.

PROPERTIES Objective F

1. **True or False** A figure and its reflection image are congruent. true

Matching In 2–4, match the matrix with the reflection.

2. $\begin{bmatrix} 0 & 1 \\ 1 & 0 \end{bmatrix}$ C
3. $\begin{bmatrix} -1 & 0 \\ 0 & 1 \end{bmatrix}$ A
4. $\begin{bmatrix} 1 & 0 \\ 0 & -1 \end{bmatrix}$ B

A r_y
B r_x
C $r_{y=x}$

5. According to the Matrix Basis Theorem, if a transformation represented by a 2 × 2 matrix maps (1, 0) onto (x_1, y_1) and (0, 1) onto (x_2, y_2), then what is the matrix for the transformation? $\begin{bmatrix} x_1 & x_2 \\ y_1 & y_2 \end{bmatrix}$

PROPERTIES Objective G

6. a. Multiply the matrix for $r_{y=x}$ by itself. $\begin{bmatrix} 0 & 1 \\ 1 & 0 \end{bmatrix}\begin{bmatrix} 0 & 1 \\ 1 & 0 \end{bmatrix} = \begin{bmatrix} 1 & 0 \\ 0 & 1 \end{bmatrix}$
   b. Explain your result. Answers vary. Sample: If a figure is reflected over the line $y = x$ and the image is then reflected over $y = x$, the image of the image then coincides with the original figure. So, the product of the matrix representing reflection over $y = x$ and itself is equal to the identity matrix.

Fill in the Blanks In 7–9, translate the matrix equation into English.

7. $\begin{bmatrix} 0 & 1 \\ 1 & 0 \end{bmatrix}\begin{bmatrix} -3 \\ 8 \end{bmatrix} = \begin{bmatrix} 8 \\ -3 \end{bmatrix}$ The reflection image of the point (−3, 8) over the line $y = x$ is the point (8, −3).

8. $\begin{bmatrix} -1 & 0 \\ 0 & 1 \end{bmatrix}\begin{bmatrix} -3 \\ 8 \end{bmatrix} = \begin{bmatrix} 3 \\ 8 \end{bmatrix}$ The reflection image of the point (−3, 8) over the y-axis is the point (3, 8).

9. $\begin{bmatrix} 1 & 0 \\ 0 & -1 \end{bmatrix}\begin{bmatrix} -3 \\ 8 \end{bmatrix} = \begin{bmatrix} -3 \\ -8 \end{bmatrix}$ The reflection image of the point (−3, 8) over the x-axis is the point (−3, −8).

216 *Advanced Algebra* 217

Lesson 4-7

GOAL

Summarize the properties of matrix multiplication; explore the fundamental relationship between matrices and the transformations they represent—products of matrices correspond to composites of transformations.

SPUR Objectives

E Recognize properties of matrix operations.

G Relate transformations to matrices, and vice versa.

K Graph figures and their transformation images.

Materials/Resources

- Lesson Masters 4-7A and 4-7B
- Resource Masters 1 and 67
- Quiz 2
- Matrix polygon application

HOMEWORK

Suggestions for Assignment

- Questions 1–25
- Question 26 (extra credit)
- Reading Lesson 4-8
- Covering the Ideas 4-8

Local Standards

Lesson 4-7 Transformations and Matrices

Vocabulary

composite of two transformations

BIG IDEA The product of two matrices corresponds to the composite of the transformations that the matrices represent.

Properties of 2 × 2 Matrix Multiplication

Multiplication of 2 × 2 matrices has some of the same properties as multiplication of real numbers, such as closure, associativity, and the existence of an identity.

1. Closure: *The set of 2 × 2 matrices is closed under multiplication.*
   Closure means that when an operation is applied to two elements in a set, the result is an element of the set. From the definition of multiplication of matrices, if you multiply two 2 × 2 matrices, the result is a 2 × 2 matrix.
2. Associativity: *Multiplication of 2 × 2 matrices is associative.* For any 2 × 2 matrices A, B, and C, it can be shown that $(AB)C = A(BC)$. You are asked to prove this in the Questions.
3. Identity: *The matrix* $I = \begin{bmatrix} 1 & 0 \\ 0 & 1 \end{bmatrix}$ *is the identity for multiplication of 2 × 2 matrices.*

   Here is a proof of the Identity Property. Recall that for the real numbers, 1 is the identity for multiplication because for all a, $1 \cdot a = a \cdot 1 = a$. In the matrix version of this property, we need to show that for all 2 × 2 matrices M, $\begin{bmatrix} 1 & 0 \\ 0 & 1 \end{bmatrix} \cdot M = M$, and $M \cdot \begin{bmatrix} 1 & 0 \\ 0 & 1 \end{bmatrix} = M$.

   Let $M = \begin{bmatrix} a & b \\ c & d \end{bmatrix}$.

   Then $\begin{bmatrix} 1 & 0 \\ 0 & 1 \end{bmatrix}\begin{bmatrix} a & b \\ c & d \end{bmatrix} = \begin{bmatrix} a & b \\ c & d \end{bmatrix}$ and $\begin{bmatrix} a & b \\ c & d \end{bmatrix}\begin{bmatrix} 1 & 0 \\ 0 & 1 \end{bmatrix} = \begin{bmatrix} a & b \\ c & d \end{bmatrix}$.

   Thus, $I = \begin{bmatrix} 1 & 0 \\ 0 & 1 \end{bmatrix}$ is the identity for multiplication of 2 × 2 matrices.

QY1

Mental Math

Azra has a collection of 35 china elephants. All the elephants are gray, white, or pink. She has twice as many pink elephants as white elephants and half as many gray elephants as white elephants.

a. How many of Azra's elephants are white? 10

b. How many are gray? 5

c. How many are pink? 20

QY1

Verify that both matrix products $\begin{bmatrix} 1 & 0 \\ 0 & 1 \end{bmatrix}\begin{bmatrix} a & b \\ c & d \end{bmatrix}$ and $\begin{bmatrix} a & b \\ c & d \end{bmatrix}\begin{bmatrix} 1 & 0 \\ 0 & 1 \end{bmatrix}$ equal $\begin{bmatrix} a & b \\ c & d \end{bmatrix}$.

1 Warm-Up

In 1–4, find the image of (100, 36) under each transformation.

1. reflection over the x-axis (100, –36)
2. the composite of a reflection over the x-axis followed by a reflection over the line $y = x$ (–36, 100)
3. the composite of a reflection over the y-axis followed by a reflection over the line $y = x$ (36, –100)
4. the composite of S_3 followed by S_4 (1200, 432)

Background

Properties of 2 × 2 matrix multiplication This lesson begins by summarizing the properties of matrix multiplication and relates those properties to the familiar properties of real number multiplication.

Matrices and composites of transformations The *composite* $T_2 \circ T_1$ of two transformations T_1 and T_2 is introduced in terms of this question: If T_1 has matrix $M1$ and T_2 has matrix $M2$, what is the matrix for the composite $T_2 \circ T_1$? The answer is the matrix product $M2M1$. The lesson contains an example of this theorem; a general proof follows here.

Suppose T_1 has matrix $M1$ and T_2 has matrix $M2$. Then for every point P, $T_1(P) = M1 \cdot P$, so $T_2 \circ T_1(P) = M2 \cdot (M1 \cdot P)$. Because matrix multiplication is associative, $M2 \cdot (M1 \cdot P) = (M2 \cdot M1) \cdot P$. By the Transitive Property of Equality, $T_2 \circ T_1(P) = (M2 \cdot M1) \cdot P$. This means that $T_2 \circ T_1$ can be described by the matrix $M2 \cdot M1$.

Notice that we wrote equal signs between the transformations and the matrices in the

Notice that both multiplications were needed in the proof because multiplication of 2×2 matrices is not always commutative.

Multiplying the Matrices of Two Transformations

The product of two 2×2 transformation matrices yields a third 2×2 matrix that also represents a transformation.

Activity

MATERIALS matrix polygon application

Step 1 Use a matrix polygon application to draw quadrilateral $ABCD$ with $A = (1, 0)$, $B = (4, -1)$, $C = (6, 2)$, and $D = (3, 5)$.

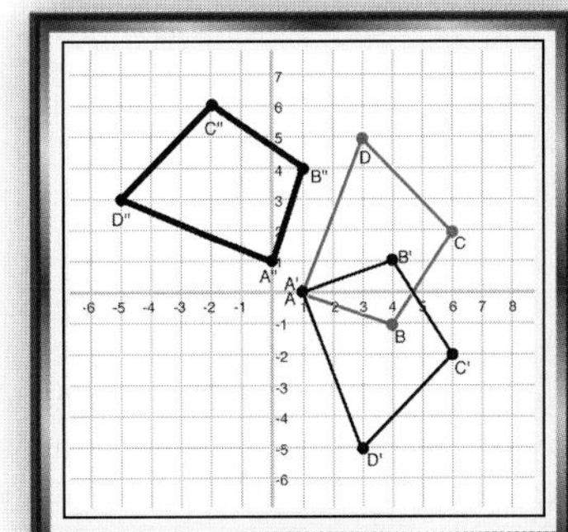

Step 2 Reflect $ABCD$ over the x-axis and call its image $A'B'C'D'$.

Step 3 Reflect $A'B'C'D'$ over the line with equation $y = x$ and call its image $A''B''C''D''$.

Step 4 Compare the coordinates of the vertices of the final image $A''B''C''D''$ to the coordinates of the vertices of your original preimage $ABCD$. What single transformation could you apply to $ABCD$ to get the image $A''B''C''D''$?

Step 5 Multiply the matrix for r_x on the left by the matrix for $r_{y=x}$. Call the product M.

Step 6 Clear the screen and redraw $ABCD$. Then draw the image of $ABCD$ after applying the transformation defined by M. Compare your results to the results of Step 3. What do you notice? See margin.

Step 4 a counterclockwise rotation 90° about (0, 0)

Step 5 $M = \begin{bmatrix} 0 & -1 \\ 1 & 0 \end{bmatrix}$

Composites of Transformations

We call the final quadrilateral $A''B''C''D''$ from the Activity the image of $ABCD$ under the *composite* of the reflections r_x and $r_{y=x}$. In general, any two transformations can be composed.

> **Definition of Composite of Transformations**
>
> Suppose transformation T_1 maps figure G onto figure G', and transformation T_2 maps figure G' onto figure G''. The transformation that maps G onto G'' is called the **composite** of T_1 and T_2, written $T_2 \circ T_1$.

preceding paragraph. This can be done because the transformations and the matrices are *isomorphic*. That is, there is a 1-to-1 correspondence between transformations and matrices so that the composition of transformations corresponds to the multiplication of matrices. Thus, transformations and matrices are two different languages for discussing the same ideas. The theorem on page 264, which expresses the basic relationship between transformations and matrices, is sometimes called the Matrix-Transformation Isomorphism (MTI) Theorem.

The MTI Theorem enables matrices for the composites of transformations to be obtained if you know the matrices for the individual transformations. The first and perhaps most important of these composites is the rotation of 90° as the composite of two reflections over lines that intersect at a 45° angle. The Example shows the derivation of a matrix for the rotation of -90° about the origin. In Lesson 4-8, the matrix is found for a rotation of 90° about the origin.

2 Teaching

Notes on the Lesson

Activity Students need to do an activity like this at least once to see how the product of two 2×2 matrices for transformations can be associated with the composite of the transformations.

Composites of transformations The idea of composition of transformations is easy, but the notation is somewhat tricky. In English, we normally read from left to right, but in mathematics we often operate "from the inside out." A solution to this problem is to read the symbol $\circ$ as "following." Thus, $r_{y=x} \circ r_x$ means $r_{y=x}$ following r_x. This means that r_x is applied first. This is the composition of functions, and each of these expressions—$(f \circ g)(x)$, $f(g(x))$, f follows g, and f is applied after g—represent the same operation.

The terminology for the composition of transformations is identical to that used for other functions, so care taken now will help students later. Try to distinguish between the words *composite* and *composition*. The first is the result; the second is the operation. They are as different as *sum* and *addition*.

Additional Answers

Activity

Step 6:

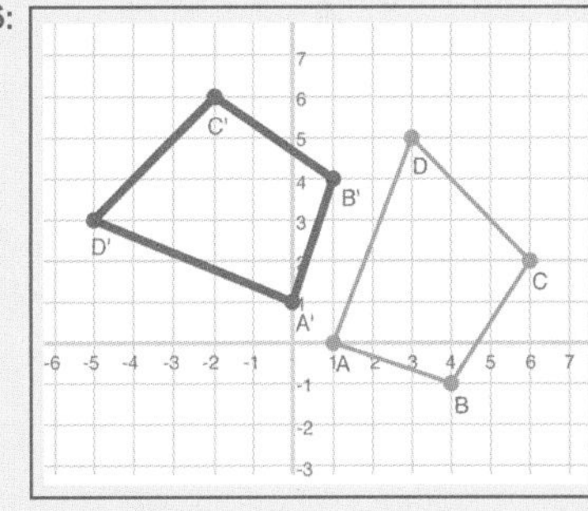

The image of $ABCD$ after applying the transformation described by M is the same as $A''B''C''D''$ from Step 3.

The symbol ∘ is read "following." In the Activity, r_x came first and then $r_{y=x}$, so we write $r_{y=x} \circ r_x$ and say "$r_{y=x}$ following r_x" or "the composite of r_x and $r_{y=x}$".

The Composite of $r_{y=x}$ and r_x

To describe $r_{y=x} \circ r_x$ as one transformation, consider the results of the previous Activity. Quadrilateral $ABCD$ is the preimage, $A'B'C'D'$ is the first image, and $A''B''C''D''$ is the final image. In Step 6 of the Activity, you plotted only the preimage $ABCD$ and the final image $A''B''C''D''$ to get a graph like the one at the right below.

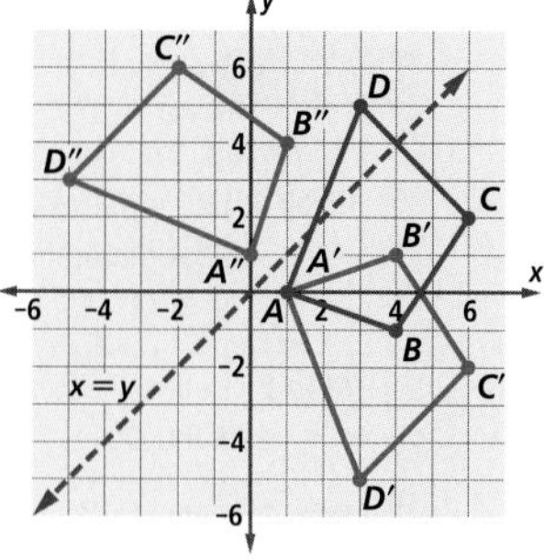

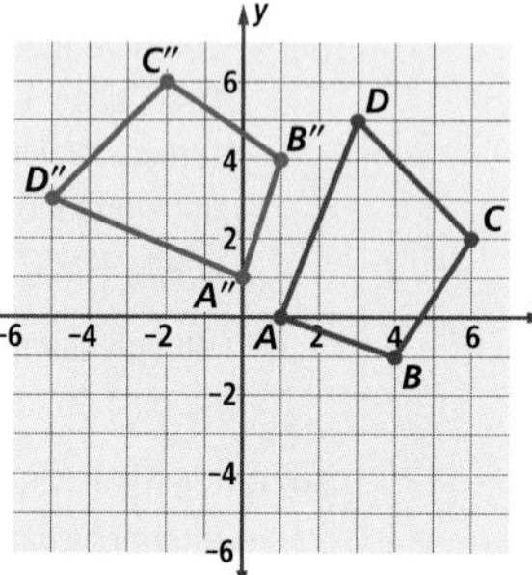

The graph shows that the composite is a *rotation* 90° counterclockwise about (0, 0). We denote this rotation by R_{90}. This rotation is the composite of the two reflections: $R_{90} = r_{y=x} \circ r_x$.

In geometry, you should have encountered the Two-Reflection Theorem for Rotations: The composite of two reflections $r_m \circ r_\ell$ over intersecting lines ℓ and m is a rotation whose center is the intersection of ℓ and m. The magnitude of rotation is twice the measure of an angle formed by ℓ and m, measured from ℓ to m. Because the x-axis and the line with equation $y = x$ intersect at the origin at a 45° angle, this theorem explains why the composite $r_{y=x} \circ r_x$ is a rotation about the origin with magnitude 90°.

Matrices and Composites of Transformations

How can you find the matrix associated with R_{90}? In Steps 5 and 6 of the Activity, you multiplied the matrices for the two reflections, then multiplied the matrix for $ABCD$ on the left by the product. The result was the matrix for $A''B''C''D''$. In symbols, we can show this as follows.

$$\underset{r_{y=x}\ \circ\ r_x}{\left(\begin{bmatrix} 0 & 1 \\ 1 & 0 \end{bmatrix}\begin{bmatrix} 1 & 0 \\ 0 & -1 \end{bmatrix}\right)}\overset{(A\ B\ C\ D)}{\begin{bmatrix} 1 & 4 & 6 & 3 \\ 0 & -1 & 2 & 5 \end{bmatrix}} =$$

$$\overset{R_{90}}{\begin{bmatrix} 0 & -1 \\ 1 & 0 \end{bmatrix}} \cdot \overset{(A\ B\ C\ D)}{\begin{bmatrix} 1 & 4 & 6 & 3 \\ 0 & -1 & 2 & 5 \end{bmatrix}} = \overset{A''\ B''\ C''\ D''}{\begin{bmatrix} 0 & 1 & -2 & -5 \\ 1 & 4 & 6 & 3 \end{bmatrix}}$$

This tells us that $\begin{bmatrix} 0 & -1 \\ 1 & 0 \end{bmatrix}$ is a matrix for R_{90}. The general idea is summarized in the following theorem.

Accommodating the Learner

Ask students to show that the composite of four 90° rotations returns a point to its original position. Answers vary. Sample: The matrix for R_{90} is $\begin{bmatrix} 0 & -1 \\ 1 & 0 \end{bmatrix}$, and

$$\left(\begin{bmatrix} 0 & -1 \\ 1 & 0 \end{bmatrix}\left(\begin{bmatrix} 0 & -1 \\ 1 & 0 \end{bmatrix}\left(\begin{bmatrix} 0 & -1 \\ 1 & 0 \end{bmatrix}\begin{bmatrix} 0 & -1 \\ 1 & 0 \end{bmatrix}\right)\right)\right)\begin{bmatrix} x \\ y \end{bmatrix} =$$

$$\left(\begin{bmatrix} 0 & -1 \\ 1 & 0 \end{bmatrix}\left(\begin{bmatrix} 0 & -1 \\ 1 & 0 \end{bmatrix}\begin{bmatrix} -1 & 0 \\ 0 & 1 \end{bmatrix}\right)\right)\begin{bmatrix} x \\ y \end{bmatrix} =$$

$$\left(\begin{bmatrix} 0 & -1 \\ 1 & 0 \end{bmatrix}\left(\begin{bmatrix} 0 & 1 \\ -1 & 0 \end{bmatrix}\right)\right)\begin{bmatrix} x \\ y \end{bmatrix} = \begin{bmatrix} 1 & 0 \\ 0 & 1 \end{bmatrix}\begin{bmatrix} x \\ y \end{bmatrix} = \begin{bmatrix} x \\ y \end{bmatrix}.$$

Matrices and Composites Theorem

If $M1$ is the matrix for transformation T_1, and $M2$ is the matrix for transformation T_2, then $M2M1$ is the matrix for $T_2 \circ T_1$.

QY2

▶ QY2

If M1 represents $r_{y=x}$ and M2 represents r_x, does $M1M2 = M2M1$? Why or why not?

Example

Golfers strive to achieve the elusive perfect swing. Assume that when looking at a right-handed golfer from the front, as a golfer begins the swing, the golf club rotates clockwise about a point near the tip of the shaft. The club starts from a vertical position at setup, then moves along a 90° arc until it is horizontal at some point during the backswing. The rotation is R_{-90}. For the left-handed golfer, the rotation will be counterclockwise, or R_{90}. The preimage golf club and the image golf club are pictured in the graph below at the right. Three points on the original golf club are $P = (1, 0)$, $G = (1, -6)$, and $A = (2, -6)$. Use matrix multiplication to find the image of PGA under R_{-90}.

Solution A counterclockwise rotation of 90° is a composite of two reflections given by $R_{90} = r_{y=x} \circ r_x$.

To find R_{-90}, a rotation 90° clockwise about (0, 0), you need to measure the angle formed in the opposite direction, that is, the angle formed by the line with equation $y = x$ and the x-axis, measured from $y = x$ to the x-axis. So reverse the order of composition: $R_{-90} = r_x \circ r_{y=x}$.

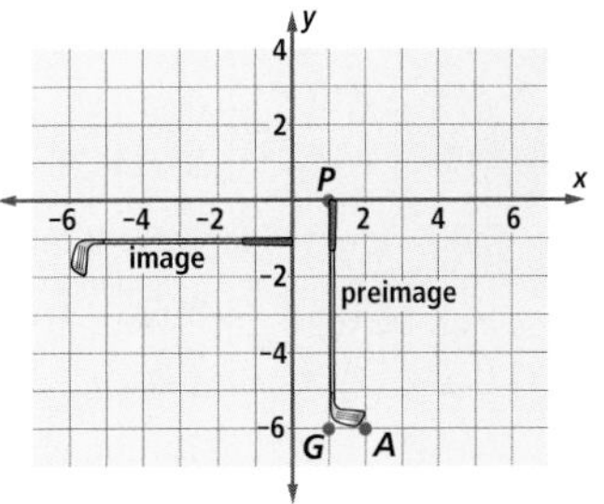

So the matrix for R_{-90} is $\underset{r_x}{\begin{bmatrix} 1 & 0 \\ 0 & -1 \end{bmatrix}} \underset{r_{y=x}}{\begin{bmatrix} 0 & 1 \\ 1 & 0 \end{bmatrix}} = \underset{R_{-90}}{\begin{bmatrix} 0 & 1 \\ -1 & 0 \end{bmatrix}}$.

To find the image of golf club PGA, multiply its matrix by the matrix for R_{-90}.

$$R_{-90}(PGA) = \underset{R_{-90}}{\begin{bmatrix} 0 & 1 \\ -1 & 0 \end{bmatrix}} \underset{(P\ G\ A)}{\begin{bmatrix} 1 & 1 & 2 \\ 0 & -6 & -6 \end{bmatrix}} = \underset{P'\ G'\ A'}{\begin{bmatrix} 0 & -6 & -6 \\ -1 & -1 & -2 \end{bmatrix}}$$

Questions

COVERING THE IDEAS

1. a. When a 2×2 matrix is multiplied by a 2×2 matrix, what are the dimensions of the product matrix? 2×2
   b. What property of 2×2 matrix multiplication does this demonstrate? closure under multiplication
2. What is the *multiplicative identity* for 2×2 matrices?

2. $I = \begin{bmatrix} 1 & 0 \\ 0 & 1 \end{bmatrix}$

Notes on the Lesson

Example Some students may have seen the property that the composite of two reflections over intersecting lines (here the lines $y = x$ and the x-axis) is a rotation whose center is the intersection of the lines and whose magnitude is twice the angle between the lines measured from the first line to the second. (In UCSMP *Geometry,* we called that property the Two-Reflection Theorem for Rotations.) There is also a similar property for translations: The composite of two reflections over parallel lines is a translation whose magnitude is twice the distance between the lines, in the direction perpendicular to the lines, from the first to the second.

Additional Example

Example Refer to the Example on page 265. Suppose three points on the original golf club are $P = (4, 0)$, $G = (4, -7)$, and $A = (5, -7)$. Use matrix multiplication to find the image of PGA under R_{-90}. $P' = (0, -4)$, $G' = (-7, -4)$, and $A' = (-7, -5)$

Note-Taking Tips

Encourage students to record (and understand!) the statement following the definition of composite that a composite described as "r_x comes first and then $r_{y=x}$" *must* be written in the order $r_{y=x} \circ r_x$. Matrix multiplication is not necessarily commutative, so the order of matrices in a multiplication statement is important.

Accommodating the Learner

Ask students to verify that matrix multiplication and composition of transformations are not always commutative by finding and comparing the matrices for $r_x \circ r_{y=x}$ and $r_{y=x} \circ r_x$.

$r_x \circ r_{y=x} = \begin{bmatrix} 1 & 0 \\ 0 & -1 \end{bmatrix} \begin{bmatrix} 0 & 1 \\ 1 & 0 \end{bmatrix} = \begin{bmatrix} 0 & 1 \\ -1 & 0 \end{bmatrix}$;

$r_{y=x} \circ r_x = \begin{bmatrix} 0 & 1 \\ 1 & 0 \end{bmatrix} \begin{bmatrix} 1 & 0 \\ 0 & -1 \end{bmatrix} = \begin{bmatrix} 0 & -1 \\ 1 & 0 \end{bmatrix}$

ENGLISH LEARNERS

Vocabulary Development

As part of a discussion of the terms *closure* and *associativity* at the beginning of the lesson, ask students to provide examples of nonclosure and nonassociativity. Answers vary. Sample: Nonclosure: subtraction of whole numbers, division of integers; nonassociativity: $(a \div b) \div c = \frac{a}{bc}$, while $a \div (b \div c) = \frac{ac}{b}$.

3 Assignment

Recommended Assignment

- Questions 1–25
- Question 26 (extra credit)
- Reading Lesson 4-8
- Covering the Ideas 4-8

Notes on the Questions

Questions 12 and 13 Stress that the order in the composition of transformations is from right to left.

4-7A Lesson Master Questions on SPUR Objectives
See Student Edition pages 293–297 for objectives.

PROPERTIES Objective E In 2–4, answers vary. Samples are given.

In 1–4, suppose *A*, *B*, and *C* are all 2 × 2 matrices. Write a statement using these matrices that demonstrates the given property.

1. The set of 2 × 2 matrices is closed under multiplication: *AC* has dimensions 2 × 2
2. Matrix multiplication is associative: $(AB)C = A(BC)$
3. Matrix multiplication is not commutative: $AB \neq BA$
4. $\begin{bmatrix} 1 & 0 \\ 0 & 1 \end{bmatrix}$ is the 2 × 2 identity matrix: $\begin{bmatrix} 1 & 0 \\ 0 & 1 \end{bmatrix}A = A$ and $A\begin{bmatrix} 1 & 0 \\ 0 & 1 \end{bmatrix} = A$
5. In the composite $r_{y=-x} \circ r_y$, which reflection is performed first? r_y
6. Write a composition that shows a reflection over the *x*-axis followed by a rotation of 90° around the origin. $R_{90} \circ r_x$

PROPERTIES Objective G

7. Find a matrix for $r_{y=x} \circ r_x$. $\begin{bmatrix} 0 & -1 \\ 1 & 0 \end{bmatrix}$
8. Find a matrix for $r_x \circ r_{y=x}$. $\begin{bmatrix} 0 & 1 \\ -1 & 0 \end{bmatrix}$
9. Which answer from question 7 or 8 is the matrix for R_{90}? $\begin{bmatrix} 0 & -1 \\ 1 & 0 \end{bmatrix}$

REPRESENTATIONS Objective K Images from 11 and 12 are graphed below.

In 10–13, use *PENTA*, graphed at the right.

10. Give a matrix for *PENTA*. $\begin{bmatrix} 2 & 2 & 5 & 6 & 4 \\ 2 & 7 & 9 & 7 & 2 \end{bmatrix}$
11. Give a matrix for $P'E'N'T'A' = r_y(PENTA)$. Graph this image at the right. $\begin{bmatrix} -2 & -2 & -5 & -6 & -4 \\ 2 & 7 & 9 & 7 & 2 \end{bmatrix}$
12. Give a matrix for $P''E''N''T''A'' = R_{90} \circ r_y(PENTA)$. Graph this image at the right. $\begin{bmatrix} -2 & -7 & -9 & -7 & -2 \\ -2 & -2 & -5 & -6 & -4 \end{bmatrix}$
13. What single transformation equals $R_{90} \circ r_y$? $r_{y=-x}$

218 *Advanced Algebra*

3. Write this product as a single matrix: $\begin{bmatrix} 1 & 0 \\ 0 & 1 \end{bmatrix} \cdot \begin{bmatrix} 5 & 2 \\ \sqrt{8} & \pi \end{bmatrix}$.
4. **Fill in the Blank** The identity transformation maps each point of a preimage onto ___?___. itself
5. In general, multiplication of 2 × 2 matrices is not commutative, but sometimes it is.
   a. Suppose *I* is the 2 × 2 identity matrix and *A* is any other 2 × 2 matrix of your choosing. Does $IA = AI$? yes
   b. Pick any 2 × 2 size change matrix *A* and any 2 × 2 matrix *B* other than the identity matrix. Does $AB = BA$? yes
   c. Give an example of two 2 × 2 matrices *A* and *B* such that $AB \neq BA$.

Multiple Choice In 6–10, identify which property is illustrated by the statement.

A closure B associativity C existence of an identity
D commutativity in some cases E noncommutativity

6. $\begin{bmatrix} 2 & 3 \\ 7 & 4 \end{bmatrix}\begin{bmatrix} 1 & 0 \\ 0 & 1 \end{bmatrix} = \begin{bmatrix} 2 & 3 \\ 7 & 4 \end{bmatrix}$ C and A
7. $\begin{bmatrix} 2 & 3 \\ 7 & 4 \end{bmatrix}\left(\begin{bmatrix} 0 & 3 \\ 8 & 6 \end{bmatrix}\begin{bmatrix} 5 & 9 \\ 1 & 2 \end{bmatrix}\right) = \left(\begin{bmatrix} 2 & 3 \\ 7 & 4 \end{bmatrix}\begin{bmatrix} 0 & 3 \\ 8 & 6 \end{bmatrix}\right)\begin{bmatrix} 5 & 9 \\ 1 & 2 \end{bmatrix}$ B
8. $\begin{bmatrix} 2 & 3 \\ 7 & 4 \end{bmatrix}\begin{bmatrix} 0 & 3 \\ 8 & 6 \end{bmatrix} \neq \begin{bmatrix} 0 & 3 \\ 8 & 6 \end{bmatrix}\begin{bmatrix} 2 & 3 \\ 7 & 4 \end{bmatrix}$ E
9. The product of any 2 × 2 matrix multiplication is a 2 × 2 matrix. A
10. $\begin{bmatrix} 3 & 0 \\ 0 & 3 \end{bmatrix}\begin{bmatrix} 3 & 5 \\ 7 & 8 \end{bmatrix} = \begin{bmatrix} 3 & 5 \\ 7 & 8 \end{bmatrix}\begin{bmatrix} 3 & 0 \\ 0 & 3 \end{bmatrix}$ D
11. Noel thought that by applying the Associative Property, the following matrix equation would be true.
$$\begin{bmatrix} 0 & 1 \\ 1 & 0 \end{bmatrix}\left(\begin{bmatrix} 1 & 0 \\ 0 & -1 \end{bmatrix}\begin{bmatrix} 1 & 1 \\ 2 & 6 \end{bmatrix}\right) = \left(\begin{bmatrix} 0 & 1 \\ 1 & 0 \end{bmatrix}\begin{bmatrix} 1 & 1 \\ 2 & 6 \end{bmatrix}\right)\begin{bmatrix} 1 & 0 \\ 0 & -1 \end{bmatrix}$$
However, when checking the matrix multiplication with a calculator, the left side of the equation did not equal the right side of the equation. Explain the mistake in Noel's logic.
12. If T_1 and T_2 are two transformations, what does $T_1 \circ T_2$ mean?
13. Does $r_{y=x} \circ r_x = r_x \circ r_{y=x}$? Explain why or why not.
14. **Fill in the Blanks** R_{-90} represents a rotation of ___?___ degrees about ___?___ in a ___?___ direction. 90; the origin; clockwise

3. $\begin{bmatrix} 5 & 2 \\ \sqrt{8} & \pi \end{bmatrix}$

5c. Answers vary. Sample: $\begin{bmatrix} 1 & 2 \\ 3 & 4 \end{bmatrix}\begin{bmatrix} 5 & 6 \\ 7 & 8 \end{bmatrix} \neq \begin{bmatrix} 5 & 6 \\ 7 & 8 \end{bmatrix}\begin{bmatrix} 1 & 2 \\ 3 & 4 \end{bmatrix}$

11. He changed the order of the matrices being multiplied, and matrix multiplication is not always commutative.

12. The transformation that is equivalent to applying T_2 first, and then applying T_1 to the first image.

13. No; one is a rotation of 90°, the other of -90°. You can also show this with matrices: $\begin{bmatrix} 1 & 0 \\ 0 & -1 \end{bmatrix}\begin{bmatrix} 0 & 1 \\ 1 & 0 \end{bmatrix} = \begin{bmatrix} 0 & 1 \\ -1 & 0 \end{bmatrix} \neq \begin{bmatrix} 0 & -1 \\ 1 & 0 \end{bmatrix} = \begin{bmatrix} 0 & 1 \\ 1 & 0 \end{bmatrix}\begin{bmatrix} 1 & 0 \\ 0 & -1 \end{bmatrix}$

Extension

Another property of the real numbers is the existence of an *additive identity,* which is 0 for all real numbers. All real numbers also have an *additive inverse:* For any real number *A*, there is a number -*A* such that $A + (-A) = 0$. An additive identity and additive inverses also exist for all 2 × 2 matrices. Ask students to find the additive identity for 2 × 2 matrices and to find the additive inverse -*A* of the general 2 × 2 matrix $A = \begin{bmatrix} a & b \\ c & d \end{bmatrix}$. Then ask them to show that the sum $A + -A$ is equal to the additive identity.

additive identity: $\begin{bmatrix} 0 & 0 \\ 0 & 0 \end{bmatrix}$; $-A = \begin{bmatrix} -a & -b \\ -c & -d \end{bmatrix}$;

$A + -A = \begin{bmatrix} a & b \\ c & d \end{bmatrix} + \begin{bmatrix} -a & -b \\ -c & -d \end{bmatrix} = \begin{bmatrix} a-a & b-b \\ c-c & d-d \end{bmatrix} = \begin{bmatrix} 0 & 0 \\ 0 & 0 \end{bmatrix}$.

15. Refer to the Example. As a right-handed golfer takes the club back the golfer cocks his or her wrist at the top of the backswing as shown in the picture. When the golfer is viewed from the back, the club appears to have rotated 270 degrees (R_{270}) from vertical.
   a. Use the Matrix Basis Theorem to find the matrix for R_{270}.
   b. Find the image of the golf club under a 270° counterclockwise rotation.
   c. Compare the results of Part b to the results of the Example. Explain your findings.

15a. $\begin{bmatrix} 0 & 1 \\ -1 & 0 \end{bmatrix}$

15b. $\begin{bmatrix} 0 & -6 & -6 \\ -1 & -1 & -2 \end{bmatrix}$

15c. They are the same. A -90° rotation is equivalent to a 270° rotation.

APPLYING THE MATHEMATICS

16. Let $G = (-1, 4)$, $R = (-3, 6)$, $E = (2, 6)$, $A = (2, -1)$, and $T = (-1, -4)$.
   a. Write the matrix for $GREAT$.
   b. Write the matrix for $R_{90}(GREAT)$.
   c. Write the matrix for $r_{y=x} \circ R_{90}(GREAT)$.
   d. What single transformation is equal to $r_{y=x} \circ R_{90}$? r_x

16a. $\begin{bmatrix} -1 & -3 & 2 & 2 & -1 \\ 4 & 6 & 6 & -1 & -4 \end{bmatrix}$

16b. $\begin{bmatrix} -4 & -6 & -6 & 1 & 4 \\ -1 & -3 & 2 & 2 & -1 \end{bmatrix}$

16c. $\begin{bmatrix} -1 & -3 & 2 & 2 & -1 \\ -4 & -6 & -6 & 1 & 4 \end{bmatrix}$

17. Refer to the Activity and quadrilateral $ABCD$ with $A = (1, 0)$, $B = (4, -1)$, $C = (6, 2)$, and $D = (3, 5)$.
   a. Find the image of $ABCD$ under the transformation $S_{\frac{1}{2}} \circ r_y$.
   b. Is the image congruent to $ABCD$? no
   c. Is the image similar to $ABCD$? yes

17a. $\begin{bmatrix} -\frac{1}{2} & -2 & -3 & -\frac{3}{2} \\ 0 & -\frac{1}{2} & 1 & \frac{5}{2} \end{bmatrix}$

18. a. To what single transformation is each of the following equivalent? a.–b. See margin.
   i. $r_x \circ r_x$ ii. $r_y \circ r_y$ iii. $r_{y=x} \circ r_{y=x}$
   b. Explain the geometric meaning of the results of Part a.

19. Consider the matrix multiplications shown at the right. Laura hypothesizes that reversing the order of a 2 × 2 matrix multiplication always results in switching the diagonal elements of the original 2 × 2 product matrix. Let $A = \begin{bmatrix} a & b \\ c & d \end{bmatrix}$ and $B = \begin{bmatrix} e & f \\ g & h \end{bmatrix}$.
   a. Find AB and BA. a.–b. See margin.
   b. Is Laura's conjecture correct? Why or why not?

$$\begin{bmatrix} 5 & 2 \\ 8 & 3 \end{bmatrix}\begin{bmatrix} 3 & 4 \\ -2 & 5 \end{bmatrix} = \begin{bmatrix} 11 & 30 \\ 18 & 47 \end{bmatrix}$$

$$\begin{bmatrix} 3 & 4 \\ -2 & 5 \end{bmatrix}\begin{bmatrix} 5 & 2 \\ 8 & 3 \end{bmatrix} = \begin{bmatrix} 47 & 18 \\ 30 & 11 \end{bmatrix}$$

20. a. Use a CAS to show that See margin.
$$\left(\begin{bmatrix} a & b \\ c & d \end{bmatrix}\begin{bmatrix} e & f \\ g & h \end{bmatrix}\right)\begin{bmatrix} i & j \\ k & \ell \end{bmatrix} = \begin{bmatrix} a & b \\ c & d \end{bmatrix}\left(\begin{bmatrix} e & f \\ g & h \end{bmatrix}\begin{bmatrix} i & j \\ k & \ell \end{bmatrix}\right).$$
   b. What property does Part a demonstrate? Associative Property of Multiplication

Notes on the Questions

Question 16d Because reflections reverse orientation and rotations preserve orientation, the composite of a reflection and a rotation will reverse orientation. This indicates that the single transformation $r_{x} = y \circ R_{90}$ is likely a reflection (because that is the only congruence transformation so far that reverses orientation).

Question 18 Some students may draw a figure and do the reflections geometrically, some may remember a theorem from geometry, others may use the algebraic rule, and still others may use matrices.

Question 20 Another similar property is that when the multiplications are possible, then matrix multiplication distributes over matrix addition. That is, for all matrices A, B, and C for which the multiplications exist, $A(B + C) = AB + AC$.

Additional Answers

18a. i. the identity transformation, ii. the identity transformation; iii. the identity transformation

18b. Reflecting a figure over the same line twice results in mapping the figure onto itself.

19a. $AB = \begin{bmatrix} ae + bg & af + bh \\ ce + dg & cf + dh \end{bmatrix}$;

$BA = \begin{bmatrix} ae + cf & be + df \\ ag + ch & bg + dh \end{bmatrix}$

19b. No, it is not. For instance, $ae + bg$ does not necessarily equal $bg + dh$.

20a. $\begin{bmatrix} a & b \\ c & d \end{bmatrix} \cdot \begin{bmatrix} e & f \\ g & h \end{bmatrix} \cdot \begin{bmatrix} i & j \\ k & l \end{bmatrix} = \begin{bmatrix} a & b \\ c & d \end{bmatrix} \cdot \begin{bmatrix} e & f \\ g & h \end{bmatrix} \cdot \begin{bmatrix} i & j \\ k & l \end{bmatrix}$ $\begin{bmatrix} \text{true} & \text{true} \\ \text{true} & \text{true} \end{bmatrix}$

Notes on the Questions

Additional Answers can be found in the back of the book.

4 Wrap-Up

Ongoing Assessment

Have students work in groups. The group should decide on a 2 × 2 matrix *M*. Some members of the group should multiply *M* by $\begin{bmatrix} 1 & 0 \\ 0 & 1 \end{bmatrix}$ on the right and other members should multiply *M* by $\begin{bmatrix} 1 & 0 \\ 0 & 1 \end{bmatrix}$ on the left. Then all the group members should compare their results. Students are multiplying by an identity matrix, so the answer matrix should match the starting matrix.

Administer Quiz 2 (or a quiz of your own) after students' complete this lesson.

4-7B page 2

4-7B Lesson Master — Questions on SPUR Objectives
See Student Edition pages 293–297 for objectives.

PROPERTIES Objective E

1. Show that multiplication of 2 × 2 matrices is not commutative.
Answers vary. Sample:
$\begin{bmatrix} 1 & 0 \\ 6 & 2 \end{bmatrix}\begin{bmatrix} 2 & 1 \\ 0 & 3 \end{bmatrix} = \begin{bmatrix} 2 & 1 \\ 12 & 12 \end{bmatrix}$, but $\begin{bmatrix} 2 & 1 \\ 0 & 3 \end{bmatrix}\begin{bmatrix} 1 & 0 \\ 6 & 2 \end{bmatrix} = \begin{bmatrix} 8 & 2 \\ 18 & 6 \end{bmatrix}$

2. a. Write the 2 × 2 identity matrix *I*.
$I = \begin{bmatrix} 1 & 0 \\ 0 & 1 \end{bmatrix}$

b. Show that $I \cdot M = M \cdot I$ for all 2 × 2 matrices *M*.
$I \cdot M = \begin{bmatrix} 1 & 0 \\ 0 & 1 \end{bmatrix}\begin{bmatrix} a & b \\ c & d \end{bmatrix} = \begin{bmatrix} a+0 & b+0 \\ 0+c & 0+d \end{bmatrix} = \begin{bmatrix} a & b \\ c & d \end{bmatrix}$;
$M \cdot I = \begin{bmatrix} a & b \\ c & d \end{bmatrix}\begin{bmatrix} 1 & 0 \\ 0 & 1 \end{bmatrix} = \begin{bmatrix} a+0 & 0+b \\ c+0 & 0+d \end{bmatrix} = \begin{bmatrix} a & b \\ c & d \end{bmatrix}$

3. Name two other properties of 2 × 2 matrices that are shared by multiplication of real numbers.
Associative Property; Closure

PROPERTIES Objective G

4. Suppose T_1 has matrix $\begin{bmatrix} 4 & 0 \\ 0 & 4 \end{bmatrix}$ and T_2 has matrix $\begin{bmatrix} 1 & 0 \\ 0 & -1 \end{bmatrix}$.

a. What is the matrix for $T_2 \circ T_1$?
$\begin{bmatrix} 4 & 0 \\ 0 & -4 \end{bmatrix}$

b. Explain what happens to a figure under $T_2 \circ T_1$.
Answers vary. Sample: The figure undergoes a size change of magnitude 4 and is reflected over the *x*-axis.

Advanced Algebra 219

REVIEW

21. Name three points that are their own images under the transformation represented by $\begin{bmatrix} 0 & 1 \\ 1 & 0 \end{bmatrix}$. (Lesson 4-6)

22. Suppose *T* is a transformation with *T*: (1, 0) → (5, 0), and *T*: (0, 1) → $\left(0, \frac{4}{5}\right)$. (Lessons 4-6, 4-5)
    a. Find a matrix that represents *T*.
    b. What kind of transformation is *T*? a scale change

23. Find a matrix for the size change that maps the triangle $\begin{bmatrix} -6 & 4 & 7 \\ 2 & 2 & 8 \end{bmatrix}$ onto the triangle $\begin{bmatrix} -9 & 6 & 10.5 \\ 3 & 3 & 12 \end{bmatrix}$. (Lesson 4-4)

24. a. Suppose *a* is a real number. For what values of *a* is there a unique line containing (*a*, 0) and (0, *a*)? $\{a \mid a \neq 0\}$
    b. If *a* is such that there is a unique line, find an equation satisfied by every point (*x*, *y*) on it. (Lesson 3-4) $y = -x + a$

25. There are two prices for used movies at the Lights, Camera, Action! video store. The regular price is \$15, but some are on sale for \$9. Let *s* represent the number of movies Bob bought on sale, and *r* represent the number of movies he bought at regular price. (Lesson 3-2)
    a. Suppose Bob spent \$78 on movies. Write an equation relating *s*, *r*, and the money Bob spent. $9s + 15r = 78$
    b. Graph the equation from Part a and list all possible combinations of regular and sale movies Bob could have bought. See margin.

EXPLORATION

26. Test whether the properties of 2 × 2 matrix multiplication extend to 3 × 3 matrices.
    a. Explain whether you think that the closure property holds for 3 × 3 matrix multiplication.
    b. There is also an identity matrix *M* for 3 × 3 matrix multiplication. Use your knowledge of matrices to guess the values of the elements of matrix *M*. Test your identity matrix *M* by multiplying it by a general 3 × 3 matrix.
    c. Test the commutative property for 3 × 3 matrix multiplication with a specific example.
    d. Test the associative property for 3 × 3 matrix multiplication with a specific example. a–d. See the Additional Answers section at the back of the book.

21. Answers vary. Sample: (0, 0), (1, 1), and (2, 2)

22a. $\begin{bmatrix} 5 & 0 \\ 0 & \frac{4}{5} \end{bmatrix}$

23. $\begin{bmatrix} \frac{3}{2} & 0 \\ 0 & \frac{3}{2} \end{bmatrix}$

QY ANSWERS

1. $\begin{bmatrix} 1 \cdot a + 0 \cdot c & 1 \cdot b + 0 \cdot d \\ 0 \cdot a + 1 \cdot c & 0 \cdot b + 1 \cdot d \end{bmatrix} = \begin{bmatrix} a & b \\ c & d \end{bmatrix}$, and $\begin{bmatrix} a \cdot 1 + b \cdot 0 & a \cdot 0 + b \cdot 1 \\ c \cdot 1 + d \cdot 0 & c \cdot 0 + d \cdot 1 \end{bmatrix} = \begin{bmatrix} a & b \\ c & d \end{bmatrix}$

2. No; $M1M2 = \begin{bmatrix} 0 & 1 \\ 1 & 0 \end{bmatrix}\begin{bmatrix} 1 & 0 \\ 0 & -1 \end{bmatrix} = \begin{bmatrix} 0 & -1 \\ 1 & 0 \end{bmatrix}$ and $M2M1 = \begin{bmatrix} 1 & 0 \\ 0 & -1 \end{bmatrix}\begin{bmatrix} 0 & 1 \\ 1 & 0 \end{bmatrix} = \begin{bmatrix} 0 & 1 \\ -1 & 0 \end{bmatrix}$. The matrices are not equal.

Additional Answers

25b.

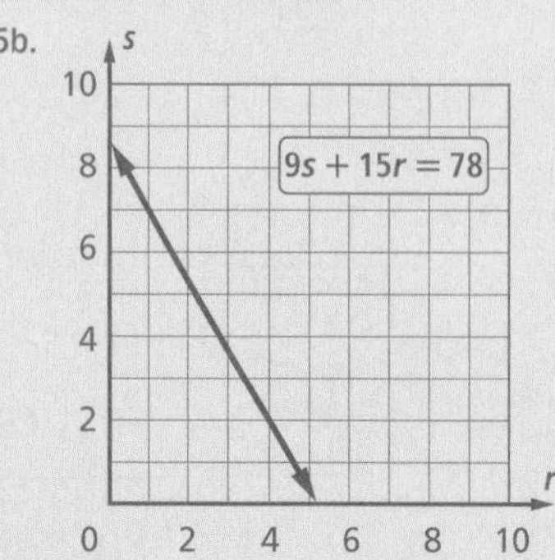

2 sale movies and 4 regular movies or
7 sale movies and 1 regular movie

Lesson 4-8 Matrices for Rotations

Vocabulary

rotation

center of a rotation

magnitude of a rotation

▸ **BIG IDEA** Matrices can represent rotations about the origin.

Mental Math

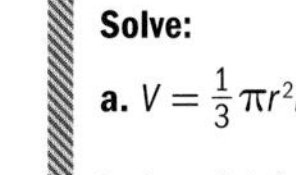

Solve:

a. $V = \frac{1}{3}\pi r^2 h$ for h. $h = \frac{3V}{\pi r^2}$

b. $h = 4.9t^2$ for t. $t = \sqrt{\frac{h}{4.9}}$

c. $M = \frac{kwt^2}{d}$ for k. $k = \frac{Md}{wt^2}$

d. $y = 4x + 12$ for x. $x = \frac{y - 12}{4}$

Recall from geometry and Lesson 4-7 that a turn, or **rotation**, is described by its *center* and *magnitude*. The **center of a rotation** is a point that coincides with its image. The **magnitude of a rotation** is positive if the rotation is counterclockwise, while the magnitude is negative if the rotation is clockwise. The rotation of magnitude $x°$ around the origin is denoted R_x.

Note that we denote a rotation with a capital R, while we identify a reflection with a lowercase r.

The Composite of Two Rotations

Rotations often occur one after the other, as when a spinner is spun twice.

Activity

MATERIALS tracing paper, protractor

At the right, figures I, II, and III are images of each other under rotations with center O.

Step 1 Trace the figures at the right.

Step 2 Measure $\angle AOE$ to determine the magnitude of the rotation that maps figure I onto figure II. 70°

Step 3 Measure $\angle EOI$ to determine the magnitude of the rotation that maps figure II onto figure III. 82°

Step 4 What is the magnitude of the rotation that maps figure I onto figure III? 152°

Step 5 What is the magnitude of the rotation that maps figure III onto figure I? -152°

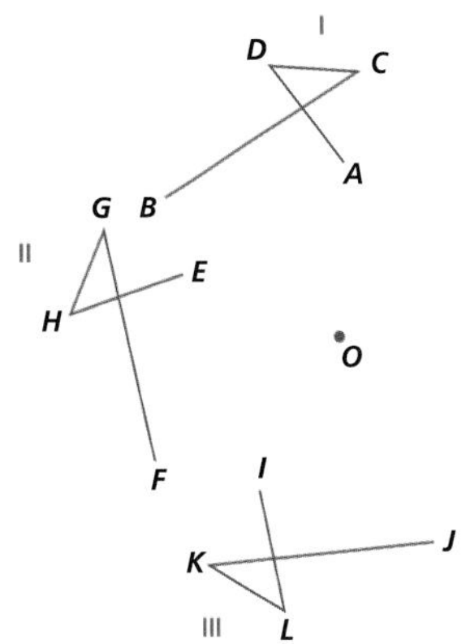

Lesson 4-8

GOAL

Apply the ideas of Lesson 4-7 to explore the matrix for R_{90}, using it as a factor two or three times to obtain matrices for R_{180} and R_{270}.

SPUR Objectives

F Recognize relationships between figures and their rotation images.

G Relate certain rotations to matrices, and vice versa.

K Graph figures and their rotation images.

Materials/Resources

- Lesson Masters 4-8A and 4-8B
- Resource Masters 1, 68 and 69
- Tracing Paper
- Protractor

HOMEWORK

Suggestions for Assignment

- Questions 1–15
- Question 16 (extra credit)
- Reading Lesson 4-9
- Covering the Ideas 4-9

Local Standards

Background

By this point in the chapter, most students should feel comfortable with transformations and the matrices that represent them. Rotations are interesting examples of transformations that will give students more practice with matrices.

But this lesson does more than give practice, and it should not be skipped under any circumstances. Rotations are used in the next lesson to prove the property that the product of the slopes of two (oblique) perpendicular lines is -1. And, in a later chapter, rotations are used to define cos x and sin x for all real numbers x.

In this lesson, we consider matrices only for rotations whose magnitudes are integer multiples of 90°. But any rotation with center (0, 0) has a 2 × 2 matrix; the transformation R_θ has matrix $\begin{bmatrix} \cos\theta & -\sin\theta \\ \sin\theta & \cos\theta \end{bmatrix}$. (Of course, at this time we do not expect students to know this.)

(continued on next page)

1 Warm-Up

Adjacent pairs of the compass directions N, E, S, and W are bisected by the directions NE, SE, SW, and NW, and adjacent pairs of those eight directions are bisected by eight others, clockwise from north: NNE, ENE, ESE, SSE, SSW, WSW, WNW, and NNW.

1. Draw a figure with these 16 directions radiating from a single point.

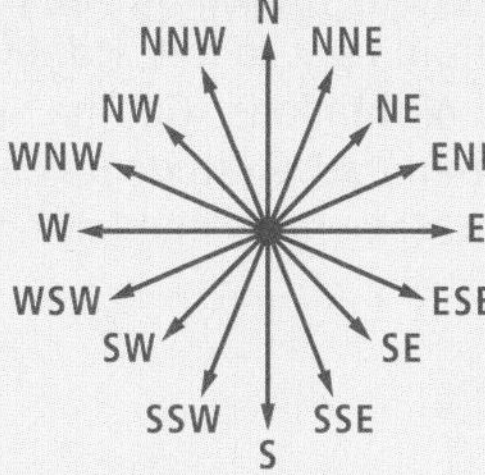

(continued on next page)

2. If NNE is rotated 90° clockwise, what direction results? ESE
3. If SSE is rotated 90° counterclockwise, what direction results? ENE
4. Suppose you rotate N to NE. How many rotations of this magnitude would it take to rotate N to SW? 5
5. Suppose you rotate NW to WSW. What is the magnitude of that rotation? -292.5° or 67.5°

2 Teaching

Note-Taking Tips

Be sure students understand the different meanings of uppercase R and lowercase r (R represents a rotation; r represents a reflection) and the different meanings of positive and negative subscripts for rotations (R_{90} represents a rotation by 90° in the counterclockwise direction; R_{-90} represents a rotation by 90° in the clockwise direction).

Notes on the Lesson

Matrices for rotations of multiples of 90° If students forget the matrices for R_{90}, R_{180}, and R_{270}, they should be able to determine the matrices by themselves. They can memorize them, memorize just the matrix for R_{90} and obtain the others through matrix multiplication, or (most efficiently) use the Matrix Basis Theorem and the images of (1, 0) and (0, 1) to derive each matrix each time they need it.

This is an appropriate time to summarize the matrices known so far.

In class, have students predict the matrix for R_{360}. Then have them derive it through repeated multiplication. It will be the 2 × 2 identity matrix $\begin{bmatrix} 1 & 0 \\ 0 & 1 \end{bmatrix}$, because a 360° rotation is equivalent to a 0° rotation. Thus, another name for this rotation is R_0.

Point out to students that an expression of the form $R_y \circ R_x$ means to rotate by x and then rotate by y; thus, we "apply" the expression from right to left. However, the composition of rotations with the same center is commutative (students can check that statement by multiplying the matrices), so $R_y \circ R_x = R_x \circ R_y$.

The relationships in the Activity result from a fundamental property of rotations, which itself is a consequence of the Angle Addition Postulate in geometry.

Composite of Rotations Theorem

A rotation of b° following a rotation of a° with the same center results in a rotation of $(a + b)$°. In symbols, $R_b \circ R_a = R_{a+b}$.

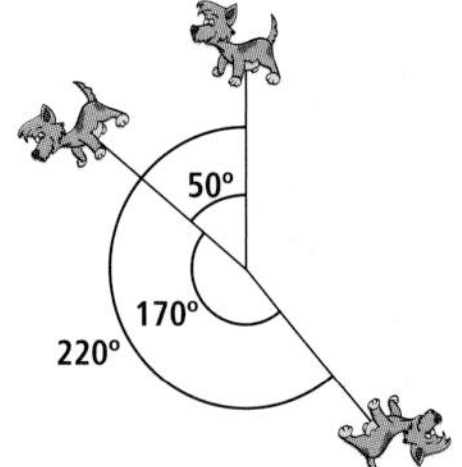

Matrices for Rotations

Rotations centered at the origin are the only rotations that can be represented by 2 × 2 matrices. This is because any transformation represented by a 2 × 2 matrix maps (0, 0) onto itself: $\begin{bmatrix} a & b \\ c & d \end{bmatrix}\begin{bmatrix} 0 \\ 0 \end{bmatrix} = \begin{bmatrix} 0 \\ 0 \end{bmatrix}$.

As you will see later in this course, you can use trigonometry to develop a rotation matrix of any magnitude. However, some rotations have matrices whose elements can be derived without trigonometry. For example, in the previous lesson you derived a matrix for R_{90}.

Matrix for R_{90} Theorem

$\begin{bmatrix} 0 & -1 \\ 1 & 0 \end{bmatrix}$ is the matrix for R_{90}.

You can verify this theorem using the Matrix Basis Theorem.

The image of (1, 0) under R_{90} is (0, 1).

The image of (0, 1) under R_{90} is (-1, 0).

So, the matrix for R_{90} is $\begin{bmatrix} 0 & -1 \\ 1 & 0 \end{bmatrix}$.

Using matrices to represent rotations lets you describe rotation images algebraically. For example, for R_{90},

$$\begin{bmatrix} 0 & -1 \\ 1 & 0 \end{bmatrix}\begin{bmatrix} x \\ y \end{bmatrix} = \begin{bmatrix} 0 \cdot x + -1 \cdot y \\ 1 \cdot x + 0 \cdot y \end{bmatrix} = \begin{bmatrix} -y \\ x \end{bmatrix}.$$

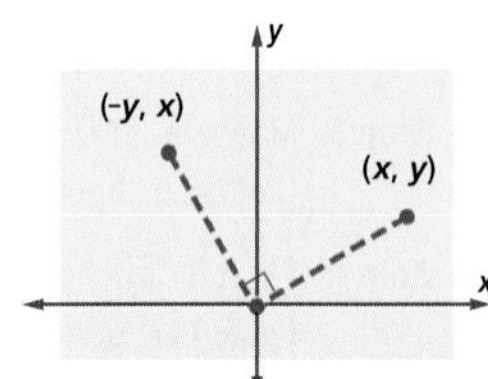

Thus, $R_{90}(x, y) = (-y, x)$. This is an important result you should memorize.

 QY1

QY1
What is the image of (3, 2) under R_{90}?

The Matrix Basis Theorem can be used to remember the various rotation matrices.

The Composite of Rotations Theorem on page 270 is a special case of a more general theorem. If $a + b \neq k \cdot 360$, where k is an integer, a rotation of b° following a rotation of a°, with any point as their center, results in a rotation of magnitude $(a + b)$°. If $a + b = k \cdot 360$, then the composite of the two rotations is a translation.

ENGLISH LEARNERS

Vocabulary Development

Help students understand that the term *composite transformation* implies a particular order for multiplying matrices. For example, in Question 9, to evaluate $R_{90} \circ r_x(6, 2)$, the first step is to evaluate $r_x(6, 2)$, getting (6, -2), and then the second step is to evaluate $R_{90}(6, -2)$, resulting in (2, 6).

Matrices for Rotations of Multiples of 90°

The rotations R_{180} and R_{270} are especially important, and their matrices can be computed straightforwardly from the matrix for R_{90}.

GUIDED

Example

Find the matrix for

a. R_{180}. b. R_{270}.

Solution

a. Because $90° + 90° = 180°$, a rotation of 180° can be considered as the composite of a 90° rotation following a first 90° rotation. That is, $R_{180} = R_{90} \circ R_{90}$.

Use matrix multiplication:

The matrix for $R_{180} = R_{90} \circ R_{90}$ is $\begin{bmatrix} 0 & -1 \\ 1 & 0 \end{bmatrix}\begin{bmatrix} 0 & -1 \\ 1 & 0 \end{bmatrix} = \begin{bmatrix} \underline{?} & \underline{?} \\ \underline{?} & \underline{?} \end{bmatrix}$. -1; 0 0; -1

Another way to write the matrix for R_{180} is $\begin{bmatrix} 0 & -1 \\ 1 & 0 \end{bmatrix}\begin{bmatrix} 0 & -1 \\ 1 & 0 \end{bmatrix} = \begin{bmatrix} 0 & -1 \\ 1 & 0 \end{bmatrix}^2$.

b. $R_{270} = R_{90} \circ R_{\underline{?}}$. 180

So, the matrix for R_{270} is $\begin{bmatrix} 0 & -1 \\ 1 & 0 \end{bmatrix}\begin{bmatrix} \underline{?} & \underline{?} \\ \underline{?} & \underline{?} \end{bmatrix} = \begin{bmatrix} \underline{?} & \underline{?} \\ \underline{?} & \underline{?} \end{bmatrix}$. -1; 0; 0; 1 0; -1; -1; 0

QY2

▶ QY2

What is the matrix for R_{-90}?

Questions

COVERING THE IDEAS

1. A rotation with negative magnitude represents a turn in which direction? clockwise

2. a. Verify that $\begin{bmatrix} a & b \\ c & d \end{bmatrix}\begin{bmatrix} 0 \\ 0 \end{bmatrix} = \begin{bmatrix} 0 \\ 0 \end{bmatrix}$.

   b. What does this computation prove about representing rotations with 2×2 matrices?

2a. $\begin{bmatrix} a & b \\ c & d \end{bmatrix}\begin{bmatrix} 0 \\ 0 \end{bmatrix} = \begin{bmatrix} a \cdot 0 + b \cdot 0 \\ c \cdot 0 + d \cdot 0 \end{bmatrix} = \begin{bmatrix} 0 \\ 0 \end{bmatrix}$

2b. Rotations centered at the origin are the only ones that can be represented by 2×2 matrices.

Additional Example

Example Use the results from Example 1 that $R_{180} = \begin{bmatrix} -1 & 0 \\ 0 & -1 \end{bmatrix}$ and $R_{270} = \begin{bmatrix} 0 & 1 \\ -1 & 0 \end{bmatrix}$ to find **(a)** R_{360} and **(b)** R_{450}.

Solution

a. Because $180° + 180° = 360°$, a rotation of 360° can be considered as the composite of a 180° rotation following an initial 180° rotation.

That is, $R_{360} = R_{180} \circ R_{180}$. Use matrix multiplication. The matrix for $R_{360} = R_{180} \circ R_{180}$ is $\begin{bmatrix} -1 & 0 \\ 0 & -1 \end{bmatrix}\begin{bmatrix} -1 & 0 \\ 0 & -1 \end{bmatrix}$

$= \underline{\quad ? \quad}$. $\begin{bmatrix} 1 & 0 \\ 0 & 1 \end{bmatrix}$

b. $R_{450} = R_{180}$, so the matrix for R_{450} is $\begin{bmatrix} -1 & 0 \\ 0 & -1 \end{bmatrix} \underline{\quad ? \quad} = \underline{\quad ? \quad}$.

$\begin{bmatrix} 0 & 1 \\ -1 & 0 \end{bmatrix}$; $\begin{bmatrix} 0 & -1 \\ 1 & 0 \end{bmatrix}$

3 Assignment

Recommended Assignment

- Questions 1–15
- Question 16 (extra credit)
- Reading Lesson 4-9
- Covering the Ideas 4-9

Accommodating the Learner

Ask students to use the Matrix Basis Theorem from Lesson 4-6 to find matrices for R_{-90}, R_{180}, and R_{-180}. Then ask the students to show that $R_{90} \circ R_{-90}(x, y) = (x, y)$ and that $R_{180} \circ R_{-180}(x, y) = (x, y)$. For R_{-90}, $(1, 0) \to (0, -1)$ and $(0, 1) \to (1, 0)$, so the matrix is $\begin{bmatrix} 0 & 1 \\ -1 & 0 \end{bmatrix}$. For both R_{180} and R_{-180}, $(1, 0) \to (-1, 0)$ and $(0, 1) \to (0, -1)$, so each matrix is $\begin{bmatrix} -1 & 0 \\ 0 & -1 \end{bmatrix}$. So $R_{90} \circ R_{-90}(x, y) =$

$$\begin{bmatrix} 0 & -1 \\ 1 & 0 \end{bmatrix}\begin{bmatrix} 0 & 1 \\ -1 & 0 \end{bmatrix}\begin{bmatrix} x \\ y \end{bmatrix} = \begin{bmatrix} 1 & 0 \\ 0 & 1 \end{bmatrix}\begin{bmatrix} x \\ y \end{bmatrix} = \begin{bmatrix} x \\ y \end{bmatrix}.$$

Also, $R_{180} \circ R_{-180}(x, y) =$

$$\begin{bmatrix} -1 & 0 \\ 0 & -1 \end{bmatrix}\begin{bmatrix} -1 & 0 \\ 0 & -1 \end{bmatrix}\begin{bmatrix} x \\ y \end{bmatrix} = \begin{bmatrix} 1 & 0 \\ 0 & 1 \end{bmatrix}\begin{bmatrix} x \\ y \end{bmatrix} = \begin{bmatrix} x \\ y \end{bmatrix}.$$

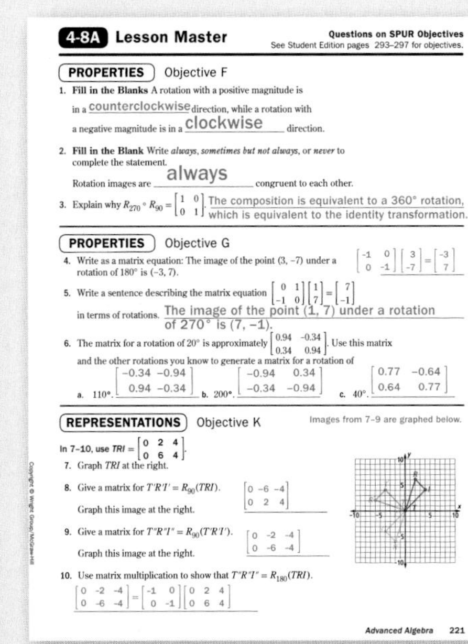

Notes on the Questions

Question 9 Suggest that students draw a picture to verify the results that might have been found algebraically.

Question 10 This matrix approximates the rotation matrix $\begin{bmatrix} \cos\theta & -\sin\theta \\ \sin\theta & \cos\theta \end{bmatrix}$ when $\theta = 60°$.

3. a. **Fill in the Blank** A rotation of 45° followed by a rotation of 90° is equivalent to a rotation of __?__. 135°
   b. Write Part a using R notation. $R_{90} \circ R_{45} = R_{135}$
4. A rotation of -120° is the same as a rotation of what positive magnitude? 240°
5. Write the matrices for R_{90}, R_{180}, R_{270}, and R_{360}.
6. Find the image of (x, y) under R_{270}. $(y, -x)$
7. Find the image of the square $\begin{bmatrix} 2 & 8 & 8 & 2 \\ 3 & 3 & 9 & 9 \end{bmatrix}$ under R_{180}.

APPLYING THE MATHEMATICS

8. Let $A = (6, 2)$, $B = R_{90}(A)$, $C = R_{180}(A)$, and $D = R_{270}(A)$. Prove that $ABCD$ is a square by showing that $AB = BC = CD = AD$ and $AO = BO = CO = DO$, where $O = (0, 0)$.
9. a. Calculate a matrix for $R_{90} \circ r_x$.
   b. Calculate a matrix for $r_x \circ R_{90}$.
   c. Your answers to Parts a and b should be different. What property of matrix multiplication does this illustrate? What property of transformations does this illustrate?
10. The matrix for R_{60} is approximately $\begin{bmatrix} 0.5 & -0.866 \\ 0.866 & 0.5 \end{bmatrix}$. Use the fact that a 150° rotation is the result of a 60° rotation followed by a 90° rotation to find an approximate matrix for R_{150}.
11. a. Find a matrix for $R_{90} \circ S_{0.5,2} \circ R_{-90} \circ S_{2,0.5}$.
    b. What does this transformation represent geometrically?

REVIEW

12. a. By what matrix can you multiply the size change matrix $\begin{bmatrix} 8 & 0 \\ 0 & 8 \end{bmatrix}$ to get the identity matrix?
    b. What does your answer to Part a represent geometrically? **(Lessons 4-7, 4-4)**
13. **True or False** The matrix for a transformation can be determined by finding the image of the point (1, 1) under the transformation. **(Lesson 4-6)** false

5. $R_{90}: \begin{bmatrix} 0 & -1 \\ 1 & 0 \end{bmatrix}$; $R_{180}: \begin{bmatrix} -1 & 0 \\ 0 & -1 \end{bmatrix}$; $R_{270}: \begin{bmatrix} 0 & 1 \\ -1 & 0 \end{bmatrix}$; $R_{360}: \begin{bmatrix} 1 & 0 \\ 0 & 1 \end{bmatrix}$

7. $\begin{bmatrix} -2 & -8 & -8 & -2 \\ -3 & -3 & -9 & -9 \end{bmatrix}$

8. $B = (-2, 6)$, $C = (-6, -2)$, $D = (2, -6)$; $AB = BC = CD = AD = 4\sqrt{5}$ and $AO = BO = CO = DO = 2\sqrt{10}$

9a. $\begin{bmatrix} 0 & 1 \\ 1 & 0 \end{bmatrix}$ b. $\begin{bmatrix} 0 & -1 \\ -1 & 0 \end{bmatrix}$

9c. Matrix multiplication is not commutative; composition of transformations is not commutative.

10. $\begin{bmatrix} -0.866 & -0.5 \\ 0.5 & -0.866 \end{bmatrix}$

11a. $\begin{bmatrix} 4 & 0 \\ 0 & 0.25 \end{bmatrix}$

11b. a horizontal stretch of magnitude 4 and a vertical shrink of magnitude 0.25

12a. $\begin{bmatrix} \frac{1}{8} & 0 \\ 0 & \frac{1}{8} \end{bmatrix}$

12b. the size change of magnitude $\frac{1}{8}$

Accommodating the Learner

Tell students that the matrix for R_{30} is approximately $\begin{bmatrix} 0.866 & -0.5 \\ 0.5 & 0.866 \end{bmatrix}$. Ask students to complete the following activities:

a. Use the information in Question 10 to verify that $R_{30} \circ R_{60} = R_{90}$.

$\begin{bmatrix} 0.866 & -0.5 \\ 0.5 & 0.866 \end{bmatrix}\begin{bmatrix} 0.5 & -0.866 \\ 0.866 & 0.5 \end{bmatrix} = \begin{bmatrix} 0 & -0.99996 \\ 0.99996 & 0.5 \end{bmatrix}$; taking rounding into account, that matrix is $\begin{bmatrix} 0 & -1 \\ 1 & 0 \end{bmatrix}$, which is the matrix for R_{90}.

b. Verify that $R_{30} \circ R_{30} \circ R_{30} = R_{90}$.

$\begin{bmatrix} 0.866 & -0.5 \\ 0.5 & 0.866 \end{bmatrix} \cdot \left(\begin{bmatrix} 0.866 & -0.5 \\ 0.5 & 0.866 \end{bmatrix}\begin{bmatrix} 0.866 & -0.5 \\ 0.5 & 0.866 \end{bmatrix}\right) = \begin{bmatrix} 0.866 & -0.5 \\ 0.5 & 0.866 \end{bmatrix}\begin{bmatrix} 0.49996 & -0.866 \\ 0.866 & 0.49996 \end{bmatrix} = \begin{bmatrix} 0 & -1 \\ 1 & 0 \end{bmatrix}$, which is the matrix for R_{90}.

14. Consider the triangle $\triangle ELK$ represented by the matrix $\begin{bmatrix} 0 & 8 & 9 \\ -2 & -4 & -6 \end{bmatrix}$, and the triangle $\triangle RAM$ represented by the matrix $\begin{bmatrix} 0 & 4 & 4.5 \\ -3 & -6 & -9 \end{bmatrix}$. (Lesson 4-5)
    a. Find a matrix for the scale change that maps $\triangle ELK$ onto $\triangle RAM$.
    b. Find a matrix for the scale change that maps $\triangle RAM$ onto $\triangle ELK$.

14a. $\begin{bmatrix} \frac{1}{2} & 0 \\ 0 & \frac{3}{2} \end{bmatrix}$

14b. $\begin{bmatrix} 2 & 0 \\ 0 & \frac{2}{3} \end{bmatrix}$

15. In 2006, about 45 million people in the U.S. did not have health insurance. The four states with the highest percent of uninsured residents were Texas (24.1%), New Mexico (21.0%), Florida (20.3%), and Arizona (19.0%). Their populations in 2006 were as follows: Texas 23,508,000; New Mexico 1,955,000; Florida 18,090,000; and Arizona 6,166,000. Use matrix multiplication to determine how many people in these four states had no health insurance. (Lessons 4-3, 4-1) about 10,920,000

The population of New Mexico increased by 20.1% between 1990 and 2000.

EXPLORATION

16. You can find a matrix for R_{45} in the following way. Suppose the matrix is $\begin{bmatrix} a & b \\ c & d \end{bmatrix}$. Then, since $R_{45} \circ R_{45} = R_{90}$,

$$\begin{bmatrix} a & b \\ c & d \end{bmatrix}\begin{bmatrix} a & b \\ c & d \end{bmatrix} = \begin{bmatrix} 0 & -1 \\ 1 & 0 \end{bmatrix}.$$

a–f. See the Additional Answers section at the back of the book.

   a. Multiply the matrices on the left side of the equation to obtain one matrix.
   b. Equate the elements of the product matrix and the matrix for R_{90}. You will have four equations in a, b, c, and d.
   c. From the equations, explain why $a^2 = d^2$, but $a \neq -d$.
   d. From the equations, explain why $b = -c$.
   e. Either by hand or with a CAS, find the two possible matrices $\begin{bmatrix} a & b \\ c & d \end{bmatrix}$.
   f. One solution is the matrix for R_{45}. The other solution is the matrix for what transformation?

QY ANSWERS

1. (-2, 3)
2. $\begin{bmatrix} 0 & 1 \\ -1 & 0 \end{bmatrix}$

Notes on the Questions

Question 16 The parts of this question carry a student through the solution of a system of equations in four variables that is not a linear system. It is instructive to discuss this question so that all students can see that algebraic methods can be used to determine a geometric result. It may motivate some students to try to solve systems like this without the hints.

Additional Answers can be found in the back of the book.

4 Wrap-Up

Ongoing Assessment

Ask students to explain and interpret this equation: $\begin{bmatrix} 0 & -1 \\ 1 & 0 \end{bmatrix}^4 \begin{bmatrix} x \\ y \end{bmatrix} = \begin{bmatrix} x \\ y \end{bmatrix}$.

Answers vary. Sample: The matrix $\begin{bmatrix} 0 & -1 \\ 1 & 0 \end{bmatrix}$ represents a rotation of 90°, so the fourth power of $\begin{bmatrix} 0 & -1 \\ 1 & 0 \end{bmatrix}$ represents a rotation of 360°. Because that is the same as a rotation of 0°, the image is the same as the preimage.

Project Update

Project 3, *Pitch, Yaw, and Roll,* on page 286 relates to the content of this lesson.

Extension

Ask students if matrix multiplication is commutative. No; in general for matrices M and N, $MN \neq NM$. Then ask students to explain why matrix multiplication, when it represents the composite of two rotations with the same center, *is* always commutative. Answers vary: Sample: If R_a and R_b are two rotations with the same center, then $R_a \circ R_b = R_{a+b}$ and $R_b \circ R_a = R_{b+a}$. Because $a + b = b + a$ (the addition of real numbers is always commutative), then $R_{a+b} = R_{b+a}$, so $R_a \circ R_b = R_b \circ R_a$.

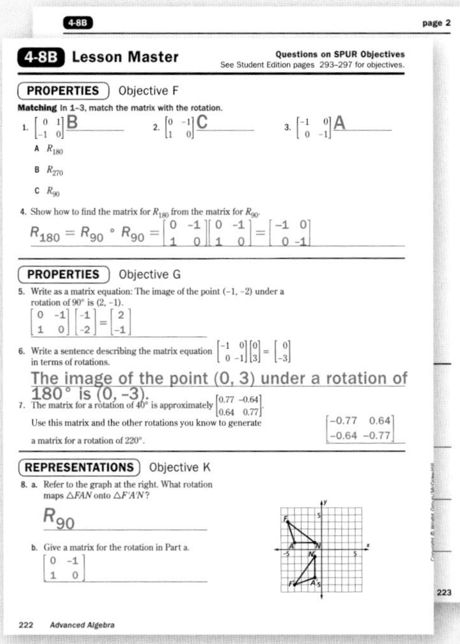

Lesson 4-9

GOAL

Use rotations to justify the biconditional statement that the product of the slopes of two (oblique) lines is -1 if and only if the two lines are perpendicular.

SPUR Objectives

D Determine equations of lines perpendicular to given lines.

F Recognize relationships between figures and their transformation images.

H Given their slopes, determine whether lines are perpendicular to each other, and vice versa.

Materials/Resources

- Lesson Masters 4-9A and 4-9B
- Resource Master 70
- Matrix polygon application

HOMEWORK

Suggestions for Assignment

- Questions 1–26
- Question 27 (extra credit)
- Reading Lesson 4-10
- Covering the Ideas 4-10

Local Standards

1 Warm-Up

1. Rotate the triangle represented by the matrix $\begin{bmatrix} 2 & 11 & 11 \\ 5 & 5 & -7 \end{bmatrix}$ by -90° about the origin. $\begin{bmatrix} 5 & 5 & -7 \\ -2 & -11 & -11 \end{bmatrix}$
2. By using the Pythagorean Distance Formula or some other means, demonstrate that your image is indeed the rotation image of the original triangle under a rotation of -90°. Answers vary. Sample: The points (2, 5), (5, -2), and (0, 0) are vertices of an isosceles right triangle. The triangle with those

Lesson 4-9 Rotations and Perpendicular Lines

▶ **BIG IDEA** If a line has slope m, any line perpendicular to it has slope $-\frac{1}{m}$.

If a rotation of magnitude 90° is applied to a line, then the image line is perpendicular to the preimage line. This is true regardless of the center of the rotation, and it explains a very nice relationship between the slopes of perpendicular lines.

Mental Math

Pete has $9.50 in nickels and dimes. How many dimes does he have if he has

a. 50 nickels? 70

b. 150 nickels? 20

c. n nickels? $\frac{950 - 5n}{10}$

Activity

MATERIALS matrix polygon application

Consider $\overline{AB}$ with endpoints $A = (-8, 3)$ and $B = (5, -1)$. See margin.

Step 1 Use a matrix polygon application to enter W, the 2×2 matrix of endpoints of $\overline{AB}$. Graph $\overline{AB}$.

Step 2 Enter the R_{90} transformation matrix as R.

Step 3 Calculate $R \cdot W$ to graph $\overline{A'B'}$, the image of $\overline{AB}$ under R_{90}. Describe any relationships you notice between these two line segments.

Step 4 Calculate the slope of $\overline{AB}$ and the slope of $\overline{A'B'}$. How is one slope related to the other?

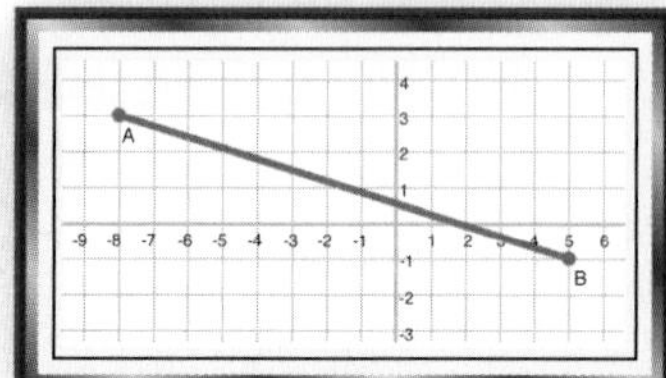

The results of the Activity can be generalized to prove the following theorem.

Perpendicular Lines and Slopes Theorem (Part 1)

If two lines with slopes m_1 and m_2 are perpendicular, then $m_1 \cdot m_2 = -1$.

Background

The major concept of this lesson is the theorem that expresses the relationship between the slopes of two perpendicular lines. The proof of this theorem is demonstrated by using a rotation of 90°, and we believe that the geometry of rotations provides both a proof and an explanation of the algebraic result. Because $R_{90}(x, y) = (-y, x)$, R_{90} switches coordinates and changes the sign of the second coordinate. When the same changes are made to the coordinates of the two points (x_1, y_1) and (x_2, y_2) in the formula for the slope m of the original line, the numerator and denominator are switched, and one switches signs. But the result is the slope of the perpendicular line. Thus, the slope is the negative reciprocal of the original slope, namely, $-\frac{1}{m}$.

Proof You are given two perpendicular lines with slopes m_1 and m_2 and need to show that the product $m_1 m_2$ is -1. The given lines either contain the origin or they are parallel to lines that contain the origin. Here we prove the theorem for two lines through the origin. In the next lesson you will show that this property holds true for perpendicular lines elsewhere.

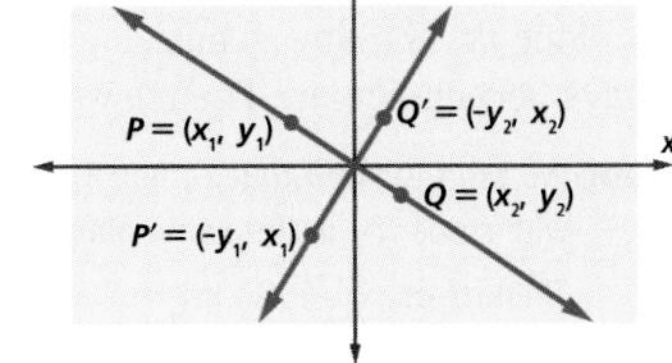

Let $P = (x_1, y_1)$ and $Q = (x_2, y_2)$ be two points on a line $\overleftrightarrow{PQ}$ that contains the origin.

From Lesson 4-8, $R_{90}(P) = (-y_1, x_1) = P'$, and $R_{90}(Q) = (-y_2, x_2) = Q'$. $\overleftrightarrow{P'Q'}$ is perpendicular to $\overleftrightarrow{PQ}$ since $\overleftrightarrow{P'Q'}$ is the image of $\overleftrightarrow{PQ}$ under a rotation of magnitude 90°.

Now, let the slope of the preimage be m_1 and the slope of the image be m_2.

$$m_1 = \text{slope of } \overleftrightarrow{PQ} = \frac{y_2 - y_1}{x_2 - x_1}$$

$$m_2 = \text{slope of } \overleftrightarrow{P'Q'} = \frac{x_2 - x_1}{-y_2 - (-y_1)} = \frac{x_2 - x_1}{-(y_2 - y_1)} = -\frac{x_2 - x_1}{y_2 - y_1}$$

The product of the slopes is

$$m_1 \cdot m_2 = \frac{y_2 - y_1}{x_2 - x_1} \cdot \left(-\frac{x_2 - x_1}{y_2 - y_1}\right) = -1.$$

This proves the theorem.

 **QY1**

Do you see why the product of the slopes is -1? The rotation of 90° switches x- and y-coordinates and changes the first coordinate to its opposite. In the slope formula, this switches numerator and denominator and multiplies the denominator by -1. So the slope $\frac{a}{b}$ becomes $\frac{-b}{a}$, and the product is -1.

> **QY1**
>
> Two perpendicular lines have slopes $\frac{1}{2}$ and s. What is s?

GUIDED

Example

Line n contains (4, -3) and is perpendicular to line ℓ, whose equation is $y = \frac{2}{5}x + 3$. Find an equation for line n.

Solution The slope of line ℓ is __?__. So by the theorem on the previous page, the slope of line n is __?__. $\frac{2}{5}$; $-\frac{5}{2}$

Since line n contains (4, -3), an equation for line n in point-slope form is __?__. $y + 3 = -\frac{5}{2}(x - 4)$

vertices has sides $\sqrt{29}$, $\sqrt{29}$, and $\sqrt{58}$, so (2, 5) has been rotated 90° to get to (5, -2); (5, -2) is in Quadrant IV, so the rotation is of magnitude -90°. The same argument can be used with either of the other two points and their images.

2 Teaching

Notes on the Lesson

Activity Have students work through the Activity, which reviews rotations and also demonstrates the truth of the Perpendicular Lines and Slopes Theorem that follows. Then review the theorem itself. The proof is algebraic and much simpler than it looks. The basis of the proof is finding the images of points on the perpendicular line by using the formula for R_{90}, then directly calculating the slopes of the two lines and showing that the product of their slopes is -1 (or that their slopes are opposite reciprocals).

Example Before discussing the solution, discuss the strategy for doing such a problem. We can find an equation for line n if we know a point on it and its slope. We already know a point on n. So we need to find its slope, which we can obtain from the slope of a line perpendicular to n.

It is important to emphasize that the meaning of *perpendicular* here is exactly the same as in geometry, so all the theorems students learned in geometry are applicable here. For instance, through a point there is exactly one perpendicular to a given line, and, because we are in a plane, two lines perpendicular to the same line are parallel. The theorems of this lesson show how geometric methods and algebraic techniques can provide separate and independent proofs of geometric properties.

Additional Answers

Activity

Step 1: $\begin{bmatrix} -8 & 5 \\ 3 & -1 \end{bmatrix}$

Step 2: $R1 = \begin{bmatrix} 0 & -1 \\ 1 & 0 \end{bmatrix}$

Step 3: Answers vary. Sample: The segments look perpendicular.

Step 4: The slope of $\overline{AB} = -\frac{4}{13}$; the slope of $\overline{A'B'} = \frac{13}{4}$; the slopes are negative reciprocals of each other.

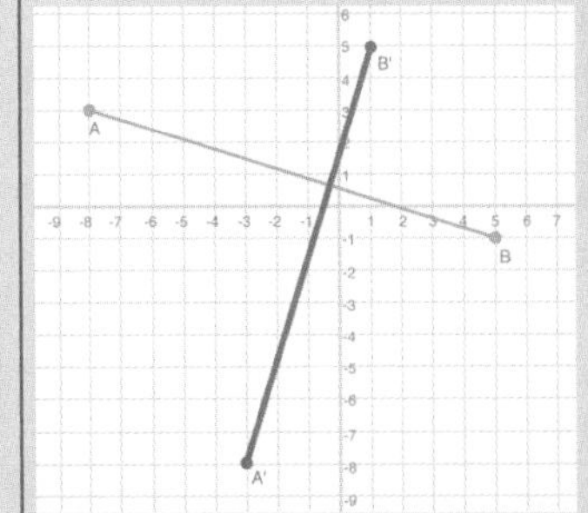

Additional Example

Example Line p contains (-2, 7) and is perpendicular to line q, whose equation is $y = \frac{4}{7}x - 8$. Find an equation for line p.

Solution The slope of line q is __?__. So by the Perpendicular Lines and Slopes Theorem, the slope of line p is __?__. Because line p contains (-2, 7), an equation for line p in point-slope form is __?__. $\frac{4}{7}$; $-\frac{7}{4}$; $y - 7 = -\frac{7}{4}(x + 2)$

4-9

Note-Taking Tips

Encourage students to distinguish, in their notes, between a 2 × 2 matrix for two points (as in Question 1) and a 2 × 2 matrix for operations (as in Question 21). One way to do that is to write a note near the matrix indicating what it represents.

3 Assignment

Recommended Assignment

- Questions 1–26
- Question 27 (extra credit)
- Reading Lesson 4-10
- Covering the Ideas 4-10

Notes on the Questions

In all the questions that involve equations of lines, remind students to sketch the lines or to use their graphing utilities to check that their answers are reasonable.

Additional Answers

2b.

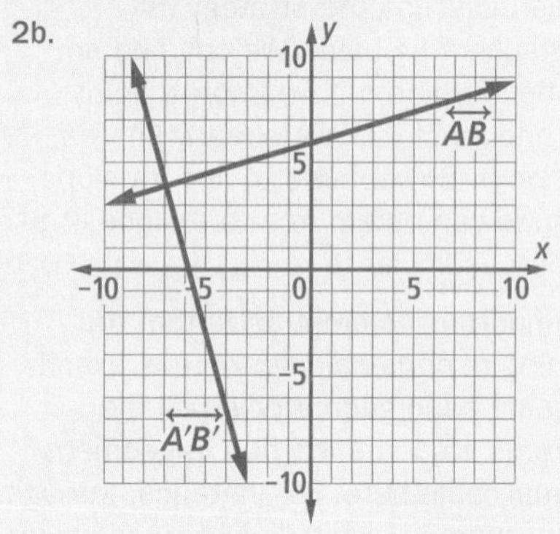

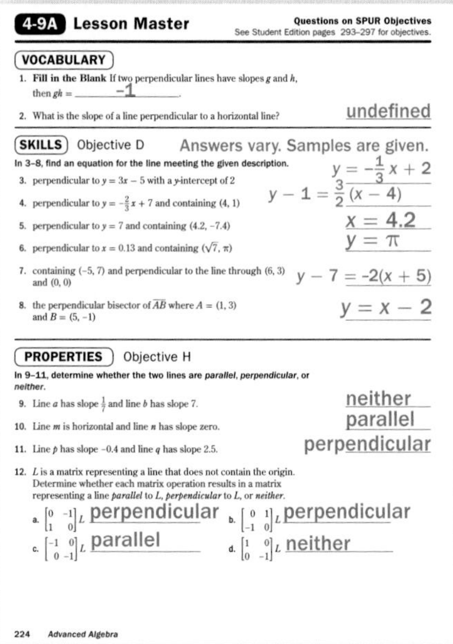

4-9A Lesson Master

Questions on SPUR Objectives
See Student Edition pages 293–297 for objectives.

VOCABULARY

1. **Fill in the Blank** If two perpendicular lines have slopes g and h, then gh = ___-1___.
2. What is the slope of a line perpendicular to a horizontal line? ___undefined___

SKILLS Objective D Answers vary. Samples are given.

In 3–8, find an equation for the line meeting the given description.

3. perpendicular to $y = 3x - 5$ with a y-intercept of 2 $y = -\frac{1}{3}x + 2$
4. perpendicular to $y = -\frac{2}{3}x + 7$ and containing (4, 1) $y - 1 = \frac{3}{2}(x - 4)$
5. perpendicular to $y = 7$ and containing (4.2, –7.4) $x = 4.2$
6. perpendicular to $x = 0.13$ and containing $(\sqrt{7}, \pi)$ $y = \pi$
7. containing (–5, 7) and perpendicular to the line through (6, 3) and (0, 0) $y - 7 = -2(x + 5)$
8. the perpendicular bisector of $\overline{AB}$ where $A = (1, 3)$ and $B = (5, -1)$ $y = x - 2$

PROPERTIES Objective H

In 9–11, determine whether the two lines are *parallel*, *perpendicular*, or *neither*.

9. Line a has slope $\frac{1}{7}$ and line b has slope 7. ___neither___
10. Line m is horizontal and line n has slope zero. ___parallel___
11. Line p has slope –0.4 and line q has slope 2.5. ___perpendicular___
12. L is a matrix representing a line that does not contain the origin. Determine whether each matrix operation results in a matrix representing a line *parallel* to L, *perpendicular* to L, or *neither*.

a. $\begin{bmatrix} 0 & -1 \\ 1 & 0 \end{bmatrix} L$ ___perpendicular___ b. $\begin{bmatrix} 0 & 1 \\ -1 & 0 \end{bmatrix} L$ ___perpendicular___

c. $\begin{bmatrix} -1 & 0 \\ 0 & -1 \end{bmatrix} L$ ___parallel___ d. $\begin{bmatrix} 1 & 0 \\ 0 & -1 \end{bmatrix} L$ ___neither___

224 *Advanced Algebra*

Consider the converse of the preceding theorem. Suppose line ℓ_1 has slope m_1 and line ℓ_2 has slope m_2, and $m_1m_2 = -1$. Are ℓ_1 and ℓ_2 always perpendicular? The answer is yes.

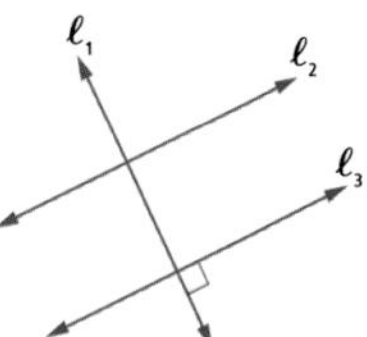

Proof We want to show that ℓ_1 and ℓ_2 are perpendicular. Think of a third line ℓ_3 with slope m_3 in the same plane as ℓ_1 and ℓ_2, and with $\ell_3 \perp \ell_1$. Then $m_1m_3 = -1$. So, $m_1m_3 = m_1m_2$. Thus, $m_3 = m_2$, so ℓ_3 and ℓ_2 have the same slope. So, $\ell_3 \parallel \ell_2$. But $\ell_1 \perp \ell_3$. Now use the theorem from geometry that if a line is perpendicular to one of two parallel lines, it must be perpendicular to the other. So, $\ell_1 \perp \ell_2$. This proves the converse of the previous theorem.

Perpendicular Lines and Slopes Theorem (Part 2)

If two lines have slopes m_1 and m_2 and $m_1m_2 = -1$, then the lines are perpendicular.

Because the original theorem and its converse are both true, we can conclude the following biconditional.

Perpendicular Lines and Slopes Theorem

Two lines with slopes m_1 and m_2 are perpendicular if and only if $m_1m_2 = -1$.

QY2

▶ QY2

Are the lines with slopes 5 and –0.2 perpendicular? Justify your answer.

Questions

COVERING THE IDEAS

1. Write a 2 × 2 matrix that represents the line containing the points (x_1, y_1) and (x_2, y_2).
2. Let $\overleftrightarrow{AB}$ contain points $A = (4, 7)$ and $B = (-3, 5)$.
   a. Find two points on the image of $\overleftrightarrow{AB}$ under R_{90}.
   b. Graph $\overleftrightarrow{AB}$ and its image $\overleftrightarrow{A'B'}$. See margin.
   c. Find the slopes of $\overleftrightarrow{AB}$ and of $\overleftrightarrow{A'B'}$.
   d. What is the product of the slopes? -1

1. $\begin{bmatrix} x_1 & x_2 \\ y_1 & y_2 \end{bmatrix}$

2a. Answers vary. Sample: (-7, 4) and (-5, -3)

2c. slope of $\overleftrightarrow{AB} = \frac{2}{7}$; slope of $\overleftrightarrow{A'B'} = -\frac{7}{2}$

Accommodating the Learner

Tell students to assume that the graph of $y = ax + b$ is not a horizontal line. Ask them to write, in point-slope form, y-intercept form, and standard form, an equation for the line through the point (p, q) that is perpendicular to $y = ax + b$. point-slope form: $y - q = -\frac{1}{a}(x - p)$; slope-intercept form: $y = -\frac{1}{a}x + \frac{p + qa}{a}$; standard form: $x + ay = p + qa$

ENGLISH LEARNERS

Vocabulary Development

Some students may recall that the phrase *negative reciprocal* or *opposite reciprocal* applies to slopes of perpendicular lines. You may want to discuss with them that if $m_1m_2 = -1$, then $m_1 = -1 \cdot \left(\frac{1}{m_2}\right)$. Because $\frac{1}{m_2}$ is the reciprocal of m_2, then m_1 is equal to -1 times the reciprocal of m_2, or "m_1 is the negative/opposite reciprocal of m_2."

In 3–5, indicate whether each statement is *true* or *false*.

3. If two lines have slopes m_1 and m_2, and $m_1m_2 = -1$, then the lines are perpendicular. true
4. If two lines are perpendicular, and they have slopes m_1 and m_2, then $m_1m_2 = -1$. true
5. Suppose m_1 and m_2 are the slopes of two perpendicular lines. Then m_1 is the reciprocal of m_2. false
6. A line has slope 0.25. What is the slope of a line
   a. parallel to this line? 0.25
   b. perpendicular to this line? -4
7. Find an equation of the line through (6, 1) and perpendicular to the line with equation $y = \frac{3}{5}x - 2$. $y = -\frac{5}{3}x + 11$
8. Find an equation of the line perpendicular to the line with equation $y - 2 = -5(x - 1)$ passing through the point (-10, 7). $y = \frac{1}{5}x + 9$

10c. $M3 = \begin{bmatrix} -5 & -9 \\ 3 & 1 \end{bmatrix}$; ℓ_1 and ℓ_3 are parallel since they have the same slope.

11. Answers vary. Sample: Lines with slopes of zero will never satisfy the condition $m_1m_2 = -1$.

APPLYING THE MATHEMATICS

9. Use the graph at the right. Find an equation for the line perpendicular to $\overline{BC}$ through point A. $y - 10 = -\frac{1}{4}(x + 5)$

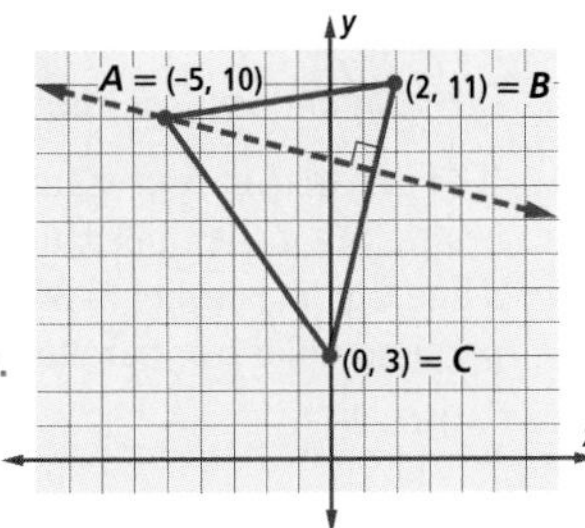

10. A line ℓ_1 contains the points (5, -3) and (9, -1).
    a. Graph ℓ_1 and write a matrix $M1$ representing this line.
    b. Find $M2 = R_{90}(M1)$ and graph the line ℓ_2 that $M2$ represents. Are ℓ_1 and ℓ_2 perpendicular? a–b. See margin.
    c. Let matrix $M3 = R_{90}(M2)$ represent line ℓ_3. What is the relationship between ℓ_1 and ℓ_3? Explain your answer.
11. Why do the statements of the theorems in this lesson apply only to lines with nonzero slopes?
12. **Multiple Choice** What is the slope of a line perpendicular to the line with equation $x = 5$? A

    A 0
    B The slope is not defined.
    C $-\frac{1}{5}$
    D 5
13. Find an equation for the line through (6, 3) and perpendicular to the line with equation $y = 8$. $x = 6$
14. Refer to the graph at the right. Find an equation for the perpendicular bisector of $\overline{PQ}$. (*Hint:* First find the midpoint of $\overline{PQ}$.) $y = x - 8$

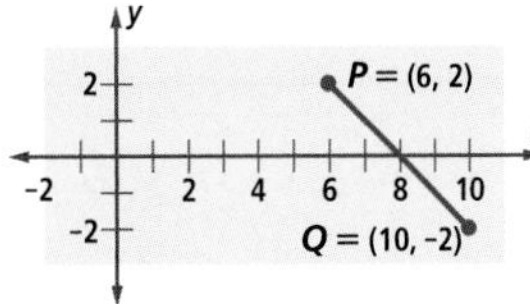

Notes on the Questions

Questions 12 and 13 These questions are computationally easier than the corresponding Questions 7 and 8, but students cannot use any ideas of slope to solve them.

Question 14 You might generalize the question to find an equation for the perpendicular bisector of the segment with endpoints (*a*, *b*) and (*c*, *d*). The midpoint is $\left(\frac{a+c}{2}, \frac{b+d}{2}\right)$, and the slope is the opposite of the reciprocal of $\frac{d-b}{c-a}$, so an equation is $y - \frac{b+d}{2} = \frac{a-c}{d-b}\left(x - \frac{a+c}{2}\right)$. Then have students check their answers using this formula. (For a related task—finding the distance between a point and a line—see the Extension on page 277.)

Additional Answers

10a.

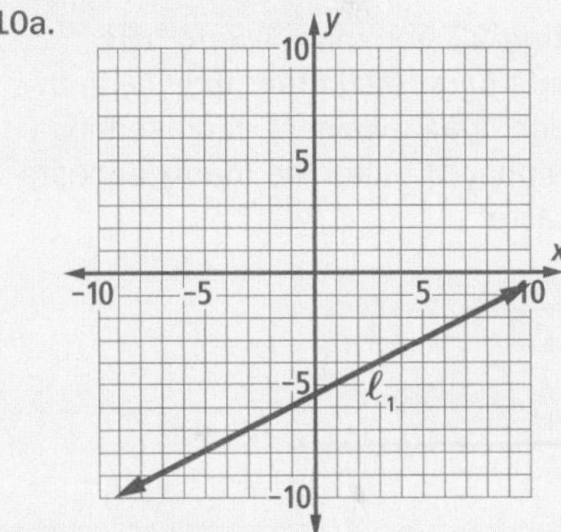

$M1 = \begin{bmatrix} 5 & 9 \\ -3 & -1 \end{bmatrix}$

10b. $M2 = \begin{bmatrix} 3 & 1 \\ 5 & 9 \end{bmatrix}$

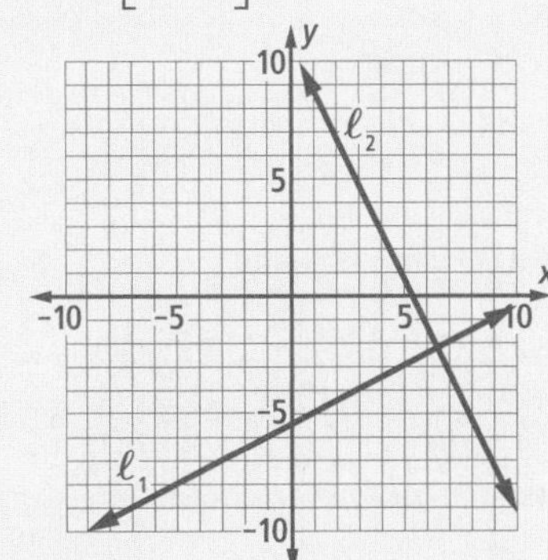

Yes, ℓ_1 and ℓ_2 are perpendicular.

Extension

Ask students to complete the following activities:

a. Describe the steps involved in calculating the distance between a line and a point. Answers vary. Sample: To find the distance between a line ℓ_1 and a point *P*, the steps are as follows: (1) Find an equation of the line ℓ_2 that contains *P* and is perpendicular to ℓ_1; (2) Find point *Q*, the intersection of ℓ_1 and ℓ_2; and (3) Find *QP*, the distance between *P* and *Q*.

b. Have students check their steps by calculating the distance between a given line such as $y = \frac{1}{2}x - 1$ and a point such as (6, 1). An equation for ℓ_2 is $y = -2x + 13$, so the point of intersection is $Q = (5.6, 1.8)$. The distance *PQ* is $\frac{2\sqrt{5}}{5}$ or approximately 0.894 units.

Notes on the Questions

Questions 17–20 Question 17 is a statement that parallelism possesses the transitive property. This is true for all lines ℓ, m, and n because we allow a line to be parallel to itself. A table with the results of these four questions looks very much like a table for the multiplication of positive and negative numbers. The results in the boxes give a relationship between ℓ and n.

m and *n*

ℓ and m	and	$\parallel$	$\perp$
	$\parallel$	$\parallel$	$\perp$
	$\perp$	$\perp$	$\parallel$

second number

first number	·	+	−
	+	+	−
	−	−	+

Question 22 You may have to help students understand that the "4" in this question is an exponent, representing the number of times the matrix appears as a factor.

Additional Answers

17b. Answers vary. Sample:

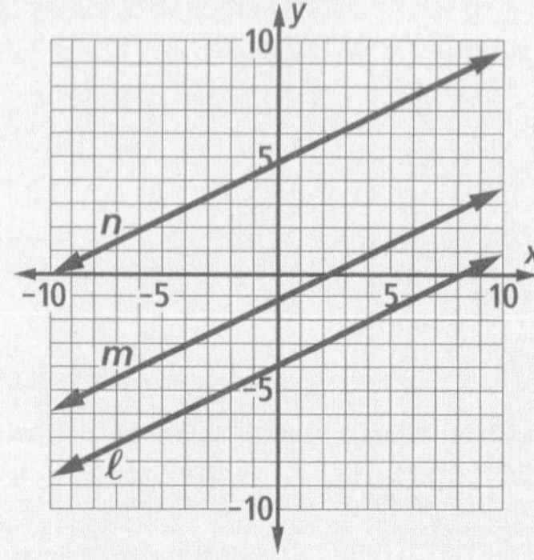

18b. Answers vary. Sample:

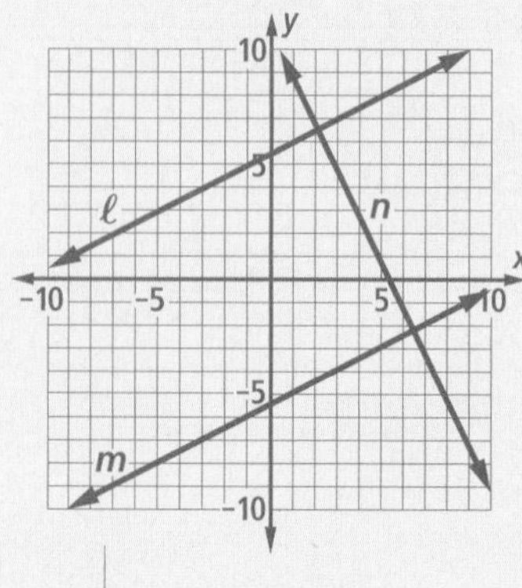

15. Let $A = (6, 2)$ and $B = (-5, 0)$.
    a. **Fill in the Blank** A counterclockwise rotation of 270° is the same as a clockwise rotation of __?__. 90°
    b. Find the coordinates of A' and B', the images of A and B under R_{270}. $A' = (2, -6)$ and $B' = (0, 5)$
    c. Find the slopes of $\overleftrightarrow{AB}$ and $\overleftrightarrow{A'B'}$.
    d. What relationship exists between the slopes? What does this tell you about the lines?

16. Consider $ABCD$, where $A = (0, 5)$, $B = (4, 3)$, $C = (1, -2)$, and $D = (-4, -1)$. Use the Perpendicular Lines and Slopes Theorem to determine if $ABCD$ is a rectangle.
not a rectangle because, for example, (slope of $\overline{AB}$)(slope of $\overline{DA}$) $\neq -1$

Fill in the Blanks In 17–20, assume all lines lie in the same plane.
   a. Fill each blank with $\parallel$ or $\perp$.
   b. Draw a picture to illustrate each situation.

17. If $\ell \parallel m$ and $m \parallel n$, then ℓ __?__ n. a. $\parallel$; b. See margin.
18. If $\ell \parallel m$ and $m \perp n$, then ℓ __?__ n. a. $\perp$; b. See margin.
19. If $\ell \perp m$ and $m \parallel n$, then ℓ __?__ n. a. $\perp$; b. See margin.
20. If $\ell \perp m$ and $m \perp n$, then ℓ __?__ n. a. $\parallel$; b. See margin.

21. If M is a matrix representing a line that does not contain the origin, tell if each operation on M gives a matrix representing a line that is parallel to M, perpendicular to M, or neither perpendicular nor parallel to M.
    a. $\begin{bmatrix} 0 & -1 \\ 1 & 0 \end{bmatrix} M$ perpendicular
    b. $\begin{bmatrix} 0 & 1 \\ 1 & 0 \end{bmatrix} M$ neither
    c. $3M$ parallel
    d. $\begin{bmatrix} -1 & 0 \\ 0 & -1 \end{bmatrix} M$ parallel
    e. $\begin{bmatrix} 3 & 3 \\ -5 & -5 \end{bmatrix} + M$ parallel
    f. $\begin{bmatrix} 3 & 0 \\ 0 & 5 \end{bmatrix} M$ neither

22. Without doing any computation, find $\begin{bmatrix} 0 & -1 \\ 1 & 0 \end{bmatrix}^4$. Explain how you know your answer is true.

Figures and their rotation images can be found in Hawaiian quilts, batik designs, and Celtic knots.

15c. slope of $\overleftrightarrow{AB} = \frac{2}{11}$; slope of $\overleftrightarrow{A'B'} = -\frac{11}{2}$

15d. (slope of $\overleftrightarrow{AB}$) • (slope of $\overleftrightarrow{A'B'}$) $= -1$, so the two lines are perpendicular.

22. $\begin{bmatrix} 1 & 0 \\ 0 & 1 \end{bmatrix}$; $90 \cdot 4 = 360$, so four 90° rotations return the figure to the original state.

Accommodating the Learner

Tell students that the matrix $\begin{bmatrix} -6 & 9 \\ -4 & 6 \end{bmatrix}$ represents two ordered pairs on the line with equation $y = \frac{2}{3}x$. Ask them to **(a)** use matrix multiplication to find the images of those two points after a rotation of 90°, **(b)** use matrix multiplication to find the images of the original two points after a roatation of 270°, and **(c)** show that each line determined in Parts a and b is perpendicular to the line with equation $y = \frac{2}{3}x$.

a. $\begin{bmatrix} 0 & -1 \\ 1 & 0 \end{bmatrix}\begin{bmatrix} -6 & 9 \\ -4 & 6 \end{bmatrix} = \begin{bmatrix} 4 & -6 \\ -6 & 9 \end{bmatrix}$;

b. $\begin{bmatrix} 0 & 1 \\ -1 & 0 \end{bmatrix}\begin{bmatrix} -6 & 9 \\ -4 & 6 \end{bmatrix} = \begin{bmatrix} -4 & 6 \\ 6 & -9 \end{bmatrix}$;

c. The slope of the line through (4, -6) and (-6, 9) is $-\frac{15}{10} = -\frac{3}{2}$, and the slope of the line through (-4, 6) and (6, -9) is $-\frac{15}{10} = -\frac{3}{2}$. Because $\left(-\frac{3}{2}\right)\left(\frac{2}{3}\right) = -1$, the two lines are perpendicular to the line with equation $y = \frac{2}{3}x$.

REVIEW

23. Find a matrix for $R_{80} \circ R_{80} \circ R_{200}$. **(Lesson 4-8)**

23. $\begin{bmatrix} 1 & 0 \\ 0 & 1 \end{bmatrix}$

24. a. Use a DGS to rotate the points (1, 0) and (0, 1) 80° about the origin. Find the coordinates of their image points. about (0.17, 0.98) and (–0.98, 0.17)

    b. Use the results of Part a to find an approximate matrix for R_{80}. **(Lessons 4-8, 4-6)**

24b. $\begin{bmatrix} 0.17 & -0.98 \\ 0.98 & 0.17 \end{bmatrix}$

25. **Multiple Choice** Which of the following is *not* a property of multiplication of 2 × 2 matrices? **(Lesson 4-7)** B

    A associativity
    B commutativity
    C existence of an identity
    D closure

26. Architects designing auditoriums use the fact that sound intensity I is inversely proportional to the square of the distance d from the sound source. **(Lessons 2-3, 2-2)**

    a. Write a variation equation that represents this situation. $I = \frac{k}{d^2}$

    b. A person moves to a seat that is 4 times as far from the sound source. How will the intensity of the sound be affected? intensity will be divided by 16

Sydney Opera House

EXPLORATION

27. a. Consider the lines with equations $\pi x + \sqrt{10}y = \sqrt[3]{6}$ and $\sqrt{10}x + \pi y = \sqrt[3]{6}$. How is the graph of one related to the graph of the other?

    b. Generalize Part a.

27a. The graphs are reflection images of each other over the line with equation $y = x$.

27b. Let A, B, and C be any real numbers. Then the graph of $Ax + By = C$ is the reflection image of the graph of $Bx + Ay = C$ over the line with equation $y = x$.

QY ANSWERS

1. $s = -2$

2. Yes; because $5(-0.2) = -1$, the lines are perpendicular.

4 Wrap-Up

Ongoing Assessment

Have students work in groups. The group should select two ordered pairs (not on a horizontal or vertical line). Then each student in the group should calculate (**1**) the slope of the line through the two points and (**2**) the slope of any line perpendicular to the line through the points. Answers vary. Check students' work.

Additional Answers

19b. Answers vary. Sample:

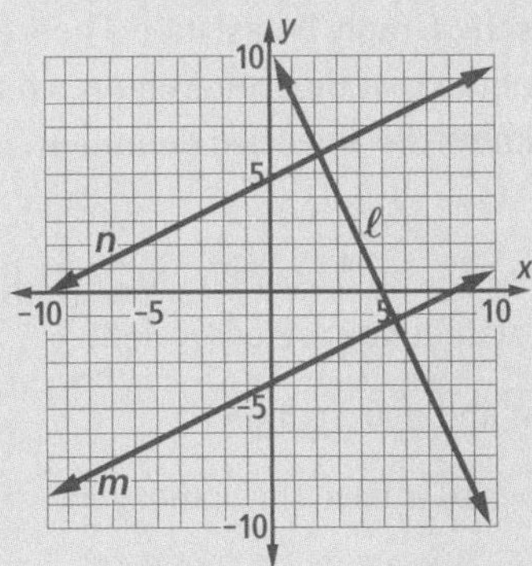

20b. Answers vary. Sample:

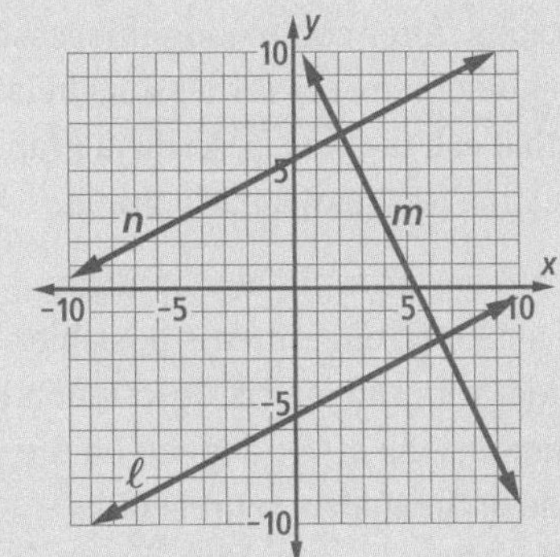

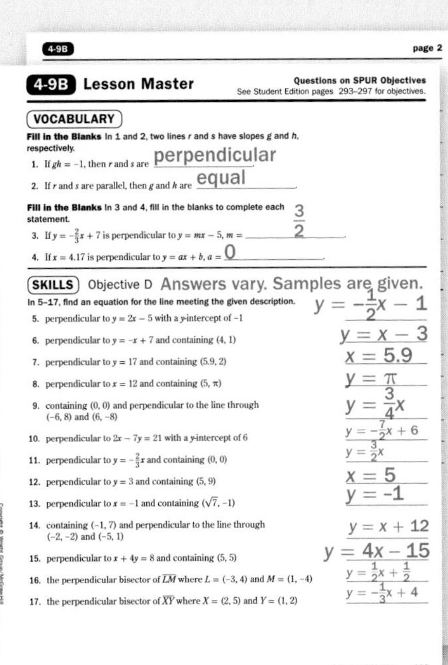

4-9B page 2

4-9B Lesson Master

Questions on SPUR Objectives
See Student Edition pages 293–297 for objectives.

VOCABULARY

Fill in the Blanks In 1 and 2, two lines r and s have slopes g and h, respectively.

1. If $gh = -1$, then r and s are perpendicular.
2. If r and s are parallel, then g and h are equal.

Fill in the Blanks In 3 and 4, fill in the blanks to complete each statement.

3. If $y = -\frac{2}{3}x + 7$ is perpendicular to $y = mx - 5$, $m =$ $\frac{3}{2}$.
4. If $x = 4.17$ is perpendicular to $y = ax + b$, $a =$ 0.

SKILLS Objective D Answers vary. Samples are given.

In 5–17, find an equation for the line meeting the given description.

5. perpendicular to $y = 2x - 5$ with a y-intercept of –1 $y = -\frac{1}{2}x - 1$
6. perpendicular to $y = -x + 7$ and containing (4, 1) $y = x - 3$
7. perpendicular to $y = 17$ and containing (5.9, 2) $x = 5.9$
8. perpendicular to $x = 12$ and containing $(5, \pi)$ $y = \pi$
9. containing (0, 0) and perpendicular to the line through (–6, 8) and (6, –8) $y = \frac{3}{4}x$
10. perpendicular to $2x - 7y = 21$ with a y-intercept of 6 $y = -\frac{7}{2}x + 6$
11. perpendicular to $y = -\frac{2}{3}x$ and containing (0, 0) $y = \frac{3}{2}x$
12. perpendicular to $y = 3$ and containing (5, 9) $x = 5$
13. perpendicular to $x = -1$ and containing $(\sqrt{7}, -1)$ $y = -1$
14. containing (–1, 7) and perpendicular to the line through (–2, –2) and (–5, 1) $y = x + 12$
15. perpendicular to $x + 4y = 8$ and containing (5, 5) $y = 4x - 15$
16. the perpendicular bisector of $\overline{LM}$ where $L = (-3, 4)$ and $M = (1, -4)$ $y = \frac{1}{2}x + \frac{1}{2}$
17. the perpendicular bisector of $\overline{XY}$ where $X = (2, 5)$ and $Y = (1, 2)$ $y = -\frac{1}{3}x + 4$

Advanced Algebra 225

Lesson

4-10

GOAL

Complete the study of the basic transformations and matrices; discuss translations; and provide another application of matrix addition.

SPUR Objectives

F Recognize relationships between figures and their translation images.

G Relate translations to matrices, and vice versa.

H Given their slopes, determine whether lines are parallel to each other, and vice versa.

K Graph figures and their translation images.

Materials/Resources

- Lesson Masters 4-10A and 4-10B
- Resource Masters 1 and 71–73

HOMEWORK

Suggestions for Assignment

- Questions 1–20
- Question 21 (extra credit)
- Self-Test

Local Standards

1 Warm-Up

1. Graph the polygon whose consecutive vertices are $\begin{bmatrix} 3 & 5 & 2 & -8 & -8 & 0 & 1 \\ -2 & 2 & 5 & 1 & -3 & -4 & -4 \end{bmatrix}$. Add the matrix $\begin{bmatrix} -2 & -2 & -2 & -2 & -2 & -2 & -2 \\ -3 & -3 & -3 & -3 & -3 & -3 & -3 \end{bmatrix}$ to the polygon matrix and graph the polygon whose image results. Answers vary. Sample:

(continued on next page)

Lesson

4-10 Translations and Parallel Lines

Vocabulary

translation

BIG IDEA By adding matrices, translation images of figures in the plane can be described.

In this chapter you have found images for many transformations by multiplying 2 × 2 matrices. There is one transformation for which images can be found by *adding* matrices.

Translations

Consider $\triangle ABC$ and its image $\triangle A'B'C'$ at the left below. Matrices M and M' representing the vertices of these triangles are given at the right below.

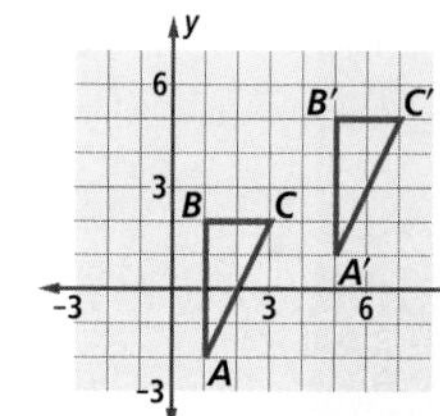

$\triangle ABC$

$$M = \begin{bmatrix} 1 & 1 & 3 \\ -2 & 2 & 2 \end{bmatrix}$$

$\triangle A'B'C'$

$$M' = \begin{bmatrix} 5 & 5 & 7 \\ 1 & 5 & 5 \end{bmatrix}$$

Activity

Use the matrices M and M' above.

Step 1. $D = \begin{bmatrix} 4 & 4 & 4 \\ 3 & 3 & 3 \end{bmatrix}$

Step 1 Calculate $D = M' - M$.

Step 2 What does the first row of D represent?

Step 3 What does the second row of D represent?

Step 4 Calculate $D + M$. What does $D + M$ represent?

Step 5 Complete this sentence: If (x, y) is any point in the preimage, then its image is ___?___. $(x + 4, y + 3)$

The transformation in the Activity is an example of a *translation* or *slide*.

Step 2. the difference in the x-coordinates of $\triangle ABC$ and $\triangle A'B'C'$

Step 3. the difference in the y-coordinates of $\triangle ABC$ and $\triangle A'B'C'$

Step 4. $D + M = \begin{bmatrix} 5 & 5 & 7 \\ 1 & 5 & 5 \end{bmatrix}$; $D + M$ represents $\triangle A'B'C'$, the image of $\triangle ABC$ shifted 4 units to the right and 3 units up.

Mental Math

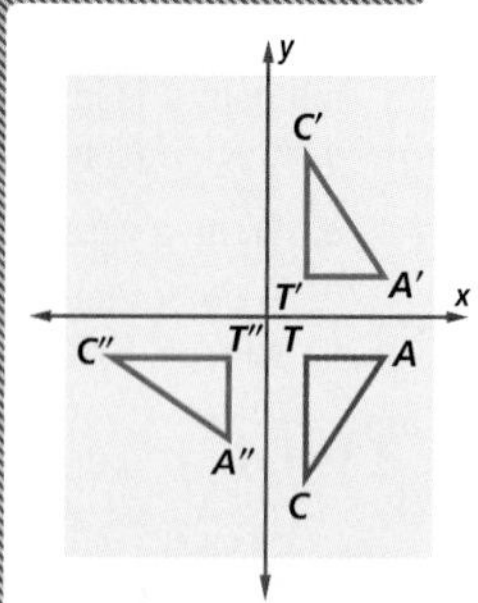

Use the graph above to identify the ransformation that maps

a. $\triangle CAT$ onto $\triangle C'A'T'$. r_x

b. $\triangle C'A'T'$ onto $\triangle C''A''T''$. $r_{y=-x}$

c. $\triangle CAT$ onto $\triangle C''A''T''$. R_{-90} or R_{270}

Background

Translations provide the most basic way to modify graphs. After completing this lesson, students should be ready for lessons in later chapters that ask them to describe a graph as a translation image of a basic graph.

It is easier to describe $T_{h,k}$ algebraically than with a matrix, but either is possible. The problem with the matrix description is that the dimensions of $T_{h,k}$ depend on the dimensions of the matrix representing preimage polygon. $T_{h,k}$ will have dimensions $2 \times n$, where n is the number of vertices in the polygon. Also, in Lesson 6-3, students encounter the Graph-Translation Theorem. Understanding that theorem requires that students know the algebraic definition of $T_{h,k}$.

Because a line can be parallel to itself, the following statements are equivalent:

- Lines m and n are parallel.
- Lines m and n have the same slope.
- Line n is a translation image of line m.

Definition of Translation

The transformation that maps (x, y) onto $(x + h, y + k)$ is a **translation** of h units horizontally and k units vertically, and is denoted by $T_{h,k}$.

Using mapping notation, $T_{h,k}$: $(x, y) \rightarrow (x + h, y + k)$.

Using $f(x)$ notation, $T_{h,k}(x, y) = (x + h, y + k)$.

In the figure on the previous page, $\triangle A'B'C'$ is the image of $\triangle ABC$ under the translation $T_{4,3}$.

Reading Math

The Latin prefix *trans* means "across." When we translate a geometric figure, we move it across the plane. Another term in this chapter with the same prefix is *transformation*.

Matrices for Translations

There is no single matrix representing a specific translation because the dimensions of the translation matrix depend on the figure being translated. Example 1 shows you how to find image coordinates with and without matrices.

GUIDED

Example 1

A quadrilateral has vertices $Q = (1, 1)$, $U = (6, 2)$, $A = (8, 4)$, and $D = (5, 5)$.

a. Find its image under the translation $T_{-8,2}$.

b. Graph the image and preimage on the same set of axes.

Solution

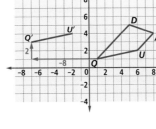

a. Using $f(x)$ notation:

$T_{-8,2}(x, y) = (x - 8, y + 2)$

$Q' = T_{-8,2}(1, 1) = (1 - 8, 1 + 2) = (-7, 3)$

$U' = T_{-8,2}(6, 2) = (\underline{?}, \underline{?}) = (-2, 4)$ 6 − 8; 2 + 2

$A' = T_{-8,2}(8, 4) = (\underline{?}, \underline{?}) = (\underline{?}, \underline{?})$ 8 − 8; 4 + 2; 0; 6

$D' = T_{-8,2}(5, 5) = (\underline{?}, \underline{?}) = (\underline{?}, \underline{?})$ 5 − 8; 5 + 2; -3; 7

To use matrices, construct the translation matrix by showing the point (-8, 2) in each of four columns.

$$\begin{matrix} T_{-8,2} & + & Q\ U\ A\ D & = & Q'\ U'\ A'\ D' \end{matrix}$$

$$\begin{bmatrix} -8 & -8 & \underline{?} & \underline{?} \\ 2 & 2 & \underline{?} & \underline{?} \end{bmatrix} + \begin{bmatrix} 1 & 6 & \underline{?} & \underline{?} \\ 1 & 2 & \underline{?} & \underline{?} \end{bmatrix} = \begin{bmatrix} -7 & -2 & \underline{?} & \underline{?} \\ 3 & 4 & \underline{?} & \underline{?} \end{bmatrix}$$

-8; -8; 8; 5; 0; -3
2; 2; 4; 5; 6; 7

b. $Q'U'A'D'$ is the image of $QUAD$ under a translation 8 units to the left and 2 units up. Copy and complete the graph shown above. See margin.

STOP QY

QY

Calculate the slopes of $\overleftrightarrow{QU}$ and $\overleftrightarrow{Q'U'}$. What is the relationship between $\overleftrightarrow{QU}$ and $\overleftrightarrow{Q'U'}$?

The last of these statements, which is studied in this lesson, is key in graphing. For instance,

- The line with equation $y = mx + b$ is the image of the line with equation $y = mx$ under $T_{0,b}$.
- The sine curve with equation $y = \sin(x - b)$ is the image of the sine curve with equation $y = \sin x$ under $T_{b,0}$.
- The parabola with equation $y = a(x - h)^2 + k$ is the image of the parabola with equation $y = ax^2$ under $T_{h,k}$.
- The circle $(x - h)^2 + (y - k)^2 = r^2$ is the image of $x^2 + y^2 = r^2$ under $T_{h,k}$.

The last two statements are common in many textbooks, and it is because of them that we have chosen the letters h and k to represent the horizontal and vertical slides in a two-dimensional translation.

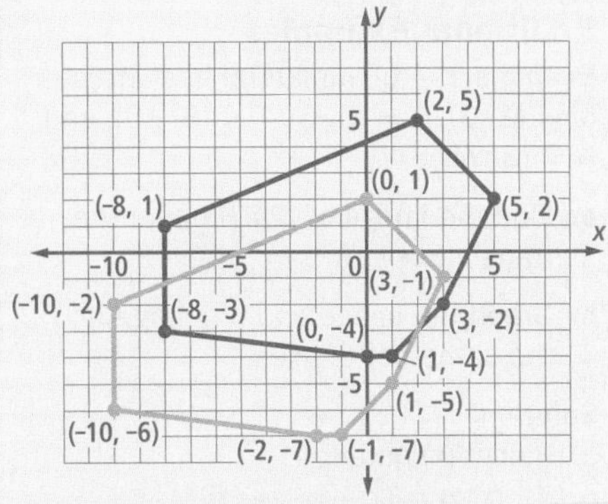

2. How are the two polygons in Warm-Up 1 related? Polygon $\begin{bmatrix} 1 & 3 & 0 & -10 & -10 & -2 & -1 \\ -5 & -1 & 2 & -2 & -6 & -7 & -7 \end{bmatrix}$ is the image of the original polygon under the translation that maps (x, y) onto $(x - 2, y - 3)$.

2 Teaching

Notes on the Lesson

It may help students to visualize the image of a figure under the translation $T_{h,k}$ if they think of $T_{h,k}$ as "sliding" the figure h units to the right (to the left if h is negative) and k units up (down if k is negative). However, emphasize to students that there is no physical sliding. The translation, like all other transformations, is simply a correspondence between a figure and its image.

This lesson provides a natural opportunity to summarize the ideas of the chapter. Review with students that transformations may be described *algebraically* (with a formula for the image (x', y') in terms of (x, y)), *arithmetically* (with a matrix), or *geometrically* (by indicating the location of image points without using coordinates). It may be worthwhile to discuss what students see as the strengths and weaknesses of each definition.

Point out to students that unlike the other transformations encountered in this chapter, translations cannot be done by multiplying by a 2 × 2 matrix. They should remember that any transformation by a 2 × 2 matrix must map (0, 0) onto itself, and the only translation that does so is $T_{0,0}$, the identity transformation.

Note-Taking Tips

Encourage students to record translations using both types of notation: $T_{a,b}$ and matrix addition.

Additional Examples

Example 1 A quadrilateral has vertices $M = (1, 3)$, $A = (5, 6)$, $T = (8, 10)$, and $H = (3, 7)$.

a. Find the image of *MATH* under the translation $T_{6,-9}$.

b. Graph the image and preimage on the same set of axes.

Solution

a. Using *f*(*x*) notation,
$T_{6,-9}(x, y) = (x + 6, y - 9)$.
$M' = T_{6,-9}(1, 3) =$
$(1 + 6, 3 - 9) = (7, -6)$
$A' = T_{6,-9}(5, 6) =$
(__?__, __?__) = (11, -3)
5 + 6; 6 − 9
$T' = T_{6,-9}(8, 10) =$
(__?__, __?__) =
(__?__, __?__)
8 + 6; 10 − 9; 14; 1
$H' = T_{6,-9}(3, 7) =$
(__?__, __?__) =
(__?__, __?__)
3 + 6; 7 − 9; 9; -2]

b. *M′A′T′H′* is the image of *MATH* under a translation of 6 units right and 9 units down.

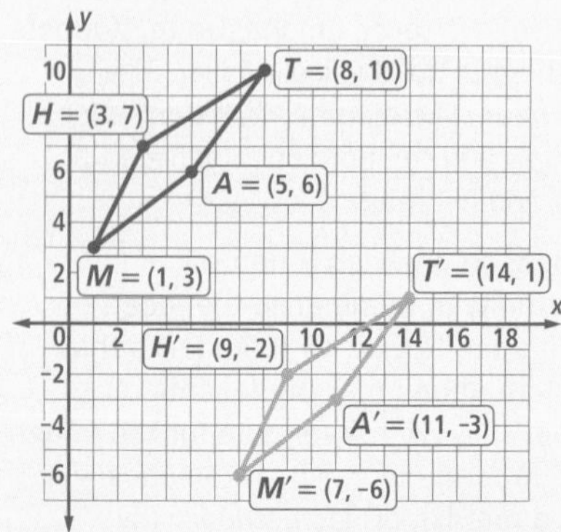

Example 2 Find the image of the line with equation $y = -2x + 7$ under the translation $T_{-4,5}$.

Solution Because the image is parallel to the original line, the slopes are equal. So, the slope of the image is __?__. -2 Pick a point on the original line. An easy one is (0, 7). Its translation image is $T_{-4,5}(0, 7)$ = (__?__, __?__). -4; 12 Using the Point-Slope Theorem, an equation for the line is *y* = __?__(*x* − __?__) + __?__. -2; -4; 12 So an equation of the line is *y* = __?__*x* + __?__. -2; 4

Properties of Translation Images

The QY illustrates a special case of the following more general result.

Parallel Lines and Translations Theorem

Under a translation, a preimage line is parallel to its image.

Proof Let $P = (x_1, y_1)$ and $Q = (x_2, y_2)$ be two different points on the line $\overleftrightarrow{PQ}$. The image of the line under $T_{h,k}$ contains the points P' and Q' such that $P' = (x_1 + h, y_1 + k)$ and $Q' = (x_2 + h, y_2 + k)$.

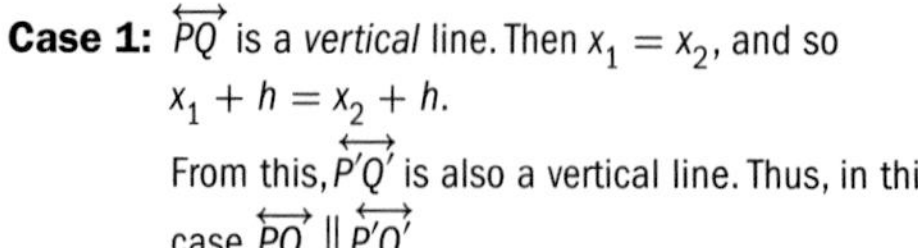

Case 1: $\overleftrightarrow{PQ}$ is a *vertical* line. Then $x_1 = x_2$, and so $x_1 + h = x_2 + h$.
From this, $\overleftrightarrow{P'Q'}$ is also a vertical line. Thus, in this case $\overleftrightarrow{PQ} \parallel \overleftrightarrow{P'Q'}$.

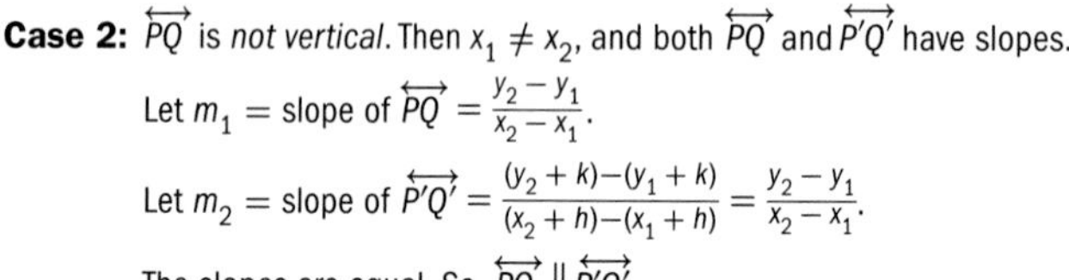

Case 2: $\overleftrightarrow{PQ}$ is *not vertical*. Then $x_1 \neq x_2$, and both $\overleftrightarrow{PQ}$ and $\overleftrightarrow{P'Q'}$ have slopes.

Let m_1 = slope of $\overleftrightarrow{PQ} = \frac{y_2 - y_1}{x_2 - x_1}$.

Let m_2 = slope of $\overleftrightarrow{P'Q'} = \frac{(y_2 + k) - (y_1 + k)}{(x_2 + h) - (x_1 + h)} = \frac{y_2 - y_1}{x_2 - x_1}$.

The slopes are equal. So, $\overleftrightarrow{PQ} \parallel \overleftrightarrow{P'Q'}$.

This theorem lets you easily find an equation for a translation image of a line.

Architect Frank Lloyd Wright used many parallel lines in designing his houses as seen in his Robie House above.

GUIDED

Example 2

Find the image of the line with equation $y = 3x - 5$ under the translation $T_{2,-1}$.

Solution Because the image is parallel to the original line, the slopes are equal. So, the slope of the image is __?__. 3

Pick a point on the original line. An easy one is (0, –5). Its translation image is $T_{2,-1}(0, -5)$ = (__?__, __?__). 2; -6

Using the Point-Slope Theorem, an equation for the line is
y = __?__(*x* − __?__) + __?__. 3; 2; -6

So an equation of the line is *y* = __?__*x* + __?__. 3; -12

Additional Answers

Example 1

b.

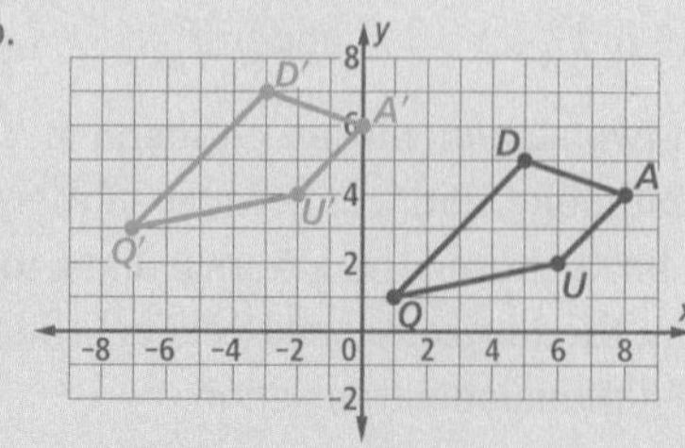

ENGLISH LEARNERS

Vocabulary Development

This lesson provides a natural opportunity to review the terms *reflection, rotation,* and *translation,* along with how to represent those transformations as matrices and as mappings.

Questions

COVERING THE IDEAS

1. Refer to $\triangle ABC$ and $\triangle A'B'C'$ at the beginning of the lesson. Using $f(x)$ notation, describe the translation that maps
   a. $\triangle ABC$ onto $\triangle A'B'C'$.
   b. $\triangle A'B'C'$ onto $\triangle ABC$.

2. **Fill in the Blank** A translation $T_{h,k}$ is a transformation mapping (x, y) onto __?__. $(x + h, y + k)$

3. **Fill in the Blanks** $T_{h,k}$ is a translation of __?__ units horizontally and __?__ units vertically. h; k

4. Find the image of the point under $T_{5,-7}$.
   a. (0, 0) (5, -7)
   b. (-50, 83) (-45, 76)
   c. (a, b) $(a + 5, b - 7)$

5. Consider $\triangle PQR$ represented by the matrix $\begin{bmatrix} 4 & 12 & -5 \\ -3 & 0 & 7 \end{bmatrix}$. Use matrix addition to find a matrix for $\triangle P'Q'R'$, the image of $\triangle PQR$ under a translation 7 units to the left and 2 units down.

6. The matrix $\begin{bmatrix} 7 & 2 & 1 & -1 & 4 \\ 2 & 13 & 8 & 4 & -5 \end{bmatrix}$ represents pentagon $AHMED$.
   a. Apply the translation $T_{-3,8}$ to the pentagon. Call the image $A'H'M'E'D'$. b. See margin.
   b. Graph the preimage and the image on the same set of axes.
   c. Verify that $AA' = HH'$. $AA' = \sqrt{73} = HH'$
   d. Why is the result in Part c not a surprise?

7. Refer to Example 1.
   a. What is the slope of $\overleftrightarrow{QA}$? $\frac{3}{7}$
   b. What is the slope of $\overleftrightarrow{Q'A'}$? $\frac{3}{7}$
   c. Is $\overleftrightarrow{QA} \parallel \overleftrightarrow{Q'A'}$? Justify your answer.

8. Suppose lines ℓ_1 and ℓ_2 are not parallel. Can they be translation images of each other? Explain your reasoning.

9. Refer to the graph at the right.
   a. What translation maps $ABCDE$ onto $A'B'C'D'E'$? $T_{2,-4}$
   b. Verify that $\overline{BC} \parallel \overline{B'C'}$.
   c. Verify that $BC = B'C'$.
   d. $BB'C'C$ is what kind of quadrilateral? parallelogram

10. Consider the line with equation $y = -2x + 7$. Find an equation for the image of this line under $T_{-4,5}$. $y = -2x + 4$

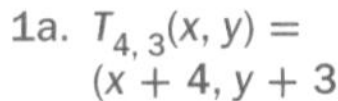

1a. $T_{4,3}(x, y) = (x + 4, y + 3)$

1b. $T_{-4,-3}(x, y) = (x - 4, y - 3)$

5. $\begin{bmatrix} -3 & 5 & -12 \\ -5 & -2 & 5 \end{bmatrix}$

6a. $\begin{bmatrix} 4 & -1 & -2 & -4 & 1 \\ 10 & 21 & 16 & 12 & 3 \end{bmatrix}$

6d. Answers vary. Sample: Each point on the preimage moves the same distance to get to its image.

7c. Yes; their slopes are equal so the two lines are parallel.

8. No: translations do not affect the slopes of lines. Image lines and preimage lines are parallel.

9b. slope of $\overline{BC}$ = slope of $\overline{B'C'} = -\frac{2}{3}$

9c. $BC = B'C' = \sqrt{13}$

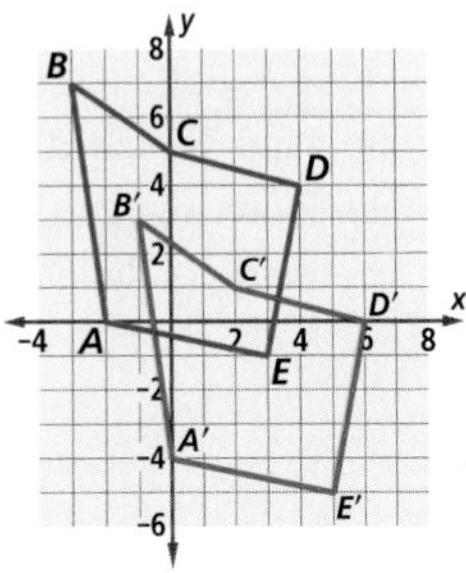

4-10

3 Assignment

Recommended Assignment

- Questions 1–20
- Question 21 (extra credit)
- Self-Test

Notes on the Questions

Question 9 Only one point and its translation image are needed to determine a translation. Students should describe the translation by giving an algebraic formula for the image of (x, y), and they should know what the translation does geometrically; that is, how far horizontally and vertically the image is from the preimage.

Additional Answers

6b.

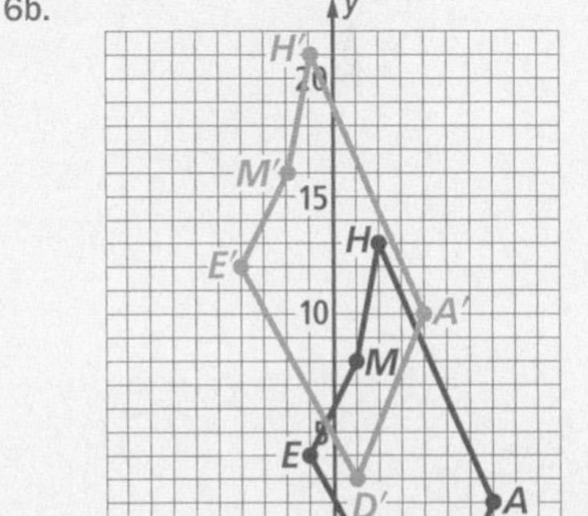

Accommodating the Learner

Show students the diagram below of a figure translated by r units along a line that forms an angle of $\theta°$ with a horizontal line.

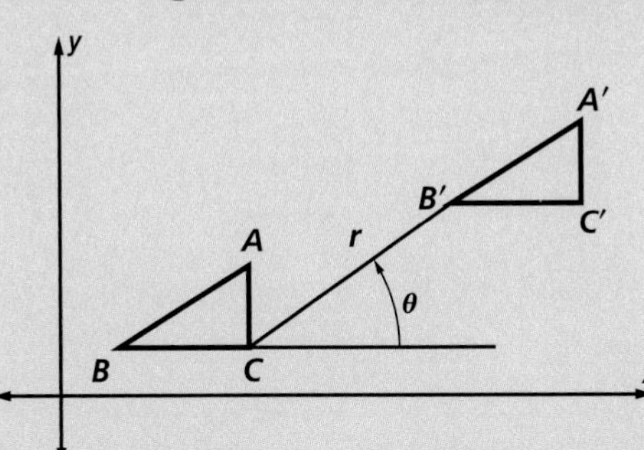

Ask students to express the translation in the form $T_{h,k}$. $T_{r \cdot \cos\theta, r \cdot \sin\theta}$

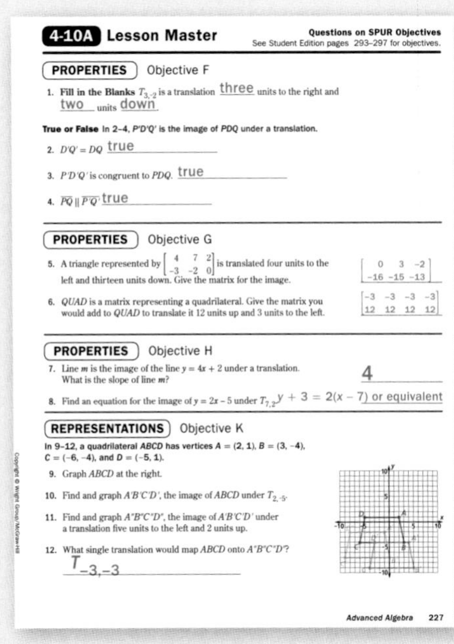

4-10A Lesson Master

Questions on SPUR Objectives
See Student Edition pages 293–297 for objectives.

PROPERTIES Objective F

1. **Fill in the Blanks** $T_{3,-2}$ is a translation three units to the right and two units down.

True or False In 2–4, $P'D'Q'$ is the image of PDQ under a translation.

2. $D'Q' = DQ$ true
3. $P'D'Q'$ is congruent to PDQ. true
4. $\overline{PQ} \parallel \overline{P'Q'}$ true

PROPERTIES Objective G

5. A triangle represented by $\begin{bmatrix} 4 & 7 & 2 \\ -3 & -2 & 0 \end{bmatrix}$ is translated four units to the left and thirteen units down. Give the matrix for the image. $\begin{bmatrix} 0 & 3 & -2 \\ -16 & -15 & -13 \end{bmatrix}$
6. $QUAD$ is a matrix representing a quadrilateral. Give the matrix you would add to $QUAD$ to translate it 12 units up and 3 units to the left. $\begin{bmatrix} -3 & -3 & -3 & -3 \\ 12 & 12 & 12 & 12 \end{bmatrix}$

PROPERTIES Objective H

7. Line m is the image of the line $y = 4x + 2$ under a translation. What is the slope of line m? 4
8. Find an equation for the image of $y = 2x - 5$ under $T_{7,2}$. $y + 3 = 2(x - 7)$ or equivalent

REPRESENTATIONS Objective K

In 9–12, a quadrilateral $ABCD$ has vertices $A = (2, 1)$, $B = (3, -4)$, $C = (-6, -4)$, and $D = (-5, 1)$.

9. Graph $ABCD$ at the right.
10. Find and graph $A'B'C'D'$, the image of $ABCD$ under $T_{2,-5}$.
11. Find and graph $A''B''C''D''$, the image of $A'B'C'D'$ under a translation five units to the left and 2 units up.
12. What single translation would map $ABCD$ onto $A''B''C''D''$? $T_{-3,-3}$

Advanced Algebra 227

Notes on the Questions

Question 11 A generalization from this question is that the composite of any two translations is commutative and so is the composite of any two rotations with the same center. However, a composite of a rotation and a translation is *not* commutative.

APPLYING THE MATHEMATICS

11. Under $T_{-2,5}$ the image of $\triangle CUB$ is $\triangle C'U'B'$. $\triangle C'U'B'$ is then translated under $T_{7,3}$ to get $\triangle C''U''B''$. a. $T_{5,8}$
    a. What single translation will give the same result as $T_{7,3} \circ T_{-2,5}$?
    b. Is $T_{7,3} \circ T_{-2,5} = T_{-2,5} \circ T_{7,3}$? yes
    c. In general, is the composition of two translations commutative? Why or why not? yes, because matrix addition is commutative

12. Line ℓ has the equation $y = 3x - 7$. Line ℓ' is the image of ℓ under a translation.
    a. If ℓ' contains the point (0, 5), find an equation for ℓ'. $y = 3x + 5$
    b. Give an example of a translation that maps line ℓ onto line ℓ'. Answers vary. Sample: $T_{0,12}$

13. In chess, each knight can move 2 squares vertically or horizontally and then one square at a right angle to the first part of its move. In the figure at the right, the black knight can move to any of the places occupied by a white pawn. As a translation, two of the knight's possible moves can be written as $T_{2,1}$ (two squares right and one square up) and $T_{-1,2}$ (one square left and two squares up). The knight has 6 other possible moves; write them as translations. $T_{-2,-1}, T_{-2,1}, T_{1,2}, T_{1,-2}, T_{-1,-2}, T_{2,-1}$

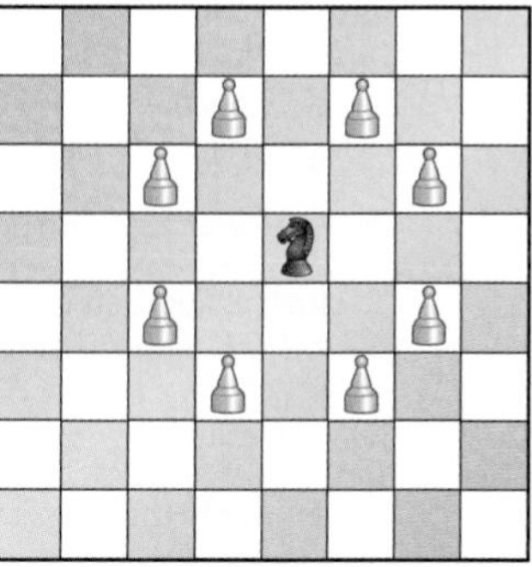

14. Consider the segments $\overline{QU}$ and $\overline{Q'U'}$ from Example 1.
    a. Find the lengths of both segments. How do they compare?
    b. Do you think it is generally true that a segment and its image under a translation are congruent? If so, try to prove it.
    c. Are there any other transformations under which a segment and its image are congruent? If so, which ones?

15. a. Find the image of the ordered pair (x, y) under $T_{h,k} \circ R_{90}$ and $R_{90} \circ T_{h,k}$. $(-y + h, x + k)$; $(-y - k, x + h)$
    b. Is translating a rotation image of a point the same as rotating its translation image? Why or why not?

14a. $QU = Q'U' = \sqrt{26}$

14b. Yes; by definition, segments and figures are congruent if one can be mapped onto the other by an isometry, and a translation is an isometry.

14c. Yes; rotations and reflections

15b. No; the two images in Part a are not equal.

REVIEW

16. Let $A = (2, 1)$ and $B = (-4, 4)$. Let $A' = R_{90}(A)$ and $B' = R_{90}(B)$. (Lessons 4-9, 4-8)
    a. Find the coordinates of A' and B'. $A' = (-1, 2)$, $B' = (-4, -4)$
    b. Find equations for $\overleftrightarrow{AB}$ and $\overleftrightarrow{A'B'}$. $y = -\frac{1}{2}x + 2$; $y = 2x + 4$
    c. Find the slopes of the two lines and verify that their product is -1. $2\left(-\frac{1}{2}\right) = -1$

Accommodating the Learner

$\triangle ABC$ is translated by $T_{5,-3}$ to $\triangle A'B'C'$, so that $A' = (4, 4)$, $B' = (7, 5)$, and $C' = (9, 9)$. Then $\triangle A'B'C'$ is translated by $T_{a,b}$ to $\triangle A''B''C''$, so that $A'' = (1, -2)$, $B'' = (4, -1)$, and $C'' = (6, 3)$. Find the values of a and b and the coordinates of the vertices of $\triangle ABC$. $a = -3$; $b = -6$; $A = (-1, 7)$; $B = (2, 8)$; $C = (4, 12)$

17. A rotation of 180° can be considered as the composite of two rotations of 90° or as the composite of a reflection over the x-axis followed by a reflection over the y-axis. **(Lessons 4-7, 4-6, 4-3)**
    a. Compute $N \cdot N$, where $N = \begin{bmatrix} 0 & -1 \\ 1 & 0 \end{bmatrix}$ is the matrix for R_{90}.
    b. Compute $\begin{bmatrix} 1 & 0 \\ 0 & -1 \end{bmatrix} \cdot \begin{bmatrix} -1 & 0 \\ 0 & 1 \end{bmatrix}$. Do you get the same answer as in Part a?

17a. $\begin{bmatrix} -1 & 0 \\ 0 & -1 \end{bmatrix}$

17b. $\begin{bmatrix} -1 & 0 \\ 0 & -1 \end{bmatrix}$; yes

18. Consider the line with equation $2x - 3y = 12$. **(Lessons 4-6, 3-3)**
    a. Find the x- and y-intercepts of this line. 6, –4
    b. Find the images of the x- and y-intercept points under R_{90}. (0, 6), (4, 0)
    c. Write an equation in standard form for the line that contains the two points from Part b. $3x + 2y = 12$

19. The Central High School debate team is selling T-shirts to raise money. They are selling small, medium, and large shirts in blue, grey, and tan. **(Lessons 4-2, 4-1)**
    a. The debate team ordered 8 of each color in small, 12 of each in medium, and 8 of each in large. Write a matrix to represent their T-shirt inventory.
    b. The first five customers bought 2 medium blue T-shirts, 1 medium grey T-shirt, 1 large grey T-shirt, and 1 small tan T-shirt. Write a matrix to represent these T-shirt purchases.
    c. Use matrix subtraction to write a matrix that represents the T-shirt inventory after the first five purchases.

This T-shirt has a logo that can be read both as printed and when it is rotated 180°.

19a.

	blue	grey	tan
S	8	8	8
M	12	12	12
L	8	8	8

19b. $\begin{bmatrix} 0 & 0 & 1 \\ 2 & 1 & 0 \\ 0 & 1 & 0 \end{bmatrix}$

19c. $\begin{bmatrix} 8 & 8 & 7 \\ 10 & 11 & 12 \\ 8 & 7 & 8 \end{bmatrix}$

20. At Mimi's Pizzeria, a large pizza costs \$8, and each additional topping costs \$0.90. Write an equation describing the total cost y of a large pizza with x toppings. Graph the resulting line, and label the y-intercept. **(Lesson 3-1)** $y = 0.9x + 8$
    See margin for graph.

EXPLORATION

21. Using translations you can find a rule for finding image points for a rotation of 90° with any point as center. Consider the rotation of 90° with center (–3, –1). Let (x, y) be any point.
    a. What is the image of (x, y) under the translation that maps (–3, –1) onto (0, 0)? $(x + 3, y + 1)$
    b. What is the image of your answer to Part a under a rotation of 90° about the origin? $(-y - 1, x + 3)$
    c. What is the image of your answer to Part b under the translation that maps (0, 0) onto (–3, –1)? $(-y - 4, x + 2)$
    d. Check that your answer to Part c is the image of (x, y) under a rotation of 90° about (–3, –1). See margin.

QY ANSWER

The slope of each line is $\frac{1}{5}$. They are parallel.

Extension

Suppose a figure is transformed by a composite of a scale change and a translation. Does it matter which transformation is performed first? Explain.

Yes; the order does matter. Consider the scale change $S_{a,b}$ and the translation $T_{h,k}$. Applying the scale change first to a point (x, y), the final image of (x, y) is $T_{h,k} \circ S_{a,b}(x, y) = T_{h,k}(ax, by) = (ax + h, by + k)$. Applying the translation first, the final image of (x, y) is $S_{a,b} \circ T_{h,k}(x, y) = S_{a,b}(x + h, y + k) = (ax + ah, by + bk)$. So $S_{a,b} \circ T_{h,k} \neq T_{h,k} \circ S_{a,b}$.

Additional Answers

20.

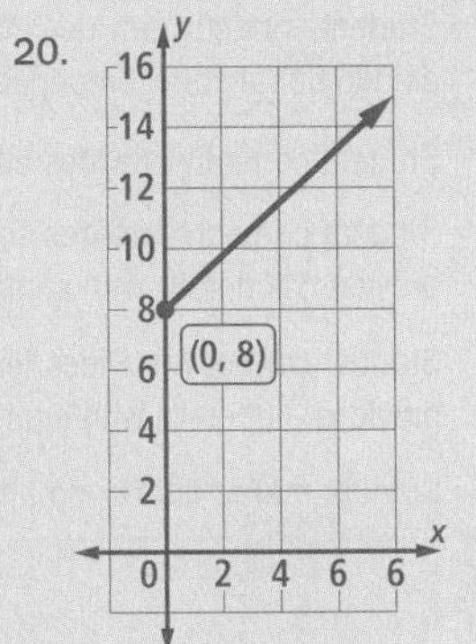

4 Wrap-Up

Ongoing Assessment

Give students the vertices of a quadrilateral and several translations, each of the form $T_{a,b}$. Ask students to write the vertices of the image of the given quadrilateral under each translation. Answers vary. Check students' work.

Additional Answers

21d. Let $(x, y) = (0, 0)$. Then my answer to Part c is (–4, 2). The two points are graphed below as P and P', along with the center of rotation, $O = (-3, -1)$. The slope of $\overleftrightarrow{PO}$ is $\frac{1}{3}$ and the slope of $\overleftrightarrow{P'O}$ is –3. So $m\angle P'OP$ is 90°. Additionally, $PO = OP' = \sqrt{10}$. So, P' is the image of P under a rotation of 90° about (–3, –1).

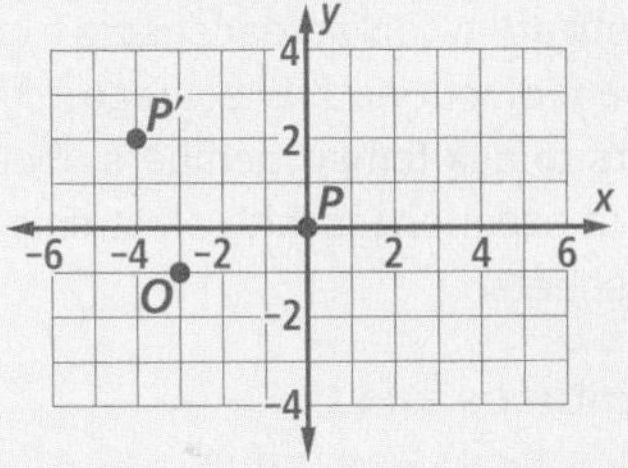

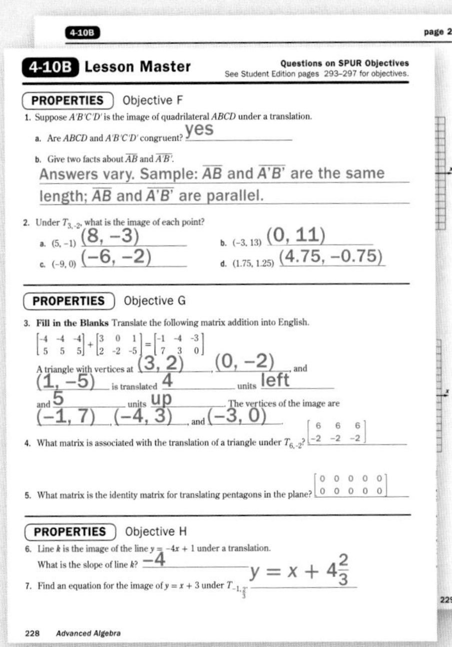

4-10B page 2

4-10B Lesson Master

Questions on SPUR Objectives
See Student Edition pages 293–297 for objectives.

PROPERTIES Objective F

1. Suppose $A'B'C'D'$ is the image of quadrilateral $ABCD$ under a translation.
   a. Are $ABCD$ and $A'B'C'D'$ congruent? yes
   b. Give two facts about $\overline{AB}$ and $\overline{A'B'}$.
   Answers vary. Sample: $\overline{AB}$ and $\overline{A'B'}$ are the same length; $\overline{AB}$ and $\overline{A'B'}$ are parallel.
2. Under $T_{3,-2}$, what is the image of each point?
   a. (5, –1) (8, –3)
   b. (–3, 13) (0, 11)
   c. (–9, 0) (–6, –2)
   d. (1.75, 1.25) (4.75, –0.75)

PROPERTIES Objective G

3. **Fill in the Blanks** Translate the following matrix addition into English.
   $\begin{bmatrix} -4 & -4 & -4 \\ 5 & 5 & 5 \end{bmatrix} + \begin{bmatrix} 3 & 0 & 1 \\ 2 & -2 & -5 \end{bmatrix} = \begin{bmatrix} -1 & -4 & -3 \\ 7 & 3 & 0 \end{bmatrix}$
   A triangle with vertices at (3, 2), (0, –2), and (1, –5) is translated 4 units left and 5 units up. The vertices of the image are (–1, 7), (–4, 3), and (–3, 0).
4. What matrix is associated with the translation of a triangle under $T_{6,-2}$? $\begin{bmatrix} 6 & 6 & 6 \\ -2 & -2 & -2 \end{bmatrix}$
5. What matrix is the identity matrix for translating pentagons in the plane? $\begin{bmatrix} 0 & 0 & 0 & 0 & 0 \\ 0 & 0 & 0 & 0 & 0 \end{bmatrix}$

PROPERTIES Objective H

6. Line k is the image of the line $y = -4x + 1$ under a translation. What is the slope of line k? –4
7. Find an equation for the image of $y = x + 3$ under $T_{-1,\frac{2}{3}}$. $y = x + 4\frac{2}{3}$

228 *Advanced Algebra* 229

Chapter 4

The projects relate to the content of the lessons of this chapter as follows:

Project	Lesson(s)
1	4-1
2	4-3
3	4-8
4	4-3
5	4-1
6	4-3

1 History of Matrices

A spreadsheet is a type of matrix, and, as an extension, ask students to investigate when spreadsheets first "went electronic." Encourage students to ask family members about their first experiences with electronic spreadsheets.

2 Matrices and the Fibonacci Sequence

As an extension, ask students to repeat Part a for $P = \begin{bmatrix} a \\ b \end{bmatrix}$ and describe the results. $A \cdot P = \begin{bmatrix} b \\ a + b \end{bmatrix}$, $A \cdot A \cdot P = \begin{bmatrix} a + b \\ 2a + b \end{bmatrix}$, $A^3 \cdot P = \begin{bmatrix} 2a + b \\ 3a + 2b \end{bmatrix}$, $A^4 \cdot P = \begin{bmatrix} 3a + 2b \\ 5a + 3b \end{bmatrix}$; in each matrix, the coefficients of a and b are consecutive terms in the Fibonacci sequence.

3 Pitch, Yaw, and Roll

Ask students to include, in their reports, descriptions of the center for each type of rotation and when each type of rotation is "positive" or "negative."

4 Transpose of a Matrix

As an extension, ask students to repeat the activity for a 3 × 3 matrix.

Chapter 4 Projects

1 History of Matrices

Investigate the development of matrices and the early work of Arthur Cayley and James Sylvester in the mid 1800s.

a. For what purposes were matrices used before they were given that name?

b. When were matrices first used to describe transformations?

c. What other mathematicians and terms are associated with the history and use of matrices?

Arthur Cayley

James Sylvester

2 Matrices and the Fibonacci Sequence

Let $A = \begin{bmatrix} 0 & 1 \\ 1 & 1 \end{bmatrix}$ and $P = \begin{bmatrix} 1 \\ 1 \end{bmatrix}$.

a. Calculate $A \cdot P$, $A \cdot A \cdot P$, $A \cdot A \cdot A \cdot P$, and $A \cdot A \cdot A \cdot A \cdot P$.

b. What do the calculations you did in Part a have to do with the Fibonacci sequence? Explain why this happens.

c. Use matrices to find the first 10 terms of the sequence a_n such that $a_1 = 3$, $a_2 = 4$, and $a_n = 3a_{n-1} + 2a_{n-2}$ for $n \geq 3$.

3 Pitch, Yaw, and Roll

Rotations are not limited to the two-dimensional coordinate plane. In order to keep their aircrafts properly oriented in space, pilots need to pay attention to *attitude, pitch, yaw,* and *roll.* Research these terms and explain how they relate to rotations in three dimensions.

4 Transpose of a Matrix

The *transpose* of a matrix M is a matrix M^T in which the rows and columns of M are switched. For example, the transpose of matrix $A = \begin{bmatrix} 1 & 2 \\ 3 & 4 \end{bmatrix}$ is $A^T = \begin{bmatrix} 1 & 2 \\ 3 & 4 \end{bmatrix}^T = \begin{bmatrix} 1 & 3 \\ 2 & 4 \end{bmatrix}$. Use a CAS to explore the following.

a. Find $(A^T)^T$. What does this suggest about the transpose of a transpose matrix?

b. Define a 2 × 2 matrix B and explore the connection between $A^T + B^T$ and $(A + B)^T$. What do you notice?

c. Using the same matrix B, explore the products $(AB)^T$, A^TB^T, and B^TA^T. What do you notice?

d. Is there a 2 × 2 matrix C such that $C^T = C$? Explain your answer.

e. Does a matrix have to be square to have a transpose? Give an example to support your answer. Do the properties in Parts a–d apply to nonsquare matrices?

Project Rubric

Advanced	Student correctly provides all of the details asked for in the project as well as additional correct independent conclusions.
Proficient	Student correctly provides all of the details asked for in the project.
Partially proficient	Student correctly provides some of the details asked for in the project or provides all details with some inaccuracies.
Not proficient	Student correctly provides few of the details asked for in the project or provides all details with many inaccuracies.
No attempt	Student makes little or no attempt to complete the project.

5 Computer Graphics

One application of matrices is in computer graphics. A graphic image is divided into a matrix of pixels, each of which is typically assigned three values: hue (or color), saturation (purity of the color), and intensity (brightness). For example, a 5×5 matrix of pixels represents an image with 25 pixels. If you use a 10-point gray scale (10 hues), you could assign each pixel a value from 1 to 10 that represents the picture's level of grayness, where $1 =$ white and $10 =$ black.

a. Find a black-and-white picture and overlay a 5-by-5 grid on it. Use a 10-point scale to assign each entry in the resulting matrix a value based on an average level of grayness in the grid square.

b. Using only your matrix and a blank 5-by-5 grid, recreate the picture using the levels of grayness you assigned. You will notice that the resolution of your image is not very good. How could you improve your resolution?

c. Computers use a grid that is much finer (has more pixels) and are able to assign values based on color rather than just shades of gray. Research what size grids are used and what properties are numerically assigned to pixels of a graphic.

6 Predicting the Weather

Matrix multiplication can be used to forecast the weather. Suppose the probability of rain or sunshine on a given day depends on the weather the previous day as shown in matrix Q below.

$$\text{Next Day} \begin{matrix} \text{Rain} \\ \text{Shine} \end{matrix} \overset{\substack{\text{Previous Day} \\ \text{Rain} \quad \text{Shine}}}{\begin{bmatrix} 0.6 & 0.2 \\ 0.4 & 0.8 \end{bmatrix}} = Q$$

a. A 30% chance of rain, 70% chance of sunshine on Monday is given by the matrix $M = \begin{bmatrix} 0.3 \\ 0.7 \end{bmatrix}$. Calculate QM to find the probabilities for Tuesday. Multiply by Q again (that is, compute QQM) to find the probabilities for Wednesday. Multiply by Q again ($QQQM$) to find the probabilities for Thursday.

b. Find the probability of rain for the remaining days of the week. What happens to the probabilities as the week goes on?

c. This matrix application is called a *Markov chain*. Find out what you can about Markov chains and report your results.

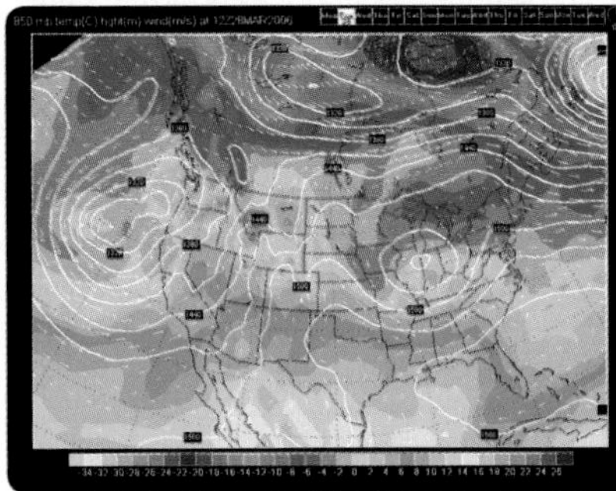

5 Computer Graphics

You may want to ask students to relate this project to images composed of many copies of some arbitrary image. Up close, you see the many copies of the arbitrary small image, but if you step back, you see that the overall image shows, say, President Abraham Lincoln.

6 Predicting the Weather

Encourage students to contact a local weather service agency over several days, obtain probabilities for various weather conditions for each coming day, and enter those data into matrices. Students can use a CAS to multiply the matrices and compare their forecasts with those of the weather service.

Sample answers for projects are in the Solution Manual in the Electronic Teacher's Edition.

Notes

Chapter 4

Summary and Vocabulary

The Summary gives an overview of the entire chapter and provides an opportunity for students to consider the material as a whole. Thus, the Summary can be used to help students relate and unify the concepts presented in the chapter.

Vocabulary words and symbols are listed by lesson to provide a checklist of concepts that students must know. Emphasize to students that they should read the vocabulary list carefully before starting the Self-Test on pages 291–292. If students do not understand the meaning of a vocabulary word, they should refer back to the indicated lesson.

Theorems and Properties covered in the chapter are listed below the Summary with page references included to lead students back to the location in the chapter where the theorem or property is stated.

Chapter 4 Summary and Vocabulary

- A **matrix** is a rectangular array of objects. Matrices are frequently used to store data and to represent **transformations**. Matrices can be added or subtracted if they have the same **dimensions**. Addition of matrices can be used to obtain translation images of figures.

- Any matrix can be multiplied by a real number, called a *scalar*. Multiplying each element in the matrix by the scalar yields the **scalar product**. However, not all matrices can be multiplied by other matrices. The product of two matrices exists only if the number of columns of the left matrix equals the number of rows of the right matrix. The element in row r and column c of AB is the product of row r of A and column c of B. Matrix multiplication is associative but not commutative.

- Matrices with 2 rows can represent points, segments, lines, polygons, and other figures in the coordinate plane. Multiplying such a matrix by a 2×2 matrix on its left may yield a transformation image of the figure. Transformations for which 2×2 matrices are given in this chapter include **reflections**, **rotations**, **size changes**, and **scale changes**. They are summarized on the next two pages. The rotation of 90° about the origin is a particularly important transformation. Based on that transformation, it can be proved that two nonvertical lines are perpendicular if and only if the product of their slopes is -1.

- The set of 2×2 matrices is closed under multiplication. The **identity matrix** for multiplying 2×2 matrices is $\begin{bmatrix} 1 & 0 \\ 0 & 1 \end{bmatrix}$. The **identity transformation** maps any figure onto itself.

  The **Matrix Basis Theorem** provides a way to generate and remember matrices for transformations. When a transformation A is represented by a 2×2 matrix, if $A(1, 0) = (x_1, y_1)$ and $A(0, 1) = (x_2, y_2)$, then A has the matrix $\begin{bmatrix} x_1 & x_2 \\ y_1 & y_2 \end{bmatrix}$.

Vocabulary

4-1
*matrix
element
*dimensions
equal matrices
point matrix

4-2
*matrix addition, sum of two matrices
scalar multiplication, scalar product
difference of two matrices

4-3
row-by-column multiplication
*matrix multiplication
matrix product

4-4
*transformation
preimage
image
*size change
center of a size change
magnitude of a size change
*identity matrix
*identity transformation
similar

4-5
*scale change
horizontal magnitude
vertical magnitude
stretch
shrink

4-6
reflection image of a point over a line
reflecting line, line of reflection
*reflection

- **Reflections, rotations,** and **translations** preserve distance. A size change S_k multiplies distances by k. These properties can be proved using the Pythagorean Distance Formula for the distance d between two points (x_1, y_1) and (x_2, y_2):

$$d = \sqrt{|x_2 - x_1|^2 + |y_2 - y_1|^2}.$$

Matrices for many specific transformations were discussed in this chapter.

Vocabulary

4-7
*composite of two transformations

4-8
*rotation
center of a rotation
magnitude of a rotation

4-10
*translation

- **Transformations Yielding Images Congruent to Preimages**

Reflections:

over x-axis

$$\begin{bmatrix} 1 & 0 \\ 0 & -1 \end{bmatrix}$$

$r_x: (x, y) \rightarrow (x, -y)$

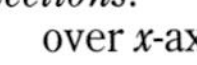

over y-axis

$$\begin{bmatrix} -1 & 0 \\ 0 & 1 \end{bmatrix}$$

$r_y: (x, y) \rightarrow (-x, y)$

over the line $y = x$

$$\begin{bmatrix} 0 & 1 \\ 1 & 0 \end{bmatrix}$$

$r_{y=x}: (x, y) \rightarrow (y, x)$

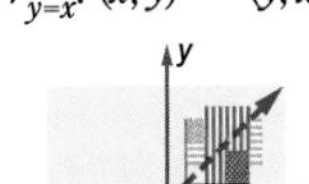

over the line $y = -x$

$$\begin{bmatrix} 0 & -1 \\ -1 & 0 \end{bmatrix}$$

$r_{y=-x}: (x, y) \rightarrow (-y, -x)$

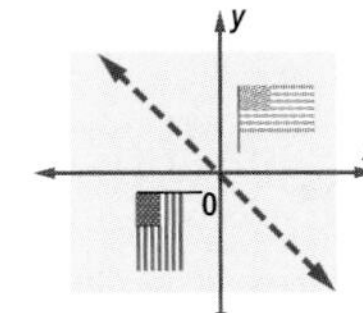

Rotations with center (0, 0):

magnitude 90°

$$\begin{bmatrix} 0 & -1 \\ 1 & 0 \end{bmatrix}$$

$R_{90}: (x, y) \rightarrow (-y, x)$

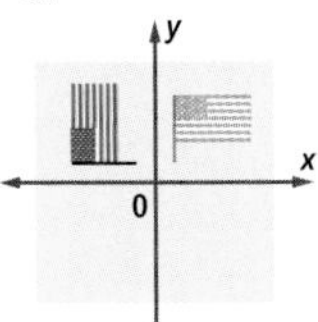

magnitude 180°

$$\begin{bmatrix} -1 & 0 \\ 0 & -1 \end{bmatrix}$$

$R_{180}: (x, y) \rightarrow (-x, -y)$

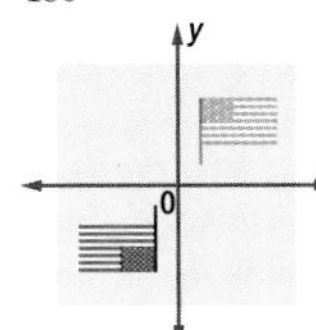

magnitude 270°

$$\begin{bmatrix} 0 & 1 \\ -1 & 0 \end{bmatrix}$$

$R_{270}: (x, y) \rightarrow (y, -x)$

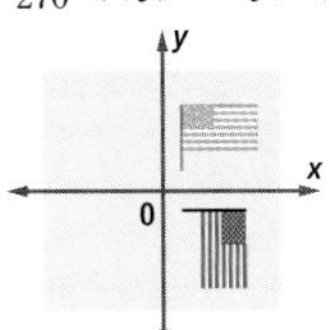

Translations:

No general matrix

$T_{h,k}: (x, y) \rightarrow (x + h, y + k)$

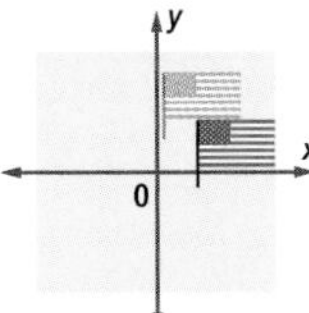

Summary and Vocabulary 289

Additional Answers

1.
$$\begin{matrix} H & U & L & K \end{matrix}$$
$$\begin{bmatrix} -2 & 5 & -2 & -4 \\ 4 & 1 & -2 & 2 \end{bmatrix}$$

2a.

	Jicamaport	Okraville	Potatotown
first-class	16	4	2
economy	107	180	321

2b.

	first-class	economy
Jicamaport	16	107
Okraville	4	180
Potatotown	2	321

3. The product will exist when the number of columns in the left matrix is equal to the number of rows in the right matrix. This is the case for *AB*, *BA*, *AC* and *CB*.

Transformations Yielding Images Similar to Preimages

Size changes with center (0, 0) and magnitude k:

$$\begin{bmatrix} k & 0 \\ 0 & k \end{bmatrix}$$

$S_k: (x, y) \to (kx, ky)$

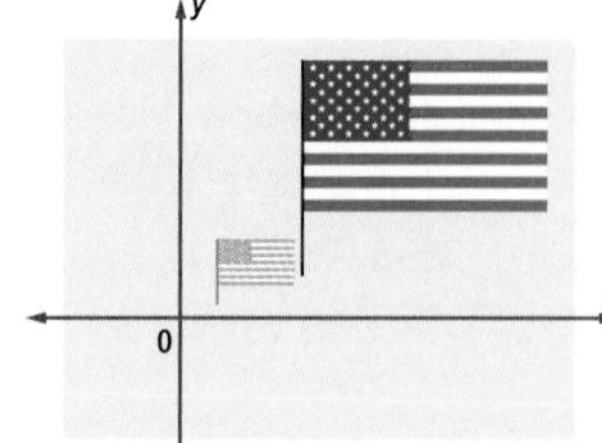

Other Transformations

Scale changes with horizontal magnitude a *and vertical magnitude* b:

$$\begin{bmatrix} a & 0 \\ 0 & b \end{bmatrix}$$

$S_{a,b}: (x, y) \to (ax, by)$

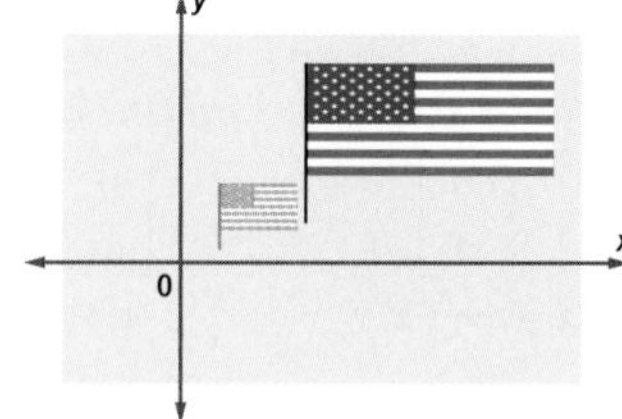

Theorems

Size Change Theorem (p. 244)
Pythagorean Distance Formula (p. 245)
Scale Change Theorem (p. 251)
Matrix for r_y Theorem (p. 256)
Matrix Basis Theorem (p.257)
Matrices for r_x, $r_{y=x}$, and $r_{y=-x}$ Theorem (p. 259)
Matrices and Composites Theorem (p. 265)
Composite of Rotations Theorem (p. 270)
Matrix for R_{90} Theorem (p. 270)
Perpendicular Lines and Slopes Theorem (pp. 274, 276)
Parallel Lines and Translations Theorem (p. 282)

Additional Answers

4. $BA = \begin{bmatrix} (5 \cdot 2) + (-2 \cdot 4) + \left(-1 \cdot \frac{1}{2}\right) & (5 \cdot 0) + (-2 \cdot (-2)) + \left(-1 \cdot \frac{1}{2}\right) \\ \left(\frac{1}{8} \cdot 2\right) + (6 \cdot 4) + \left(5 \cdot \left(-\frac{1}{2}\right)\right) & \left(\frac{1}{8} \cdot 0\right) + (6 \cdot (-2)) + \left(5 \cdot \frac{1}{2}\right) \end{bmatrix} = \begin{bmatrix} 2.5 & 3.5 \\ 21.75 & -9.5 \end{bmatrix}$

5. not possible; *A* and *C* have different dimensions

Chapter 4 Self-Test

Take this test as you would take a test in class. You will need a calculator. Then use the Selected Answers section in the back of the book to check your work.

1. Write a matrix to represent polygon $HULK$ if $H = (-2, 4)$, $U = (5, 1)$, $L = (-2, -2)$, and $K = (-4, 2)$.
1–13. See margin.
2. One day on a Veggie-Air flight from Iceburg, there were 16 first-class and 107 economy passengers going to Jicamaport, 4 first-class and 180 economy passengers bound for Okraville, and 2 first-class and 321 economy passengers flying to Potatotown.
   a. Write a 2×3 matrix to store this information. Include appropriate column and row headings.
   b. Write a 3×2 matrix to store this information. Include appropriate column and row headings.

In 3–6, use matrices *A*, *B*, and *C* below.

$$A = \begin{bmatrix} 2 & 0 \\ 4 & -2 \\ -\frac{1}{2} & \frac{1}{2} \end{bmatrix} \quad B = \begin{bmatrix} 5 & -2 & -1 \\ \frac{1}{8} & 6 & 5 \end{bmatrix} \quad C = \begin{bmatrix} 17 & 4 \\ \frac{1}{3} & \sqrt{2} \end{bmatrix}$$

3. Determine which of the following products exist: AB, BA, AC, CA, BC, and CB.
4. If possible, find BA. If it is not possible, explain why.
5. If possible, find $A - C$. If it is not possible, explain why.
6. Calculate $\frac{1}{3}B$.
7. Why is $\begin{bmatrix} 1 & 0 \\ 0 & 1 \end{bmatrix}$ called the identity matrix?
8. Are the two lines with equations $y = 5x - 3$ and $y = \frac{1}{5}x + 2$ perpendicular? Explain your answer.
9. Find an equation for the line through $\left(\frac{1}{4}, -1\right)$ that is perpendicular to $y = \frac{1}{7}x + 4$.
10. Calculate the matrix for $r_y \circ R_{270}$.

In 11–12, refer to the graph below.

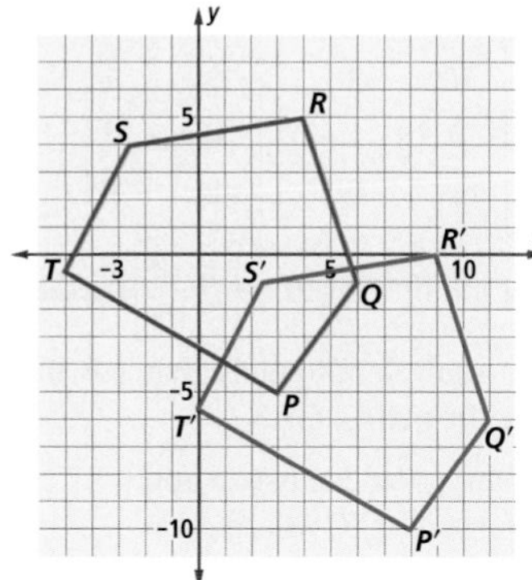

11. What translation maps $PQRST$ onto $P'Q'R'S'T'$?
12. Graph the image of $PQRST$ under the transformation r_x.
13. The 4-Star Movie Theater has four screens. The number and type of theater attendees is summarized in the following matrix for one show time of four different movies.

	Children	Adults	Students
Movie 1	38	135	169
Movie 2	84	101	152
Movie 3	84	118	135
Movie 4	67	236	34

Ticket prices for children, adults, and students are \$4.00, \$6.50, and \$5.00, respectively. Use matrix multiplication to determine the total ticket sales revenue for each movie.

Additional Answers

12.

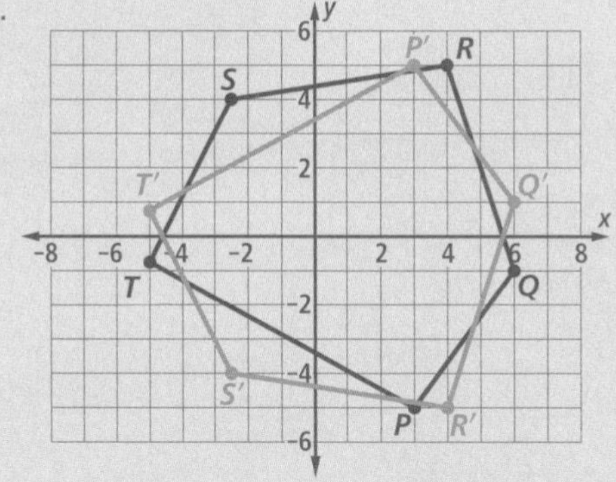

13. $\begin{bmatrix} (38 \cdot 4) + (135 \cdot 6.5) + (169 \cdot 5) \\ (84 \cdot 4) + (101 \cdot 6.5) + (152 \cdot 5) \\ (84 \cdot 4) + (118 \cdot 6.5) + (135 \cdot 5) \\ (67 \cdot 4) + (236 \cdot 6.5) + (34 \cdot 5) \end{bmatrix} =$

Movie 1	1874.5
Movie 2	1752.5
Movie 3	1778
Movie 4	1972

Self-Test

For the development of mathematical competence, feedback and correction, along with the opportunity for practice, are necessary. The Self-Test provides the opportunity for feedback and correction; the Chapter Review provides additional opportunities for practice. We cannot overemphasize the importance of these end-of-chapter materials. It is at this point that the material gels for many students, allowing them to solidify skills and understanding. In general, student performance should improve after these pages.

Assign the Self-Test as a one-night assignment. Worked-out solutions for all questions are in the Selected Answers section of the student book. Encourage students to take the Self-Test honestly, grade themselves, and then be prepared to discuss the test in class.

Advise students to pay special attention to those Chapter Review questions (pages 293–297) that correspond to the questions they missed on the Self-Test.

Additional Answers

6. $\frac{1}{3}B = \begin{bmatrix} \frac{1}{3} \cdot 5 & \frac{1}{3} \cdot (-2) & \frac{1}{3} \cdot -1 \\ \frac{1}{3} \cdot \frac{1}{8} & \frac{1}{3} \cdot 6 & \frac{1}{3} \cdot 5 \end{bmatrix} = \begin{bmatrix} \frac{5}{3} & -\frac{2}{3} & -\frac{1}{3} \\ \frac{1}{24} & 2 & \frac{5}{3} \end{bmatrix}$

7. Answers vary. Sample: Multiplication by $\begin{bmatrix} 1 & 0 \\ 0 & 1 \end{bmatrix}$ maps each point $\begin{bmatrix} x \\ y \end{bmatrix}$ onto itself.

8. No; $m_1 = 5$, $m_2 = \frac{1}{5}$, and $m_1 m_2 = 5 \cdot \frac{1}{5} = 1$. For perpendicular lines, $m_1 m_2 = -1$.

9. $m_1 \cdot \frac{1}{7} = -1$, $m = -7$, $y - (-1) = -7\left(x - \frac{3}{4}\right)$; $y = -7x + \frac{3}{4}$

10. The matrix for $r_y \circ R_{270}$ is $\begin{bmatrix} -1 & 0 \\ 0 & 1 \end{bmatrix} \begin{bmatrix} 0 & 1 \\ -1 & 0 \end{bmatrix} = \begin{bmatrix} (-1 \cdot 0) + (0 \cdot (-1)) & (-1 \cdot 1) + (0 \cdot 0) \\ (0 \cdot 0) + (1 \cdot (-1)) & (0 \cdot 1) + (1 \cdot 0) \end{bmatrix} = \begin{bmatrix} 0 & -1 \\ -1 & 0 \end{bmatrix}$

11. $P = (3, -5)$ maps onto $P' = (8, -10)$, so the translation is $T_{5,-5}$.

Additional Answers

14. $\begin{bmatrix} 42+5 & 15+2 \\ 10+3 & 2+1 \\ 7+0 & 1+3 \\ 4+2 & 0+0 \end{bmatrix} =$

	fiction	nonfiction
Paperbacks	47	17
Hardbacks	13	3
Audiotapes	7	4
Audio CDs	6	0

15. $\begin{bmatrix} 2 & 0 \\ 0 & 2 \end{bmatrix}\begin{bmatrix} 2 & -9 \\ 7 & 5 \end{bmatrix} =$

$\begin{bmatrix} (2 \cdot 2) + (0 \cdot -9) & (2 \cdot -9) + (0 \cdot 5) \\ (0 \cdot 2) + (2 \cdot 7) & (0 \cdot -9) + (2 \cdot 5) \end{bmatrix} =$

$\begin{bmatrix} 4 & -18 \\ 14 & 10 \end{bmatrix} = 2\begin{bmatrix} 2 & -9 \\ 7 & 5 \end{bmatrix}$

19a. $\begin{bmatrix} 4 & 0 \\ 0 & 3 \end{bmatrix}\begin{bmatrix} 2.5 & 1 & -6 \\ -5 & 4 & -12 \end{bmatrix} =$

$\begin{bmatrix} 2.5 \cdot 4 & 1 \cdot 4 & -6 \cdot 4 \\ -5 \cdot 3 & 4 \cdot 3 & -12 \cdot 3 \end{bmatrix} =$

$\begin{bmatrix} 10 & 4 & -24 \\ -15 & 12 & -36 \end{bmatrix}$

19b. $\begin{bmatrix} 2.5 & 1 & -6 \\ -5 & 4 & -12 \end{bmatrix} + \begin{bmatrix} 2.5 & 2.5 & 2.5 \\ -1 & -1 & -1 \end{bmatrix} =$

$\begin{bmatrix} 2.5+2.5 & 1+2.5 & -6+2.5 \\ -5-1 & 4-1 & -12-1 \end{bmatrix} =$

$\begin{bmatrix} 5 & 3.5 & -3.5 \\ -6 & 3 & -13 \end{bmatrix}$

22a. $S_7(a, b) = (7a, 7b)$

22b. $PQ = \sqrt{|3-2|^2 + |9-5|^2} = \sqrt{17}$;

$S_7(2, 5) = (7 \cdot 2, 7 \cdot 5) = (14, 35)$;

$S_7(3, 9) = (7 \cdot 3, 7 \cdot 9) = (21, 63)$;

$P'Q' = \sqrt{|21-14|^2 + |63-35|^2} = \sqrt{833}$;

$\frac{\sqrt{833}}{\sqrt{17}} = \sqrt{\frac{833}{17}} = \sqrt{49} = 7.$

Thus, $P'Q' = 7PQ$.

14. Savannah Reed and Denise Wright have decided to merge their book inventories and hold a book sale. If the matrices below represent each person's inventory, write a matrix for the inventory of books after merging. 14–15. See margin.

	Savannah Fiction	Savannah Nonfiction	Denise Fiction	Denise Nonfiction
Paperbacks	42	15	5	2
Hardbacks	10	2	3	1
Audiotapes	7	1	0	3
Audio CDs	4	0	2	0

15. Show that multiplying $A = \begin{bmatrix} 2 & -9 \\ 7 & 5 \end{bmatrix}$ by the scalar 2 is equivalent to multiplying A on the left by the matrix for S_2.

16. Write a matrix you can use to apply the transformation T, where $T: (x, y) \rightarrow (-y, x)$, to a figure in the coordinate plane.

16. $\begin{bmatrix} 0 & -1 \\ 1 & 0 \end{bmatrix}$

17. The reflection of $\triangle XYZ$ over the y-axis gives a triangle with vertices $X' = (4, 5)$, $Y' = (-2, 6)$, and $Z' = (3, 1)$.

18. $R_{270}(X) = (5, 4)$, $R_{270}(Y) = (6, -2)$, $R_{270}(Z) = (1, 3)$

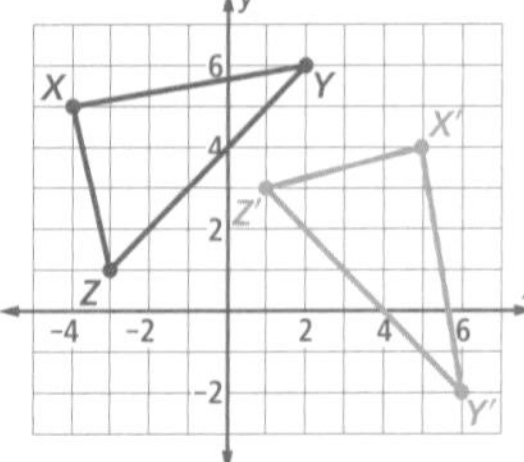

In 17 and 18, $\triangle XYZ$ has vertices $X = (-4, 5)$, $Y = (2, 6)$, and $Z = (-3, 1)$.

17. Write a sentence that describes this matrix multiplication geometrically:

$$\begin{bmatrix} -1 & 0 \\ 0 & 1 \end{bmatrix}\begin{bmatrix} -4 & 2 & -3 \\ 5 & 6 & 1 \end{bmatrix} = \begin{bmatrix} 4 & -2 & 3 \\ 5 & 6 & 1 \end{bmatrix}.$$

18. Graph $\triangle XYZ$ and $R_{270}(\triangle XYZ)$.

19. Find the matrix of the image of $\begin{bmatrix} 2.5 & 1 & -6 \\ -5 & 4 & -12 \end{bmatrix}$ under each transformation. a–b. See margin.

a. $S_{4,3}$

b. $T_{2.5,-1}$

True or False In 20 and 21, if the statement is false, give an example to show that it is false.

20. A line and its translation image are always parallel. true

21. A line and its rotation image are always perpendicular.

22. Consider the transformation S_7.

a. What is the image of (a, b) under S_7?

b. If $P = (2, 5)$ and $Q = (3, 9)$, show that the distance between $S_7(P)$ and $S_7(Q)$ is 7 times the distance between P and Q. a–b. See margin.

23. Find an equation for the perpendicular bisector of $\overline{PQ}$ in Question 22.

21. False; Examples vary. Sample: $y = x$ rotated 135° is the line $y = 0$. $m_1 m_2 = (1 \cdot 0) = 0 \neq -1$.

23. $m_2 = \frac{9-5}{3-2} = 4$; $m_1 \cdot 4 = -1$; $m_1 = -\frac{1}{4}$; midpoint $= \left(\frac{2+3}{2}, \frac{5+9}{2}\right) = \left(\frac{5}{2}, 7\right)$; $y - 7 = -\frac{1}{4}\left(x - \frac{5}{2}\right)$

Chapter 4 Chapter Review

SKILLS
PROPERTIES
USES
REPRESENTATIONS

SKILLS Procedures used to get answers

OBJECTIVE A Write matrices for points and polygons. (Lesson 4-1)

1. Write a matrix to represent each point.
   a. $U = (4, 5)$ a. $\begin{bmatrix}4\\5\end{bmatrix}$ b. $\begin{bmatrix}3\\-4\end{bmatrix}$
   b. $E = (3, -4)$
   c. $D = (-4, 1)$ c. $\begin{bmatrix}-4\\1\end{bmatrix}$ d. $\begin{bmatrix}-2\\-4\end{bmatrix}$
   d. $G = (-2, -4)$ e. $\begin{bmatrix}3\\1\end{bmatrix}$
   e. $F = (3, 1)$
2. Write a matrix to represent polygon *FUDGE*, if its vertices are those defined in Question 1. See margin.

OBJECTIVE B Add, subtract, and find scalar multiples of matrices. (Lesson 4-2)

In 3-6, let $A = \begin{bmatrix}2 & 2 & 5\\6 & 4 & -2\\0 & -3 & -3\end{bmatrix}$ and $B = \begin{bmatrix}-2 & 4 & 7\\3 & 3 & -5\\4 & 1 & -10\end{bmatrix}$. Calculate. 3–6. See margin.

3. $A - B$
4. $A - 3B$
5. $B - 2A$
6. $B + A$

In 7 and 8, find *p* and *q*.

7. $2\begin{bmatrix}4 & p\\q & -3\end{bmatrix} + \begin{bmatrix}2 & 3\\5q & 7\end{bmatrix} = \begin{bmatrix}10 & 9\\21 & 1\end{bmatrix}$ $p = 3$; $q = 3$
8. $\begin{bmatrix}8 & -2\\-3 & p\end{bmatrix} - 2\begin{bmatrix}q & 4\\-7 & 3\end{bmatrix} = \begin{bmatrix}5 & -10\\11 & 7\end{bmatrix}$ $p = 13$; $q = \frac{3}{2}$

OBJECTIVE C Multiply matrices. (Lesson 4-3)

In 9–12, multiply the matrices if possible.

9. $\begin{bmatrix}4 & 1\\6 & -3\end{bmatrix}\begin{bmatrix}1 & 2\\-3 & 4\end{bmatrix}$ $\begin{bmatrix}1 & 12\\15 & 0\end{bmatrix}$
10. $\begin{bmatrix}4\\3\end{bmatrix}\begin{bmatrix}1 & -2 & 0\end{bmatrix}$ $\begin{bmatrix}4 & -8 & 0\\3 & -6 & 0\end{bmatrix}$
11. $\begin{bmatrix}2 & 2 & 5\\6 & 4 & -2\end{bmatrix}\begin{bmatrix}-2 & 4\\3 & 3\\4 & 1\end{bmatrix}$ $\begin{bmatrix}22 & 19\\-8 & 34\end{bmatrix}$
12. $\begin{bmatrix}1 & 2\\-1 & 0\end{bmatrix}\begin{bmatrix}4 & 3 & -1\\-1 & 1 & -1\end{bmatrix}\begin{bmatrix}2\\2\\2\end{bmatrix}$ $\begin{bmatrix}8\\-12\end{bmatrix}$

In 13 and 14, find *p* and *q*.

13. $\begin{bmatrix}p & 0\\0 & q\end{bmatrix}\begin{bmatrix}4\\-2\end{bmatrix} = \begin{bmatrix}16\\-4\end{bmatrix}$ $p = 4$; $q = 2$
14. $\begin{bmatrix}0 & -2\\1 & 0\end{bmatrix}\begin{bmatrix}p\\q\end{bmatrix} = \begin{bmatrix}12\\5\end{bmatrix}$ $p = 5$; $q = -6$

OBJECTIVE D Determine equations of lines perpendicular to given lines. (Lesson 4-9)

15. Find an equation of the line through (2, -5) perpendicular to the line $y = \frac{1}{3}x + 1$. $y = -3x + 1$
16. Find an equation of the line through (4, -6) perpendicular to the line $y = 5$. $x = 4$
17. Given $A = (4, 7)$ and $B = (-6, 1)$, find an equation for the perpendicular bisector of $\overline{AB}$. $y = -\frac{5}{3}x + \frac{7}{3}$
18. Consider two lines. One is the image of the other under R_{90}. The slope of one of the lines is $\frac{1}{8}$. What is the slope of the other line? -8

Additional Answers

2. $\begin{bmatrix}3 & 4 & -4 & -2 & 3\\1 & 5 & 1 & -4 & -4\end{bmatrix}$
3. $\begin{bmatrix}4 & -2 & -2\\3 & 1 & 3\\-4 & -4 & 7\end{bmatrix}$
4. $\begin{bmatrix}8 & -10 & -16\\-3 & -5 & 13\\-12 & -6 & 27\end{bmatrix}$
5. $\begin{bmatrix}-6 & 0 & -3\\-9 & -5 & -1\\4 & 7 & -4\end{bmatrix}$
6. $\begin{bmatrix}0 & 6 & 12\\9 & 7 & -7\\4 & -2 & -13\end{bmatrix}$

Chapter Review

The main objectives for the chapter are organized in the Chapter Review under the four types of understanding this book promotes: Skills, Properties, Uses, and Representations.

Whereas end-of-chapter material may be considered optional in some texts, in UCSMP *Advanced Algebra* we have selected these objectives and questions with the expectation that they will be covered. Students should be able to answer these questions with about 85% accuracy after studying the chapter.

You may assign these questions over a single night to help students prepare for a test the next day or you may assign the questions over a two-day period. If you work the questions over two days, we recommend assigning the evens for homework the first night so that students get feedback in class the next day, and then assigning the odds the night before the test because the answers are provided to the odd-numbered questions in the Selected Answers section at the back of the book.

It is effective to ask students which questions they still do not understand and use the day as a total class discussion of the material that the class finds most difficult.

Resources

- Assessment Resources: Chapter 4 Test Forms A–D; Chapter 4 Test, Cumulative Form

Technology Resources

Teacher's Assessment Assistant, Ch. 4
Electronic Teacher's Edition, Ch. 4

Additional Answers

19a. true

19b. Answers vary. Sample:
$\left(\begin{bmatrix} 4 & 3 \\ 7 & 1 \end{bmatrix}\begin{bmatrix} 2 & 9 \\ -1 & -3 \end{bmatrix}\right)\begin{bmatrix} -4 \\ -4 \end{bmatrix} = \begin{bmatrix} 4 & 3 \\ 7 & 1 \end{bmatrix}\left(\begin{bmatrix} 2 & 9 \\ -1 & -3 \end{bmatrix}\begin{bmatrix} -4 \\ -4 \end{bmatrix}\right)$

20a. false

20b. Answers vary. Sample:
$\begin{bmatrix} 4 & 3 \\ 7 & 1 \end{bmatrix}\begin{bmatrix} 2 & 9 \\ -1 & -3 \end{bmatrix} \neq \begin{bmatrix} 2 & 9 \\ -1 & -3 \end{bmatrix}\begin{bmatrix} 4 & 3 \\ 7 & 1 \end{bmatrix}$

21a. false

21b. Answers vary. Sample:
$\begin{bmatrix} 1 & 2 \\ 3 & 4 \end{bmatrix} - \begin{bmatrix} 5 & 6 \\ 7 & 8 \end{bmatrix} \neq \begin{bmatrix} 5 & 6 \\ 7 & 8 \end{bmatrix} - \begin{bmatrix} 1 & 2 \\ 3 & 4 \end{bmatrix}$

22a. true

22b. Answers vary. Sample:
$5\begin{bmatrix} 1 & 2 \\ 3 & 4 \end{bmatrix} = \begin{bmatrix} 5 & 10 \\ 15 & 20 \end{bmatrix} = \begin{bmatrix} 1 & 2 \\ 3 & 4 \end{bmatrix}5$

28. Answers vary. Sample:

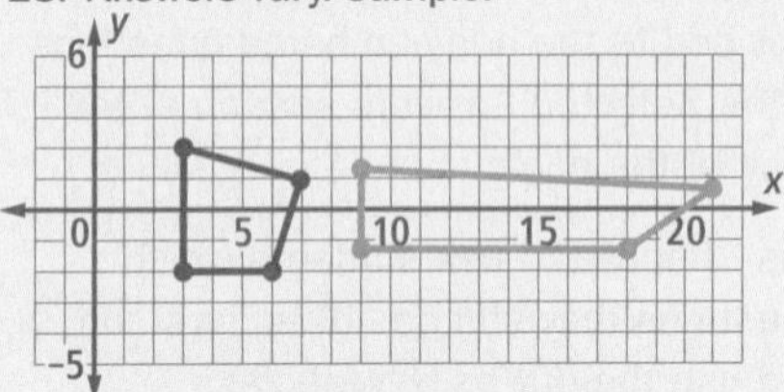

29. $\sqrt{(2x_2 - 2x_1)^2 + (2y_2 - 2y_1)^2} = \sqrt{4(x_2 - x_1)^2 + 4(y_2 - y_1)^2} = 2\sqrt{(x_2 - x_1)^2 + (y_2 - y_1)^2}$

PROPERTIES Principles behind the mathematics

OBJECTIVE E Recognize properties of matrix operations. (Lessons 4-2, 4-3, 4-7)

In 19–22, a statement is given. 19–22. See margin.

a. **Is the statement true or false?**

b. **Give an example to support your answer.**

19. Matrix multiplication is associative.

20. Matrix multiplication is commutative.

21. Matrix subtraction is commutative.

22. Scalar multiplication of matrices is commutative.

In 23 and 24, suppose *Y* and *P* are matrices. *Y* has dimensions 1 × 7 and *P* has dimensions *m* × *n*.

23. If the sum $Y + P$ exists, what are the values of m and n? $m = 1$; $n = 7$

24. If the product PY exists, what is the value of n? $n = 1$

25. What matrix is the identity for multiplication of 2 × 2 matrices? $\begin{bmatrix} 1 & 0 \\ 0 & 1 \end{bmatrix}$

OBJECTIVE F Recognize relationships between figures and their transformation images. (Lessons 4-4, 4-5, 4-6, 4-8, 4-9, 4-10)

In 26 and 27, fill in the blank with A, B, or C to make a true statement.

A not necessarily similar or congruent

B similar, but not necessarily congruent

C congruent

26. A figure and its size change image are __?__. B

27. A figure and its reflection image are __?__. C

28. Give an example to show that a figure and its image under $S_{3,\frac{2}{3}}$ are not similar. 28–29. See margin.

29. Use the Pythagorean Distance Formula to show that S_2 multiplies distances by 2.

30. Find an equation for the image of the line $2x + 3y = 60$ under R_{90}. $-3x + 2y = 60$

31. Repeat Question 30 if the transformation is the translation $T_{-1,3}$. $2x + 3y = 67$

OBJECTIVE G Relate transformations to matrices, and vice versa. (Lessons 4-4, 4-5, 4-6, 4-7, 4-8, 4-10)

32. Translate the matrix equation $\begin{bmatrix} -1 & 0 \\ 0 & -1 \end{bmatrix}\begin{bmatrix} 4 \\ 3 \end{bmatrix} = \begin{bmatrix} -4 \\ -3 \end{bmatrix}$ into English by filling in the blanks.

The image of the point __(4, ? 3)__ under a rotation with center __(0, ? 0)__ and magnitude __?__ 180° is the point __(-4, ? -3)__.

33. Multiply the matrix for $r_{y=x}$ by itself, and tell what transformation the product represents. $\begin{bmatrix} 1 & 0 \\ 0 & 1 \end{bmatrix}$; the identity transformation

34. Write a matrix for a scale change with horizontal magnitude 5 and vertical magnitude 3.5.

35. a. Calculate a matrix for $R_{180} \circ r_x$.

b. What single transformation corresponds to your answer? r_y

36. a. Find two reflections whose composite is R_{180}. Answers vary. Sample: r_x and r_y

b. Use matrix multiplication and your answer to Part a to generate the matrix for R_{180}.

34. $\begin{bmatrix} 5 & 0 \\ 0 & 3.5 \end{bmatrix}$

35a. $\begin{bmatrix} -1 & 0 \\ 0 & 1 \end{bmatrix}$

36b. $\begin{bmatrix} -1 & 0 \\ 0 & -1 \end{bmatrix}$

37. a. What size change maps FIG onto $F'I'G'$ as shown below? S_2

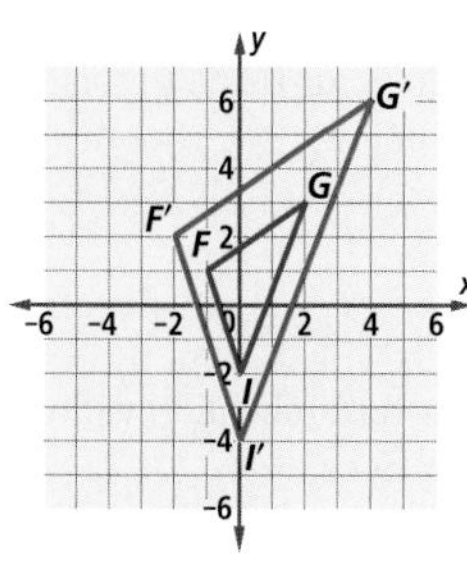

b. Explain how to use a matrix operation to transform FIG to $F'I'G'$. See margin.

Multiple Choice In 38–40, choose the matrix for each transformation.

A $\begin{bmatrix} 0 & -1 \\ 1 & 0 \end{bmatrix}$ B $\begin{bmatrix} 0 & 1 \\ 1 & 0 \end{bmatrix}$ C $\begin{bmatrix} 0 & 3 \\ 3 & 0 \end{bmatrix}$

D $\begin{bmatrix} -1 & 0 \\ 0 & 1 \end{bmatrix}$ E $\begin{bmatrix} 1 & 0 \\ 0 & -1 \end{bmatrix}$ F $\begin{bmatrix} 3 & 0 \\ 0 & 3 \end{bmatrix}$

38. $r_{y=x}$ B 39. S_3 F 40. R_{90} A

41. Find the image of $\begin{bmatrix} 2 & -1 & 4 & 3 \\ 0.7 & 0 & -1 & 5 \end{bmatrix}$ under r_x.
41–43. See margin.

42. $HARP$ has coordinates $H = (-2, 2)$, $A = (-1, -2)$, $R = (0, 0)$, and $P = (1, 4)$. Find the matrix of $HARP$ under R_{270}.

43. Find the matrix of $\begin{bmatrix} 0 & -8 & 6 \\ 4 & 0 & 4 \end{bmatrix}$ under $S_{0.5}$.

OBJECTIVE H Given their slopes, determine whether lines are parallel or perpendicular to each other, and vice versa. (Lessons 4-9, 4-10)

44. Line ℓ has equation $y = 3x$, and line m has equation $y = kx$. If $\ell \perp m$, find the value of k. $k = -\frac{1}{3}$

45. Suppose $A = (0, 3)$, $B = (2, 4)$, $C = (7, 8)$, and $D = (2, 9)$. Is $\overleftrightarrow{AB} \parallel \overleftrightarrow{CD}$? Explain. See margin.

46. **Multiple Choice** Line a has slope –4. Which of the following is the slope of a line perpendicular to a? B

A 4 B $\frac{1}{4}$ C $-\frac{1}{4}$ D -4

47. Lines j and k are parallel. j has slope 8 and k passes through the point (0, 0). Find another point on k. Answers vary. Sample: (1, 8)

48. Let $\triangle NSA$ be represented by the matrix $\begin{bmatrix} 152 & -12 & 87 \\ 16 & 113 & -23 \end{bmatrix}$.
Let $\triangle N'S'A' = R_{270}(\triangle NSA)$.

a. What is the slope of $\overleftrightarrow{NA}$? $\frac{3}{5}$

b. What is the product of the slopes of $\overleftrightarrow{NA}$ and $\overleftrightarrow{N'A'}$? -1

c. Use your answers to Parts a and b to find the slope of $\overleftrightarrow{N'A'}$. $-\frac{5}{3}$

USES Applications of mathematics in real-world situations

OBJECTIVE I Use matrices to store data. (Lesson 4-1)

49. In 2005, the average loss for people who were victims of three common online scams was \$240 for credit or debit card fraud, \$410 for nondelivery of merchandise, and \$2000 for investment fraud. In 2006, the amounts lost to these scams averaged \$427.50, \$585, and \$2694.99, respectively. Store these data in a 2 × 3 matrix. See margin.

50. The recommended daily allowance (RDA) of vitamin K is 60 µg for a 9- to 13-year-old male, 75 µg for a 14- to 18-year-old male, and 120 µg for a 19- to 30-year-old male. (Note: µg means micrograms, or one-millionth of a gram.) The RDA of thiamin is 0.9 mg for a 9- to 13-year-old male, 1.2 mg for a 14- to 18-year-old male, and 1.2 mg for a 19- to 30-year-old male. The RDAs of vitamin C for these age categories are 45 mg, 75 mg, and 90 mg, respectively. The RDAs of niacin for these age categories are 12 mg, 16 mg, and 16 mg, respectively. Store these data in a 3 × 4 matrix. See margin.

Additional Answers

37b. Multiply the matrix of the points for FIG by the size change matrix $\begin{bmatrix} 2 & 0 \\ 0 & 2 \end{bmatrix}$.

41. $\begin{bmatrix} 2 & -1 & 4 & 3 \\ -0.7 & 0 & 1 & -5 \end{bmatrix}$

42. H' A' R' P'
$\begin{bmatrix} 2 & -2 & 0 & 4 \\ 2 & 1 & 0 & -1 \end{bmatrix}$

43. $\begin{bmatrix} 0 & -4 & 3 \\ 2 & 0 & 2 \end{bmatrix}$

45. No; their slopes are not equal.

49.

	CC/DC fraud	nondelivery	investment fraud
2005	240	410	2000
2006	427.50	585	2694.99

50.

	Vit. K	thiamin	Vit. C	niacin
9–13	0.06	0.9	45	12
14–18	0.075	1.2	75	16
19–30	0.12	1.2	90	16

Additional Answers

51. the element in the second row and first column (1:01)

53a. $\begin{bmatrix} 822 & 456 & 977 \\ 784 & 739 & 879 \end{bmatrix}$

54a. $1.05\begin{bmatrix} 14 & 95 & 80 \\ 7 & 60 & 20 \end{bmatrix}$

54b. $\begin{bmatrix} 14.7 & 99.75 & 84 \\ 7.35 & 63 & 21 \end{bmatrix}$

55. $B = \begin{bmatrix} 9 & 11 & 2 \\ 5 & 7 & 5 \end{bmatrix}$; $P = \begin{bmatrix} 1 \\ 2 \\ 3 \end{bmatrix}$; $BP = \begin{bmatrix} 37 \\ 34 \end{bmatrix}$

57a.

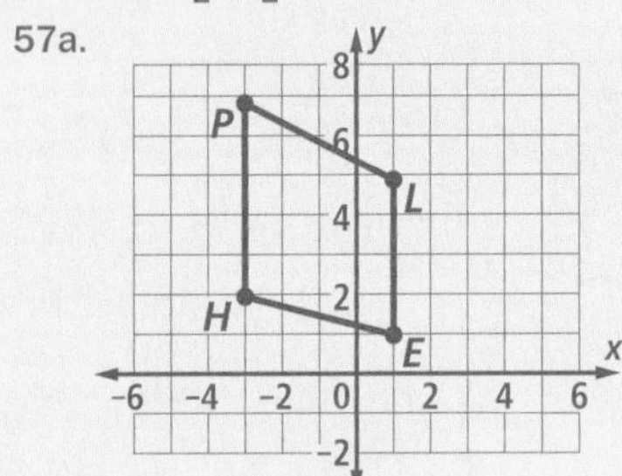

57b. $\begin{bmatrix} -6 & 2 & 2 & -6 \\ 6 & 3 & 15 & 21 \end{bmatrix}$

57c.

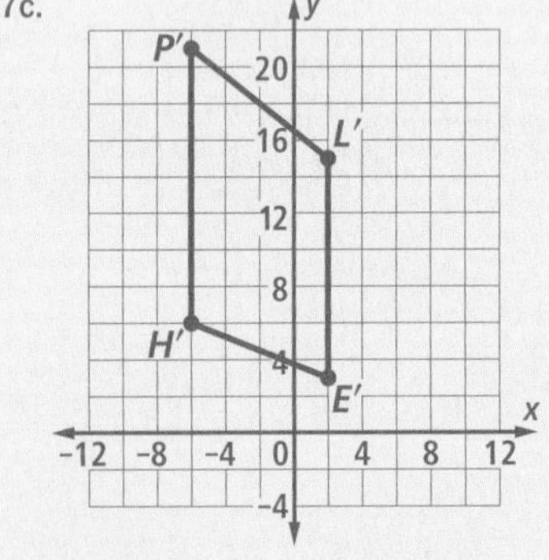

57d. No; magnitude is not the same for the horizontal and vertical directions.

In 51 and 52, the matrix gives the time (in minutes and seconds) behind Lance Armstrong's time each competitor in the Tour de France finished in each of three years.

	2003	2004	2005
Lance Armstrong	0:00	0:00	0:00
Jan Ulrich	1:01	8:50	6:21
Francisco Mancebo	19:15	18:01	9:59

51. Which element represents the time behind Armstrong's time that Jan Ullrich finished in 2003? See margin.

52. How much time behind Jan Ullrich's time did Francisco Mancebo finish in 2005? 3:38

OBJECTIVE J Use matrix addition, matrix multiplication, and scalar multiplication to solve real-world problems. (Lessons 4-2, 4-3)

53. The matrices below contain box office data for three popular movie series. One matrix contains the movies' domestic gross earnings, in millions of dollars, for both the first and second movie in the series, while the other matrix contains the movies' foreign gross earnings.

Domestic Gross (10^6 dollars)

	Spiderman	*The Matrix*	*Harry Potter*
Original	404	171	318
Sequel	374	282	262

Foreign Gross (10^6 dollars)

	Spiderman	*The Matrix*	*Harry Potter*
Original	418	285	659
Sequel	410	457	617

a. Calculate the matrix that stores the worldwide total amount of money each movie made (in millions of dollars). See margin.

b. Of these movies, which made the most money worldwide? *Harry Potter* (original)

c. Which sequel made more money worldwide than its original movie? *The Matrix* sequel

54. Suppose the New York Yankees and Seattle Mariners both decided to raise their ticket prices by 5%. Prices of tickets in dollars in 2008 for three tiers are given in the matrix below. See margin.

	Bleachers	Premium Box	Upper Deck
Yankees	14	95	80
Mariners	7	60	20

a. What scalar multiplication will yield the new ticket prices?

b. Find a matrix that stores the new ticket prices for each team.

55. In basketball, a free throw is worth 1 point, a shot made from inside the three-point arc is worth 2 points, and a shot made from behind the three-point arc is worth 3 points. Suppose that in one game, Brenda made 9 free throws, 11 shots from inside the three-point arc, and 2 shots from behind the three-point arc. In the same game, Marisa made 5 free throws, 7 shots from inside the three-point arc, and 5 shots from behind the three-point arc. Write a matrix B for the number of each type of basket each player made and a matrix P for the number of points the baskets are worth, then calculate BP to find the total points each player scored. See margin.

56. An office supply store sells three different models of graphing calculators. Model X sells for \$150, model Y sells for \$130, and model Z sells for \$100. The following matrix multiplication represents a teacher's order at the store.

$$\begin{bmatrix} 5 & 11 & 7 \end{bmatrix}\begin{bmatrix} 150 \\ 130 \\ 100 \end{bmatrix}$$

a. How many of each model did the teacher order? 5 of X, 11 of Y, and 7 of Z

b. What is the total cost of the order? \$2880

REPRESENTATIONS Pictures, graphs, or objects that illustrate concepts

OBJECTIVE K Graph figures and their transformation images. (Lessons 4-4, 4-5, 4-6, 4-7, 4-8, 4-10) 57. See margin.

57. a. Graph the polygon $HELP$ described by the matrix $\begin{bmatrix} -3 & 1 & 1 & -3 \\ 2 & 1 & 5 & 7 \end{bmatrix}$.
    b. Use matrix multiplication to find the image of $HELP$ under $S_{2,3}$.
    c. Graph the image of $HELP$.
    d. Is the image similar to the preimage? Explain why or why not.

58. A popular road atlas company uses a 1:7,500,000 scale to represent roads on a map. Consider the actual road to be the preimage. Write a matrix that could be used to transform the road to its map representation.

59. Consider $\triangle ABC$ defined by $\begin{bmatrix} -5 & 0 & -3 \\ 1 & 0 & -3 \end{bmatrix}$.
    a. Graph $\triangle ABC$ and $\triangle A'B'C'$, the image of $\triangle ABC$ under $r_{y=x} \circ r_x$.
    b. What single transformation maps $\triangle ABC$ to $\triangle A'B'C'$? R_{90}

58. $\begin{bmatrix} \frac{1}{7{,}500{,}000} & 0 \\ 0 & \frac{1}{7{,}500{,}000} \end{bmatrix}$

59a.

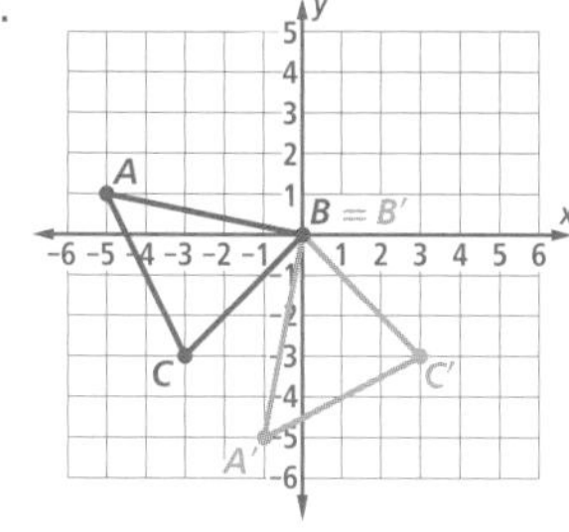

In 60 and 61, refer to polygon BRUCE and its image $B'R'U'C'E'$ shown below.

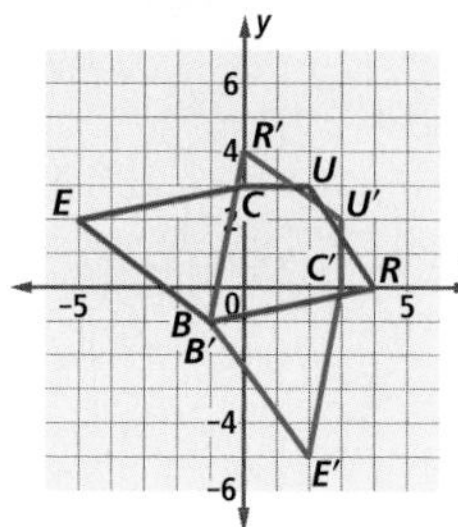

60. a. What transformation maps $BRUCE$ onto $B'R'U'C'E'$? $r_{y=x}$
    b. Show how the coordinates of $B'R'U'C'E'$ can be derived by matrix multiplication.

61. a. Write the image $B''R''U''C''E''$ of $B'R'U'C'E'$ under r_x as a matrix and draw the image. a–c. See margin.
    b. Is $B''R''U''C''E''$ congruent to $B'R'U'C'E'$? Explain.
    c. Are the two images similar? Explain.

60b. $\overset{r_{y=x}}{\begin{bmatrix} 0 & 1 \\ 1 & 0 \end{bmatrix}} \overset{B\ R\ U\ C\ E}{\begin{bmatrix} -1 & 4 & 2 & 0 & -5 \\ -1 & 0 & 3 & 3 & 2 \end{bmatrix}} = \overset{B'\ R'\ U'\ C'\ E'}{\begin{bmatrix} -1 & 0 & 3 & 3 & 2 \\ -1 & 4 & 2 & 0 & -5 \end{bmatrix}}$

Assessment

Evaluation The *Assessment Resources* provide four forms of the Chapter 4 Test. Forms A and B present parallel versions of a short-answer format. Form C consists of four to six short-response questions that cover the SPUR objectives from Chapter 4. Form D offers performance assessment that covers a subset (or even just one) of the SPUR objectives for the chapter. The fifth type of test is a Chapter 4 Test, Cumulative Form. About 50% of this test covers Chapter 4, and the remaining 50% covers the previous chapters evenly.

Feedback After students have taken the test for Chapter 4 and you have scored the results, return the tests to students for discussion. Class discussion on the questions that caused trouble for most students can be very effective in identifying and clarifying misunderstandings. You might want to have them note the items they missed and work either in groups or at home to correct them. It is important for students to receive feedback on every chapter test, and we recommend that students see and correct their mistakes before proceeding too far into the next chapter.

Suggestions for Assignment Assign Lesson 5-1 for homework the evening of the test. It gives students work to do after they have completed the test and keeps the class moving. If you do not do this, you may cover one less chapter over the course of the year.

Additional Answers

61a. $\begin{bmatrix} -1 & 0 & 3 & 3 & 2 \\ 1 & -4 & -2 & 0 & 5 \end{bmatrix}$;

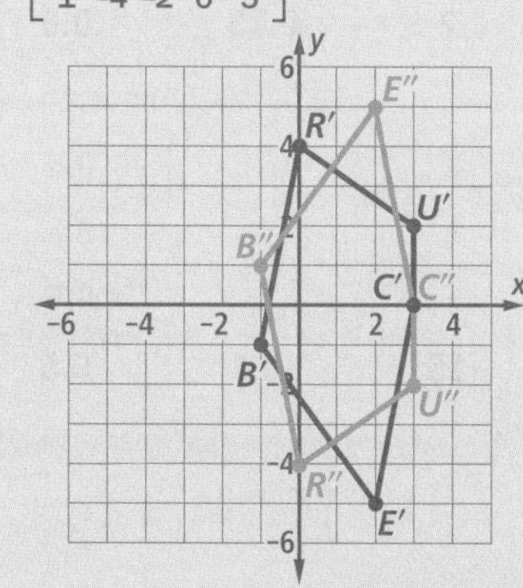

61b. Yes; reflection is a congruence transformation.

61c. Yes; reflections preserve angle measure and slope.

Chapter

5 Systems

Chapter Overview

		Local Standards	Pacing (in days) Average	Advanced	Block
5-1	**Inequalities and Compound Sentences** **H** Solve and graph linear inequalities in one variable.		1	0.75	0.5
5-2	**Solving Systems Using Tables, Graphs, or a CAS** **D** Recognize properties of systems of equations. **F** Use systems of two or three linear equations to solve real-world problems. **I** Estimate solutions to systems by graphing.		1	0.75	0.5
5-3	**Solving Systems Using Substitution** **A** Solve 2×2 and 3×3 systems using the linear-combination method or substitution. **D** Recognize properties of systems of equations. **F** Use systems of two or three linear equations to solve real-world problems.		1	0.75	0.5
	QUIZ 1		0.5	0.5	0.25
5-4	**Solving Systems Using Linear Combinations** **A** Solve 2×2 and 3×3 systems using the linear-combination method or substitution. **D** Recognize properties of systems of equations. **F** Use systems of two or three linear equations to solve real-world problems.		1	0.75	0.5
5-5	**Inverse of Matrices** **B** Find the determinant and inverse of a square matrix.		1	0.75	0.5
5-6	**Solving Systems Using Matrices** **C** Use matrices to solve systems of two or three linear equations. **D** Recognize properties of systems of equations. **F** Use systems of two or three linear equations to solve real-world problems.		1	0.75	0.5
	QUIZ 2		0.5	0.5	0.25
5-7	**Graphing Inequalities in the Coordinate Plane** **J** Graph linear inequalities in two variables.		1	0.75	0.5
5-8	**Systems of Linear Inequalities** **E** Recognize properties of systems of inequalities. **K** Solve systems of inequalities by graphing.		1	0.75	0.5
5-9	**Linear Programming** **E** Recognize properties of systems of inequalities. **G** Solve problems using linear programming.		2	0.75	0.5
		Self-Test	1	0.75	0.5
		Chapter Review	2	1	0.5
		Test	1	1	0.5
		TOTAL	15	10.5	6.5

Technology Resources

Teacher's Assessment Assistant, Ch. 5

Electronic Teacher's Edition, Ch. 5

Differentiated Options  Universal Access

	Accommodating the Learner	Vocabulary Development	Ongoing Assessment	Materials
5-1	pp. 301, 302–303	p. 305	group, p. 306	CAS
5-2	pp. 308, 309	p. 310	written, p. 313	
5-3	pp. 316, 317	p. 315	written, p. 320	CAS
5-4	pp. 322,324	p. 323	group, p. 327	CAS
5-5	pp. 331, 332	p. 330	group, p. 335	CAS or graphing calculator
5-6	pp. 338, 339	p. 340	written, p. 341	
5-7	pp. 344, 346	p. 343	group, p. 347	
5-8	pp. 349, 352	p. 351	group, p. 354	
5-9	pp. 356, 358	p. 357	written, p. 361	CAS

Objectives

Skills	Lessons	Self-Test Questions	Chapter Review Questions
A Solve 2 × 2 and 3 × 3 systems using the linear-combination method or substitution.	5-3, 5-4	5, 6	1-8
B Find the determinant and inverse of a square matrix.	5-5	8b, 9	9-16
C Use matrices to solve systems of two or three linear equations.	5-6	8	17-20
Properties			
D Recognize properties of systems of equations.	5-2, 5-3, 5-4, 5-6	4	21-30
E Recognize properties of systems of inequalities.	5-8, 5-9	12	31-35
Uses			
F Use systems of two or three linear equations to solve real-world problems.	5-2, 5-3, 5-4, 5-6	7	36-40
G Solve problems using linear programming.	5-9	13	41-42
Representations			
H Solve and graph linear inequalities in one variable.	5-1	1, 2	43-52
I Estimate solutions to systems by graphing.	5-2	3	53-55
J Graph linear inequalities in two variables.	5-7	10	56-60
K Solve systems of inequalities by graphing.	5-8	11	61-65

Resource Masters Chapter 5

Resource Master 2, Four-Quadrant Graph Paper (page 3), can be used with Lessons 5-2 and 5-7. **Resource Master 4, Blank Number Lines** (page 5), can be used with Lesson 5-1.

Resource Master 75 Lesson 5-1

Resource Master 74 Lesson 5-1

Warm-Up

Refer to the constraints on a soccer ball listed on page 298.

1. What is the least possible circumference of a tournament soccer ball?
2. What is the greatest possible circumference of a tournament soccer ball?
3. Give the least and greatest possible diameters of a soccer ball, to the nearest tench of a centimeter.

Additional Example

A ticket agency has 300 tickets to a playoff game. Each customer can purchase 2 tickets. When the agency has 50 tickets or fewer, the agency tries to obtain more tickets to sell.

a. How many customers can purchase tickets before the agency needs more tickets?

b. How many tickets will be left after the first 75 customers have each purchased 2 tickets?

Resource Masters for Lesson 5-1

Resource Master 76 Lesson 5-2

Warm-Up

1. Graph all solutions (x, y) to the equation $xy = 6$.
2. On the same grid, graph $\{(x, y) \mid x - y = 5\}$.
3. Find the coordinates of the points of intersection of the two graphs.

Additional Examples

1. Solve the system $\begin{cases} y = 3x + 2 \\ y = 2x - 4 \end{cases}$.
2. Fred wants to enclose a 400-square-meter rectangular garden with 70 meters of fencing. To do this, he must use one side of his barn as a side of the garden. What can the dimensions of the garden be?
3. Solve the system $\begin{cases} xy = 30 \\ x - y = 1 \end{cases}$.

   Solution Solve both equations for y: $y = \frac{30}{\_\_\_\_}$ and $y = x - $ ____. Graph both equations in a window that shows all points of intersection. The window dimensions are ____ $< x <$ ____ and ____ $< y <$ ____.

   Use the intersection feature of your grapher to identify the points of intersection. The graphs intersect at (____, ____) and (____, ____).

Resource Master for Lesson 5-2

Resource Master 77 Lesson 5-3

Warm-Up

In 1–3, solve the equation.

1. $5x + 2(10 - 4x) = 12$
2. $y - 2(y + 1) = 3$
3. $2(r + 7) + 11 + r = 0$

Additional Example

1. Trevian Stadium has a seating capacity of 4216. There are four times as many lower-level seats as upper-level seats. There are three times as many mezzanine seats as upper-level seats. How many seats of each type are there?

Solution Solve by hand using substitution. Let L = the number of lower-level seats, M = the number of mezzanine seats, and U = the number of upper-level seats. Then the system to be solved is

$$\begin{cases} L + M + U = 4216 \\ L = \_\_\_\_ \\ M = \_\_\_\_ \end{cases}.$$

Substitute your expressions for L and M in the last two equations into the first equation and solve for U: ____ + ____ + $U = 4216$. Because $8U = 4216$, $U =$ ____. Now substitute to find L and M: $L =$ ____ and $M =$ ____. Trevian Stadium has ____ upper-level seats, ____ lower-level seats, and ____ mezzanine seats.

Check Does $L = 4U$? Does $M = 3U$? Does $L + M + U = 4216$? If the answers are yes, then your solution to the system is correct.

Resource Master for Lesson 5-3

Resource Master 78 Lesson 5-3

Additional Examples

2. Solve the system $\begin{cases} y = 3x \\ xy = 48 \end{cases}$.
3. Solve the system $\begin{cases} x = 3 - 2y \\ 3x + 6y = 6 \end{cases}$.
4. Solve the system $\begin{cases} y = 6 - \frac{x}{8} \\ \frac{x}{3} + 2y = 12 \end{cases}$.

Resource Master for Lesson 5-3

Resource Master 80 Lesson 5-4

Resource Master 79 Lesson 5-4

Warm-Up

1. Find values of m and n so that $3m - 4n = 0$.
2. Find values of a and b so that $12a + 3b = 0$.
3. If $m(3x + 4y) + n(15x + 45y) = py$ for all x and y, find possible values of m, n, and p.

Additional Example

1. Solve the system $\begin{cases} 5x - 6y = 3 \\ 2x + 12y = 12 \end{cases}$ by the linear-combination method.

Resource Masters for Lesson 5-4

Resource Master 81 Lesson 5-4

Additional Example 2 Continued

Use the linear-combination method on this system. Subtract the second equation from the first and solve for z: ____ $= 12$; $z =$ ____.

Substitute this value of z into an equation involving just two variables, such as: $6x + 16z = 12$. Thus,

$6x + 16\left(\frac{3}{2}\right) = 12$

$6x =$ ____

$x =$ ____

Finally, substitute the values for z and x into one of the original equations: $5x + y + 6z = 3$. Thus,

$5(-2) + y + 6\left(\frac{3}{2}\right) = 3$, so

$y =$ ____.

The solution is $x =$ ____, $y =$ ____, and $z =$ ____, which can be written as the ordered triple $(x, y, z) =$ (____, ____, ____).

Resource Master for Lesson 5-4

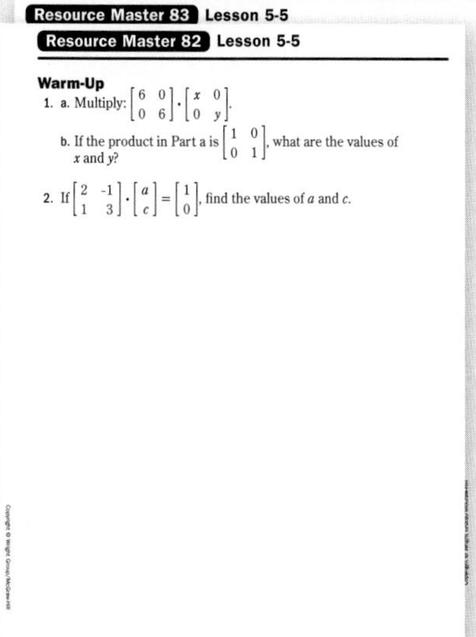

Resource Master 83 Lesson 5-5

Resource Master 82 Lesson 5-5

Warm-Up

1. a. Multiply: $\begin{bmatrix} 6 & 0 \\ 0 & 6 \end{bmatrix} \cdot \begin{bmatrix} x & 0 \\ 0 & y \end{bmatrix}$.

   b. If the product in Part a is $\begin{bmatrix} 1 & 0 \\ 0 & 1 \end{bmatrix}$, what are the values of x and y?

2. If $\begin{bmatrix} 2 & -1 \\ 1 & 3 \end{bmatrix} \cdot \begin{bmatrix} a \\ c \end{bmatrix} = \begin{bmatrix} 1 \\ 0 \end{bmatrix}$, find the values of a and c.

Resource Masters for Lesson 5-5

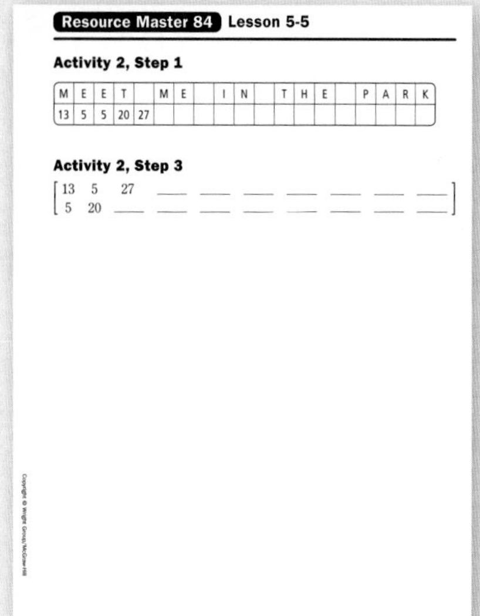

Resource Master 84 Lesson 5-5

Activity 2, Step 1

M	E	E	T		M	E		I	N		T	H	E		P	A	R	K
13	5	5	20	27														

Activity 2, Step 3

$\begin{bmatrix} 13 & 5 & 27 & \_\_ & \_\_ & \_\_ & \_\_ & \_\_ & \_\_ & \_\_ & \_\_ \\ 5 & 20 & \_\_ & \_\_ & \_\_ & \_\_ & \_\_ & \_\_ & \_\_ & \_\_ & \_\_ \end{bmatrix}$

Resource Master for Lesson 5-5

Resource Master 86 Lesson 5-6

Resource Master 85 Lesson 5-6

Warm-Up

1. Multiply: $\begin{bmatrix} -8 & 3 \\ 5 & -2 \end{bmatrix} \begin{bmatrix} x \\ y \end{bmatrix}$.

2. Solve for x and y: $\begin{bmatrix} -8 & 3 \\ 5 & -2 \end{bmatrix} \begin{bmatrix} x \\ y \end{bmatrix} = \begin{bmatrix} 12 \\ -17 \end{bmatrix}$.

Additional Example

1. Solve the system $\begin{bmatrix} 1 & 3 \\ 2 & -1 \end{bmatrix} \begin{bmatrix} x \\ y \end{bmatrix} = \begin{bmatrix} 22 \\ 2 \end{bmatrix}$.

   Solution First, find the inverse of the coefficient matrix:

   $\begin{bmatrix} 1 & 3 \\ 2 & -1 \end{bmatrix}^{-1} = \begin{bmatrix} \_\_ & \_\_ \\ \_\_ & \_\_ \end{bmatrix} = \begin{bmatrix} \_\_ & \_\_ \\ \_\_ & \_\_ \end{bmatrix}$.

   Next, multiply both sides of the equation on the left by the inverse:

   $\begin{bmatrix} \_\_ & \_\_ \\ \_\_ & \_\_ \end{bmatrix} \cdot \begin{bmatrix} 1 & 3 \\ 2 & -1 \end{bmatrix} \begin{bmatrix} x \\ y \end{bmatrix} = \begin{bmatrix} \_\_ & \_\_ \\ \_\_ & \_\_ \end{bmatrix} \begin{bmatrix} 22 \\ 2 \end{bmatrix}$.

   Find the product of each side:

   $\begin{bmatrix} \_\_ & \_\_ \\ \_\_ & \_\_ \end{bmatrix} \begin{bmatrix} x \\ y \end{bmatrix} = \begin{bmatrix} \_\_ \\ \_\_ \end{bmatrix}$.

   Because you multiplied by the inverse, the left side of the equation should now be $\begin{bmatrix} 1 & 0 \\ 0 & 1 \end{bmatrix} \begin{bmatrix} x \\ y \end{bmatrix}$. Thus,

   $\begin{bmatrix} x \\ y \end{bmatrix} = \begin{bmatrix} 4 \\ 6 \end{bmatrix}$, so $x =$ ____ and $y =$ ____.

Resource Masters for Lesson 5-6

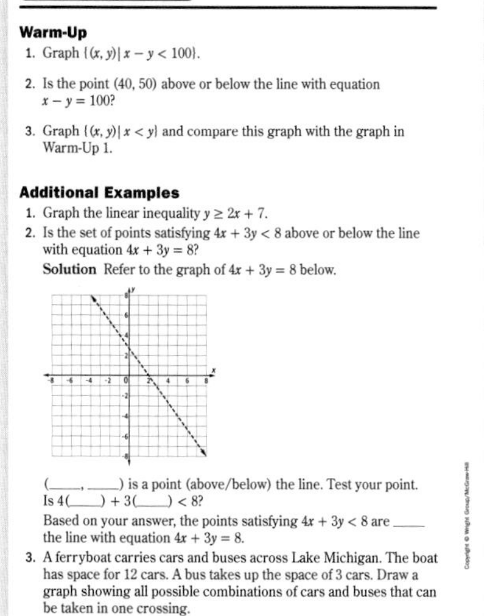

Resource Master 87 Lesson 5-7

Warm-Up

1. Graph $\{(x, y) | x - y < 100\}$.
2. Is the point (40, 50) above or below the line with equation $x - y = 100$?
3. Graph $\{(x, y) | x < y\}$ and compare this graph with the graph in Warm-Up 1.

Additional Examples

1. Graph the linear inequality $y \geq 2x + 7$.
2. Is the set of points satisfying $4x + 3y < 8$ above or below the line with equation $4x + 3y = 8$?

   Solution Refer to the graph of $4x + 3y = 8$ below.

   (____, ____) is a point (above/below) the line. Test your point. Is 4(____) + 3(____) < 8?

   Based on your answer, the points satisfying $4x + 3y < 8$ are ____ the line with equation $4x + 3y = 8$.
3. A ferryboat carries cars and buses across Lake Michigan. The boat has space for 12 cars. A bus takes up the space of 3 cars. Draw a graph showing all possible combinations of cars and buses that can be taken in one crossing.

Resource Master for Lesson 5-7

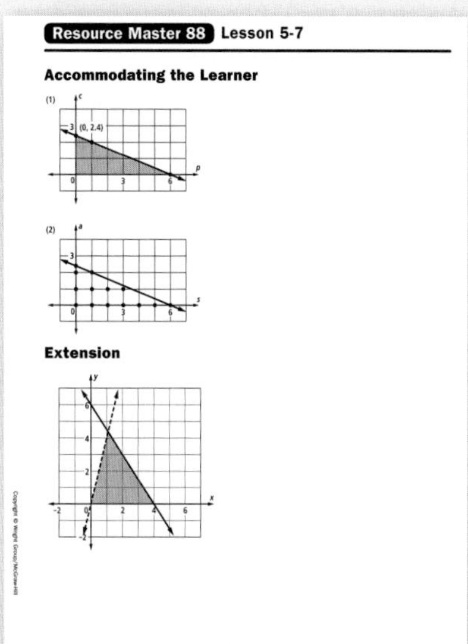

Resource Master 88 Lesson 5-7

Accommodating the Learner

Extension

Resource Master for Lesson 5-7

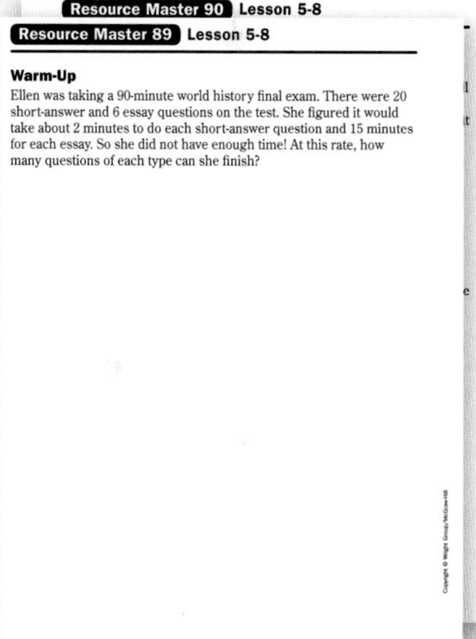

Resource Master 90 Lesson 5-8

Resource Master 89 Lesson 5-8

Warm-Up

Ellen was taking a 90-minute world history final exam. There were 20 short-answer and 6 essay questions on the test. She figured it would take about 2 minutes to do each short-answer question and 15 minutes for each essay. So she did not have enough time! At this rate, how many questions of each type can she finish?

Resource Masters for Lesson 5-8

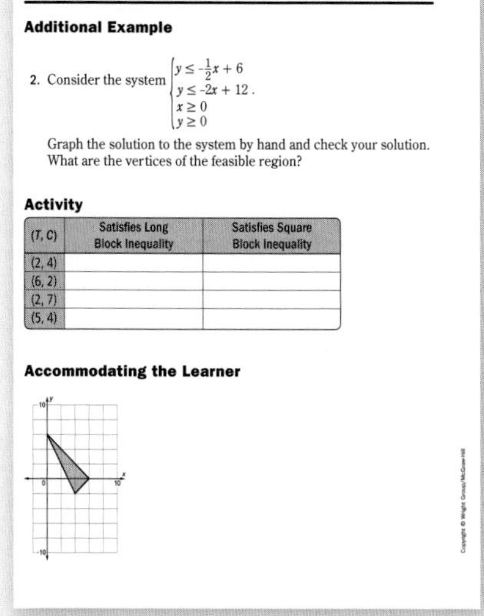

Resource Master 91 Lesson 5-8

Additional Example

2. Consider the system $\begin{cases} y \leq -\frac{1}{2}x + 6 \\ y \leq -2x + 12 \\ x \geq 0 \\ y \geq 0 \end{cases}$.

   Graph the solution to the system by hand and check your solution. What are the vertices of the feasible region?

Activity

(T, C)	Satisfies Long Block Inequality	Satisfies Square Block Inequality
(2, 4)		
(6, 2)		
(2, 7)		
(5, 4)		

Accommodating the Learner

Resource Master for Lesson 5-8

Resource Master 92 Lesson 5-9

Warm-Up

Consider the situation of the Warm-Up in Lesson 5-8. If Ellen correctly answers every question that she finishes, and if short-answer questions are worth 3 points each and essay questions 8 points each, what strategy should she use to maximize her score?

Additional Example

Lisa makes necklaces and bracelets in her spare time and sells all that she makes. Each week, she has 10,000 grams of metal and 20 hours (1200 minutes) to work. It takes 500 grams of metal for a necklace and 50 grams for a bracelet. Each necklace takes 30 minutes to make, and each bracelet takes 15 minutes.

a. Let n = the number of necklaces and b = the number of bracelets Lisa makes each week. Find the vertices of the region of pairs (n, b) Lisa can make each week. Draw a graph of the feasible region.

b. Lisa's weekly profit is \$8 on each necklace and \$5 on each bracelet. How many of each type of jewelry should Lisa make (and sell) each week to maximize her profit?

Resource Master for Lesson 5-9

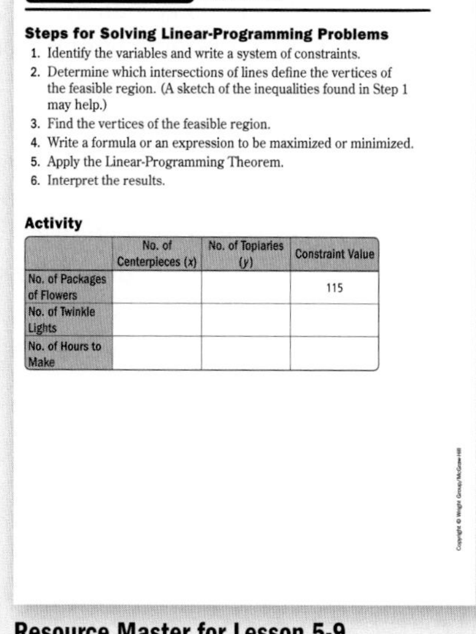

Resource Master 93 Lesson 5-9

Steps for Solving Linear-Programming Problems

1. Identify the variables and write a system of constraints.
2. Determine which intersections of lines define the vertices of the feasible region. (A sketch of the inequalities found in Step 1 may help.)
3. Find the vertices of the feasible region.
4. Write a formula or an expression to be maximized or minimized.
5. Apply the Linear-Programming Theorem.
6. Interpret the results.

Activity

	No. of Centerpieces (x)	No. of Topiaries (y)	Constraint Value
No. of Packages of Flowers			115
No. of Twinkle Lights			
No. of Hours to Make			

Resource Master for Lesson 5-9

Chapter 5

Pacing

Each lesson in this chapter is designed to be covered in 1 day except for Lesson 5-9, which may take up to 2 days. At the end of the chapter, you should plan to spend 1 day to review the Self-Test, 1 to 2 days for the Chapter Review, and 1 day for a test. You may wish to spend a day on projects and possibly a day is needed for quizzes. This chapter should therefore take 14 to 18 days. We strongly advise you not to spend more than 18 days on this chapter.

Overview

Some of the greatest mathematicians of all time have been involved in the history of developing methods for solving systems. The German mathematician Carl Gauss (who is mentioned in the text), Jean-Baptiste Joseph Fourier of France, and Arthur Cayley of Great Britain did important work in the theory of solving systems.

The importance of systems is evident by the fact that great mathematicians devoted time to them and also by the variety of uses to which systems have been applied. Some of these uses are mentioned in this chapter opener; students will see others as they study this chapter.

Chapter 5 reviews and extends the methods of solving systems of equations from first-year algebra and introduces two new concepts: solving systems using matrices and solving systems of linear inequalities, applying the latter to linear programming. Linear programming is an exciting application, and the chapter is structured so that students master all the prerequisite skills before solving linear-programming problems.

The authors use "punny" names quite often in this chapter. We hope your students enjoy them.

Chapter 5 Systems

Contents

The Fédération Internationale de Football Association (FIFA) is the international body that governs the game known in the United States as soccer. FIFA makes the rules for the soccer balls allowed in tournament play. Some requirements are:

- The circumference of the ball must be from 68 to 70 cm.
- The weight of the ball must be from 410 to 450 grams at the start of a match.
- The inflated pressure of the ball should be from 8.5 to 15.6 psi (pounds per square inch) at sea level.

Chapter 5 Overview

The first two lessons review the graphing associated with systems. Lesson 5-1 uses number lines to compare and contrast solutions to compound sentences of one variable connected by *and* or *or*. Lesson 5-2 reviews graphing 2×2 linear systems to estimate and find solutions. It then extends the technique to nonlinear systems with familiar curves, such as parabolas and rectangular hyperbolas. Additionally, Lesson 5-2 addresses finding solutions with tables.

Lessons 5-3 and 5-4 review the methods of substitution and linear combination with some important applications and extend these techniques to simple nonlinear or 3×3 linear systems. In Lesson 5-5, students are taught how to find the inverse of a 2×2 matrix and then how to use the inverse to code and decode messages. In Lesson 5-6, 2×2 linear systems are solved by using matrices, and the System-Determinant Theorem

Suppose C represents the circumference of the ball, w represents its weight, and p represents its pressure. The requirements on the previous page imply that a soccer ball must satisfy the following constraints:

$$\begin{cases} 68 \text{ cm} \le C \le 70 \text{ cm} \\ 410 \text{ grams} \le w \le 450 \text{ grams} \\ 8.5 \text{ psi} \le p \le 15.6 \text{ psi} \end{cases}$$

Notice that each *constraint* above involves just one variable. In other situations, a constraint may involve more than one variable.

When mathematical conditions are joined by the word *and*, the set of conditions or sentences is called a *system*. Systems have many applications. For instance, in the early 19th century, the German mathematician Carl Friedrich Gauss used systems of equations to calculate the orbits of asteroids from sightings made by a few astronomers. During World War II, the American mathematician George Dantzig was charged with the task of optimizing the distribution of forces and equipment for the U.S. Air Force. His work in this area led to advances in the field of *linear programming*. In 1945, the American economist George Stigler used linear programming to determine a best diet for the least cost. For his work, Stigler received a Nobel Prize in 1982. (This prize was in economics; there is no Nobel Prize in mathematics.) In this chapter you will study systems of equations and inequalities and their applications in the field of linear programming.

helps to identify the number of solutions for a 2×2 linear system. Some 3×3 linear systems are discussed in Lessons 5-3, 5-4, and 5-6. We expect students to solve them using substitution, linear combinations, or technology.

Lessons 5-7 and 5-8 set the stage for linear programming, which is studied in Lesson 5-9. Linear inequalities in two variables are graphed in Lesson 5-7.

Lesson 5-8 extends the idea of systems of inequalities, introduced in Lesson 5-1, to 2-dimensional inequalities. Lesson 5-9 introduces the technique for solving linear-programming problems that have been set up mathematically.

Using Pages 298–299

The three algebraic sentences on page 299 correspond to the bulleted list on the previous page. Because all of the sentences must be satisfied at once, taken together they form a system. Each inequality involves only one variable, and the problem is a 3-dimensional problem because three variables are involved.

Ask students to explain the meaning of the word *constraints,* which may be a new word to many of them. **Constraints are conditions that make it impossible for complete freedom in a situation; mathematically, they are restrictions on the values that variables can take.**

Students should not be surprised that soccer balls must be of a certain size and weight. They may be surprised that certain bounds on pressure must also be met. Also, the weight of a FIFA soccer ball cannot increase more than 10% as a result of water absorption.

Chapter 5 Projects

At the end of each chapter, you will find projects related to the chapter. At this time you might want to have students look over the projects on pages 362 and 363. You might want to have students tentatively select a project on which to work. Then, as students read and progress through the chapter, they can finalize their project choices.

Sometimes students might work alone. At other times, you might let them collaborate with classmates for a presentation and discussion. We recommend that you allow for diversity and encourage students to use their imaginations when presenting their projects. As students work on projects throughout the year, they should see many uses of mathematics in the real world.

Lesson 5-1

GOAL

Review the graphing of inequalities on the number line, the distinction between the words *and* and *or*, and the symbols for the union and intersection of sets.

SPUR Objectives

The SPUR Objectives for all of Chapter 5 are found in the Chapter Review on pages 367–371.

H Solve and graph linear inequalities in one variable.

Materials/Resources

- Lesson Masters 5-1A and 5-1B
- Resource Masters 4, 74, and 75
- CAS

HOMEWORK

Suggestions for Assignment

- Questions 1–24
- Questions 25 and 26 (extra credit)
- Reading Lesson 5-2
- Covering the Ideas 5-2

Local Standards

1 Warm-Up

Refer to the constraints on a soccer ball listed on page 298.

1. What is the least possible circumference of a tournament soccer ball? 68 cm
2. What is the greatest possible circumference of a tournament soccer ball? 70 cm
3. Give the least and greatest possible diameters of a soccer ball, to the nearest tenth of a centimeter. 21.6 cm; 22.3 cm

Lesson 5-1 Inequalities and Compound Sentences

Vocabulary

compound sentence
intersection of two sets
double inequality
union of two sets

▶ **BIG IDEA** The graph of a linear inequality in one variable is a ray either with or without its endpoint.

Compound Sentences

In English, you can use the words *and* and *or* as conjunctions to join two or more clauses. In mathematics, these two words are used in a similar way. A sentence in which two clauses are connected by the word *and* or by the word *or* is called a **compound sentence**. For example, the requirement that a soccer ball's circumference C satisfy the single sentence $68 \text{ cm} \le C \le 70 \text{ cm}$ is mathematical shorthand for the compound sentence "$68 \text{ cm} \le C$ *and* $C \le 70$ cm."

You can enter compound sentences on a CAS.

Mental Math

Find the union or intersection.

a. $\{1, 4, 7, 11\} \cap \{3, 5, 7, 9, 11\}$ $\{7, 11\}$

b. the set of all odd integers $\cup$ the set of all even integers the set of all integers

c. the set of all odd integers $\cap$ the set of all even integers $\emptyset$

d. the set of all real numbers $\cup$ the set of all integers the set of all real numbers

Activity

MATERIALS CAS

Step 1 Make a table like the one below. Clear all variables in your CAS memory, then enter each compound sentence into your CAS and record the output.

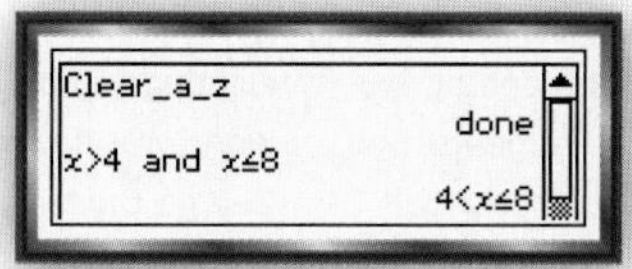

Compound Sentence Entry	$x > 4$ and $x \le 8$	$x > 4$ or $x \le 8$	$a < 5$ and $a < 20$	$a < 5$ or $a < 20$	$n < 0$ and $n > 5$	$n < 0$ or $n > 5$
CAS Output	?	?	?	?	?	?

$4 < x \le 8$; true; $a < 5$; $a < 20$; false; $n < 0$ or $n > 5$

Step 2 In some cases, the output is only one word, either true or false. What do you notice about situations that lead to these results? See margin.

Step 3 Examine each pair of compound sentences that only differ by the connecting word *and* versus *or* (such as "$x > 4$ and $x \le 8$" and "$x > 4$ or $x \le 8$"). In each pair, which output includes more values in its solution? Explain why you think this is the case. See margin.

Background

In this book, inequalities are often discussed with equations. We do this for two major reasons: (1) There are analogies between equation solving and inequality solving that help students understand both procedures. (2) The application situations that lead to equations can almost always lead to inequalities.

The content of this lesson should not be new to students. Solving and graphing the solutions of inequalities are topics that most have seen in a previous algebra course. Translating application situations into inequalities, however, may be new to students who have not studied from previous UCSMP courses.

Step 4 Store values for variables x, a, and n, as indicated in the table below. Then enter each sentence and record the output.

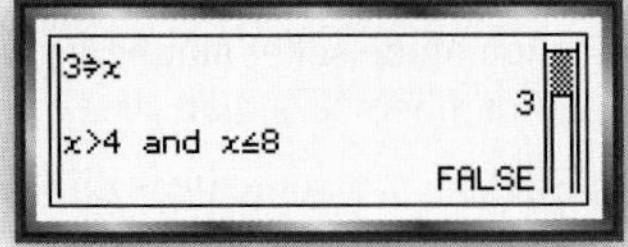

Stored Variable	$3 \rightarrow x$	$3 \rightarrow x$	$1 \rightarrow a$	$1 \rightarrow a$	$2 \rightarrow n$	$2 \rightarrow n$
Compound Sentence Entry	$x > 4$ and $x \leq 8$	$x > 4$ or $x \leq 8$	$a < 5$ and $a < 20$	$a < 5$ or $a < 20$	$n < 0$ and $n > 5$	$n < 0$ or $n > 5$
CAS Output	?	?	?	?	?	?

false; true; true; true; false; false

Step 5 Summarize the results of Step 4. In general, when are outputs of compound sentences with assigned variables true and when are they false? See margin.

QY1

> **QY1**
> If 8 is stored as x, what output do you expect from your CAS if you enter "$x = 8$ and $x = 5$"? If you enter "$x = 8$ or $x = 5$"?

Compound Sentences Using the Word *and*

The solution set for a compound sentence using *and* consists of the *intersection* of the solution sets of the individual sentences. Recall that the **intersection of two sets** is the set consisting of those values common to both sets. The graph of the intersection consists of the points common to the graphs of the individual sets.

For instance, roller coasters are classified according to maximum height achieved during the ride. A gigacoaster is a roller coaster that reaches a height of at least 300 feet, but less than 400 feet. In symbols, $H \geq 300$ and $H < 400$. The solution sets of the individual sentences, $\{H \mid H \geq 300\}$ and $\{H \mid H < 400\}$, are *intervals*.

The graph of the interval $\{H \mid H \geq 300\}$ is a ray. The graph of $\{H \mid H < 400\}$ is a ray without its endpoint.

The intersection of these two graphs is the graph of required height. The intersection can be described by the single compound sentence $300 \leq H < 400$, which is called a **double inequality** because it has two inequality symbols.

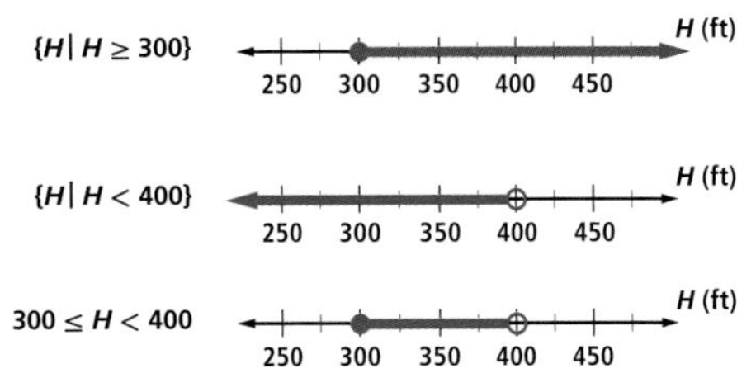

Recall that the symbol used for intersection is $\cap$. So the intersection of sets A and B is written $A \cap B$. In set notation,

$$\{H \mid 300 \leq H < 400\} = \{H \mid H \geq 300\} \cap \{H \mid H < 400\}.$$

2 Teaching

Notes on the Lesson

Activity In this Activity, students enter "$x > 4$ and $x \leq 8$" into a CAS and record the CAS output. The answer key shows the result as "$4 < x \leq 8$"; however, not all CAS will show the compressed format of the inequality. They may simply repeat what was entered.

Compound sentences using the word *and* The open-circle, shaded-circle distinction in the graphs of inequalities is troublesome for some students. Stress that any time a sentence is graphed, only those points belonging to the solution set are to be graphed (or shaded). The open circle is an efficient way to mark a nonincluded endpoint of a ray or segment.

Additional Answers

Activity

Step 2: *True* is displayed when all real numbers satisfy the compound sentence, and *false* is displayed when no real numbers satisfy the compound sentence.

Step 3: Compound sentences involving the word *or* include more values in their solution set than compound sentences involving the word *and* because solutions to *or* sentences have to satisfy only part of the sentence.

Step 5: When the stored value satisfies the compound sentence, the output is *true;* when the stored value does not satisfy the compound sentence, the output is *false.*

This lesson requires attention to detail, and even students who know the concepts will need to pay close attention when answering the Questions. Students need to carefully compare and contrast solutions to compound sentences using the words *and* and *or,* along with using set notation and the symbols $\cup$ and $\cap$, which represent *union* and *intersection,* respectively.

Accommodating the Learner

Ask students to explain why it is necessary to reverse the inequality sign when multiplying by a negative number. Explanations should be based on the fact that the greater the negative number, the less its absolute value. If a and b are positive and $a > b$, then $|-a| > |-b|$ and $-a < -b$. If a and b are positive and $-a < -b$, then $|-a| > |-b|$ and $a > b$. Have students supply numerical values to verify their reasoning.

Notes on the Lesson

Compound sentences using the word *or* The distinctions between *and* and *or* and between *union* and *intersection* are key concepts in this lesson. To distinguish between union and intersection, suggest that students think of a labor union wanting as many members as possible and street intersections containing only those points that are in both crossing streets. Point out that the symbol ∪ looks like a U for union.

This can be read "the set of numbers from 300 up to but not including 400 equals the intersection of the set of numbers greater than or equal to 300 and the set of numbers less than 400."

When describing an interval in English, it is sometimes difficult to know whether endpoints are included. In this book, we use the following language:

"x is *from* 3 to 4" means $3 \le x \le 4$. The endpoints are included.

"x is *between* 3 and 4" means $3 < x < 4$. The endpoints are not included.

This is consistent with the use of the word "between" in geometry. When just one endpoint is included, as in "$3 \le x < 4$," we say "x is 3 or between 3 and 4," or "x is at least 3 and less than 4."

 QY2

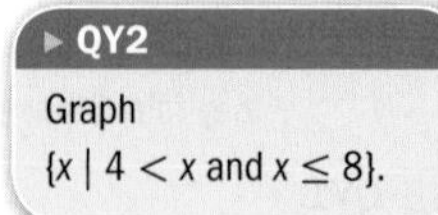

▶ QY2
Graph $\{x \mid 4 < x \text{ and } x \le 8\}$.

Compound Sentences Using the Word *or*

Recall that the **union of two sets** is the set consisting of those values in *either one or both* sets. This meaning of *or* is somewhat different from the everyday meaning *either, but not both*. The symbol often used for union is ∪. The union of sets A and B is written $A \cup B$.

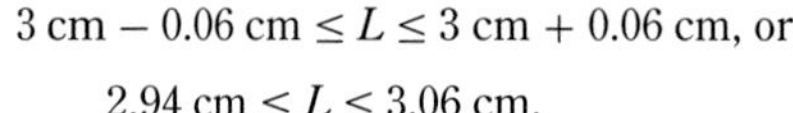

The solution set for a compound sentence using *or* consists of the union of the solution sets to the individual sentences. For example, suppose you are the quality-control examiner in a factory that produces cell-phone batteries. For one type of battery, the specification states that battery length L must be 3 cm ± 0.06 cm. (Recall that the symbol ± means *plus or minus*.) Batteries produced with a length outside the acceptable range are rejected. L must lie in the interval

$$3 \text{ cm} - 0.06 \text{ cm} \le L \le 3 \text{ cm} + 0.06 \text{ cm, or}$$

$$2.94 \text{ cm} \le L \le 3.06 \text{ cm}.$$

So, the battery will be rejected if $L < 2.94$ or $L > 3.06$.

In set notation, $\{L \mid L < 2.94 \text{ or } L > 3.06\} = \{L \mid L < 2.94\} \cup \{L \mid L > 3.06\}$.

These sets are graphed below.

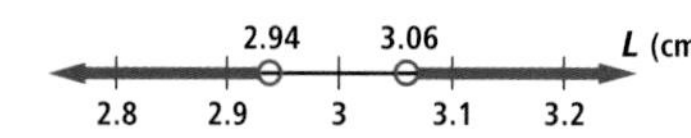

 QY3

▶ QY3
Graph $\{A \mid A < 12 \text{ or } A > 65\}$.

Accommodating the Learner

Have students compare and contrast compound sentences that are similar but not identical. Have them graph the compound inequalities in 1–4.

1. $x > 8$ and $x > 4$

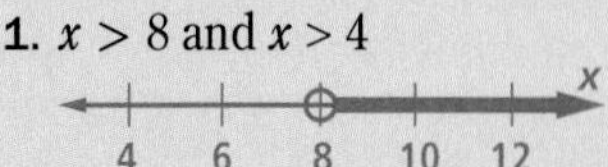

2. $x < 8$ and $x < 4$

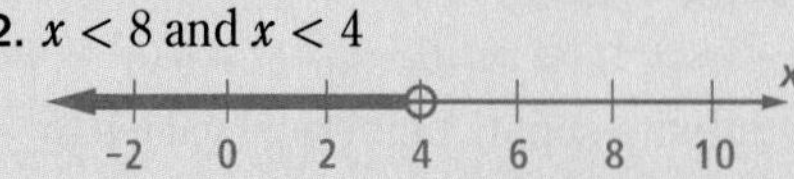

3. $x > 8$ and $x < 4$

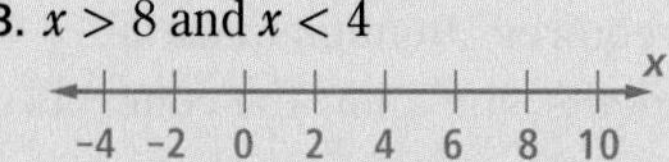

4. $x < 8$ and $x > 4$

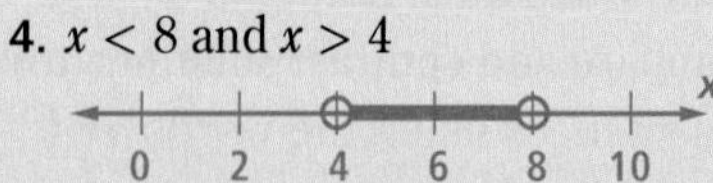

Solving Linear Inequalities

Solving a linear inequality is very much like solving a linear equation. The only difference is that when you multiply or divide each side of an inequality by a negative number, you must *reverse* the inequality sign.

Properties of Inequality

For all real numbers a, b, and c:

Addition Property of Inequality
If $a < b$, then $a + c < b + c$.

Multiplication Property of Inequality
If $a < b$ and $c > 0$, then $ac < bc$.
If $a < b$ and $c < 0$, then $ac > bc$.

This Example illustrates an application of linear inequalities.

Example

Penny Nichols has $500 to buy stock options at $17.50 per option. She wants to stop buying options as soon as she has less than $100. (Stock options from a company give an employee the right to buy shares of the company's stock at a designated price.)

a. How many options should she buy before stopping?

b. How much money will she have left?

Solution

a. Let s = the number of options bought. After buying s options Penny will have $500 - 17.50s$ dollars left. She will stop buying stock as soon as $500 - 17.50s < 100$. Solve the inequality.

$500 - 17.50s < 100$

$-17.50s < -400$ Subtract 500 from both sides.

$s > \frac{-400}{-17.5}$ Divide both sides by -17.5. (Notice that the inequality sign is reversed in this step.)

$s > 22.86$

So, Penny will have less than $100 left when $s > 22.86$. Penny should purchase 23 options before stopping.

b. To find how much money Penny has left, we substitute 23 into the expression in Part a. Penny has $\$500 - \$17.50(23) = \$97.50$ left.

Check To check the solution, use the `solve` command on a CAS. It gives the same result.

Notes on the Lesson

Example Students will probably know that the techniques used to solve inequalities are essentially the same as those used to solve equations, and they see this here. However, students need to be reminded that the direction of the inequality reverses when multiplying or dividing by a negative number. You can illustrate why the direction must be changed by using $3 < 5$. If you multiply both sides by 2, the inequality is still true—$3(2) < 5(2)$. However, if you multiply both sides by -2, the less than sign must be changed to a greater than sign for the inequality to be true—$3(-2) > 5(-2)$.

Remind students that doing a check is an important part of solving a problem. To determine whether an answer is correct, one must be able to check it. The worst way to check a problem is to do it using the same method, because errors are likely to be repeated. Encourage your students to check using a different method.

Sometimes, students are unsure if a sentence should be graphed on a number line or on a coordinate plane. Point out that when a sentence is expressed in set-builder notation, the variables preceding the vertical bar indicate whether a solution is to be found in one dimension or two. For example, the letter s in $\{s \mid 45 \le s \le 55\}$ and the ordered pair (x, y) in $\{(x, y) \mid x \le 3\}$ indicate to find a solution in 1 dimension and 2 dimensions, respectively.

Additional Example

Example A ticket agency has 300 tickets for a playoff game. Each customer can purchase 2 tickets. When the agency has 50 tickets or fewer, the agency tries to obtain more tickets to sell.

a. How many customers can purchase tickets before the agency needs more tickets? 125

b. How many tickets will be left after the first 75 customers have each purchased 2 tickets? 150

Now have students graph the compound inequalities in 5–8.

5. $x > 8$ or $x > 4$

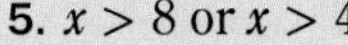
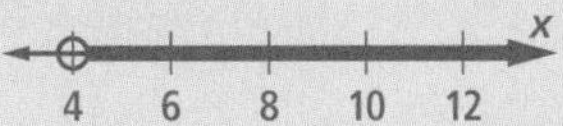

6. $x < 8$ or $x < 4$

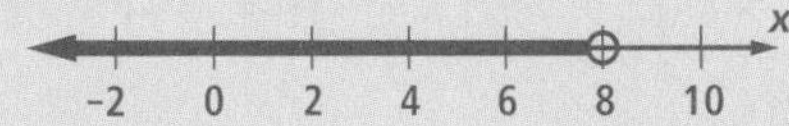

7. $x > 8$ or $x < 4$

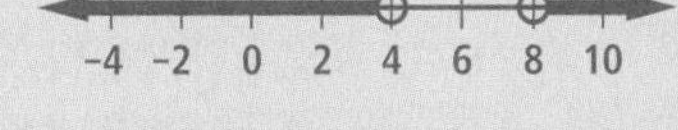

8. $x < 8$ or $x > 4$

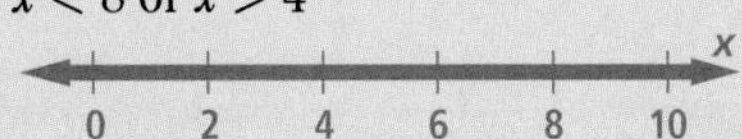

Discuss with students how the graphs in 5–8 differ from those in 1–4, respectively. Answers vary. Students should notice that the sentences with *or* have more solutions.

3 Assignment

Recommended Assignment

- Questions 1–24
- Questions 25 and 26 (extra credit)
- Reading Lesson 5-2
- Covering the Ideas 5-2

Notes on the Questions

Question 3 Point out that either of the following two answers is correct: 14 hr 48 min $\geq h \geq$ 9 hr 29 min or 9 hr 29 min $\leq h \leq$ 14 hr 48 min. If students are uncomfortable with the mixed units on the left and right sides of these double inequalities, point out that the times could be changed to either hours or minutes. In hours, $14\frac{4}{5} \geq h \geq 9\frac{29}{60}$. In minutes, $888 \geq h \geq 569$.

Questions 7, 9, 10, and 18 These questions are especially useful for comparing and contrasting *and* with *or* and *union* with *intersection*.

5-1A Lesson Master

Questions on SPUR Objectives
See Student Edition pages 367–371 for objectives.

REPRESENTATIONS Objective H

In 1 and 2, write the inequality for the set of numbers that is graphed on the number line.

1. $a > -4.2$
2. $t \leq 0.03$

In 3 and 4, solve the inequality, and then graph the solution set on the number line.

3. $2.5a + 7 \geq 22$ $a \geq 6$
4. $10 - 3x > -2$ $x < 4$

In 5 and 6, write the compound inequality for the set of numbers that is graphed on the number line.

5. $-2 < x < 3$
6. $u \leq 17.76$ or $u > 17.83$

In 7 and 8, graph the solution set on a number line.

7. $\{x \mid -3 \leq x \leq 5\}$
8. $\{t \mid 0 \leq t \leq 4\} \cup \{t \mid t > 6\}$

9. Suppose people 18 and under or 65 and older are eligible for discount fares on city buses.
   a. Write a compound inequality in set notation for a, the ages of people eligible for discount fares. $\{a \mid 0 < a \leq 18\} \cup \{a \mid a \geq 65\}$
   b. Graph your inequality.

10. Give the CAS output when each of the compound sentences is entered, assuming the variable a is first cleared. Then graph the solution set on the number line at the right of each compound sentence.
    a. $a > -1$ and $a < 2$ $-1 < a < 2$
    b. $a > -1$ or $a < 2$ true
    c. $a < -1$ and $a > 2$ false; no solution to graph
    d. $a < -1$ or $a > 2$ $a \leq -1$ or $a > 2$

230 Advanced Algebra

Questions

COVERING THE IDEAS

In 1–3, translate the statement into a mathematical inequality and graph the inequality.

1. To ride the T-Bar in Blizzard Beach at Disney World, you must be under 4' tall. $0 < h < 4$
2. In order to fit snugly into the box, the paperweight has to be between 7.5 and 7.6 cm in diameter. $7.5 < d < 7.6$
3. In Louisville, Kentucky, the number of hours of daylight in a day ranges over a year from about 14 hr 48 min to about 9 hr 29 min. $9\frac{29}{60} \leq h \leq 14\frac{48}{60}$
4. A new soccer ball was manufactured for the 2006 World Cup Soccer Tournament. The ball had a circumference between 69 and 69.25 cm, a weight between 441 and 444 g, and a possible weight gain due to water absorption less than 0.1%.
   a. Represent circumference C, weight w, and percent weight gain g due to water absorption as inequalities. $69 < C < 69.25$, $441 < w < 444$, $0 \leq g < 0.001$
   b. Refer to the first page of the chapter. Does this ball meet the FIFA requirements for circumference and weight? yes
5. **Multiple Choice** Which inequality represents the statement "The weight L of airplane carry-on luggage may be no more than 25 pounds"? B

   A $25 < L$ B $L \leq 25$
   C $25 > L$ D $L \geq 25$
6. Write an inequality for the set of numbers graphed at the right. $-\frac{1}{3} \leq x < 3$

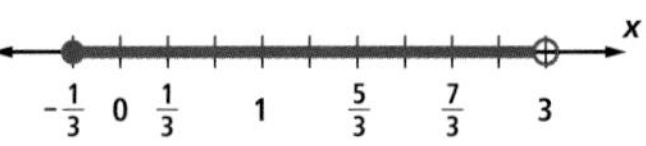

7. a. The solution set for a compound sentence using ***and*** is the __?__ of the solution sets to the individual sentences. intersection
   b. The solution set for a compound sentence using ***or*** is the __?__ of solution sets to the individual sentences. union
8. Assume all variables are cleared in a CAS memory.
   a. **Matching** Match each CAS entry at the left with its output at the right.

      i. $x > 1$ and $x < 4$ C A `x < 1 or x > 4`
      ii. $x > 1$ or $x < 4$ D B `false`
      iii. $x < 1$ or $x > 4$ A C `1 < x < 4`
      iv. $x < 1$ and $x > 4$ B D `true`
   b. Graph the solution set for each compound sentence. See margin.

In 9 and 10, graph the solution set on a number line. See margin.

9. $x \leq -7$ or $x > -2$
10. $t \leq -7$ and $t > -2$

Additional Answers

8b.

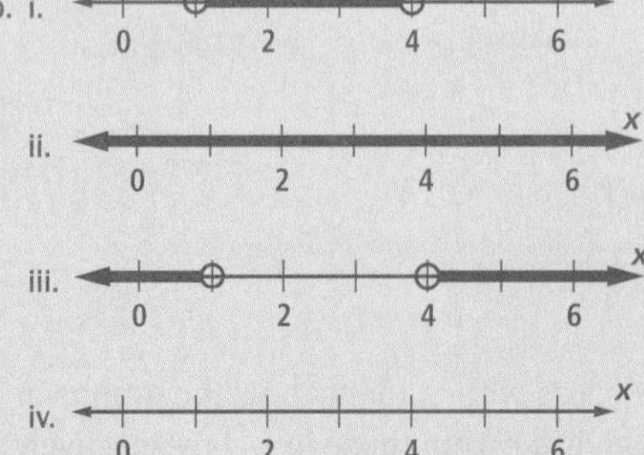

9.

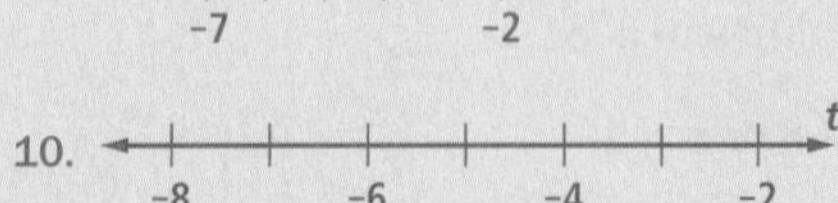

10.

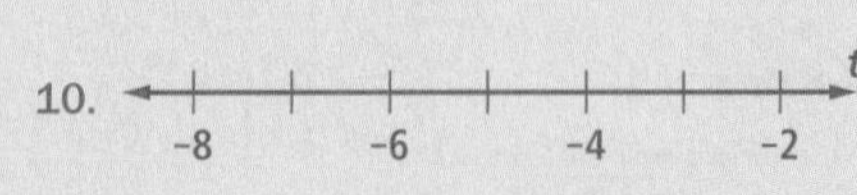

11. Three roller coasters and their maximum heights are listed below. Which ones are gigacoasters? Steel Dragon 2000

Rollercoaster	Location	Maximum Height (ft)
Kingda Ka	Jackson, NJ	456
Steel Dragon 2000	Nagashima, Japan	318
Superman El Último Escape	Mexico City, Mexico	220

Source: Ultimate Rollercoaster

12. In the Example, suppose Penny had \$750 to spend and stock options cost \$19.00 per share. If she stops buying stock when she first has \$50 or less left, how many shares of stock will she buy? 37

13. **Fill in the Blanks** When you __?__ or __?__ both sides of an inequality by a negative number, you must __?__ the inequality sign. multiply; divide; reverse

In 14 and 15, solve by hand or with a CAS. Graph all solutions.

14. $\frac{2}{3}x \leq \frac{1}{2}$

15. $-5m - 0.4 > 1$

14. $x \leq \frac{3}{4}$

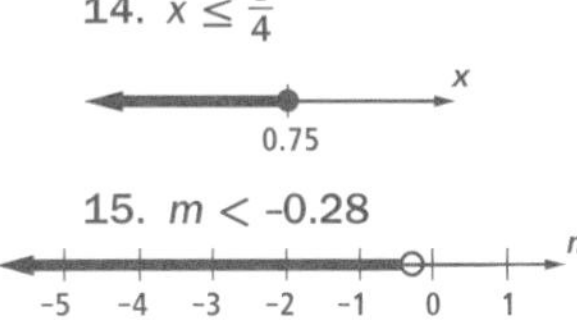

15. $m < -0.28$

m
-5 -4 -3 -2 -1 0 1

APPLYING THE MATHEMATICS

16. Suppose a small plane weighs 1615 pounds and an average passenger weighs 146 pounds.
    a. Write an expression representing the total weight of the airplane with p people on board. $1615 + 146p$
    b. How many people can the airplane hold if the total weight limit is 2300 pounds? 4

17. *From The Mixed-up Files of Mrs. Basil E. Frankweiler* (Konigsburg, 1967) tells the story of Claudia and Jamie, who run away from home and live in the Metropolitan Museum of Art in New York City for a short while. Short on money, Jamie argues with Claudia about spending money to ride the bus. He wants to save their \$24.43 for food and other necessities.
    a. In 1967, it cost 20 cents per person to ride the bus in New York City. If Jamie and Claudia both ride the bus, how many rides r could they take together? Write your answer as a double inequality that includes all possible values. $0 \leq r \leq 61$
    b. In 2008, it cost \$2.00 to ride the bus in New York City. Write a double inequality that includes all possible values for r in 2008. $0 \leq r \leq 6$

Six New York City bus routes have stops for the Metropolitan Museum of Art.

Notes on the Questions

Question 11 *Gigacoaster* is defined in the lesson on page 301.

Question 17 Students may need help in writing the inequalities for this question. They should not be upset at this point if they are unable to do it by themselves. Point out that in the following lessons there will be numerous opportunities to practice translating application problems into inequalities.

ENGLISH LEARNERS

Vocabulary Development

Have volunteers give real-world examples of compound sentences using *and* and *or.* Then use the following activity to help students distinguish *union* from *intersection.*

Identify two sets of students, making sure that at least one student is in both sets, for example, students wearing blue slacks and students wearing white tops. Have those students wearing blue slacks stand. Then have all students wearing white tops stand. Explain that the joining of all students in one or the other set forms the *union* of the two sets. Now have all students wearing both blue slacks and white tops remain standing. Explain that these students are in both sets and form the *intersection* of the sets.

Notes on the Questions

Questions 20–23 These questions help to introduce the next lesson by reminding students of equations and graphs of lines.

Question 26 This is an engaging question that can also be very instructive in showing the difference between *and* and *or* outside mathematics.

4 Wrap-Up

Ongoing Assessment

Have students work in pairs. Have one student write an inequality in one variable that uses <, >, ≤, or ≥ and draw its graph. Have the other student write a second inequality and draw the graph of that inequality. Then have the pair graph the intersection and the union of the two inequalities. Students should demonstrate that they can graph compound sentences that use *and* or *or*.

Project Update

Project 5, *Programming and CAS*, on page 363 relates to the content of this lesson.

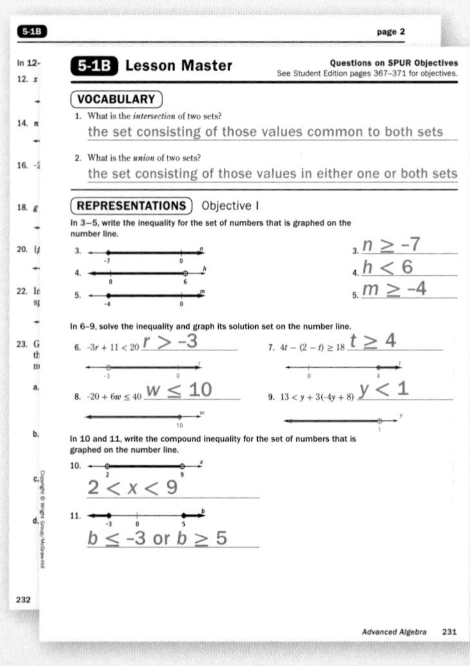

5-1B page 2

5-1B Lesson Master — Questions on SPUR Objectives. See Student Edition pages 367–371 for objectives.

VOCABULARY

1. What is the *intersection* of two sets? the set consisting of those values common to both sets
2. What is the *union* of two sets? the set consisting of those values in either one or both sets

REPRESENTATIONS Objective I

In 3–5, write the inequality for the set of numbers that is graphed on the number line.

3. $n \geq -7$
4. $h < 6$
5. $m \geq -4$

In 6–9, solve the inequality and graph its solution set on the number line.

6. $-3r + 11 < 20$ $r > -3$
7. $4t - (2 - t) \geq 18$ $t \geq 4$
8. $-20 + 6w \leq 40$ $w \leq 10$
9. $13 < y + 3(-4y + 8)$ $y < 1$

In 10 and 11, write the compound inequality for the set of numbers that is graphed on the number line.

10. $2 < x < 9$
11. $b \leq -3$ or $b \geq 5$

Copyright © Wright Group/McGraw-Hill

232

Advanced Algebra 231

18. Omar solved $x^2 = 5$ and wrote "$x = \sqrt{5}$ and $x = -\sqrt{5}$." What is wrong with Omar's answer?

19. Solve the compound sentence $7m + 2 < 23$ and $8 - 3m \leq 9$ for m. Write the final answer using set-builder notation and provide a graph of the solution set.

18. Omar used the wrong connecting word. He should have written "$x = \sqrt{5}$ or $x = -\sqrt{5}$."

19. $\{m \mid -\frac{1}{3} \leq m < 3\}$

REVIEW

In 20 and 21, line m has equation $y = -2x + 8$. Line m' is the image of line m under a translation. Suppose line m' contains the point (4, 8).

20. Find an equation for m'. **(Lessons 4-10, 3-4)**
21. Find a translation that maps m onto m'. **(Lesson 4-10)**

20. Answers vary, Sample: $y = -2x + 16$

21. Answers vary, Sample: $T_{0,8}$

22. Find an equation for the line that passes through the origin and is perpendicular to the line with equation $2x - 3y = -6$. **(Lessons 4-9, 3-4)** $y = -\frac{3}{2}x$

23. **Multiple Choice** Which of the equations below is equivalent to the equation $4x - 3y = 12$? **(Lesson 3-3)** C

    A $4x + 3y = 12$ B $-3x + 4y = 12$
    C $8x - 6y = 24$ D $-8x + 6y = 2$

24. A *duathlon* is a sporting event involving running and cycling. While training for a duathlon, Gustavo ran for R hours at 10 kilometers per hour and cycled for C hours at 28 kilometers per hour. He went a total of 50 kilometers. **(Lessons 3-3, 3-2)**
    a. Write a linear combination equation describing this situation.
    b. Graph your equation from Part a with R as the independent variable.
    c. What does the point (1.5, 1.25) represent on the graph?

24a. $10R + 28C = 50$

24b.

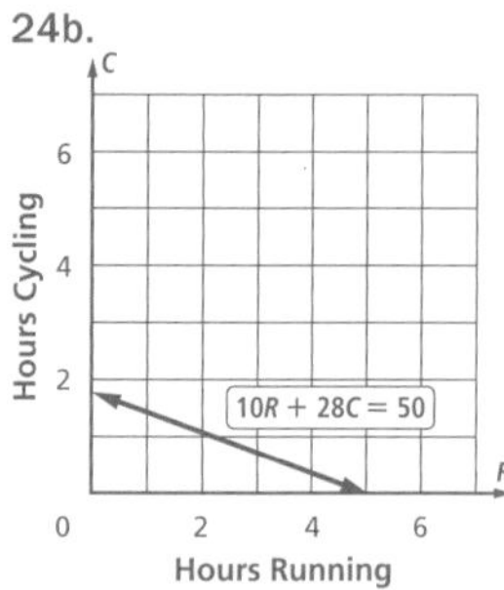

24c. This represents the case where Gustavo runs for 1.5 hr and cycles for 1.25 hr.

EXPLORATION

25. Data on average daily temperature highs and lows are collected for many cities by month, and published on the Internet. Find January temperature data for three different cities. For each city, write the temperature range of average daily lows and highs as a compound inequality. See margin.

26. In ordinary usage, replacing *or* by *and* can dramatically change the meaning of a sentence. For instance, "Give me liberty and give me death" differs from Patrick Henry's famous saying only by that one word. Find examples of other sayings that have a change in meaning when "and" is replaced with "or," or vice versa. See margin.

QY ANSWERS

1. false; true
2.
3.

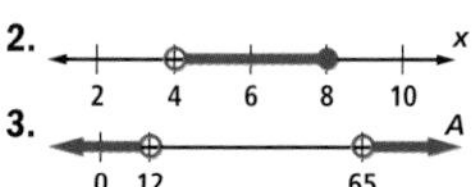

Additional Answers

25. Answers vary. Sample:

City	Temp. Range of Avg. Daily Highs (°F)	Temp. Range of Avg. Daily Lows (°F)
Chicago	$31 \leq T \leq 33$	$18 \leq T \leq 20$
New York	$36 \leq T \leq 38$	$29 \leq T \leq 31$
Miami	$76 \leq T \leq 77$	$59 \leq T \leq 60$

26. Answers vary. Sample: Yoda, in *The Empire Strikes Back*, says, "Do or do not. There is no 'try.'" Replacing "or" with "and" makes the quote incomprehensible.

Extension

Have students solve the following inequalities. You might suggest that they use a graphing utility and graph the left side of each inequality as y_1 and the right side as y_2. They can use the trace key to find values of x for which y_1 is less than or greater than y_2.

1. $x^2 + 5x - 6 < 0$ $-6 < x < 1$
2. $\frac{2}{x-4} > 1$ $4 < x < 6$
3. $|2x - 5| > 7$ $x < -1$ or $x > 6$

Lesson 5-2 Solving Systems Using Tables, Graphs, or a CAS

Vocabulary

system

solution set of a system

▸ **BIG IDEA** The solution(s) to a system of equations in two variables can be estimated by examining a table or graph and often solved exactly by using a CAS.

Minnie Strikes and Noah Spares are in a bowling league in which players are ranked using a handicap system. The maximum handicap is 50 pins per game and depends on the player's average. Minnie has a high average, so she has a low 5-pin handicap. Noah has a low average; his handicap is 45 pins. Noah practices, and his handicap decreases by 5 pins each month. Minnie does not practice, and her handicap increases by 3 pins per month. So after x months; Noah's handicap $N(x)$ is $45 - 5x$ and Minnie's handicap $M(x)$ is $5 + 3x$.

If the situation continues, then at some point Minnie's and Noah's handicaps will be the same. To determine when this will happen, you can solve a *system of equations*. Remember that a **system** is a set of conditions joined by the word *and*. Thus, if we call the handicaps y, the following compound sentence models the situation where the handicaps are equal: $y = 45 - 5x$ *and* $y = 5 + 3x$.

A system is often denoted by a brace: $\begin{cases} y = 45 - 5x \\ y = 5 + 3x \end{cases}$.

The **solution set of a system** is the intersection of the solution sets of the individual sentences in the system.

Mental Math

Suppose that the amount of hair a cat sheds varies directly as the square of the cat's height.

a. Fraidy is 3 times as tall as she was when she was a kitten. How much hair does she shed now compared to when she was a kitten? 9 times as much

b. Mittens is 1.2 times as tall as Fluffy. How much hair does Mittens shed compared to Fluffy? 1.44 times as much

c. Suppose that a Burmese sheds four times as much as a Siamese. How many times as tall as the Siamese is the Burmese? 2 times as tall

Finding Solutions Using Tables and Graphs

To solve a system, you can create a table or a graph. To speed up graphing, use the equations in slope-intercept form.

Noah's handicap $N(x) = -5x + 45$

Minnie's handicap $M(x) = 3x + 5$

The table and graph show that the handicaps $M(x)$ and $N(x)$ both equal 20 when $x = 5$. They also show that when $x < 5$, Minnie has a lower handicap than Noah. When $x > 5$, Noah's handicap is lower.

Month	$N(x)$	$M(x)$
0	45	5
1	40	8
2	35	11
3	30	14
4	25	17
5	20	20
6	15	23
7	10	26

Lesson 5-2

GOAL

Learn how to solve systems of equations (both linear systems and systems in which one equation is not linear) without using algebraic equation-solving techniques.

SPUR Objectives

D Recognize properties of systems of equations.

F Use systems of two linear equations to solve real-world problems.

I Estimate solutions to systems by graphing.

Materials/Resources

- Lesson Masters 5-2A and 5-2B
- Resource Masters 2 and 76

HOMEWORK

Suggestions for Assignment

- Questions 1–21
- Question 22 (extra credit)
- Reading Lesson 5-3
- Covering the Ideas 5-3

Local Standards

1 Warm-Up

1. Graph all solutions (x, y) to the equation $xy = 6$.
2. On the same grid, graph $\{(x, y) \mid x - y = 5\}$.
3. Find the coordinates of the points of intersection of the two graphs.

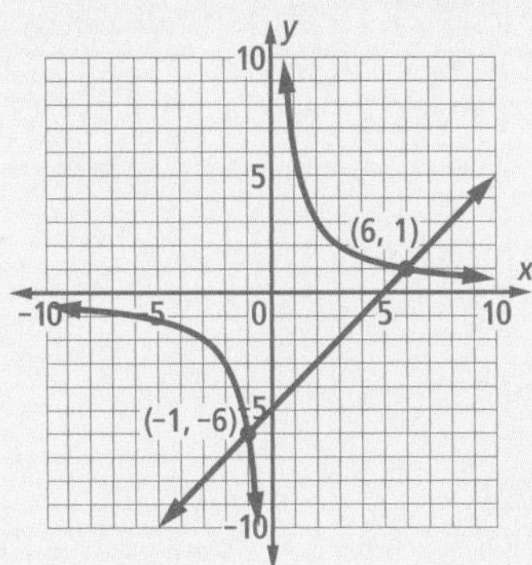

Background

In contrast to Lesson 5-1, this lesson focuses on *systems* only, that is, compound sentences using the word *and*. The lesson reviews the idea that the solution to a system of equations is represented by the point(s) of intersection of the graphs of the equations.

In the past, graphing was a weak method for solving a system because it was very difficult to draw an accurate graph. Thus graphing was often used to determine the number of solutions, not to get the actual solutions. Graphing utilities have increased the importance of graphing.

The same can be said for using tables and successive approximation to solve systems. The ability of computers to iterate quickly makes these methods quite practical, and they are very common in the solution of large systems.

(continued on next page)

2 Teaching

Notes on the Lesson

This lesson begins by describing the handicaps of two bowlers over time. You may need to inform your students that a bowling handicap system allows bowlers of different abilities to compete against one another by increasing a less skilled bowler's score for competition against a bowler of greater skill. These handicaps *help* a bowler. (A poorer bowler has a higher handicap than a better bowler.) Point out that because the handicaps increase or decrease at a constant rate, each handicap is a linear function of time. With two points on each line easily obtained from the description, one can determine an equation for each line. Then each equation can be solved for y. Point out that we call the handicaps $M(x)$ and $N(x)$ when we want to distinguish them, but when we want to determine when they are equal, we denote each handicap by y.

Finding solutions using tables and graphs After the equations are found, the lesson shows two ways of determining when the handicaps are equal: with a graph and with a table. With either method, you can determine the times when Minnie's handicap will be less than or equal to Noah's handicap.

Additional Example

Example 1 Solve the system $\begin{cases} y = 3x + 2 \\ y = 2x - 4 \end{cases}$.

Two different approaches on one CAS are shown here. The first approach enters the system as a compound sentence. The second enters the system using a brace.

solve(y=3·x+2 and y=2·x−4,{x,y}) x=-6 and y=-16

solve({y=3·x+2, y=2·x−4},{x,y}) x=-6 and y=-16

The solution is (-6, -16).

Solutions to systems of equations can be written in several ways. For example, the solution to Minnie and Noah's system can be expressed by

(1) listing the solution: (5, 20).

(2) writing the solution set: {(5, 20)}.

(3) writing a simplified equivalent system: $\begin{cases} x = 5 \\ y = 20 \end{cases}$.

QY1

Solving Systems with a CAS

You can also use a CAS to solve a system of equations. This is a good method if solutions are not easily found in tables or on graphs.

> **QY1**
> If Minnie's handicap increased by 5 pins each month, when would her handicap be equal to Noah's?

Example 1

Solve the system $\begin{cases} y = \frac{1}{2}x - 5 \\ y = 2x - 1 \end{cases}$.

Solution Most CAS have more than one way to enter and solve systems. Two different approaches on one machine are shown at the right. The first approach enters the system as a compound sentence. The second enters the system using a brace. You should find out how to do this on your CAS.

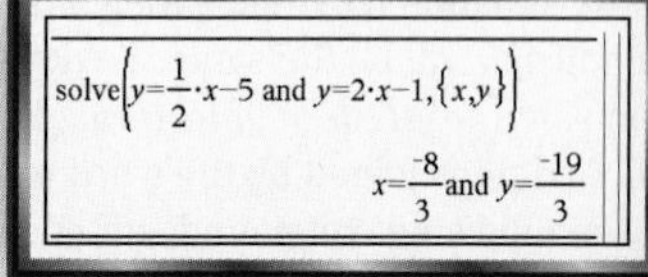

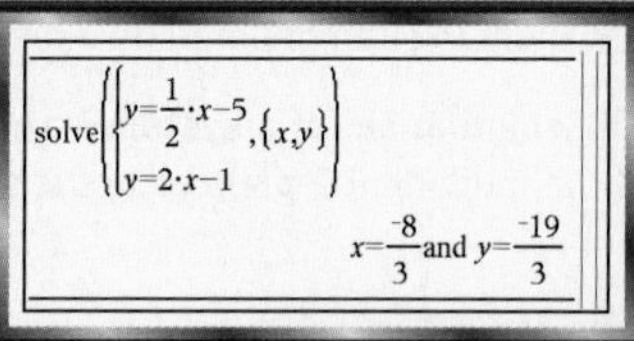

So the solution is $\left(-\frac{8}{3}, -\frac{19}{3}\right)$.

QY2

> **QY2**
> Verify the solution to Example 1 on your CAS.

Solving Nonlinear Systems

Systems can involve nonlinear equations.

It is ironic that we usually find the *intersection* of two or more curves by first graphing their *union*.

Students who have studied from UCSMP *Algebra* and UCSMP *Geometry* have studied linear systems. Thus, the material in this lesson and the next two lessons may be a review for them.

Accommodating the Learner

Some students may not be comfortable with systems of equations that have no solution. Demonstrate by graphing that pairs of parallel lines, such as those with equations $y = 5x$ and $y = 5x - 3$, do not intersect. Then demonstrate that the graphs of a quadratic function and a linear function, such as those with equations $y = 2x^2$ and $y = -4$, also have no point of intersection. You can further verify that these two systems have no solution by applying algebraic methods.

Example 2

Kaila is a packaging engineer at Healthy Soup Company. The marketing department has requested that she design a new soup can. The new can must hold 360 mL of soup and be in the shape of a cylinder. An eye-catching new label must be large enough to show the product name and all the nutrition content data. Marketing wants the area of the label to be about 225 cm^2. What are the dimensions of this new can?

Solution Define variables. Let h = the height of the can and r = the radius of the can.

Draw a picture, as shown at the right.

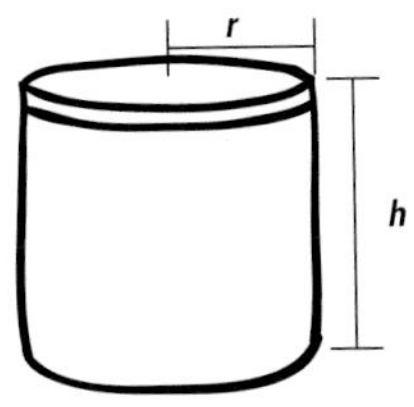

Write a system of equations. The volume of the can is given by the formula $V = \pi r^2 h$. The can must hold 360 cm^3 of soup (1 mL = 1 cm^3). So, $\pi r^2 h = 360$.

The area of the rectangular label that wraps around the can is the product of the can's circumference $2\pi r$ and its height h. Marketing wants the area to be about 225 cm^2. So, $2\pi rh = 225$.

So, a system describing the situation is $\begin{cases} \pi r^2 h = 360 \\ 2\pi rh = 225 \end{cases}$.

Solve the system. One way to solve this system is by graphing. First, solve each equation for h so that you can enter the functions into a graphing utility.

$$\begin{cases} h = \frac{360}{\pi r^2} \\ h = \frac{225}{2\pi r} \end{cases}$$

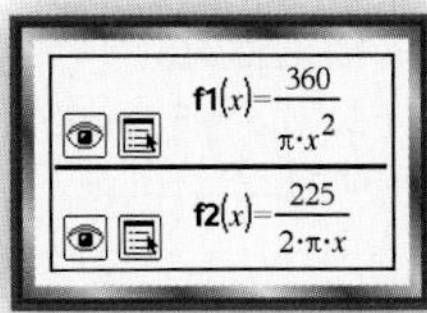

Think of r as the independent variable and h as the dependent variable. Enter the equations into a graphing utility as shown at the right. r becomes x and h becomes $f(x)$.

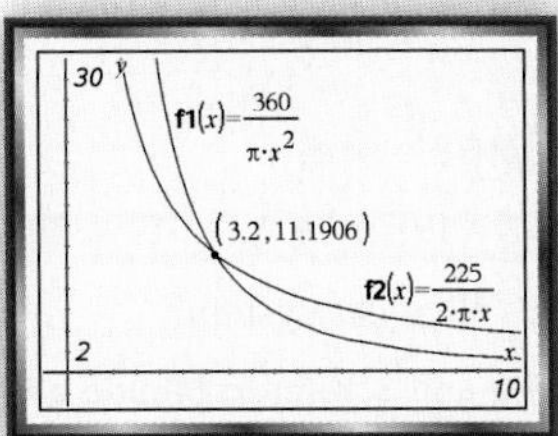

Both r and h must be positive, so only consider the branches of these inverse variation and inverse square variation graphs in the first quadrant. These branches intersect at only one point. Use the `intersect` command on your graphing utility to find the coordinates of the point of intersection.

The display shows the point of intersection is about (3.2, 11.2), so the radius of the can is approximately 3.2 cm and the height is approximately 11.2 cm.

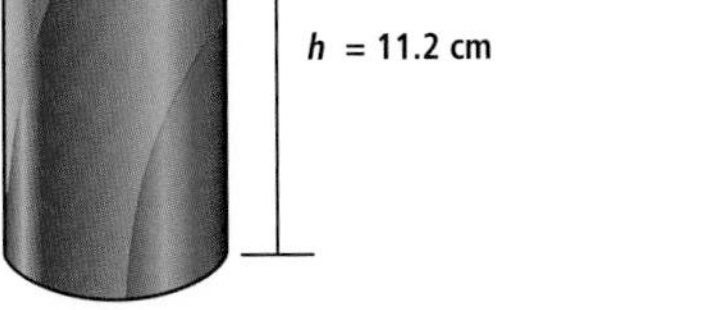

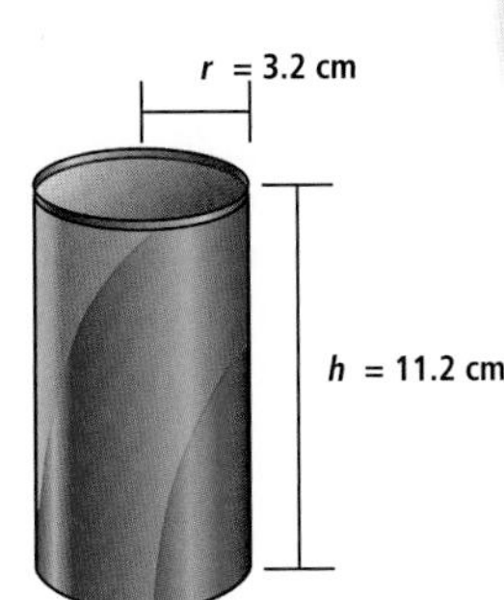

This is the only solution that meets the criteria of a 360 mL volume and a 225 cm^2 label area.

Notes on the Lesson

Solving nonlinear systems Emphasize how a graphing utility can zoom in on the solution to a nonlinear system. You might want to have students emulate Example 2 with their calculators and zoom in until the two graphs look like lines.

Example 2 The nonlinear system can be solved by a method that students likely have not seen. Given $\pi r^2 h = 360$ and $2\pi rh = 225$, divide the first equation by the second equation to obtain $\frac{\pi r^2 h}{2\pi rh} = \frac{360}{225}$. Simplify each side of the equation to get $\frac{r}{2} = \frac{8}{5}$, from which we see that $r = 3.2$ exactly. Now $h = \frac{225}{2\pi r}$, so $h = \frac{225}{6.4\pi}$ exactly, or about 11.19.

Additional Example

Example 2 Fred wants to enclose a 400-square-meter rectangular garden with 70 meters of fencing. To do this, he must use one side of his barn as a side of the garden. What can the dimensions of the garden be? Let W be the dimension along the barn and let S be the other dimension. Draw a picture.

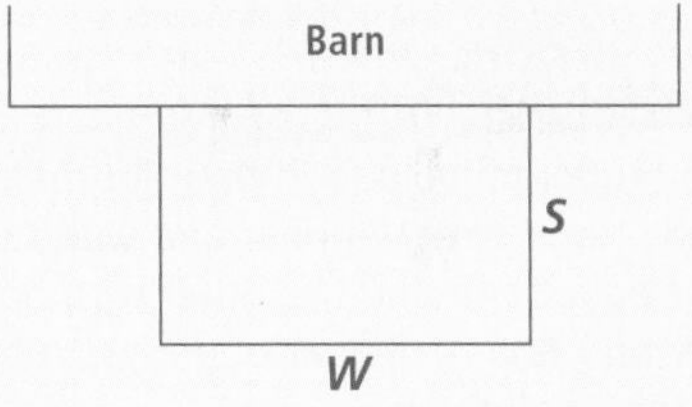

Then $W + 2S = 70$ and $WS = 400$.

Let W be the dependent variable and S be the independent variable. Solve the system $\begin{cases} W = -2S + 70 \\ W = \frac{400}{S} \end{cases}$ by graphing.

Because both S and W must be positive, consider only those parts of the graphs in Quadrant I. The solutions (S, W) are near (7, 56) and (28, 14). Thus, the dimensions of the garden are close to either 7 by 56 or 14 by 28.

Accommodating the Learner

Have students work in groups. Tell each group to write a system of two linear equation whose solution is the given point.

1. (0, 0) Answers vary. Sample: $\begin{cases} y = 5x \\ y = -x \end{cases}$
2. (–3, 5) Answers vary. Sample: $\begin{cases} y = x + 8 \\ y = 2x + 11 \end{cases}$
3. No solution any two equations for parallel lines, such as $y = x + 2$ and $y = x + 4$
4. Infinitely many solutions any two equations for the same line, such as $y = x + 2$ and $2y = 2x + 4$

Additional Example

Example 3 Solve the system $\begin{cases} xy = 30 \\ x - y = 1 \end{cases}$.

Solution Solve both equations for y: $y = \frac{30}{?}$ and $y = x - $ __?__. x; 1

Graph both equations in a window that shows all points of intersection. The window dimensions are __?__ < x < __?__ and __?__ < y < __?__. Answers vary. Sample: 15; 15; 15; 15 Use the intersection feature of your graphing utility to identify the points of intersection. The graphs intersect at __?__ and __?__. (6, 5); (-5, -6)

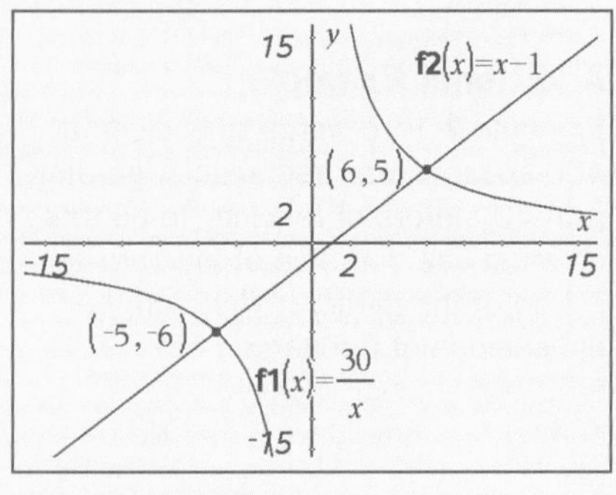

Note-Taking Tips

Have students include in their journals two systems of equations, one with two linear equations and the other with one linear and one nonlinear equation, along with their solutions.

3 Assignment

Recommended Assignment

- Questions 1–21
- Question 22 (extra credit)
- Reading Lesson 5-3
- Covering the Ideas 5-3

When a system is nonlinear, it is possible for it to have more than one solution, as in Example 3.

GUIDED

Example 3

Solve the system $\begin{cases} y = 4x^2 \\ 2y + 6x = 14 \end{cases}$.

Solution 1 First, solve both equations for y.

The first equation is already solved for y. The second equation is equivalent to y = __?__ + 7. -3x

Graph both equations in a window that shows all the points of intersection.

Window dimensions: __?__ ≤ x ≤ __?__ and __?__ ≤ y ≤ __?__. -3; 3; -5; 15

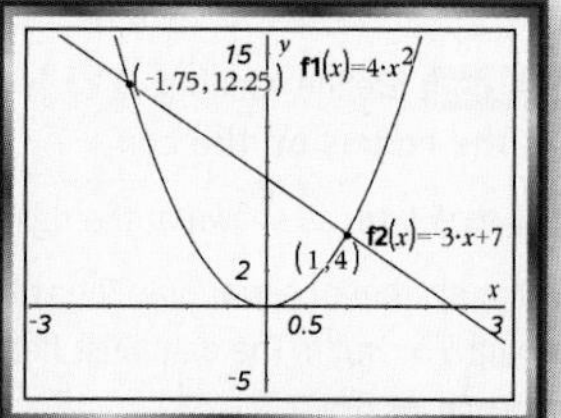

Use the intersection feature of the graphing utility to identify both intersection points.

The graphs intersect at (__?__, __?__) and (__?__, __?__). -1.75; 12.25; 1; 4

Solution 2 Solve on a CAS.

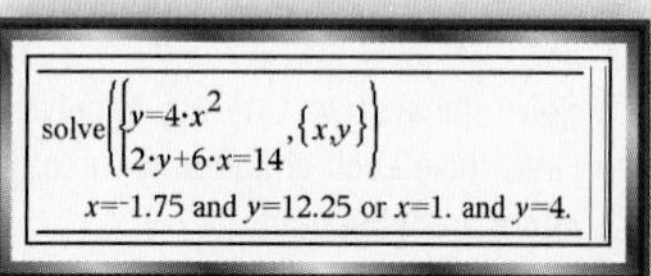

So the two possible solutions are (__?__, __?__) and (__?__, __?__). -1.75; 12.25; 1; 4

You will learn an algebraic method of solution later in this book.

Questions

COVERING THE IDEAS

1. What is a system?

In 2 and 3, refer to Minnie and Noah's situation.

2. After how many months is Noah's handicap less than Minnie's?
3. Suppose Noah's handicap has decreased to 40 pins, while Minnie's handicap has increased to 20 pins. If Noah's handicap continues decreasing by 3 pins each month and Minnie's declines by 1 pin each month, when will their handicaps be equal? 3a–c. See margin.
   a. Solve this new system of equations by using the `solve` command.
   b. Solve the system by graphing.
   c. Which method do you prefer and why?

1. A system is a set of conditions joined by the word *and*.
2. 5 months

ENGLISH LEARNERS

Vocabulary Development

Use equations like $x + y = 12$ and $x - y = 6$ to define *system* and *solution set of a system.* Explain that a system is "a set of things or parts that are considered together." We consider the two equations together, so the equations are called a system. The equation $x + y = 12$ requires that the sum of x and y is 12. The equation $x - y = 6$ requires that the difference of x and y is 6. The solution of the system is those ordered pairs that satisfy both equations. For these equations, the solution set of the system is {(9, 3)}.

Extension

Ask students to determine how many solutions are possible for each system described. Assume all equations represent functions.

1. Both equations are linear. 0, 1, or infinitely many
2. One equation is linear, and the other equation is quadratic. 0, 1, or 2
3. Both equations are quadratic. 0, 1, 2, or infinitely many

4. a. Use brace notation to write the system $y = 7x - 4$ and $y = 10$.
   b. Solve the system in Part a using any of the four methods below. Check your solution with any of the other methods.
      i. by hand 4b–c. See margin.
      ii. using the `solve` command
      iii. using a graphing utililty to find the intersection points
      iv. using a table of values
   c. Explain why you chose the methods that you used in Part b.

4a. $\begin{cases} y = 7x - 4 \\ y = 10 \end{cases}$

5. a. Solve the system $\begin{cases} y = \frac{1}{2}x - 1.5 \\ y = 2x + 3 \end{cases}$ by graphing. 5a–c. See margin.
   b. What do you notice about the relationship between the two lines graphed in Part a?
   c. Check your answer to Part a on a CAS using the `solve` command.

In 6 and 7, refer to Example 2.

6. We only looked for intersection points in the first quadrant. Why?

6. It is impossible to have a negative height or a negative radius.

7. a. How can you tell that (3.2, 11.2) is an approximate and not an exact solution?
   b. A CAS gives the solution (3.2, 11.190582). Is it an exact solution? Justify your answer. 7a–b. See margin.

8. Refer to Example 3. Would a window with $-2 \le x \le 4$ and $1 \le y \le 13$ show both intersections of the graphs? Why or why not?

8. Yes; the x- and y-values of the solutions satisfy the inequalities representing the window.

APPLYING THE MATHEMATICS

In 9–11, use the given systems and their graphs.

a. Tell how many solutions the system has.

b. Estimate the solutions, if there are any, to the nearest hundredth. Answers vary. Sample estimates are given.

c. Verify that your solutions satisfy all equations of the system.

9. $\begin{cases} y = 2x^2 \\ y = -3x + 4 \end{cases}$

10. 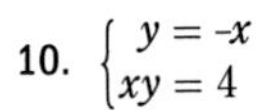
$\begin{cases} y = -x \\ xy = 4 \end{cases}$

11. 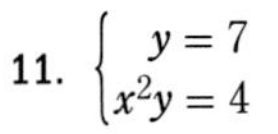
$\begin{cases} y = 7 \\ x^2y = 4 \end{cases}$

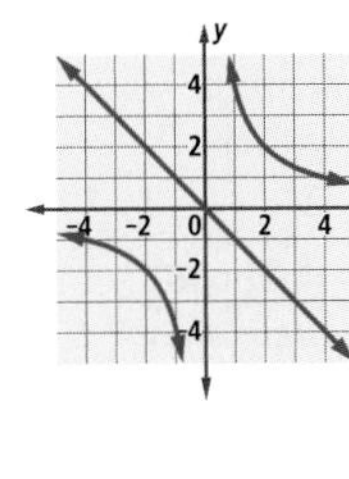

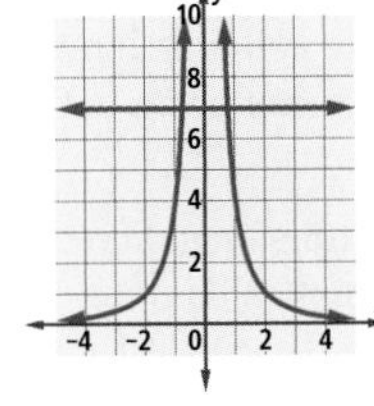

9a. 2

9b. (0.85, 1.45), (-2.35, 11.05)

9c. $2(0.85)^2 \approx 1.45$; $-3(0.85) + 4 = 1.45$; $2(-2.35)^2 \approx 11.05$; $-3(-2.35) + 4 = 11.05$

10a. 0

10b. no solutions

10c. no solutions

11a. 2

11b. (−0.76, 7), (0.76, 7)

11c. $(-0.76)^2 \cdot 7 \approx 4$; $(0.76)^2 \cdot 7 \approx 4$

Notes on the Questions

Questions 5–13 Emphasize that although there may be cases in which exact solutions can be read directly from a graph, most solutions read from a graph are approximations.

Additional Answers

3a.

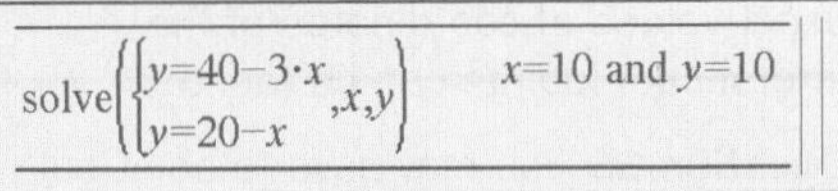
solve$\left(\begin{cases} y=40-3\cdot x \\ y=20-x \end{cases}, x, y\right)$ $x=10$ and $y=10$

3b.

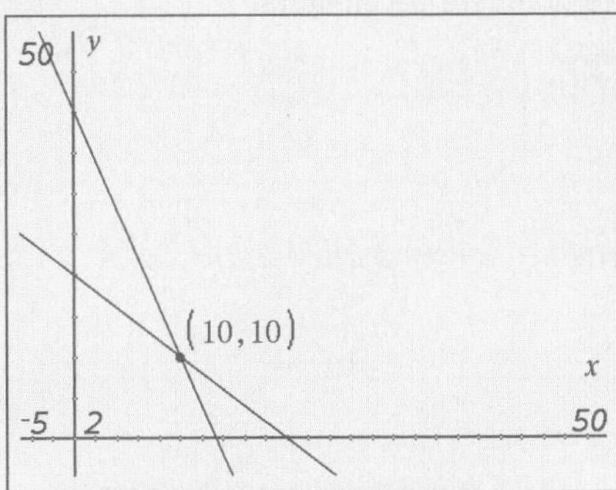

3c. Answers vary. Sample: The "solve" command because it involved fewer steps.

4b. Answers vary. Sample: $10 = 7x - 4$; $\frac{14}{7} = x$; $x = 2$; so the solution is (2, 10).

Check:

solve($y=7\cdot x-4$ and $y=10, x, y$) $x=2$ and $y=10$

Additional Answers

4c. Answers vary. Sample: It is good to not be dependent on a calculator to solve a problem, which is why I solved by hand. On the other hand, the solve command provides a quick and accurate check for the answer.

5a.

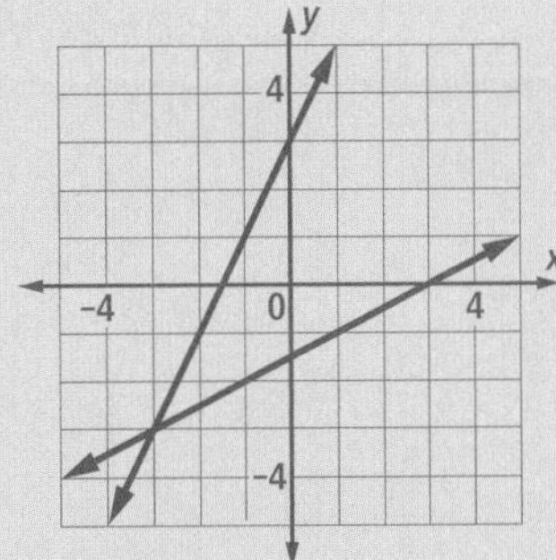

$x = -3$; $y = -3$

5b. Answers vary. Sample: The lines have their x- and y-intercepts exchanged.

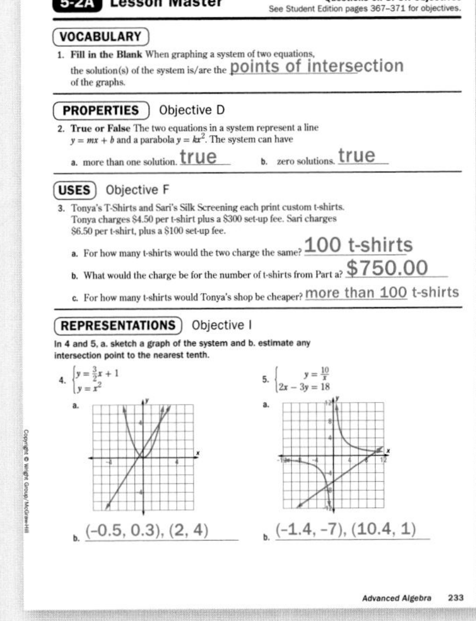

5-2A Lesson Master Questions on SPUR Objectives See Student Edition pages 367–371 for objectives.

VOCABULARY

1. **Fill in the Blank** When graphing a system of two equations, the solution(s) of the system is/are the points of intersection of the graphs.

PROPERTIES Objective D

2. **True or False** The two equations in a system represent a line $y = mx + b$ and a parabola $y = kx^2$. The system can have
   a. more than one solution. true
   b. zero solutions. true

USES Objective F

3. Tonya's T-Shirts and Sari's Silk Screening each print custom t-shirts. Tonya charges $4.50 per t-shirt plus a $300 set-up fee. Sari charges $6.50 per t-shirt, plus a $100 set-up fee.
   a. For how many t-shirts would the two charge the same? 100 t-shirts
   b. What would the charge be for the number of t-shirts from Part a? $750.00
   c. For how many t-shirts would Tonya's shop be cheaper? more than 100 t-shirts

REPRESENTATIONS Objective I

In 4 and 5, a. sketch a graph of the system and b. estimate any intersection point to the nearest tenth.

4. $\begin{cases} y = \frac{3}{2}x + 1 \\ y = x^2 \end{cases}$
   b. (−0.5, 0.3), (2, 4)

5. $\begin{cases} y = \frac{10}{x} \\ 2x - 3y = 18 \end{cases}$
   b. (−1.4, −7), (10.4, 1)

Advanced Algebra 233

Notes on the Questions

Question 10 Substitution of $-x$ for y in the second equation yields $x^2 = -4$, indicating why there are no points of intersection.

Question 11 Dividing the sides of the second equation by the corresponding sides of the first equation gives $x^2 = \frac{4}{7}$. From this, $x = \pm\sqrt{\frac{4}{7}}$, and exact values of coordinates of the intersection points can be found.

Question 15 You may have to point out that the question does not require that the numbers be integers.

Additional Answers

5c.

solve$\left(y=\frac{1}{2}\cdot x-1.5 \text{ and } y=2\cdot x+3,x,y\right)$

$x=-3.$ and $y=-3.$

7a. Answers vary. Sample: The graphing utility shows more decimal places for the y-coordinate, so 11.2 must be a rounded value.

7b. Answers vary. Sample: No, this is also an estimate. Since the solution involves the irrational number π, no exact decimal answer can be written.

12a.

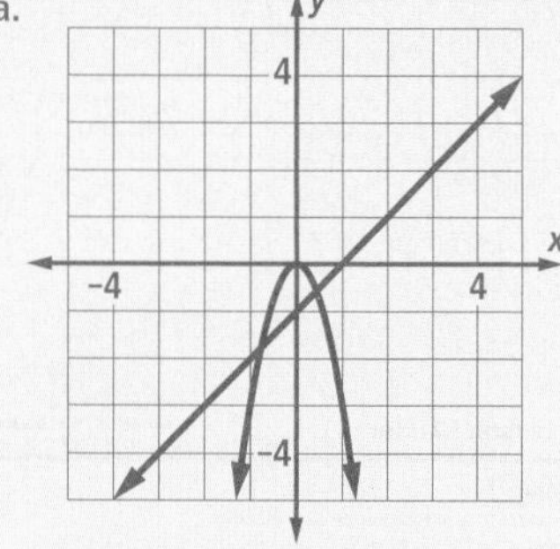

In 12 and 13, a system is given.

a. Graph the system. 12a, 13a. See margin.

b. Tell how many solutions the system has.

c. Estimate any solutions to the nearest tenth.

12. $\begin{cases} y = -3x^2 \\ x - y = 1 \end{cases}$

13. $\begin{cases} y = \frac{-6}{t^2} \\ y = 12 \end{cases}$

12b. 2

12c. (0.4, -0.6), (-0.8, -1.8)

13b. 0

13c. no solutions

14. The Aguilar family needs to hire a moving company. They received two quotes.
    Company 1: \$1000 plus \$0.10 per pound
    Company 2: \$750 plus \$0.20 per pound
    The Aguilars would like to find the value of the *break-even* point, where the cost is the same with both movers.
    a. Write a system describing this situation.
    b. Find the break-even point on a CAS by making a table of values starting at 0 and with a step size of 500.
    c. What is an appropriate domain for the functions of this system? Explain. 14a–c. See margin.

15. Use a graph to find out if there is a pair of numbers x and y whose product is 1740 and whose sum is 89. See margin.

16. Tomi is planting a vegetable garden that will be rectangular in shape. He has purchased 72 linear feet of fencing material to enclose the garden. He has enough fertilizer to take care of 320 square feet of garden.
    a. Write a system of equations relating the length L and width W of the rectangle to represent this situation.
    b. Assume that L is the independent variable. Rewrite each equation of the system to give W in terms of L.
    c. Solve the system using any method. 16 ft by 20 ft

16a. $\begin{cases} 72 = 2L + 2W \\ 320 = LW \end{cases}$

16b. $\begin{cases} W = -L + 36 \\ W = \frac{320}{L} \end{cases}$

REVIEW

17. Solve $2 - 4x < 5$ and graph your solution on a number line. (Lesson 5-1)

17. $x > -\frac{3}{4}$

18. Alkas is throwing a party. She tells Felix to bring a friend, but no more than 5 friends. Write a double inequality describing the number F of friends Felix can bring to the party without upsetting Alkas. (Lesson 5-1) $1 \leq F \leq 5$

19. Find the 2×2 matrix for a transformation that maps the point (1, 0) onto (-4, 1) and the point (0, 1) onto (-1, -4). (Lesson 4-7)

19. $\begin{bmatrix} -4 & -1 \\ 1 & -4 \end{bmatrix}$

Additional Answers

13a.

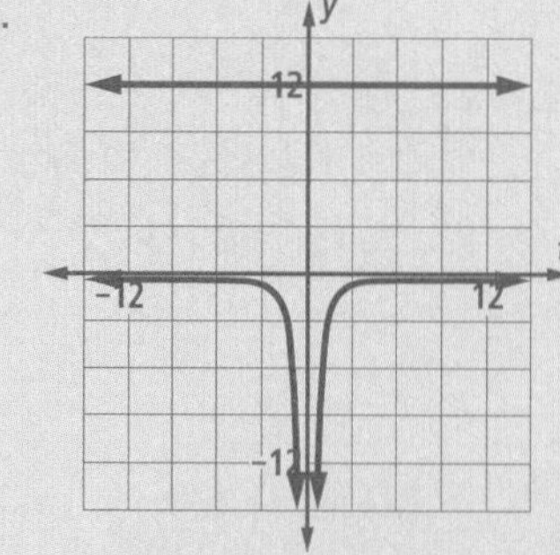

14a. $\begin{cases} c = 1000 + 0.1p \\ c = 750 + 0.2p \end{cases}$

14b.

x	f1(x):...	f2(x):...
	1000+..	750+.2.
0.	1000.	750.
500.	1050.	850.
1.E3	1100.	950.
1.5E3	1150.	1050.
2.E3	1200.	1150.
2.5E3	1250.	1250.

2500.

The breakeven point is at 2500 pounds, where the cost is \$1250 with either company.

20. **True or False** If $Ax + By$ is a linear combination of x and y, and $Cx + Dy$ is another linear combination of x and y, then the sum of these two expressions is a linear combination of x and y. **(Lesson 3-2)** true

21. In basketball, a player's effective shooting percentage e is given by the formula $e = \frac{f + 1.5t}{a}$, where f is the total number of two-point shots made, t is the number of three-point shots made, and a is the total number of shots attempted. Write a formula for the number t of three-point shots a player has made in terms of e, f, and a. **(Lesson 1-7)** $t = \frac{ea - f}{1.5} = \frac{2}{3}(ea - f)$

EXPLORATION

22. The break-even point is used often when making business decisions. Do some research about how the break-even point is applied in different types of financial analyses. Write a summary of your findings.

22. Answers vary. Sample: The break-even point in a cost analysis is the point where the costs equal the revenue (i.e., there is no net loss or gain).

QY ANSWERS

1. after 4 months
2. Answers vary. Sample:

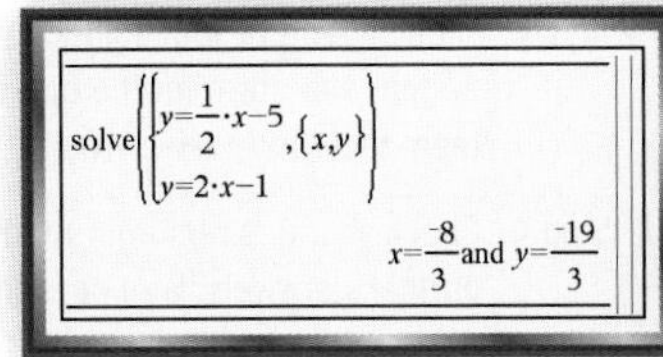

solve$\left(\begin{cases} y=\frac{1}{2}\cdot x-5 \\ y=2\cdot x-1 \end{cases},\{x,y\}\right)$
$x=\frac{-8}{3}$ and $y=\frac{-19}{3}$

Notes on the Questions

Question 21 A field goal may be worth 2 or 3 points, so adding $1.5t$ for t 3-point field goals accounts for the extra value of the 3-point field goal. The greatest possible value of e is 1.5, which occurs if a person attempts only 3-point field goals and makes all of them. This formula is used by many people, but a more intuitive formula might be $e = \frac{2f + 3t}{a}$, where f is the number of 2-point field goals made, t is the number of 3-point field goals made, and a is the total number of field-goal attempts. Then e is the number of points per attempt.

4 Wrap-Up

Ongoing Assessment

Have each student write a paragraph explaining how a graphing utility can be helpful when solving a system of equations. Then have students share their responses with the class. Students should demonstrate that they understand the concept of solving a system of two equations by graphing and that a graphing utility can provide precise approximations of the solution to some systems of equations.

Additional Answers

14c. Answers vary. Sample: $100 \le p \le 20{,}000$; the Aguilar family may need to move only a kitchen table and chairs (which would be around 100 lb), or they could need to move all the furniture in a 5-bedroom house, which could be about 20,000 lb.

15. Yes; The graphs of $xy = 1740$ and $x + y = 89$ intersect in two points, (29, 60) and (60, 29).

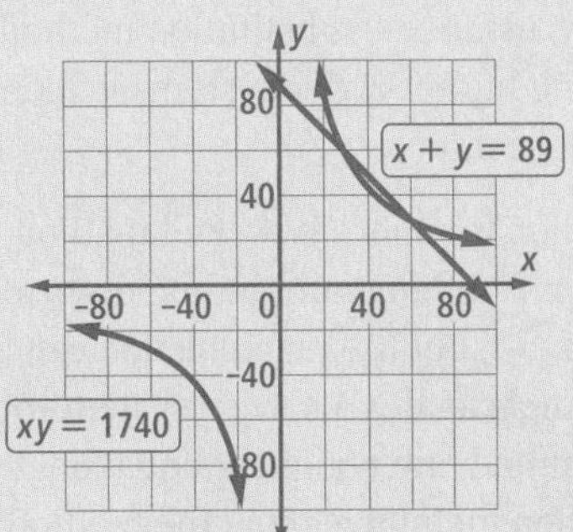

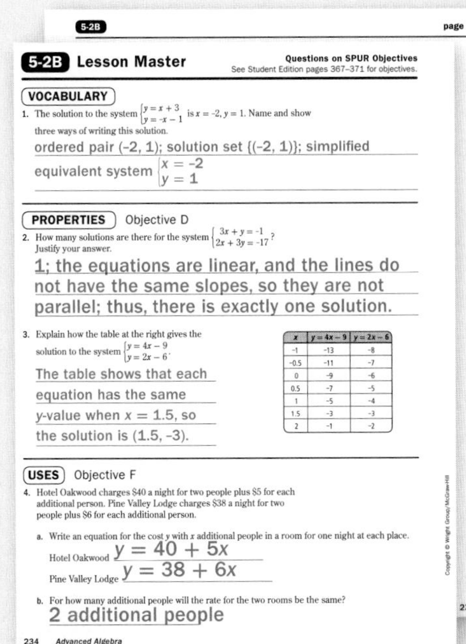

5-2B page 2

5-2B Lesson Master

Questions on SPUR Objectives
See Student Edition pages 367–371 for objectives.

VOCABULARY

1. The solution to the system $\begin{cases} y = x + 3 \\ y = -x - 1 \end{cases}$ is $x = -2$, $y = 1$. Name and show three ways of writing this solution.

ordered pair (–2, 1); solution set {(–2, 1)}; simplified equivalent system $\begin{cases} x = -2 \\ y = 1 \end{cases}$

PROPERTIES Objective D

2. How many solutions are there for the system $\begin{cases} 3x + y = -1 \\ 2x + 3y = -17 \end{cases}$? Justify your answer.

1; the equations are linear, and the lines do not have the same slopes, so they are not parallel; thus, there is exactly one solution.

3. Explain how the table at the right gives the solution to the system $\begin{cases} y = 4x - 9 \\ y = 2x - 6 \end{cases}$.

The table shows that each equation has the same y-value when $x = 1.5$, so the solution is (1.5, –3).

x	$y = 4x - 9$	$y = 2x - 6$
-1	-13	-8
-0.5	-11	-7
0	-9	-6
0.5	-7	-5
1	-5	-4
1.5	-3	-3
2	-1	-2

USES Objective F

4. Hotel Oakwood charges $40 a night for two people plus $5 for each additional person. Pine Valley Lodge charges $38 a night for two people plus $6 for each additional person.

a. Write an equation for the cost y with x additional people in a room for one night at each place.

Hotel Oakwood $y = 40 + 5x$

Pine Valley Lodge $y = 38 + 6x$

b. For how many additional people will the rate for the two rooms be the same?

2 additional people

234 *Advanced Algebra*

235

Lesson 5-3

GOAL

Review the substitution method for solving systems of equations and the terminology of consistent and inconsistent systems.

SPUR Objectives

A Solve 2 × 2 and 3 × 3 systems using substitution.

D Recognize properties of systems of equations.

F Use systems of two or three linear equations to solve real-world problems.

Materials/Resources

- Lesson Masters 5-3A and 5-3B
- Resource Masters 77 and 78
- Quiz 1
- CAS

HOMEWORK

Suggestions for Assignment

- Questions 1–20
- Question 21 (extra credit)
- Reading Lesson 5-4
- Covering the Ideas 5-4

Local Standards

1 Warm-Up

In 1–3, solve the equation.

1. $5x + 2(10 - 4x) = 12$ $x = \frac{8}{3}$
2. $y - 2(y + 1) = 3$ $y = -5$
3. $2(r + 7) + 11 + r = 0$ $r = -\frac{25}{3}$

Lesson 5-3 Solving Systems Using Substitution

Vocabulary

substitution method
consistent system
inconsistent system

BIG IDEA Some systems of equations in two (or more) variables can be solved by solving one equation for one variable, substituting the expression for that variable into the other equation, and solving the resulting equation.

Tables and graphs can be used to solve systems, but they do not always give exact solutions. You can find exact solutions with paper and pencil or on a CAS by using the **Substitution Property of Equality**: if $a = b$, then a may be substituted for b in any arithmetic or algebraic expression. For instance, if $H = 4V$, you can substitute $4V$ for H in any other expression. The following Activity illustrates how to use the Substitution Property of Equality as part of a **substitution method** to solve a system of two equations.

Mental Math

Find the perimeter of the polygon.

a. a square with side length $x + 1$ $4x + 4$

b. a right triangle with leg lengths 3 and 5 $8 + \sqrt{34}$

c. a parallelogram with one side of length 5 and one side of length L $2L + 10$

d. a regular n-gon with side length $\frac{\sqrt{3}}{2}$ $\frac{n\sqrt{3}}{2}$

Activity

MATERIALS CAS

The Policeville Bandits sports stadium seats 60,000 people. Suppose 600 tickets are reserved for the two teams. The home team gets 4 times as many tickets as the visiting team. Let H be the number of tickets for the Bandits and V be the number of tickets for the visiting team. How many tickets does each team receive?

Step 1 Work with a partner. Write a system of equations describing this situation. $\begin{cases} H + V = 600 \\ H = 4V \end{cases}$

Step 2 Have one partner solve one equation in the system for H and use the Substitution Property of Equality to rewrite the other equation in terms of V only. Have the other partner solve one equation in the system for V and then rewrite the other equation in terms of H only. See margin.

Step 3 Solve your last equation in Step 2 for the remaining variable. Then substitute your solution in one of the equations in the original system and solve for the other variable. How many tickets does each team receive? See margin.

Step 4 Check your answers from Step 3 by comparing them to your partner's answers. Was one substitution easier than the other? Why or why not? See margin.

Background

Using substitution for 2 × 2 linear systems should be familiar to students. However, using the substitution method for solving higher-order systems is most likely new content.

Substitution is a more powerful method than the Linear-Combination Method discussed in Lesson 5-4, but the manipulation can be more complicated. To solve a system with one linear and one nonlinear equation, the substitution method is often the method of choice, as illustrated in Example 2.

Consistent and inconsistent systems The terms *consistent* and *inconsistent,* as used in mathematics, may be new to students. For students who may be confused by a system of equivalent equations such as the one in Example 4, stress that when one equation is equivalent to another, the system is always consistent.

Step 5 A CAS applies the Substitution Property of Equality when the `such that` command is used. Enter the equations into a CAS using the `such that` command, and explain the result.

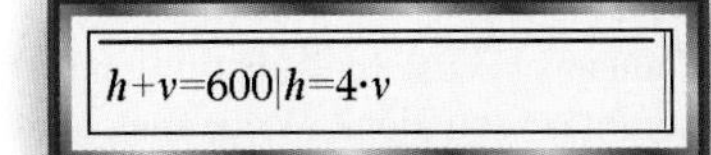

Step 6 Solve the result of Step 5 for V. $V = 120$

Step 7 Use the second equation in the system and the such that command to find H for your value of V from Step 6.

Step 5: The CAS command substitutes $4V$ for H in the first equation.
Step 7: $H = 480$

$h=4\cdot v|v=120 \qquad h=480$

Solving Systems with Three or More Linear Equations

You can also use the substitution method when there are more than two variables and two equations.

GUIDED

Example 1

Able Baker makes a total of 160 dozen regular muffins, mini-muffins, and jumbo muffins for his stores each day. He makes twice as many regular muffins as mini-muffins and 5 times as many jumbo muffins as mini-muffins. How many of each does he make?

Solution Solve by hand using substitution.

Let R = the number of dozens of regular muffins,
M = the number of dozens of mini-muffins, and
J = the number of dozens of jumbo muffins.

Then the system to be solved is $\begin{cases} R + M + J = 160 \\ R = \underline{\ ?\ } \\ J = \underline{\ ?\ } \end{cases}$ 2M; 5M

Substitute your expressions for R and J in the last two equations into the first equation and solve for M.

$\underline{\ \ ?\ \ } + M + \underline{\ \ ?\ \ } = 160$ 2M; 5M

$8M = 160$

$M = \underline{\ ?\ }$ dozen 20

Substitute to find R. $R = \underline{\ ?\ }$ dozen 40

Substitute to find J. $J = \underline{\ ?\ }$ dozen 100

Carl makes ___?___ dozen regular muffins, ___?___ dozen mini-muffins, and ___?___ dozen jumbo muffins. 40; 20; 100

Check Does $R = 2M$? ___?___ Does $J = 5M$? ___?___ Does $R + M + J = 160$? ___?___ If the answers are yes, then your solution to the system is correct. yes; yes; yes

CAS distinguish between consistent and inconsistent systems in different ways. For example, one CAS might give an output of "false" for inconsistent systems, while another CAS might give an output of "no solution." Be sure to indicate to your class the particular syntax and outputs used for their technology.

ENGLISH LEARNERS

Vocabulary Development

Stress that the mathematical meaning of the term *consistent* is "having one or more solutions." Then point out that the prefix *in* frequently means "not," "the opposite of," or "the absence of." The *in-* in the term *inconsistent* has this meaning, so an inconsistent system does not have one or more solutions; it has no solutions.

2 Teaching

Notes on the Lesson

Example 1 This is an important example to discuss. Some students may not have seen a system with more than two equations or may not remember seeing such a system. Example 1 is an excellent illustration of a system of three equations that is easily solved by substitution.

Additional Example

Example 1 Trevian Stadium has a seating capacity of 4216. There are four times as many lower-level seats as there are upper-level seats. And there are three times as many mezzanine seats as there are upper-level seats. How many seats of each type are there?

Solution Solve by hand using substitution. Let L = the number of lower-level seats, M = the number of mezzanine seats, and U = the number of upper-level seats. Then the system to be solved is

$\begin{cases} L + M + U = 4216 \\ L = \underline{\ ?\ } \\ M = \underline{\ ?\ } \end{cases}$ $4U$; $3U$

Substitute your expressions for L and M into the first equation and solve for U: ___?___ + ___?___ + $U = 4216$. $4U$; $3U$

Because $8U = 4216$, U = ___?___. 527

Now substitute to find L and M: L = ___?___ and M = ___?___. $4 \cdot 527 = 2108$; $3 \cdot 527 = 1581$

Trevian Stadium has ___?___ upper-level seats, ___?___ lower-level seats, and ___?___ mezzanine seats. 527; 2108; 1581

Check Does $L = 4U$? Does $M = 3U$? Does $L + M + U = 4216$? If the answers are yes, then your solution to the system is correct.

Notes on the Lesson

Examples 2–4 These systems are presented in a form in which substitution is the natural method of solution.

Example 2 Relate the solutions to the graph of the system. Stress that the graph indicates that there are two solutions. Because the graphs of the two equations do not intersect outside the window, there are only two solutions.

Additional Example

Example 2 Solve the system $\begin{cases} y = 3x \\ xy = 48 \end{cases}$.
{(4, 12), (-4, -12)}

Note-Taking Tips

Have students include in their journals an example of a consistent system and an example of an inconsistent system.

Additional Answers

Activity

Step 2: $H = 4V$; $4V + V = 600$; $V = 600 - H$; $H = 4(600 - H)$

Step 3: $V = 120$; $H = 480$; the home team gets 480 tickets, and the visiting team gets 120 tickets.

Step 4: Answers vary. Sample: Yes; one substitution was easier because it required less arithmetic.

Solving Nonlinear Systems

You can also use the substitution method to solve some systems with nonlinear equations. Write one equation in terms of a single variable, and substitute the expression into the other equation.

Example 2

Solve the system $\begin{cases} y = 4x \\ xy = 36 \end{cases}$.

Solution Substitute $4x$ for y in the second equation and solve for x.

$x(4x) = 36$ Substitute.

$4x^2 = 36$ Simplify.

$x^2 = 9$ Divide both sides by 4.

$x = 3$ or $x = -3$ Take the square root of both sides.

The word *or* means that the solution set is the union of all possible answers. So substitute each value of x into either of the original equations to get two corresponding values of y. We substitute into $y = 4x$.

If $x = 3$, then $y = 4(3) = 12$. If $x = -3$, then $y = 4(-3) = -12$.

The solution set is {(3, 12), (-3, -12)}.

Check Graph the equations. This calculator display shows the two solutions (3, 12) and (-3, -12). It checks.

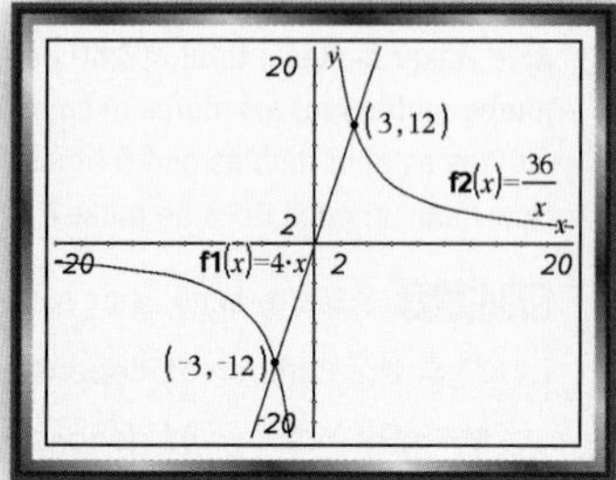

Consistent and Inconsistent Systems

A system that has *one or more solutions* is called a **consistent system**. Examples 1 and 2 involve consistent systems. A system that has *no solutions* is called an **inconsistent system**. Example 3 illustrates an inconsistent system.

Example 3

Solve the system $\begin{cases} x = 4 - 3y \\ 2x + 6y = -2 \end{cases}$.

Solution 1 Substitute $4 - 3y$ for x in the second equation.

$2(4 - 3y) + 6y = -2$

$8 - 6y + 6y = -2$ Use the Distributive Property.

$8 = -2$ Add like terms.

Accommodating the Learner

As an example of the idea in Question 15, give students this recipe for 5 cups of French dressing that includes tomato juice, vinegar, and olive oil. The recipe calls for 3 times as much vinegar as tomato juice and 2 times as much olive oil as vinegar. Have students write a system of three equations to describe this recipe and then solve the system to determine how much of each ingredient should be used.

$\begin{cases} T + V + O = 5 \\ V = 3T \\ O = 2V \end{cases}$; $\frac{1}{2}$ cup tomato juice, $1\frac{1}{2}$ cups vinegar; 3 cups olive oil

We came up with the statement $8 = -2$, which is never true! This false conclusion indicates that what we started with is impossible. That is, the system has no solutions. In other words, the solution is ∅, the empty set. A graph of the system shows parallel lines, which supports this conclusion.

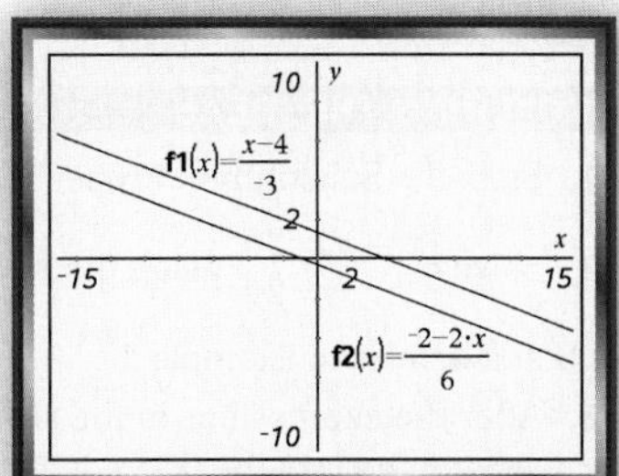

Solution 2 Solving the system on a CAS returns `false`, as shown below. This indicates that the system is inconsistent and has no solution.

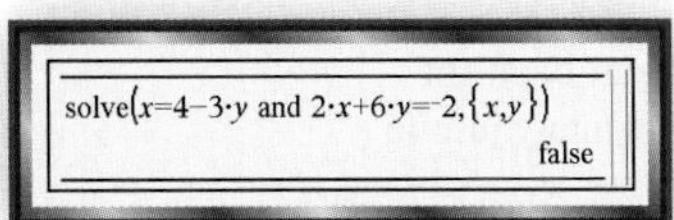

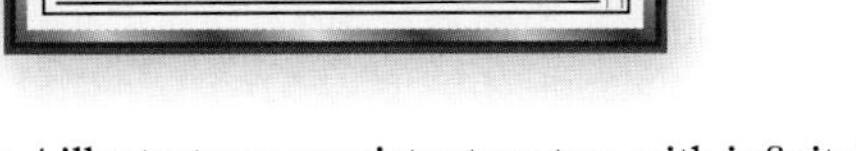

Example 4 illustrates a consistent system with infinitely many solutions.

Example 4

Solve the system $\begin{cases} y = -3x + 2 \\ 15x + 5y = 10 \end{cases}$.

Solution 1 Substitute $-3x + 2$ for y in the second equation.

$15x + 5(-3x+2) = 10$ Substitute.

$15x - 15x + 10 = 10$ Use the Distributive Property.

$10 = 10$ Add like terms.

The statement $10 = 10$ is *always* true. The solutions to the system are all ordered pairs satisfying either equation: $\{(x, y) | y = -3x + 2\}$. The graph of each equation is the same line. So, this system has an *infinite number of solutions.*

Solution 2 Substituting the first equation into the second on a CAS returns `true`. This means that every solution to the first equation is a solution to the second equation.

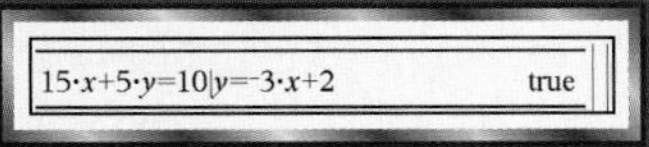

QY

▶ **QY**

Show that the two equations in Example 4 are equations describing the same line by putting the second one in slope-intercept form.

Notes on the Lesson

When using the substitution method, most students will solve for one variable correctly. However, some students will not multiply through by the variable's coefficient after the substitution is made into the second equation. In Example 3, when $4 - 3y$ is substituted for x in the second equation, $2x + 6y = -2$, the new equation may incorrectly be written as $8 - 3y + 6y = -2$ instead of $2(4 - 3y) + 6y = -2$. Stress the importance of multiplying through by the variable's coefficient.

Another difficulty is when the coefficient is negative or the variable is subtracted. In this case, students often make careless errors in sign. Remind students to work carefully.

Additional Examples

Example 3 Solve the system $\begin{cases} x = 3 - 2y \\ 3x + 6y = 6 \end{cases}$.

Solution 1. Substitute $3 - 2y$ for x in the second equation and solve: $3(3 - 2y) + 6y = 6$. A false conclusion, $9 = 6$, results, indicating that the system has no solutions. A graph of the system shows parallel lines, which support this conclusion.

Solution 2. Solving the system on a CAS returns false, as shown. This indicates that the system is inconsistent and has no solution.

solve(x=3−2·y and 3·x+6·y=6,{x,y}) false

Example 4 Solve the system $\begin{cases} y = 6 - \frac{x}{8} \\ \frac{x}{3} + 2y = 12 \end{cases}$. (0, 6)

Accommodating the Learner

To give students more practice solving systems of three equations, have them solve the following systems of three equations by using substitution. Have them check each solution by substituting the solution values into each equation.

1. $\begin{cases} x + y + z = 9 \\ x + y = 3 \\ y = 2 \end{cases}$ $(x, y, z) = (1, 2, 6)$

2. $\begin{cases} x + 2y + z = 6 \\ x - 4y - z = 2 \\ z + 1 = 0 \end{cases}$ $(x, y, z) = (5, 1, -1)$

3 Assignment

Recommended Assignment

- Questions 1–20
- Question 21 (extra credit)
- Reading Lesson 5-4
- Covering the Ideas 5-4

Notes on the Questions

Question 9 It is as easy to substitute for x in the first equation as it is to substitute for y in the second equation.

Additional Answers

2.

$x+y=20 \mid x=2\cdot y$	$3\cdot y=20$
$\frac{3\cdot y=20}{3}$	$y=\frac{20}{3}$
$x=2\cdot y \mid y=\frac{20}{3}$	$x=\frac{40}{3}$

$(x, y) = \left(\frac{40}{3}, \frac{20}{3}\right)$

8c.

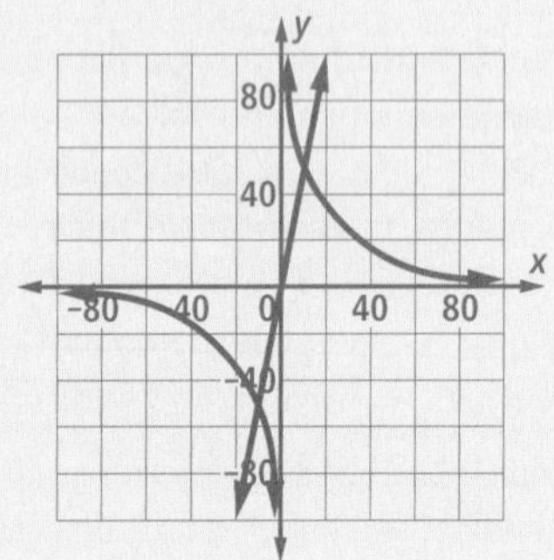

5-3A Lesson Master

Questions on SPUR Objectives
See Student Edition pages 367–371 for objectives.

SKILLS Objective A

In 1–4, solve using the substitution method.

1. $\begin{cases} 2a + 3b = 19 \\ b = 3a - 1 \end{cases}$ (2, 5)

2. $\begin{cases} y = 3x \\ xy = 1200 \end{cases}$ (20, 60), (–20, –60)

3. $\begin{cases} 5x - 2y = 10 \\ y = 2.5x + 3 \end{cases}$ no solution

4. $\begin{cases} 3p - q + 2r = 26 \\ q = 4p - 20 \\ 3p = 2r \end{cases}$ $p = 3$, $q = -8$, and $r = 4.5$

PROPERTIES Objective D

5. For what value of m is the system $\begin{cases} 5x - 2y = 12 \\ y = mx + 2 \end{cases}$ inconsistent? $\frac{5}{2}$

6. Without finding the actual solution(s), tell how many solutions each system has.

   a. $\begin{cases} 3x + 4y = 24 \\ 2x + 5y = 30 \end{cases}$ one

   b. $\begin{cases} 6x - 3y = 19 \\ 6x - 3y = 24 \end{cases}$ none

   c. $\begin{cases} y = x^2 \\ y = 25 \end{cases}$ two

USES Objective F

7. A movie download service has two different plans. Under the "unlimited" plan, they charge $11.95 per month for unlimited downloads. Under the "budget" plan, they charge $3.95 per month, plus $2.00 for each download.

   a. Write two equations, one for the cost of each plan, where C is the cost to download m movies in a month. $\begin{cases} C = 11.95 \\ C = 3.95 + 2m \end{cases}$

   b. Solve your system from Part a. (4, 11.95)

   c. What does your solution mean in the context of the problem? The cost of the two plans is the same if you download exactly four movies in a month.

8. In a basketball game, Chamique scored twice as many points as Sheryl, and Merlakia scored five points more than Chamique. Together, they scored 40 points. How many points did each woman score? Chamique scored 14, Sheryl scored 7, Merlakia scored 19.

236 *Advanced Algebra*

Questions

COVERING THE IDEAS

1. State the Substitution Property of Equality.

   1. If $a = b$, then a may be substituted for b in any arithmetic or algebraic expression.

2. Solve $\begin{cases} x + y = 20 \\ x = 2y \end{cases}$ using the `such that` comand on a CAS. See margin.

In 3 and 4, refer to Example 1.

3. After the expressions in the second and third equations are substituted into the first equation, how many variables are in this new equation? one

4. For a holiday when business was slow, Able Baker cut back the total number of muffins he made to 120 dozen. How many jumbo muffins did he make? 75 dozen

5. Verify that (-3, -12) is a solution to the system of Example 2.

   5. $-12 = 4(-3)$; $(-12)(-3) = 36$; the original equations are both true when the values are substituted.

In 6 and 7, solve the system by hand using the substitution method.

6. $\begin{cases} y = 4 - 2x \\ 3x + 4y = 11 \end{cases}$ $x = 1, y = 2$

7. $\begin{cases} x - 2y + 4z = 9 \\ x = 2z + 2 \\ y = -4z \end{cases}$ $x = 3, y = -2, z = \frac{1}{2}$

In 8–10, a system is given.

a. Solve the system using substitution.

b. Tell whether the system is consistent or inconsistent.

c. Graph the system to verify your answers to Parts a and b.

8. $\begin{cases} y = 5x \\ xy = 500 \end{cases}$

9. $\begin{cases} y = \frac{2}{3}x + 3 \\ x = \frac{3}{2}y - 4 \end{cases}$

10. $\begin{cases} y = 2.75x - 1 \\ 11x - 4y = 4 \end{cases}$

8c–10c. See margin.

8a. {(10, 50), (–10, -50)}

8b. consistent

9a. no solution

9b. inconsistent

10a. infinitely many solutions

10b. consistent

11. Two lines in a plane are either the same line, parallel non-intersecting lines, or lines that intersect in a single point. What does this tell you about the possible number of points in the solution set of a system of linear equations in two variables?

   11. There are either no solutions, one solution, or infinitely many solutions.

Additional Answers

9c.

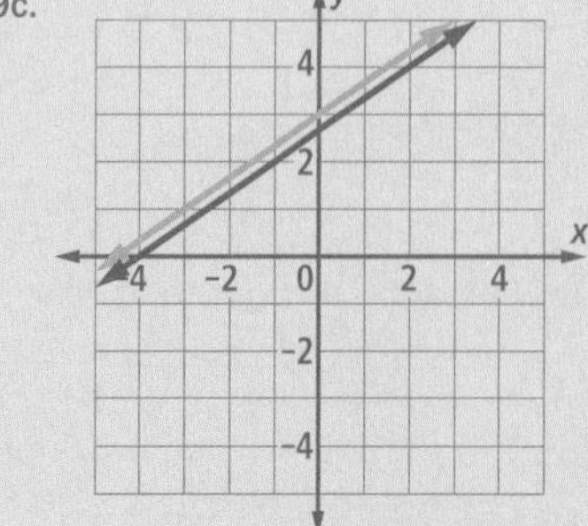

10c.

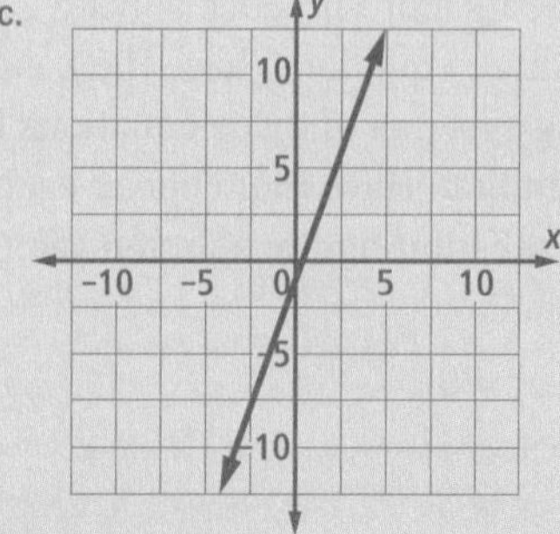

APPLYING THE MATHEMATICS

12. Cheap Airways offers to fly the Underdog team to the playoffs for \$250 per person. Comfort Flights offers to take the team for \$1500 plus \$100 per person. Let x = the number of team members on the flight and y = the total cost of the flight. The Underdog coach, who is also a math teacher, wants to analyze the rates to get the best deal.
   a. Write a system of equations to describe the relationship between x and y for the two airlines.
   b. For what number of passengers will the cost be the same for both airlines? 10 passengers
   c. What is this cost? \$2500
   d. The Underdog team and staff consists of 23 people. Which airline will cost the least? How much is saved over the other airline?

12a. 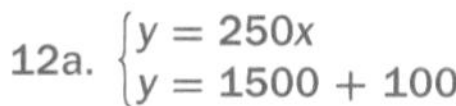
$\begin{cases} y = 250x \\ y = 1500 + 100x \end{cases}$

12d. Comfort Flights is cheaper; \$1950

13. Consider the system $\begin{cases} y = x^2 \\ y = x - 3 \end{cases}$.
   a. Solve the system by substitution. There are no solutions.
   b. Tell whether the system is consistent or inconsistent. inconsistent
   c. Graph the system to verify your answer to Parts a and b. See margin.

14. For the system $\begin{cases} xy = 4 \\ y = x \end{cases}$, a student wrote "The solution is x = -2 or 2 and y = -2 or 2." Explain why this is *not* a correct answer. See margin.

15. Sand, gravel, and cement are mixed with water to produce concrete. One mixture has these three components in the extended ratio 2:4:1. For a total of 50 cubic yards of concrete, how much sand, gravel, and cement should be mixed?
   a. Write a system of three equations to describe this situation.
   b. Solve the system to determine how much of each ingredient should be used.

To test the consistency of concrete, inspectors perform a slump test by forming a cone of concrete and measuring how much it slumps due to gravity.

16. Suppose the circumference C of a circle is 1 meter longer than the diameter d of the circle.
   a. Write a system of equations relating C and d. $\begin{cases} C = \pi d \\ C = d + 1 \end{cases}$
   b. Solve the system. $d = \frac{1}{\pi - 1}$, $C = \frac{\pi}{\pi - 1}$
   c. Estimate the radius of the circle to the nearest millimeter. $r \approx 233$ mm

15a. Answers vary. Sample: $\begin{cases} S = 2C \\ G = 4C \\ S + G + C = 50 \end{cases}$.

15b. $C = \frac{50}{7}$, $G = \frac{200}{7}$, $S = \frac{100}{7}$; use about 14.3 yd^3 of sand, 28.6 yd^3 of gravel, and 7.1 yd^3 of cement.

Notes on the Questions

Question 13 To solve $x^2 = x - 3$ algebraically, students may use trial and error, factoring, or the Quadratic Formula. Allow any method. For students who are concerned that they have forgotten how to solve quadratics, you might tell them that Chapter 6 includes a thorough treatment of quadratic equations.

Question 15 You may have to explain that an extended ratio such as 2 : 4 : 1 means that if there are x cubic yards of cement (the 1 in the extended ratio), then there are $2x$ cubic yards of sand and $4x$ cubic yards of gravel. You might want to refer to Example 1, noting that if there are m mini-muffins, then there are $2m$ regular muffins and $5m$ jumbo muffins, so these are in the ratio $m : 2m : 5m$, or 1 : 2 : 5. Thus, this question can be solved by using equations involving one or more of three identified variables (one for the amount of each ingredient in concrete).

Additional Answers

13c.

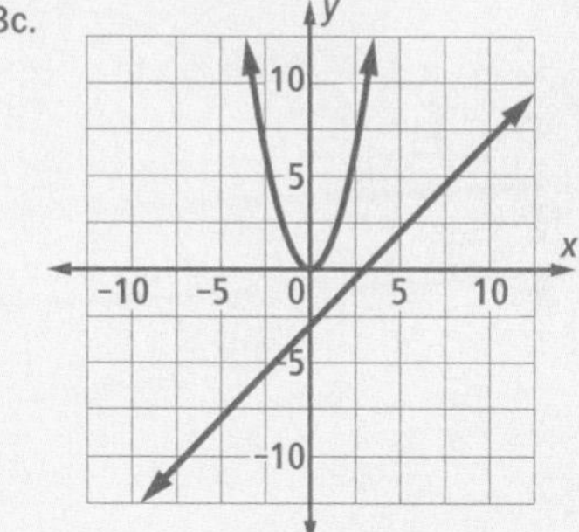

14. The correct solutions are x = -2 and y = -2, or x = 2 and y = 2. The student's answer implies that x = -2 and y = 2 or x = 2 and y = -2 are also solutions, which they are not.

4 Wrap-Up

Ongoing Assessment

Have students write a paragraph describing the difference between consistent and inconsistent systems. Have them include an example of each kind of system. Students should demonstrate that they understand the difference between consistent and inconsistent systems.

Administer Quiz 1 (or a quiz of your own) after students complete this lesson.

Additional Answers

19a. domain: all real numbers except 0; range: all real numbers except 0

19b. domain: all real numbers; range: all real numbers less than or equal to 0

19c. domain: all real numbers except 0; range: all positive real numbers

19d. domain: all real numbers; range: all real numbers

5-3B Lesson Master page 2

Questions on SPUR Objectives
See Student Edition pages 367–371 for objectives.

VOCABULARY

1. **Fill in the Blanks** A *consistent system* has one or more solution(s), while an *inconsistent system* has no solution(s).

SKILLS Objective A

In 2–9, solve using the substitution method.

2. $\begin{cases} y = x - 7 \\ y = -2x + 5 \end{cases}$ (4, -3)

3. $\begin{cases} y = 3x + 13 \\ y = x + 1 \end{cases}$ (-6, -5)

4. $\begin{cases} 3m - 2n = 1 \\ 21m - 6n = 11 \end{cases}$ $\left(\frac{2}{3}, \frac{1}{2}\right)$

5. $\begin{cases} xy = -4 \\ x = -4y \end{cases}$ (-4, 1), (4, -1)

6. $\begin{cases} 0.25x + 0.1y = 78 \\ 7.5y - 1.5x = 990 \end{cases}$ (240, 180)

7. $\begin{cases} 4a + 6b - 3c = -26 \\ b = a + 3 \\ c = -4a \end{cases}$ (-2, 1, 8)

8. $\begin{cases} xy + z = 10 \\ z = -x + 1 \\ y = x + 1 \end{cases}$ (3, 4, -2), (-3, -2, 4)

9. $\begin{cases} y = \frac{1}{2}x + 1 \\ x - 2y = -2 \end{cases}$ infinitely many solutions

PROPERTIES Objective D

In 10–12, determine whether the system is *consistent* or *inconsistent*.

10. $\begin{cases} 5y = 10x + 20 \\ y = 2x + 4 \end{cases}$ consistent

11. $\begin{cases} y = -\frac{1}{4}x + 6 \\ 4y + x = 48 \end{cases}$ inconsistent

12. $\begin{cases} 7x - y = -3 \\ 2x + y = -6 \end{cases}$ consistent

238

Advanced Algebra 237

REVIEW

17. The Outdoors Club at Larkchester High School budgeted \$20 for the year to print color flyers for their trips. Printing costs 9 cents per page. **(Lesson 5-1)**
   a. Write an inequality relating the number x of flyers the Outdoors Club can print this year. $0.09x \le 20$
   b. Solve your inequality from Part a. $x \le 222.2$
   c. How many flyers can the club print? 222 one-page flyers

18. a. Write a matrix for $\triangle HAW$ at the right. $\begin{bmatrix} -4 & -2 & 2 \\ 0 & 3 & 3 \end{bmatrix}$
   b. Use matrix multiplication to determine the coordinates of $\triangle H'A'W'$, the reflection image of $\triangle HAW$ over the line $y = x$. **(Lessons 4-6, 4-1)** $\begin{bmatrix} 0 & 3 & 3 \\ -4 & -2 & 2 \end{bmatrix}$

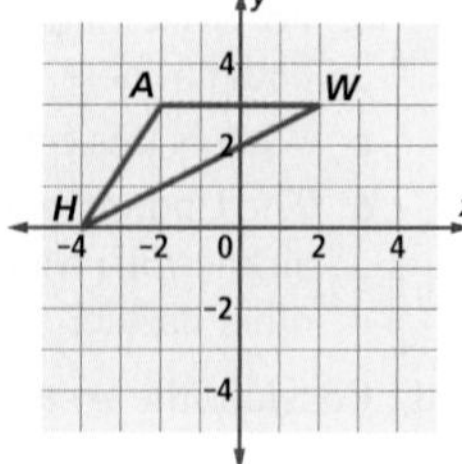

19. Give the domain and range of each variation function. **(Lessons 2-6, 2-5, 2-4)** 19a–d. See margin.
   a. $d = \frac{10}{t}$
   b. $y = -2.5x^2$
   c. $I = \frac{300}{d^2}$
   d. $C = 10.09n$

20. Tell whether each relation is a function. Justify your answer. **(Lesson 1-2)**
   a. $g: x \to 3x^2$
   b. $\{(-2, 0), (1, 4), (2, 14), (1, 3), (-2, -5)\}$
   c.

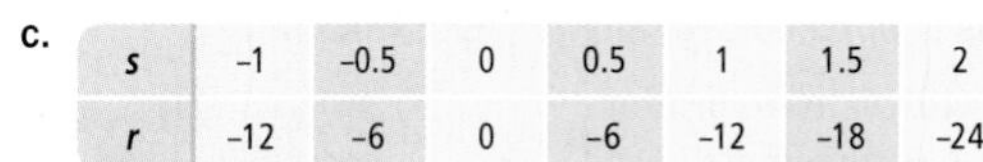

s	-1	-0.5	0	0.5	1	1.5	2
r	-12	-6	0	-6	-12	-18	-24

   (Treat s as the independent variable.)
   d. The relation that maps Blake's age onto his height at that age.

20a. Yes; it is a function because each x is paired with only one output.

20b. No; -2 is paired with both 0 and -5, and 1 is paired with both 4 and 3.

20c. Yes; each s is paired with only one r.

20d. Yes; Blake can be only one height at a time.

EXPLORATION

21. Consider the system $\begin{cases} y = x^2 \\ y = x + k \end{cases}$. Explore these equations and find the values of k for which this system has
   a. two solutions. $k > -\frac{1}{4}$
   b. exactly one solution. $k = -\frac{1}{4}$
   c. no solution. $k < -\frac{1}{4}$

QY ANSWER

$15x + 5y = 10$

$5y = 10 - 15x$

$y = \frac{1}{5}(10 - 15x)$

$y = -3x + 2$

Lesson

5-4 Solving Systems Using Linear Combinations

Vocabulary

linear-combination method

▸ **BIG IDEA** Some systems of equations can be solved by creating a new equation that is a linear combination of the original equations.

Mental Math

Write a linear combination to answer the question. How much did I spend if I bought

a. p pairs of shoes at \$39 each and s pairs of socks at \$4 each?

b. 3 pairs of shoes at $\$d_1$ each and 6 pairs of socks at $\$d_2$ each?

c. x pairs of shoes at $\$d_1$ each and y pairs of socks at $\$d_2$ each?

a. $39p + 4s$ dollars
b. $3d_1 + 6d_2$ dollars
c. $xd_1 + yd_2$ dollars

In the last lesson, you solved systems using the Substitution Property, which may be faster than using a CAS in cases when one equation is already solved for one variable in terms of the other variables. When linear equations are written in standard form, it may be more efficient to solve the system using the Addition and Multiplication Properties of Equality.

Recall that an expression of the form $Am + Bn$ is called a *linear combination* of m and n. In this lesson we use what we call the **linear-combination method** of solving systems because it involves adding multiples of the given equations.

Example 1

Solve the system $\begin{cases} x + 2y = 11 \\ 3x - 9y = 23 \end{cases}$ by the linear-combination method.

Solution The equations in this system represent the lines graphed at the right. The solution to the system is the point of intersection of the lines.

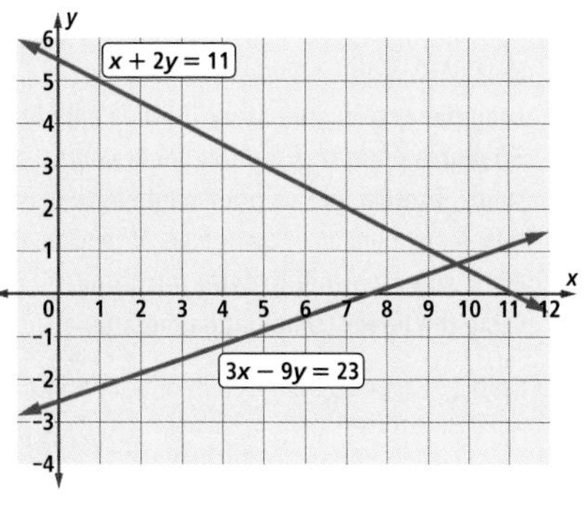

To solve the system using linear combinations, multiply the first equation by -3.

$-3(x + 2y) = -3 \cdot 11$ Multiplication Property of Equality

$-3x - 6y = -33$ Distributive Property, arithmetic

This equation is equivalent to the first equation of the original system. So, rewrite the system using this equation.

$$\begin{cases} -3x - 6y = -33 \\ 3x - 9y = 23 \end{cases}$$

Add these two equations. The result has no term in x.

$-15y = -10$ Addition Property of Equality

(continued on next page)

Background

The method in this lesson is called the linear-combination method because the resulting equation is a linear combination of the given equations. In general, given $ax + by = e$ and $cx + dy = f$ that intersect in a single point, *any* linear combination of these equations $m(ax + by) + n(cx + dy) = me + nf$ will contain that point. The multipliers m and n are chosen so that the resulting combination has only x or only y in it. That is, the combination will be a horizontal or vertical line containing the point of intersection.

Example 1 Some teachers prefer to multiply equations by numbers so that the equations being added have one less variable in the sum. Others are comfortable with having students multiply by the opposites of those numbers and subtract. In Example 1, we followed the first preference.

(continued on next page)

Lesson

5-4

GOAL

Learn how to use the Addition and Multiplication Properties of Equality to find solutions to certain systems.

SPUR Objectives

A Solve 2 × 2 and 3 × 3 systems using the linear-combination method.

D Recognize properties of systems of equations.

F Use systems of two or three linear equations to solve real-world problems.

Materials/Resources

- Lesson Masters 5-4A and 5-4B
- Resource Masters 79–81
- CAS

HOMEWORK

Suggestions for Assignment

- Questions 1–21
- Question 22 (extra credit)
- Reading Lesson 5-5
- Covering the Ideas 5-5

Local Standards

1 Warm-Up

1. Find values of m and n so that $3m - 4n = 0$. Answers vary. Sample: $m = 4$ and $n = 3$
2. Find values of a and b so that $12a + 3b = 0$. Answers vary. Sample: $a = 1$ and $b = -4$
3. If $m(3x + 4y) + n(15x + 45y) = py$ for all x and y, find possible values of m, n, and p. Answers vary. Sample: $m = 5$, $n = -1$, and $p = -25$.

2 Teaching

Notes on the Lesson

Most students will be familiar with using the linear-combination method to solve 2 × 2 systems from their previous work in algebra. Stress the need to work accurately. Encourage students to organize their work carefully.

Additional Example

Example 1 Solve the system $\begin{cases} 5x - 6y = 3 \\ 2x + 12y = 12 \end{cases}$ by the linear-combination method.
$(x, y) = (1.5, 0.75)$

Notes on the Lesson

Activity We urge you to do this Activity, even though it seems long. The work in setting up the equations will help in later lessons of this chapter.

Solve this equation for y.

$$y = \frac{-10}{-15} = \frac{2}{3}$$

Thus, $\frac{2}{3}$ is the y-coordinate of the point of intersection.

Substitute $\frac{2}{3}$ for y in any equation above to find x. We choose the first equation.

$$x + 2\left(\frac{2}{3}\right) = 11$$

$$x = 11 - \frac{4}{3} = \frac{29}{3}$$

So the solution to the system is $\begin{cases} x = \frac{29}{3} \\ y = \frac{2}{3} \end{cases}$.

You can write $(x, y) = \left(\frac{29}{3}, \frac{2}{3}\right)$.

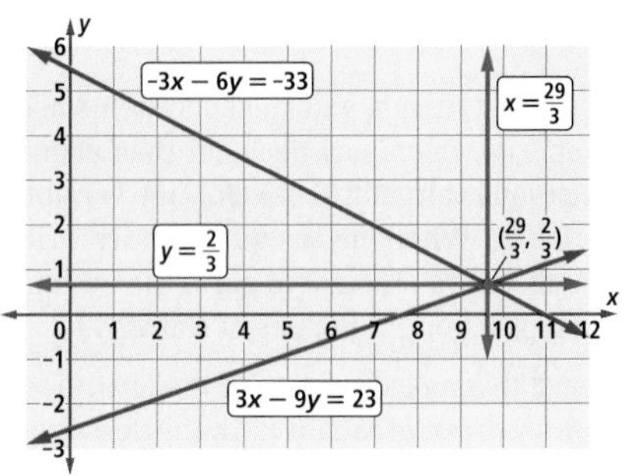

Check 1 Substitute $\frac{29}{3}$ for x and $\frac{2}{3}$ for y in the second equation. Does $3 \cdot \frac{29}{3} - 9 \cdot \frac{2}{3} = 23$? Yes. It checks.

Check 2 The graphs of the lines with the equations $x = \frac{29}{3}$ and $y = \frac{2}{3}$ intersect at the same point as the lines in the other systems. The last system is equivalent to the other two systems on the previous page.

Systems arise in important practical endeavors. For example, we all need to eat foods that meet minimum requirements of protein, vitamins, minerals, and calories.

Activity

MATERIALS CAS (optional)

Long-distance runner Mary Thawn wants to get 800 calories and 50 grams of protein from a dinner course of chicken and pasta with sauce. Protein and calorie counts for each item are given below. How many ounces of each type of food does Mary need to eat? Work with a partner to solve this problem in two different ways using the linear-combination method.

Scientific studies suggest that marathoners eat 0.8–1.7 grams of protein per kilogram of body weight per day.

Step 1 Organize the given information into a table.

	Chicken	Pasta with Sauce	Total Needed
Protein	9 g/oz	2 g/oz	50 g
Calories	65 cal/oz	45 cal/oz	800 cal

Step 2 Together, write a system to model this situation if c = the number of ounces of chicken Mary should eat, and p = the number of ounces of pasta with sauce that Mary should eat. $\begin{cases} 9c + 2p = 50 \\ 65c + 45p = 800 \end{cases}$

That is, we multiplied the first equation by -3 so that we could add the equations. We could have multiplied by 3 and then subtracted one equation from the other.

We use the shorthand informal language of "adding equations" when we mean "adding corresponding sides of two equations." This language is symbolically shown in the CAS display on page 323.

Accommodating the Learner

When asked to solve a system of three equations, as in Example 2, some students are confused about how to pair the equations. Explain that they can begin by choosing equations 1 and 2, 1 and 3, or 2 and 3. They can eliminate any of the three variables from the pair that they choose and then eliminate the *same* variable from another pair of equations.

Step 3 In the linear-combination method, you want to eliminate a variable by making the coefficients for that variable into opposites. Have one partner work to eliminate c and the other to eliminate p. By what numbers can you multiply the equations in the system to make the coefficients of your variable opposites? **Steps 3–6. See margin.**

Step 4 Carry out your multiplications from Step 3 and add to eliminate your variable. You can do this on a CAS or by hand. If you use a CAS, you might want to assign the two original equations to variables such as eq1 and eq2. Then you can multiply eq1 and eq2 by constants and add the results without retyping whole equations.

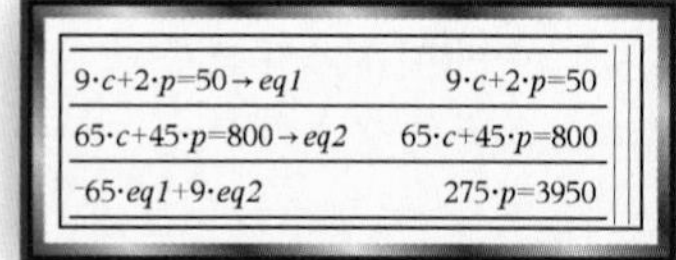

Step 5 Solve for the remaining variable and substitute into one of the original equations to find the value of the other variable. Then answer the question in the problem.

Step 6 Compare your results with those of your partner. Did you get the same solution? Was eliminating p easier than eliminating c, or vice versa? Was using a CAS easier or harder than doing it by hand?

QY

> **QY**
>
> If m is one of your equations in the Activity, and n is the other equation, then $Am + Bn$ is the linear combination you used to eliminate your variable. What were your A and B? What were your partner's A and B?

Linear Combinations with Systems of Three Equations

The linear-combination method can also be used to solve a system with three linear equations. First, use a linear combination of any pair of equations to eliminate one of the variables. Then eliminate the same variable from another pair of equations by using another linear combination. The result is a system of two equations with two variables. Then you can solve the simpler system using the methods of Example 1 and the Activity.

GUIDED

Example 2

Solve the system $\begin{cases} 2x + y + 4z = 20 \\ 3x - 3y + 2z = 27 \\ 4x + 5y - 2z = 4 \end{cases}$.

Solution We choose to eliminate z first because its coefficients in the last two equations are already opposites. Add the last two equations to get an equation in terms of x and y.

(continued on next page)

Notes on the Lesson

Example 2 In Check 2, we use a CAS to solve a system. Some graphing utilities can solve linear systems. Technology is particularly useful for systems larger than 2 × 2.

Additional Answers

Activity

Step 3: Answers vary. Sample: To eliminate c, multiply the second equation by $-\frac{1}{5}$ and multiply the first equation by $\frac{13}{9}$. To eliminate p, multiply the first equation by -45 and the second equation by 2.

Step 4: Answers vary. Sample: $\frac{-55}{9}p = \frac{-790}{9}$; $-275c = -650$

Step 5: $p = \frac{158}{11}$; $c = \frac{26}{11}$; she should eat about 14.4 oz of pasta and 2.4 oz of chicken for dinner.

Step 6: Answers vary. Sample: The easier variable to eliminate is usually the one where the coefficients have factors in common. Using a CAS can make this easier.

ENGLISH LEARNERS

Vocabulary Development

As introduced in Lesson 3-2, a *linear combination* is a sum of terms in which all the variables are raised to the first power and are not multiplied or divided by each other. For example, a linear combination of m and n is $-3m + n$. Point out that if we let m be the equation $x + 2y = 11$ and let n be the equation $3x - 9y = 23$, then $-3(x + 2y = 11) + 1 \cdot (3x - 9y = 23)$, as calculated in Example 1, is also a linear combination. This explains why the name *linear-combination method* is given to the method of solving systems that involves adding multiples of given equations.

Additional Example

Example 2 Solve the system $\begin{cases} 5x + y + 6z = 3 \\ x - y + 10z = 9 \\ 5x + y - 2z = -9 \end{cases}$.

Solution Add the first two equations to eliminate y and get an equation in terms of x and z:

$$\begin{array}{r} 5x + y + 6z = 3 \\ x - y + 10z = 9 \\ \hline \end{array}$$

$\underline{?} + \underline{?} = 12$ 6x; 16z

Now add the second and third equations to eliminate y and get another equation in terms of x and z:

$$\begin{array}{r} x - y + 10z = 9 \\ 5x + y - 2z = -9 \\ \hline \end{array}$$

$\underline{?} + \underline{?} = 0$ 6x; 8z

The result of adding the two sets of of equations is the system $\begin{cases} 6x + 16z = 12 \\ \underline{?} \end{cases}$. $6x + 8z = 0$

Use the linear-combination method on this system. Subtract the second equation from the first and solve for z: $\underline{?} = 12$; $z = \underline{?}$. $8z; \frac{3}{2}$

Substitute this value of z into an equation involving just two variables, such as: $6x + 16z = 12$. Thus, $6x + 16\left(\frac{3}{2}\right) = 12$; $6x = \underline{?}$; $x = \underline{?}$. -12; -2

Finally, substitute the values for z and x into one of the original equations, such as: $5x + y + 6z = 3$. Thus, $5(-2) + y + 6\left(\frac{3}{2}\right) = 3$, so $y = \underline{?}$ 4

The solution is $x = \underline{?}$, $y = \underline{?}$, and $z = \underline{?}$, which can be written as the ordered triple $(x, y, z) = \underline{?}$.

$-2; 4; \frac{3}{2}; \left(-2, 4, \frac{3}{2}\right)$

$$\begin{array}{r} 3x - 3y + 2z = 27 \\ 4x + 5y - 2z = 4 \\ \hline \underline{?} + \underline{?} = 31 \end{array}$$ Add. 7x; 2y

Now consider the first two equations. The coefficients of z are 4 and 2, so you can multiply the second equation by -2, then add the result to the first equation to get an equation in terms of x and y.

$2x + y + 4z = 20 \rightarrow \quad 2x + y + 4z = 20$

$3x - 3y + 2z = 27 \rightarrow \underline{?} + \underline{?} - 4z = \underline{?}$ Multiply by -2. -6x; 6y; -54

$\underline{?} + \underline{?} = -34$ Add. -4x; 7y

The result is the system below.

$\begin{cases} -4x + 7y = -34 \\ \underline{?} + \underline{?} = \underline{?} \end{cases}$ 7x; 2y; 31

Continue using the linear-combination method on this system of two equations in two variables. We choose to eliminate x.

$-4x + 7y = -34 \rightarrow \quad -28x + \underline{?} = \underline{?}$ Multiply by 7. 49y; -238

$7x + 2y = 31 \rightarrow \quad \underline{?} + 8y = \underline{?}$ Multiply by 4. 28x; 124

$\underline{?} = -114$ Add. 57y

$y = \underline{?}$ Solve for y. -2

Substitute $y = -2$ into one of the two equations involving just two variables. We substitute into $-4x + 7y = -34$.

$-4x + 7(-2) = -34$

$-4x = \underline{?}$ -20

$x = \underline{?}$ 5

Now substitute $x = 5$ and $y = -2$ into one of the original equations of the system. We use $2x + y + 4z = 20$.

$2(5) + (-2) + 4z = 20$

$4z = \underline{?}$ 12

$z = \underline{?}$ 3

So the solution is $x = \underline{?}$, $y = \underline{?}$, and $z = \underline{?}$. This can be written as the ordered triple $(x, y, z) = (\underline{?}, \underline{?}, \underline{?})$. 5; -2; 3 5; -2; 3

Check 1 Substitute the values for x, y, and z in each of the original equations to make sure they check.

Check 2 Solve using a CAS. One CAS solution is shown at the right.

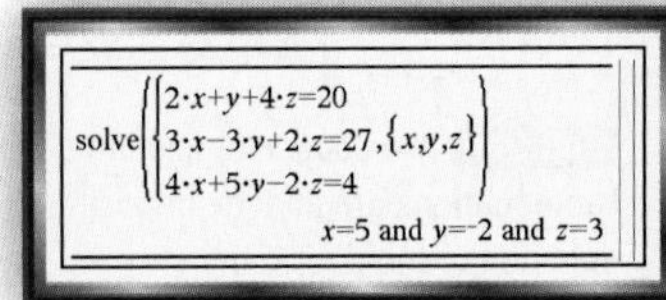

Accommodating the Learner

Have students explain how to use the linear combination method to find b if the y-coordinate of the solution to the system $\begin{cases} 4x + y = 6 \\ 2x + by = 4 \end{cases}$ is 2. Then have them find the solution to the system. To eliminate x, multiply the second equation by -2 and add to the first equation to get $(1 - 2b)y = 14$. Substitute 2 for y to get $2 - 4b = 14$, which implies that $b = -3$. Substitute -3 for b into the original system and solve it to find that the solution is (1, 2).

The systems in Examples 1 and 2 are consistent, and each has a unique solution. However, suppose you try to solve systems such as

$$\begin{cases} x + 2y = 11 \\ x + 2y = 12 \end{cases} \text{ or } \begin{cases} x + 2y = 11 \\ 2x + 4y = 22 \end{cases}.$$

If you use the linear-combination method with the first system, the result is a false statement, such as $0 = 1$, so the system is inconsistent and has no solutions. However, with the second system, the linear-combination method yields a result that is always true, such as $0 = 0$. This means the system is consistent, and there are infinitely many solutions.

As Example 2 shows, the linear-combination method takes some work with a 3×3 system. This method is more complicated and impractical when there are large numbers of variables and equations in the system. In Lesson 5-6, you will see how matrices provide an efficient way to solve large systems.

Questions

COVERING THE IDEAS

1. Refer to Example 1. What properties are used to obtain the equation $-15y = -10$ from the two original equations?
2. What equation results when $5x - 4y = 12$ is multiplied by -2? What property is being applied?
3. Refer to the Activity. One student graphed the equations she obtained in Steps 4 and 5. Her graph is at the right.
   a. Which variable was eliminated in Step 4? p
   b. What is an equation for the horizontal line? What is the equation for the vertical line? $p = 14.36$; $c = 2.36$
   c. What is the solution to the system? (2.36, 14.36)
4. Refer to the system involving only x and y in Example 2. Multiply the first equation by $\frac{7}{4}$ and solve the resulting system.
5. The table at the right gives the number of grams of protein and the number of calories in one ounce of each of two foods. Mary Thawn from the Activity still wants to get 800 calories from her meal and obtain 50 grams of protein.
   a. Let h be the number of ounces of chicken strips and r be the number of ounces of french fries she eats. Write a system of equations that describes these conditions.
   b. How many ounces of each food should Mary eat?

1. Addition and Multiplication Properties of Equality, Distributive Property
2. $-10x + 8y = -24$; Multiplication Property of Equality
4. $-7x + 12.25y = -59.5$; $14.25y = -28.5$; (5, -2)

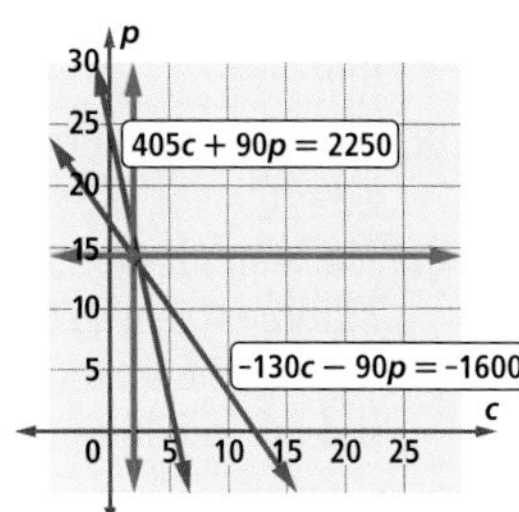

	Chicken Strips	French Fries
Protein	5 g/oz	1 g/oz
Calories	80 cal/oz	95 cal/oz

5a. $\begin{cases} 5h + r = 50 \\ 80h + 95r = 800 \end{cases}$

5b. 10 oz of chicken, 0 oz of fries

3 Assignment

Recommended Assignment

- Questions 1–21
- Question 22 (extra credit)
- Reading Lesson 5-5
- Covering the Ideas 5-5

Notes on the Questions

Questions 1–12 These questions have been carefully ordered to summarize the main ideas of the lesson.

Question 2 Here we speak of multiplying an equation by a number. Although this is technically incorrect—we are multiplying both sides of the equation by the number—in some technology this is exactly what is entered symbolically. We think it is a convenient phrase, and as far as we know it does not lead to misunderstandings.

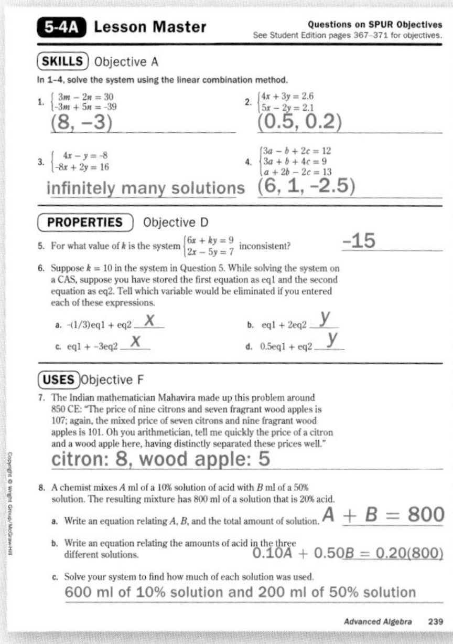

5-4A Lesson Master

Questions on SPUR Objectives
See Student Edition pages 367–371 for objectives.

SKILLS Objective A

In 1–4, solve the system using the linear combination method.

1. $\begin{cases} 3m - 2n = 30 \\ -3m + 5n = -39 \end{cases}$ (8, −3)
2. $\begin{cases} 4x + 3y = 2.6 \\ 5x - 2y = 2.1 \end{cases}$ (0.5, 0.2)
3. $\begin{cases} 4x - y = -8 \\ -8x + 2y = 16 \end{cases}$ infinitely many solutions
4. $\begin{cases} 3a - b + 2c = 12 \\ 3a + b + 4c = 9 \\ a + 2b - 2c = 13 \end{cases}$ (6, 1, −2.5)

PROPERTIES Objective D

5. For what value of k is the system $\begin{cases} 6x + ky = 9 \\ 2x - 5y = 7 \end{cases}$ inconsistent? −15
6. Suppose $k = 10$ in the system in Question 5. While solving the system on a CAS, suppose you have stored the first equation as eq1 and the second equation as eq2. Tell which variable would be eliminated if you entered each of these expressions.
   a. -(1/3)eq1 + eq2 x
   b. eq1 + 2eq2 y
   c. eq1 + -3eq2 x
   d. 0.5eq1 + eq2 y

USES Objective F

7. The Indian mathematician Mahavira made up this problem around 850 CE: "The price of nine citrons and seven fragrant wood apples is 107; again, the mixed price of seven citrons and nine fragrant wood apples is 101. Oh you arithmetician, tell me quickly the price of a citron and a wood apple here, having distinctly separated these prices well." citron: 8, wood apple: 5
8. A chemist mixes A ml of a 10% solution of acid with B ml of a 50% solution. The resulting mixture has 800 ml of a solution that is 20% acid.
   a. Write an equation relating A, B, and the total amount of solution. $A + B = 800$
   b. Write an equation relating the amounts of acid in the three different solutions. $0.10A + 0.50B = 0.20(800)$
   c. Solve your system to find how much of each solution was used. 600 ml of 10% solution and 200 ml of 50% solution

Advanced Algebra 239

Notes on the Questions

Questions 11 and 12 These questions can lead to a discussion of the relationship between constants and consistency. A criterion will be discussed in Lesson 5-6. However, you could initiate the discussion at this time.

Question 13 Question 22b asks students to show how to answer this question without using algebra or trial and error.

Question 14 This question uses linear combinations in a chemistry application that students may also encounter in their science classes.

In 6–9, solve the system using the linear-combination method.

6. $\begin{cases} a + b = \frac{1}{2} \\ a - b = \frac{1}{3} \end{cases}$

7. $\begin{cases} 4u - 2v = 24 \\ 5u + 6v = 13 \end{cases}$

8. $\begin{cases} 10g + 15h = 60 \\ 0.02g + 0.12h = 0.3 \end{cases}$

9. $\begin{cases} 2x - y + 2z = 4 \\ 5x + 2y - 3z = 43 \\ x + y - z = 11 \end{cases}$

6. $a = \frac{5}{12}$, and $b = \frac{1}{12}$
7. $u = 5$ and $v = -2$
8. $g = 3$ and $h = 2$
9. $x = 6$, $y = 2$, and $z = -3$

10. In the process of solving a system using the linear-combination method, a student obtained the result $0 = 0$. How should the result be interpreted? The system has infinitely many solutions.

In 11 and 12, use the linear-combination method to determine whether the system is inconsistent or consistent.

11. $\begin{cases} 5x + y = 16 \\ 10x + 2y = 20 \end{cases}$ inconsistent

12. $\begin{cases} 4a + 10b = 12 \\ 6a + 15b = 18 \end{cases}$ consistent

APPLYING THE MATHEMATICS

13. Suppose 3 turkey wraps and 2 juices cost \$26.50, while 2 turkey wraps and 3 juices cost \$24.75. What is the cost of one juice? \$4.25

14. N liters of a 1.3 moles per liter (mol/L) nitric acid solution are mixed with A liters of a 6.8 mol/L nitric acid solution. The result is 2 liters of a solution that is 3.5 mol/L.
   a. Write an equation relating N, A, and the total number of liters. $N + A = 2$
   b. The amount of nitric acid in the resulting solution is 2 liters • 3.5 mol/L, or 7 mols. Write an equation relating the amount of nitric acid in the two initial solutions and the resulting solution. $1.3N + 6.8A = 7$
   c. Solve the system represented by your answers in Parts a and b. How many liters of each solution are needed?

Nitric acid is sometimes used in etching as a *mordant*, a solution that eats away unwanted metal.

14c. $A = 0.8$ and $N = 1.2$; 1.2 L of the 1.3 mol/L solution and 0.8 L of the 6.8 mol/L solution are needed.

15. Refer to Example 2.
   a. Suppose you use the first and second equations to eliminate x. What can you multiply each equation by so that when you add the results, you get an equation in terms of y and z only?
   b. Suppose you use the first and third equations to eliminate x. What can you multiply each equation by so that when you add the results, you get an equation in terms of y and z only?
   c. Do the multiplications in Parts a and b and solve the resulting system of 2 equations in y and z. Then substitute to find x. $y = -2$ and $z = 3$; $x = 5$
   d. **True or False** The method used in Parts a–c gives the same solution as in Example 2. true

15a. Answers vary. Sample: Multiply the first equation by −3 and the second equation by 2.

15b. Answers vary. Sample: Multiply the first equation by −2.

16. Solve the system $\begin{cases} 3x^2 - 2y^2 = 40 \\ 2x^2 + 4y^2 = 48 \end{cases}$ using the linear-combination method. {(-4, -2), (-4, 2), (4, -2), (4, 2)}

REVIEW

17. Solve by substitution and check: $\begin{cases} x - 3y + 2z = 18 \\ y + z = -9 \\ z = 1 \end{cases}$. **(Lesson 5-3)** (-14, -10, 1)

18. Consider the scale change transformations with matrices $\begin{bmatrix} 2 & 0 \\ 0 & 1 \end{bmatrix}$ and $\begin{bmatrix} 1 & 0 \\ 0 & 2 \end{bmatrix}$. **(Lessons 4-7, 4-5, 4-4)**

a. What is the matrix for the composite of these two transformations? $\begin{bmatrix} 2 & 0 \\ 0 & 2 \end{bmatrix}$

b. What type of transformation is represented by the matrix you found in Part a? a size change of magnitude 2

In 19 and 20, find the product. (Lesson 4-3)

19. $\begin{bmatrix} 4 & 3 \\ -2 & 6 \end{bmatrix}\begin{bmatrix} x \\ y \end{bmatrix}$

20. $\begin{bmatrix} 2 & -4 \\ 1 & 8 \end{bmatrix}\begin{bmatrix} 0.4 & 0.2 \\ -0.05 & 0.1 \end{bmatrix}$

21. a. Rewrite the following using scalar multiples.

$$\begin{bmatrix} 4 & -6 & 5.5 \\ 0 & 3 & 0 \end{bmatrix} + \begin{bmatrix} 4 & -6 & 5.5 \\ 0 & 3 & 0 \end{bmatrix} + \begin{bmatrix} 4 & -6 & 5.5 \\ 0 & 3 & 0 \end{bmatrix} - \begin{bmatrix} 7 & 2 & 0 \\ 0 & 0 & -1 \end{bmatrix} - \begin{bmatrix} 7 & 2 & 0 \\ 0 & 0 & -1 \end{bmatrix}$$

b. Find the sum in Part a. **(Lesson 4-2)**

EXPLORATION

22. In a talk to students, mathematician Raymond Smullyan gave this problem as an example of one that can be solved without algebra:

> A family has 12 pets, a combination of cats and dogs. Every night, they give each cat two treats and each dog three treats. If they give 27 treats a night, how many of each kind of pet do they have?

a. Show how to solve this problem without any algebra and without using trial-and-error.

b. Show how to answer Question 14 without algebra or trial-and-error. See margin.

19. $\begin{bmatrix} 4x + 3y \\ -2x + 6y \end{bmatrix}$

20. $\begin{bmatrix} 1 & 0 \\ 0 & 1 \end{bmatrix}$

21a. $3\begin{bmatrix} 4 & -6 & 5.5 \\ 0 & 3 & 0 \end{bmatrix} - 2\begin{bmatrix} 7 & 2 & 0 \\ 0 & 0 & -1 \end{bmatrix}$

21b. $\begin{bmatrix} -2 & -22 & 16.5 \\ 0 & 9 & 2 \end{bmatrix}$

22a. Since an odd number of treats is distributed each night, we know there must be an odd number of dogs. We also know the number of dogs must be less than 9 in order for the total number of treats to be 27. If we give each pet 2 treats, that is 24 treats. There are 3 left over, so there must be 3 dogs and 9 cats.

QY ANSWER

Answers vary. Sample: one partner, $A = 65$, $B = -9$; the other partner, $A = -45$, $B = 2$

Additional Answers

22b. We know that the difference between t and j is $26.5 - 24.75 = 1.75$, and $t > j$. So $t = j + 1.75$. Take away 1.75 for each turkey wrap in either combination and divide the result by 5 to see that a juice costs \$4.25.

Notes on the Questions

Question 16 The linear-combination method is extended to quadratic systems in this question. The graph of the first equation is a hyperbola, and the graph of the second is an ellipse. Quadratic systems are discussed in a later chapter.

Question 20 Note that the product of these two matrices is the identity matrix for multiplication. That these matrices are *inverse matrices* is discussed in the next lesson.

Question 22 Some research suggests that students who have not had algebra are more likely to be able to answer the question than those who have had algebra. This is not because the algebra is difficult, but because a solution without algebra is not difficult.

4 Wrap-Up

Ongoing Assessment

Have students work in pairs, with each student writing a system of equations. Each equation should be written in standard form. Have partners exchange papers and use the linear-combination method to solve the system. Students should demonstrate that they can solve a system of two equations by using the linear-combination method.

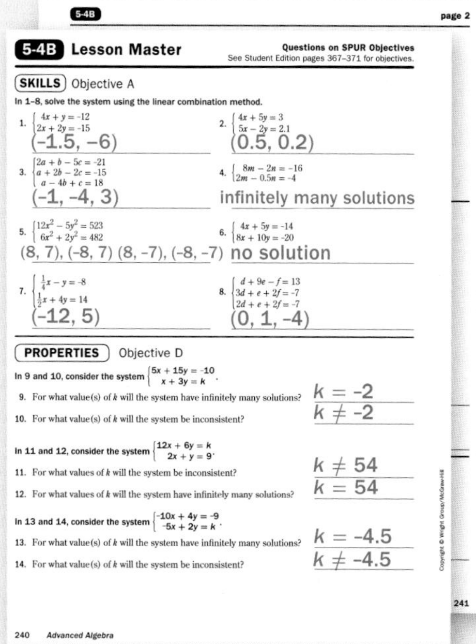
5-4B page 2

5-4B Lesson Master — Questions on SPUR Objectives. See Student Edition pages 367–371 for objectives.

SKILLS Objective A

In 1–8, solve the system using the linear combination method.

1. $\begin{cases} 4x + y = -12 \\ 2x + 2y = -15 \end{cases}$ (-1.5, -6)
2. $\begin{cases} 4x + 5y = 3 \\ 5x - 2y = 2.1 \end{cases}$ (0.5, 0.2)
3. $\begin{cases} 2a + b - 5c = -21 \\ a + 2b - 2c = -15 \\ a - 4b + c = 18 \end{cases}$ (-1, -4, 3)
4. $\begin{cases} 8m - 2n = -16 \\ 2m - 0.5n = -4 \end{cases}$ infinitely many solutions
5. $\begin{cases} 12x^2 - 5y^2 = 523 \\ 6x^2 + 2y^2 = 482 \end{cases}$ (8, 7), (-8, 7) (8, -7), (-8, -7)
6. $\begin{cases} 4x + 5y = -14 \\ 8x + 10y = -20 \end{cases}$ no solution
7. $\begin{cases} \frac{1}{4}x - y = -8 \\ \frac{1}{2}x + 4y = 14 \end{cases}$ (-12, 5)
8. $\begin{cases} d + 9e - f = 13 \\ 3d + e + 2f = -7 \\ 2d + e + 2f = -7 \end{cases}$ (0, 1, -4)

PROPERTIES Objective D

In 9 and 10, consider the system $\begin{cases} 5x + 15y = -10 \\ x + 3y = k \end{cases}$.

9. For what value(s) of k will the system have infinitely many solutions? $k = -2$
10. For what value(s) of k will the system be inconsistent? $k \neq -2$

In 11 and 12, consider the system $\begin{cases} 12x + 6y = k \\ 2x + y = 9 \end{cases}$.

11. For what values of k will the system be inconsistent? $k \neq 54$
12. For what values of k will the system have infinitely many solutions? $k = 54$

In 13 and 14, consider the system $\begin{cases} -10x + 4y = -9 \\ -5x + 2y = k \end{cases}$.

13. For what value(s) of k will the system have infinitely many solutions? $k = -4.5$
14. For what value(s) of k will the system be inconsistent? $k \neq -4.5$

240 Advanced Algebra 241

Lesson 5-5

GOAL

Relate the matrix concepts in Chapter 4 to systems of equations. Find the inverse of a 2 × 2 matrix and apply it to codes.

SPUR Objectives

B Find the determinant and inverse of a square matrix.

Materials/Resources

- Lesson Masters 5-5A and 5-5B
- Resource Masters 82–84
- CAS or graphing calculator

HOMEWORK

Suggestions for Assignment

- Questions 1–19
- Question 20 (extra credit)
- Reading Lesson 5-6
- Covering the Ideas 5-6

Local Standards

1 Warm-Up

1. a. Multiply: $\begin{bmatrix} 6 & 0 \\ 0 & 6 \end{bmatrix} \cdot \begin{bmatrix} x & 0 \\ 0 & y \end{bmatrix}$.

$\begin{bmatrix} 6x & 0 \\ 0 & 6y \end{bmatrix}$

b. If the product in Part a is $\begin{bmatrix} 1 & 0 \\ 0 & 1 \end{bmatrix}$, what are the values of x and y?

$x = \frac{1}{6}$; $y = \frac{1}{6}$

2. If $\begin{bmatrix} 2 & -1 \\ 1 & 3 \end{bmatrix} \cdot \begin{bmatrix} a \\ c \end{bmatrix} = \begin{bmatrix} 1 \\ 0 \end{bmatrix}$, find the values of a and c. $a = \frac{3}{7}$; $c = -\frac{1}{7}$

Lesson 5-5 Inverses of Matrices

Vocabulary

inverse matrices
square matrix
singular matrix
determinant

BIG IDEA Most 2 × 2 and most 3 × 3 matrices A have an inverse, A^{-1}, of the same dimensions, that satisfies $A^{-1}A = AA^{-1} = I$, where I is the identity matrix for their dimensions.

Are there ever times when you want to send a friend a note, but you want only your friend to be able to read it? To do this, you could use cryptography. Cryptography, which comes from the Greek words *kryptos* (hidden) and *graphia* (writing), is the study of encoding and decoding messages. In this lesson you will see how to use the *inverses of matrices* in cryptography.

Mental Math

Sheila tosses a fair 6-sided die. What is the probability that the die shows

a. a 4? $\frac{1}{6}$

b. an even number? $\frac{1}{2}$

c. a prime number? $\frac{1}{2}$

d. a rational number? 1

What Are Inverse Matrices?

The idea of an inverse of an operation runs throughout mathematics. Recall that two real numbers a and b are *additive inverses* (or *opposites*) if and only if $a + b = 0$. For example, 7.3 and -7.3 are additive inverses. The sum of two additive inverses is 0, the additive identity. Two real numbers a and b are *multiplicative inverses* (or *reciprocals*) if and only if $ab = 1$. For example, π and $\frac{1}{\pi}$ are multiplicative inverses. The product of two multiplicative inverses is 1, the multiplicative identity.

The definition of *inverse matrices* under multiplication follows the same idea as the inverses mentioned above. The 2 × 2 matrices A and B are called **inverse matrices** if and only if their product is the 2 × 2 identity matrix for multiplication, that is, if and only if

$AB = BA = \begin{bmatrix} 1 & 0 \\ 0 & 1 \end{bmatrix}$.

Because matrix multiplication is not commutative, the definition of *inverse matrices* requires that the product in both orders of multiplication be the identity. To be multiplied in both directions, the matrices must be **square matrices**, those with the same number of rows and columns.

So there can be inverse 3 × 3 matrices, inverse 4 × 4 matrices, and so on. But there cannot be inverse 2 × 3 matrices. Furthermore, as you will see, not all square matrices are *invertible* (have inverses).

Background

A system of linear equations can be considered as a *single* matrix equation $AX = B$, where A is a matrix of coefficients, X is a matrix of variables to be found, and B is a matrix of constants. This equation is solved by multiplying both sides by the multiplicative inverse of the matrix A. This process, being analogous to the process of solving the linear equation $ax = b$, reinforces that earlier work. The only difficulty in the process is finding the inverse of A. As one might expect from the process of matrix multiplication, the formula for the inverse under this operation is not at all obvious. However, that it works is quite amazing to many students, and this lesson and the next can be engaging lessons.

Determinants and inverses Determinants were first used by the Japanese mathematician Seki Kowa in 1683 and independently 10 years later by the German mathematician Gottfried Leibniz (1646–1716). The determinant

Notation for Inverse Matrices

The real number x^{-1} is equal to $\frac{1}{x}$, the multiplicative inverse of x, for all $x \neq 0$. Similarly, the symbol M^{-1} stands for the inverse of the square matrix M, if M has an inverse. Many graphing calculators and all CAS can display matrices and their inverses. To verify that two matrices are inverses, multiply.

Activity 1

MATERIALS CAS or graphing calculator

Step 1 Clear the variable a on your calculator. Store $\begin{bmatrix} -3 & 5 \\ 7 & -11 \end{bmatrix}$ in your calculator as variable a.

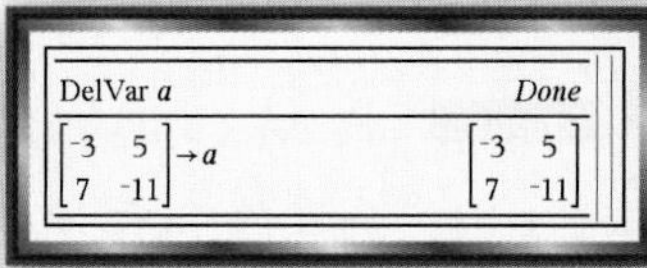

Step 2 Calculate a^{-1} by using the inverse key on your calculator, or by entering a^-1.

Step 3 Find the product aa^{-1}.

Step 4 Find the product $a^{-1}a$.

Activity 1

Step 2. $\begin{bmatrix} 5.5 & 2.5 \\ 3.5 & 1.5 \end{bmatrix}$

Step 3. $\begin{bmatrix} 1 & 0 \\ 0 & 1 \end{bmatrix}$

Step 4. $\begin{bmatrix} 1 & 0 \\ 0 & 1 \end{bmatrix}$

A Formula for the Inverse of a 2 × 2 Matrix

You do not need a calculator to obtain the inverse of a 2 × 2 matrix. There is a formula.

Inverse Matrix Theorem

If $ad - bc \neq 0$ and $M = \begin{bmatrix} a & b \\ c & d \end{bmatrix}$, then $M^{-1} = \begin{bmatrix} \frac{d}{ad-bc} & \frac{-b}{ad-bc} \\ \frac{-c}{ad-bc} & \frac{a}{ad-bc} \end{bmatrix}$.

Proof We need to show that the product of the two matrices in either order is the identity matrix. Below, we show one order. In Question 9, you are asked to verify the multiplication in the reverse order.

$$\begin{bmatrix} a & b \\ c & d \end{bmatrix} \begin{bmatrix} \frac{d}{ad-bc} & \frac{-b}{ad-bc} \\ \frac{-c}{ad-bc} & \frac{a}{ad-bc} \end{bmatrix}$$

$$= \begin{bmatrix} \frac{ad}{ad-bc} + \frac{-bc}{ad-bc} & \frac{-ab}{ad-bc} + \frac{ab}{ad-bc} \\ \frac{cd}{ad-bc} + \frac{-cd}{ad-bc} & \frac{-bc}{ad-bc} + \frac{ad}{ad-bc} \end{bmatrix} \quad \text{Matrix multiplication}$$

$$= \begin{bmatrix} \frac{ad-bc}{ad-bc} & \frac{0}{ad-bc} \\ \frac{0}{ad-bc} & \frac{ad-bc}{ad-bc} \end{bmatrix} = \begin{bmatrix} 1 & 0 \\ 0 & 1 \end{bmatrix} \quad \text{Addition of fractions, definition of subtraction}$$

2 Teaching

Notes on the Lesson

Point out that the inverse of a 2 × 2 matrix is also a 2 × 2 matrix, which allows the two matrices to be multiplied in either order. Multiplication of 2 × 2 matrices is not generally commutative, but it is always commutative when the matrices are inverses. Have students verify the matrix multiplication in the proof of the Inverse Matrix Theorem.

The key or command for the inverse of a matrix varies from calculator to calculator. On many it is [x^{-1}]. The sequence a[^][-][1] gives the inverse of the matrix a on all graphing calculators and CASs. The - key ([+/−]) is not typically the same as the minus key ([−]).

Activity 1 Many graphing utilities can automatically obtain the inverse of a 2 × 2 matrix. If your students have such technology, they should learn how to find the inverse of a matrix. It is usually a surprise for students to see that the same [x^{-1}] key used to find the multiplicative inverse of a real number is used to find the multiplicative inverse of a matrix. The Example on page 330 can be used to check the above procedure. We note that some calculators use the term *singular matrix* to identify a matrix that has no inverse. A *nonsingular matrix* is one that has an inverse.

Some teachers like to make finding an inverse to a matrix a "discovery" activity. If you have the time, or curious students, you might give them an equation of the form $AX = \begin{bmatrix} 1 & 0 \\ 0 & 1 \end{bmatrix}$ and let them try to find matrix X for a given matrix A. Be sure that A has an inverse before having students work on their own.

key/command varies from calculator to calculator, but for most it is [DET].

Using matrices to encode and decode Matrices provide a simple way to encode and decode a message. (If students are confused by these words, compare them with *enable* and *disable*.) The idea is to transform the original message by a mathematical rule that has an inverse. It is possible to use a simple function, rather than matrices, to map a letter with number x onto the letter with number $3x - 2$, working with remainders when numbers are divided by 27. But, then the same letter is always encoded in the same way, and a person not knowing the coding function could determine the original message by looking at the frequencies of letters. Working with frequencies is done in many cryptograms in puzzle books.

Breaking the code can be made more difficult by not coding spaces between words.

Notes on the Lesson

A formula for the inverse of a 2 × 2 matrix The proof of the Inverse Matrix Theorem does not tell how we knew in advance that $\begin{bmatrix} \frac{d}{ad-bc} & \frac{-b}{ad-bc} \\ \frac{-c}{ad-bc} & \frac{a}{ad-bc} \end{bmatrix}$ is the inverse of $\begin{bmatrix} a & b \\ c & d \end{bmatrix}$. The inverse can be derived as follows, which is a generalization of the technique illustrated in Question 14. If the inverse of $\begin{bmatrix} a & b \\ c & d \end{bmatrix}$ exists, it must be a 2 × 2 matrix; so we can multiply it on either the left or right. Call the inverse $\begin{bmatrix} w & x \\ y & z \end{bmatrix}$. Then we need to find w, x, y, and z such that

$$\begin{bmatrix} a & b \\ c & d \end{bmatrix}\begin{bmatrix} w & x \\ y & z \end{bmatrix} = \begin{bmatrix} 1 & 0 \\ 0 & 1 \end{bmatrix} \text{ or}$$

$$\begin{bmatrix} w & x \\ y & z \end{bmatrix}\begin{bmatrix} a & b \\ c & d \end{bmatrix} = \begin{bmatrix} 1 & 0 \\ 0 & 1 \end{bmatrix}.$$

Multiplying the matrices on the left and equating the entries yields the following system: $\begin{cases} aw + by = 1 \\ ax + bz = 0 \\ cw + dy = 0 \\ cx + dz = 1 \end{cases}$.

By using linear-combination techniques, you can solve for w, x, y, and z. For example, if you multiply the first equation by c and the third by $-a$ and add the resulting equations, you can solve for y: $y = \frac{c}{bc-ad} = \frac{-c}{ad-bc}$. Other linear combinations will allow you to find w, x, and z. We do not suggest you do the complete derivation for all four variables, but some students might enjoy working through the complete derivation independently.

Not only does the Inverse Matrix Theorem tell you how to find an inverse without a calculator, it gives you a quick test for whether an inverse exists. Note that $ad - bc$ cannot be zero because it is in the denominator of all the fractions. The inverse of a 2 × 2 matrix $\begin{bmatrix} a & b \\ c & d \end{bmatrix}$ exists only if $ad - bc \neq 0$.

GUIDED

Example

Use the Inverse Matrix Theorem to find the inverse of each matrix, if it exists.

a. $\begin{bmatrix} -2 & 4 \\ -1 & 6 \end{bmatrix}$ b. $\begin{bmatrix} 5 & 10 \\ 3 & 6 \end{bmatrix}$

Solution

a. In $\begin{bmatrix} -2 & 4 \\ -1 & 6 \end{bmatrix}$, a = _?_, b, = _?_, c = _?_, and d = _?_. -2; 4; -1; 6

So, ad − bc = (_?_ • _?_ − _?_ • _?_) = _?_, and the matrix has an inverse. -2; 6; 4; -1; -8

Now substitute into the formula. The inverse is $\begin{bmatrix} \frac{?}{?} & \frac{?}{?} \\ \frac{?}{?} & \frac{-2}{-8} \end{bmatrix}$, which $-\frac{6}{8}; \frac{-4}{-8}; -\frac{1}{8}$

simplifies to $\begin{bmatrix} \frac{?}{?} & \frac{?}{?} \\ \frac{?}{?} & \frac{?}{?} \end{bmatrix}$. $-\frac{3}{4}; \frac{1}{2}; -\frac{1}{8}; \frac{1}{4}$

b. In $\begin{bmatrix} 5 & 10 \\ 3 & 6 \end{bmatrix}$, a = _?_, b, = _?_, c = _?_, and d = _?_. 5; 10; 3; 6

So ad − bc = (_?_ • _?_ − _?_ • _?_) = _?_. 5; 6; 10; 3; 0

Because ad − bc = _?_, $\begin{bmatrix} 5 & 10 \\ 3 & 6 \end{bmatrix}$ has _?_. 0; no inverse

If a matrix has no inverse, trying to find it on a calculator leads to an error message. Some calculators say the inverse is undefined, while others say the original matrix is a **singular matrix**, meaning that its inverse does not exist.

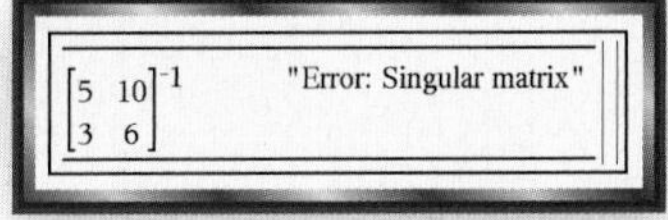

ENGLISH LEARNERS

Vocabulary Development

Stress that the *inverse of a matrix* is analogous to the inverse of a real number. When added, additive inverses (or opposites) add to zero, the identity for addition. When multiplied, multiplicative inverses (or reciprocals) yield 1, the identity for multiplication; and when multiplied, matrix inverses yield the identity matrix.

Then discuss *square matrices,* which have the same number of rows and columns and thus form a "square" of elements. Students can relate "singular" to "single," so a *singular matrix* has no mate or inverse.

Finally, the term *determinant* is related to the word *determine,* which can mean "to be a deciding factor in reaching a certain result." Tell students that the determinant has this name because it determines whether the matrix has an inverse or not.

Determinants and Inverses

The formula in the Inverse Matrix Theorem can be simplified using scalar multiplication. When $ad - bc \neq 0$,

$$\begin{bmatrix} \frac{d}{ad-bc} & \frac{-b}{ad-bc} \\ \frac{-c}{ad-bc} & \frac{a}{ad-bc} \end{bmatrix} = \frac{1}{ad-bc}\begin{bmatrix} d & -b \\ -c & a \end{bmatrix}.$$

Because the number $ad - bc$ determines whether or not a matrix has an inverse, it is called the **determinant** of the matrix. We abbreviate the word *determinant* as *det*. Thus, the Inverse Matrix Theorem can be written:

If $M = \begin{bmatrix} a & b \\ c & d \end{bmatrix}$, then $M^{-1} = \frac{1}{\det M}\begin{bmatrix} d & -b \\ -c & a \end{bmatrix}$ if and only if $\det M \neq 0$.

Calculators that handle matrices have a determinant function, usually called `det`.

QY

Using Matrices to Encode and Decode

How can matrices and their inverses help in cryptography? At the right is a picture of a decoder ring, created as part of a promotional offer in May, 2000. On the outside circle are the letters of the alphabet and on the inside circle are the numbers 1 through 26. You are able to turn the inside dial so the number 1 can correspond to any of the letters in the alphabet. In the configuration in the photo at the right, 1 corresponds to C. This is the *key* to the code. A message gets encoded as a set of numbers. To decode the message, the recipient sets the dial according to the key and reads the letters corresponding to the numbers. For example, the code 9, 16, 4, 4, 15 in this configuration decodes as HELLO.

While encoding phrases using the ring is easy to do, it is also relatively easy to decode them. For one thing, each number always stands for the same letter. For example, each E is encoded as 16. Also, it is easy to tell the length of a word. For these reasons it would not be too difficult to break the code. Businesses and governments need a more powerful method of encryption. One such method is to use matrices.

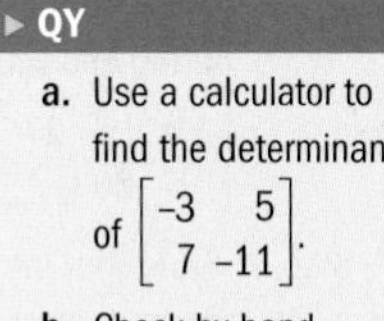
QY

a. Use a calculator to find the determinant of $\begin{bmatrix} -3 & 5 \\ 7 & -11 \end{bmatrix}$.

b. Check by hand.

Additional Example

Example Use the Inverse Matrix Theorem to find the inverse of each matrix, if it exists.

a. $\begin{bmatrix} 0 & -2 \\ 2 & 1 \end{bmatrix}$ **b.** $\begin{bmatrix} 2 & -4 \\ 5 & -10 \end{bmatrix}$

Solution

a. In $\begin{bmatrix} 0 & -2 \\ 2 & 1 \end{bmatrix}$, $a =$ __?__, $b =$ __?__, $c =$ __?__, and $d =$ __?__. 0; -2; 2; 1

So, $ad - bc =$ (__?__)(__?__) − (__?__)(__?__) = __?__, and the matrix has an inverse. 0; 1; -2; 2; 4

Now substitute into the formula.

The inverse is __?__, which simplifies to __?__. $\begin{bmatrix} \frac{1}{4} & \frac{2}{4} \\ -\frac{2}{4} & \frac{0}{4} \end{bmatrix}$; $\begin{bmatrix} \frac{1}{4} & \frac{1}{2} \\ -\frac{1}{2} & 0 \end{bmatrix}$

b. In $\begin{bmatrix} 2 & -4 \\ 5 & -10 \end{bmatrix}$, $a =$ __?__, $b =$ __?__, $c =$ __?__, and $d =$ __?__. 2; -4; 5; -10 So $ad - bc =$ (__?__)(__?__) − (__?__)(__?__) = __?__. 2; -10; -4; 5; 0 Because $ad - bc =$ __?__, $\begin{bmatrix} 2 & -4 \\ 5 & -10 \end{bmatrix}$ has __?__. 0; no inverse

Accommodating the Learner

To show that the inverse of the inverse of a matrix is the matrix itself, have students use the Inverse Matrix Theorem to show that $\left(\begin{bmatrix} w & x \\ y & z \end{bmatrix}^{-1}\right)^{-1} = \begin{bmatrix} \frac{z}{wz-xy} & \frac{-x}{wz-xy} \\ \frac{-y}{wz-xy} & \frac{w}{wz-xy} \end{bmatrix}^{-1} = \begin{bmatrix} w & x \\ y & z \end{bmatrix}$. det $\begin{bmatrix} \frac{z}{wz-xy} & \frac{-x}{wz-xy} \\ \frac{-y}{wz-xy} & \frac{w}{wz-xy} \end{bmatrix} = \left(\frac{z}{wz-xy}\right)\left(\frac{w}{wz-xy}\right) - \left(\frac{-x}{wz-xy}\right)\left(\frac{-y}{wz-xy}\right) = \frac{xy}{(wz-xy)^2} = \frac{1}{(wz-xy)}$. So, by the Inverse Matrix Theorem, $\begin{bmatrix} \frac{z}{wz-xy} & \frac{-x}{wz-xy} \\ \frac{-y}{wz-xy} & \frac{w}{wz-xy} \end{bmatrix}^{-1} = \begin{bmatrix} \frac{w(wz-xy)}{wz-xy} & \frac{x(wz-xy)}{wz-xy} \\ \frac{y(wz-xy)}{wz-xy} & \frac{z(wz-xy)}{wz-xy} \end{bmatrix} = \begin{bmatrix} w & x \\ y & z \end{bmatrix}$.

Notes on the Lesson

Activity 2 In an actual coding situation, the message would not be given as numbers but as letters. The letters would be found by dividing each number by 27 and using the letter in the key that corresponds to the remainder. For example, in Step 5, instead of 1, 51, 145, 110, ..., the matrix would begin 1, 24, 10, 2, ... and the coded message would be given as AXJB....

Note-Taking Tips

Have students include in their journals examples of two 2 × 2 matrices, one that has an inverse and one that does not. They should include the determinant of each matrix and the inverse of the appropriate matrix.

Additional Answers

Activity 2

Step 5: 1, 51, 145, 110, 23, 119, 201, 145, 85, 88, 79, 154, 16, 41, 47, 134, 141, 92, 183, 157

Step 6: $e^{-1} = \begin{bmatrix} -\frac{5}{31} & \frac{8}{31} \\ \frac{2}{31} & \frac{3}{31} \end{bmatrix}$; $e^{-1} \cdot V =$

$$\begin{bmatrix} 13 & 5 & 27 & 5 & 9 & 27 & 8 & 27 & 1 & 11 \\ 5 & 20 & 13 & 27 & 14 & 20 & 5 & 16 & 18 & 27 \end{bmatrix}$$

Activity 2

MATERIALS CAS or graphing calculator

Step 1 To encode a phrase using matrices, first make a *key* by assigning a number to each letter like the ring does on the previous page. For this Activity, let $A = 1$, $B = 2$, and so on, and assign the number 27 to spaces between words. Use this method to make a key for MEET ME IN THE PARK in the table below. It has been started for you.

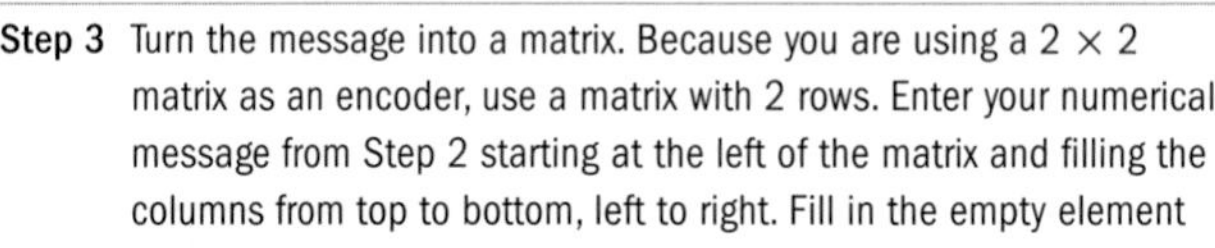

M	E	E	T		M	E		I	N		T	H	E		P	A	R	K
13	5	5	20	27	? 13	? 5	? 27	? 9	? 14	? 27	? 20	? 8	? 5	? 27	? 16	? 1	? 18	? 11

Step 2 Create a 2 × 2 *encoder matrix* e that has an inverse, for example, $e = \begin{bmatrix} -3 & 8 \\ 2 & 5 \end{bmatrix}$. Store this matrix in variable e in a calculator. Although we are using a 2 × 2 matrix for an encoder, any size square matrix with an inverse could be used.

$\begin{bmatrix} -3 & 8 \\ 2 & 5 \end{bmatrix} \rightarrow e$ $\quad \begin{bmatrix} -3 & 8 \\ 2 & 5 \end{bmatrix}$

Step 3 Turn the message into a matrix. Because you are using a 2 × 2 matrix as an encoder, use a matrix with 2 rows. Enter your numerical message from Step 2 starting at the left of the matrix and filling the columns from top to bottom, left to right. Fill in the empty element at the end with a 27, like the other spaces.

$$\begin{bmatrix} 13 & 5 & 27 & ? & ? & ? & ? & ? & ? & ? \\ 5 & 20 & ? & ? & ? & ? & ? & ? & ? & ? \end{bmatrix}$$

5; 9; 27; 8; 27; 1; 11; 13; 27; 14; 20; 5; 16; 18; 27

Step 4 Store your matrix from Step 3 as *m*. Multiply the encoder matrix e by *m* and store the product as *v*.

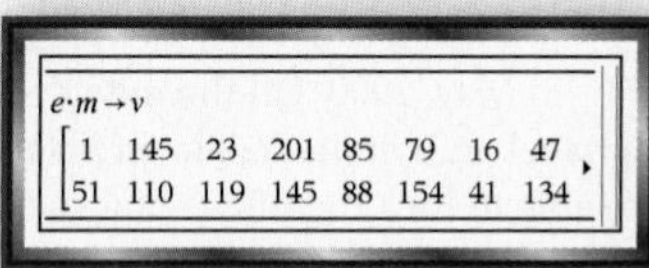

Step 5 To send the encoded message, record it as 1, 51, 145, 110, and so on, reading down the columns of *v*. Notice that with this encoding method, each E (or any other letter) does not get encoded to the same number, making it a more difficult code to break. See margin.

Step 6 Imagine that you gave your encoded message to a friend. The friend is a *receiver*. The receiver first needs to rewrite the message as a 2 × 10 matrix (the one you named *v*). Your friend then needs a *decoder matrix* to undo the multiplication by your encoder matrix e. This matrix is e^{-1}. Multiply the inverse matrix by matrix *v*. This is how the receiver would get your keyed message. He or she could then use the key to read the message. See margin.

Accommodating the Learner

Give students these steps to help them remember the Inverse Matrix Theorem.

Use the following steps to find the inverse of a 2 × 2 matrix $M = \begin{bmatrix} a & b \\ c & d \end{bmatrix}$:

1. Find det *M;* if det $M = 0$, the inverse of *M* does not exist.
2. Reverse the positions of *a* and *d.*
3. Take the opposites of *b* and *c.*
4. Divide each element by det *M.*

The final result is the inverse matrix.

Step 7 If you want to send encoded messages this way, the receiver needs to know only the encoding matrix and the key. The receiver can then find the inverse matrix and apply it.

Use the encoding matrix $\begin{bmatrix} -89 & 120 \\ 35 & 6 \end{bmatrix}$ and the key from this Activity (A = 1, B = 2, . . .) to decode the following message: –1304, 566, 589, 779, –843, 1023, 2311, 155, 2528, 442 PASS MATH

Questions

COVERING THE IDEAS

1. Identify the identity for each operation.
   a. real-number multiplication 1
   b. real-number addition 0
   c. 2×2 matrix multiplication $\begin{bmatrix} 1 & 0 \\ 0 & 1 \end{bmatrix}$
2. Explain why only square matrices can have inverses.
3. If N is a 2×2 matrix and N^{-1} exists, find each product.
   a. NN^{-1} $\begin{bmatrix} 1 & 0 \\ 0 & 1 \end{bmatrix}$ b. $N^{-1}N$ $\begin{bmatrix} 1 & 0 \\ 0 & 1 \end{bmatrix}$
4. Verify that $\begin{bmatrix} -\frac{3}{4} & \frac{1}{2} \\ -\frac{1}{8} & \frac{1}{4} \end{bmatrix}$ is the inverse of $\begin{bmatrix} -2 & 4 \\ -1 & 6 \end{bmatrix}$ using matrix multiplication. See margin.
5. a. When does the matrix $\begin{bmatrix} a & b \\ c & d \end{bmatrix}$ have an inverse? when $ad - bc \neq 0$
   b. What is that inverse?
6. Determine whether each matrix has an inverse.
   a. $\begin{bmatrix} 3 & 2 \\ 3 & 2 \end{bmatrix}$ no b. $\begin{bmatrix} 3 & -2 \\ -3 & 2 \end{bmatrix}$ no c. $\begin{bmatrix} 3 & -2 \\ 3 & 2 \end{bmatrix}$ yes

In 7 and 8, give the determinant of the matrix. Give the inverse of the matrix if it exists.

7. $\begin{bmatrix} 2 & 9 \\ -7 & 6 \end{bmatrix}$
8. $\begin{bmatrix} 12 & -2 \\ 25 & 5 \end{bmatrix}$
9. Complete the second part of the proof of the Inverse Matrix Theorem. That is, show that the identity matrix is the product of the two matrices in the reverse order. See margin.

2. To be inverse matrices, the matrices must be able to be multiplied in both directions.

5b. $\begin{bmatrix} \frac{d}{ad-bc} & \frac{-b}{ad-bc} \\ \frac{-c}{ad-bc} & \frac{a}{ad-bc} \end{bmatrix}$

7. 75, $\begin{bmatrix} \frac{2}{25} & -\frac{3}{25} \\ \frac{7}{75} & \frac{2}{75} \end{bmatrix}$

8. 110, $\begin{bmatrix} \frac{1}{22} & \frac{1}{55} \\ -\frac{5}{22} & \frac{6}{55} \end{bmatrix}$

5-5

3 Assignment

Recommended Assignment

- Questions 1–19
- Question 20 (extra credit)
- Reading Lesson 5-6
- Covering the Ideas 5-6

Additional Answers

4. $\begin{bmatrix} -\frac{3}{4} & \frac{1}{2} \\ -\frac{1}{8} & \frac{1}{4} \end{bmatrix} \begin{bmatrix} -2 & 4 \\ -1 & 6 \end{bmatrix} = \begin{bmatrix} 1 & 0 \\ 0 & 1 \end{bmatrix}$;

$\begin{bmatrix} -2 & 4 \\ -1 & 6 \end{bmatrix} \begin{bmatrix} -\frac{3}{4} & \frac{1}{2} \\ -\frac{1}{8} & \frac{1}{4} \end{bmatrix} = \begin{bmatrix} 1 & 0 \\ 0 & 1 \end{bmatrix}$

9. $\begin{bmatrix} \frac{d}{ad - bc} & \frac{-b}{ad - bc} \\ \frac{-c}{ad - bc} & \frac{a}{ad - bc} \end{bmatrix} \begin{bmatrix} a & b \\ c & d \end{bmatrix} =$

$\begin{bmatrix} \frac{da}{ad - bc} + \frac{-bc}{ad - bc} & \frac{db}{ad - bc} + \frac{-bd}{ad - bc} \\ \frac{-ca}{ad - bc} + \frac{ac}{ad - bc} & \frac{-cb}{ad - bc} + \frac{ad}{ad - bc} \end{bmatrix} =$

$\begin{bmatrix} \frac{ad - bc}{ad - bc} & \frac{0}{ab - bc} \\ \frac{0}{ad - bc} & \frac{ad - bc}{ad - bc} \end{bmatrix} = \begin{bmatrix} 1 & 0 \\ 0 & 1 \end{bmatrix}$

5-5A Lesson Master Questions on SPUR Objectives
See Student Edition pages 367–371 for objectives.

SKILLS Objective B

In 1–4, for each matrix, find a. the determinant and b. the inverse, if it exists.

1. $\begin{bmatrix} 7 & 5 \\ 4 & 3 \end{bmatrix}$
   a. 1
   b. $\begin{bmatrix} 3 & -5 \\ -4 & 7 \end{bmatrix}$
2. $\begin{bmatrix} 3 & 1 \\ -2 & 6 \end{bmatrix}$
   a. 20
   b. $\begin{bmatrix} \frac{3}{10} & -\frac{1}{20} \\ \frac{1}{10} & \frac{3}{20} \end{bmatrix}$
3. $\begin{bmatrix} -2 & 10 \\ 1 & -5 \end{bmatrix}$
   a. 0
   b. no inverse
4. $\begin{bmatrix} a & b \\ c & d \end{bmatrix}$
   a. $ad - bc$
   b. $\begin{bmatrix} \frac{d}{ad - bc} & \frac{-b}{ad - bc} \\ \frac{-c}{ad - bc} & \frac{a}{ad - bc} \end{bmatrix}$

In 5 and 6, find a value of x so that the matrix does not have an inverse.

5. $\begin{bmatrix} 3 & 5 \\ 6 & x \end{bmatrix}$ 10
6. $\begin{bmatrix} 9 & 15 \\ x & -4 \end{bmatrix}$ $-\frac{12}{5}$
7. The matrix for S_3 is $\begin{bmatrix} 3 & 0 \\ 0 & 3 \end{bmatrix}$.
   a. Find the inverse of this matrix. $\begin{bmatrix} \frac{1}{3} & 0 \\ 0 & \frac{1}{3} \end{bmatrix}$
   b. Explain your result geometrically.
   The inverse of the matrix for a stretch by 3 is the matrix for a shrink by $\frac{1}{3}$.
8. Use a calculator to find a. the determinant and b. the inverse of $\begin{bmatrix} 3 & 1 & 0 \\ 4 & 5 & 1 \\ 0 & -3 & 1 \end{bmatrix}$.
   a. 20
   b. $\begin{bmatrix} \frac{2}{5} & -\frac{1}{20} & \frac{1}{20} \\ -\frac{1}{5} & \frac{3}{20} & -\frac{3}{20} \\ -\frac{3}{5} & \frac{9}{20} & \frac{11}{20} \end{bmatrix}$
9. Melissa receives a message that has been encoded using the matrix $\begin{bmatrix} 3 & 2 \\ 7 & 5 \end{bmatrix}$ and the key A = 1, B = 2, . . ., Y = 25, Z = 26, [space] = 27. The message she receives is 41, 96, 96, 230, 33, 78, 53, 130, 83, 194, 64, 151, 93, 219, 91, 217.
   a. Find the decoding matrix. $\begin{bmatrix} 5 & -2 \\ -7 & 3 \end{bmatrix}$
   b. Write the coded message in a 2×8 matrix. $\begin{bmatrix} 41 & 96 & 33 & 53 & 83 & 64 & 93 & 91 \\ 96 & 230 & 78 & 130 & 194 & 151 & 219 & 217 \end{bmatrix}$
   c. Multiply your answers to Parts a and b, and decode the message. MATRICES ARE FUN

242 *Advanced Algebra*

Notes on the Questions

Question 14 The inverse of a matrix, if it exists, can always be found using the method of this question. Using the Inverse Matrix Theorem, however, is faster.

Additional Answers

14b. $\begin{bmatrix} 1 & 4 \\ 2 & -2 \end{bmatrix}\begin{bmatrix} \frac{1}{5} & \frac{2}{5} \\ \frac{1}{5} & -\frac{1}{10} \end{bmatrix} =$

$\begin{bmatrix} \frac{1}{5}+\frac{4}{5} & \frac{2}{5}-\frac{2}{5} \\ \frac{2}{5}-\frac{2}{5} & \frac{4}{5}+\frac{1}{5} \end{bmatrix} = \begin{bmatrix} 1 & 0 \\ 0 & 1 \end{bmatrix}$

$\begin{bmatrix} \frac{1}{5} & \frac{2}{5} \\ \frac{1}{5} & -\frac{1}{10} \end{bmatrix}\begin{bmatrix} 1 & 4 \\ 2 & -2 \end{bmatrix} =$

$\begin{bmatrix} \frac{1}{5}+\frac{4}{5} & \frac{4}{5}-\frac{4}{5} \\ \frac{1}{5}-\frac{1}{5} & \frac{4}{5}+\frac{1}{5} \end{bmatrix} = \begin{bmatrix} 1 & 0 \\ 0 & 1 \end{bmatrix}$

15a. $\begin{bmatrix} 0 & -1 \\ 1 & 0 \end{bmatrix}\begin{bmatrix} 0 & 1 \\ -1 & 0 \end{bmatrix} = \begin{bmatrix} 1 & 0 \\ 0 & 1 \end{bmatrix}$

$\begin{bmatrix} 0 & 1 \\ -1 & 0 \end{bmatrix}\begin{bmatrix} 0 & -1 \\ 1 & 0 \end{bmatrix} = \begin{bmatrix} 1 & 0 \\ 0 & 1 \end{bmatrix}$

15b. They are inverses. If you rotate an object 90° and then 270° or vice versa, you end up in the same place where you started.

15c. It is the matrix for R_{180}, $\begin{bmatrix} -1 & 0 \\ 0 & -1 \end{bmatrix}$, because $R_{180} \circ R_{180} = R_{360}$.

10. Refer to Activity 2. A message has the encoder matrix $\begin{bmatrix} 4 & -8 \\ 10 & -10 \end{bmatrix}$. Find its decoder matrix.

10. $\begin{bmatrix} -\frac{1}{4} & \frac{1}{5} \\ -\frac{1}{4} & \frac{1}{10} \end{bmatrix}$

In 11 and 12, use the following key.

A	B	C	D	E	F	G	H	I	J	K	L	M
2	4	6	8	10	12	14	16	18	20	22	24	26
N	O	P	Q	R	S	T	U	V	W	X	Y	Z
1	3	5	7	9	11	13	15	17	19	21	23	25

11. Encode the message MATRICES DO CODES using the matrix $\begin{bmatrix} 2 & 1 \\ 7 & 4 \end{bmatrix}$. Use 27 to represent a space.

11. 54, 190, 35, 127, 42, 150, 31, 114, 62, 221, 33, 129, 15, 54, 26, 96, 49, 185

12. Kendra got the message 378, -202, 294, -56, 504, -162, 343, -7, 273, -51, 203, 73, the encoder matrix $\begin{bmatrix} 14 & 7 \\ -8 & 3 \end{bmatrix}$, and the key above.
   a. What is the decoding matrix?
   b. Decode the message. MATH IS FUN

12a. $\begin{bmatrix} \frac{3}{98} & -\frac{1}{14} \\ \frac{4}{49} & \frac{1}{7} \end{bmatrix}$

APPLYING THE MATHEMATICS

13. Give an example of a 2×2 matrix not mentioned in this lesson that does not have an inverse. Answers vary. Sample: $\begin{bmatrix} 2 & 6 \\ 1 & 3 \end{bmatrix}$

14. If it has one, the inverse of a 2×2 matrix can be found by solving a pair of systems of linear equations. For example, if the inverse of $\begin{bmatrix} 1 & 4 \\ 2 & -2 \end{bmatrix}$ is $\begin{bmatrix} a & b \\ c & d \end{bmatrix}$, then $\begin{bmatrix} 1 & 4 \\ 2 & -2 \end{bmatrix}\begin{bmatrix} a & b \\ c & d \end{bmatrix} = \begin{bmatrix} 1 & 0 \\ 0 & 1 \end{bmatrix}$.

   This yields the systems $\begin{cases} a + 4c = 1 \\ 2a - 2c = 0 \end{cases}$ and $\begin{cases} b + 4d = 0 \\ 2b - 2d = 1 \end{cases}$.
   a. Solve these two systems and determine the inverse matrix.
   b. Check your answer to Part a using matrix multiplication. See margin.

14a. $a = c = \frac{1}{5}$, $d = -\frac{1}{10}$, and $b = \frac{2}{5}$; $\begin{bmatrix} \frac{1}{5} & \frac{2}{5} \\ \frac{1}{5} & -\frac{1}{10} \end{bmatrix}$

15. a. Multiply the matrix for R_{90} by the matrix for R_{270} in both orders.
   b. Based on your answer to Part a, what can you say about the two matrices? Why do you think this is so?
   c. Based on your answer to Part b, find the inverse of the matrix for R_{180}. Try to get the answer *without* doing any calculations. 15a–c. See margin.

Additional Answers

17a. $\begin{cases} 50e + 30d = 160 \\ 10e = 20 \\ 0.75d + 0.75b = 3 \end{cases}$

17b. $e = 2$; $d = 2$; $b = 2$; 2 energy bars, 2 energy drink bottles, and 2 bottles of water

17c. Answers vary. Sample: I used the substitution method because it was easy to solve the second equation for e.

19b.

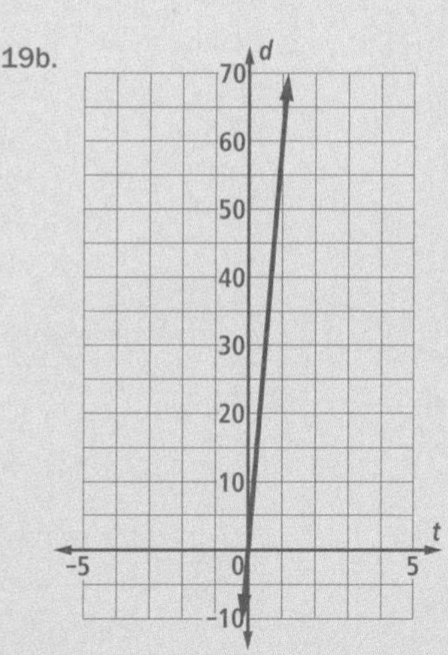

REVIEW

In 16 and 17, a situation is presented and a question is asked.

a. Set up a system of equations to represent the situation.

b. Solve the system using any method and answer the question.

c. Explain why you chose the method you did in Part b.
(Lessons 5-4, 5-3, 5-2)

16. Javier is making mango-and-banana fruit salad to take to a party. Mangos cost \$2.19/pound and bananas cost \$0.89/pound. Javier decides to buy 5 pounds of fruit for \$7.50. How many pounds of each fruit does he buy? See below.

17. Trevon is going on a long mountain bike ride. During the ride, he wants to make sure he consumes 160 g of carbohydrates, 20 g of protein, and 3 liters of fluids. An energy bar contains 50 g of carbohydrates, 10 g of protein, and no fluids. An energy drink bottle contains 30 g of carbohydrates, no protein, and 750 mL of fluid. A water bottle contains no carbohydrates, no protein, and 750 mL of fluid. How many energy bars, energy drink bottles, and water bottles should Trevon pack for his ride? 17a–c. See margin.

18. Translate into a single formula: P varies directly as w and inversely as m and r^2. (Lesson 2-9) $P = \frac{kw}{mr^2}$

19. A car is traveling at 60 miles per hour. (Lessons 2-4, 2-1)
    a. Write a variation equation to describe the distance d in miles the car travels in t hours. $d = 60t$
    b. Graph your equation from Part a. See margin.

Banana plants commonly grow to full size in just a few weeks.

20a. det A = 3, det B = 3, and det AB = 9, so det AB is equal to det A • det B.

EXPLORATION

20. Let $A = \begin{bmatrix} 2 & 1 \\ 1 & 2 \end{bmatrix}$ and $B = \begin{bmatrix} 0 & -1 \\ 3 & 0 \end{bmatrix}$.
    a. Calculate det A, det B, and det AB. What do you notice about these values?
    b. Make a conjecture about the determinant of the product of two 2×2 matrices. Check it for two pairs of 2×2 matrices of your choosing. See margin.

16a. $\begin{cases} 2.19m + 0.89b = 7.50 \\ m + b = 5 \end{cases}$

b. $m = 2.35$ and $b = 2.65$; 2.35 pounds of mangos and 2.65 pounds of bananas

c. Answers vary. Sample: I used the substitution method because it was easy to solve the second equation for m or b.

QY ANSWER

a. -2

b. $-3 \cdot -11 - 5 \cdot 7 = 33 - 35 = -2$

Notes on the Questions

Question 16 To lead into the next lesson, you might wish to check this using the matrix method. Equations that are set up for linear combinations are also set up for matrices.

Question 17 You might have interested students enter this information as a 3×3 matrix and then use technology to solve the system, finding the inverse of that matrix. This would also anticipate the next lesson.

4 Wrap-Up

Ongoing Assessment

Have students work in groups of four. Have one student write a 2×2 matrix and have a second student find its determinant. Have a third student find the inverse (if it exists) and a fourth student check the results by multiplying. Have students switch roles and repeat the activity. Students should demonstrate that they understand how to find the determinant of a 2×2 matrix and use the determinant to write the inverse matrix (if it exists).

Project Update

Project 3, *The Enigma Machine,* and Project 4, *Using Matrices to Code and Decode Messsages,* on page 362 relate to the content of this lesson.

Additional Answers

20a. det A = 3, det B = 3, and det AB = 9; so det AB is equal to det A • det B

20b. det AB = det A • det B; Answers vary. Sample:

(1) $A = \begin{bmatrix} 3 & 0 \\ 1 & 2 \end{bmatrix}, B = \begin{bmatrix} 1 & 2 \\ 3 & 2 \end{bmatrix}, AB = \begin{bmatrix} 3 & 6 \\ 7 & 6 \end{bmatrix}$;

det A = 6, det B = -4, det AB = -24; det A • det B = 6 • -4 = -24

(2) $A = \begin{bmatrix} 0 & 1 \\ 4 & 2 \end{bmatrix}, B = \begin{bmatrix} 3 & 1 \\ 3 & 2 \end{bmatrix}, AB = \begin{bmatrix} 3 & 2 \\ 18 & 8 \end{bmatrix}$;

det A = -4, det B = 3, det AB = -12; det A • det B = -4 • 3 = -12

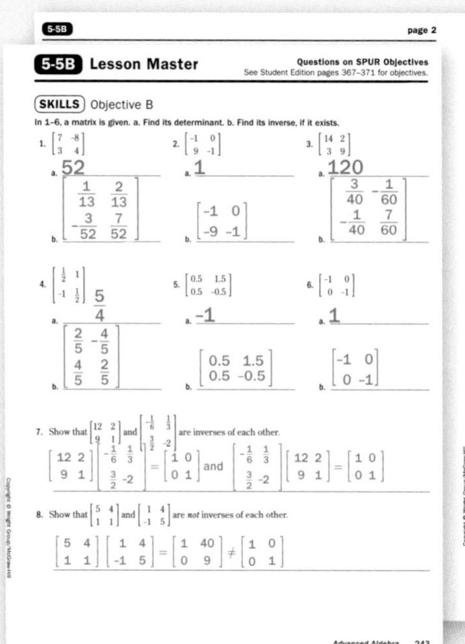

5-5B page 2

5-5B Lesson Master — Questions on SPUR Objectives. See Student Edition pages 367–371 for objectives.

SKILLS Objective B

In 1–6, a matrix is given. a. Find its determinant. b. Find its inverse, if it exists.

1. $\begin{bmatrix} 7 & -8 \\ 3 & 4 \end{bmatrix}$ a. 52 b. $\begin{bmatrix} \frac{1}{13} & \frac{2}{13} \\ -\frac{3}{52} & \frac{7}{52} \end{bmatrix}$

2. $\begin{bmatrix} -1 & 0 \\ 9 & -1 \end{bmatrix}$ a. 1 b. $\begin{bmatrix} -1 & 0 \\ -9 & -1 \end{bmatrix}$

3. $\begin{bmatrix} 14 & 2 \\ 3 & 9 \end{bmatrix}$ a. 120 b. $\begin{bmatrix} \frac{3}{40} & -\frac{1}{60} \\ -\frac{1}{40} & \frac{7}{60} \end{bmatrix}$

4. $\begin{bmatrix} \frac{1}{2} & 1 \\ -1 & \frac{1}{2} \end{bmatrix}$ a. $\frac{5}{4}$ b. $\begin{bmatrix} \frac{2}{5} & -\frac{4}{5} \\ \frac{4}{5} & \frac{2}{5} \end{bmatrix}$

5. $\begin{bmatrix} 0.5 & 1.5 \\ 0.5 & -0.5 \end{bmatrix}$ a. -1 b. $\begin{bmatrix} 0.5 & 1.5 \\ 0.5 & -0.5 \end{bmatrix}$

6. $\begin{bmatrix} -1 & 0 \\ 0 & -1 \end{bmatrix}$ a. 1 b. $\begin{bmatrix} -1 & 0 \\ 0 & -1 \end{bmatrix}$

7. Show that $\begin{bmatrix} 12 & 2 \\ 9 & 1 \end{bmatrix}$ and $\begin{bmatrix} -\frac{1}{6} & \frac{1}{3} \\ \frac{3}{2} & -2 \end{bmatrix}$ are inverses of each other.

$\begin{bmatrix} 12 & 2 \\ 9 & 1 \end{bmatrix}\begin{bmatrix} -\frac{1}{6} & \frac{1}{3} \\ \frac{3}{2} & -2 \end{bmatrix} = \begin{bmatrix} 1 & 0 \\ 0 & 1 \end{bmatrix}$ and $\begin{bmatrix} -\frac{1}{6} & \frac{1}{3} \\ \frac{3}{2} & -2 \end{bmatrix}\begin{bmatrix} 12 & 2 \\ 9 & 1 \end{bmatrix} = \begin{bmatrix} 1 & 0 \\ 0 & 1 \end{bmatrix}$

8. Show that $\begin{bmatrix} 5 & 4 \\ 1 & 1 \end{bmatrix}$ and $\begin{bmatrix} 1 & 4 \\ -1 & 5 \end{bmatrix}$ are *not* inverses of each other.

$\begin{bmatrix} 5 & 4 \\ 1 & 1 \end{bmatrix}\begin{bmatrix} 1 & 4 \\ -1 & 5 \end{bmatrix} = \begin{bmatrix} 1 & 40 \\ 0 & 9 \end{bmatrix} \neq \begin{bmatrix} 1 & 0 \\ 0 & 1 \end{bmatrix}$

Advanced Algebra 243

Lesson

5-6

GOAL

Learn how to solve 2×2 and 3×3 linear systems by representing the system as a matrix equation and then multiplying each side of the matrix equation by the inverse of the coefficient matrix.

SPUR Objectives

C Use matrices to solve systems of two or three linear equations.

D Recognize properties of systems of equations.

F Use systems of two or three linear equations to solve real-world problems.

Materials/Resources

- Lesson Masters 5-6A and 5-6B
- Resource Masters 85 and 86
- Quiz 2

HOMEWORK

Suggestions for Assignment

- Questions 1–20
- Question 21 (extra credit)
- Reading Lesson 5-7
- Covering the Ideas 5-7

Local Standards

1 Warm-Up

1. Multiply: $\begin{bmatrix} -8 & 3 \\ 5 & -2 \end{bmatrix}\begin{bmatrix} x \\ y \end{bmatrix}$. $\begin{bmatrix} -8x + 3y \\ 5x - 2y \end{bmatrix}$

2. Solve for x and y:

$$\begin{bmatrix} -8 & 3 \\ 5 & -2 \end{bmatrix}\begin{bmatrix} x \\ y \end{bmatrix} = \begin{bmatrix} 12 \\ -17 \end{bmatrix}.$$

$(x, y) = (27, 76)$

Lesson

5-6 Solving Systems Using Matrices

Vocabulary

matrix form of a system

coefficient matrix

constant matrix

BIG IDEA A system of linear equations in standard form can be written as a matrix equation that can often be solved by multiplying both sides of the equation by the inverse of the *coefficient matrix.*

The matrix equation $\begin{bmatrix} 3 & -1 \\ 2 & 4 \end{bmatrix}\begin{bmatrix} x \\ y \end{bmatrix} = \begin{bmatrix} 14 \\ 0 \end{bmatrix}$ is called the **matrix form of the system** $\begin{cases} 3x - y = 14 \\ 2x + 4y = 0 \end{cases}$. The matrix $\begin{bmatrix} 3 & -1 \\ 2 & 4 \end{bmatrix}$ is called the **coefficient matrix** because it contains the coefficients of the variables in the system. The matrix $\begin{bmatrix} 14 \\ 0 \end{bmatrix}$ is called the **constant matrix** because it contains the constants on the right side of the equations in the system.

 **QY1**

How do you solve a system in matrix form? Think of how you solve the equation $3x = 6$. You might divide both sides of the equation by 3, or multiply both sides of the equation by $\frac{1}{3}$, the multiplicative inverse of 3. This idea is employed to solve linear systems in matrix form.

GUIDED

Example 1

Solve the system $\begin{bmatrix} 3 & -1 \\ 2 & 4 \end{bmatrix}\begin{bmatrix} x \\ y \end{bmatrix} = \begin{bmatrix} 14 \\ 0 \end{bmatrix}$.

Solution First, find the inverse of the coefficient matrix.

$$\begin{bmatrix} 3 & -1 \\ 2 & 4 \end{bmatrix}^{-1} = \begin{bmatrix} \underline{?} & \underline{?} \\ \underline{?} & \underline{?} \end{bmatrix} \quad \frac{2}{7}; \frac{1}{14}; -\frac{1}{7}; \frac{3}{14}$$

Next, multiply both sides of the equation on the left by the inverse.

$$\begin{bmatrix} \underline{?} & \underline{?} \\ \underline{?} & \underline{?} \end{bmatrix} \cdot \begin{bmatrix} 3 & -1 \\ 2 & 4 \end{bmatrix} \cdot \begin{bmatrix} x \\ y \end{bmatrix} = \begin{bmatrix} \underline{?} & \underline{?} \\ \underline{?} & \underline{?} \end{bmatrix} \cdot \begin{bmatrix} 14 \\ 0 \end{bmatrix} \quad \frac{2}{7}; \frac{1}{14}; \frac{2}{7}; \frac{1}{14}; -\frac{1}{7}; \frac{3}{14}; -\frac{1}{7}; \frac{3}{14}$$

$$\begin{bmatrix} \underline{1?} & \underline{0?} \\ \underline{0?} & \underline{1?} \end{bmatrix} \cdot \begin{bmatrix} x \\ y \end{bmatrix} = \begin{bmatrix} \underline{4?} \\ \underline{-2?} \end{bmatrix}$$

Mental Math

Calculate the determinant of the matrix.

a. $\begin{bmatrix} 2 & 0 \\ 0 & 2 \end{bmatrix}$ 4

b. $\begin{bmatrix} 7 & 3 \\ 4 & 2 \end{bmatrix}$ 2

c. $\begin{bmatrix} -1 & 5 \\ -2 & -1 \end{bmatrix}$ 11

d. $\begin{bmatrix} a & b \\ c & d \end{bmatrix}$ $ad - bc$

QY1

Expand $\begin{bmatrix} 3 & -1 \\ 2 & 4 \end{bmatrix}\begin{bmatrix} x \\ y \end{bmatrix} = \begin{bmatrix} 14 \\ 0 \end{bmatrix}$ to verify that it represents $\begin{cases} 3x - y = 14 \\ 2x + 4y = 0 \end{cases}$.

Background

For the 2×2 case, students can use the Inverse Matrix Theorem to find the inverse of the coefficient matrix when it exists. For the 3×3 case, in this book, students are always given the inverse of the coefficient matrix or expected to use technology to find it. The methods for finding the inverse of a 3×3 matrix are beyond the scope of this course.

With the availability of both calculator and computer technology that can find inverses of matrices, matrix methods for solving systems are widely used. To create your own 3×3 examples, if you do not have such technology available, begin with $M = \begin{bmatrix} a_{11} & a_{12} & a_{13} \\ a_{21} & a_{22} & a_{23} \\ a_{31} & a_{32} & a_{33} \end{bmatrix}$. The cofactor C_{ij} of the component a_{ij} in a 3×3 matrix is the product of $(-1)^{i+j}$, and the determinant of the 2×2 submatrix is determined by deleting the ith row and jth column of M. Calculate the cofactor of each element

Because you multiplied by the inverse, the left side of the equation should now be $\begin{bmatrix} 1 & 0 \\ 0 & 1 \end{bmatrix} \cdot \begin{bmatrix} x \\ y \end{bmatrix} = \begin{bmatrix} x \\ y \end{bmatrix}$. Thus $\begin{bmatrix} x \\ y \end{bmatrix} = \begin{bmatrix} 4? \\ -2? \end{bmatrix}$, so x = 4? and y = ?-2

Check Check your answer by substituting your values for *x* and *y* into the original matrix equation.

$\begin{bmatrix} 3 & -1 \\ 2 & 4 \end{bmatrix} \begin{bmatrix} 4 \\ -2 \end{bmatrix} = \begin{bmatrix} 14 \\ 0 \end{bmatrix}$ It checks.

This method for solving a system of linear equations with matrices was developed in the middle of the nineteenth century by the British mathematician Arthur Cayley and can be generalized. For any invertible coefficient matrix A and constant matrix B, with $X = \begin{bmatrix} x \\ y \end{bmatrix}$, the solution to the matrix equation $AX = B$ is $X = A^{-1}B$. Example 2 shows how this method works on systems with three linear equations in three variables.

Example 2

Use matrices to solve $\begin{cases} 4x + 2y - 2z = 2 \\ 2x + 4z = 28 \\ 3y - 2z = -16 \end{cases}$.

Solution Write the matrix form of the system.

$$\underset{A}{\begin{bmatrix} 4 & 2 & -2 \\ 2 & 0 & 4 \\ 0 & 3 & -2 \end{bmatrix}} \cdot \underset{X}{\begin{bmatrix} x \\ y \\ z \end{bmatrix}} = \underset{B}{\begin{bmatrix} 2 \\ 28 \\ -16 \end{bmatrix}}$$

For each side of the equation use a CAS to multiply on the left by the inverse of the coefficient matrix.

$A^{-1} \cdot A \cdot X \quad = \quad A^{-1} \cdot B$

$$\begin{bmatrix} 4 & 2 & -2 \\ 2 & 0 & 4 \\ 0 & 3 & -2 \end{bmatrix}^{-1} \cdot \begin{bmatrix} 4 & 2 & -2 \\ 2 & 0 & 4 \\ 0 & 3 & -2 \end{bmatrix} \cdot \begin{bmatrix} x \\ y \\ z \end{bmatrix} \quad \begin{bmatrix} x \\ y \\ z \end{bmatrix}$$

$$\begin{bmatrix} 4 & 2 & -2 \\ 2 & 0 & 4 \\ 0 & 3 & -2 \end{bmatrix}^{-1} \cdot \begin{bmatrix} 2 \\ 28 \\ -16 \end{bmatrix} \quad \begin{bmatrix} 4 \\ -2 \\ 5 \end{bmatrix}$$

(continued on next page)

2 Teaching

Notes on the Lesson

Stress that each equation must be in the form of $ax + by = c$ or $ax + by + cz = d$ before the matrix method of solution can be applied. Emphasize that the inverse matrix must be to the left of the constant matrix; otherwise the multiplication cannot be done.

There are four reasons why matrices are used to solve systems: (1) These methods generalize the solving of systems with many equations and many variables; (2) these methods are used by computers; (3) these methods indicate exactly when a system has a solution; and (4) the System-Determinant Theorem extends to any linear system of *n* equations and *n* variables.

Additional Example

Example 1 Solve the system $\begin{bmatrix} 1 & 3 \\ 2 & -1 \end{bmatrix} \begin{bmatrix} x \\ y \end{bmatrix} = \begin{bmatrix} 22 \\ 2 \end{bmatrix}$.

Solution First, find the inverse of the coefficient matrix:

$\begin{bmatrix} 1 & 3 \\ 2 & -1 \end{bmatrix}^{-1} = \underline{\quad ? \quad} = \underline{\quad ? \quad}$.

$\begin{bmatrix} \frac{-1}{-7} & \frac{-3}{-7} \\ \frac{-2}{-7} & \frac{1}{-7} \end{bmatrix}$; $\begin{bmatrix} \frac{1}{7} & \frac{3}{7} \\ \frac{2}{7} & -\frac{1}{7} \end{bmatrix}$ Next, multiply both sides of the equation on the left by the inverse:

$\underline{\quad ? \quad} \cdot \begin{bmatrix} 1 & 3 \\ 2 & -1 \end{bmatrix} \begin{bmatrix} x \\ y \end{bmatrix} = \underline{\quad ? \quad}$

$\begin{bmatrix} 22 \\ 2 \end{bmatrix} \cdot \begin{bmatrix} \frac{1}{7} & \frac{3}{7} \\ \frac{2}{7} & -\frac{1}{7} \end{bmatrix}$; $\begin{bmatrix} \frac{1}{7} & \frac{3}{7} \\ \frac{2}{7} & -\frac{1}{7} \end{bmatrix}$

Find the product of each side: $\underline{\quad ? \quad}$

$\begin{bmatrix} x \\ y \end{bmatrix} = \underline{\quad ? \quad}$.

$\begin{bmatrix} 1 & 0 \\ 0 & 1 \end{bmatrix}$; $\begin{bmatrix} 4 \\ 6 \end{bmatrix}$ Because you multiplied by the inverse, the left side of the equation should now be $\begin{bmatrix} 1 & 0 \\ 0 & 1 \end{bmatrix} \begin{bmatrix} x \\ y \end{bmatrix}$.

Thus, $\begin{bmatrix} x \\ y \end{bmatrix} = \begin{bmatrix} 4 \\ 6 \end{bmatrix}$, so $x = \underline{\quad ? \quad}$ and $y = \underline{\quad ? \quad}$. 4; 6

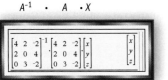

and then calculate $\det M = a_{11}C_{11} + a_{12}C_{12} + a_{13}C_{13}$. The inverse M^{-1} of the matrix exists if and only if $\det M \neq 0$. If $\det M \neq 0$, then

$$M^{-1} = \begin{bmatrix} \frac{C_{11}}{\det M} & \frac{C_{12}}{\det M} & \frac{C_{13}}{\det M} \\ \frac{C_{21}}{\det M} & \frac{C_{22}}{\det M} & \frac{C_{23}}{\det M} \\ \frac{C_{31}}{\det M} & \frac{C_{32}}{\det M} & \frac{C_{33}}{\det M} \end{bmatrix} = \frac{1}{\det M} \begin{bmatrix} C_{11} & C_{12} & C_{13} \\ C_{21} & C_{22} & C_{23} \\ C_{31} & C_{32} & C_{33} \end{bmatrix}.$$

Generalizations of these formulas to higher-order $n \times n$ systems are in any standard linear algebra text. The matrix method of solving a system of equations is especially useful for applications in which the coefficients of the variables remain the same while the constants change.

Notes on the Lesson

Example 1 Work through this example with students. If you have students read the lines aloud, you may find that some students do not know how to read a matrix orally. Point out that matrices are read row by row. For example, $\begin{bmatrix} 4 & 2.3 \\ 0 & -8 \end{bmatrix}$ is read "the 2 by 2 matrix 4, 2 point 3, 0, negative 8."

Additional Example

Example 2 Use matrices to solve

$$\begin{cases} x - y + 3z = 9 \\ x + 2z = 3 \\ 2x + 2y + z = 10 \end{cases} \cdot \begin{bmatrix} x \\ y \\ z \end{bmatrix} = \begin{bmatrix} 35 \\ -22 \\ -16 \end{bmatrix}$$

Write an equation with the results from the multiplications.

$X = A^{-1} \cdot B$

$\begin{bmatrix} x \\ y \\ z \end{bmatrix} = \begin{bmatrix} 4 \\ -2 \\ 5 \end{bmatrix}$. So, $x = 4$, $y = -2$, and $z = 5$.

Check Substitute for x, y, and z in each of the three given equations.

Does $4(4) + 2(-2) - 2(5) = 2$? Yes, $16 + -4 - 10 = 2$.

Does $2(4) + 4(5) = 28$? Yes, $8 + 20 = 28$.

Does $3(-2) + -2(5) = -16$? Yes, $-6 + -10 = -16$.

The Number of Solutions to Linear Systems

Matrices can be used to determine the number of solutions to a linear system. For example, consider the system $\begin{cases} ax + by = e \\ cx + dy = f \end{cases}$. If the determinant $ad - bc$ of the coefficient matrix $\begin{bmatrix} a & b \\ c & d \end{bmatrix}$ is not 0, the matrix has an inverse and the system has exactly one solution. When $ad - bc = 0$, the coefficient matrix has no inverse. In that case, the system has either infinitely many solutions or none at all.

System-Determinant Theorem

An $n \times n$ system of linear equations has exactly one solution if and only if the determinant of the coefficient matrix is *not* zero.

In the previous lesson you calculated the determinant of a 2×2 matrix. While the calculation of a determinant of a larger square matrix is tedious by hand, a calculator can find the determinant automatically.

QY2

When the determinant of the coefficient matrix is zero, to determine whether there are no solutions or infinitely many solutions, find a solution to one of the equations and test it in the other equations. If it satisfies all the other equations, there are infinitely many solutions to the system. If the solution does not satisfy all the other equations, there are no solutions to the system.

▶ QY2

Use a calculator to find the determinant of the coefficient matrix in Example 2. Does its value support the solution to that Example?

Accommodating the Learner

Watch for students who misplace the zeros in the coefficient matrix when some of the equations in a system do not have a term in every variable. For instance, they may write the coefficient matrix for Example 2 as $\begin{bmatrix} 4 & 2 & -2 \\ 0 & 2 & 4 \\ 0 & 3 & -2 \end{bmatrix}$ to match how the system appears when written with a brace. To help avoid these errors, encourage students to rewrite the system in Example 2 as $\begin{cases} 4x + 2y - 2z = 2 \\ 2x + 0y + 4z = 28 \\ 0x + 3y - 2z = -16 \end{cases}$ before writing the system in matrix form. This technique can also be used in Question 7.

Example 3

Consider the system $\begin{cases} 3x + 2y = 14 \\ 6x + 4y = 10 \end{cases}$.

a. Show that this system does not have exactly one solution.

b. Determine how many solutions this system has.

Solution 1

a. Let A be the coefficient matrix $\begin{bmatrix} 3 & 2 \\ 6 & 4 \end{bmatrix}$.

Then $\det A = (3)(4) - (2)(6) = 0$.

So, by the System-Determinant Theorem, the system does not have exactly one solution.

b. Either the system has infinitely many solutions or no solutions. To decide, find an ordered pair that satisfies one equation.

(4, 1) satisfies the first equation.

Next, does it satisfy the other equation?

Does $6(4) + 4(1) = 10$? No. Thus, because (4, 1) does not satisfy all the equations, the system has no solutions.

Solution 2

a. Use a calculator to solve the system with matrices. One calculator gives the result at the right. The error message means .that the coefficient matrix does not have an inverse.

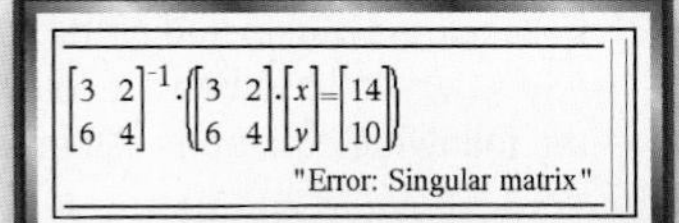

b. Proceed as in Part b of Solution 1.

STOP QY3

Questions

COVERING THE IDEAS

1. a. Write the matrix form of the system $\begin{cases} 0.5x - y = 1.75 \\ 3x + 8y = 5 \end{cases}$.
   b. Solve the system.

1a. $\begin{bmatrix} 0.5 & -1 \\ 3 & 8 \end{bmatrix}\begin{bmatrix} x \\ y \end{bmatrix} = \begin{bmatrix} 1.75 \\ 5 \end{bmatrix}$

1b. about (2.71, -0.39)

2. a. Write a system of equations whose matrix form is
   $\begin{bmatrix} 2 & 0 & -1 \\ 5 & 5 & 2 \\ 3 & 1 & 0 \end{bmatrix} \cdot \begin{bmatrix} x \\ y \\ z \end{bmatrix} = \begin{bmatrix} 2 \\ -3 \\ 10 \end{bmatrix}$. $\begin{cases} 2x - z = 2 \\ 5x + 5y + 2z = -3 \\ 3x + y = 10 \end{cases}$
   b. Which matrix in Part a is the coefficient matrix? Which is the constant matrix?
   c. Use technology to solve this system. $x = \frac{49}{6}$, $y = -\frac{29}{2}$, and $z = \frac{43}{3}$

2b. $\begin{bmatrix} 2 & 0 & -1 \\ 5 & 5 & 2 \\ 3 & 1 & 0 \end{bmatrix}$; $\begin{bmatrix} 2 \\ -3 \\ 10 \end{bmatrix}$

▶ **QY3**

Is the system in Example 3 consistent or inconsistent?

Additional Example

Example 3 Consider the system $\begin{cases} 6x - 9y = 12 \\ 2x - 3y = 4 \end{cases}$.

a. Show that this system does not have exactly one solution. Let A be the coefficient matrix $\begin{bmatrix} 6 & -9 \\ 2 & -3 \end{bmatrix}$. Then $\det A = (6)(-3) - (-9)(2) = 0$. So, by the System-Determinant Theorem, the system does not have exactly one solution.

b. Determine how many solutions this system has. The system has either infinitely many solutions or no solutions. To decide, find an ordered pair that satisfies one equation; (8, 4) satisfies the first equation. Next, does it satisfy the other equation, $2x - 3y = 4$? Does $2(8) - 3(4) = 4$? Yes. Thus, because (8, 4) satisfies both equations, the two equations describe the same line and the system has infinitely many solutions.

3 Assignment

Recommended Assignment

- Questions 1–20
- Question 21 (extra credit)
- Reading Lesson 5-7
- Covering the Ideas 5-7

Accommodating the Learner

After completing the lesson, have students work in groups to discuss the three methods for solving systems of equations: substitution, linear combinations, and matrices. Have them provide examples of systems that they would solve using each method. Answers vary. Sample: substitution: $\begin{cases} 8x + 12y = 16 \\ 3y = 12 \end{cases}$; linear combinations: $\begin{cases} 8x + 12y = 20 \\ 2x + 3y = 4 \end{cases}$; matrices: any system, when using technology

Extension

Have students use matrices to find a formula for the solution to this general system of equations: $\begin{cases} ax + by = c \\ dx + ey = f \end{cases}$. If students need a hint, tell them to use the matrix formula $X = A^{-1} \cdot B$, where $A = \begin{bmatrix} a & b \\ d & e \end{bmatrix}$ and $B = \begin{bmatrix} c \\ f \end{bmatrix}$.

$\begin{bmatrix} x \\ y \end{bmatrix} = \begin{bmatrix} \frac{ec - bf}{ae - bd} \\ \frac{af - dc}{ae - bd} \end{bmatrix}$

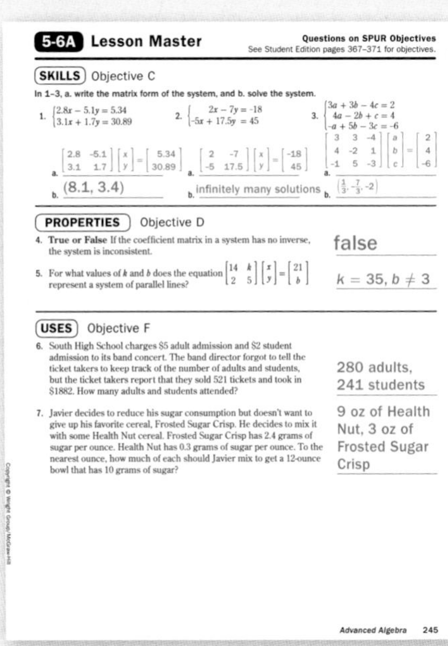

5-6A Lesson Master

Questions on SPUR Objectives
See Student Edition pages 367–371 for objectives.

SKILLS Objective C

In 1–3, a. write the matrix form of the system, and b. solve the system.

1. $\begin{cases} 2.8x - 5.1y = 5.34 \\ 3.1x + 1.7y = 30.89 \end{cases}$
   a. $\begin{bmatrix} 2.8 & -5.1 \\ 3.1 & 1.7 \end{bmatrix}\begin{bmatrix} x \\ y \end{bmatrix} = \begin{bmatrix} 5.34 \\ 30.89 \end{bmatrix}$
   b. (8.1, 3.4)

2. $\begin{cases} 2x - 7y = -18 \\ -5x + 17.5y = 45 \end{cases}$
   a. $\begin{bmatrix} 2 & -7 \\ -5 & 17.5 \end{bmatrix}\begin{bmatrix} x \\ y \end{bmatrix} = \begin{bmatrix} -18 \\ 45 \end{bmatrix}$
   b. infinitely many solutions

3. $\begin{cases} 3a + 3b - 4c = 2 \\ 4a - 2b + c = 4 \\ -a + 5b - 3c = -6 \end{cases}$
   a. $\begin{bmatrix} 3 & 3 & -4 \\ 4 & -2 & 1 \\ -1 & 5 & -3 \end{bmatrix}\begin{bmatrix} a \\ b \\ c \end{bmatrix} = \begin{bmatrix} 2 \\ 4 \\ -6 \end{bmatrix}$
   b. $\left(\frac{1}{3}, -\frac{7}{3}, -2\right)$

PROPERTIES Objective D

4. **True or False** If the coefficient matrix in a system has no inverse, the system is inconsistent. false

5. For what values of k and b does the equation $\begin{bmatrix} 14 & k \\ 2 & 5 \end{bmatrix}\begin{bmatrix} x \\ y \end{bmatrix} = \begin{bmatrix} 21 \\ b \end{bmatrix}$ represent a system of parallel lines? $k = 35, b \neq 3$

USES Objective F

6. South High School charges \$5 adult admission and \$2 student admission to its band concert. The band director forgot to tell the ticket takers to keep track of the number of adults and students, but the ticket takers report that they sold 521 tickets and took in \$1882. How many adults and students attended? 280 adults, 241 students

7. Javier decides to reduce his sugar consumption but doesn't want to give up his favorite cereal, Frosted Sugar Crisp. He decides to mix it with some Health Nut cereal. Frosted Sugar Crisp has 2.4 grams of sugar per ounce. Health Nut has 0.3 grams of sugar per ounce. To the nearest ounce, how much of each should Javier mix to get a 12-ounce bowl that has 10 grams of sugar? 9 oz of Health Nut, 3 oz of Frosted Sugar Crisp

Advanced Algebra 245

Notes on the Questions

Questions 6 and 7 Emphasize that the inverse matrix must be to the *left* of the constant matrix to multiply the matrices.

Question 9 David Auburn's play *Proof* was made into a movie; some of the movie was filmed at the University of Chicago.

Question 10 With the popularity of television shows involving forensics, what was at one time an obscure context is now relatively familiar.

Additional Answers

3. zero; the determinant of the coefficient matrix is 0, and (2, 2) satisfies the first equation but not the second.
4. one; the determinant of the coefficient matrix is not 0.
5. infinitely many; the determinant of the coefficient matrix is 0, and (2, 2) satisfies both equations.
8. $6x + 4y = 28$
   $\underline{-6x - 4y = -10}$
   $0 + 0 = 18$

   The linear combination method produces a false statement, so the system is inconsistent, and there are no solutions.
9. $\begin{bmatrix} 3 & 5 \\ 1 & 1 \end{bmatrix}\begin{bmatrix} s \\ n \end{bmatrix} = \begin{bmatrix} 3943 \\ 937 \end{bmatrix}$;
   $\begin{bmatrix} s \\ n \end{bmatrix} = \begin{bmatrix} 371 \\ 566 \end{bmatrix}$; 371 student tickets and 566 nonstudent tickets

10a. The line for female height has a steeper slope, so eventually the female height will catch up to the male height.

10b. $\begin{bmatrix} -1.880 & 1 \\ -1.945 & 1 \end{bmatrix}\begin{bmatrix} b \\ h \end{bmatrix} = \begin{bmatrix} 32.010 \\ 28.679 \end{bmatrix}$;
   $\begin{bmatrix} b \\ h \end{bmatrix} = \begin{bmatrix} 51.246 \\ 128.353 \end{bmatrix}$

16. $\begin{bmatrix} a & 0 \\ 0 & b \end{bmatrix}^{-1} = \begin{bmatrix} \frac{b}{ab} & 0 \\ 0 & \frac{a}{ab} \end{bmatrix} = \begin{bmatrix} \frac{1}{a} & 0 \\ 0 & \frac{1}{b} \end{bmatrix}$

In 3–5, determine how many solutions the system has. Justify your answer. 3–5. See margin.

3. $\begin{cases} 8x + 12y = 40 \\ 4x + 6y = 25 \end{cases}$ 4. $\begin{cases} 8x + 12y = 40 \\ 6x + 20y = 52 \end{cases}$ 5. $\begin{cases} 8x + 12y = 40 \\ 6x + 9y = 30 \end{cases}$

In 6 and 7, solve each system using matrices.

6. $\begin{cases} 18 = 2d - 3h \\ 7 = 5d + 2h \end{cases}$ $\begin{bmatrix} d \\ h \end{bmatrix} = \begin{bmatrix} 3 \\ -4 \end{bmatrix}$ 7. $\begin{cases} 4x - 3y + z = 4 \\ 2x = -2 \\ 3y + 5z = 40 \end{cases}$ $\begin{bmatrix} x \\ y \\ z \end{bmatrix} = \begin{bmatrix} -1 \\ 0 \\ 8 \end{bmatrix}$

8. Solve the system in Example 3 using the linear-combination method. Explain how that method shows there is no solution. See margin.

APPLYING THE MATHEMATICS

9. Set up a system and solve it using matrices to answer this question: Two types of tickets are available for Lincoln High School plays. Student tickets cost \$3 each, and nonstudent tickets cost \$5 each. On opening night of the play *Proof* by David Auburn, 937 total tickets were sold for \$3943. How many of each type of ticket were sold? See margin.

10. Forensic scientists and anthropologists can estimate the height h of a person based on the length b of the person's femur using the following equations. All lengths are measured in inches.

    Male: $h = 32.010 + 1.880b$

    Female: $h = 28.679 + 1.945b$

    a. Even though the equation for male height has a larger h-intercept, there is a point where males and females are expected to have the same height and length of femur. How do you know this from the equations? See margin.

    b. Use matrices to find the point of intersection of the lines represented by the equations. (Hint: Remember to put the system in standard form before setting up each matrix.) See margin.

    c. **Fill in the Blanks** According to these linear models, a man and a woman with the same height and femur length are _?_ inches tall and have a femur length of _?_ inches. 128.353; 51.246

11. A hotel has standard, special, and deluxe rooms. A meeting planner needs 15 rooms. If 6 standard, 6 special, and 3 deluxe rooms are booked, the cost will be \$2835 a night. Is this enough information to determine the cost of each kind of room? If so, determine the costs. If not, explain why not.

11. No; you need three equations to find three unknowns.

Additional Answers

17b. $\begin{bmatrix} 1 & -1 \\ 0 & 1 \end{bmatrix}\begin{bmatrix} 1 & 1 \\ 0 & 1 \end{bmatrix} = \begin{bmatrix} 1 & 1 \\ 0 & 1 \end{bmatrix}\begin{bmatrix} 1 & -1 \\ 0 & 1 \end{bmatrix} = \begin{bmatrix} 1 & 0 \\ 0 & 1 \end{bmatrix}$

ENGLISH LEARNERS

Vocabulary Development

On the board, write a system of linear equations, such as $\begin{cases} x + 7y = 28 \\ 3x - 4y = 10 \end{cases}$. Review with students the terms *coefficient* (a number that a variable is multiplied by) and *constant* (a number that is not multiplied by a variable). Have them identify the coefficients and constants in the two equations. Then write the system in matrix form, relating *coefficient* to *coefficient matrix* and constant *to constant matrix*. Give students practice in writing systems of equations in matrix form.

12. a. Write the matrix form of the system $\begin{cases} 4x = 12 \\ 8y = 16 \end{cases}$ and solve.

b. Give a geometric interpretation of the solution to the system.

In 13 and 14, determine all values of n that satisfy the condition.

13. $\begin{cases} 5x + 3y = 4 \\ 20x - ny = 16 \end{cases}$ has infinitely many solutions. $n = -12$

14. $\begin{cases} 2x + 7y = 1 \\ 4x + 14y = n \end{cases}$ has no solution. $n \neq 2$

15. Solve the system $\begin{cases} 2w - x - y + z = -1 \\ 3.2w + 1.4z = 2.4 \\ 1.8x - 3y + 7z = 23.8 \\ 5w - 3x + 7y + z = 10 \end{cases}$. $(w, x, y, z) = (-1, 1, 2, 4)$

12a. $\begin{bmatrix} 4 & 0 \\ 0 & 8 \end{bmatrix}\begin{bmatrix} x \\ y \end{bmatrix} = \begin{bmatrix} 12 \\ 16 \end{bmatrix}$; $\begin{bmatrix} x \\ y \end{bmatrix} = \begin{bmatrix} 3 \\ 2 \end{bmatrix}$

12b. The vertical line $x = 3$ and the horizontal line $y = 2$ intersect at the point (3, 2).

REVIEW

16. A 2×2 *diagonal matrix* is of the form $\begin{bmatrix} a & 0 \\ 0 & b \end{bmatrix}$. Show that the inverse (if it exists) of a diagonal matrix is another diagonal matrix. **(Lesson 5-5)** See margin.

17. a. Find the inverse of $\begin{bmatrix} 1 & 1 \\ 0 & 1 \end{bmatrix}$. $\begin{bmatrix} 1 & -1 \\ 0 & 1 \end{bmatrix}$

b. Check your answer using matrix multiplication. **(Lessons 5-5, 4-3)** See margin.

18. Solve and check: $\begin{cases} A = 19 - 3D \\ 2A - 4D = -12 \end{cases}$. **(Lesson 5-3)**

18. $A = 4$ and $D = 5$; $19 - 3(5) = 4$; $2(4) - 4(5) = -12$

19. Find the equation in slope-intercept form for the line through the origin and perpendicular to the line with equation $8x - 5y = 20$. **(Lesson 4-9)** $y = -\frac{5}{8}x$

20. A sequence L has the explicit formula $L_n = 4 - 2.5n$. Write a recursive formula for the sequence. **(Lesson 3-8)** $\begin{cases} L_1 = 1.5 \\ L_n = L_{n-1} - 2.5 \text{ for } n \geq 2 \end{cases}$

EXPLORATION

21. From a reference, find a formula for the determinant and inverse of a 3×3 matrix. Check the formula for the inverse for the matrix $A = \begin{bmatrix} 2 & -2 & 5 \\ 4 & 6 & 12 \\ 3 & 1 & 7 \end{bmatrix}$. See margin.

QY ANSWERS

1. $\begin{bmatrix} 3 & -1 \\ 2 & 4 \end{bmatrix}\begin{bmatrix} x \\ y \end{bmatrix} = \begin{bmatrix} 3x - y \\ 2x + 4y \end{bmatrix}$, so, $\begin{bmatrix} 3x - y \\ 2x + 4y \end{bmatrix} = \begin{bmatrix} 14 \\ 0 \end{bmatrix}$, which represents $\begin{cases} 3x - y = 14 \\ 2x + 4y = 0 \end{cases}$.

2. -52; yes; it does.

3. inconsistent

5-6

Notes on the Questions

Question 14 Point out that the graphs of all equations of the form $4x + 14y = n$ are lines parallel to each other and to the graph of $2x + 7y = 1$, so the question is looking for the values of n for which the two equations are not equivalent.

Question 15 This question can be used to check whether students know how to obtain the inverse of a matrix with calculator technology.

4 Wrap-Up

Ongoing Assessment

Have students write a paragraph that summarizes the procedure for solving a 2×2 linear system of equations with matrices. Students should demonstrate that they understand how to solve a 2×2 linear system of equations with matrices.

Administer Quiz 2 (or a quiz of your own) after students complete this lesson.

Additional Answers

21. For $M = \begin{bmatrix} a & b & c \\ d & e & f \\ g & h & i \end{bmatrix}$, $\det M = (aei + bfg + cdh) - (gec + hfa + idb)$; for $\det M \neq 0$,

$$M^{-1} = \begin{bmatrix} \frac{ei - fh}{\det M} & \frac{ch - bi}{\det M} & \frac{bf - ce}{\det M} \\ \frac{fg - di}{\det M} & \frac{ai - cg}{\det M} & \frac{cd - af}{\det M} \\ \frac{dh - eg}{\det M} & \frac{bg - ah}{\det M} & \frac{ae - bd}{\det M} \end{bmatrix}; A^{-1} = \begin{bmatrix} -\frac{15}{13} & -\frac{19}{26} & \frac{27}{13} \\ -\frac{4}{13} & \frac{1}{26} & \frac{2}{13} \\ \frac{7}{13} & \frac{4}{13} & -\frac{10}{13} \end{bmatrix}$$

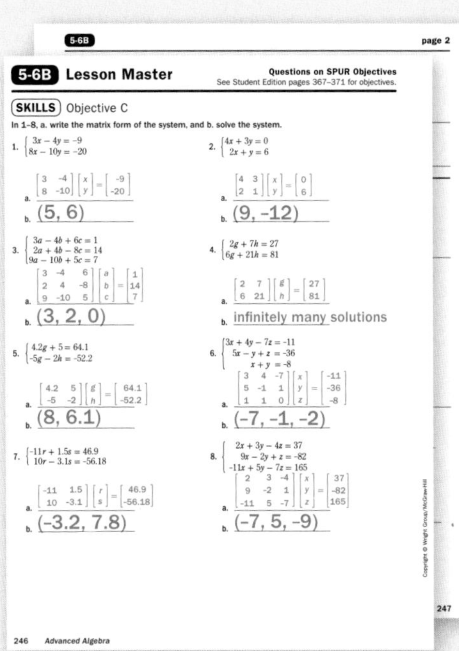

5-6B page 2

5-6B Lesson Master — Questions on SPUR Objectives. See Student Edition pages 367–371 for objectives.

SKILLS Objective C

In 1–8, a. write the matrix form of the system, and b. solve the system.

1. $\begin{cases} 3x - 4y = -9 \\ 8x - 10y = -20 \end{cases}$
   a. $\begin{bmatrix} 3 & -4 \\ 8 & -10 \end{bmatrix}\begin{bmatrix} x \\ y \end{bmatrix} = \begin{bmatrix} -9 \\ -20 \end{bmatrix}$
   b. (5, 6)

2. $\begin{cases} 4x + 3y = 0 \\ 2x + y = 6 \end{cases}$
   a. $\begin{bmatrix} 4 & 3 \\ 2 & 1 \end{bmatrix}\begin{bmatrix} x \\ y \end{bmatrix} = \begin{bmatrix} 0 \\ 6 \end{bmatrix}$
   b. (9, -12)

3. $\begin{cases} 3a - 4b + 6c = 1 \\ 2a + 4b - 8c = 14 \\ 9a - 10b + 5c = 7 \end{cases}$
   a. $\begin{bmatrix} 3 & -4 & 6 \\ 2 & 4 & -8 \\ 9 & -10 & 5 \end{bmatrix}\begin{bmatrix} a \\ b \\ c \end{bmatrix} = \begin{bmatrix} 1 \\ 14 \\ 7 \end{bmatrix}$
   b. (3, 2, 0)

4. $\begin{cases} 2g + 7h = 27 \\ 6g + 21h = 81 \end{cases}$
   a. $\begin{bmatrix} 2 & 7 \\ 6 & 21 \end{bmatrix}\begin{bmatrix} g \\ h \end{bmatrix} = \begin{bmatrix} 27 \\ 81 \end{bmatrix}$
   b. infinitely many solutions

5. $\begin{cases} 4.2g + 5 = 64.1 \\ -5g - 2h = -52.2 \end{cases}$
   a. $\begin{bmatrix} 4.2 & 5 \\ -5 & -2 \end{bmatrix}\begin{bmatrix} g \\ h \end{bmatrix} = \begin{bmatrix} 64.1 \\ -52.2 \end{bmatrix}$
   b. (8, 6.1)

6. $\begin{cases} 3x + 4y - 7z = -11 \\ 5x - y + z = -36 \\ x + y = -8 \end{cases}$
   a. $\begin{bmatrix} 3 & 4 & -7 \\ 5 & -1 & 1 \\ 1 & 1 & 0 \end{bmatrix}\begin{bmatrix} x \\ y \\ z \end{bmatrix} = \begin{bmatrix} -11 \\ -36 \\ -8 \end{bmatrix}$
   b. (-7, -1, -2)

7. $\begin{cases} -11r + 1.5s = 46.9 \\ 10r - 3.1s = -56.18 \end{cases}$
   a. $\begin{bmatrix} -11 & 1.5 \\ 10 & -3.1 \end{bmatrix}\begin{bmatrix} r \\ s \end{bmatrix} = \begin{bmatrix} 46.9 \\ -56.18 \end{bmatrix}$
   b. (-3.2, 7.8)

8. $\begin{cases} 2x + 3y - 4z = 37 \\ 9x - 2y + z = -82 \\ -11x + 5y - 7z = 165 \end{cases}$
   a. $\begin{bmatrix} 2 & 3 & -4 \\ 9 & -2 & 1 \\ -11 & 5 & -7 \end{bmatrix}\begin{bmatrix} x \\ y \\ z \end{bmatrix} = \begin{bmatrix} 37 \\ -82 \\ 165 \end{bmatrix}$
   b. (-7, 5, -9)

247

246 Advanced Algebra

Lesson 5-7

GOAL

Expand the idea of graphing inequalities on a number line (from Lesson 5-1) to graphing inequalities in a coordinate plane.

SPUR Objectives

J Graph linear inequalities in two variables.

Materials/Resources

- Lesson Masters 5-7A and 5-7B
- Resource Masters 2, 87, and 88

HOMEWORK

Suggestions for Assignment

- Questions 1–22
- Questions 23 and 24 (extra credit)
- Reading Lesson 5-8
- Covering the Ideas 5-8

Local Standards

1 Warm-Up

1. Graph $\{(x, y) \mid x - y < 100\}$.

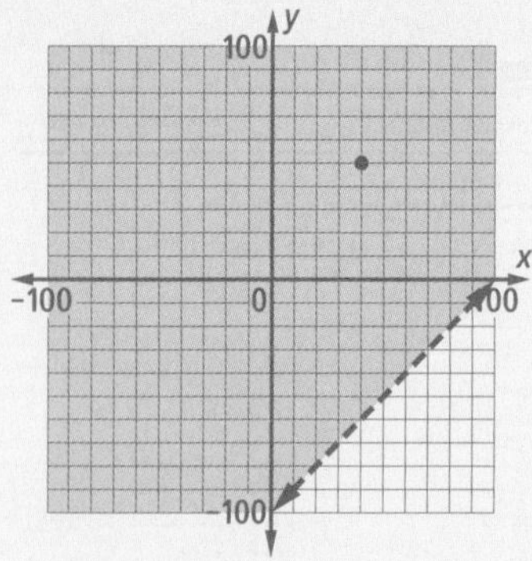

2. Is the point (40, 50) above or below the line with equation $x - y = 100$? Above; it is one of the points on the graph in Warm-Up 1.
3. Graph $\{(x, y) \mid x < y\}$ and compare this graph with the graph in Warm-Up 1. It is the image of the half-plane of Warm-Up 1 under a translation that maps (x, y) onto $(x, y + 100)$.

Lesson 5-7 Graphing Inequalities in the Coordinate Plane

Vocabulary

half-plane
boundary of a half-plane
lattice point

BIG IDEA The graph of a linear inequality in two variables consists of the points on one side of a line, either with or without the line.

As you learned in Lesson 5-1, solutions to compound sentences with inequalities involving only one variable can be graphed on a number line. In this lesson, we review the graphs of inequalities in two variables.

half-plane
boundary
half-plane

When a line is drawn in a plane, the line separates the plane into three distinct sets of points: two regions called **half-planes** and the line itself. The line is called the **boundary of the half-planes**. The boundary does *not* belong to either half-plane.

Mental Math

Kelley's hair is 8 inches long and grows at a rate of 0.5 inch per month.

a. How long will Kelley's hair be m months from now? $8 + 0.5m$ in.

b. How long will Kelley's hair be 3 months from now? 9.5 in.

c. How long was Kelley's hair 3 months ago? 6.5 in.

d. Four months ago, Kelley got a hair cut. She cut 3 inches off her hair. How long was her hair before her hair cut? 9 in.

Inequalities with Horizontal or Vertical Boundaries

Inequalities with one variable can be graphed on either a number line or in the coordinate plane. In the plane, think of $x < 3$ as $x + 0 \cdot y < 3$. The solution set is the set of all points (x, y) with x-coordinates less than 3. Graph $x = 3$ with a dashed line because the points on this line are *not* part of the solution set. Shade the half-plane to the left of the line $x = 3$. Shaded is $\{(x, y) \mid x < 3\}$.

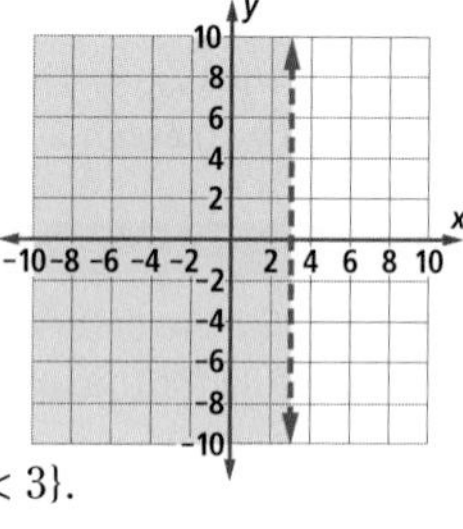
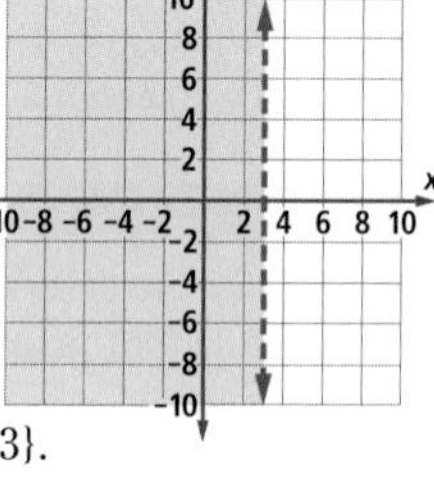

STOP QY1

QY1

Describe the graph of $\{(x, y) \mid y \geq -100\}$.

Half-Planes with Oblique Boundaries

The line $y = mx + b$ is oblique when $m \neq 0$. The half-planes of this line are described by the inequalities $y > mx + b$ (the half-plane above the line) and $y < mx + b$ (the half-plane below the line). Read $y > mx + b$ as "the set of all points where the y-coordinate is greater than $mx + b$."

Background

The graphing of half-planes will be a review for students who studied from UCSMP *Algebra* or UCSMP *Geometry*. The idea is usually quite easy for students.

The graphing of linear inequalities is critical for the graphing of systems of inequalities in Lessons 5–8 and 5–9. It also reviews the graphing encountered in Chapter 3.

The boundary for a linear inequality separates the coordinate plane into three disjoint sets of points: points on each side of the boundary and points on the boundary line itself. Because the same idea will be used later to graph inequalities relating to circles and parabolas, it should be stressed here.

Examples 1 and 2 familiarize students with graphing inequalities in the coordinate plane by hand and by using technology. Example 3 offers a discrete situation in the first quadrant that previews the kinds of inequalities students will see in Lessons 5-8 and 5-9.

Example 1

Graph the linear inequality $y > -\frac{1}{2}x + 2$.

Solution 1 First, graph the boundary $y = -\frac{1}{2}x + 2$. Use a dashed line because the boundary points do not satisfy the inequality. For the points on the boundary, the y-coordinates are equal to $-\frac{1}{2}x + 2$. The y-coordinates are greater than $-\frac{1}{2}x + 2$ for all points above the line. So the solution is the set of all points above the line. Shade the half-plane above the line to show this.

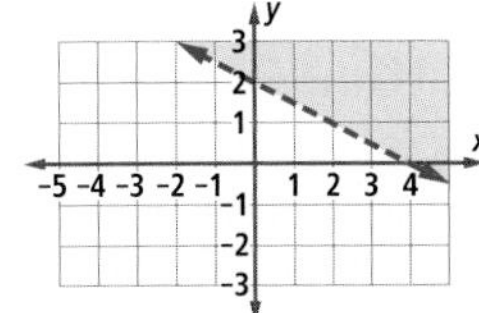

Solution 2 Use a graphing utility to graph the inequality. On the grapher shown, you can enter the inequality symbol directly. On other graphers, you may have to choose "$y >$" from a menu, then enter the rest of the inequality.

Graphers may also differ in the appearance of the boundary line itself. Although this inequality calls for a dotted line, many graphing utilities only show a solid line. The display at the right shows a dotted line, but it is difficult to see.

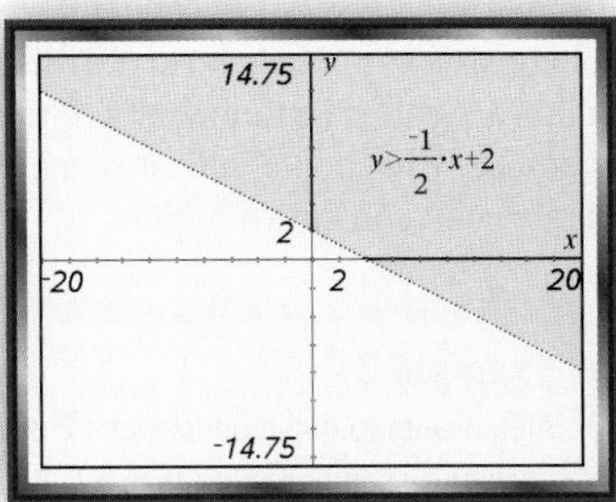

Check Pick a point in the shaded region. We pick (4, 6). Do the coordinates satisfy $y > -\frac{1}{2}x + 2$? Is $6 > -\frac{1}{2}(4) + 2$? Yes, it checks.

STOP QY2

> **QY2**
> How do you enter $y > -\frac{1}{2}x + 2$ on your grapher? Does the boundary line show as dotted or solid?

If the equation for a line is not in slope-intercept form, you can still describe its half-planes rather easily. The half-planes of the line with equation $Ax + By = C$ are described by

$$Ax + By < C \text{ and } Ax + By > C.$$

To decide which inequality describes which side of the line, pick a point not on the line and test it in the inequality.

GUIDED

Example 2

Is the set of points satisfying $3x - 2y > 6$ above or below the line with equation $3x - 2y = 6$?

Solution Refer to the graph of $3x - 2y = 6$ at the right. Pick a point not on the line:

(_?_, _?_) is a point _?_ (above/below) the line. Answers vary. Sample: 0; 0; above

Test your point.

Is 3 • _?_ − 2 • _?_ > 6? Answers vary. Sample: 0; 0

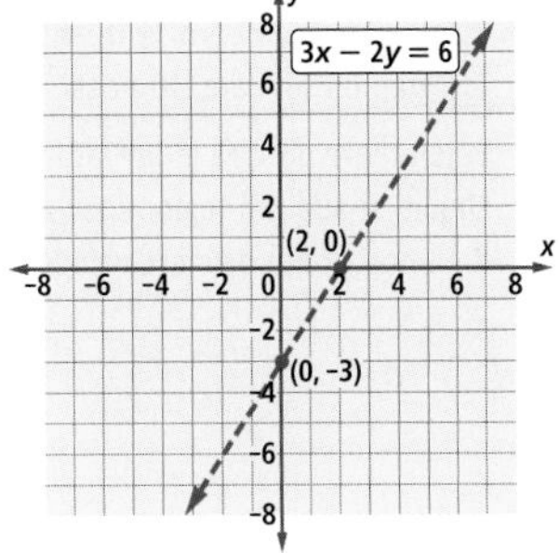

(continued on next page)

ENGLISH LEARNERS

Vocabulary Development

To help students understand the term boundary, name a *boundary* that is familiar to students. For example, "The Mississippi River forms a boundary between Illinois and Iowa. The river separates these two states from each other." You might point this out on a map of the United States.

Tell students that a coordinate grid is a type of *lattice,* which is a structure of strips with open spaces between them. The points at which the grid lines, or strips, intersect are *lattice points.*

2 Teaching

Notes on the Lesson

Inequalities with horizontal or vertical boundaries Point out that we distinguish between the number-line and the coordinate-plane graphs of $x < 3$ by using the set-builder notations $\{x \mid x < 3\}$ for the number line and $\{(x, y) \mid x < 3\}$ for the coordinate plane. Read $\{(x, y) \mid x < 3\}$ as "the set of all points where the x-coordinate is less than 3." Encourage students to utilize this reading technique with other inequalities.

Example 1 Read $y > -\frac{1}{2}x + 2$ as "the set of all points where the y-coordinates are greater than $-\frac{1}{2}x + 2$." Such reading helps students realize that the half-plane of the solution set includes the half-plane where the y-values are greater—that is, the half-plane *above* the boundary. It will greatly speed up the graphing of systems and linear-programming problems if students recognize where to shade simply by reading the inequality sign. However, to emphasize that the inequalities must be solved for y, with y *on the left* side before such a reading is possible. Picking a point and substituting should still be used as a check. In set-builder notation, this example graphs $\{(x, y) \mid y > -\frac{1}{2}x + 2\}$. As pointed out in Solution 2, various models of graphing utilities handle inequalities very differently. For some problems, it may be easier for the students to graph by hand. You will want to find out and discuss some of the limitations of the graphing utilities that students are using to graph inequalities.

Additional Example

Example 1 Graph the linear inequality $y \geq 2x + 7$.

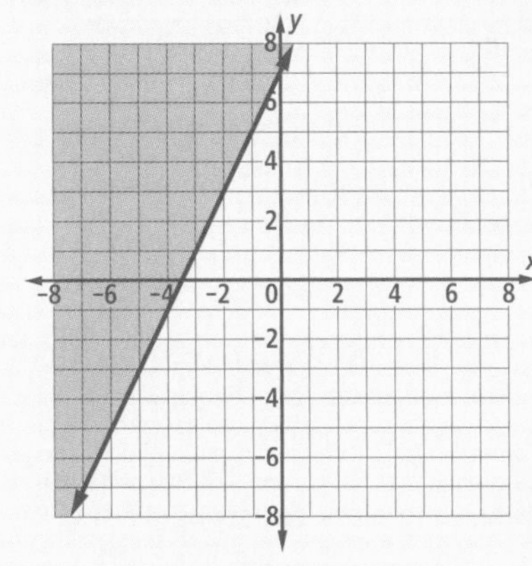

Notes on the Lesson

Example 2 Encourage students to use (0, 0) as a test point because of its ease of substitution in most inequalities. Stress, however, that (0, 0) should not be used when it is on the boundary because a point on the boundary will not enable the student to determine which half-plane is in the solution set.

Example 3 This example can be interpreted as an introduction to a simple system of inequalities, namely $\begin{cases} p \geq 0 \\ r \geq 0 \\ 12p + 15r \leq 100, \end{cases}$ where p and r are integers. Caution students to be watchful for the domains of the variables, for these determine whether the graph is a discrete set of points or consists of all points in a region.

Students may see that there are no solutions shown on the line $12p + 15r = 100$. Why is that the case? Because $12p + 15r = 3(4p + 5r)$, $3(4p + 5r) = 100$, or $4p + 5r = \frac{100}{3}$. Because p and r are integers, $4p + 5r$ is an integer and could never equal $\frac{100}{3}$. Another way of describing this is that if p and r are integers, then the left side of $12p + 15r = 100$ is divisible by 3, but the right side is not.

Additional Examples

Example 2 Is the set of points satisfying $4x + 3y < 8$ above or below the line with equation $4x + 3y = 8$?

Solution Look at the graph of $4x + 3y = 8$.

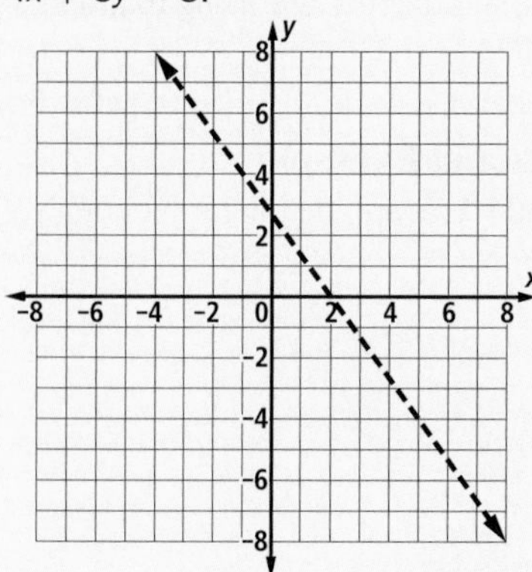

__?__ is a point __?__ (above/below) the line. Answers vary. Sample: (0, 0); below Test your point. Is $4(\underline{\ ?\ }) + 3(\underline{\ ?\ }) < 8$? 0; 0; yes Based on your answer, the points satisfying $4x + 3y < 8$ are __?__ the line with equation $4x + 3y = 8$. below

This point __?__ (does/does not) satisfy the inequality. Answers vary. Sample: does not

Based on your answer, the points satisfying $3x - 2y > 6$ are __?__ below (above/below) the line with equation $3x - 2y = 6$.

Lattice Points

In the examples you have seen, the domain of all variables is the set of real numbers or a subset of the real numbers. In these cases, the graph of an inequality consists of all points in a region, indicated by shading. However, in some situations the domain of each variable is a discrete set, such as the set of integers. In these cases, the solution set consists of points whose coordinates are both integers. These points are called **lattice points**. If there are not too many lattice-point solutions, you should indicate each with a dot on the plane, rather than shading an entire region.

> **READING MATH**
> A *lattice* is an open framework of interwoven strips forming regular patterned spaces. The grid lines on an *x-y* graph form a lattice. You may see a lattice on a window or gate, or as the top crust of a pie.

Example 3

Aleta wants to buy *p* pencils at 12 cents each and *r* erasers at 15 cents each and spend no more than \$1. What combinations (*p*, *r*) are possible?

Solution The domains of the variables p and r are nonnegative integers, so every solution is a lattice point, $p \geq 0$, and $r \geq 0$.

Write an inequality to represent the situation.

The cost of the pencils is 12p cents.

The cost of the erasers is 15r cents.

So $12p + 15r \leq 100$.

Now graph the corresponding equation $12p + 15r = 100$. The p-intercept is $\frac{100}{12} = 8\frac{1}{3}$ and the r-intercept is $\frac{100}{15} = 6\frac{2}{3}$. A graph is shown at the right. Notice that the line is dashed. This is because the restricted domains of p and r mean that a point on the boundary is included in the solution set only if both coordinates of the point are integers.

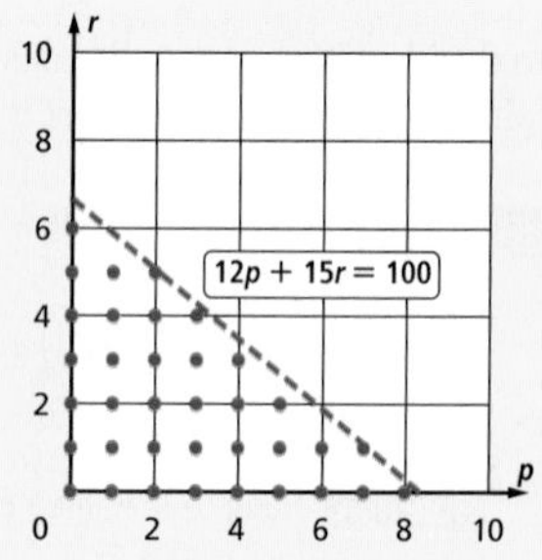

Identify all lattice points satisfying the three inequalities $12p + 15r \leq 100$, $p \geq 0$, and $r \geq 0$ and mark them on the graph. There are 36 possible points.

When there are too many lattice points to graph them all, you should shade the region they are in and make a note that only the appropriate discrete values are solutions.

Accommodating the Learner

After completing the lesson, give students the two graphs at the right. Ask them to write a word problem for each graph such that the graph shows the solution set for the problem. Answers vary. Sample: (1) Peanuts cost \$2 per pound and cashews cost \$5 per pound. Find all possible combinations of pounds of peanuts and cashews that you can buy for \$12 or less. (2) What combinations of \$2 student tickets and \$5 adult tickets can you purchase for \$12 or less?

(1)

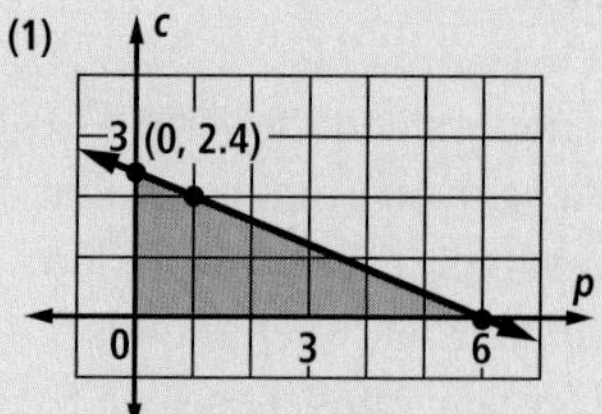

(2)

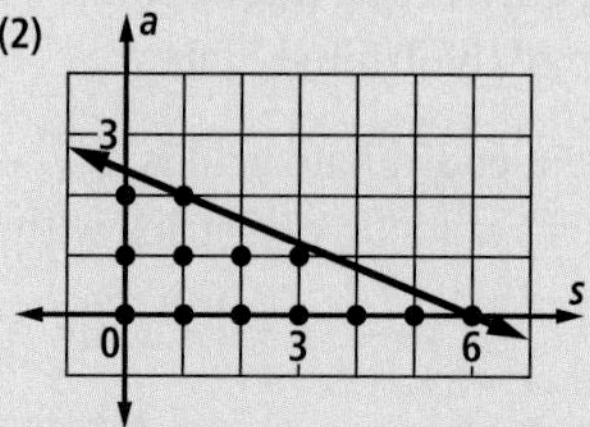

Questions

COVERING THE IDEAS

1. **Fill in the Blanks** A line separates a plane into two distinct regions called __?__. The line itself is called the __?__ of these regions. half-planes; boundary
2. Graph the solutions to $x \le 4.93$ 2a–b. See margin.
   a. on a number line.
   b. in the coordinate plane.
3. Does the graph in the coordinate plane of all solutions to $y < 3$ consist of the points above or below the line with equation $y = 3$? below
4. To graph the inequality $y > 5 - 3x$, should you shade above or below the line with equation $y = 5 - 3x$? above
5. **Matching** Tell which sentence each point satisfies.

a. (-4, 4) ii	i. $y > -\frac{1}{2}x + 2$
b. (11, 2) i	ii. $y = -\frac{1}{2}x + 2$
c. (0, 0) iii	iii. $y < -\frac{1}{2}x + 2$

In 6 and 7, graph the inequality. 6–7. See margin.

6. $100x - 80y > 200$
7. $y - \frac{x}{3} \le 6$
8. What name is given to a point with integer coordinates? lattice point

In 9–11, refer to Example 3.

9. What is the greatest number of pencils Aleta can purchase? 8
10. What is the greatest number of erasers Aleta can purchase? 6
11. If Aleta wants an equal number of pencils and erasers, what is the greatest number of each she can purchase? 3
12. Norma Lee Lucid wants to buy d DVDs at \$19.95 each and m music CDs at \$14.95 each. She wants to spend less than \$100.00.
    a. Write an inequality in d and m describing this situation. $19.95d + 14.95m < 100$
    b. Graph all solutions. 12b–c. See margin.
    c. What pairs (d, m) are possible?

Additional Example

Example 3 A ferryboat carries cars and buses across Lake Michigan. The boat has space for 12 cars. A bus takes up the space of 3 cars. Draw a graph showing all possible combinations of cars and buses that can be taken in one crossing. Write an inequality to represent the situation: $x + 3y \le 12$. Because x and y are nonnegative integers, only lattice points in the first quadrant are possible. Graph the boundary $x + 3y = 12$. The lattice points on this line and those in the first quadrant below this line satisfy the inequality. Mark and count these lattice points. There are 35 combinations.

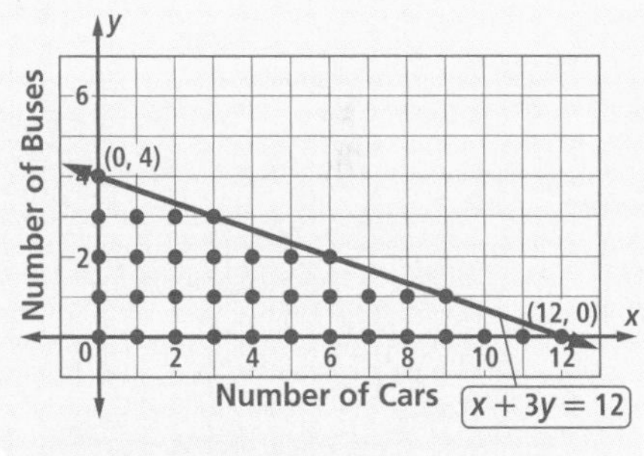

3 Assignment

Recommended Assignment

- Questions 1–22
- Question 23 and 24 (extra credit)
- Reading Lesson 5-8
- Covering the Ideas 5-8

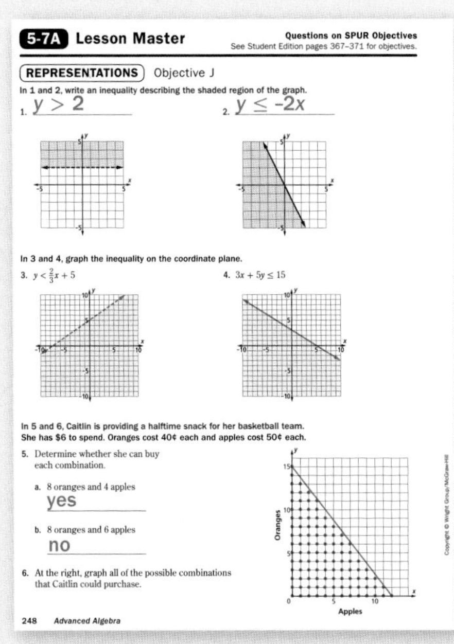
5-7A Lesson Master — Questions on SPUR Objectives. See Student Edition pages 367–371 for objectives.

REPRESENTATIONS Objective J

In 1 and 2, write an inequality describing the shaded region of the graph.

1. $y > 2$
2. $y \le -2x$

In 3 and 4, graph the inequality on the coordinate plane.

3. $y < \frac{2}{3}x + 5$
4. $3x + 5y \le 15$

In 5 and 6, Caitlin is providing a halftime snack for her basketball team. She has \$6 to spend. Oranges cost 40¢ each and apples cost 50¢ each.

5. Determine whether she can buy each combination.
   a. 8 oranges and 4 apples yes
   b. 8 oranges and 6 apples no
6. At the right, graph all of the possible combinations that Caitlin could purchase.

248 Advanced Algebra

Extension

Have students write a system of inequalities whose solution set shown on the graph below.

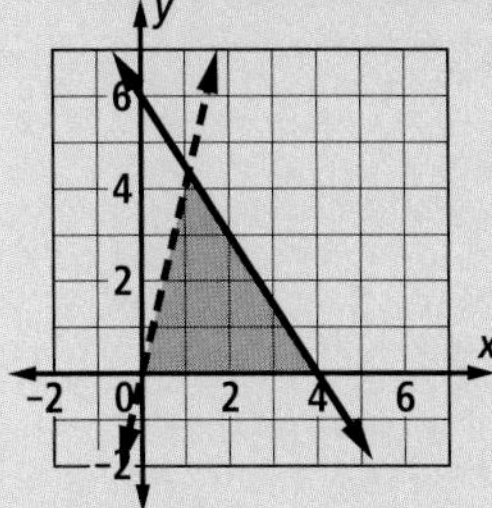

$$\begin{cases} x \ge 0 \\ y \le -\frac{3}{2}x + 6 \\ y < 4x \end{cases}$$

Notes on the Questions

Questions 15 and 16 It is interesting to focus on the difference between the mathematical domain and range and a realistic domain and range, which takes into account the real-world restrictions of the problem itself, such as the fact that the number of children and adults must be nonnegative integers. Some students' graphs for this problem will have infinite domains and ranges, while others will restrict theirs. We consider both of these interpretations useful. However, a correct graph should display only lattice points or indicate that only lattice points are meant to be shaded.

Additional Answers

2a.

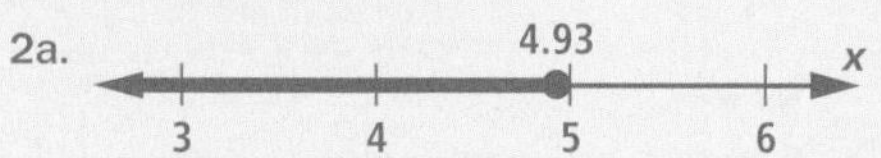

2b.

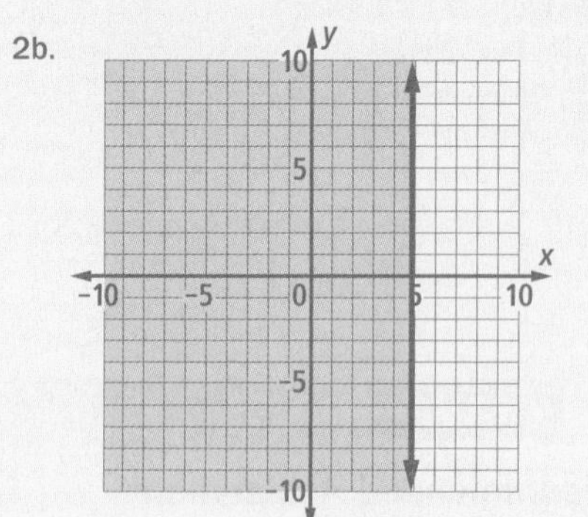

6.

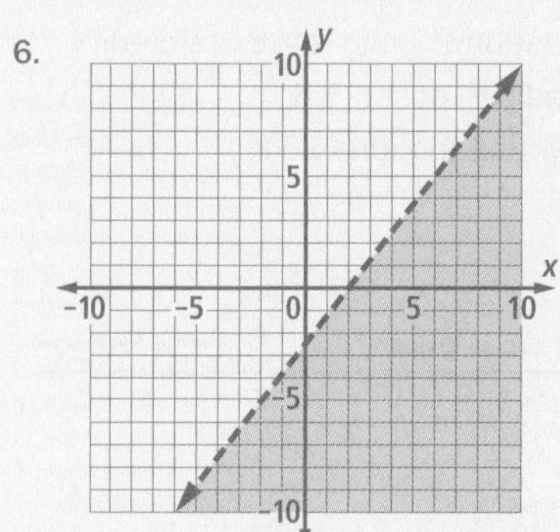

7.

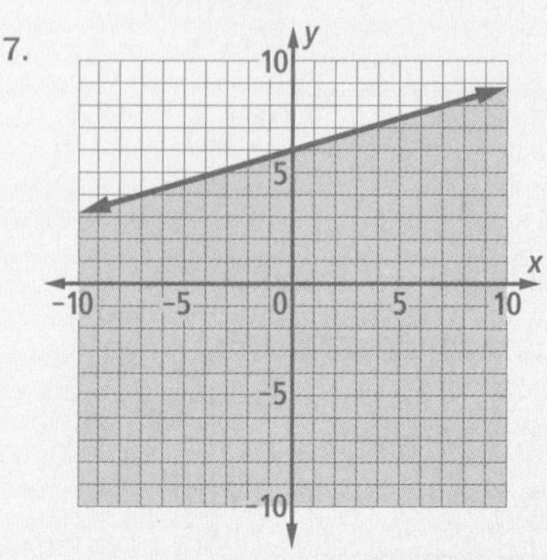

APPLYING THE MATHEMATICS

In 13 and 14, write an inequality that describes the graph.

13.

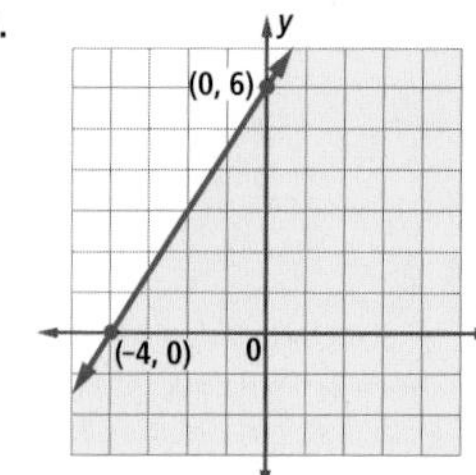

14.

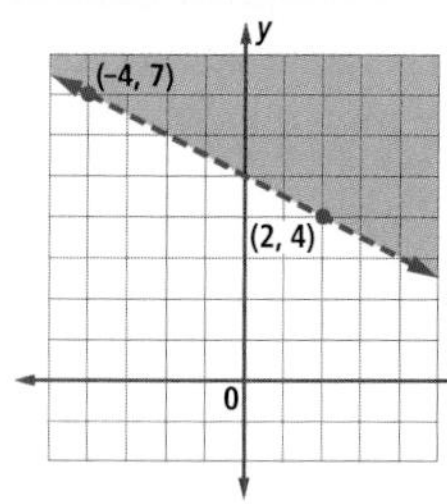

13. $-3x + 2y \leq 12$

14. $y > -\frac{1}{2}x + 5$

In 15 and 16, a group of 4 adults and 8 children are planning to attend a family reunion at an amusement park. Children's tickets cost $24.95 each and adult tickets cost $32.50 each. The group budgeted $300.00 for the trip, which is not quite enough money for everyone to attend. Some children and adults will have to stay home.

15. State whether each of these combinations will be able to attend.
    a. 4 children and 4 adults yes
    b. 6 children and 3 adults yes
    c. 7 children and 4 adults no

16. a. Graph all pairs of numbers of children and adults who can attend. See margin.
    b. How many pairs are there? 43

17. Can the graph of a linear inequality in two variables also be the graph of a function? Explain why or why not.

17. No; a single x-value is paired with multiple y-values.

REVIEW

18. a. Write the matrix form of the system $\begin{cases} 3x + 6y = 18 \\ -4x - 5y = 20 \end{cases}$.
    b. Solve the system. (Lesson 5-6)

18a. $\begin{bmatrix} 3 & 6 \\ -4 & -5 \end{bmatrix}\begin{bmatrix} x \\ y \end{bmatrix} = \begin{bmatrix} 18 \\ 20 \end{bmatrix}$

18b. $x = -\frac{70}{3}, y = \frac{44}{3}$

19. Use the System-Determinant Theorem to determine whether the system $\begin{cases} A + 3B - 2C = 5.5 \\ 7A - 5B + C = 1 \\ B - C = -1 \end{cases}$ has exactly one solution. (Use a calculator to find the determinant.) (Lesson 5-6) Yes; it has exactly one solution.

Accommodating the Learner

Review with students the four inequality symbols ($<$, $>$, $\leq$, and $\geq$). Also review inequality graphing on a number line: An open circle signifies that the endpoint *is not* included in the graph, and a solid circle signifies that the endpoint *is* included in the graph. Then explain that a dashed or dotted line as a boundary line is analogous to an open circle, and a solid line is analogous to a solid circle. Stress to students that when graphing an inequality, they should always check their solutions with one or more test points.

Additional Answers

12b.

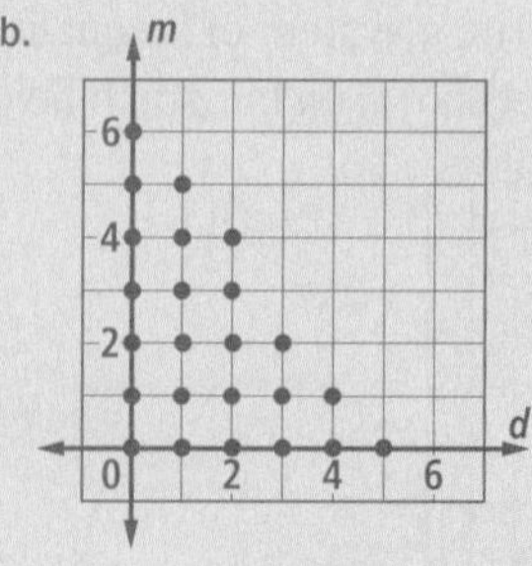

12c. (5, 0), (4, 1), (4, 0), (3, 2), (3, 1), (3, 0), (2, 4), (2, 3), (2, 2), (2, 1), (2, 0), (1, 5), (1, 4), (1, 3), (1, 2), (1, 1), (1, 0), (0, 6), (0, 5), (0, 4), (0, 3), (0, 2), (0, 1), and (0, 0)

20. Antonio claims to have a shortcut for determining if the matrix $\begin{bmatrix} a & b \\ c & d \end{bmatrix}$ has an inverse whenever c and d are nonzero. If the fractions $\frac{a}{c}$ and $\frac{b}{d}$ are equal, Antonio argues, then the matrix has no inverse. Otherwise, it does. Does Antonio's method work? Explain your answer. **(Lesson 5-5)**

20. Yes. If $\frac{a}{c} = \frac{b}{c}$, then $ad = bc$ so $ad - bc = 0$. This corresponds to the matrix not having an inverse.

21. Solve $37w + 3 > 77$ and $8 - 4w \geq -10$. Write the solution in set-builder notation and graph it on a number line. **(Lesson 5-1)**

21. $\{w \mid 2 < w \leq 4.5\}$

22. Meteor Crater in Arizona is approximately in the shape of a cylinder 1500 meters in diameter and 180 meters deep. Scientists estimate that the meteor that created it weighed about 300,000 tons at entry. Assuming the volume of the crater varies directly with the weight of the meteor, what volume of crater would you expect for a meteor weighing 500,000 tons? **(Lesson 2-1)** about 530,000,000 m^3

When the crater was first discovered, it was surrounded by about 30 tons of meteoritic iron chunks, scattered over an area 12 to 15 kilometers in diameter.

EXPLORATION

23. This problem was made up by the Indian mathematician Mahavira and dates from about 850 CE. "The price of nine citrons and seven fragrant wood apples is 107; again, the mixed price of seven citrons and nine fragrant wood apples is 101. Oh you arithmetician, tell me quickly the price of a citron and a wood apple here, having distinctly separated these prices well." At this time algebra had not been developed yet. How could this question be answered by someone without using algebra? See margin.

24. Write a system of three inequalities that describes the shaded region below.

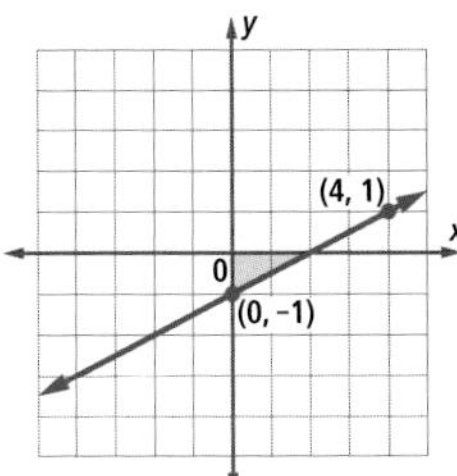

24. $\begin{cases} x > 0 \\ y < 0 \\ y \geq \frac{1}{2}x - 1 \end{cases}$

QY ANSWERS

1. It is the half plane together with its boundary consisting of all points whose y-coordinate is greater than or equal to –100.

2. Answers vary.

Notes on the Questions

Question 24 This question can be used to set up Lesson 5-8.

4 Wrap-Up

Ongoing Assessment

Have students work in pairs, with each student writing a linear inequality. Have students exchange inequalities and draw the graph of the inequality in a coordinate plane. Have students check each other's work. Students should correctly draw the graph of a linear inequality in a coordinate plane.

Additional Answers

16a.

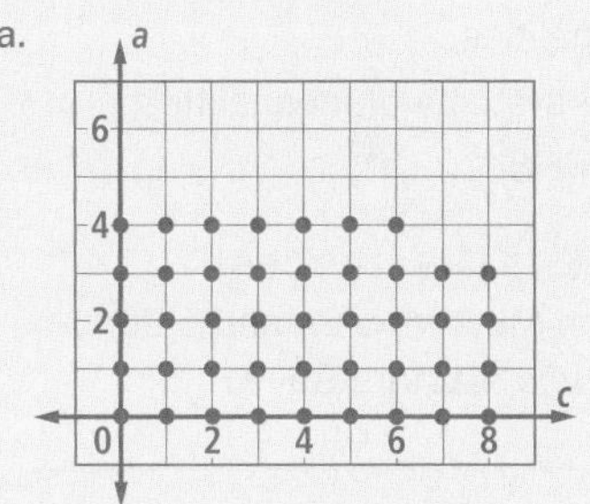

23. One could guess and check. Because these are integer solutions, this is not particularly difficult. Also, one can deduce that 2 citrons cost $107 - 101 = 6$ more than 2 wood apples, so 1 wood apple costs 3 less than 1 citron.

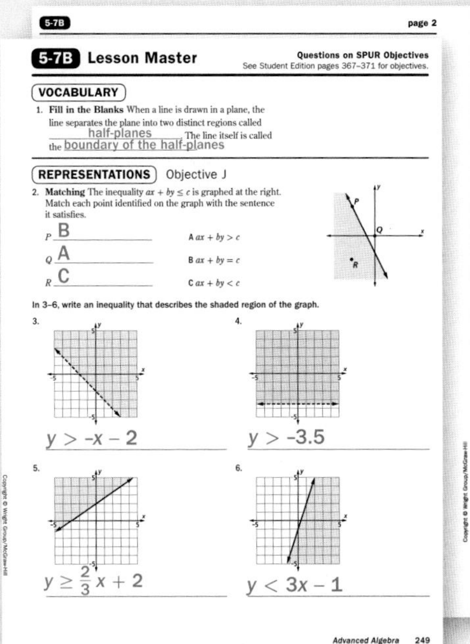
5-7B page 2

5-7B Lesson Master — Questions on SPUR Objectives. See Student Edition pages 367–371 for objectives.

VOCABULARY

1. Fill in the Blanks When a line is drawn in a plane, the line separates the plane into two distinct regions called half-planes. The line itself is called the boundary of the half-planes

REPRESENTATIONS Objective J

2. Matching The inequality $ax + by \leq c$ is graphed at the right. Match each point identified on the graph with the sentence it satisfies.

P B — A $ax + by > c$

Q A — B $ax + by = c$

R C — C $ax + by < c$

In 3–6, write an inequality that describes the shaded region of the graph.

3. $y > -x - 2$

4. $y > -3.5$

5. $y \geq \frac{2}{3}x + 2$

6. $y < 3x - 1$

Copyright © Wright Group/McGraw-Hill

Advanced Algebra 249

Lesson 5-8

GOAL

Solve systems of linear inequalities using graphs of inequalities and systems of equations. Learn the terms *feasible set* or *feasible region* for the solution set of a system of inequalities as the groundwork for using the linear-programming method in Lesson 5-9.

SPUR Objectives

E Recognize properties of systems of inequalities.

K Solve systems of inequalities by graphing.

Materials/Resources

- Lesson Masters 5-8A and 5-8B
- Resource Masters 89–91

HOMEWORK

Suggestions for Assignment

- Questions 1–19
- Question 20 (extra credit)
- Reading Lesson 5-9
- Covering the Ideas 5-9

Local Standards

1 Warm-Up

Ellen was taking a 90-minute world history final exam. There were 20 short-answer and 6 essay questions on the test. She figured it would take about 2 minutes to do each short-answer question and 15 minutes for each essay. So she did not have enough time! At this rate, how many questions of each type can she finish? Let s be the number of short-answer questions Ellen answers and e be the number of essay questions she answers. Then the possible values of (s, e) are the points on and in the interior of the convex polygonal region that is the intersection of the solution sets to the three inequalities $2s + 15e \leq 90$, $0 \leq s \leq 20$, and $0 \leq e \leq 6$.

Lesson 5-8 Systems of Linear Inequalities

Vocabulary

feasible set, feasible region

BIG IDEA The solution to a system of linear inequalities in two variables is either the empty set, the interior of a polygon, or a region bounded by line segments and rays.

A linear inequality in two or more variables may be used to model a situation in which one or more resources limit, or *constrain*, the values of the variables. In the previous lesson, Aleta's money limited the number of pencils and erasers she could buy. In this lesson we show how systems of linear inequalities can model even more complicated situations.

Mental Math

What inequality is represented by the graph?

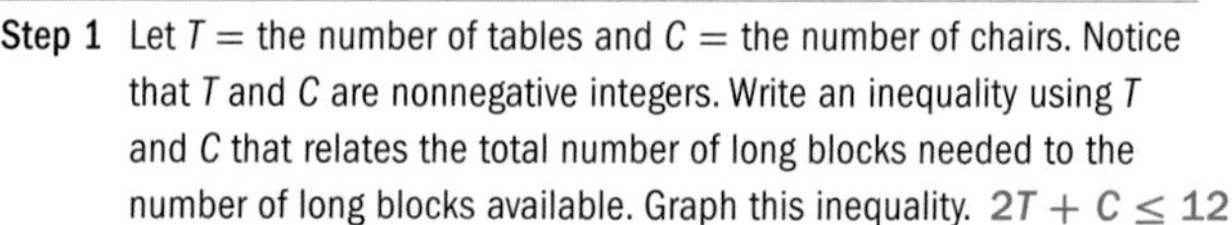

a. (number line, variable p; labels 0, 12)

b. (number line, variable c; labels -3, 0)

c. (number line, variable x; labels 23, 31)

d. (number line, variable t; labels 0.7, 0.9)

a. $p \leq 12$
b. $c > -3$
c. $23 < x \leq 31$
d. $t < 0.7$ or $t > 0.9$

Activity

Suppose you have a collection of 16 square (2 × 2) and 12 long (2 × 4) interlocking blocks to form into tables and chairs. It takes 2 long blocks and 2 square blocks to make a table. It takes 1 long block and 2 square blocks to make a chair. What combinations of tables and chairs can you make with your collection? Steps 1–3. See margin for graphs.

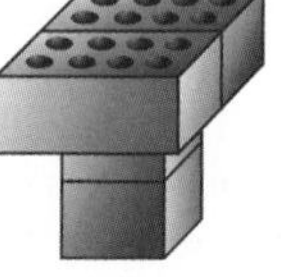

	Table	Chair
Long Blocks Needed	2	1
Square Blocks Needed	2	2

Step 1 Let T = the number of tables and C = the number of chairs. Notice that T and C are nonnegative integers. Write an inequality using T and C that relates the total number of long blocks needed to the number of long blocks available. Graph this inequality. $2T + C \leq 12$

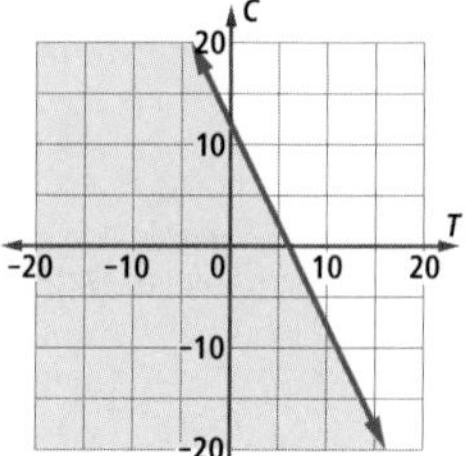

Step 2 Write an inequality using T and C that relates the total number of square blocks needed to the number of square blocks available. Graph this inequality on the same axes as the inequality from Step 1. $2T + 2C \leq 16$

Step 3 Determine whether each ordered pair (T, C) in the table on the next page satisfies the inequalities from Steps 1 and 2. Then plot the four ordered pairs on your graph.

Background

Solving systems of linear inequalities is important in mathematics. Linear programming is used by many corporations and is encountered by almost all those who major in business in college. Linear programming also provides an opportunity to review and solidify concepts related to linear equations. Linear programming also opens students' eyes to the subject of optimization, an important topic in both pure and applied mathematics.

The Activity and Example 1 present the kind of translation problem that is required in a linear-programming situation. But they are not yet linear-programming problems because there is no expression to be maximized or minimized. That will come in Lesson 5-9. You may wish to do the Activity slowly so that all students understand how the formula for each constraint was obtained.

(T, C)	Satisfies Long Block Inequality	Satisfies Square Block Inequality
(2, 4)	? yes	? yes
(6, 2)	? no	? yes
(2, 7)	? yes	? no
(5, 4)	? no	? no

Step 4 Which point(s) from Step 3 satisfy both the long-block inequality and the square-block inequality? Where do these points appear on the graph? See margin.

In the Activity, the limited numbers of square and long blocks are constraints to solving the problem. These constraints are represented by the inequalities $2T + C \leq 12$, $2T + 2C \leq 16$, $T \geq 0$, and $C \geq 0$. The set of possible combinations of tables and chairs is the intersection of the solution sets of all these inequalities, as shown in the graph at the right.

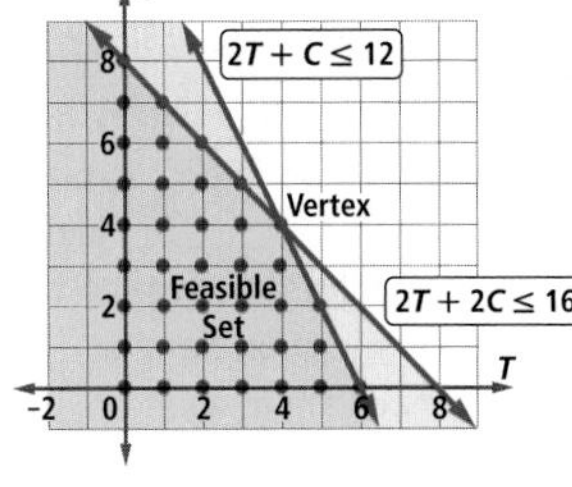

Because the graph of a linear inequality in two variables is a half-plane, the graph of the solution to a system of linear inequalities is the intersection of half-planes. Points in this intersection are often called the **feasible set** or **feasible region** for the system.

STOP QY

A feasible region is always bounded by either segments or rays. The intersections of boundary segments or rays are *vertices* of the feasible region. One vertex of the feasible region from the Activity is labeled in the graph. Because the boundary may not be included in the solution set of an inequality, the vertices and boundary segments or rays may not be part of the feasible region.

▶ QY

Multiple Choice
Which of these combinations of tables and chairs are in the feasible region from the Activity?

A (5, 2) B (6, 1)
C (0, 12) D (0, 0)
E (4, 4)

GUIDED

Example 1

An electronics firm makes two kinds of televisions: plasma and projection. The firm assumes it will sell all the sets it makes. It profits $2000 on each plasma set it sells and $1500 on each projection TV. If it wants a profit of over $100,000, how many plasma sets and how many projection TVs should it make?

Solution Let L = the number of plasma sets made. Then the profit the firm makes on these sets is ? $\frac{\text{dollars}}{\text{set}}$ · ? sets = ? dollars. Similarly, let R = the number of projection sets made. The profit on these sets is ? dollars. 2000; L; $2000L$; $1500R$

(continued on next page)

2 Teaching

Notes on the Lesson

As in the case of graphing systems of lines and curves (Lesson 5-2), we usually find the intersection of the solution sets by first graphing their union. However, point out to students that in this lesson, the feasible region is highlighted by redrawing it with only the points that belong to the intersection. Students do not have to redraw their graphs in this manner; a graph of the union is sufficient, provided that the shading is clear.

Activity It is important to do this Activity. Engage the class in a discussion of how the inequalities are derived. Graph the feasible set together and use what has been learned about solving systems of equations to find the vertices. Emphasize that the feasible set includes *all* the points that satisfy the conditions stated in the inequalities and *only* those points.

In linear-programming problems, some teachers like to have students shade all the areas that do *not* satisfy the constraints. Then what is left is the feasible region. This idea has the advantage that overlapping shadings are not needed but the disadvantage of being rather confusing because students are generally familiar with shading solutions.

Students may think the word *feasible,* being new for them in mathematics, indicates a totally new concept. Emphasize that the feasible set is simply the intersection of the solution sets of the individual inequalities. Its name comes from its application, not from any new mathematical idea.

Example 2 Solution sets to systems of linear inequalities are always convex because they are the intersection of convex sets. In this example, the solution set is an infinite convex set. In Question 24 of Lesson 5-7, the shaded region is a bounded convex set.

Accommodating the Learner

Some students may find a feasible region difficult to identify. For these students, it may help to denote the region represented by each inequality with a different color or a different form of highlighting: vertical lines, horizontal lines, or oblique lines.

Additional Example

Example 1 The Lines School Social Club is holding a flower sale. They will sell baskets of geraniums and petunias and plan to sell all the plants they have. Their profit on each basket of geraniums is $4 and on each basket of petunias is $2.50. If the club wants a profit of $500 or more, how many baskets of each kind of flower should they sell?

Solution Let G = the number of geranium baskets. Then the profit made on geraniums is

_?_ $\frac{\text{dollars}}{\text{basket}}$ • _?_ baskets = _?_ dollars. Similarly, let P = the number of petunia baskets. Then the profit on petunias is _?_ dollars. So the total profit is _?_ + _?_ dollars, and the pair of numbers (G, P) of baskets the club should sell to satisfy _?_ + _?_ $\geq$ \$500. 4; *G*; 4*G*; 2.5*P*; 4*G*; 2.5*P*; 4*G*; 2.5*P* Because G and P are the number of baskets, they must be nonnegative integers. So $G \geq 0$ and $P \geq 0$. These three inequalities form the boundary of the feasible region. Graph the three boundary lines. Shade the feasible region as shown.

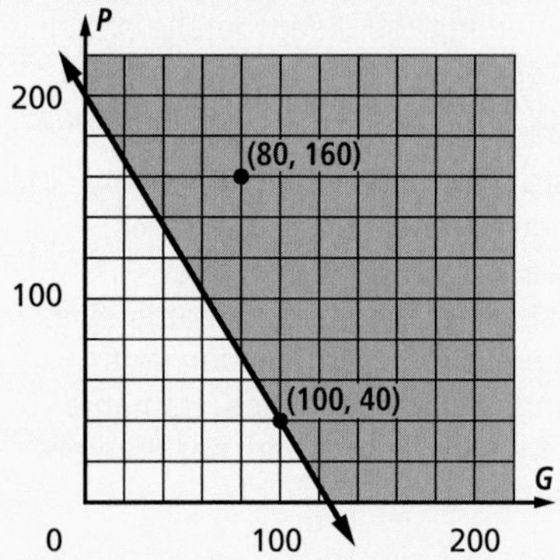

The club can sell any pair (G, P) of numbers of baskets that is a lattice point in the feasible region. In this situation, there are too many lattice points to plot distinctly, so the feasible region is shaded and two discrete solutions—_?_ and _?_— are noted in the graph. (100, 40); (80, 160) These points mean that the club can sell _?_ geranium baskets and _?_ petunia baskets or _?_ geranium baskets and _?_ petunia baskets and meet the \$500 or more goal. 100; 40; 80; 160

So the total profit is _?_ + _?_ dollars, and the pair (L, R) of numbers of televisions the firm should make needs to satisfy 1500*R*; 2000*L*

$$\_?\_ + \_?\_ > 100{,}000.$$ 1500*R*; 2000*L*

Divide both sides by 100 to make the numbers easier to manage.

$$\_?\_ + \_?\_ > 1000$$ 15*R*; 20*L*

Because *L* and *R* are numbers of televisions, they are nonnegative integers. So $L \geq 0$ and $R \geq 0$. These three inequalities form the boundary of the feasible region.

Graph the three boundary lines. Shade the feasible region as shown at the right.

The firm can make any pair (L, R) of numbers of televisions that is a lattice point in the feasible region.

In this situation, there are too many lattice points to plot distinctly, so the feasible region is shaded and two discrete solutions, (_?_, _?_) and (_?_, _?_), are noted on the graph. 30; 40; 50; 20 These points mean that the firm could sell _?_ plasma sets and _?_ projection sets or _?_ plasma sets and _?_ projection sets and meet their goal. 30; 40; 50; 20

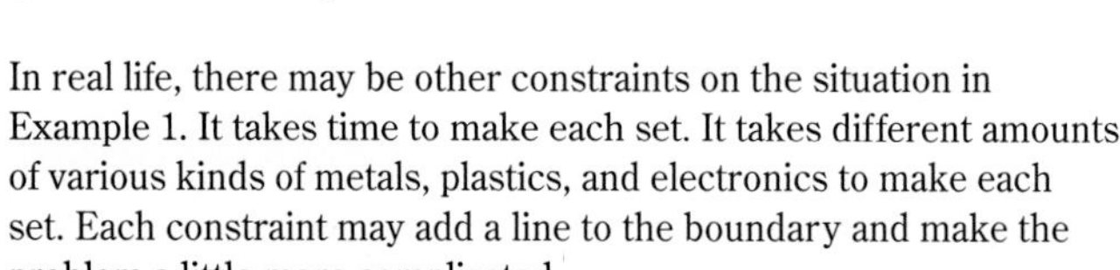
In real life, there may be other constraints on the situation in Example 1. It takes time to make each set. It takes different amounts of various kinds of metals, plastics, and electronics to make each set. Each constraint may add a line to the boundary and make the problem a little more complicated.

Example 2

Consider the system $\begin{cases} y > -\frac{1}{2}x \\ y \leq \frac{1}{2}x + 4. \\ y \leq 6 \end{cases}$

a. **Graph the solution to the system by hand and check your solution.**

b. **Find the vertices of the feasible region.**

Solution

a. The boundary lines for all the inequalities are easily sketched because the inequalities are in slope-intercept form.

The first inequality has a dotted boundary, and the half-plane above is shaded. The second has a solid boundary, and the half-plane below it is shaded. The third inequality has a solid boundary, and the half-plane below it is shaded. The three inequalities are graphed on the same grid shown here.

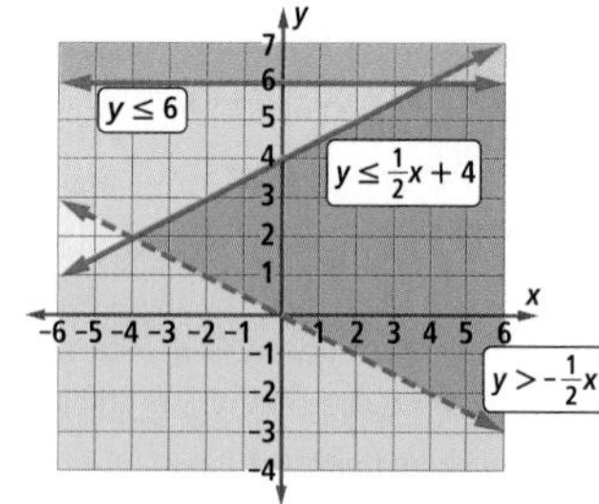

Additional Answers

Activity

Steps 1–3:

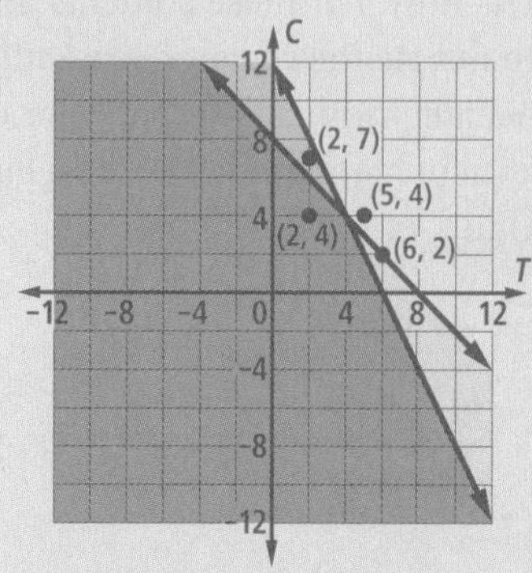

Step 4: (2, 4); it appears in the region where the solutions to the two inequalities overlap.

The solution to the system is all the points in the intersection of the three half-planes. A graph of the feasible region is shown at the right. The region extends forever to the right, below and on $y = 6$ and $y = -\frac{1}{2}x + 4$ and above $y = -\frac{1}{2}x$.

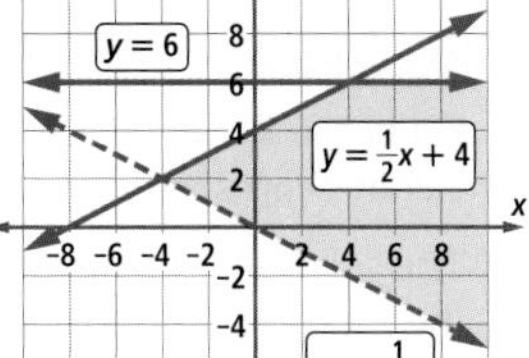

Choose an ordered pair in the feasible region to see if it satisfies all three inequalities. We choose (1, 0).

Is $0 > -\frac{1}{2}(1)$? Yes.
Is $0 \le \frac{1}{2}(1) + 4$? Yes.
Is $0 \le 6$? Yes, so the solution checks.

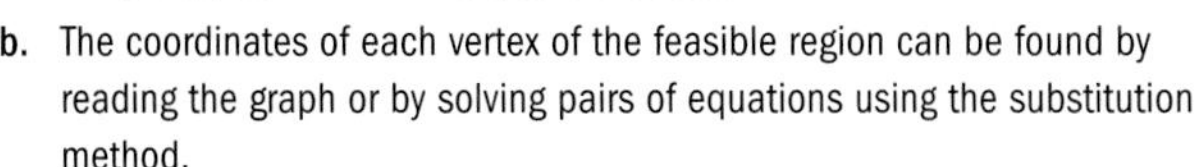

b. The coordinates of each vertex of the feasible region can be found by reading the graph or by solving pairs of equations using the substitution method.

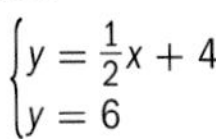

$$\begin{cases} y = \frac{1}{2}x + 4 \\ y = 6 \end{cases}$$

Substitute 6 for y in $y = \frac{1}{2}x + 4$.

$$6 = \frac{1}{2}x + 4$$
$$x = 4$$

(4, 6) is one vertex.

$$\begin{cases} y = \frac{1}{2}x + 4 \\ y = -\frac{1}{2}x \end{cases}$$

Substitute $-\frac{1}{2}x$ for y in $y = \frac{1}{2}x + 4$.

$$-\frac{1}{2}x = \frac{1}{2}x + 4$$
$$x = -4$$

Substitute –4 for x in either equation to find that $y = 2$.

(-4, 2) is the other vertex.

A graphing utility can graph systems of inequalities. However, the feasible region may not be clear on all machines. A graph of the system from Example 2 on one grapher is shown below. The darkest region is the feasible region.

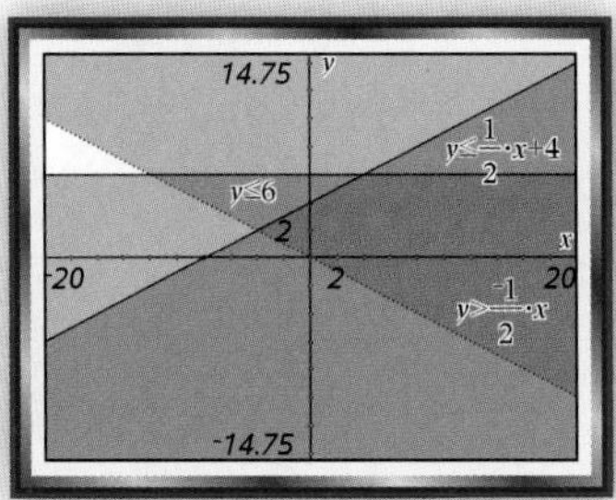

Additional Example

Example 2

Consider the system $\begin{cases} y \le -\frac{1}{2}x + 6 \\ y \le -2x + 12. \\ x \ge 0 \\ y \ge 0 \end{cases}$

Graph the solution to the system by hand and check your solution. What are the vertices of the feasible region?

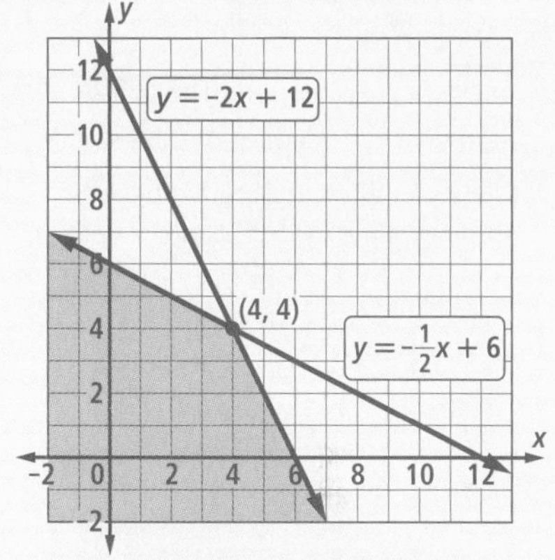

(0, 0), (0, 6), (6, 0), and (4, 4)

ENGLISH LEARNERS

Vocabulary Development

Tell students that the term *feasible* means "possible." Then point out that the graphs in the Activity and the Examples are different. The Activity graph is a *feasible set* or *region* of lattice points, while the graph in Example 1 is a shaded region because there are too many lattice points to plot distinctly. The graph in Example 2 is a shaded region because it includes all real numbers in the feasible region. Review the use of dashed and solid boundary lines.

Because a feasible region is a convex region bounded by parts of lines, feasible regions that are finite may be thought of as polygons and a vertex of such a feasible region corresponds to the vertex of a polygon. You might ask students to find each vertex of the feasible region in Question 6.

3 Assignment

Recommended Assignment

- Questions 1–19
- Question 20 (extra credit)
- Reading Lesson 5-9
- Covering the Ideas 5-9

Additional Answers

4. Answers vary. Sample: The points represent the number of tables and chairs, so the coordinates must be integers; thus (3, 2.5) is not a solution.

9a.

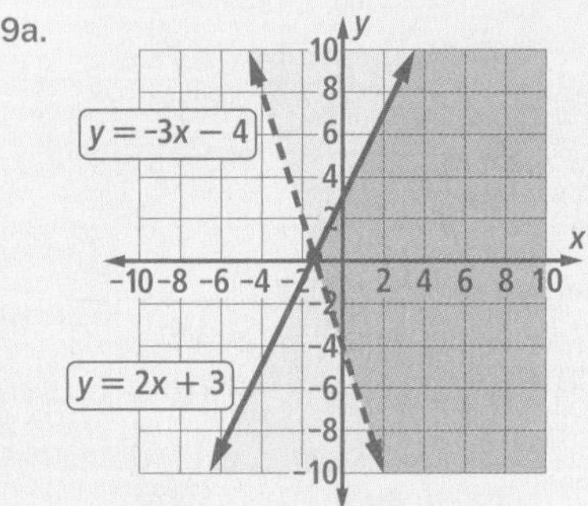

10a.

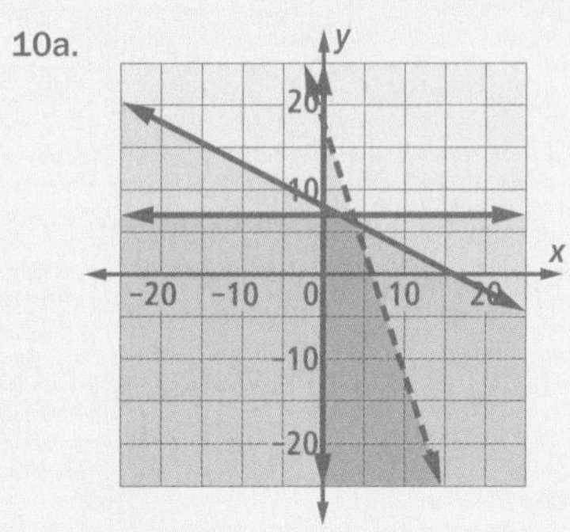

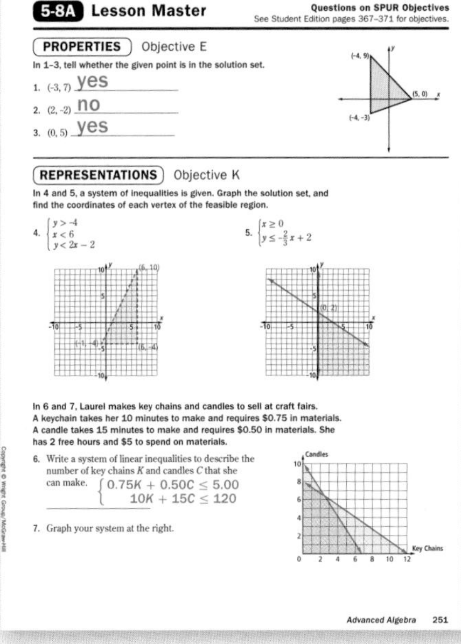

5-8A Lesson Master

Questions on SPUR Objectives
See Student Edition pages 367–371 for objectives.

PROPERTIES Objective E

In 1–3, tell whether the given point is in the solution set.

1. (-3, 7) yes
2. (2, -2) no
3. (0, 5) yes

(-4, 9) (5, 0) (-4, -3)

REPRESENTATIONS Objective K

In 4 and 5, a system of inequalities is given. Graph the solution set, and find the coordinates of each vertex of the feasible region.

4. $\begin{cases} y > -4 \\ x < 6 \\ y < 2x - 2 \end{cases}$

(6, 10) (-1, -4) (6, -4)

5. $\begin{cases} x \geq 0 \\ y \leq -\frac{2}{3}x + 2 \end{cases}$

(0, 2)

In 6 and 7, Laurel makes key chains and candles to sell at craft fairs. A keychain takes her 10 minutes to make and requires $0.75 in materials. A candle takes 15 minutes to make and requires $0.50 in materials. She has 2 free hours and $5 to spend on materials.

6. Write a system of linear inequalities to describe the number of key chains K and candles C that she can make. $\begin{cases} 0.75K + 0.50C \leq 5.00 \\ 10K + 15C \leq 120 \end{cases}$
7. Graph your system at the right.

Candles
Key Chains

Advanced Algebra 251

Questions

COVERING THE IDEAS

1. **Fill in the Blank** The solution to a system of linear inequalities can be represented by the ___?___ of half-planes. intersection
2. The solution set to a system of linear inequalities is often called the ___?___. feasible set or feasible region

In 3–5, refer to the Activity.

3. Use your graph to determine whether each combination of tables and chairs is possible. If it is not, describe which block, long or square, is in short supply.
   a. 7 tables and 2 chairs not possible; not enough long blocks or square blocks
   b. 5 tables and 2 chairs possible
   c. 2 tables and 5 chairs possible
   d. 2 tables and 7 chairs not possible; not enough square blocks
4. The point (3, 2.5) satisfies all the constraints, but it is not a solution in this situation. Explain why not. See margin.
5. a. What system of equations can you solve to find the vertex of the feasible region located in the first quadrant?
   b. Solve the system from Part a to find the coordinates of the vertex. (4, 4)

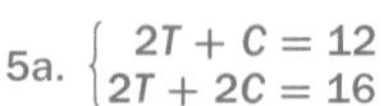

5a. $\begin{cases} 2T + C = 12 \\ 2T + 2C = 16 \end{cases}$

6. The graph at the right represents a system of inequalities. In what region(s) are the solutions to each system, with $x > 0$ and $y > 0$?
   a. $y + 2x < 600$ and $x + 2y < 600$ III
   b. $y + 2x > 600$ and $x + 2y < 600$ IV
   c. $y + 2x < 600$ and $x + 2y > 600$ I
   d. $y + 2x > 600$ and $x + 2y > 600$ II

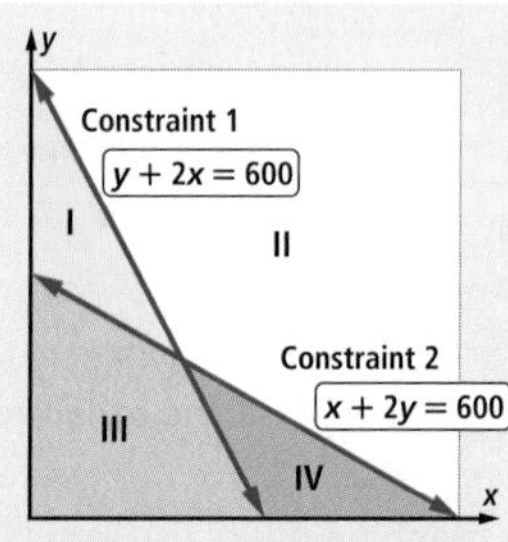

In 7 and 8, refer to Example 1.

7. How much profit will the company make if it sells
   a. 50 plasma sets and 40 projection TVs? $160,000
   b. 20 plasma sets and 40 projection TVs? $100,000
   c. 50 plasma sets and 5 projection TVs? $107,500
8. Will the firm meet its goal of surpassing a $100,000 profit if it sells 11 plasma sets and 45 projection TVs? no

Most projection TVs are rear-projection systems; the image is displayed on the back of the screen and the projector is contained in the TV.

Accommodating the Learner

Give students the diagram at the right. Alternatively, have them graph a triangle with vertices (0, 6), (6, 0), and (4, -2) and shade the interior. Explain that the shaded region is a feasible region for a system. Have them write a system whose solution set is this feasible region.

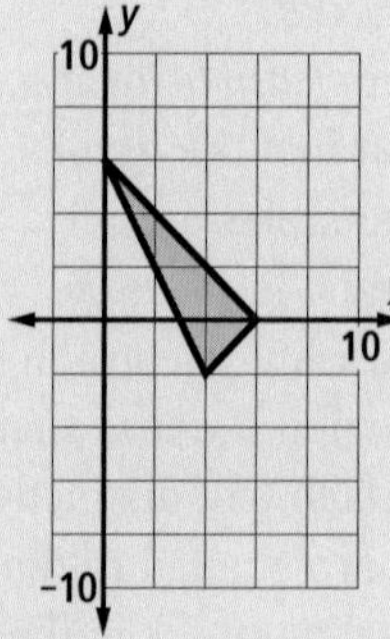

Answers vary. Sample: $\begin{cases} x + y \leq 6 \\ x - y \leq 6 \\ 2x + y \geq 6 \end{cases}$

In 9 and 10, a system of inequalities is given.

a. Graph the solution set. 9a, 10a. See margin.

b. Find the coordinates of each vertex of the feasible region.

9. $\begin{cases} y \le 2x + 3 \\ y > -3x - 4 \end{cases}$

10. $\begin{cases} x + 2y \le 16 \\ 3x + y < 18 \\ y \le 7 \\ x \ge 0 \end{cases}$

9b. (-1.4, 0.2)

10b. (2, 7), (4, 6), (0, 7)

APPLYING THE MATHEMATICS

11. A school's film club shows movies after school and sells popcorn in small and large sizes. The bags cost \$0.15 for a small and \$0.20 for a large. A small bag holds 1.25 ounces of popcorn; a large bag holds 2.5 ounces of popcorn. The club has 400 ounces of popcorn and a budget of \$40 for popcorn bags.

   a. **Fill in the Blanks** Let S be the number of small bags and L be the number of large bags. Complete the translation of this situation into a system of inequalities.

   $$\begin{cases} S \ge \underline{\ ?\ }\ 0 \\ L \ge \underline{\ ?\ }\ 0 \\ 0.15S + 0.2L \le \underline{\ ?\ }\ 40 \\ \underline{\ ?\ } \le 400 \quad 1.25S + 2.5L \end{cases}$$

   b. Graph the feasible region of points (S, L) for this system and label the vertices. See margin.

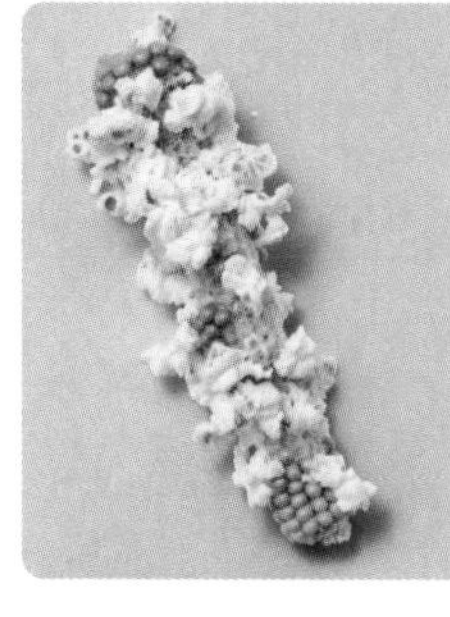

Americans consume an average of 17.3 billion quarts of popcorn each year.

12. Graph the solutions to the system $\begin{cases} y < 2x + 4 \\ 4x - 2y \le 6 \end{cases}$. See margin.

13. In his shop, Hammond Wrye makes two kinds of sandwiches: plain turkey and turkey-and-cheese. Each sandwich uses 2 pieces of bread. The plain turkey sandwiches use 3.5 ounces of turkey, while the turkey-and-cheese sandwiches use 2.5 ounces of turkey and 1 slice of cheese. Hammond has 100 slices of bread, 40 slices of cheese, and 150 ounces of turkey. Let x be the number of turkey-and-cheese sandwiches and y be the number of plain turkey sandwiches he makes.

   a. Translate the situation into a system of inequalities.

   b. Graph the feasible set for this system, and label the vertices. See margin.

13a.

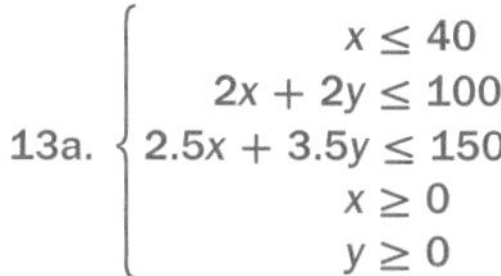

$$\begin{cases} x \le 40 \\ 2x + 2y \le 100 \\ 2.5x + 3.5y \le 150 \\ x \ge 0 \\ y \ge 0 \end{cases}$$

14. Refer to Example 1. Suppose it takes 30 worker-hours to make a plasma TV and 25 worker-hours to make a projection TV. If the company has 15,000 worker-hours available, can it make its desired profit of \$100,000? Explain your answer. See margin.

Additional Answers

14. Yes; Answers vary. Sample: If the company makes 30 plasma TVs and 540 projection TVs, they will use 14,400 worker hours and make \$870,000.

Notes on the Questions

Question 11 and 13 Stress the importance of using a table to organize the information in each problem. Because mathematical prose is often very dense, a table helps students to separate and clarify the given information.

Additional Answers

11b.

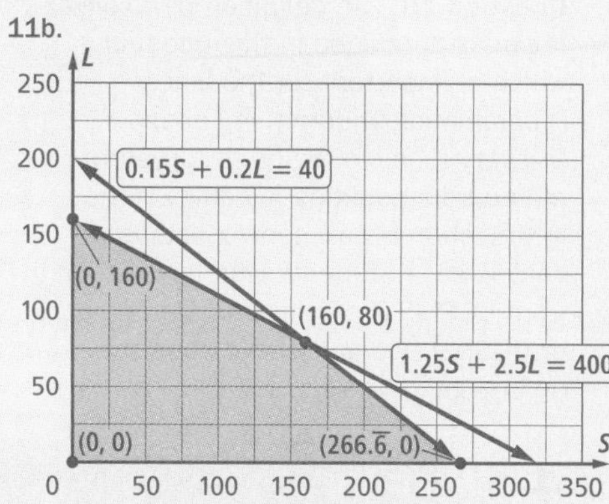

12.

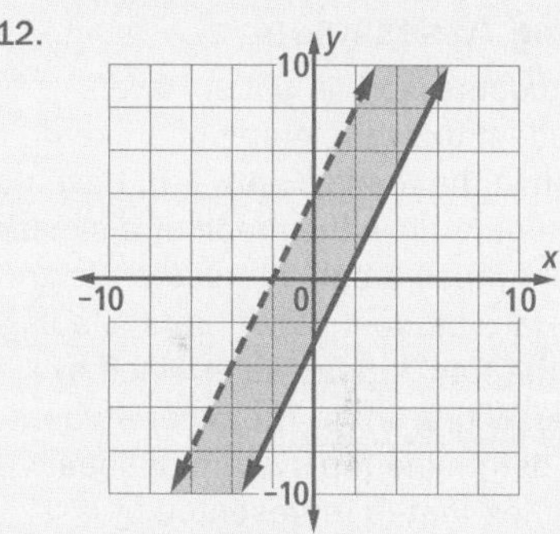

13b.

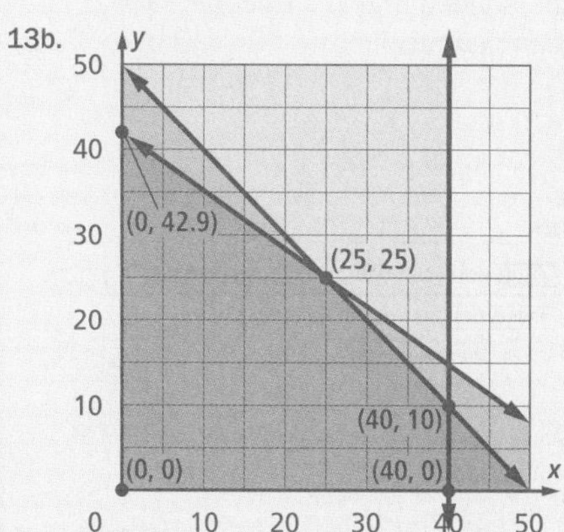

Ongoing Assessment

Questions 15 and 16 Focus on the difference between Questions 1–10, which cover the main ideas of the lesson, and these questions, which refer back to Lesson 5-7. Questions 15 and 16 each deal with one linear inequality, whereas Questions 1–10 deal with systems of inequalities.

Question 18 The definition of a *convex region* is contained in this question, which is important for the Linear-Programming Theorem in Lesson 5-9. Every feasible region to a system of linear inequalities is convex. (The intersection of two convex sets is a convex set.) Students who have studied from UCSMP *Pre-Transition Mathematics* or UCSMP *Geometry* have seen this definition.

4 Wrap-Up

Ongoing Assessment

Have students work in pairs. Have one student draw the graph of a linear equation in the form $y = mx + b$. Have the other student draw the graph of a similar equation whose graph intersects the first graph. Have students take turns shading one of the four regions determined by the intersecting lines. The other student should determine the system of linear inequalities that is represented by the shaded region. Students should demonstrate that they understand the graphing technique for finding the intersection of the solution sets of two linear inequalities.

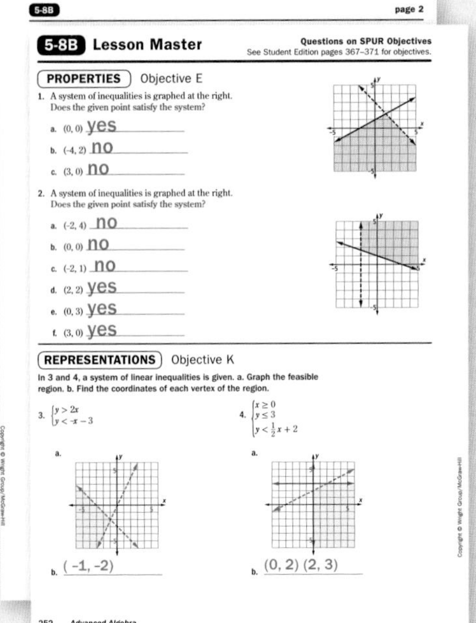
5-8B page 2

5-8B Lesson Master Questions on SPUR Objectives
See Student Edition pages 367–371 for objectives.

PROPERTIES Objective E

1. A system of inequalities is graphed at the right. Does the given point satisfy the system?
   a. (0, 0) yes
   b. (-4, 2) no
   c. (3, 0) no

2. A system of inequalities is graphed at the right. Does the given point satisfy the system?
   a. (-2, 4) no
   b. (0, 0) no
   c. (-2, 1) no
   d. (2, 2) yes
   e. (0, 3) yes
   f. (3, 0) yes

REPRESENTATIONS Objective K

In 3 and 4, a system of linear inequalities is given. a. Graph the feasible region. b. Find the coordinates of each vertex of the region.

3. $\begin{cases} y > 2x \\ y < -x - 3 \end{cases}$
   a.
   b. (−1, -2)

4. $\begin{cases} x \geq 0 \\ y \leq 3 \\ y < \frac{1}{2}x + 2 \end{cases}$
   a.
   b. (0, 2) (2, 3)

Copyright © Wright Group/McGraw-Hill

252 Advanced Algebra

REVIEW

In 15 and 16, graph the inequality. (Lesson 5-7) See margin.

15. $y \leq -4x + 3$

16. $3x - 2y > 14$

17. **True or False** If the coefficient matrix of a system has determinant zero, then the system has no solutions. **(Lesson 5-6)** false

18. Recall from geometry that a region of the plane is said to be *convex* if and only if any two points of the region can be connected by a line segment which is itself entirely within the region. The pentagonal region at the right is convex, but the quadrilateral region is not.

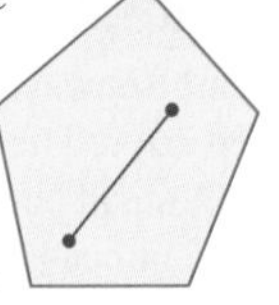

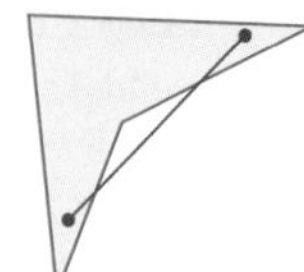

Tell whether the shaded region is convex. **(Previous Course)**

a.

b.

c.

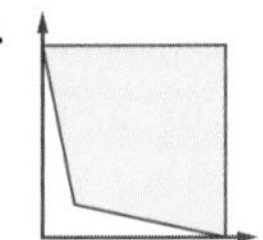

d.

18a. yes
18b. no
18c. yes
18d. yes

19. Cesar runs for x to $x + 5$ minutes every Tuesday. Every year has either 365 or 366 days in it (depending on whether or not it is a leap year). What are the minimum and maximum amounts of time Cesar could spend on his weekly runs in any given year? **(Previous Course)** $52x$ to $53x + 265$ min

EXPLORATION

20. Consider the system $\begin{cases} x > 0 \\ y > 0 \\ y < mx + b \end{cases}$.
    a. For what values of m and b is the graph of the solution set to this system the interior of a triangle? $m < 0, b > 0$
    b. Find the area of the triangle in terms of m and b. $A = -\frac{b^2}{2m}$

QY ANSWER

A, D, and E

Additional Answers

15.

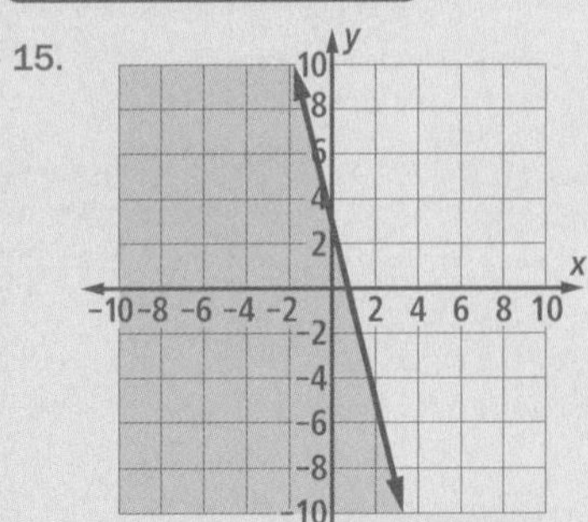

16.

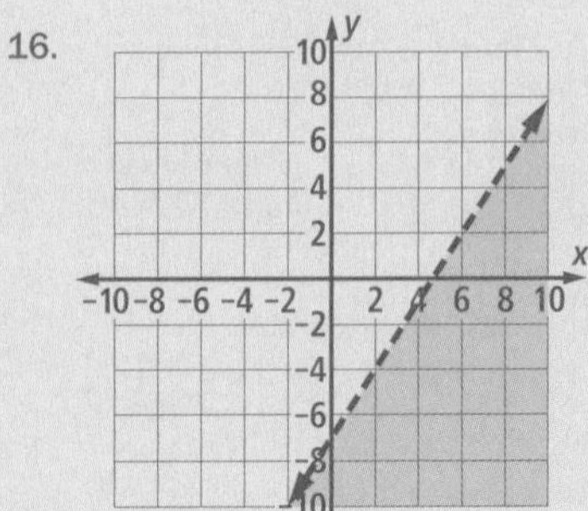

Lesson 5-9 Linear Programming

Vocabulary

linear-programming problem

▸ **BIG IDEA** A *linear-programming problem* is one in which you wish to find a solution to a system of inequalities that minimizes or maximizes a linear combination of the variables.

In Lesson 5-8, you graphed a system of linear inequalities to see the numbers of tables and chairs that could be made from a certain set of blocks. In this lesson, we consider combinations of actual tables and chairs that a furniture maker, Tim Burr, can build under the same constraints:

$$\begin{cases} 2T + C \leq 12 \\ 2T + 2C \leq 16 \\ T \geq 0 \\ C \geq 0 \end{cases}$$

Suppose that Tim earns \$900 for each table and \$600 for each chair he makes and sells. Under these constraints and assuming that Tim sells all the tables and chairs that he makes, how many of each should he produce to maximize revenue?

If T tables and C chairs are sold, the revenue R in dollars is given by the formula

$$900T + 600C = R.$$

For instance, suppose 3000 is substituted for R in the formula. The solutions (T, C) to $900T + 600C = 3000$ are ordered pairs that represent combinations of tables and chairs that will yield \$3000 in earnings. Two such solutions are (2, 2) and (0, 5). This means that Tim could make 2 tables and 2 chairs, or 0 tables and 5 chairs, and he would earn \$3000.

The feasible set for Tim's system of inequalities is the set of lattice points in the shaded region of the graph on the next page. The graph also includes the line for a \$3000 revenue and five other revenue lines that result from substituting different values of R into the revenue formula. Notice that all lines with equations of the form $900T + 600C = R$ are parallel because each has a slope of -1.5.

Mental Math

Suppose a cleaning service charges a flat rate of \$25 for the first hour plus \$10 for each additional half hour or part of a half hour. What would the cleaning service charge if the time spent cleaning were

a. 2 hours? \$45

b. 1 hour and 35 minutes? \$45

c. 3 hours and 15 minutes? \$75

d. 4 hours and 5 minutes? \$95

Background

In Lesson 5-8, the situations presented to students led to a set of inequalities. In this lesson, students must translate a given situation into a system of inequalities that represent the constraints of the problem and an expression to be maximized or minimized for solving the problem. Initially, linear-programming problems may seem formidable to students. However, when students realize how the mathematics they know can be applied to solve such seemingly complex problems, they usually enjoy such problems.

The Linear-Programming Theorem gives a numerical shortcut for finding the maximum or minimum value of an expression without having to graph a family of lines. The linear combination expression to be maximized or minimized is often called the *objective function.*

(continued on next page)

Lesson 5-9

GOAL

Solve a linear-programming problem from scratch, given adequate information in prose.

SPUR Objectives

E Recognize properties of systems of inequalities.

G Solve problems using linear programming.

Materials/Resources

- Lesson Masters 5-9A and 5-9B
- Resource Masters 92 and 93
- CAS

HOMEWORK

Suggestions for Assignment

- Questions 1–18
- Question 19 (extra credit)
- Self-Test

Local Standards

1 Warm-Up

Consider the situation of the Warm-Up on page 348. If Ellen correctly answers every question that she finishes, and if short-answer questions are worth 3 points each and essay questions 8 points each, what strategy should she use to maximize her score? The possible values of (s, e) are the points on and in the interior of the convex polygonal region that is the intersection of the solution sets to the inequalities $2s + 15e \leq 90$, $0 \leq s \leq 20$, and $0 \leq e \leq 6$. Test points in this region to find Ellen's score if she answers these numbers of questions. She can get the highest score if she answers 20 short answer questions and 3 essay questions.

2 Teaching

Notes on the Lesson

Generally one wishes to maximize profit or minimize cost in a linear-programming situation. Most of the lesson deals with maximizing profit. Questions 9b and 12 involve minimizing cost.

We suggest that you do the Warm-Up on page 355. Then review the furniture situation and the Example with students.

Before class, investigate how your graphing utility handles the intersection of several inequalities. For example, your graphing utility output may be difficult to read when you are looking for the feasible region; in such cases, graphing by hand may be the better option. Software exists that will solve linear-programming problems. You might wish to demonstrate such software; in the business world, virtually all linear-programming problems are solved with software.

It is possible that the boundaries of the feasible region intersect in a point that is not a lattice point. Then you need to check all nearby lattice points in the feasible region for a point that might maximize or minimize the expression that needs to be optimized.

Some of these lines intersect the feasible region and some do not. Lines such as L_3 and L_4 that do intersect the feasible region indicate possible revenues. The highest revenue line that intersects the feasible region represents the greatest possible revenue. This is the line L_3, where the revenue line passes through vertex (4, 4). So, to maximize revenue, Tim should make 4 tables and 4 chairs each week. The maximum revenue under these conditions is $900 \cdot 4 + 600 \cdot 4 = \$6000$.

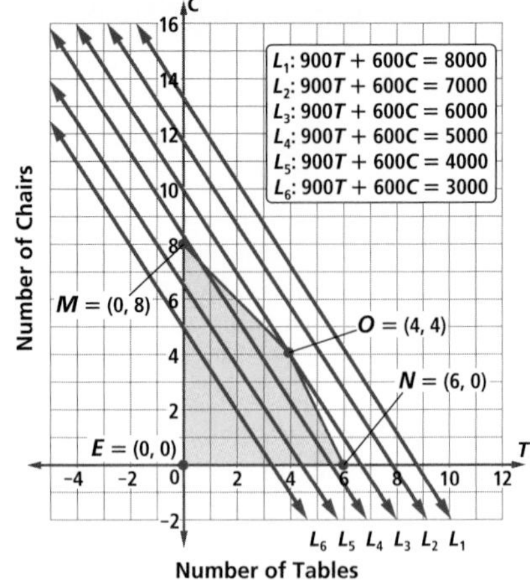

Problems such as this one, that involve wanting to maximize or minimize a quantity based on solutions to a system of linear inequalities, are called **linear-programming problems**. The word *programming* does not refer to a computer; it means that the solution gives a program, or course of action, to follow.

In 1826, the French mathematician Jean-Baptiste Joseph Fourier proved the following theorem. It tells you where to look for the greatest or least value of a linear-combination expression in a linear-programming situation, without having to draw any lines through the feasible region.

Linear-Programming Theorem

The feasible region of every linear-programming problem is convex, and the maximum or minimum quantity is determined at one of the vertices of this feasible region.

Linear programming is often used in industries in which all the competitors make the same product (such as gasoline, paper, appliances, clothing, and so on). Their efficiency in the use of labor and materials greatly affects their profits. These situations can involve as many as 5000 variables and 10,000 inequalities.

Testing vertices is a good solution method for problems involving a few constraints and only two variables. There are procedures for solving large linear-programming problems such as the *simplex algorithm* invented in 1947 by the mathematician George Dantzig, who worked on it with the econometrician Leonid Hurwicz, and the mathematician T.C. Koopmans, all from the United States. It is for this work, as well as other contributions, that Koopmans shared the Nobel Prize in 1975.

The Nobel Prize medal is made of 18-karat green gold plated with 24-karat gold.

Linear-programming problems take a long time to do. We suggest giving no more than two such problems in an assignment, though you may wish to assign other questions at the same time. It is not uncommon to spend 2 days on this lesson.

Accommodating the Learner

Point out to students that linear-programming problems often fall into two categories. In one type, the objective is to maximize revenue and profits, as in the Example and the Activity. In the other type, the objective is to minimize costs, as in Questions 9b and 12. You may want to have students work in pairs or small groups to write the appropriate inequalities needed to complete the questions in this lesson.

Example

For a certain company, a bed sheet requires 2 pounds of cotton, 9 minutes of dyeing time, and 2 minutes of packaging time. A set of pillowcases requires 1 pound of cotton, 1.5 minutes of dyeing time, and 7.25 minutes of packaging time. Each day, the company has available 110 pounds of cotton, 405 minutes of dyeing time, and 435 minutes of packaging time.

a. Let b = the number of bed sheets made per day and p = the number of sets of pillowcases made per day. Find the vertices of the region of pairs (b, p) the company can make.

b. The company's daily revenue will be \$12 for each sheet and \$8 for each set of pillowcases. Assuming they sell everything they make, how many of each product should the company produce per day to maximize revenue?

Solution

a. From the given information, write the constraints.

Available cotton: $2b + p \le 110$

Dyeing time: $9b + 1.5p \le 405$

Packaging time: $2b + 7.25p \le 435$

$b \ge 0, p \ge 0$

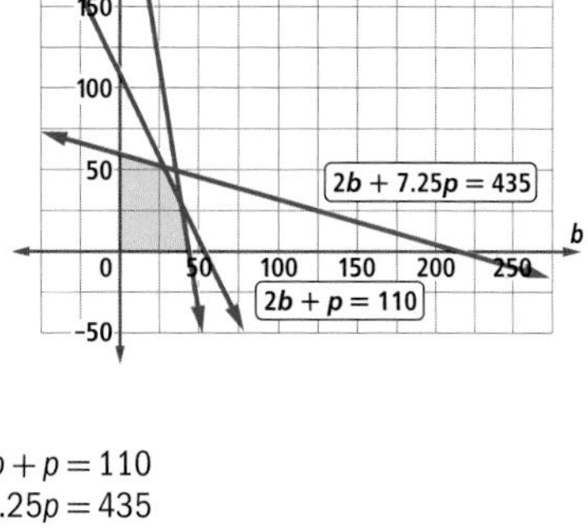

Graph the constraints. The graph at the right shows the feasible region. Because of the Linear-Programming Theorem, the revenue will be maximized at one of the vertices of this region.

There are 5 vertices to consider for the solution of this linear-programming problem. Each of these vertices is the intersection of two lines and is the solution to one of the five systems shown below.

$$\begin{cases} p = 0 \\ 9b + 1.5p = 405 \end{cases} \quad \begin{cases} 2b + p = 110 \\ 9b + 1.5p = 405 \end{cases} \quad \begin{cases} 2b + p = 110 \\ 2b + 7.25p = 435 \end{cases}$$

$$\begin{cases} b = 0 \\ 2b + 7.25p = 435 \end{cases} \quad \begin{cases} b = 0 \\ p = 0 \end{cases}$$

Use solve to find each vertex (b, p).

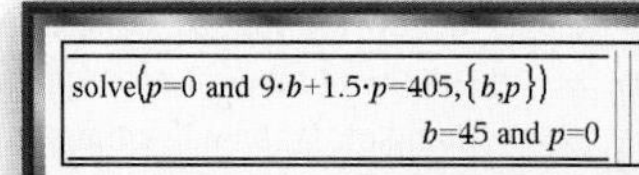

The vertices are (45, 0), (40, 30), (29, 52), (0, 60), and (0, 0).

(continued on next page)

Additional Example

Example Lisa makes necklaces and bracelets in her spare time and sells all that she makes. Each week, she has 10,000 grams of metal and 20 hours (1200 minutes) to work. It takes 500 grams of metal for a necklace and 50 grams for a bracelet. Each necklace takes 30 minutes to make, and each bracelet takes 15 minutes.

a. Let n = the number of necklaces and b = the number of bracelets Lisa makes each week. Find the vertices of the region of pairs (n, b) Lisa can make each week. Draw a graph of the feasible region.
metal used: $500n + 50b \le 10{,}000$; time used: $30n + 15b \le 1200$; other constraints: $n \ge 0$; $b \ge 0$; the four vertices are (0, 0), (0, 80), (15, 50), and (20, 0).

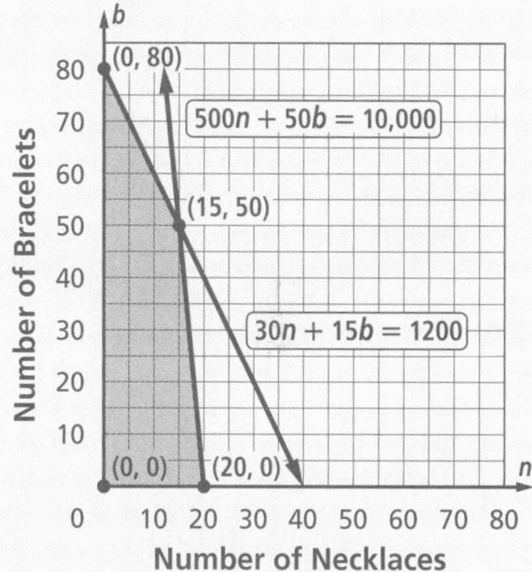

b. Lisa's weekly profit is \$8 on each necklace and \$5 on each bracelet. How many of each type of jewelry should Lisa make (and sell) each week to maximize her profit? A profit formula is $P = 8n + 5b$. At (0, 0), there is no profit. At (0, 80), the profit is \$400. At (15, 50), the profit is \$370. At (20, 0), the profit is \$160. The maximum weekly profit is \$320 when $n = 0$ and $b = 80$, that is, when Lisa makes 0 necklaces and 80 bracelets.

ENGLISH LEARNERS

Vocabulary Development

Students have been working with "programs" throughout their mathematical careers. The new concept here is linear programming. Focus on the *program* part of linear programming. Ask: What is a *program*? Answers vary. Sample: a course of action, computer software, a way to proceed Explain that linear programming is a method to solve systems of linear inequalities, which students did in Lesson 5-8. Alternatively, you may want to show a variety of programs (or schedules) that illustrate a process, such as the program from a musical or a schedule of classes.

Additional Answers

Activity

Step 1: $\begin{cases} 5x + 3y \le 115 \\ 2x + 6y \le 130 \\ 2.5x + 4y \le 120 \\ x \ge 10 \\ y \ge 1 \end{cases}$

Step 2:

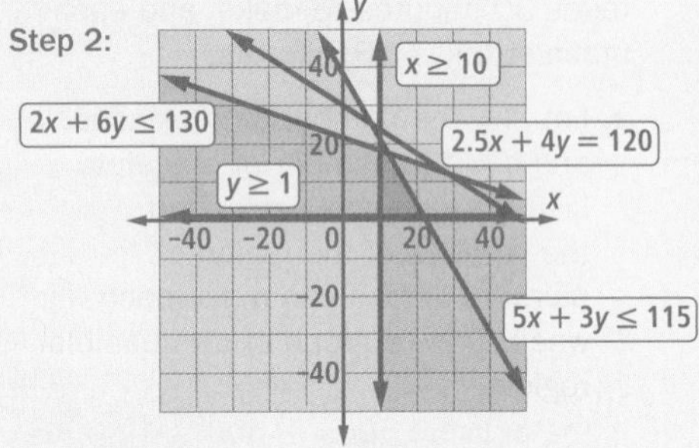

$2x + 6y = 130$; $5x + 3y = 115$;

$2x + 6y = 130$; $5x + 3y = 115$;

$2.5x + 4y \le 120$ does not help define the feasible region.

Step 5: $R_1 = 20(10) + 15(1) = 215$;
$R_2 = 20(10) + 15(18) = 470$;
$R_3 = 20(22) + 15(1) = 455$;
$R_4 = 20(12) + 15(17) = 495$

Step 6: To maximize profits, 12 centerpieces and 17 topiaries should be made. \$495 would be made from the sales.

b. The company wants to maximize daily revenue R. Because the company sells bed sheets for \$12 and sets of pillowcases for \$8, a revenue formula is $R = 12b + 8p$.

Use the Linear-Programming Theorem. The maximum value of R occurs at a vertex of the feasible region. Evaluate R at each vertex to see which combination of p and b gives the maximum revenue.

The maximum daily revenue of \$764 is obtained when b = 29 and p = 52, that is, when the company produces 29 bed sheets and 52 sets of pillowcases.

Define $f(b,p)=12\cdot b+8\cdot p$	Done
$f(45,0)$	540
$f(40,30)$	720
$f(29,52)$	764
$f(0,60)$	480
$f(0,0)$	0

Steps for Solving Linear-Programming Problems

The steps at the right are a good way to organize your work when solving a linear-programming problem. Use the steps in the following Activity.

LINEAR-PROGRAMMING PROBLEMS

1. Identify the variables and write a system of constraints.
2. Determine which intersections of lines define the vertices of the feasible region. (A sketch of the inequalities found in Step 1 may help.)
3. Find the vertices of the feasible region.
4. Write a formula or an expression to be maximized or minimized.
5. Apply the Linear-Programming Theorem.
6. Interpret the results.

Activity

MATERIALS CAS (optional)

A Prom Committee is responsible for prom decorations. There are two types of decorations needed; centerpieces for tables and topiaries for the dance floor. The committee decides to make its own decorations.

Each centerpiece requires 5 packages of artificial flowers and 2 twinkle lights; each topiary requires 3 packages of artificial flowers and 6 twinkle lights. A local florist helps out by donating 115 packages of artificial flowers and 130 twinkle lights.

Twenty prom committee members will meet for 6 hours to assemble the decorations, so they must complete the assembly job in 120 person-hours. Each centerpiece requires 2.5 hours, while each topiary requires 4 hours of labor. At least 10 centerpieces and at least 1 topiary will be needed.

After the prom, the committee plans on selling the decorations. Centerpieces will sell for \$20 each and topiaries will sell for \$15 each.

Step 1 *Identify the variables and write a system of constraints.* Let x = number of centerpieces and y = number of topiaries. Complete a table like the one at the top of the next page to organize the information. Then write three constraints that summarize the table, and two more that represent the minimum values for x and y. See margin.

Accommodating the Learner

Have pairs of students work together to write a real-world linear-programming problem similar to those in this lesson. Have them provide solutions to the problem and share their work with the rest of the class. Answers vary. Check students' work.

	Number of Centerpieces (x)	Number of Topiaries (y)	Constraint Value
No. of packages of flowers	? $5x$	? $3y$	115
No. of packages of twinkle lights	? $2x$	? $6y$	? 130
No. of hours to make	? $2.5x$	? $4y$	? 120

Step 2 *Determine which intersections of lines define the vertices of the feasible region.* Make a sketch of the feasible region. There are four vertices of the feasible region, defined by the solutions of four systems. Fill in the blanks below to record the systems. Which constraint, if any, does not help define the feasible region? See margin.

$\begin{cases} x = 10 \\ y = 1 \end{cases}$ $\begin{cases} x = 10 \\ \underline{\quad ? \quad} \end{cases}$ $\begin{cases} y = 1 \\ \underline{\quad ? \quad} \end{cases}$ $\begin{cases} \underline{\quad ? \quad} \\ \underline{\quad ? \quad} \end{cases}$

Step 3 *Find the vertices of the feasible region.* Use a CAS to solve the four systems from Step 2.
The four vertices of the region are __?__, __?__, __?__, and __?__.

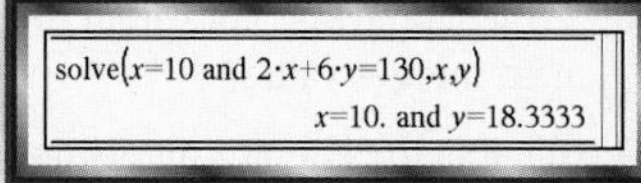

Step 3. (10, 1), (10, $\frac{55}{3}$), (22.4, 1), (12.5, 17.5)

Step 4 *Write a formula or an expression to be maximized or minimized.* Write an equation for the revenue R if all decorations made are sold. $R = 20x + 15y$

Step 5 *Apply the Linear-Programming Theorem.* Using your results from Steps 3 and 4, find the revenue for each vertex. Round vertex coordinates down because the committee cannot sell partial centerpieces or topiaries. See margin.

Step 6 *Interpret the results.* To maximize profits, how many centerpieces and topiaries should be made? What would be the maximum revenue from the sales? See margin.

Questions

COVERING THE IDEAS

1. Refer to the discussion of Tim Burr at the beginning of this lesson.
   a. What is Tim trying to maximize? How is it represented? revenue, $R = 900T + 600C$
   b. Find the revenue for making 5 tables and 1 chair. \$5100
   c. What do the coordinates of points with integer coordinates inside the feasible region represent? possible combinations of tables and chairs
   d. **True or False** The line $900T + 600C = 950$ intersects the feasible region. true

5-9

3 Assignment

Recommended Assignment

- Questions 1–18
- Question 19 (extra credit)
- Self-Test

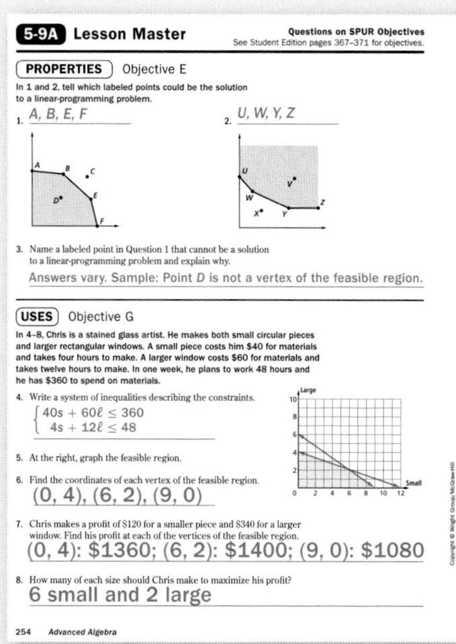

Notes on the Questions

Question 10 The context of this problem, diets, is a famous context for linear-programming problems. During World War II, the U.S. government searched for ways in which minimum daily amounts of vitamins and minerals could be achieved through varying kinds of foods. Linear-programming techniques were used to solve such diet problems.

Questions 10 and 11 These questions are scaffolded to provide direction to students as they work their way through the problems. Encourage them to do as complete a solution as possible on their own. Students already have all the tools to do these aids themselves, but we offer these aids to focus on the solution process, not the setup process.

Additional Answers

10a. Let A = apples, O = oranges;

$$\begin{cases} 10A + 600 \geq 1000 \\ 73A + 200 \geq 1000 \\ A \geq 0 \\ O \geq 0 \end{cases}$$

11a. Let M = trays of muffins, N = loaves of nut bread;

$$\begin{cases} \frac{9}{16}M + \frac{1}{2}N \leq 50 \\ \frac{3}{4}M + \frac{3}{4}N \leq 48 \\ \frac{3}{4}M + \frac{1}{6}N \leq 15 \\ M \geq 0 \\ N \geq 0 \end{cases}$$

11b.

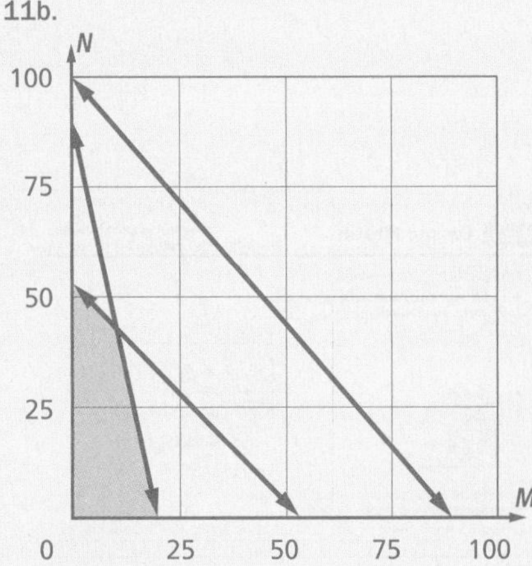

$\frac{9}{16}M + \frac{1}{2}N = 50$ is not a boundary of the feasible region. The feasible set is the set of lattice points in the shaded region.

11c. 53 loaves of nut bread and 0 trays of muffins

2. Refer to the Example.
   a. What does the linear combination R represent? daily revenue
   b. Why is the vertex (52, 29) a solution to the problem?
   c. Why is $p \geq 0$ and $b \geq 0$?
   d. Assume that the available cotton has changed from 110 pounds to 120 pounds. Write a new constraint for cotton. $2b + p \leq 120$
3. What does Jean-Baptiste Fourier have to do with the content of this lesson? He proved the Linear-Programming Theorem.
4. Why do industries test vertices of the feasible region of a system of inequalities? Answers vary. Sample: It provides a method for evaluating their efficiency and profits compared to their competitors.

In 5 and 6, refer to the Activity.

5. Write the coordinates of the vertex that maximizes revenue. What does this vertex mean for the committee?
6. Why should you not round the vertex values up to the next integer value?
7. What is the simplex algorithm?
8. Who developed the simplex algorithm, and when?
9. Use the feasible set graphed at the right.
   a. Which vertex maximizes the profit equation $P = 30x + 18y$? (7, 10)
   b. Which vertex minimizes the cost equation $C = 25x + 13y$? (1, 2)

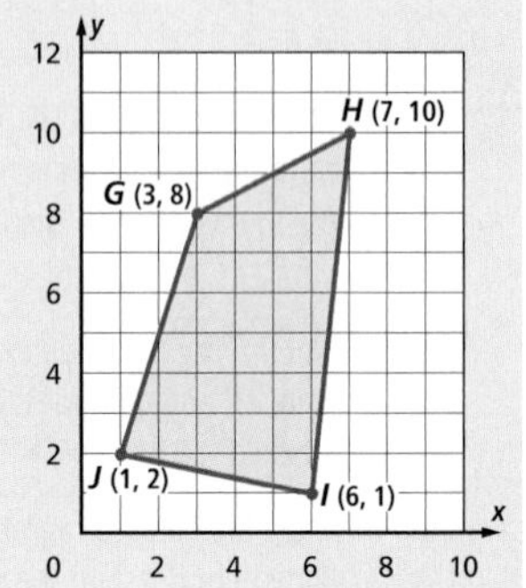

APPLYING THE MATHEMATICS

10. Apples and oranges can meet certain nutritional needs. Suppose a person needs to consume at least 1000 mg of calcium and at least 1000 IU (international units) of vitamin A each day. An apple has about 73 IU of vitamin A and 10 mg calcium and an orange has about 20 IU of vitamin A and 60 mg calcium. Suppose an apple costs 30¢ and an orange costs 45¢. You want to minimize costs, yet meet the nutritional needs.
    a. Identify the variables and constraints. Translate them into a system of inequalities. See margin.
    b. Use a CAS and find the vertices of the feasible region.
    c. Write the expression to be minimized. $0.30A + 0.45O$
    d. Find the number of apples and oranges that will minimize the cost. 10 apples and 15 oranges

2b. According to the Linear-Programming Theorem, the solution must be one of the vertices, and this vertex produced the highest revenue.

2c. Negative numbers of bed sheets and pillowcases cannot be produced.

5. (12, 17); It means that they should make 12 centerpieces and 17 topiaries.

6. The students would not be able to produce that many if the amount were rounded up.

7. a procedure for solving large linear programming problems

8. George Dantzig, Leonid Hurwicz, and T.C. Koopmans in 1947

10b. (9.57, 15.07), (0, 50), (100, 0)

Additional Answers

12a.

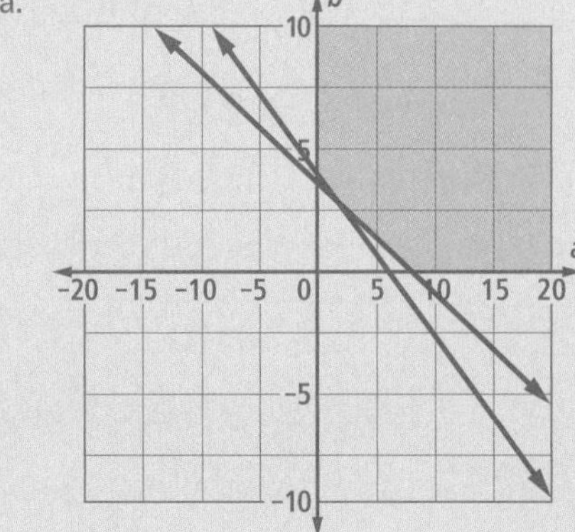

11. A muffin recipe uses $\frac{9}{16}$ pound of flour, $\frac{3}{4}$ pound of sugar, and $\frac{3}{4}$ pound of nuts to make 1 tray of muffins. A nut-bread recipe uses $\frac{1}{2}$ pound of flour, $\frac{3}{4}$ pound of sugar, and $\frac{1}{6}$ pound of nuts to yield 1 loaf of nut bread. Able Baker Carl has 50 pounds of flour, 40 pounds of sugar, and 15 pounds of nuts available.
    a. Identify the variables and constraints. Translate them into a system of inequalities.
    b. Sketch a graph of the feasible region. Which constraint from Part a is not a boundary of the feasible region?
    c. How many of each item should Carl make to maximize his revenue, if each tray of muffins sells for \$8.00 and each loaf of nut bread sells for \$12.00? 11a–c. See margin.

12. Landscaping contractor Pete Moss uses a combination of two brands of fertilizers, each containing different amounts of phosphates and nitrates as shown in the table. A certain lawn requires a mixture of at least 24 lb of phosphates and at least 16 lb of nitrates. If Pete uses a packages of Brand A and b packages of Brand B, then the constraints of the problem are given by the system of inequalities at the right.

	Brand A	Brand B
Phosphates (lb)	4	6
Nitrates (lb)	2	5

$$\begin{cases} a \geq 0 \\ b \geq 0 \\ 4a + 6b \geq 24 \\ 2a + 5b \geq 16 \end{cases}$$

    a. Graph the feasible region for this situation. See margin.
    b. If a package of Brand A costs \$6.99 and a package of Brand B costs \$17.99, which acceptable combination of packages (a, b) will cost Pete the least? (8, 0)

REVIEW

In 13 and 14, graph the solution set to the system. (Lesson 5-8) See margin.

13. $\begin{cases} y > 3 - x \\ y < x - 3 \end{cases}$ 14. $\begin{cases} x + y \geq 10 \\ x - y \leq 10 \end{cases}$

15. Write an inequality to describe the shaded region at the right. (Lesson 5-7) $y \geq -\frac{2}{3}x + 2$

In 16–18, consider the system $\begin{cases} A = s^2 \\ A + 2s = 8 \end{cases}$.

16. Solve the system by substitution. (Lesson 5-3)
17. Solve the system using a CAS. (Lesson 5-2)
18. Solve the system by graphing. (Lesson 5-1)

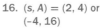

16. $(s, A) = (2, 4)$ or $(-4, 16)$
17. $(s, A) = (2, 4)$ or $(-4, 16)$
18. $(s, A) = (2, 4)$ or $(-4, 16)$

EXPLORATION

19. Suppose $a, b, c, d, e,$ and f are positive integers and $a + b + c + d + e + f = 1000$. What integer values of a, b, c, d, e and f will make the product $abcdef$
    a. as large as possible? 166, 166, 167, 167, 167, 167
    b. as small as possible? 1, 1, 1, 1, 1, 995

Notes on the Questions

Question 19 Because a product of numbers (rather than a linear combination) is to be maximized, this question is not a linear-programming situation. However, each part is an optimization problem. The problem may not be as difficult as it looks.

4 Wrap-Up

Ongoing Assessment

Have students write a paragraph explaining some of the techniques that they find useful in solving linear-programming problems. Students should write a meaningful paragraph that demonstrates an understanding of linear-programming techniques.

Project Update

Project 1, *Nutrition: Low Cost vs. Low Cal*, and Project 2, *Simplexes*, on page 362 relate to the content of this lesson.

Additional Answers

13.

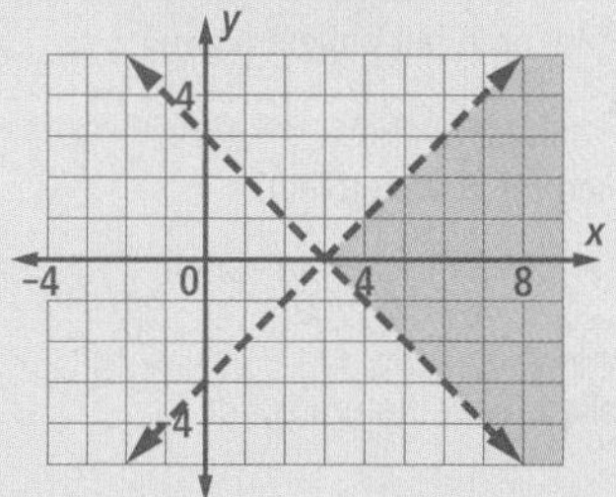

14.

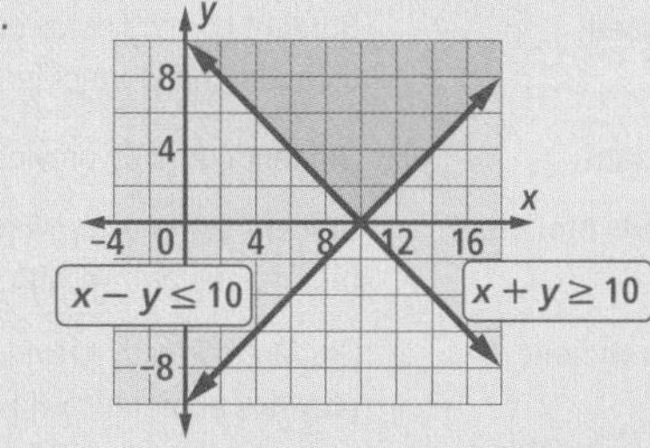

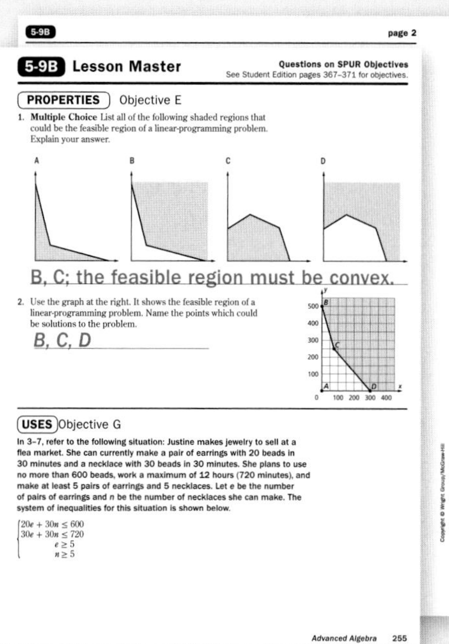

5-9B page 2

5-9B Lesson Master Questions on SPUR Objectives
See Student Edition pages 367–371 for objectives.

PROPERTIES Objective E

1. **Multiple Choice** List all of the following shaded regions that could be the feasible region of a linear-programming problem. Explain your answer.

A B C D

B, C; the feasible region must be convex.

2. Use the graph at the right. It shows the feasible region of a linear-programming problem. Name the points which could be solutions to the problem.

B, C, D

USES Objective G

In 3–7, refer to the following situation: Justine makes jewelry to sell at a flea market. She can currently make a pair of earrings with 20 beads in 30 minutes and a necklace with 30 beads in 30 minutes. She plans to use no more than 600 beads, work a maximum of 12 hours (720 minutes), and make at least 5 pairs of earrings and 5 necklaces. Let e be the number of pairs of earrings and n be the number of necklaces she can make. The system of inequalities for this situation is shown below.

$$\begin{cases} 20e + 30n \leq 600 \\ 30e + 30n \leq 720 \\ e \geq 5 \\ n \geq 5 \end{cases}$$

Advanced Algebra 255

Chapter 5

The projects relate to the content of the lessons of this chapter as follows:

Project	Lesson(s)
1	5-9
2	5-9
3	5-5
4	5-5
5	5-1

1 Nutrition: Low Cost vs. Low Cal

Students can find recommended daily dietary allowances in almanacs, health books, encyclopedias, and the Internet. You might want to have students prepare a report or a poster on their findings and share it with the class.

2 Simplexes

As an extension, have students use Internet or library resources to learn more about the originator of the simplex algorithm (George B. Dantzig). Suggest that students who complete this project present a short report to the class.

3 The Enigma Machine

The Enigma machine was the most sophisticated coding device ever used by its time, and the top mathematicians of Great Britain were employed to try to break it. It was broken when a decoding manual was found on a captured German vessel. The Allies never let the Germans know that this vessel had been captured and, until the end of the war, the Germans did not realize that their intelligence had been breached. The breaking of codes is so important to national security that the largest employer of Ph.D. mathematicians in the United States is the National Security Agency.

Chapter 5 Projects

1 Nutrition, Low Cost vs. Low Cal

a. Look up the Dietary Reference Intake (DRI) for protein, fiber, calcium, vitamin A, and vitamin C for a person of your age and gender.

b. Name two foods that contain these nutrients and find the cost and number of calories per serving for each food.

c. Use linear programming to find out how many servings of these foods you would need to eat each day in order to get the DRI of these nutrients at the lowest possible cost.

d. Use linear programming to find out how many servings of these foods you would need to eat each day in order to get the DRI of these nutrients with the fewest number of calories.

e. Compare and contrast the low-cost diet to the low-calorie diet.

2 Simplexes

What is a *simplex*? Describe how the simplex algorithm works.

3 The Enigma Machine

One of the biggest decoding breakthroughs of World War II was deciphering messages encoded by the German Enigma machine. Research the Enigma machine and the mathematicians associated with deciphering this code algorithm. Write a summary of your findings.

4 Using Matrices to Code and Decode Messages

Between 1929 and 1931, the mathematician Lester Hill devised a method of encoding messages using matrices. Every positive integer is assigned a letter according to the scheme:

$1 \rightarrow A, 2 \rightarrow B, 3 \rightarrow C, \ldots, 25 \rightarrow Y, 26 \rightarrow Z, 27 \rightarrow A, 28 \rightarrow B, \ldots$.

To encode or encipher a message, follow these steps:

Step 1 Put the numbers for the letters into 2×2 matrices: $\begin{bmatrix} \text{1st letter} & \text{2nd letter} \\ \text{3rd letter} & \text{4th letter} \end{bmatrix}$.

For instance, to encode the word FOUR, with $6 = F$, $15 = O$, $21 = U$, $18 = R$, use the matrix $\begin{bmatrix} 6 & 15 \\ 21 & 18 \end{bmatrix}$.

Project Rubric

Advanced	Student correctly provides all of the details asked for in the project as well as additional correct independent conclusions.
Proficient	Student correctly provides all of the details asked for in the project.
Partially proficient	Student correctly provides some of the details asked for in the project or provides all details with some inaccuracies.
Not proficient	Student correctly provides few of the details asked for in the project or provides all details with many inaccuracies.
No attempt	Student makes little or no attempt to complete the project.

Step 2 Choose a 2×2 matrix as a coding matrix, such as $\begin{bmatrix} 0 & 1 \\ 1 & 2 \end{bmatrix}$. Multiply each 2×2 matrix from Step 1 on the left by the coding matrix. For instance, $\begin{bmatrix} 0 & 1 \\ 1 & 2 \end{bmatrix}\begin{bmatrix} 6 & 15 \\ 21 & 18 \end{bmatrix} = \begin{bmatrix} 21 & 18 \\ 48 & 51 \end{bmatrix}$.

Step 3 Change the resulting matrices back to letters to write the coded message. In our example, since 21 = U, 18 = R, 48 = V, and 51 = Y, FOUR is encoded as URVY.

To decode or decipher a message, follow these steps:

Step 1 Break the message into groups of four letters and write as matrices using the corresponding numbers: $\begin{bmatrix} \text{1st letter} & \text{2nd letter} \\ \text{3rd letter} & \text{4th letter} \end{bmatrix}$.

Step 2 Find the inverse of the coding matrix and multiply each letter-group matrix by the inverse.

Step 3 Translate the resulting matrices back into letters to read the message. (Note that $0 \rightarrow$ Z, $-1 \rightarrow$ Y, $-2 \rightarrow$ X, and so on.)

a. Code MEET ME AT NOON using the coding matrix $\begin{bmatrix} 0 & 1 \\ 1 & 2 \end{bmatrix}$.

b. A message was encoded as YTKOFOTISBGVITWKOULO using the coding matrix $\begin{bmatrix} 0 & 1 \\ 1 & 2 \end{bmatrix}$. What was the original message?

c. Make up a coding matrix and a coded message of your own. (Note: In order for Hill's method to work, the determinant of your coding matrix must be 1 or -1.)

5 Programming and CAS

Many CAS programs use the words *and* and *or*. In the program below, X is assigned each value of 1 through 50 incrementally. The IF/THEN statements test if the value Y is in the appropriate interval for display. Research how your CAS can be used to run the following program.

```
For (X, 1, 50)
2X → Y
If Y > 50 and Y < 84
Then: Disp X
EndIf
EndFor
```

a. What numbers will be displayed when this program is run?

b. Explain why this program will display an arithmetic sequence.

c. What numbers will be displayed if the word AND in the program is changed to OR?

d. If the word AND in the third line is changed to XOR, the numbers displayed are (1, 2, 3, 4, …, 25, 42, 43, 44, …, 50). What do you think XOR means?

e. Change the line "`If Y > 50 XOR Y < 84`" so that the numbers displayed will be (1, 2, 3, 4, …, 12, 45, 46, 47, …, 50).

4 Using Matrices to Code and Decode Messages

Students should be able to find information on secret codes in the library or on the Internet. The book *Sophisticated Ciphers,* by Josephine P. Andree and Richard V. Andree (and later distributed by Mu Alpha Theta), explains in detail the use of matrices for codes.

5 Programming and CAS

If this particular program does not work exactly as shown here on a student's CAS, challenge the student to determine what changes may be necessary in the program.

Sample answers for projects are in the Solution Manual in Electronic Teacher's Edition.

Notes

Chapter 5

Summary and Vocabulary

The Summary gives an overview of the entire chapter and provides an opportunity for students to consider the material as a whole. Thus, the Summary can be used to help students relate and unify the concepts presented in the chapter.

Vocabulary words and symbols are listed by lesson to provide a checklist of concepts that students must know. Emphasize to students that they should read the vocabulary list carefully before starting the Self-Test on page 365–366. If students do not understand the meaning of a vocabulary word, they should refer back to the indicated lesson.

Theorems and Properties covered in the chapter are listed below the Summary with page references included to lead students back to the location in the chapter where the theorem or property is stated.

Additional Answers

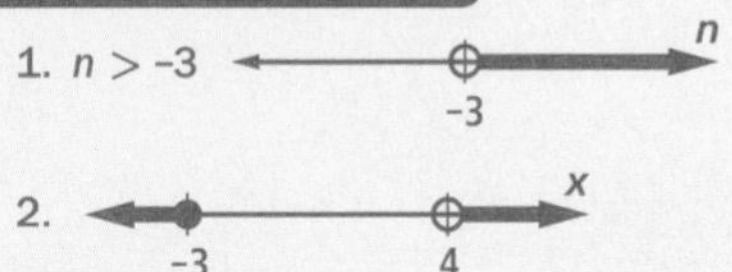

5. Substituting the first two equations into the third yields $3(q + 4) - 2(3q) = 3$, or $-3q + 12 = 3$, so $q = 3$. Substituting this value back into the first two equations gives $p = 3(3) = 9$ and $r = 3 + 4 = 7$. Thus, the solution to this system is $p = 9$, $q = 3$, and $r = 7$. Substituting these values back into the system of equations confirms this solution: $9 = 3 \cdot 3$; $7 = 3 + 4$; $3 \cdot 7 - 2 \cdot 9 = 3$.

Chapter 5 Summary and Vocabulary

- A **compound sentence** is the result of joining two or more sentences with the word *and* or *or*. The solution set for *A or B* is the **union** of the solution sets of *A* and *B*. The compound sentence *A and B* is called a **system.** The solution set to the system *A and B* is the **intersection** of the solution sets of *A* and *B*.
- Systems may contain any number of variables. If the system contains one variable, then its solutions may be graphed on a number line. If the system contains two variables, then its solutions may be graphed in the plane. The graph often tells you the number of solutions the system has, but may not yield the exact solutions.
- Systems of equations can be solved by hand or with technology. Some systems can be solved with tables and graphs. Algebraic methods use **linear combinations, substitution,** and matrices. The matrix method converts a system of *n* equations in *n* unknowns to a single matrix equation. To find the solution to a system in **matrix form,** multiply both sides of the equation by the **inverse** of the **coefficient matrix.**
- The graph of a linear inequality in two variables is a **half-plane** or a half-plane with its **boundary.** For a system of two linear inequalities, if the boundary lines intersect, then the **feasible region** is the interior of an angle plus perhaps one or both of its sides.
- Systems with two variables but more than two inequalities arise in **linear-programming problems.** In such a problem, you look for a solution to the system that maximizes or minimizes the value of a particular expression or formula.
- The Linear-Programming Theorem states that the feasible region of every linear-programming problem is always convex and that the solution that will maximize or minimize the pertinent expression must be a vertex of the feasible region.

Vocabulary

Lesson 5-1
compound sentence
double inequality
*union of two sets
*intersection of two sets

Lesson 5-2
system
*solution set of a system

Lesson 5-3
substitution method
consistent system
inconsistent system

Lesson 5-4
linear-combination method

Lesson 5-5
*inverse matrices
square matrix
singular matrix
*determinant

Lesson 5-6
matrix form of a system
coefficient matrix
constant matrix

Lesson 5-7
half-planes
boundary of the half-planes
lattice point

Lesson 5-8
feasible set, feasible region

Lesson 5-9
linear-programming problem

Theorems and Properties

Addition Property of Inequality (p. 303)
Multiplication Property of Inequality (p. 303)
Substitution Property of Equality (p. 314)
Inverse Matrix Theorem (p. 329)
System-Determinant Theorem (p. 338)
Linear-Programming Theorem (p. 356)

Additional Answers

6. Multiplying the first equation by 2, multiplying the second by 7, and subtracting yields $-53y = -74$, so $y = \frac{74}{53}$. Substituting this into either equation yields $x = \frac{38}{53}$. We can substitute to check: $7\left(\frac{38}{53}\right) + 5\left(\frac{74}{53}\right) = 12$ and $2\left(\frac{38}{53}\right) + 9\left(\frac{74}{53}\right) = 14$.

7a. $\begin{cases} H + P = 20 \\ 7.83H + 11.50P = 200 \end{cases}$; H is the number of pounds of organic hazelnuts, and P is the number of pounds of organic pecans.

7b. Solving the first equation for H and substituting into the second yields $7.83(20 - P) + 11.50P = 200$, so $P \approx 11.8$. The first equation then implies $H = 20 - P \approx 8.2$. Thus, about 11.8 lb of organic pecans must be mixed with about 8.2 lb of organic hazelnuts to obtain 20 lb of mixed nuts worth \$10/lb.

Chapter 5 Self-Test

Take this test as you would take a test in class. You will need a calculator. Then use the Selected Answers section in the back of the book to check your work.

1. Solve $-4n + 18 < 30$ and graph the solution set on a number line. See margin.
2. On a number line, graph $\{x | x \le -3 \text{ or } x > 4\}$. See margin.
3. A graph of the system $\begin{cases} y = 0.5x - 2 \\ y = -x^2 \end{cases}$ is shown below. Approximate the solutions to the system to the nearest tenth.

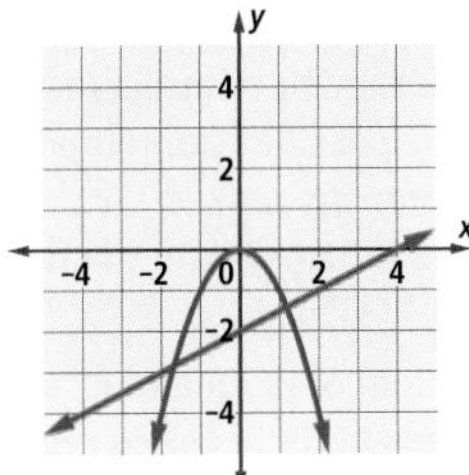

4. Consider the system $\begin{cases} x + 4y = 16 \\ 2x + 8y = 30 \end{cases}$. Is this system consistent or inconsistent? How do you know?

In 5 and 6, solve each system using an algebraic method and show how to check your answer.

5. $\begin{cases} p = 3q \\ r = q + 4 \\ 3r - 2p = 3 \end{cases}$ 5–6. See margin.
6. $\begin{cases} 7x + 5y = 12 \\ 2x + 9y = 14 \end{cases}$

3. Estimating the intersection points from the graph, the solutions are approximately (-1.7, -2.8) and (1.2, -1.4).
4. This system is inconsistent because there is no solution. The system describes two lines that do not intersect because they are parallel.

7. The Natural Nut Company sells organic nuts. How many pounds of organic hazelnuts priced at \$7.83 per pound should be mixed with organic pecans priced at \$11.50 per pound to obtain 20 pounds of mixed nuts priced at \$10 per pound?
   a. Write a system of equations representing this situation. Tell what each variable stands for in this problem.
   b. Solve the system and answer the question. 7a–b. See margin.
8. Consider the system $\begin{cases} 3x + 2y = 24 \\ -2x + 7y = 39 \end{cases}$.
   a. What is the coefficient matrix? $\begin{bmatrix} 3 & 2 \\ -2 & 7 \end{bmatrix}$
   b. Find the inverse of the coefficient matrix. 8b–c. See margin.
   c. Use a matrix equation to solve the system.
9. a. Give an example of a 2 × 2 matrix that does not have an inverse. Answers vary. Sample: $\begin{bmatrix} 1 & 1 \\ 1 & 1 \end{bmatrix}$
   b. How can you tell that the inverse does not exist? The determinant of the matrix is zero: (1)(1) − (1)(1) = 0.
10. Graph the solution set of $y > -\frac{5}{2}x - 2$.

First, graph the boundary $y = -\frac{5}{2}x - 2$ with a dotted line, then shade above it.

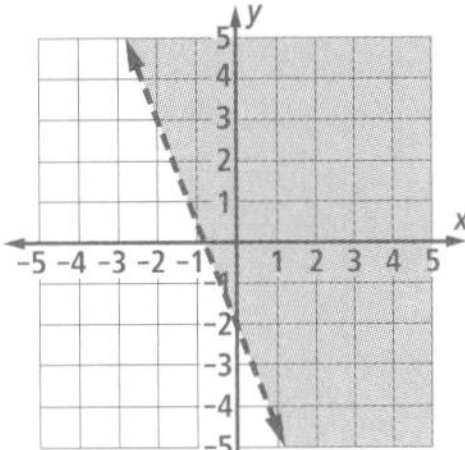

Self-Test

For the development of mathematical competence, feedback and correction, along with the opportunity for practice, are necessary. The Self-Test provides the opportunity for feedback and correction; the Chapter Review provides additional opportunities for practice. We cannot overemphasize the importance of these end-of-chapter materials. It is at this point that the material gels for many students, allowing them to solidify skills and understanding. In general, student performance should improve after these pages.

Assign the Self-Test as a one-night assignment. Worked-out solutions for all questions are in the Selected Answers section of the student book. Encourage students to take the Self-Test honestly, grade themselves, and then be prepared to discuss the test in class.

Advise students to pay special attention to those Chapter Review questions (pages 367–371) that correspond to the questions they missed on the Self-Test.

Additional Answers

8b. Because $(3)(7) - (2)(-2) = 25 \neq 0$, the Inverse Matrix Theorem says that the inverse of the coefficient matrix is $\begin{bmatrix} \frac{7}{25} & \frac{-2}{25} \\ \frac{2}{25} & \frac{3}{25} \end{bmatrix}$.

8c. $\begin{bmatrix} 3 & 2 \\ -2 & 7 \end{bmatrix}\begin{bmatrix} x \\ y \end{bmatrix} = \begin{bmatrix} 24 \\ 39 \end{bmatrix}$;

$\begin{bmatrix} \frac{7}{25} & \frac{-2}{25} \\ \frac{2}{25} & \frac{3}{25} \end{bmatrix}\begin{bmatrix} 3 & 2 \\ -2 & 7 \end{bmatrix}\begin{bmatrix} x \\ y \end{bmatrix} =$

$\begin{bmatrix} \frac{7}{25} & \frac{-2}{25} \\ \frac{2}{25} & \frac{3}{25} \end{bmatrix}\begin{bmatrix} 24 \\ 39 \end{bmatrix}$; $\begin{bmatrix} 1 & 0 \\ 0 & 1 \end{bmatrix}\begin{bmatrix} x \\ y \end{bmatrix} = \begin{bmatrix} \frac{18}{5} \\ \frac{33}{5} \end{bmatrix}$;

$x = \frac{18}{5}$; $y = \frac{33}{5}$

11. The graph below shows the feasible region for what system? $y < -x$ and $y \geq -2$

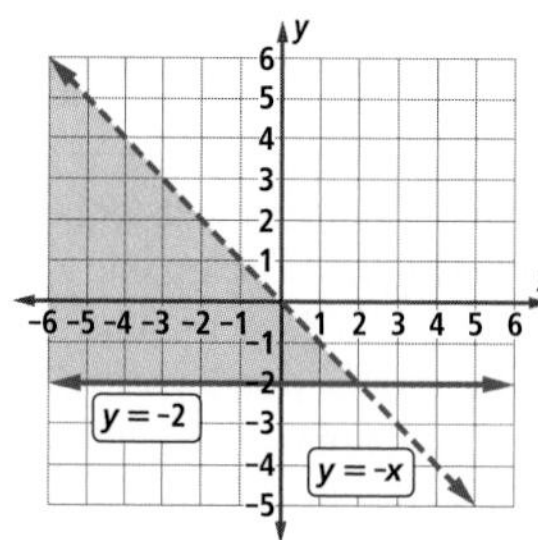

12. Tell whether the following points are solutions to the system from Question 11.
   a. (2.5, 3.2) no
   b. (-4, 0.5) yes
   c. (-2, 2) no

13a. $\begin{cases} \frac{1}{3}e + \frac{1}{6}c \leq 48 \\ \frac{1}{6}e + \frac{1}{3}c \leq 64 \\ e \geq 0 \\ c \geq 0 \end{cases}$

b. vertices: (0, 0); (0, 144); (160, 64); (192, 0)

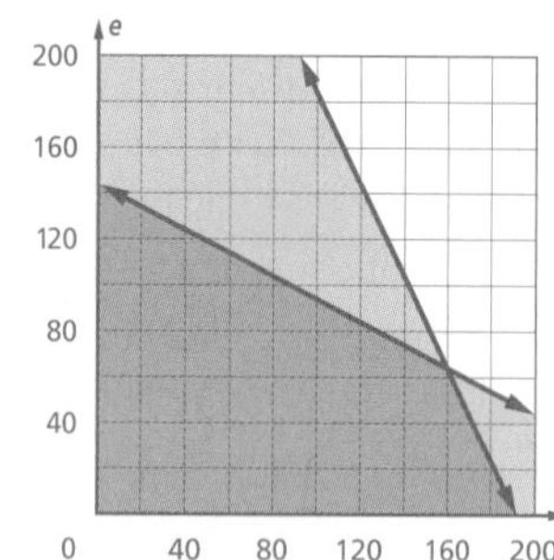

c. The Linear-Programming Theorem states that one of the vertices from Part b will maximize $15e + 12c = profits$. Substituting each vertex's values into this profit expression, we find that the company maximizes its profits at $2880 by making 160 Cool Contemporary shelves and 64 Olde English shelves.

13. Surehold Shelving Company produces two types of decorative shelves. The Olde English style takes 20 minutes to assemble and 10 minutes to finish. The Cool Contemporary style takes 10 minutes to assemble and 20 minutes to finish. Each day there are at most 48 worker-hours available in the assembly department and at most 64 worker-hours available in the finishing department. If Surehold Shelving makes a $15 profit on each Olde English shelf and a $12 profit on each Cool Contemporary shelf, how many of each shelf should the company make to maximize its profit?
   a. Let e = number of Olde English shelves and c = number of Cool Contemporary shelves the company makes. Translate the constraints into a system of linear inequalities.
   b. Graph the system of inequalities and find the vertices of the feasible region.
   c. Apply the Linear-Programming Theorem and interpret the results.

Additional Answers

9a. 4

9b. $\begin{bmatrix} \frac{1}{4} & 0 \\ 0 & 1 \end{bmatrix}$

10a. 16

10b. $\begin{bmatrix} \frac{1}{8} & -\frac{1}{8} \\ \frac{3}{16} & \frac{5}{16} \end{bmatrix}$

11a. 0

11b. does not exist

12a. $wz - xy$

12b. $\begin{bmatrix} \frac{z}{wz - xy} & \frac{-x}{wz - xy} \\ \frac{-y}{wz - xy} & \frac{w}{wz - xy} \end{bmatrix}$

16a. $\begin{bmatrix} -\frac{1}{18} & \frac{1}{9} & -\frac{1}{18} \\ \frac{1}{9} & -\frac{5}{9} & \frac{13}{9} \\ -\frac{1}{18} & \frac{7}{9} & \frac{31}{18} \end{bmatrix}$

Chapter 5 Chapter Review

SKILLS
PROPERTIES
USES
REPRESENTATIONS

SKILLS Procedures used to get answers

OBJECTIVE A Solve 2 × 2 and 3 × 3 systems using the linear-combination method or substitution. (Lessons 5-3, 5-4)

1. **Multiple Choice** After which of the following operations does the system $\begin{cases}-2x + 3y = 13\\ 6x + y = 5\end{cases}$ yield $20x = 2$? D
   A Multiply the first equation by 3 and add.
   B Multiply the second equation by 3 and add.
   C Multiply the first equation by -3 and add the second equation.
   D Multiply the second equation by -3 and add the first equation.

In 2–7, solve and check.

2. $\begin{cases}3z - 6w = 15\\ 0.5z - w = 22\end{cases}$
3. $\begin{cases}2x + 10y = 16\\ x = -3y\end{cases}$
4. $\begin{cases}r = s - 5\\ 2r - s = -3\end{cases}$
5. $\begin{cases}-7 = 2x + 6y\\ 0 = -4x - 8y + 22\end{cases}$
6. $\begin{cases}3r + 12t = 6\\ r = 2s\\ t = \frac{7}{12}s\end{cases}$
7. $\begin{cases}a = 2b - 4\\ b = 2c + 2\\ c = 4a + 6\end{cases}$

2–7. Checks are not shown.
2. no solutions
3. $x = -12, y = 4$
4. $r = 2, s = 7$
5. $x = \frac{47}{2}, y = -9$
6. $r = \frac{12}{13}, s = \frac{6}{13}, t = \frac{7}{26}$
7. $a = -\frac{8}{5}, b = \frac{6}{5}, c = -\frac{2}{5}$

8. Consider the system $\begin{cases}y = -3x\\ -5x + 3y = -28\end{cases}$.
   a. Which method do you prefer to use to solve this system, substitution or the linear-combination method? Answers vary. Sample: substitution
   b. Solve and check the system using your method from Part a. $-5x + 3(-3x) = -28$; $x = 2, y = -6$

OBJECTIVE B Find the determinant and inverse of a square matrix. (Lesson 5-5)

In 9–12, a matrix is given. 9–12. See margin.
a. Calculate its determinant.
b. Find the inverse, if it exists.

9. $\begin{bmatrix}4 & 0\\ 0 & 1\end{bmatrix}$
10. $\begin{bmatrix}5 & 2\\ -3 & 2\end{bmatrix}$
11. $\begin{bmatrix}2 & -2\\ 5 & -5\end{bmatrix}$
12. $\begin{bmatrix}w & x\\ y & z\end{bmatrix}$

13. Suppose $M = \begin{bmatrix}1 & 2\\ -5 & 3\end{bmatrix}$. Find M^{-1}. $\begin{bmatrix}\frac{3}{13} & -\frac{2}{13}\\ \frac{5}{13} & \frac{1}{13}\end{bmatrix}$

14. If the inverse of $\begin{bmatrix}a & b\\ c & d\end{bmatrix}$ does not exist, what must be true about its determinant? It must be equal to 0.

15. Explain why the matrix $\begin{bmatrix}3 & 1\\ 6 & 2\end{bmatrix}$ does not have an inverse. The determinant equals 0.

16. a. Find $\begin{bmatrix}-9 & 8 & 7\\ 6 & 5 & 4\\ 3 & 2 & 1\end{bmatrix}^{-1}$ using a calculator.
    b. Check your answer using matrix multiplication. 16a–b. See margin.

Chapter 5 Review

Chapter Review

The main objectives for the chapter are organized in the Chapter Review under the four types of understanding this book promotes: Skills, Properties, Uses, and Representations.

Whereas end-of-chapter material may be considered optional in some texts, in UCSMP *Advanced Algebra* we have selected these objectives and questions with the expectation that they will be covered. Students should be able to answer these questions with about 85% accuracy after studying the chapter.

You may assign these questions over a single night to help students prepare for a test the next day or you may assign the questions over a two-day period. If you work the questions over two days, we recommend assigning the evens for homework the first night so that students get feedback in class the next day, and then assigning the odds the night before the test because the answers are provided to the odd-numbered questions in the Selected Answers section at the back of the book.

It is effective to ask students which questions they still do not understand and use the day as a total class discussion of the material that the class finds most difficult.

Resources

- Assessment Resources: Chapter 5 Test Forms A–D; Chapter 5 Test, Cumulative Form

Technology Resources

Teacher's Assessment Assistant, Ch. 5
Electronic Teacher's Edition, Ch. 5

Additional Answers

16b. $\begin{bmatrix}-\frac{1}{18} & \frac{1}{9} & -\frac{1}{18}\\ \frac{1}{9} & -\frac{5}{9} & \frac{13}{9}\\ -\frac{1}{18} & \frac{7}{9} & \frac{31}{18}\end{bmatrix}\begin{bmatrix}-9 & 8 & 7\\ 6 & 5 & 4\\ 3 & 2 & 1\end{bmatrix} = \begin{bmatrix}-9 & 8 & 7\\ 6 & 5 & 4\\ 3 & 2 & 1\end{bmatrix}\begin{bmatrix}-\frac{1}{18} & \frac{1}{9} & -\frac{1}{18}\\ \frac{1}{9} & \frac{5}{9} & \frac{13}{9}\\ -\frac{1}{18} & \frac{7}{9} & \frac{31}{18}\end{bmatrix} = \begin{bmatrix}1 & 0 & 0\\ 0 & 1 & 0\\ 0 & 0 & 1\end{bmatrix}$

Additional Answers

17. $\begin{bmatrix}3 & -4\\4 & -6\end{bmatrix}\begin{bmatrix}x\\y\end{bmatrix}=\begin{bmatrix}12\\48\end{bmatrix}$; $\begin{bmatrix}x\\y\end{bmatrix}=\begin{bmatrix}-60\\-48\end{bmatrix}$

18. $\begin{bmatrix}4 & -2\\3 & 5\end{bmatrix}\begin{bmatrix}a\\b\end{bmatrix}=\begin{bmatrix}-3\\15\end{bmatrix}$; $\begin{bmatrix}a\\b\end{bmatrix}=\begin{bmatrix}\frac{15}{26}\\\frac{69}{26}\end{bmatrix}$

19. $\begin{bmatrix}2 & -5\\3 & -6\end{bmatrix}\begin{bmatrix}m\\n\end{bmatrix}=\begin{bmatrix}4\\-3\end{bmatrix}$; $\begin{bmatrix}m\\n\end{bmatrix}=\begin{bmatrix}-13\\-6\end{bmatrix}$

20. $\begin{bmatrix}3 & -4 & 2\\1 & 9 & 0\\2 & -3 & 6\end{bmatrix}\begin{bmatrix}x\\y\\z\end{bmatrix}=\begin{bmatrix}24\\6\\12\end{bmatrix}$; $\begin{bmatrix}x\\y\\z\end{bmatrix}=\begin{bmatrix}\frac{33}{4}\\-\frac{1}{4}\\-\frac{7}{8}\end{bmatrix}$

24a. inconsistent
24b. 0
25a. consistent
25b. 1
26a. consistent
26b. 1
27a. consistent
27b. 2
32a. Yes; the boundary going through (-2, 7) and (6, -2) has the equation $y = -\frac{9}{8}x + \frac{19}{4}$ and contains the point $\left(2, \frac{5}{2}\right)$. Because (2, 4) is above this point, it is a solution to the system of inequalities.
32b. No; the boundary going through (8, 9) and (6, -2) has the equation $y = \frac{11}{2}x - 35$ and contains the point (8, 9). Since (8, 2) is below (8, 9), this point is not a solution to this system of inequalities.
33a. Yes; this is a convex region.
33b. No; the region is not convex.
33c. Yes; the region is convex.
33d. No; the region is not convex.

OBJECTIVE C Use matrices to solve systems of two or three linear equations. (Lesson 5-6)

In 17–20, solve each system using matrices. See margin.

17. $\begin{cases}3x - 4y = 12\\4x - 6y = 48\end{cases}$

18. $\begin{cases}4a - 2b = -3\\3a + 5b = 15\end{cases}$

19. $\begin{cases}2m = 5n + 4\\3m = 6n - 3\end{cases}$

20. $\begin{cases}24 = 3x - 4y + 2z\\6 = x + 9y\\12 = 2x - 3y + 6z\end{cases}$

PROPERTIES Principles behind the mathematics

OBJECTIVE D Recognize properties of systems of equations. (Lessons 5-2, 5-3, 5-4, 5-6)

21. Are the systems $\begin{cases}7x - 3y = 7\\3x + 2y = 19\end{cases}$ and $\begin{cases}y = 5\\x + y = 8\end{cases}$ equivalent? Why or why not? No; they have different solutions.

22. Give the simplest system equivalent to $4x = 8$ and $x + y = 6$. $x = 2$ and $y = 4$

23. What is a system with no solutions called? an inconsistent system

In 24–27, a system is given.
a. Identify the system as inconsistent or consistent. See margin.
b. Determine the number of solutions. See margin.

24. $\begin{cases}2x + 7y = 14\\2x + 7y = 28\end{cases}$

25. $\begin{cases}6m - 2n = 7\\-3m = -2n - \frac{7}{2}\end{cases}$

26. $\begin{cases}4a - 5b = 20\\2a + 3b = -6\end{cases}$

27. $\begin{cases}r = -t^2\\r = t - 3\end{cases}$

28. For what value of k does $\begin{cases}3x + ky = 6\\15x + 5y = 30\end{cases}$ have infinitely many solutions? $k = 1$

29. Find a value of t for which $\begin{cases}2x + 8y = t\\3x + 12y = 7\end{cases}$ has no solutions. Answers vary. Sample: $t = 1$

30. Suppose the determinant of the coefficient matrix of a system of equations is not zero. What can you conclude about the system? The system has exactly one solution.

OBJECTIVE E Recognize properties of systems of inequalities. (Lessons 5-8, 5-9)

31. **True or False** The boundaries are included in the graph of the solution set of $\begin{cases}y > 5\\y < 6 - x\end{cases}$. false

32. A system of inequalities is graphed below. Tell whether the point is a solution to the system. Justify your answer. 32a–b. See margin.
a. (2, 4)
b. (8, 2)

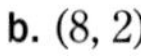

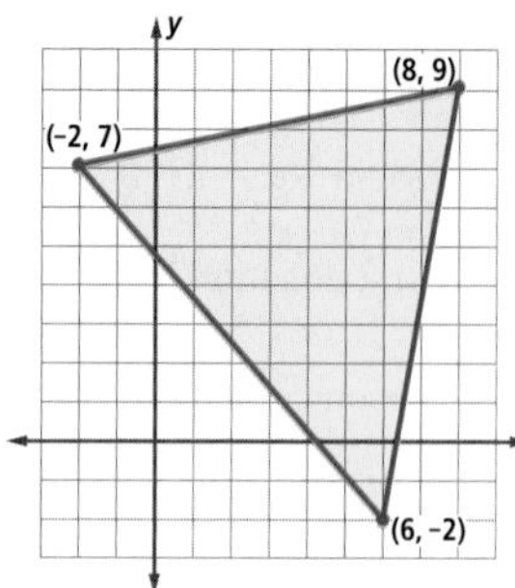

33. Tell whether the shaded region could be a feasible set in a linear-programming situation. Justify your answer. See margin.

a.
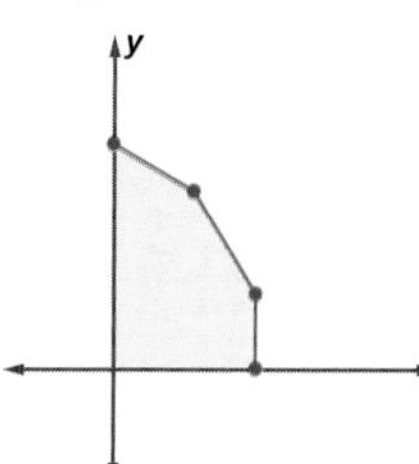

b.
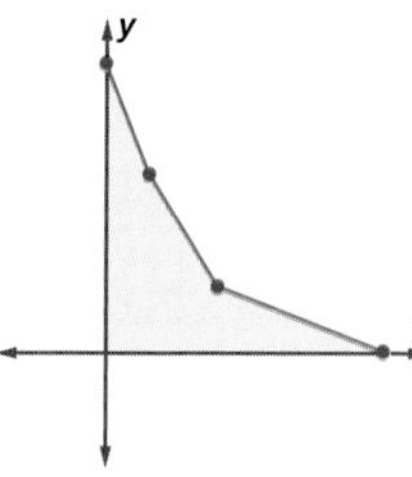

c.
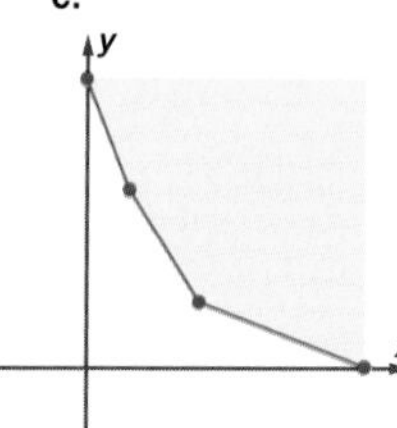

d.
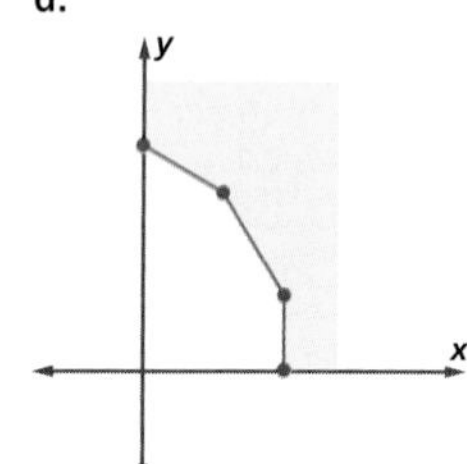

Additional Answers

41a. $\begin{cases}c \geq 0\\r \geq 0\\c \leq 30{,}000\\c + r \leq 40{,}000\\185c + 225r \leq 8{,}500{,}000\end{cases}$

41b.
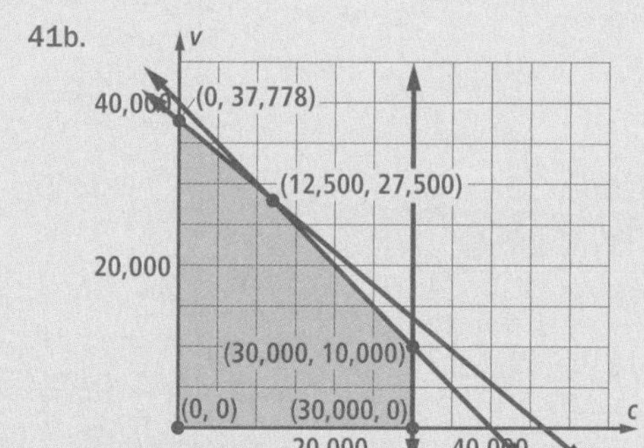

34. Where in a feasible set are the possible solutions to a linear-programming problem? at the vertices

35. Does the point *M* in the region below represent a possible solution to a linear programming problem? Why or why not? Yes; it is a vertex.

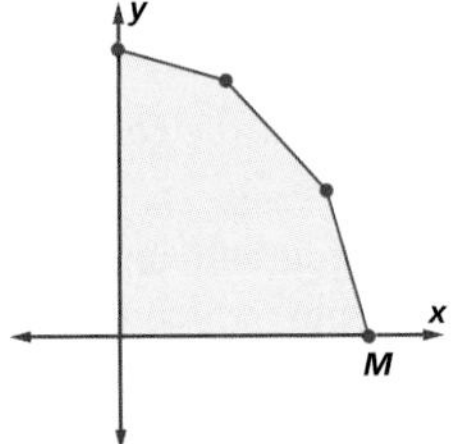

USES Applications of mathematics in real-world situations

OBJECTIVE F Use systems of two or three linear equations to solve real-world problems. (Lessons 5-2, 5-3, 5-4, 5-6)

36. A painter is creating a shade of pink by mixing 5 parts white for every 2 parts red. If 3 gallons of this shade are needed, how much white and how much red is needed?

37. To make longer dives, scuba divers breathe oxygen-enriched air. A diver wants to create a tank of air that contains 36% oxygen by combining two sources. The first source is standard compressed air that contains 20% oxygen. The second source contains 60% oxygen. What percent of each source will the diver need to put into the tank?

38. After three tests, Rachelle's average in math was 76. After four tests, her average was 81. If the teacher drops Rachelle's lowest test score, Rachelle's average will be 85. What was Rachelle's lowest test score? 69

39. A nutritionist plans a dinner menu that provides 5 grams of protein and 6 grams of carbohydrates per serving. The meat she is serving contains 0.6 gram of protein and 0.4 gram of carbohydrates per ounce. The vegetables have 0.2 gram of protein and 0.8 gram of carbohydrates per ounce. How many ounces of meat and how many ounces of vegetables will be in each serving? 7 oz of meat and 4 oz of vegetables

40. Molly Millions makes \$6000 per month, while Mike Myzer makes \$2800 per month. The following table shows average daily expenses for Molly and Mike. Both are paid on the first day of the month.

	Molly	Mike
Housing	\$127	\$28
Transportation	\$22	\$3
Food	\$21	\$6
Other	\$15	\$2

a. Who has more money left from their paycheck at the end of the month? Mike

b. On which day of the month do Mike and Molly have about the same amount left from their pay? the 22nd day

36. $\frac{15}{7}$ gal of white, $\frac{6}{7}$ gal of red

37. The tank must contain 60% from the first source and 40% from the second source.

Additional Answers

42a. h = ounces of hamburger;
p = number of medium potatoes

42b. $\begin{cases} 0.7h + 1.9p \geq 5 \\ 17.3p \geq 15 \\ 7.4h + 4.3p \geq 35 \\ h \geq 0 \\ p \geq 0 \end{cases}$

42c.

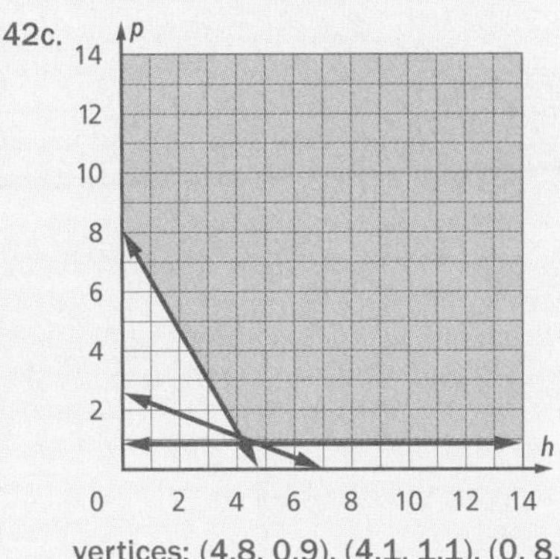

vertices: (4.8, 0.9), (4.1, 1.1), (0, 8.1)

42f. At one meal, 4.1 oz of hamburger and 1.1 potatoes per person give the proper nutrition for the lowest cost.

43a.

45. $x < -4$;

46. $n \geq 9$;

48.

49.

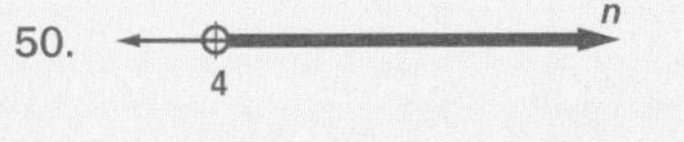

50.

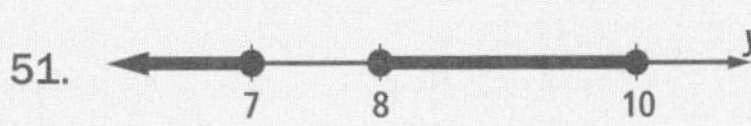

51.

53. (2.3, 4.1)

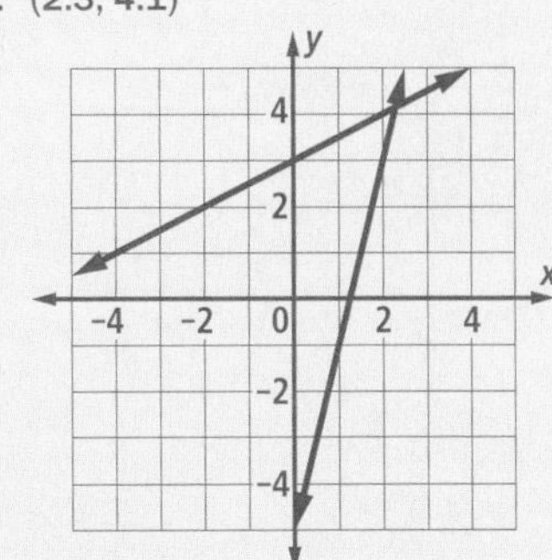

Additional Answers

54. (–1.1, 1.3), (2.6, 7.0)

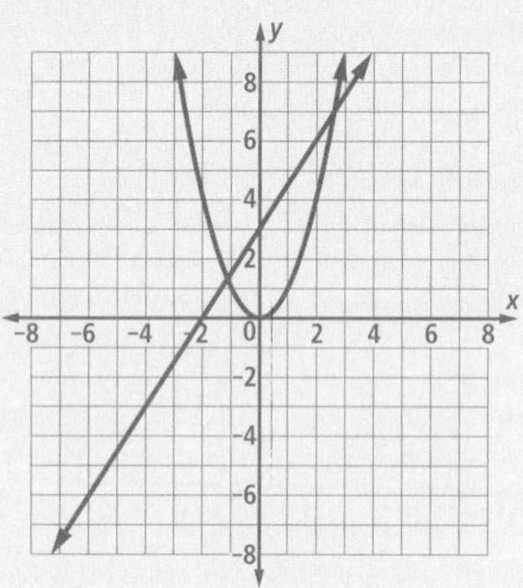

55. no solutions

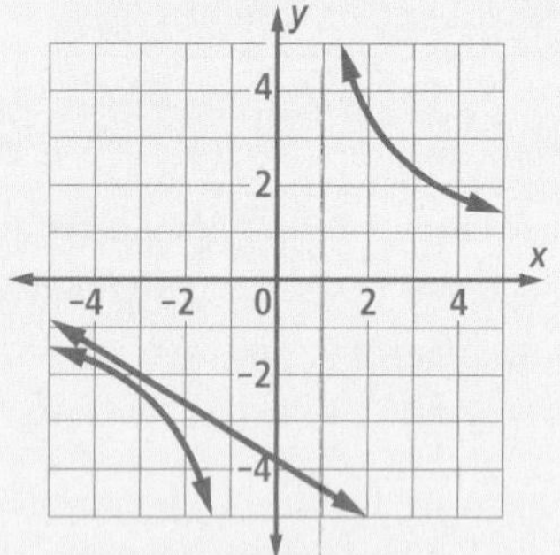

56.

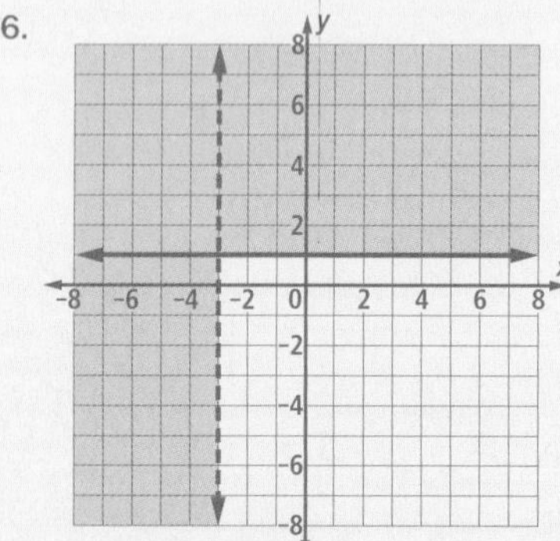

57.

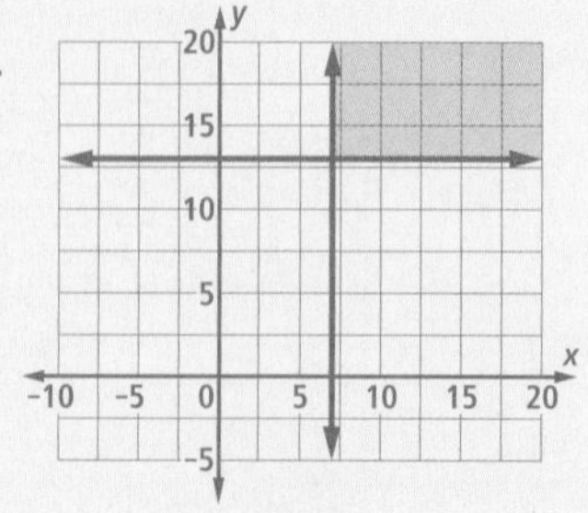

OBJECTIVE G Solve problems using linear programming. (Lesson 5-9)

41. A real estate developer is planning a building that will combine commercial space (offices and stores) with residential space. The total development will have 40,000 square feet. Construction costs are \$225 per square foot for residential space and \$185 per square foot for commercial space, and the developer has a construction budget of \$8,500,000. Zoning laws dictate that there be no more than 30,000 square feet of commercial space in the development. The developer plans to sell the property and anticipates a profit of \$70 per square foot for residential space and \$60 per square foot for commercial space.
    a. Let c = number of square feet of commercial space and r = number of square feet of residential space. Translate the constraints into a system of linear inequalities. See margin.
    b. Graph the system of inequalities and find the vertices of the feasible region. See margin.
    c. Find the solution (c, r) that maximizes profit. (12,500, 27,500)

42. Some parents shopping for their family want to know how much hamburger and how many potatoes to buy. From a nutrition table, they find that one ounce of hamburger has 0.7 mg of iron, 0 IU of vitamin A, and 7.4 grams of protein. One medium potato has 1.9 mg of iron, 17.3 IU of vitamin A, and 4.3 grams of protein. For this meal the parents want each member of the family to have at least 5 mg of iron, 15 IU of vitamin A, and 35 grams of protein. One potato costs \$0.10 and 1 ounce of hamburger costs \$0.15. The parents want to minimize their costs, yet meet daily requirements. What quantities of hamburger and potatoes should they buy for the family? 42a–c, f. See margin.
    a. Identify the variables for this problem.
    b. Translate the constraints of the problem into a system of inequalities. (You should have five inequalities; a table may help.)
    c. Graph the system of inequalities from Part b and find the vertices of the feasible region.
    d. Write an expression for the cost to be minimized. $C = 0.15h + 0.10p$
    e. Apply the Linear-Programming Theorem to determine which vertex minimizes the cost expression of Part d. (4.1, 1.1
    f. Interpret your answer to Part e. What is the best buy for this family?

REPRESENTATIONS Pictures, graphs, or objects that illustrate concepts

OBJECTIVE H Solve and graph linear inequalities in one variable. (Lesson 5-1)

43. Other weather conditions aside, the Space Shuttle will not delay or cancel a launch as long as the temperature is greater than 48°F and no more than 99°F.
    a. Graph the allowable launch temperatures. See margin.
    b. Write the set of allowable launch temperatures in set-builder notation. $\{t \mid 48 < t \le 99$

44. **Multiple Choice** Which inequality is graphed below? C

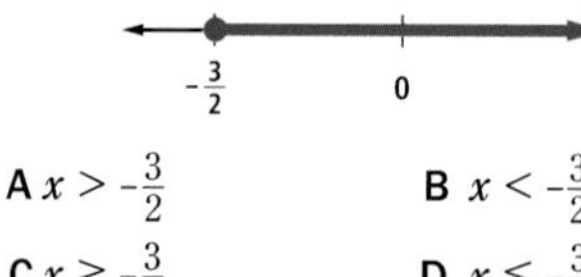

A $x > -\frac{3}{2}$ B $x < -\frac{3}{2}$
C $x \ge -\frac{3}{2}$ D $x \le -\frac{3}{2}$

In 45 and 46, solve the inequality and graph its solution set. See margin.

45. $-3x + 9 > 21$
46. $2n + 3(n - 12) \ge 9$

Additional Answers

58.

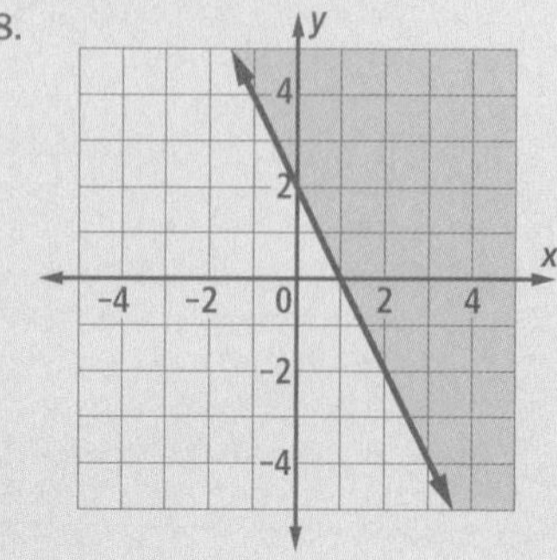

59.

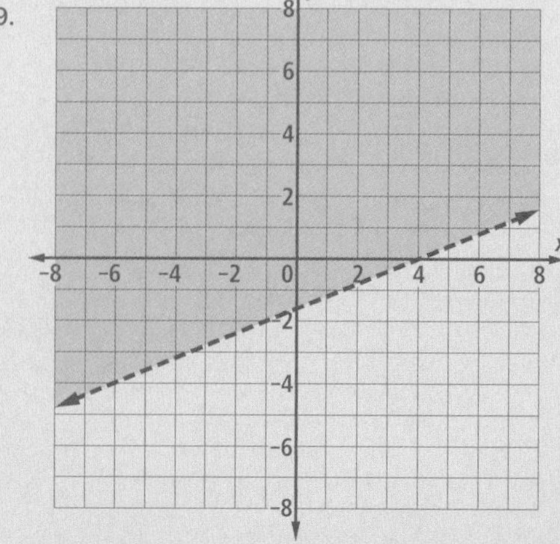

47. Write an inequality that describes the graph below. $t \le 5$

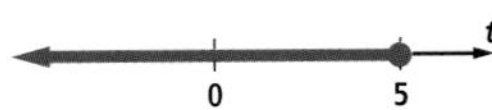

In 48–51, graph on a number line. See margin.

48. $\{x \mid x > 7 \text{ and } x < 11\}$

49. $\{t \mid -3 \le t < 5\} \cap \{t \mid t \ge 1\}$

50. $\{n \mid n > 9\} \cup \{n \mid n > 4\}$

51. $\{y \mid y \le 7 \text{ or } 8 \le y \le 10\}$

52. Write the compound sentence that is graphed below. $x < -2$ or $x \ge 6$

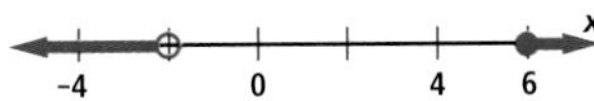

OBJECTIVE I **Estimate solutions to systems by graphing.** (Lesson 5-2)

In 53–55, estimate all solutions to the system by graphing. See margin.

53. $\begin{cases} y = 4x - 5 \\ y = 0.5x + 3 \end{cases}$

54. $\begin{cases} 3x - 2y = -6 \\ y = x^2 \end{cases}$

55. $\begin{cases} 3x + 5y = -19 \\ xy = 7 \end{cases}$

OBJECTIVE J **Graph linear inequalities in two variables.** (Lesson 5-7)

In 56–59, graph on a coordinate plane. See margin.

56. $x < -3$ or $y \ge 1$

57. $x \ge 7$ and $y \ge 13$

58. $y \ge -2x + 2$

59. $2x - 5y < 8$

60. Write an inequality to describe the shaded region below. $y \ge -\frac{5}{8}x + \frac{5}{2}$

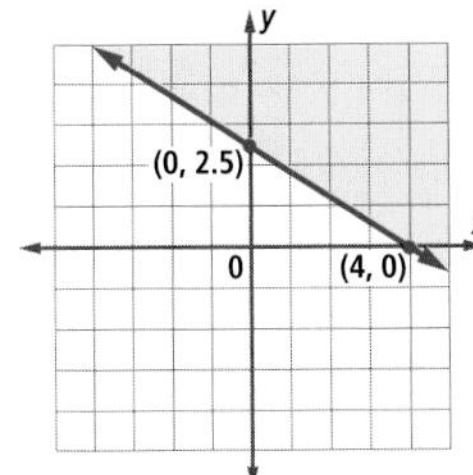

OBJECTIVE K **Solve systems of inequalities by graphing.** (Lesson 5-8)

In 61–63, graph the solution set. See margin.

61. $\begin{cases} x \ge 3 \\ y \le -2 \end{cases}$

62. $\begin{cases} 5c + 7d < 35 \\ 5c - 7d > -1 \end{cases}$

63. $\begin{cases} 3x \ge -6 \\ 2(x + y) \le 6 \\ 6 > y - 2x \end{cases}$

64. Use a compound sentence to describe the shaded region below. $x \ge 2$ and $y \le -1$

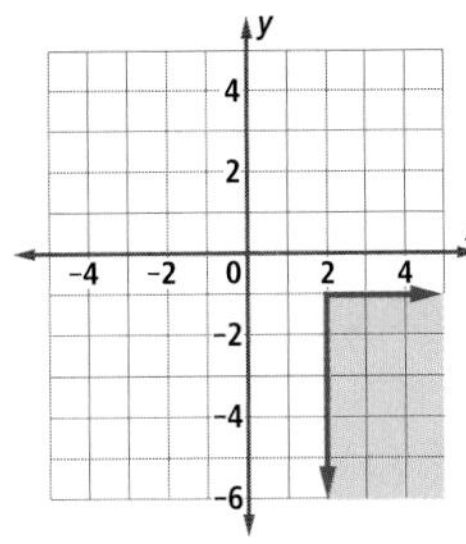

65. **Multiple Choice** Which of the following systems describes the shaded region below? C

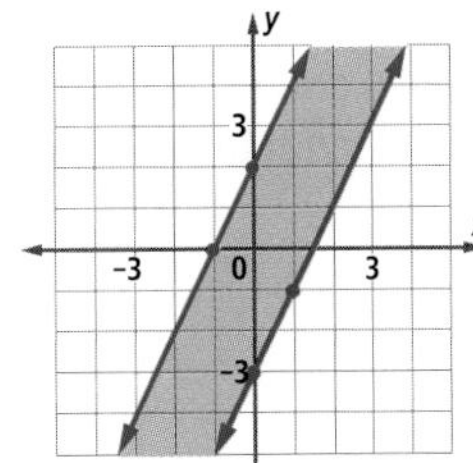

A $\begin{cases} y < \frac{1}{2}x + 2 \\ y < \frac{1}{2}x - 3 \end{cases}$

B $\begin{cases} y > 2x + 2 \\ y < x - 3 \end{cases}$

C $\begin{cases} y \le 2x + 2 \\ y \ge 2x - 3 \end{cases}$

D $\begin{cases} y \le x - 1 \\ y \ge 2x + 1.5 \end{cases}$

Assessment

Evaluation The *Assessment Resources* provide four forms of the Chapter 5 Test. Forms A and B present parallel versions of a short-answer format. Form C consists of four to six short-response questions that cover the SPUR objectives from Chapter 5. Form D offers performance assessment that covers a subset (or even just one) of the SPUR objectives for the chapter. The fifth type of test is a Chapter 5 Test, Cumulative Form. About 50% of this test covers Chapter 5, and the remaining 50% covers the previous chapters evenly.

Feedback After students have taken the test for Chapter 5 and you have scored the results, return the tests to students for discussion. Class discussion on the questions that caused trouble for most students can be very effective in identifying and clarifying misunderstandings. You might want to have them note the items they missed and work either in groups or at home to correct them. It is important for students to receive feedback on every chapter test, and we recommend that students see and correct their mistakes before proceeding too far into the next chapter.

Suggestions for Assignment Assign Lesson 6-1 for homework the evening of the test. It gives students work to do after they have completed the test and keeps the class moving. If you do not do this, you may cover one less chapter over the course of the year.

Additional Answers

61.

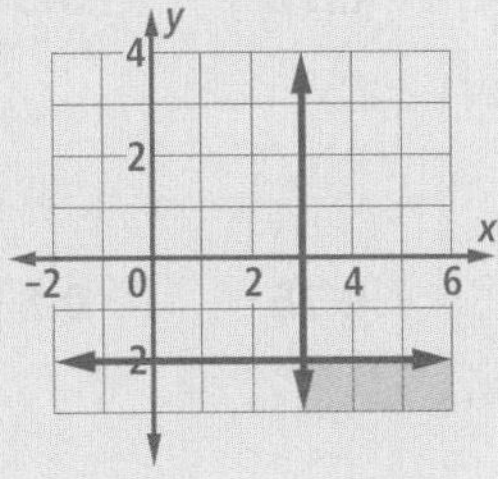

62.

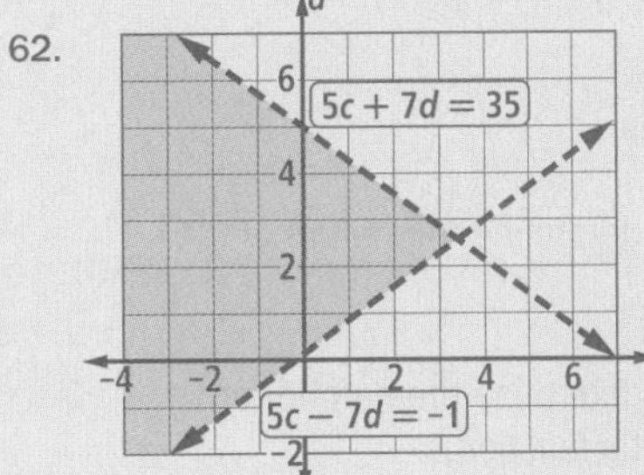

63.

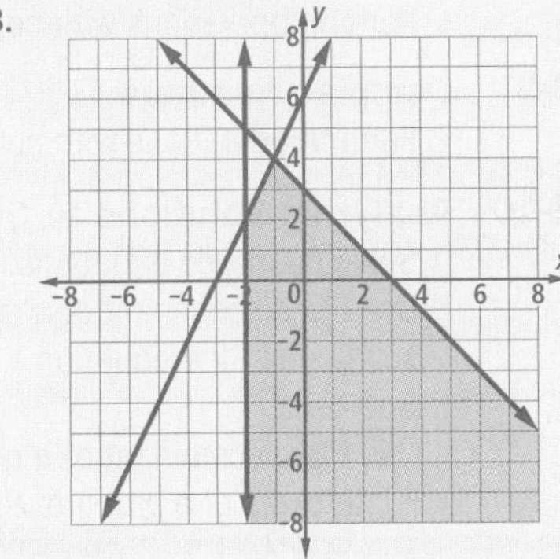

Chapter

6 Quadratic Functions

Chapter Overview

		Local Standards	Pacing (in days) Average	Advanced	Block
6-1	**Quadratic Expressions, Rectangles, and Squares** **A** Expand products and squares of binomials. **I** Use quadratic equations to solve area problems or problems dealing with distance, velocity, and acceleration.		1	0.75	0.5
6-2	**Absolute Value, Square Roots, and Quadratic Equations** **C** Solve quadratic equations. **D** Solve absolute-value equations. **F** Apply the definition of absolute value and the Absolute Value-Square Root Theorem. **K** Graph quadratic functions and absolute-value functions and interpret them.		1	0.75	0.5
6-3	**The Graph-Translation Theorem** **G** Use the Graph-Translation Theorem to interpret equations and graphs. **K** Graph quadratic functions and absolute-value functions and interpret them.		1	0.75	0.5
6-4	**The Graph of $y = ax^2 + bx + c$** **B** Convert quadratic equations from vertex to standard form, and vice versa. **G, K** See **6-3.** **I** See **6-1.**		1	0.75	0.5
	QUIZ 1		0.5	0.5	0.25
6-5	**Completing the Square** **B** Convert quadratic equations from vertex to standard form, and vice versa. **I** See **6-1.**		1	0.75	0.5
6-6	**Fitting a Quadratic Model to Data** **J** Fit a quadratic model to data.		1	0.75	0.5
6-7	**The Quadratic Formula** **C** Solve quadratic equations. **I** See **6-1.**		1	0.75	0.5
	QUIZ 2		0.5	0.5	0.25
6-8	**Pure Imaginary Numbers** **C** Solve quadratic equations. **E** Perform operations with complex numbers.		1	0.75	0.5
6-9	**Complex Numbers** **E** Perform operations with complex numbers.		1	0.75	0.5
6-10	**Analyzing Solutions to Quadratic Equations** **C** Solve quadratic equations. **H** Use the discriminant of a quadratic equation to determine the nature of the solutions to the equation. **K** See **6-2.** **L** Use the discriminant of a quadratic equation to determine the number of x-intercepts of a graph of the associated quadratic function.		1	0.75	0.5
		Self-Test	1	0.75	0.5
		Chapter Review	2	1	0.5
		Test	1	1	0.5
		TOTAL	15	11.25	7

Technology Resources

Teacher's Assessment Assistant, Ch. 6
Electronic Teacher's Edition, Ch. 6

Differentiated Options  Universal Access

	Accommodating the Learner	Vocabulary Development	Ongoing Assessment	Materials
6-1	p. 376	p. 375	oral, p. 379	
6-2	pp. 382, 387	p. 382	group, p. 385	
6-3	pp. 387, 388	p. 389	written, p. 392	graphing utility
6-4	p. 396	p. 395	oral, p. 400	stopwatch, meter stick, tape, rubber ball
6-5	pp. 403, 404	p. 406	group, p. 407	
6-6	pp. 410, 411		written, p. 413	old CD that can get scratched up, two $8\frac{1}{2}$-inch by 11-inch pieces of paper, quarter, CAS or graphing calculator
6-7	pp. 416, 418	p. 415	oral, p. 419	
6-8	pp. 421, 422	p. 421	written, p. 426	calculator
6-9	pp. 429, 430	p. 429	group, p. 433	
6-10	pp. 436, 437	p. 435	oral, p. 440	

Objectives

	Lessons	Self-Test Questions	Chapter Review Questions
Skills			
A Expand products and squares of binomials.	6-1	17	1-8
B Convert quadratic equations from vertex to standard form, and vice versa.	6-4, 6-5	1	9-13
C Solve quadratic equations.	6-2, 6-7, 6-8, 6-10	3, 14, 15	14-22
D Solve absolute-value equations.	6-2	12, 13	23-28
E Perform operations with complex numbers.	6-8, 6-9	4-8	29-42
Properties			
F Apply the definition of absolute value and the Absolute Value-Square Root Theorem.	6-2	16	43-47
G Use the Graph-Translation Theorem to interpret equations and graphs.	6-3, 6-4	2, 9, 11, 23	48-54
H Use the discriminant of a quadratic equation to determine the nature of the solutions to the equation.	6-10	18	55-57
Uses			
I Use quadratic equations to solve area problems or problems dealing with distance, velocity, and acceleration.	6-1, 6-4, 6-5, 6-7	20-22	58-60
Representations			
J Fit a quadratic model to data.	6-6	24	61-63
K Graph quadratic functions and absolute-value functions and interpret them.	6-2, 6-3, 6-4, 6-10	10	64-70
L Use the discriminant of a quadratic equation to determine the number of x-intercepts of a graph of the associated quadratic function.	6-10	19	71-74

Resource Masters Chapter 6

Resource Master 2, Four-Quadrant Graph Paper (page 3), can be used with Lessons 6-2, 6-3, 6-4, 6-5, 6-6, 6-7, 6-9, and 6-10. **Resource Master 3, Automatic Grapher Grids** (page 4), can be used with Lessons 6-2, 6-3, 6-5, and 6-6.

Resource Master 95 Lesson 6-1

Resource Master 94 Lesson 6-1

Warm-Up

1. Give an example of a quadratic expression of the form $ax^2 + bx + c$ in which a, b, and c are all negative integers.
2. Give the quadratic equation and function corresponding to your answer to Warm-Up 1.
3. Give an example of a quadratic expression of the form $ax^2 + bx + c$ in which a, b, and c are all irrational numbers.

Additional Examples

1. A portrait is 20 centimeters by 90 centimeters. A frame around the portrait is f centimeters wide. Write the total area of the portrait and the frame in standard form.
2. Write the area of a square with sides of length $2a + b$ in standard form.

Resource Masters for Lesson 6-1

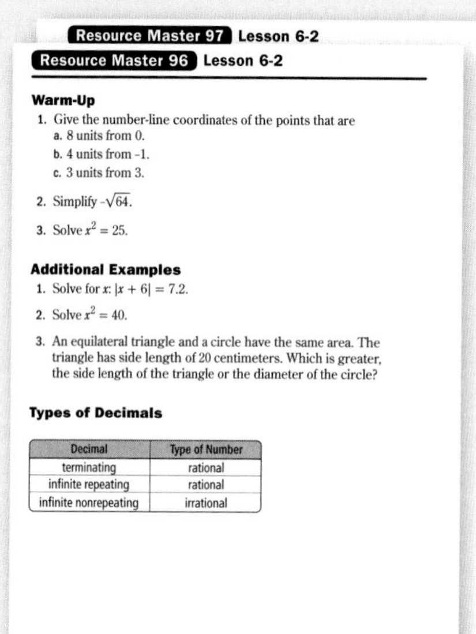

Resource Master 97 Lesson 6-2

Resource Master 96 Lesson 6-2

Warm-Up

1. Give the number-line coordinates of the points that are
   a. 8 units from 0.
   b. 4 units from -1.
   c. 3 units from 3.
2. Simplify $-\sqrt{64}$.
3. Solve $x^2 = 25$.

Additional Examples

1. Solve for x: $|x + 6| = 7.2$.
2. Solve $x^2 = 40$.
3. An equilateral triangle and a circle have the same area. The triangle has side length of 20 centimeters. Which is greater, the side length of the triangle or the diameter of the circle?

Types of Decimals

Decimal	Type of Number
terminating	rational
infinite repeating	rational
infinite nonrepeating	irrational

Resource Masters for Lesson 6-2

Resource Master 99 Lesson 6-3

Resource Master 98 Lesson 6-3

Warm-Up

Do the Activity in the lesson as a Warm-Up.

Additional Example

1. Find an equation for the image of the graph below of $y = |x|$ under the translation $T_{3,-5}$.

Resource Masters for Lesson 6-3

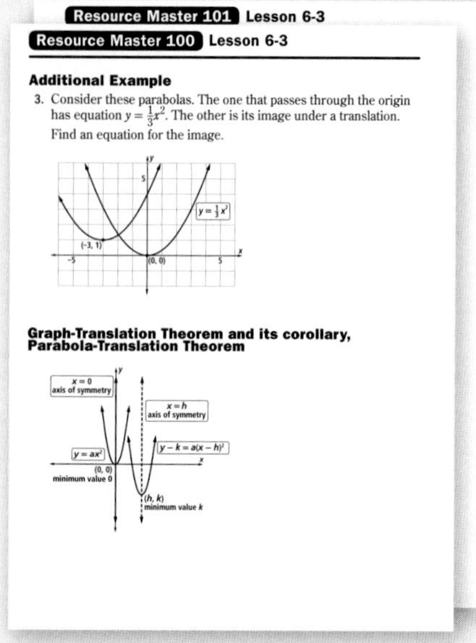

Resource Master 101 Lesson 6-3

Resource Master 100 Lesson 6-3

Additional Example

3. Consider these parabolas. The one that passes through the origin has equation $y = \frac{1}{3}x^2$. The other is its image under a translation. Find an equation for the image.

Graph-Translation Theorem and its corollary, Parabola-Translation Theorem

Resource Masters for Lesson 6-3

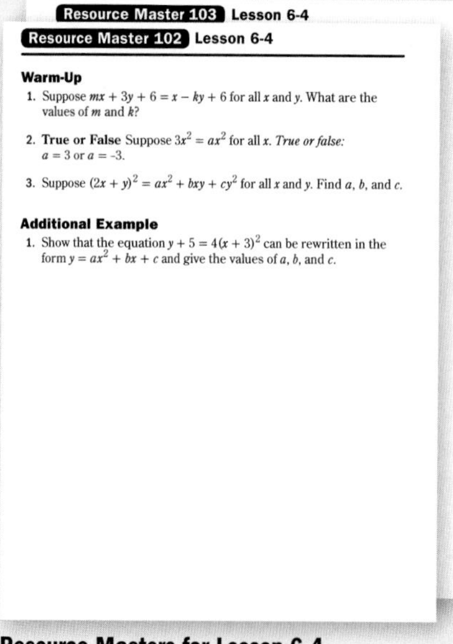

Resource Master 103 Lesson 6-4

Resource Master 102 Lesson 6-4

Warm-Up

1. Suppose $mx + 3y + 6 = x - ky + 6$ for all x and y. What are the values of m and k?
2. **True or False** Suppose $3x^2 = ax^2$ for all x. *True or false:* $a = 3$ or $a = -3$.
3. Suppose $(2x + y)^2 = ax^2 + bxy + cy^2$ for all x and y. Find a, b, and c.

Additional Example

1. Show that the equation $y + 5 = 4(x + 3)^2$ can be rewritten in the form $y = ax^2 + bx + c$ and give the values of a, b, and c.

Resource Masters for Lesson 6-4

Resource Master 104 Lesson 6-4

Activity

	Partner 1	Partner 2
Initial Height h_0 (m)		
Elapsed Time Trial 1 (sec)		
Elapsed Time Trial 2 (sec)		
Elapsed Time Trial 3 (sec)		
Elapsed Time Average t (sec)		

Resource Master for Lesson 6-4

Resource Master 106 Lesson 6-5

Resource Master 105 Lesson 6-5

Warm-Up

1. Suppose $(3x - 4)^2 = ax^2 + bx + c$ for all x. What are the values of a, b, and c?
2. Suppose $n^2 + 400n + 12 = (n + k)^2 + t$ for all n. Find k and t.

Additional Examples

1. a. What number should be added to $x^2 + 14x$ to make a perfect-square trinomial?
   b. Write the perfect-square trinomial as the square of a binomial.
2. a. Rewrite the equation $y = x^2 + 10x - 4$ in vertex form.
   b. Find the vertex of the parabola.
   Solution
   a. Rewrite the equation so that only terms with x are on one side: $y + \_\_\_\_ = x^2 + 10x$.
   Use the Completing the Square Theorem.
   Here, $b = \_\_\_\_$, so $\left(\frac{b}{2}\right)^2 = \_\_\_\_$.
   Thus, $y + \_\_\_\_ + \_\_\_\_ = x^2 + 10x + \_\_\_\_$ and
   $y + \_\_\_\_ = (x + \_\_\_\_)^2$
   b. We can read the vertex from the vertex form of the equation. The vertex of the parabola is ______.

Resource Masters for Lesson 6-5

Resource Master 108 Lesson 6-6

Resource Master 107 Lesson 6-6

Warm-Up

Robin forgot the formula for the sum of the integers from 1 to n, but she knew that it was a quadratic function of n. If $f(x) = ax^2 + bx + c$ and $f(x)$ is the sum of the integers from 1 to x,

1. find numerical values for $f(1)$, $f(2)$, and $f(3)$.
2. find algebraic expressions for $f(1)$, $f(2)$, and $f(3)$ in terms of a, b, and c.
3. Equate your answers to Warm-Ups 1 and 2 to obtain a 3×3 linear system in a, b, and c.
4. Solve the system in Warm-Up 3.

Additional Example

A parabola contains the points (-1, 8), (1, 2), and (3, 4). Find its equation.

Resource Masters for Lesson 6-6

Resource Master 110 Lesson 6-7

Resource Master 109 Lesson 6-7

Warm-Up

In 1–4, put the equation in the form $ax^2 + bx + c = 0$ and indicate the values of a, b, and c.

1. $3x^2 - 4x = 10$
2. $y = y^2$
3. $1 + 2z^2 + 3z = 4 + 5z + 6z^2$
4. $(d - 14)^2 = (d + 6)^2$

Additional Examples

1. Using the equation $h = -0.00132x^2 + 0.545x + 4$ to model the path of a ball, suppose an outfielder makes a "shoestring" catch and catches the ball when it is 2 feet above the ground. To the nearest foot, how far from home plate was the ball caught?
2. Solve $3x^2 - 10x - 25 = 0$.
   Solution Use the Quadratic Formula.
   $a = \_\_\_\_$, $b = \_\_\_\_$, and $c = \_\_\_\_$
   $x = \frac{-b \pm \sqrt{b^2 - 4ac}}{2a} = \_\_\_\_$
   $x = \_\_\_\_$.
   So $x = \_\_\_\_$ or $x = \_\_\_\_$.

Resource Masters for Lesson 6-7

Resource Master 112 Lesson 6-8

Resource Master 111 Lesson 6-8

Warm-Up

1. Write the product $(12 + 7\sqrt{2})(9 - 10\sqrt{2})$ in $a + b\sqrt{2}$ form.
2. Generalize Warm-Up 1.

Additional Examples

1. Solve $x^2 = -625$.
2. a. Show that $i\sqrt{10}$ is a square root of -10.
   b. What is the other square root of -10?
3. Simplify the following.
   a. $(7i)(-10i)$
   b. $-\sqrt{-25} - \sqrt{-100}$
   c. $\sqrt{-3} + \sqrt{-3}$
   d. $\frac{\sqrt{-25}}{\sqrt{-64}}$

Resource Masters for Lesson 6-8

Resource Master 113 Lesson 6-9

Warm-Up

1. Multiply both the numerator and the denominator of $\frac{30 + 17\sqrt{3}}{4 - 12\sqrt{3}}$ by $30 - 17\sqrt{3}$. What is the effect?
2. Multiply both the numerator and the denominator of $\frac{30 + 17\sqrt{3}}{4 - 12\sqrt{3}}$ by $4 + 12\sqrt{3}$. What is the effect?

Additional Examples

1. Write $7i(9 - 6i)$ in $a + bi$ form.
2. Multiply and simplify: $(5 + 7i)(6 - 2i)$.
3. Simplify $\frac{5 - 2i}{3 + 4i}$.
   Solution Multiply the numerator and denominator by $3 - 4i$, the conjugate of $3 + 4i$.
   $\frac{5 - 2i}{3 + 4i} = \frac{5 - 2i}{3 + 4i} \cdot \frac{3 - 4i}{3 - 4i} = \frac{(5 - 2i)(3 - 4i)}{(3 + 4i)(3 - 4i)} = \_\_\_\_ =$
   $\frac{\_\_\_\_}{9 - 16(\_\_\_)} = \frac{\_\_\_}{25} + \frac{\_\_\_}{25}i$

Question 20

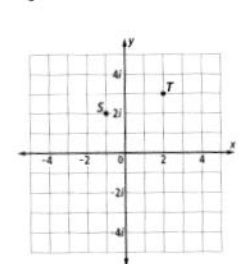

Resource Master for Lesson 6-9

Resource Master 114 Lesson 6-9

Additional Example

4. Find the total impedance in a parallel circuit if $Z_1 = 1 + i$ ohms and $Z_2 = 2 - 6i$ ohms.

Solution Substitute the values of Z_1 and Z_2 into the impedance formula for parallel circuits: $Z_T = \frac{Z_1 Z_2}{Z_1 + Z_2}$.

$Z_T = \frac{(1 + i)(2 - 6i)}{\_\_\_ + \_\_\_}$.

$= \frac{\_\_\_ - \_\_\_i}{\_\_\_ - \_\_\_i}$

$= \frac{\_\_\_ - \_\_\_i}{\_\_\_ - \_\_\_i} \cdot \frac{\_\_\_ + \_\_\_i}{\_\_\_ + \_\_\_i}$

$Z_T = \frac{\_\_\_}{34}$. The total impedance is $\frac{\_\_\_}{34}$ ohms.

Complex Numbers

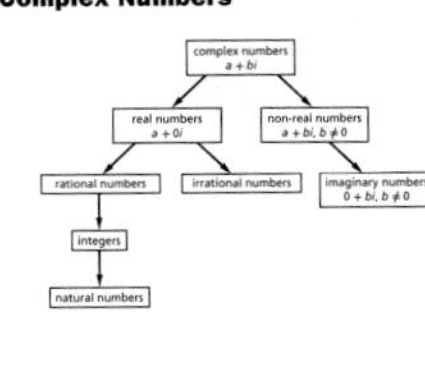

Resource Master for Lesson 6-9

Resource Master 115 Lesson 6-10

Warm-Up

In 1–3, graph the function defined by the equation and determine the number of x-intercepts.

1. $f(x) = x^2 - 18x + 6$
2. $g(x) = x^2 - 18x + 100$
3. $h(x) = x^2 - 18x + 81$

Additional Examples

1. Determine the nature of the roots of each equation.
   a. $6x^2 + 2x + 5 = 0$
   b. $9x^2 - 12x + 4 = 0$
   c. $3x^2 + x - 2 = 0$
   Solution
   Use the Discriminant Theorem. Let $D = b^2 - 4ac$.
   a. $a = 6$, $b = 2$, $c = 5$, so $D = (2)^2 - 4(6)(5) = -116$. Because D is negative, the equation has ____ real roots.
   b. $a = 9$, $b = -12$, $c = 4$, so $D =$ ___. The equation has ____ real roots.
   c. $a = 3$, $b = 1$, $c = -2$, so $D =$ ___. This equation has ____ real roots. Because D is ____, the roots are ____.
2. The equation $h = -0.4x^2 + 2x + 2$ models the path of a ball, where x is the horizontal distance in feet that the ball has traveled and h is the ball's height in feet above the ground. Use the Discriminant Theorem to determine whether the ball ever reaches a height of 4 feet.

Resource Master for Lesson 6-10

Resource Master 116 Lesson 6-10

Activity

$y = ax^2 + bx + c$	Number of x-intercepts of Graph	Solutions to $ax^2 + bx + c = 0$	Number of Real Solutions to $ax^2 + bx + c = 0$	Value of $b^2 - 4ac$
a. $y = 4x^2 - 24x + 27$				
b. $y = 4x^2 - 24x + 36$				
c. $y = 4x^2 - 24x + 45$				
d. $y = -6x^2 + 36x - 54$				
e. $y = -6x^2 + 36x - 48$				
f. $y = -6x^2 + 36x - 60$				

Resource Master for Lesson 6-10

Resource Master 117 Lesson 6-10

Discriminants

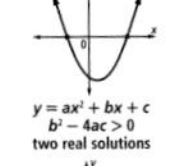

$y = ax^2 + bx + c$
$b^2 - 4ac > 0$
two real solutions

$y = ax^2 + bx + c$
$b^2 - 4ac = 0$
one real solution

$y = ax^2 + bx + c$
$b^2 - 4ac < 0$
two non-real solutions

Extension

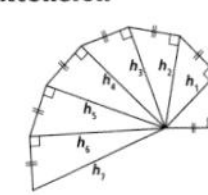

Resource Master for Lesson 6-10

Chapter 6

Pacing

Each lesson in this chapter is designed to be covered in 1 day. At the end of the chapter, you should plan to spend 1 day to review the Self-Test, 1 to 2 days for the Chapter Review, and 1 day for a test. You may wish to spend a day on projects and possibly a day is needed for quizzes. This chapter should therefore take 13 to 16 days. We strongly advise you not to spend more than 17 days on this chapter.

Overview

The opener introduces some of the vocabulary that students will encounter in the chapter: quadratic expressions, quadratic functions, parabolas, and square roots of negative numbers.

In this chapter, quadratic equations will not be solved by factoring trinomials. We approach quadratic equations by teaching problem-solving strategies that generalize easily. In addition, few realistic applications are modeled by equations that can be solved by factoring over rational numbers only. Factoring trinomials and the Factor Theorem will be discussed in Chapter 11.

Using Pages 372–373

Even in the same school, students may differ widely in their experiences with quadratic equations. Ask students to write a one-page essay that describes some of the things they remember about quadratic equations. Also ask them to indicate if they have ever studied square roots of negative numbers. Their responses can help you plan your teaching for this chapter.

Chapter 6 Quadratic Functions

Contents

The word *quadratic* comes from the Latin word *quadratus*, which means "to make square." Many situations lead to quadratic functions. The area formulas $A = s^2$ (for a square) and $A = \pi r^2$ (for a circle) are equations for quadratic functions. You studied direct-variation quadratic functions of the form $f(x) = kx^2$ in Chapter 2. The area of a rectangle with length x and width y is xy, a quadratic expression in the two variables x and y.

$A = s^2$

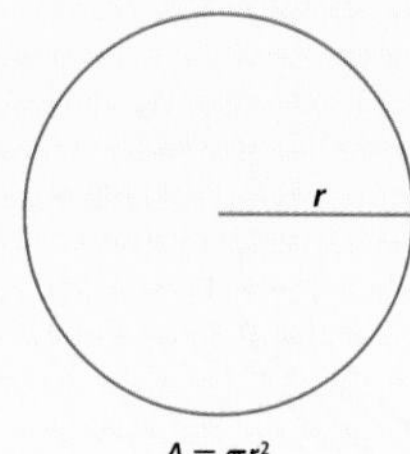

$A = \pi r^2$

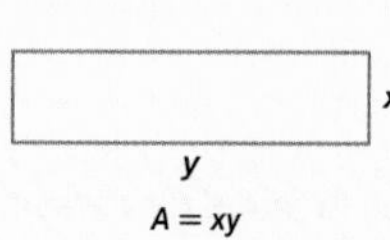

$A = xy$

Chapter 6 Overview

This chapter continues the study of quadratic equations, first introduced in Chapter 2 with a discussion of $y = kx^2$. We balance the traditional paper-and-pencil skills of manipulating expressions and solving equations with an analysis of the relationship between parameters of equations and the properties of graphs.

The first two lessons provide the basic foundation for the skills required in the chapter. Lesson 6-1 explores situations that lead to quadratic expressions and the squares of binomials. Lesson 6-2 defines the absolute-value function and applies the theorem $\sqrt{x^2} = |x|$ to solve equations of the form $ax^2 = k$.

The middle lessons deal with graphing quadratic functions and solving quadratic equations. Lesson 6-3 applies the Graph-Translation Theorem to derive the vertex form of the equation for a parabola: $y - k = a(x - h)^2$. Lesson 6-4 relates equations of the form $y = ax^2 + bx + c$ to distance, time, velocity, and acceleration applications. In

Quadratic functions also arise from studying the paths of objects. Consider the picture at the right of water spouting from a water fountain. Let y be the height (in inches) of the water above the spout and let x be the horizontal distance (in inches) from the spout. Then quadratic regression can be used to find the equation $y = -0.58x^2 + 2.7x$ to represent the path of the water.

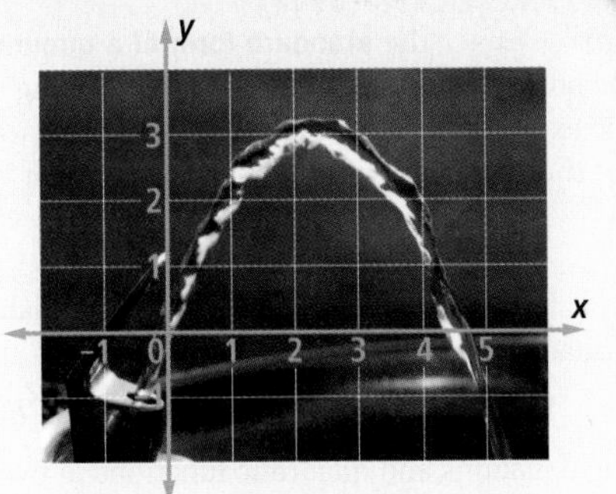

The water's path closely follows a parabola, as do the paths traveled by a batted baseball or thrown basketball. All parabolas can be described by quadratic equations.

In this chapter, you will study many uses of quadratic expressions and functions. You also will learn how to solve all quadratic equations, including those whose solutions involve square roots of negative numbers.

373

Lesson 6-5, students complete the square to rewrite the equation $y = ax^2 + bx + c$ in vertex form. Lesson 6-6 shows how parabolas can be fit to data, and Lesson 6-7 derives the Quadratic Formula and uses it to solve equations.

The last three lessons embed quadratic equations in the domain of complex numbers. Lessons 6-8 and 6-9 introduce imaginary numbers and complex numbers, respectively. Finally, Lesson 6-10 uses the Quadratic Formula to solve all types of quadratic equations with real coefficients and uses the discriminant to describe the nature and number of those solutions.

For some students, graphing $y = ax^2 + bx + c$, completing the square, and solving quadratics with the Quadratic Formula may be review topics, while fitting quadratics to data and working with nonreal numbers will be new material. Most teachers report that all students benefit by completing all the lessons in this chapter.

The simplest quadratic equations, which all students should have seen previously, are $A = s^2$ and $A = xy$. Perhaps the most common application of quadratics other than to area is to the paths of projectiles, including water spouting from a water fountain, as pictured. To get a sense of the shape of a parabola, you might have students graph $y = x^2$ with a graphing utility and zoom in and out of the graph near its vertex.

Chapter 6 Projects

At the end of each chapter, you will find projects related to the chapter. At this time you might want to have students look over the projects on pages 441 and 442. You might want to have students tentatively select a project on which to work. Then, as students read and progress through the chapter, they can finalize their project choices.

Sometimes students might work alone. At other times, you might let them collaborate with classmates for a presentation and discussion. We recommend that you allow for diversity and encourage students to use their imaginations when presenting their projects. As students work on projects throughout the year, they should see many uses of mathematics in the real world.

Lesson

6-1

GOAL

Review rectangles, squares, and quadratic expressions, which are basic to the study of quadratic functions.

SPUR Objectives

The SPUR Objectives for all of Chapter 6 are found in the Chapter Review on pages 446–449.

A Expand products and squares of binomials.

I Use quadratic equations to solve area problems.

Materials/Resources

- Lesson Masters 6-1A and 6-1B
- Resource Masters 94 and 95

HOMEWORK

Suggestions for Assignment

- Questions 1–28
- Question 29 (extra credit)
- Reading Lesson 6-2
- Covering the Ideas 6-2

Local Standards

1 Warm-Up

1. Give an example of a quadratic expression of the form $ax^2 + bx + c$ in which a, b, and c are all negative integers. Answers vary. Sample: $-2x^2 - x - 17$
2. Give the quadratic equation and function corresponding to your answer to Warm-Up 1. $-2x^2 - x - 17 = 0$; $f: x \to -2x^2 - x - 17$
3. Give an example of a quadratic expression of the form $ax^2 + bx + c$ in which a, b, and c are all irrational numbers. Answers vary. Sample: $\pi x^2 + \frac{\pi}{3}x + \sqrt{2}$

Lesson

6-1 Quadratic Expressions, Rectangles, and Squares

Vocabulary

quadratic expression
quadratic equation
quadratic function
standard form of a quadratic
binomial

BIG IDEA Some quadratic expressions arise from problems involving the areas of rectangles.

Recall that the degree of a monomial is the sum of the exponents of the variables in the monomial, and the degree of a polynomial is the highest degree among its monomial terms. For instance, the monomials $20x^5$ and $\frac{1}{3}ab^4$ have degree 5, while the polynomial $x^5 - x^6$ has degree 6. The word *quadratic* in today's mathematics refers to expressions, equations, and functions that involve sums of constants and first and second powers of variables and no higher powers. That is, they are of degree 2. Specifically, if a, b, and c are real numbers, $a \neq 0$, and x is a variable,

$ax^2 + bx + c$ is the general **quadratic expression** in x,

$ax^2 + bx + c = 0$ is the general **quadratic equation** in x, and

$f: x \to ax^2 + bx + c$ is the general **quadratic function** in x.

We call $ax^2 + bx + c$ the **standard form of a quadratic**. In standard form, the powers of the variable are in decreasing order. Some quadratic expressions, equations, and functions are not in standard form, but they can be rewritten in standard form.

 QY1

There can also be quadratics in two or more variables. The general quadratic expression in two variables is

$$Ax^2 + Bxy + Cy^2 + Dx + Ey + F.$$

Quadratic equations and quadratic functions in two variables are discussed in Chapter 12.

The simplest quadratic expression x^2 is the product of the simplest linear expressions x and x. More generally, the product of any two linear expressions $ax + b$ and $cx + d$ is a quadratic expression for any real numbers a, b, c, and d, provided a and c are not zero. Because all area formulas involve the product of two lengths, they all involve quadratic expressions.

Mental Math

A 6′ by 3.5′ mural is surrounded by a 1.5′-wide border.

a. What is the area of the mural? 21 ft^2

b. What is the area of the mural plus the border? 58.5 ft^2

c. What is the area of just the border? 37.5 ft^2

d. The border is narrowed to 1 foot wide. Now what is the area of the mural and border? 44 ft^2

QY1

Write $3x - (5 - 2x^2)$ in standard form.

Background

The first paragraph of the lesson provides an opportunity to clarify the distinction between expressions, equations, and functions. It should be noted, however, that some types of software do not make these distinctions. For example, you can ask a CAS to "solve $x^2 - 5$," and it might read this as "solve $x^2 - 5 = 0$." Certain types of software may also refer to the function f as $f(x)$.

Quadratic expressions from rectangles
This type of problem, which is a consequence of the Area Model for Multiplication, recurs throughout the chapter.

Quadratic expressions from squares
Be certain to review the Binomial Square Theorem. The theorem will help students in each lesson in this chapter, and it is explicitly used in Lesson 6-5 (see page 403) to complete the square.

Quadratic Expressions from Rectangles

Example 1

Hector and Francisca are remodeling their kitchen. They purchase a 6-foot by 2-foot pantry door, and are looking at different widths of molding to trim the door frame. If the trim is w inches wide, write the total area of the door and trim in standard form.

Solution Draw a picture. The door is surrounded by trim on 3 sides. The door with trim occupies a rectangle with length $72 + w$ inches and width $24 + 2w$ inches. The area of this rectangle is $(72 + w)(24 + 2w)$ square inches.

Use the Distributive Property to multiply $(72 + w)(24 + 2w)$. Think of $(72 + w)$ as a single number.

$$(72 + w)(24 + 2w) = (72 + w) \cdot 24 + (72 + w) \cdot 2w$$

Now apply the Distributive Property twice more.

$$= 72 \cdot 24 + w \cdot 24 + 72 \cdot 2w + w \cdot 2w$$

$$= 1728 + 24w + 144w + 2w^2 \quad \text{Arithmetic}$$

$$= 1728 + 168w + 2w^2 \quad \text{Combine like terms.}$$

In standard form, the total area of the door and the trim is $2w^2 + 168w + 1728$ square inches.

Check Use a CAS to expand the expression.

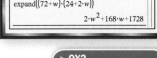

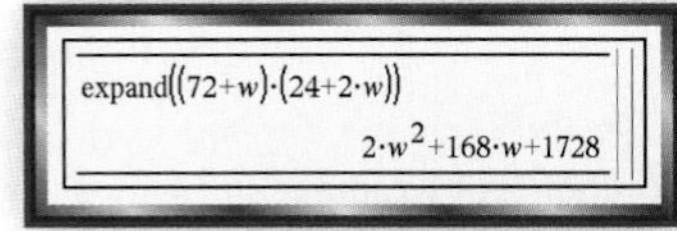
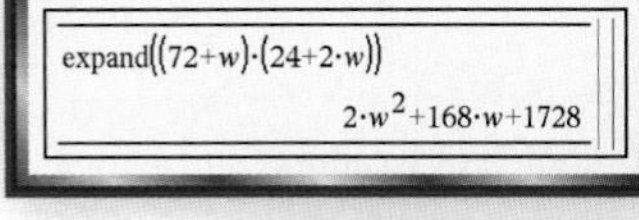

QY2

▶ QY2

The expression $2w^2 + 168w + 1728$ is in the form $ax^2 + bx + c$. What are a, b, c, and x?

Quadratic Expressions from Squares

The expression $x + y$ is an example of a *binomial*. In general, a **binomial** is an expression with two terms. The square of a binomial can be thought of as the area of a square whose side length is the binomial.

Example 2

Write the area of the square with sides of length $x + y$ in standard form.

Solution 1 Draw a picture of the square. Notice that its area is the sum of four smaller areas: a square of area x^2, two rectangles, each with area xy, and a square with area y^2. So, the area of the original square is $x^2 + 2xy + y^2$.

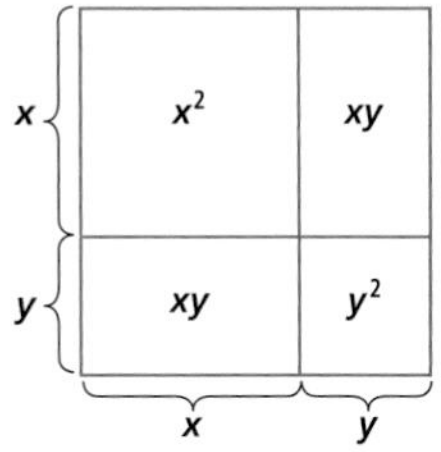

(continued on next page)

ENGLISH LEARNERS

Vocabulary Development

Be sure students understand the term *expand* in the Check for Example 1. To *expand an expression* means to write the expression as a sum of (positive or negative) terms without grouping symbols.

2 Teaching

Notes on the Lesson

Example 1 Encourage all students to describe how to set up and solve Example 1. This type of problem provides additional practice in translating real situations into quadratic equations and often occurs in algebra and geometry texts. Have students explain in their own words where the expressions $72 + w$ and $24 + 2w$ come from. Question 4 is related to Example 1.

Additional Examples

Example 1 A portrait is 20 centimeters by 90 centimeters. A frame around the portrait is f centimeters wide. Write the total area of the portrait and the frame in standard form. $(20 + 2f)(90 + 2f) = 4f^2 + 220f + 1800$ cm^2

Example 2 Write the area of a square with sides of length $2a + b$ in standard form. $4a^2 + 4ab + b^2$

Quadratic expressions from squares Some students find it easier to understand and use the Binomial Square Theorem if it is presented both verbally and as a formula. Verbally, the theorem would read: "To square a binomial, square the first term, add twice the product of the two terms (the product of the two terms may have a negative sign), and then add the square of the second term." Although the Binomial Square Theorem does not need to be learned as an isolated theorem (students could use the Distributive Property or FOIL in its place), it is helpful if students learn the pattern for quickly squaring a binomial. The most common error students make on this type of problem is to assume that powers distribute over addition and subtraction. Use specific values to demonstrate that $(x + y)^2 \neq x^2 + y^2$ unless $x = 0$ or $y = 0$, or prove that $(x + y)^2 = x^2 + y^2$ only if $x = 0$ or $y = 0$:

$(x + y)^2 = x^2 + y^2$	Given
$(x + y)^2 = x^2 + 2xy + y^2$	Binomial Square Theorem
$x^2 + 2xy + y^2 = x^2 + y^2$	Substitution
$2xy = 0$	Add $-x^2 + -y^2$ to both sides.
$x = 0$ or $y = 0$	Zero Product Property

Solution 2 The area of a square with side $x + y$ is $(x + y)^2$. Rewrite $(x + y)^2$.

$(x + y)^2 = (x + y)(x + y)$	Definition of second power
$= (x + y)x + (x + y)y$	Distributive Property
$= x^2 + yx + xy + y^2$	Distributive Property
$= x^2 + 2xy + y^2$	Commutative Property of Multiplication and Distributive Property

The area of the square is $x^2 + 2xy + y^2$.

When a linear expression is multiplied by itself, or squared, the result is a quadratic expression. In Example 2, the linear expression $x + y$ is squared. You can also say it is "taken to the 2nd power." Writing this power as a quadratic expression is called *expanding* the power. Squares of binomials occur so often that their expansions are identified as a theorem.

Binomial Square Theorem

For all real numbers x and y,
$(x + y)^2 = x^2 + 2xy + y^2$ and
$(x - y)^2 = x^2 - 2xy + y^2$.

Solution 2 of Example 2 provides the proof of the first part of this theorem. You are asked to complete the second part of this proof in Question 13. The Binomial Square Theorem is so useful that you will want to be able to apply it automatically.

QY3

▸ QY3

Use the Binomial Square Theorem to expand $(3x - y)^2$.

GUIDED

Example 3

A city wants to cover the seating area around a circular fountain with mosaic tiles. The radius of the fountain, including s feet for seating, is 15 feet.

a. **Write a quadratic expression in standard form for the area of the fountain, not including the seating area.**

b. **How many square feet are in the seating area in terms of s?**

Solution

a. Draw a picture. The radius of the fountain without seating is __?__ ft. $15 - s$,
So, the fountain area without seating is π(__?__)^2 ft^2. $15 - s$
To expand (__?__ − __?__)^2, use the Binomial Square Theorem with x = __?__ and $y = s$. 15; s; 15

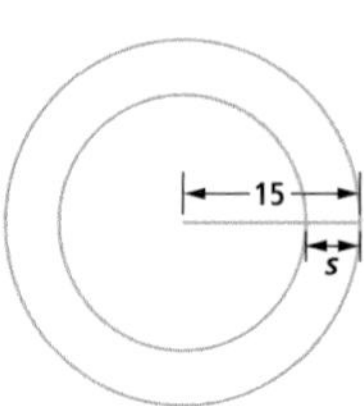

Additional Example

Example 3 A large circular pipe coming up from the ground is surrounded by a circular region of drainage stones. The distance from the edge of the pipe to the outer edge of the drainage stones is w feet, and the radius of the drainage stones, including the large pipe, is 7 feet.

a. Write a quadratic expression in standard form for the area of the opening of the circular pipe, not including the drainage stones.

b. How many square feet are covered by drainage stones, in terms of w?

Solution

a. Draw a picture.

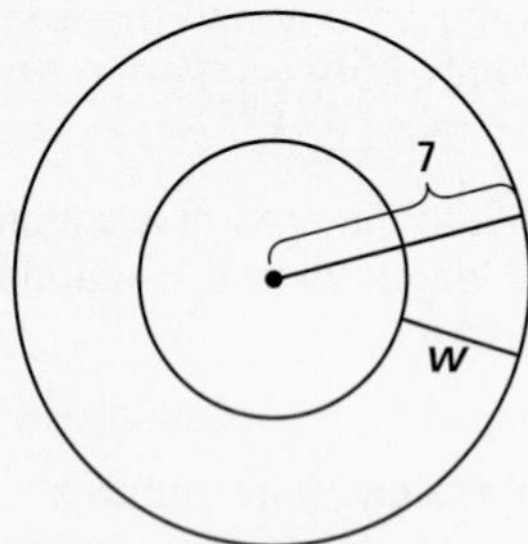

The radius of the pipe within the drainage stones is __?__ feet. $7 - w$ So, the area of the pipe is __?__ square feet. $\pi(7 - w)^2$ To expand __?__, use the Binomial Square Theorem with x = __?__ and $y = w$: (__?__ $- w)^2$ = __?__ − 2 • __?__ • $w + w^2 = w^2$ − __?__w + __?__. $(7 - w)^2$; 7; 7; 7^2; 7; 14; 49 Thus the area of the open pipe is $\pi w^2 - 14\pi w + 49\pi$ square feet.

b. The drainage stones' area is the total area minus the area of the open pipe. $7^2\pi$ − __?__π = 49π − __?__ + __?__ − __?__ = __?__ − __?__. $(7 - w)^2$; 49π; $14\pi w$; πw^2; $14\pi w$; πw^2 So the area of the drainage stones is __?__ square feet. $14\pi w - \pi w^2$

Accommodating the Learner ⬇

A frame of constant width w surrounds a rectangle whose dimensions are a and b. Find the area of the frame. The outer dimensions of the frame are $a + 2w$ and $b + 2w$, so the area of the frame is $(a + 2w)(b + 2w) - ab = ab + 2aw + 2bw + 4w^2 - ab = 2aw + 2bw + 4w^2$.

Accommodating the Learner ⬆

Three concentric circles have radii a, $2a$, and $3a$. Find the area of the outer ring and the area of the middle ring. Outer ring: $A = \pi(3a)^2 - \pi(2a)^2 = 9\pi a^2 - 4\pi a^2 = 5\pi a^2$; Inner ring: $A = \pi(2a)^2 - \pi a^2 = 4\pi a^2 - \pi a^2 = 3\pi a^2$

$(\underline{\ ?\ } - s)^2 = \underline{\ ?\ }^2 - 2 \cdot \underline{\ ?\ } \cdot s + s^2$ 15; 15

$= s^2 - \underline{\ ?\ }s + \underline{\ ?\ }$ 30; 225

So the area of the fountain not including seating is $\pi(\underline{\ ?\ })^2$ or $\pi \underline{\ ?\ } - 30\pi s + 225\pi$ ft². $15 - s$; s^2

b. The seating area is the total area minus the fountain area without seating. $15 - s$ 225 30s s^2

$15^2\pi - (\underline{\ ?\ })^2\pi = 225\pi - (\underline{\ ?\ } - \underline{\ ?\ } + \underline{\ ?\ })\pi$

$= \underline{\ ?\ } - \underline{\ ?\ }$ $30s\pi$; $s^2\pi$

So the area of the seating area is $\underline{\ ?\ }$ ft². $30\pi s - \pi s^2$

Questions

COVERING THE IDEAS

1. **Multiple Choice** Which is not a quadratic equation? Explain your answer. B; it is not a second-degree equation.

   A $y = \frac{x^2}{6}$ B $y = 2(x - 4)$

   C $\frac{x^2}{4} - \frac{y^2}{9} = 25$ D $y = (x + 3)(2x - 5)$

2. Is $x^2 + \sqrt{7}$ a quadratic expression? Explain your answer.

3. Name two geometric figures for which quadratic expressions describe their area. Answers vary. Sample: square, circle

4. A door is 7 feet high and 30 inches wide, with trim of w inches wide on three sides of the door frame. Write the total area (in square inches) of the door and trim in standard form.

In 5–8, the product of two linear expressions is given.

a. Rewrite the product as a single polynomial.

b. Check your results using the expand command on a CAS. 5–8. See margin.

5. $(3x + 5y)(2x + 7y)$
6. $(x - 3)(x + 2)$
7. $(1 - 2y)(2 - 3y)$
8. $(6 + b)(2 - b)$

In 9–11, expand the square of the binomial.

9. $(10 + 3)^2$ 169
10. $(d - 6)^2$
11. $(p + w)^2$

12. Draw a geometric diagram of the expansion of $(x + 5)^2$. See margin.

13. Prove the second part of the Binomial Square Theorem. See margin.

In 14 and 15, rewrite the expression in the form $ax^2 + bx + c$.

14. $\left(3t - \frac{1}{3}\right)^2$
15. $(1 - p)^2$

2. Yes; it is in the form $ax^2 + bx + c$, where $a = 1$, $b = 0$, and $c = \sqrt{7}$.

4. $2w^2 + 198w + 2520$ in²

This doorway in Dublin, Ireland, has very ornate trim.

10. $d^2 - 12d + 36$

11. $p^2 + 2pw + w^2$

14. $9t^2 - 2t + \frac{1}{9}$

15. $p^2 - 2p + 1$

6-1

Note-Taking Tips

Emphasize the need for clear writing when students write exponents or use a centered dot to represent multiplication. You might ask students to write a set of notes on the lesson, exchange those notes with another student, and report to each other if any parts of the other student's notes are ambiguous or difficult to understand.

3 Assignment

Recommended Assignment

- Questions 1–28
- Question 29 (extra credit)
- Reading Lesson 6-2
- Covering the Ideas 6-2

Notes on the Questions

Question 9 Do this question two ways—first using the Binomial Square Theorem and then using the order of operations and arithmetic.

Additional Answers

5a. $6x^2 + 31xy + 35y^2$

5b.

```
expand((3·x+5·y)·(2·x+7·y))
                    6·x^2+31·x·y+35·y^2
```

6a. $x^2 - x - 6$

6b.

```
expand((x-3)·(x+2))        x^2-x-6
```

Additional Answers

7a. $6y^2 - 7y + 2$

7b.

```
expand((1-2·y)·(2-3·y))    6·y^2-7·y+2
```

8a. $-b^2 - 4b + 12$

8b.

```
expand((6+b)·(2-b))        -b^2-4·b+12
```

12.

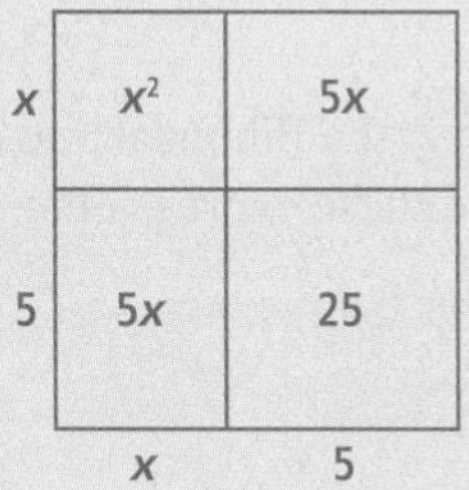

	x	5
x	x^2	$5x$
5	$5x$	25

13. $(x - y)^2 =$

$= (x - y)(x - y)$, Definition of 2nd power;

$= (x - y)x - (x - y)y$, Distributive Property;

$= x^2 - yx - xy + y^2$, Distributive Property;

$= x^2 - 2xy + y^2$, Commutative and Associative Properties

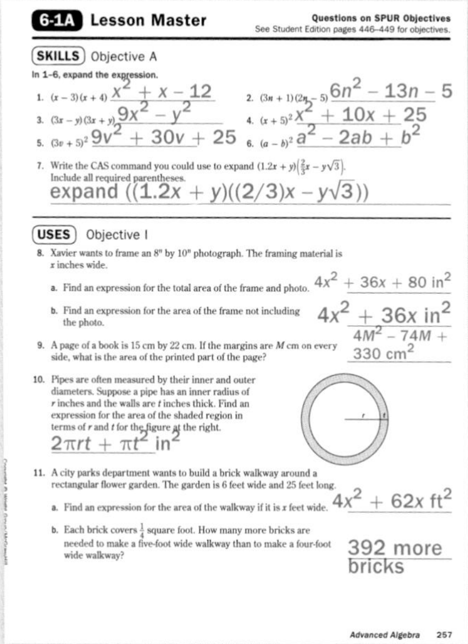

6-1A Lesson Master

Questions on SPUR Objectives
See Student Edition pages 446–449 for objectives.

SKILLS Objective A

In 1–6, expand the expression.

1. $(x - 3)(x + 4)$ $x^2 + x - 12$
2. $(3n + 1)(2n - 5)$ $6n^2 - 13n - 5$
3. $(3x - y)(3x + y)$ $9x^2 - y^2$
4. $(x + 5)^2$ $x^2 + 10x + 25$
5. $(3v + 5)^2$ $9v^2 + 30v + 25$
6. $(a - b)^2$ $a^2 - 2ab + b^2$
7. Write the CAS command you could use to expand $(1.2x + y)\left(\frac{2}{3}x - y\sqrt{3}\right)$. Include all required parentheses. expand $((1.2x + y)((2/3)x - y\sqrt{3}))$

USES Objective I

8. Xavier wants to frame an 8" by 10" photograph. The framing material is x inches wide.

   a. Find an expression for the total area of the frame and photo. $4x^2 + 36x + 80$ in²

   b. Find an expression for the area of the frame not including the photo. $4x^2 + 36x$ in²

9. A page of a book is 15 cm by 22 cm. If the margins are M cm on every side, what is the area of the printed part of the page? $4M^2 - 74M + 330$ cm²

10. Pipes are often measured by their inner and outer diameters. Suppose a pipe has an inner radius of r inches and the walls are t inches thick. Find an expression for the area of the shaded region in terms of r and t for the figure at the right. $2\pi rt + \pi t^2$ in²

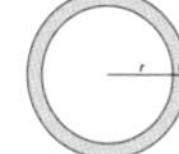

11. A city parks department wants to build a brick walkway around a rectangular flower garden. The garden is 6 feet wide and 25 feet long.

   a. Find an expression for the area of the walkway if it is x feet wide. $4x^2 + 62x$ ft²

   b. Each brick covers $\frac{1}{4}$ square foot. How many more bricks are needed to make a five-foot wide walkway than to make a four-foot wide walkway? 392 more bricks

Advanced Algebra 257

Notes on the Questions

Questions 23 and 24 These questions are advance preparation for Lesson 6-5, where students need to be able to recognize perfect square trinomials in order to complete the square. You might substitute integer values for x to demonstrate that the quadratic trinomial on the left is always equivalent to the square of a binomial.

Additional Answers

22a.

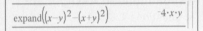

16. Refer to the quadratic expression in Example 1. Graph $y = (72 + x)(24 + 2x)$ and $y = 2x^2 + 168x + 1728$ in the window $\{x \mid -160 \le x \le 160\}$, $\{y \mid -2250 \le y \le 5750\}$.
   a. Trace the graph and toggle between the two graphs for at least three different values of x. What do you notice about the ordered pairs when you switch between the graphs? 16a. They are the same.
   b. Look at a table of values for the two functions. Does the table support your observation from Part a? 16b. yes
   c. Based on your results in Parts a and b, what do you conclude about the two equations you graphed? 16c. The equations are equivalent.

17. Suppose a rectangular swimming pool with dimensions of 100 feet by 12 feet is surrounded by a walkway of width w.
   a. Write a quadratic expression in standard form that gives the area of the pool and walkway together.
   b. Write an expression that gives the area of the walkway only.

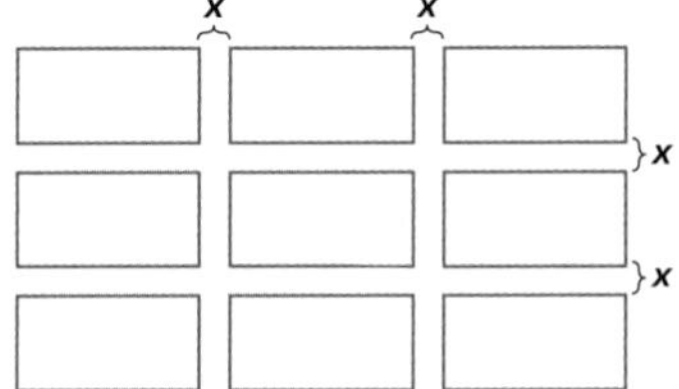

17a. $4w^2 + 224w + 1200$
17b. $4w^2 + 224w$

APPLYING THE MATHEMATICS

In 18 and 19, rewrite the expression in the form $ax^2 + bxy + cy^2$.

18. $(2a + 3b)^2$ $4a^2 + 12ab + 9b^2$ 19. $\left(2t - \frac{k}{3}\right)^2$ $4t^2 - \frac{4}{3}kt + \frac{1}{9}k^2$

20. Refer to Example 3. If $s = 3$ feet and 12 mosaic tiles cover one square foot, how many tiles would be needed to cover the seating area around the fountain? 3054 tiles

21. Certain ceramic tiles are 4 inches by 8 inches and are separated by grout seams that are x inches wide.
   a. Write a quadratic expression in standard form for the area covered by each tile and its share of the grout. (The grout in each seam is shared by two tiles, so each tile's share is only half the grout in each seam.) $x^2 + 12x + 32$
   b. If the grout seams are $\frac{1}{2}$ inch wide, approximately how many tiles will it take to cover a 5-foot by 10-foot wall? about 189 tiles
   c. What percent of the wall in Part b is grout? about 16%
   d. If the grout seams are $\frac{3}{4}$-inch wide, what percent of the wall will be grout? about 23%

22. a. Expand $(x - y)^2 - (x + y)^2$ on a CAS. See margin.
   b. Verify the CAS solution by using the Binomial Square Theorem. $x^2 - 2xy + y^2 - x^2 - 2xy - y^2 = -4xy$

In 23 and 24, find h so that the given equation is true.

23. $x^2 + 20x + 100 = (x + h)^2$ $h = 10$ 24. $x^2 - hx + h = (x - \sqrt{h})^2$ $h = 4$ or $h = 0$

Extension

Ask students to apply the Binomial Square Theorem to expand these expressions:

a. $(5ay - 2bx)^2$ $(5ay - 2bx)^2 = (5ay)^2 - 2(5ay)(2bx) + (2bx)^2 = 25a^2y^2 - 20abxy + 4b^2x^2$

b. $(12xy^3 + 5x^4y^2)^2$ $(12xy^3 + 5x^4y^2)^2 = (12xy^3)^2 + 2(12xy^3)(5x^4y^2) + (5x^4y^2)^2 = 144x^2y^6 + 120x^5y^5 + 25x^8y^4$

REVIEW

In 25 and 26, use the following data about the United States National Parks. (Lessons 3-5, 2-4)

Year	Number of Recreation Visits (millions)	Federal Appropriations (billions of $)
1999	287.1	2.030
2000	285.9	2.112
2001	279.9	2.568
2002	277.3	2.654
2003	266.1	2.546

Source: National Park Service

25. Find the rate of change from 1999 to 2003 for each of the following:
    a. number of recreation visits b. federal appropriations
26. a. Find an equation for the line of best fit describing the number of recreation visits as a function of the year using only the years 1999, 2001, and 2003. Let x be the number of years after 1999.
    b. How well does the line of best fit predict the value for 2002?
27. a. Draw $\triangle ABC$ with vertices $A = (0, 0)$, $B = (1, 1)$, and $C = (2, 4)$.
    b. Draw $\triangle A'B'C'$, its image under the transformation $(x, y) \to (x - 5, y + 2)$. 27a–b. See margin.
    c. Describe the effect of this transformation on $\triangle ABC$. (Lesson 4-10)
28. If m varies inversely as t^2, and $m = 14$ when $t = 2.5$, find the value of m when $t = 7$. (Lesson 2-2) $m = 1.79$

EXPLORATION

29. Doorway trim comes in various widths.
    a. Find out the prices of at least three different widths of doorway trim.
    b. Suppose you want to frame a 7-foot by 3-foot door. Find the area of the door moldings for each of the three different sizes you have found.
    c. How much will it cost to frame the door with each size of molding?
    d. Does the cost in Part b vary directly as the area of the molding? If so, how?

25a. -5.25 million visits/yr

25b. 0.129 billion dollars/yr

26a. $y = -5.25x + 288.2$

26b. $-5.25(3) + 288.2 = 272.45$; the equation predicts the value only moderately well.

27c. The transformation translates $\triangle ABC$ 5 units to the left and 2 units up.

29a. Answers vary. Sample:
$5\frac{9}{16}''$: \$22 for 8';
$3''$: \$18 for 8';
$2\frac{3}{4}''$: \$16 for 8'

29b. 1196.63 in^2; 630 in^2; 576.125 in^2

29c. \$51.85; \$40.50; \$35.83, assuming trim may be purchased in less than full board lengths and that beveling is required.

29d. Yes, somewhat. The cost is roughly 0.04 to 0.06 times the area given in square inches.

QY ANSWERS

1. $2x^2 + 3x - 5$
2. $a = 2, b = 168, c = 1728$, and $x = w$
3. $(3x)^2 - 2(3x)y + y^2 = 9x^2 - 6xy + y^2$

4 Wrap-Up

Ongoing Assessment

Ask students to explain how to find the area of a square if the side length is (1) $p + q$ units or (2) $m - n$ units. Answers vary. Sample: Use the Binomial Square Theorem. (1) If the side is $p + q$, then the area is $(p + q)^2 = p^2 + 2pq + q^2$. (2) If the side is $m - n$, then the area is $(m - n)^2 = m^2 - 2mn + n^2$.

Additional Answers

27a.

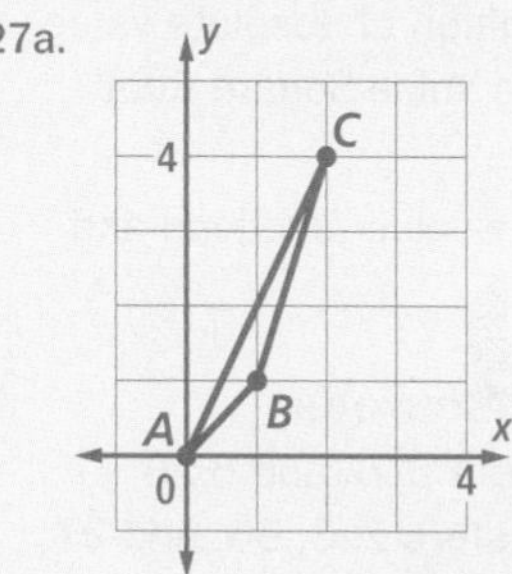

27b.

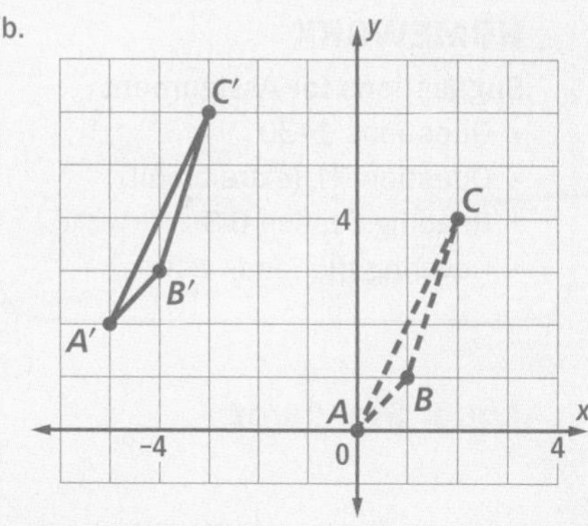

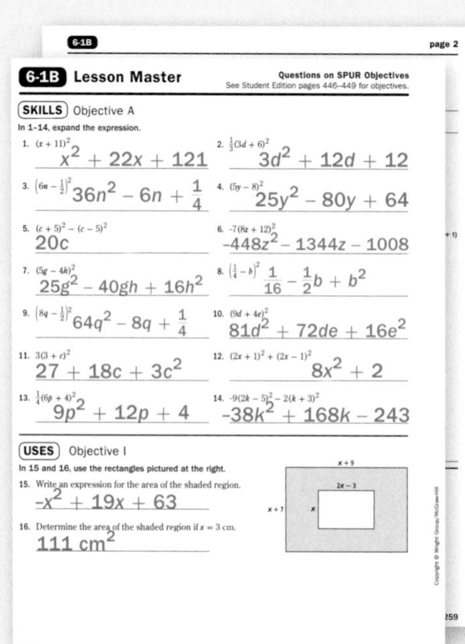
6-1B Lesson Master

Questions on SPUR Objectives
See Student Edition pages 446–449 for objectives.

SKILLS Objective A

In 1–14, expand the expression.

1. $(x+11)^2$ — $x^2 + 22x + 121$
2. $\frac{1}{3}(3d+6)^2$ — $3d^2 + 12d + 12$
3. $(6n - \frac{1}{2})^2$ — $36n^2 - 6n + \frac{1}{4}$
4. $(5y-8)^2$ — $25y^2 - 80y + 64$
5. $(c+5)^2 - (c-5)^2$ — $20c$
6. $-7(8z+12)^2$ — $-448z^2 - 1344z - 1008$
7. $(5g-4h)^2$ — $25g^2 - 40gh + 16h^2$
8. $(\frac{1}{4} - b)^2$ — $\frac{1}{16} - \frac{1}{2}b + b^2$
9. $(8q - \frac{1}{2})^2$ — $64q^2 - 8q + \frac{1}{4}$
10. $(9d+4e)^2$ — $81d^2 + 72de + 16e^2$
11. $3(3+c)^2$ — $27 + 18c + 3c^2$
12. $(2x+1)^2 + (2x-1)^2$ — $8x^2 + 2$
13. $\frac{1}{4}(6p+4)^2$ — $9p^2 + 12p + 4$
14. $-9(2k-5)^2 - 2(k+3)^2$ — $-38k^2 + 168k - 243$

USES Objective I

In 15 and 16, use the rectangles pictured at the right.

15. Write an expression for the area of the shaded region. $-x^2 + 19x + 63$
16. Determine the area of the shaded region if $x = 3$ cm. 111 cm^2

258 Advanced Algebra

Lesson

6-2

GOAL

Review and apply the relationship between square roots and absolute value: $\sqrt{x^2} = |x|$.

SPUR Objectives

C Solve quadratic equations.

D Solve absolute-value equations.

F Apply the definition of absolute value and the Absolute Value-Square Root Theorem.

K Graph absolute-value functions and interpret them.

Materials/Resources

- Lesson Masters 6-2A and 6-2B
- Resource Masters 2, 3, 96, and 97

HOMEWORK

Suggestions for Assignment

- Questions 1–30
- Question 31 (extra credit)
- Reading Lesson 6-3
- Covering the Ideas 6-3

Local Standards

1 Warm-Up

1. Give the number-line coordinates of the points that are
   a. 8 units from 0. 8, -8
   b. 4 units from -1. -5, 3
   c. 3 units from 3. 0, 6
2. Simplify $-\sqrt{64}$. -8
3. Solve $x^2 = 25$. $x = 5$ or $x = -5$

Lesson 6-2

Absolute Value, Square Roots, and Quadratic Equations

Vocabulary

absolute value
absolute-value function
square root
rational number
irrational number

BIG IDEA Geometrically, the *absolute value* of a number is its distance on a number line from 0. Algebraically, the absolute value of a number equals the nonnegative square root of its square.

The **absolute value** of a number n, written $|n|$, can be described geometrically as the distance of n from 0 on the number line. For instance, $|42| = 42$ and $|-42| = 42$. Both 42 and -42 are 42 units from zero.

-42 42
-60 -40 -20 0 20 40 60

Algebraically, the absolute value of a number can be defined piecewise as follows.

$$|x| = \begin{cases} x, \text{ for } x \geq 0 \\ -x, \text{ for } x < 0 \end{cases}$$

Examine the definition carefully. Because $-x$ is the opposite of x, $-x$ is positive when x is negative. For instance, $|-7.4| = -(-7.4) = 7.4$. Thus $|x|$ are $|-x|$ are never negative, and, in fact, $|x| = |-x|$.

On many graphing utilities, spreadsheets, and CAS, the absolute-value function is denoted `abs`. For example, `abs(x-3) = |x-3|`.

Mental Math

A company makes \$6 dollars in revenue for every teacup it sells and \$5 in revenue for every saucer it sells. How much revenue will the company make if they sell

a. 500 teacups and no saucers? \$3000

b. 400 teacups and 200 saucers? \$3400

c. 500 saucers and no teacups? \$2500

Example 1

Solve for x: $|x - 4| = 8.1$.

Solution Use the algebraic definition of absolute value.

Either $x - 4 = 8.1$ or $x - 4 = -8.1$.

So, $x = 12.1$ or $x = -4.1$.

Check Use a CAS.

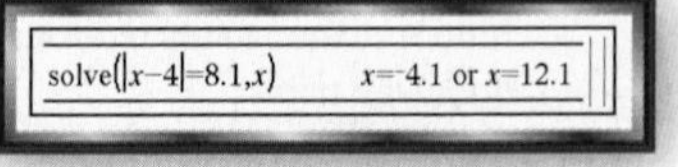

QY1

QY1

Suppose $f(x) = |x - 1|$. Write a piecewise definition for f.

Background

The absolute-value function Students saw piecewise definitions of functions in Chapter 3. Here is perhaps the most familiar example of a piecewise linear function. Students should remember how to calculate absolute value from both algebra and geometry, though coverage in those courses may not have included the function aspect of absolute value.

Absolute value and square roots The Absolute Value–Square Root Theorem ($\sqrt{x^2} = |x|$) is needed later for changing distance (which involves absolute value) into squares in the derivation of equations of parabolas. This theorem has the advantage of changing an expression that is defined piecewise (the absolute value) into a single expression that is related to powers and roots and thus can be dealt with by using properties of powers and roots.

The Absolute-Value Function

Because every real number has exactly one absolute value, $f: x \to |x|$ is a function. The graph of $f(x) = |x|$ is shown at the right. When $x \geq 0, f(x) = x$, and the graph is a ray with slope 1 and endpoint (0, 0). This is the ray in the first quadrant. When $x \leq 0, f(x) = -x$, and the graph is the ray with slope -1 and endpoint (0, 0). This is the ray in the second quadrant. The graph of $f(x) = |x|$ is the union of two rays, so the graph of $f(x) = |x|$ is an angle.

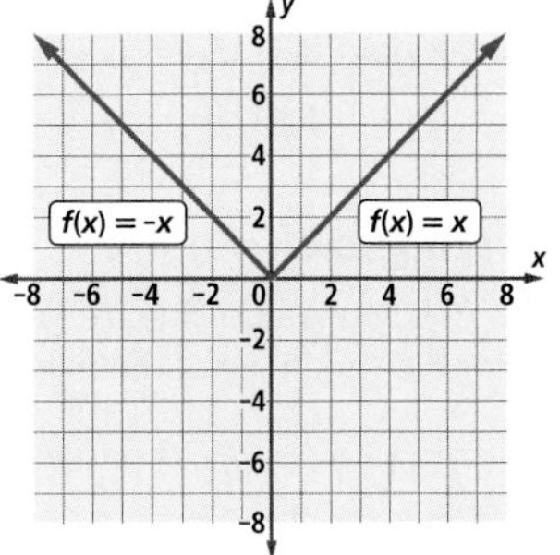

This function is called the **absolute-value function**. Its domain is the set of real numbers, and its range is the set of nonnegative real numbers.

Absolute Value and Square Roots

The simplest quadratic equations are of the form $x^2 = k$. When $k \geq 0$, the solutions to $x^2 = k$ are the positive and negative **square roots** of k, namely $\sqrt{k}$ and $-\sqrt{k}$. Square roots are intimately connected to absolute value.

Activity

Consider the functions f and g with equations $f(x) = \sqrt{x^2}$ and $g(x) = |x|$. See margin.

Step 1 In each row of the table, choose a value of x satisfying the constraint. Then evaluate $f(x)$ and $g(x)$. One row is completed for you.

Step 2 Make a conjecture about the relationship between f and g.

Step 3 Graph f and g on the same axes.

Step 4 Trace and toggle between the graphs to compare $f(x)$ and $g(x)$ for several values of x. Explain the apparent relationship between the graphs of f and g.

Constraint	x	$f(x)$	$g(x)$
$x < -10$	?	?	?
$-10 \leq x \leq -1$	?	?	?
$-1 < x < 0$	?	?	?
$x = 0$	0	0	0
$0 < x < 1$	?	?	?
$1 \leq x \leq 10$	?	?	?
$x > 10$	?	?	?

The Activity suggests that, for all real numbers x, $\sqrt{x^2}$ is equal to $|x|$.

Absolute Value–Square Root Theorem

For all real numbers x, $\sqrt{x^2} = |x|$.

Extension

Example 1 shows that the equation $|x - 4| = 8.1$ has solutions -4.1 or 12.1. The diagram below shows that the equation $|x - 4| = 8.1$ represents the statement "the distance between x and 4 is 8.1." Write and solve an absolute-value equation to find the value of x in each situation.

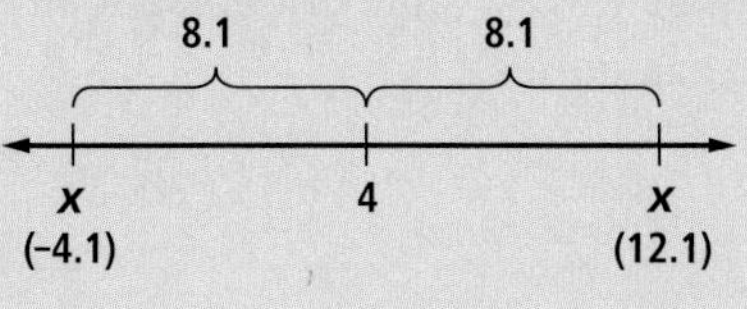

a. The distance between x and -13.6 is 22.8. $|x - (-13.6)| = 22.8$; $|x + 13.6| = 22.8$; $x + 13.6 = 22.8$ or $-(x + 13.6) = -22.8$; $x = 9.2$ or $x = -36.4$

b. The distance between -7.2 and x is 10.5. $|-7.2 - x| = 10.5$; $-7.2 - x = 10.5$ or $(-7.2 - x) = -10.5$; $x = -17.7$, or $x = 3.3$

6-2

2 Teaching

Notes on the Lesson

When x is positive, the symbol $\sqrt{x}$ is often called the square root of x, but really that symbol refers to the *positive* square root only. To denote the negative square root, we use $-\sqrt{x}$. You may wish to anticipate complex numbers by mentioning that Lessons 6-8 and 6-9 explore the meaning of the symbol $\sqrt{x}$ when x is negative.

Another way to demonstrate the Absolute Value–Square Root Theorem is to have students graph $y = \sqrt{x^2}$ with a graphing utility, using the domain $\{x \mid -10 \leq x \leq 10\}$. Many students are surprised that their graphs are the same as the absolute-value function.

Additional Example

Example 1 Solve for x: $|x + 6| = 7.2$. $x = 1.2$ or $x = -13.2$

Additional Answers

Activity

Step 1: Answers vary. Sample:

	x	$f(x)$	$g(x)$
$x < -10$	-15	15	15
$-10 \leq x \leq -1$	-6	6	6
$-1 < x < 0$	$-\frac{1}{2}$	$\frac{1}{2}$	$\frac{1}{2}$
$x = 0$	0	0	0
$0 < x < 1$	$\frac{1}{3}$	$\frac{1}{3}$	$\frac{1}{3}$
$1 \leq x \leq 10$	7	7	7
$x > 10$	12	12	12

Step 2: $f(x) = g(x)$ for all real numbers x.

Step 3:

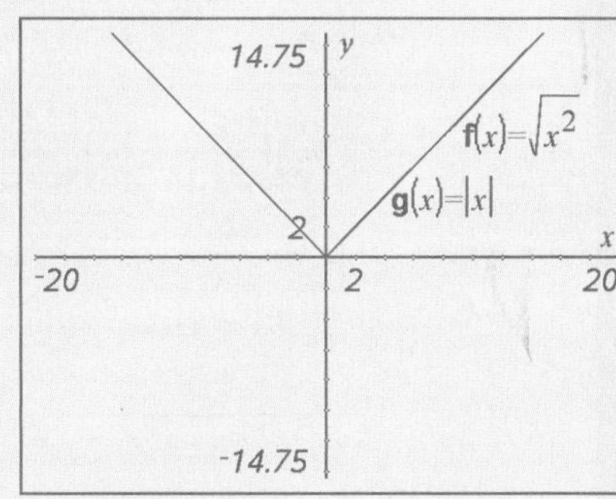

Step 4: The graphs are the same.

Notes on the Lesson

Example 2 The answer given by the CAS model shown provides a rationale for "simplifying" square roots of integers. Students should be able to recognize equalities such as $\sqrt{12} = 2\sqrt{3}$. This will help them to not only recognize the equivalence of ratios when dealing with similar figures and trigonometry but also help them deal with properties of complex numbers. If students do not understand why $\sqrt{12} = 2\sqrt{3}$, show them the intermediate steps: $\sqrt{12} = \sqrt{4 \cdot 3} = \sqrt{4}\sqrt{3} = 2\sqrt{3}$.

Note-Taking Tips

Encourage students to include in their notes a key sequence for evaluating expressions that have radicals and negative signs. For example, to evaluate $(-\sqrt{12})^2$ in the Check for Example 2, students could write the key sequence [(] [1][2] [√][(-)][)][x^2]

Additional Examples

Example 2 Solve $x^2 = 40$.
$x = \sqrt{40}$ or $x = -\sqrt{40}$

Example 3 An equilateral triangle and a circle have the same area. The triangle has a side length of 20 centimeters. Which is greater, the side length of the triangle or the diameter of the circle? The area of the triangle is $100\sqrt{3}$, so $\pi r^2 = 100\sqrt{3}$, and the radius of the circle is about 7.425 cm. Its diameter is about 14.85 cm, so the side length of the triangle is greater than the diameter of the circle.

Proof Either $x > 0$, $x = 0$, or $x < 0$.
If $x > 0$, then $\sqrt{x^2} = x$, and also $|x| = x$, so $\sqrt{x^2} = |x|$.
If $x = 0$, then $\sqrt{x^2} = 0$, and also $|x| = |0| = 0$, so $\sqrt{x^2} = |x|$.
If $x < 0$, then $\sqrt{x^2} = -x$, and also $|x| = -x$, so $\sqrt{x^2} = |x|$.

Solving $ax^2 = b$

The Absolute Value–Square Root Theorem can be used to solve quadratic equations of the form $ax^2 = b$.

Example 2

Solve $x^2 = 12$.

Solution 1 Take the positive square root of each side.

$\sqrt{x^2} = \sqrt{12}$

Use the Absolute Value-Square Root Theorem.

$|x| = \sqrt{12}$

So, either $x = \sqrt{12}$ or $x = -\sqrt{12}$.

Check Use your calculator to evaluate $(\sqrt{12})^2$ and $(-\sqrt{12})^2$. Each equals 12. It checks.

Solution 2 Use a CAS.

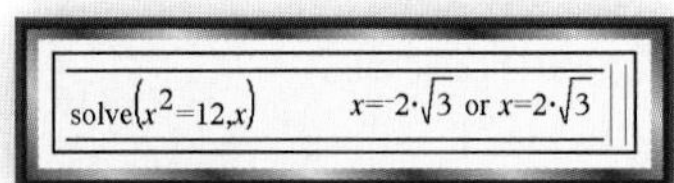

Check The solutions are shown as $-2\sqrt{3}$ and $2\sqrt{3}$, so multiply to show that $(-2\sqrt{3})^2$ and $(2\sqrt{3})^2$ both equal 12.

When $x = a$ or $x = -a$, you can write $x = \pm a$. In Example 2, $x = \pm\sqrt{12} = \pm 2\sqrt{3}$.

Example 3

A square and circle have the same area. The square has side length 15 units. Which is longer, a side of the square or the diameter of the circle?

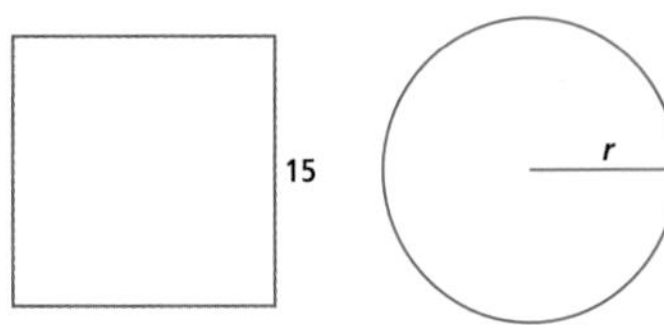

Solution The area of the square is $15 \cdot 15 = 225$ square units.

Accommodating the Learner

The area of a square is 15 square centimeters. Write an equation that involves the side length s of the square and write an expression for the exact value of s.
$s^2 = 15$ cm, $s = \sqrt{15}$ cm

ENGLISH LEARNERS

Vocabulary Development

Some students may be bothered that the definition of absolute value has two parts. It may help to discuss that the two conditions, $x \geq 0$ and $x < 0$, form categories that are *mutually exclusive* (no value of x can belong to both categories), and the two categories are *exhaustive* (every value of x must fit into one of the categories).

Since we know a formula for the area of a circle in terms of its radius, let r be the radius of the circle.

$$\pi r^2 = 225$$

$$r^2 = \frac{225}{\pi}$$ Divide by π.

$$|r| = \sqrt{\frac{225}{\pi}}$$ Take the square root of each side and use the Absolute Value-Square Root Theorem.

$$r = \pm\sqrt{\frac{225}{\pi}}$$ Definition of absolute value

$$\approx \pm 8.46 \text{ units}$$

You can ignore the negative solution because a radius cannot be negative. The radius of the circle is approximately 8.5 units. So the diameter is about 17 units and is longer than a side of the square.

QY2

▶ QY2

Check the solution to Example 3. Is $\pi(8.5)^2 \approx 225$?

Rational and Irrational Numbers

Recall from earlier courses that a *simple fraction* is a fraction of the form $\frac{a}{b}$, where a and b are integers and $b \neq 0$. And recall from Chapter 1 that a number that can be written as a simple fraction is called a **rational number**. Around 430 BCE, the Greeks proved that unless an integer is a perfect square (like 49, 625, or 10,000), its square root is an *irrational number*. An **irrational number** is a real number that cannot be written as a simple fraction. Irrational numbers, including most square roots, have infinite nonrepeating decimal expansions. The exact answers to Examples 2 and 3 are irrational numbers.

▶ READING MATH

As used in algebra, the word *rational* comes from the word *ratio*. A *rational number* is a number that can be written as the *ratio* of two integers.

Questions

COVERING THE IDEAS

1. Evaluate without a calculator.
   a. $|17.8|$ b. $|-17.8|$ c. $-|17.8|$ d. $-|-17.8|$
2. A classmate believes $|-t| = t$ for all real numbers t. Is this correct? Explain your answer. No; for $t < 0$, $-t > 0$, so $|-t| = -t$.
3. A classmate believes `abs(x) = -abs(x)` for all real numbers x. Is this correct? Why or why not?
4. Sketch a graph of f and g with equations $f(x) = |x - 4|$ and $g(x) = 8.1$, and label the coordinates of the points of intersection to verify the answer to Example 1. See margin.
5. The two numbers at a distance 90 from 0 on a number line are the solutions to what equation? $|x| = 90$

1a. 17.8

1b. 17.8

1c. -17.8

1d. -17.8

3. No; Consider $x \neq 0$. Then $|x| > 0$, so $-|x| < 0$ and $|x| \neq -|x|$.

Additional Answers

4.

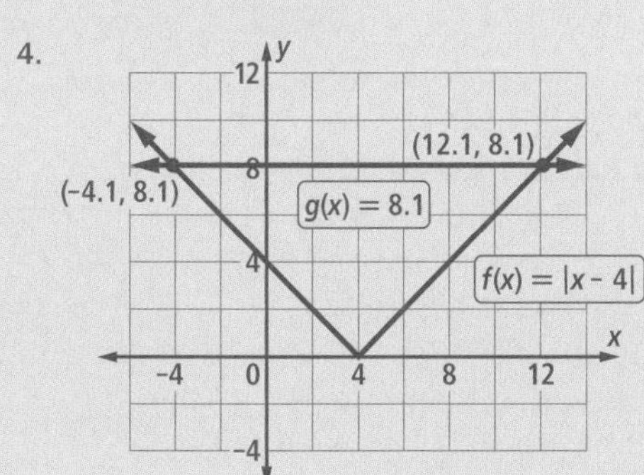

Notes on the Lesson

You may wish to display the following table categorizing decimals as rational or irrational numbers. Ask students for examples of each type of decimal.

Decimal	Type of Number
terminating	rational
infinite repeating	rational
infinite nonrepeating	irrational

3 Assignment

Recommended Assignment

- Questions 1–30
- Question 31 (extra credit)
- Reading Lesson 6-3
- Covering the Ideas 6-3

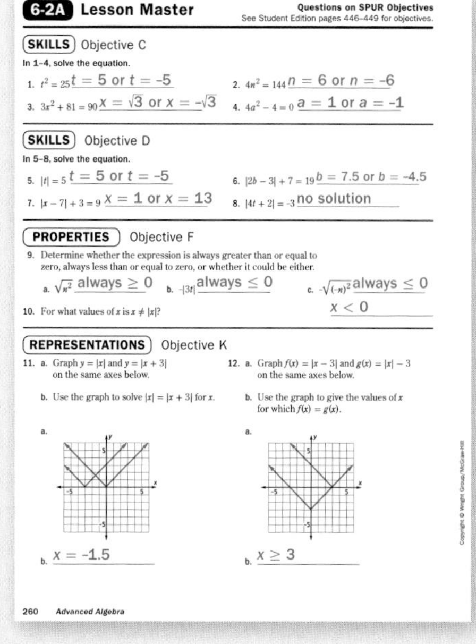

6-2A Lesson Master

Questions on SPUR Objectives
See Student Edition pages 446–449 for objectives.

SKILLS Objective C

In 1–4, solve the equation.

1. $t^2 = 25$ $t = 5$ or $t = -5$
2. $4n^2 = 144$ $n = 6$ or $n = -6$
3. $3x^2 + 81 = 90$ $x = \sqrt{3}$ or $x = -\sqrt{3}$
4. $4a^2 - 4 = 0$ $a = 1$ or $a = -1$

SKILLS Objective D

In 5–8, solve the equation.

5. $|t| = 5$ $t = 5$ or $t = -5$
6. $|2b - 3| + 7 = 19$ $b = 7.5$ or $b = -4.5$
7. $|x - 7| + 3 = 9$ $x = 1$ or $x = 13$
8. $|4t + 2| = -3$ no solution

PROPERTIES Objective F

9. Determine whether the expression is always greater than or equal to zero, always less than or equal to zero, or whether it could be either.
   a. $\sqrt{n^2}$ always ≥ 0 b. $-|3t|$ always ≤ 0 c. $-\sqrt{(-n)^2}$ always ≤ 0
10. For what values of x is $x \neq |x|$? $x < 0$

REPRESENTATIONS Objective K

11. a. Graph $y = |x|$ and $y = |x + 3|$ on the same axes below.
    b. Use the graph to solve $|x| = |x + 3|$ for x.
    b. $x = -1.5$
12. a. Graph $f(x) = |x - 3|$ and $g(x) = |x| - 3$ on the same axes below.
    b. Use the graph to give the values of x for which $f(x) = g(x)$.
    b. $x \geq 3$

260 *Advanced Algebra*

Notes on the Questions

Question 11 The answer 27 is correct; students do not have to write 27.000 to show the answer is to the nearest thousandth. However, you might have them write "27 (exactly)."

Additional Answers

22a.

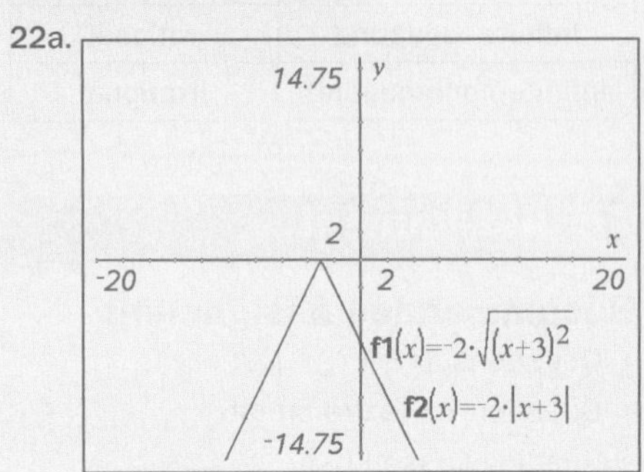

24.

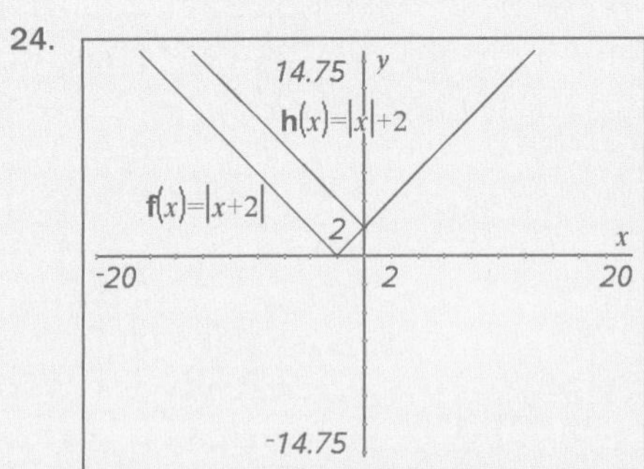

25. Answers vary. Sample: Each small square with dimensions $\sqrt{3} \times \sqrt{3}$ has an area of $(\sqrt{3})^2 = 3$. So the large square, which is made up of four small squares, has an area of $4 \cdot 3 = 12$. You can also find the area of the large square by squaring its side length: $(\sqrt{3} + \sqrt{3})^2 = (2\sqrt{3})^2$. So $(2\sqrt{3})^2 = 12$. Taking the square root of both sides gives $2\sqrt{3} = \sqrt{12}$. (Since the side length must be positive, the absolute value can be ignored.)

29a.

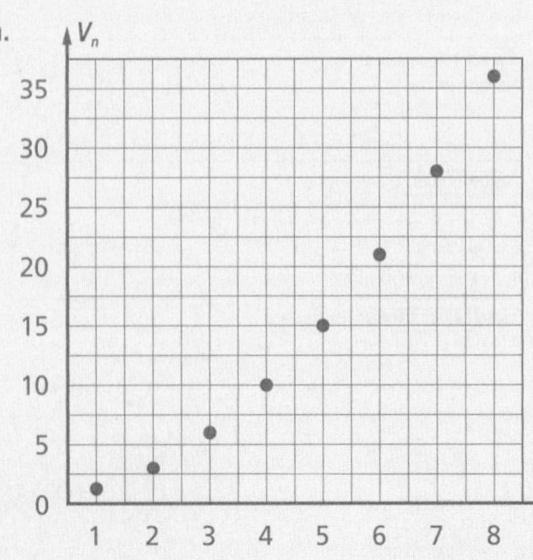

In 6 and 7, solve.

6. $|3.4 - y| = 6.5$ $y = 9.9$ or $y = -3.1$

7. $|2n + 7| = 5$ $n = -1$ or $n = -6$

8. Consider the function f with equation $f(x) = -|x|$.
   a. State its domain and its range.
   b. **True or False** The graph of f is piecewise linear. Justify your answer.

8a. domain: the set of all real numbers, range: $\{y \mid y \le 0\}$

8b. True; because $f(x) = -|x| = \begin{cases} -x, & \text{for } x \ge 0 \\ x, & \text{for } x < 0 \end{cases}$, it can be described by two linear functions.

9. **Multiple Choice** What is the solution set to $\sqrt{x^2} = |x|$? A
   A the set of all real numbers
   B the set of all nonnegative real numbers
   C the set of all positive real numbers

In 10 and 11, find all real-number solutions to the nearest thousandth.

10. $k^2 = 261$ ± 16.155

11. $3x^2 = 2187$ ± 27

12. a. Find the exact radius of a circle whose area is 150 square meters.
    b. Estimate the answer to Part a to the nearest thousandth.

12a. $\sqrt{\frac{150}{\pi}}$

12b. 6.910

13. A circle has the same area as a square with side length 8. What is the radius of the circle to the nearest hundredth? 4.51

14. A square has the same area as a circle with radius 9. What is the length of a side of the square to the nearest hundredth? 15.95

In 15–20, tell whether the number is rational or irrational. If it is rational, write the number as an integer or a simple fraction.

15. $\sqrt{8}$
16. $\sqrt{100} - 2$
17. $\sqrt{36}$
18. $\frac{0.13}{713}$
19. $\frac{2}{\sqrt{2}}$
20. π

15. irrational
16. rational, 8
17. rational, 6
18. rational, $\frac{13}{71{,}300}$
19. irrational
20. irrational

APPLYING THE MATHEMATICS

21. The formula $e = |p - I|$ gives the allowable margin of error e for a given measurement p when I is the ideal measurement. A certain soccer ball manufacturer aims for a weight of 442.5 g with an acceptable value of e being no more than 1.5 g.
    a. Use absolute value to write a mathematical sentence for the allowable margin of error for soccer ball weights p.
    b. What is the most a soccer ball from this manufacturer should weigh? 444 g

21a. $1.5 \ge |p - 442.5|$

22. a. Graph $f(x) = -2\sqrt{(x + 3)^2}$ and $g(x) = -2|x + 3|$ on the same set of axes in a standard window. See margin.
    b. How do the two graphs appear to be related? They are the same graph.

Additional Answers

31a. Answers vary. Sample: $a_1 = 2$, $a_2 = 2.25$, $a_3 \approx 2.23611$, $a_4 \approx 2.23607$, $a_5 \approx 2.23607$; $\sqrt{5} - a_5 \approx 0$

31b. Answers vary. Sample: $|\sqrt{5} - a_3| = 0.000043 < 0.0001$

31c. Answers vary. Sample: $a_1 = 6$, $a_2 \approx 6.333333$, $a_3 \approx 6.324561$, $a_4 \approx 6.324555$; $|\sqrt{40} - a_4| < 0.000001$

23. The directions on a brand-name pizza box read, "Spread dough to edges of a round pizza pan or onto a 10" by 14" rectangular baking sheet." How big a circular pizza could you make with this dough, assuming it is spread the same thickness as for the rectangular pizza? a pizza with about a 13.4-in. diameter

24. Graph $f(x) = |x + 2|$ and $h(x) = |x| + 2$ on the same set of axes in a standard window. See margin for graph.
    a. According to the graph, for which values of x does $f(x) = g(x)$? $x \geq 0$
    b. Describe the set of numbers for which $f(x) \neq g(x)$. $x < 0$

25. Use the drawing at the right to explain why $2\sqrt{3} = \sqrt{12}$. See margin.

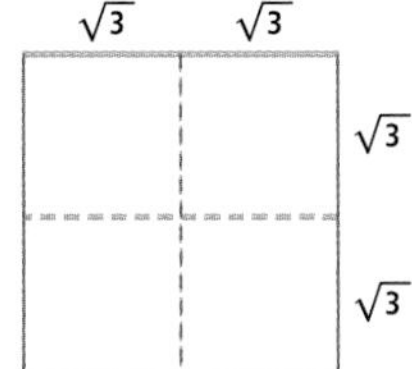

REVIEW

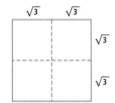

In 26 and 27, multiply and simplify. (Lesson 6-1)

26. $(x + 3y)(x - 2y)$ $x^2 + xy - 6y^2$ 27. $(8 + x)(8 - x)$ $64 - x^2$

28. Consider the line with equation $y = \frac{4}{3}x + 3$. Find an equation for the image of this line under the translation $T_{3,1}$. (Lesson 4-10) $y = \frac{4}{3}x$

29. a. Graph the first eight terms of the sequence defined recursively by $\begin{cases} v_1 = 1 \\ v_n = v_{n-1} + n, \text{ for integers } n \geq 2 \end{cases}$. See margin.
    b. Rewrite the second line of the formula in Part a if v_n represents the previous term of the sequence. (Lessons 3-7, 3-6) $v_{n+1} = v_n + (n + 1)$, for integers $n \geq 1$

30. A graph of $y = kx^2$ is shown at the right. Find the value of k. (Lesson 2-5) $k = -\frac{5}{2}$

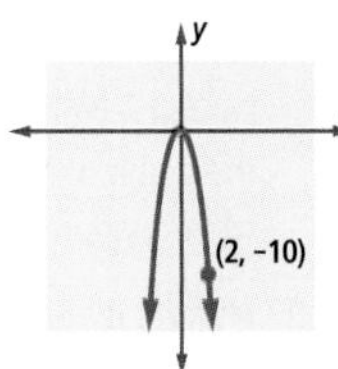

EXPLORATION

31. One way to estimate $\sqrt{k}$ without using a square root command on a calculator or computer uses the following sequence:
$$\begin{cases} a_1 = \text{initial guess at the root} \\ a_n = \frac{1}{2}\left(a_{n-1} + \frac{k}{a_{n-1}}\right), \text{ for integers } n \geq 2. \end{cases}$$
See margin.
    a. Let $k = 5$. Give a rational number approximation for $\sqrt{5}$ and use that number as a_1. Then find a_2, a_3, a_4, and a_5. Use a calculator to check the difference between a_5 and $\sqrt{5}$.
    b. Continue to generate terms of the sequence until you are within 0.0001 of $\sqrt{5}$.
    c. Use the sequence to estimate the positive square root of 40 to the nearest millionth.

QY ANSWERS

1. $f(x) = |x-1| = \begin{cases} x - 1, \text{ for } x \geq 1 \\ -x + 1, \text{ for } x < 1 \end{cases}$

2. $\pi(8.5)^2 \approx 226.98$, close enough given that 8.5 is an approximation. (In fact, $\pi(8.46)^2 \approx 224.85$, much closer to 225.)

Notes on the Questions

Question 23 These directions come from an actual package of dough. Encourage students to make a sketch for this question.

Question 25 Students may be surprised by this drawing, not realizing that an irrational number can be the side length of a rectangle.

Question 31 This procedure is known as the "divide and average" algorithm for square roots. It is sometimes called "Newton's method," although the Babylonians knew it 4000 years ago. For some history of the methods of calculating square roots, see http://www.pballew.net/oldsqrt.htm.

4 Wrap-Up

Ongoing Assessment

Have students work in small groups. In each group, one student should select a positive decimal for A and a second student should select a positive decimal for B. Then all students in the group should solve the absolute-value equations $|x - A| = B$ and $|y - B| = A$ and check each other's work. Answers vary. Sample: If $A = 5.3$ and $B = 8.1$, then the solution to $|x - 5.3| = 8.1$ is $x = 13.4$ or $x = -2.8$, and the solution to $|y - 8.1| = 5.3$ is $y = 13.4$ or $y = 2.8$.

Project Update

Project 4, *Minimum Distance,* on page 441 relates to the content of this lesson.

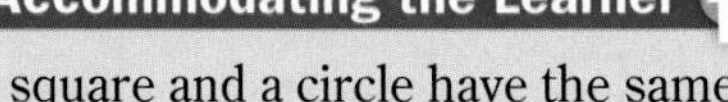

Accommodating the Learner

A square and a circle have the same perimeter.

a. If the area of the square is A square units, find the diameter of the circle. The side length of the square is $\sqrt{A}$, so its perimeter is $4\sqrt{A}$. Then $4\sqrt{A} = \pi d$ and $d = \frac{4\sqrt{A}}{\pi}$ units.

b. If the radius of the circle is r units, find the diagonal of the square. The circumference of the circle is $2\pi r$, so each side of the square is $\frac{2\pi r}{4} = \frac{\pi r}{2}$, and the diagonal is $\frac{\pi r\sqrt{2}}{2}$ units.

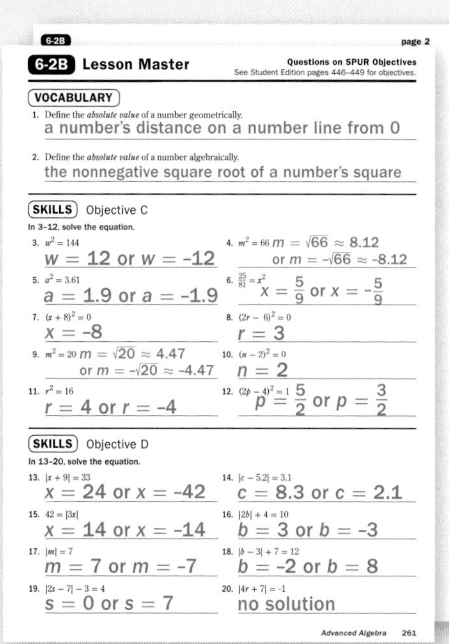

6-2B page 2

6-2B Lesson Master Questions on SPUR Objectives
See Student Edition pages 446–449 for objectives.

VOCABULARY

1. Define the *absolute value* of a number geometrically.
a number's distance on a number line from 0

2. Define the *absolute value* of a number algebraically.
the nonnegative square root of a number's square

SKILLS Objective C

In 3–12, solve the equation.

3. $w^2 = 144$ $w = 12$ or $w = -12$
4. $m^2 = 66$ $m = \sqrt{66} \approx 8.12$ or $m = -\sqrt{66} \approx -8.12$
5. $a^2 = 3.61$ $a = 1.9$ or $a = -1.9$
6. $\frac{25}{81} = x^2$ $x = \frac{5}{9}$ or $x = -\frac{5}{9}$
7. $(x + 8)^2 = 0$ $x = -8$
8. $(2r - 6)^2 = 0$ $r = 3$
9. $m^2 = 20$ $m = \sqrt{20} \approx 4.47$ or $m = -\sqrt{20} \approx -4.47$
10. $(n - 2)^2 = 0$ $n = 2$
11. $r^2 = 16$ $r = 4$ or $r = -4$
12. $(2p - 4)^2 = 1$ $p = \frac{5}{2}$ or $p = \frac{3}{2}$

SKILLS Objective D

In 13–20, solve the equation.

13. $|x + 9| = 33$ $x = 24$ or $x = -42$
14. $|c - 5.2| = 3.1$ $c = 8.3$ or $c = 2.1$
15. $42 = |3x|$ $x = 14$ or $x = -14$
16. $|2b| + 4 = 10$ $b = 3$ or $b = -3$
17. $|m| = 7$ $m = 7$ or $m = -7$
18. $|b - 3| + 7 = 12$ $b = -2$ or $b = 8$
19. $|2s - 7| - 3 = 4$ $s = 0$ or $s = 7$
20. $|4r + 7| = -1$ no solution

Advanced Algebra 261

Lesson

6-3

GOAL

Apply the Graph-Translation Theorem to parabolas and absolute-value functions.

SPUR Objectives

G Use the Graph-Translation Theorem to interpret equations and graphs.

K Graph quadratic functions and absolute-value functions and interpret them.

Materials/Resources

- Lesson Masters 6-3A and 6-3B
- Resource Masters 2, 3, and 98–101
- Graphing utility

HOMEWORK

Suggestions for Assignment

- Questions 1–25
- Question 26 (extra credit)
- Reading Lesson 6-4
- Covering the Ideas 6-4

Local Standards

1 Warm-Up

If the Activity has not been done, it can be used as a prelude to the lesson. Step 1 is easy if students can graph the parabolas with a graphing utility. You might challenge groups to predict the vertex without graphing and then use a graph as a check. In Step 5, each person in the group should choose different values for h and k.

Alternatively, if your students have dynamic graphing utilities that allow them to drag graphs, tell them to drag the graph of $y = x^2$ and observe how the equation changes. To simulate the steps of the Activity, have them drag the graph horizontally, then vertically, then both horizontally and vertically. This makes it easy to see the pattern.

Lesson

6-3 The Graph-Translation Theorem

Vocabulary

corollary
vertex form
axis of symmetry
minimum, maximum

▶ **BIG IDEA** If you know an equation for a graph, then you can easily find an equation for any translation image of the graph.

Mental Math

Let $x = 3$. Find

a. $x^2 + 7$. 16

b. $(x + 7)^2$. 100

c. $7x^2$. 63

d. $(7x)^2$. 441

You can quickly graph functions whose graphs are translation images of functions with which you are already familiar.

Activity

MATERIALS graphing utility

Work with a partner. Steps 1 and 2. See the Additional Answers section at the back of the book.

Step 1 Graph each group of equations below on the same axes. Print or sketch each group and label the individual parabolas.

Group A	Group B	Group C
$f1(x) = x^2$	$f1(x) = x^2$	$f1(x) = x^2$
$f2(x) = (x - 4)^2$	$f2(x) = x^2 - 5$	$f2(x) = (x - 3)^2 + 2$
$f3(x) = (x + 2)^2$	$f3(x) = x^2 + 3$	$f3(x) = (x + 4)^2 - 1$

Step 2 For each group, describe the translations that map the graph of $f(x) = x^2$ onto the graphs of the other two equations.

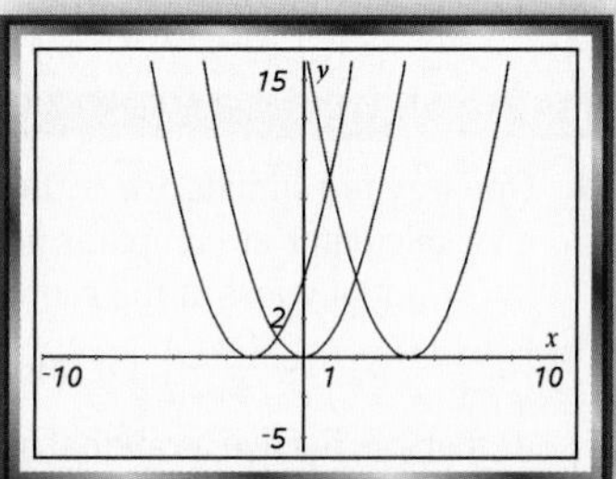

Step 3 Without graphing, describe the graph of each equation below as a translation image of the graph of $y = x^2$.

a. $y = (x + 5)^2$

b. $y = x^2 - 1$ translation 1 unit down

c. $y = (x + 2)^2 - 5$

Step 3a. translation 5 units to the left

Step 3c. translation 2 units to the left and 5 units down

Step 4 Make some conjectures. For any real numbers h and k, what translation maps $y = x^2$ onto the graph of a–c. See the Additional Answers section at the back of the book.

a. $y = (x - h)^2$? b. $y = x^2 + k$? c. $y = (x - h)^2 + k$?

Step 5 Test your conjectures from Step 4 for some other positive values of h and k. The conjecture is true.

Background

This is a very important lesson. The Graph-Translation Theorem is a powerful theorem, one that can be used repeatedly throughout a student's study of mathematics. Here are some instances:

- You can obtain the equation of a circle with center (h, k) and radius r by applying $T_{h,k}$ to $x^2 + y^2 = r^2$. The image has equation $(x - h)^2 + (y - k)^2 = r^2$. The same goes for any conic section.
- You can obtain the point-slope equation of the line with slope m through (x_0, y_0) by applying T_{x_0,y_0} to $y = mx$. An equation for the image in point-slope form is $y - y_0 = m(x - x_0)$. For the special case when $x_0 = 0$, the image of $y = mx$ under $T_{0,b}$ is $y - b = mx$.

The Graph-Translation Theorem

Your sketch of Group A in the Activity should show that when x is replaced by $(x - 4)$, the preimage is translated 4 units to the right, and when x is replaced by $(x + 2)$, the preimage is translated 2 units to the left. In general, replacing x with $x - h$ in a mathematical sentence translates its graph h units horizontally.

Similarly, replacing y with $y - k$ in a sentence translates its graph k units vertically. For example, your sketch of Group B should show that the graph of $y = x^2 + 3$ is 3 units above the graph of $y = x^2$. Note that you can rewrite this equation as $y - 3 = x^2$, so replacing y with $y - 3$ in the equation for a function translates its graph 3 units up.

Recall that the translation $T_{h,k}$ creates an image of a figure h units to the right and k units up from its preimage. The graph of $y - 2 = (x - 3)^2$ is the translation image of the graph $y = x^2$ under $T_{3,2}$. The results of the Activity are summarized in the Graph-Translation Theorem.

Graph-Translation Theorem

In a relation described by a sentence in x and y, the following two processes yield the same graph:

1. replacing x by $x - h$ and y by $y - k$;
2. applying the translation $T_{h,k}$ to the graph of the original relation.

The Graph-Translation Theorem applies to all relations that can be described by a sentence in x and y.

Example 1

Find an equation for the image of the graph of $y = |x|$ under the translation $T_{-2,4}$.

Solution Applying $T_{-2,4}$ is equivalent to replacing x with $x - (-2)$, or $x + 2$, and y with $y - 4$ in the equation for the preimage. An equation for the image is $y - 4 = |x - (-2)|$, or $y = |x + 2| + 4$.

Check $T_{-2,4}$ is the translation that slides a figure 2 units left and 4 units up. Graph $y = |x|$ and $y = |x + 2| + 4$ on the same set of axes. As shown at the right, the graph of the second equation is the image of the graph of the first equation under a translation 2 units to the left and 4 units up. It checks.

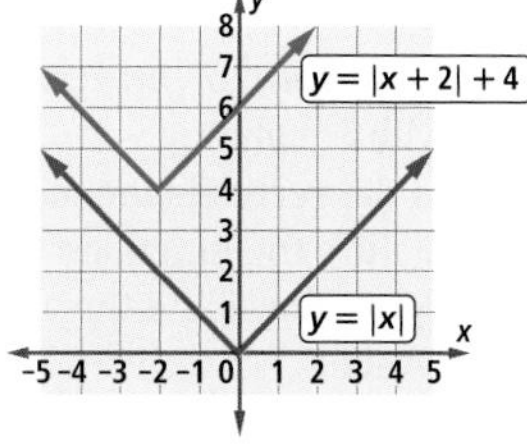

2 Teaching

Notes on the Lesson

In this lesson we apply the Graph-Translation Theorem to parabolas. From Chapter 2, we know that the parabola $y = ax^2$ has vertex (0, 0) and is symmetric to the line $x = 0$. If we translate that parabola h units to the right and k units up, we obtain a curve with equation $y - k = a(x - h)^2$, which is a parabola with vertex (h, k) and line of symmetry $x = h$.

The Graph-Translation Theorem is used to develop the vertex form of the equation of a parabola, but the theorem applies to any curve and tells how the equations representing the image and preimage are related. Here is a proof of the Graph-Translation Theorem. Let $T_{h,k} : (x, y) \rightarrow (x', y')$. Then $(x', y') = (x + h, y + k)$. Thus $x' = x + h$ and $y' = y + k$. It follows that $x = x' - h$ and $y = y' - k$. Thus, if we start with an equation relating x and y, we can substitute $x' - h$ for x and $y' - k$ for y and obtain an equation relating the coordinates of the image points under this translation. This is exactly what the Graph-Translation Theorem says; x' and y' are not in the equation for the image because we customarily drop the prime symbols.

You may wish to mention that the Graph-Translation Theorem will be used many times in the rest of this book plus in later mathematics courses.

Additional Answers can be found in the back of the book.

Additional Example

Example 1 Find an equation for the image of the graph of $y = |x|$ under the translation $T_{3,-5}$.

$y = |x - 3| - 5$

- Applying a phase shift π units to the right to the function $y = \sin x$ is the same as applying $T_{\pi,0}$ to the graph of $y = \sin x$. The image has equation $y = \sin(x - \pi)$. Any phase shift can be dealt with in this way. More generally, the graph of $y = A\sin(Bx + C) + D$ is the translation image of the graph of $y = A\sin(Bx)$ under the translation $T_{-\frac{C}{B},D}$.

Accommodating the Learner

Point out to students that the equation $y = |2x|$ can be written without absolute-value notation as $y = \begin{cases} 2x, \text{ if } x \geq 0 \\ -2x, \text{ if } x < 0 \end{cases}$. Ask students to write each equation without absolute-value notation.

1. $y = |x - 7|$ $y = \begin{cases} x - 7, \text{ if } x \geq 7 \\ -x + 7, \text{ if } x < 7 \end{cases}$

2. $y - 4 = |x + 3.5|$

$y = \begin{cases} x + 7.5, \text{ if } x \geq -3.5 \\ -x + 0.5, \text{ if } x < -3.5 \end{cases}$

Notes on the Lesson

The window used on a graphing utility can affect and/or distort the viewer's perception of a graph. For instance, some students may think that the graphs in Example 1 are not congruent. Have such students view these graphs in a different window (particularly by zooming out). Also, have them describe the angle made by the two rays and note that each angle is a right angle.

Point out that one important use of the corollary to the Graph-Translation Theorem (the Parabola-Translation Theorem) is that it tells a student how to graph any parabola that is a translation image of $y = ax^2$. Emphasize that the vertex form of the equation for a parabola has three important constants: h, k, and a. Because translations are isometries, the graphs of $y = ax^2$ and $y - k = a(x - h)^2$ are congruent, with a determining the parabola's width and whether it opens up or down.

In Example 2, we picked the point (-2, -3) to substitute, but any point can be used. Verify that there is a corresponding point on the graph of the image. Only with actual substitution does the Graph-Translation Theorem seem reasonable. Students should see how the subtraction of h and k compensates for the larger values that are substituted for x and y.

Using the Graph-Translation Theorem to Graph Parabolas

Recall from Chapter 2 that the graph of $y = ax^2$ is a parabola. If we replace x with $x - h$ and y with $y - k$ in the equation $y = ax^2$, we obtain $y - k = a(x - h)^2$. Because a figure is congruent to its translation image, the graph of this equation is also a parabola.

This argument proves the following *corollary* to the Graph-Translation Theorem. A **corollary** is a theorem that follows immediately from another theorem.

Parabola-Translation Theorem

The image of the parabola with equation $y = ax^2$ under the translation $T_{h,k}$ is the parabola with the equation

$$y - k = a(x - h)^2 \text{ or}$$
$$y = a(x - h)^2 + k.$$

The Graph-Translation Theorem and the Parabola-Translation Theorem can help you identify characteristics of a parabola by looking at its equation. As you read about these characteristics below, look at the graphs of $y = ax^2$ and $y - k = a(x - h)^2$ at the right.

- *Vertex* You know that (0, 0) is the vertex of the parabola $y = ax^2$. Under $T_{h,k}$, the translation image of (0, 0) is $T_{h,k}(0, 0) = (0 + h, 0 + k) = (h, k)$. So, the vertex of the parabola with equation $y - k = a(x - h)^2$ is (h, k). For this reason, the equation $y - k = a(x - h)^2$ is called the **vertex form** of an equation of a parabola.

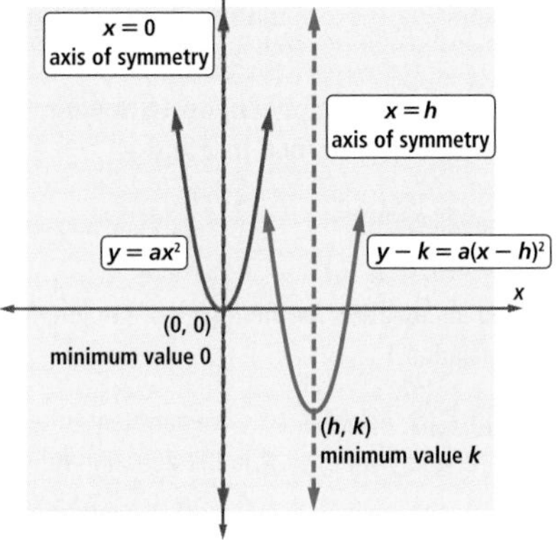

- *Axis of symmetry* The parabola with equation $y = ax^2$ is reflection-symmetric to the y-axis, which has equation $x = 0$. Since the parabola is translated h units to the right under $T_{h,k}$, the line with equation $x = h$ is the symmetry line or **axis of symmetry** of the parabola with equation $y - k = a(x - h)^2$.
- *Maximum or minimum y-value* If $a > 0$, then the parabola with equation $y - k = a(x - h)^2$ opens up and the y-coordinate of the vertex is the **minimum** y-value. The graphs at the right picture the functions when $a > 0$. If $a < 0$, then the parabola opens down and the y-coordinate of the vertex is the **maximum** y-value.

Accommodating the Learner

Ask students to explain how to find the axis of symmetry and the minimum value of the parabola described by $y = x^2$ after it undergoes the translation $T_{-2,-7}$. Answers vary. Sample: The vertex (0, 0) of $y = x^2$ is translated to (-2, -7) by $T_{-2,-7}$. So the axis of symmetry of the image is $x = -2$, and the minimum value of the image is $y = -7$.

Knowing these facts helps you to quickly sketch parabolas by hand and to better understand what you see when you use a graphing utility.

GUIDED

Example 2

a. State the coordinates of the vertex of the parabola with equation $y - 5 = -2(x + 3)^2$.

b. Write an equation for the axis of symmetry of the parabola.

c. Sketch a graph of the equation by hand.

Solution

a. The equation $y - 5 = -2(x + 3)^2$ results from replacing x with __?__ and y with __?__ in $y = -2x^2$. So its graph is the image of $y = -2x^2$ under the translation __?__. The graph is a parabola with vertex (__?__, __?__). $x + 3$; $y - 5$; $T_{-3,5}$; -3; 5

b. Since the axis of symmetry of $y = -2x^2$ has equation __?__, the axis of symmetry of this parabola is the line with equation $x =$ __?__. $x = 0$; -3

c. Because the graph of $y = -2x^2$ opens down, so does the graph of $y - 5 = -2(x + 3)^2$. Find a point on the graph other than the vertex. For example, let $x = -2$. Then $y - 5 = -2($__?__$ + 3)^2$, so $y =$ __?__ $+ 5$ $=$ __?__, and (-2, __?__) is a point on the graph. Sketch a parabola with vertex __?__, opening downward through the point (-2, __?__) and symmetric to the line $x =$ __?__. -2; -2; 3; 3; (-3, 5); 3; -3

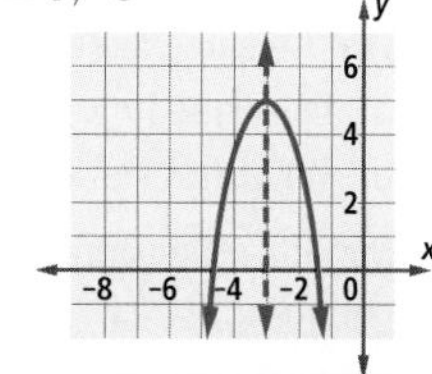

 QY

▶ QY

Describe the graph of $y - 15 = (x + 40)^2$.

Finding Equations for Parabolas

You can apply the Graph-Translation Theorem to a known parabola to find an equation for its image under a given translation.

Example 3

Consider the parabolas at the right. The one that passes through the origin has equation $y = \frac{1}{5}x^2$. The other is its image under a translation. Find an equation for the image.

Solution The translation image appears to be 4 units to the right and 2 units down from the preimage. So the translation is $T_{4,-2}$. Applying $T_{4,-2}$ is equivalent to replacing x with $x - 4$ and y with $y - (-2) = y + 2$ in the equation for the preimage. An equation for the image is $y + 2 = \frac{1}{5}(x - 4)^2$.

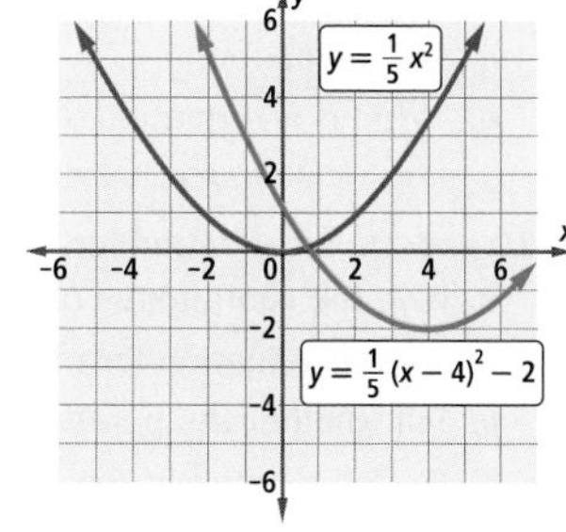

(continued on next page)

ENGLISH LEARNERS

Vocabulary Development

Just as students learned about different forms for a linear equation (slope-intercept form, point-slope form, and standard form), they will learn different forms of equations for parabolas. The form studied in this lesson, $y - k = a(x - h)^2$, is called the *vertex form* because it directly gives the vertex (h, k). Lesson 6-4 focuses on $y = ax^2 + bx + c$, the *standard* form, and Lesson 6-5 includes the process of rewriting a standard-form equation in vertex form.

Additional Example

Example 2

a. What are the coordinates of the vertex of the parabola with equation $y + 4 = 3(x - 2)^2$?

b. Write an equation for the axis of symmetry of the parabola.

c. Graph the parabola by hand.

Solution

a. The equation $y + 4 = 3(x - 2)^2$ results from replacing x by __?__ and y by __?__ in $y = 3x^2$. $x - 2$; $y + 4$ So its graph is the image of $y = 3x^2$ under the translation __?__. $T_{2,-4}$ The graph is a parabola with vertex __?__. (2, -4)

b. Because the axis of symmetry of $y = 3x^2$ has equation __?__, the axis of symmetry of this parabola is the line with equation __?__. $x = 0$; $x = 2$

c. Because the graph of $y = 3x^2$ opens up, so does the graph of $y + 4 = 3(x - 2)^2$. Find a point on the graph other than the vertex. For example, let $x = 3$. Then $y + 4 = 3($__?__$ - 2)^2$, so $y =$ __?__ $- 4 =$ __?__, and (3, __?__) is a point on the graph. 3; 3; -1; -1 Graph a parabola with vertex __?__ opening upward through the point (3, __?__) and symmetric to the line $x =$ __?__. (2, -4); -1; 2

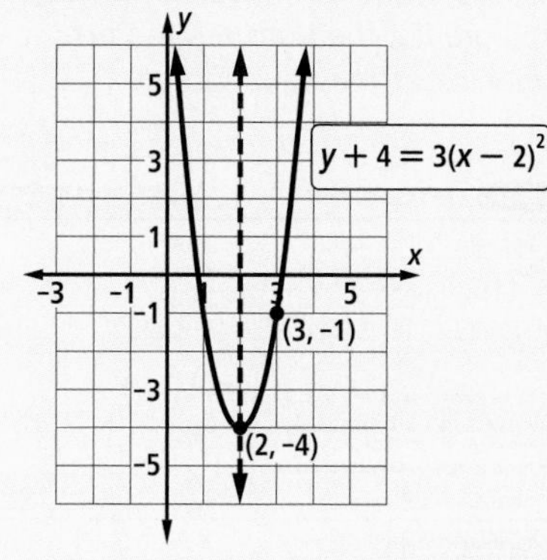

Additional Example

Example 3 Consider these parabolas.

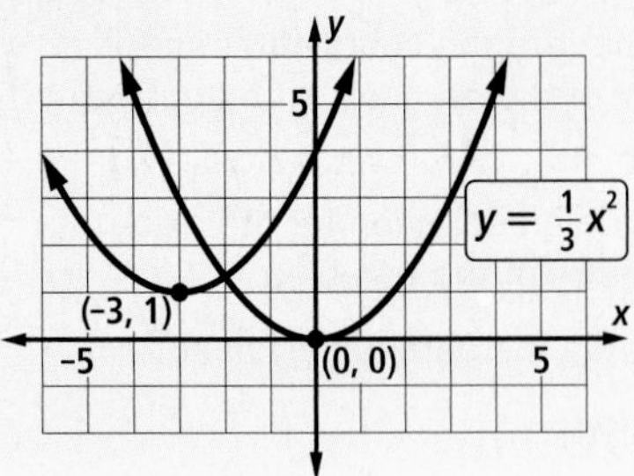

The one that passes through the origin has equation $y = \frac{1}{3}x^2$. The other is its image under a translation. Find an equation for the image. The translation is $T_{-3,1}$, and applying this translation is equivalent to replacing x by $x + 3$ and y by $y - 1$; an equation for the image is $y - 1 = \frac{1}{3}(x + 3)^2$.

3 Assignment

Recommended Assignment

- Questions 1–25
- Question 26 (extra credit)
- Reading Lesson 6-4
- Covering the Ideas 6-4

Notes on the Questions

Questions 3b, 5, 12, and 13 Encourage students to check their answers by graphing.

Questions 10 and 11 Have students describe in their own words how they could predict the answers to Parts a–c by looking at the equation only.

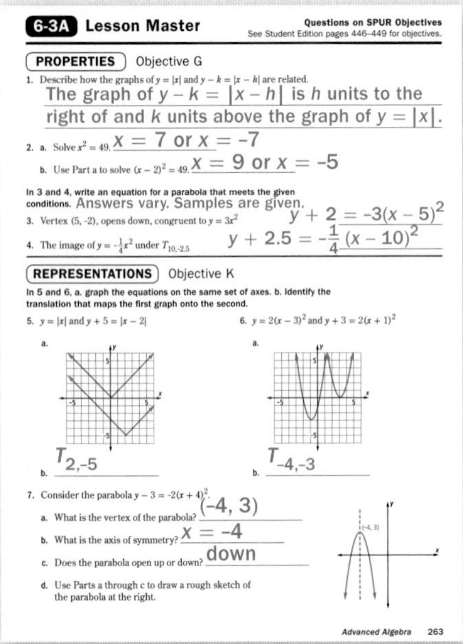

6-3A Lesson Master

Questions on SPUR Objectives
See Student Edition pages 446–449 for objectives.

PROPERTIES Objective G

1. Describe how the graphs of $y = |x|$ and $y - k = |x - h|$ are related. The graph of $y - k = |x - h|$ is h units to the right of and k units above the graph of $y = |x|$.
2. a. Solve $x^2 = 49$. $x = 7$ or $x = -7$
   b. Use Part a to solve $(x - 2)^2 = 49$. $x = 9$ or $x = -5$

In 3 and 4, write an equation for a parabola that meets the given conditions. Answers vary. Samples are given.

3. Vertex (5, -2), opens down, congruent to $y = 3x^2$ $y + 2 = -3(x - 5)^2$
4. The image of $y = -\frac{1}{4}x^2$ under $T_{10,-2.5}$ $y + 2.5 = -\frac{1}{4}(x - 10)^2$

REPRESENTATIONS Objective K

In 5 and 6, a. graph the equations on the same set of axes. b. Identify the translation that maps the first graph onto the second.

5. $y = |x|$ and $y + 5 = |x - 2|$
   a.
   b. $T_{2,-5}$
6. $y = 2(x - 3)^2$ and $y + 3 = 2(x + 1)^2$
   a.
   b. $T_{-4,-3}$
7. Consider the parabola $y - 3 = -2(x + 4)^2$.
   a. What is the vertex of the parabola? (-4, 3)
   b. What is the axis of symmetry? $x = -4$
   c. Does the parabola open up or down? down
   d. Use Parts a through c to draw a rough sketch of the parabola at the right.

Advanced Algebra 263

Check Use a graphing utility. Because $y + 2 = \frac{1}{5}(x - 4)^2$ is equivalent to $y = \frac{1}{5}(x - 4)^2 - 2$, plot $y = \frac{1}{5}x^2$ and $y = \frac{1}{5}(x - 4)^2 - 2$ in the same window. You should see that the graph of the second equation is the image of the graph of the first under $T_{4,-2}$.

You will see more applications of the Graph-Translation Theorem in later chapters.

Questions

COVERING THE IDEAS

In 1 and 2, tell how the graphs of the two equations are related.

1. $y_1 = x^2$ and $y_2 = (x - 5)^2$
2. $y_1 = x^2$ and $y_2 + 6 = x^2$
3. a. What is the image of (x, y) under $T_{7,0}$? $(x + 7, y)$
   b. Under $T_{7,0}$, what is an equation for the image of the graph of $y = x^2$? $y = (x - 7)^2$
4. On the same axes, sketch $y = |x|$ and $y + 1 = |x - 4|$.
   a. Describe how the two graphs are related.
   b. What translation maps the first onto the second? $T_{4,-1}$
5. Suppose the translation $T_{4,-7}$ is applied to the parabola with equation $y = \frac{7}{5}x^2$. Find an equation for the image. $y = \frac{7}{5}(x - 4)^2 - 7$
6. **Fill in the Blanks** The graph of $y - k = a(x - h)^2$ is __?__ units above and __?__ units to the right of the graph of $y = ax^2$. k; h
7. **True or False** For all values of h and k, the graphs of $y = ax^2$ and $y = a(x - h)^2 + k$ are congruent. true
8. a. What is the vertex of the parabola with equation $y - 7 = -3(x + 5)^2$? (-5, 7)
   b. What is the vertex of the parabola with equation $y - k = a(x - h)^2$? (h, k)
9. a. What is an equation of the axis of symmetry of the parabola with equation $y - 7 = -3(x + 5)^2$ $x = -5$
   b. What is an equation of the axis of symmetry of the parabola with equation $y - k = a(x - h)^2$? $x = h$

In 10 and 11, an equation for a parabola is given.

a. Give the coordinates of the vertex of the parabola.

b. Give an equation for the axis of symmetry.

c. Tell whether the parabola opens up or opens down.

d. Sketch a graph of the equation. 10–11. See margin.

10. $y + 1 = 5(x + 10)^2$
11. $y = 5 - (x - 4)^2$

1. The translation $T_{5,0}$ maps the first graph onto the second.

2.

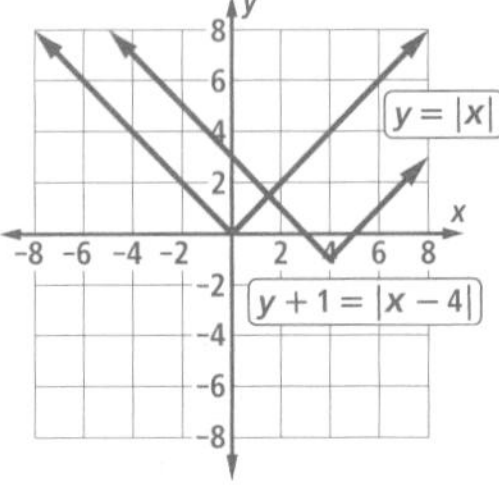

4a. They are translation images of each other.

Parabolic arcs can often be found in art and architecture, as in Casa Mila, located in Barcelona, Spain, shown here.

Additional Answers

10a. (-10, -1)

10b. $x = -10$

10c. up

10d.

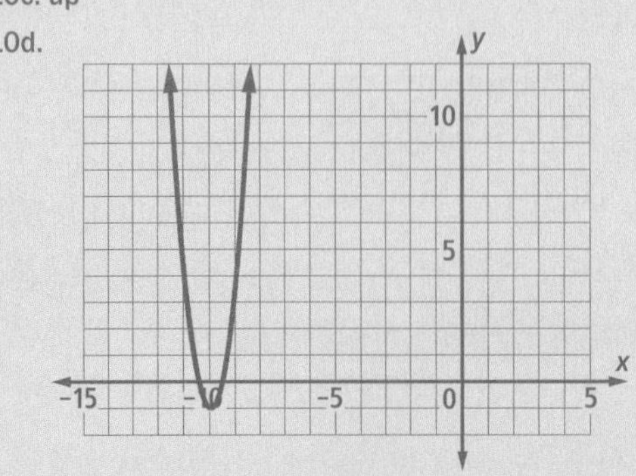

11a. (4, 5)

11b. $x = 4$

11c. down

11d.

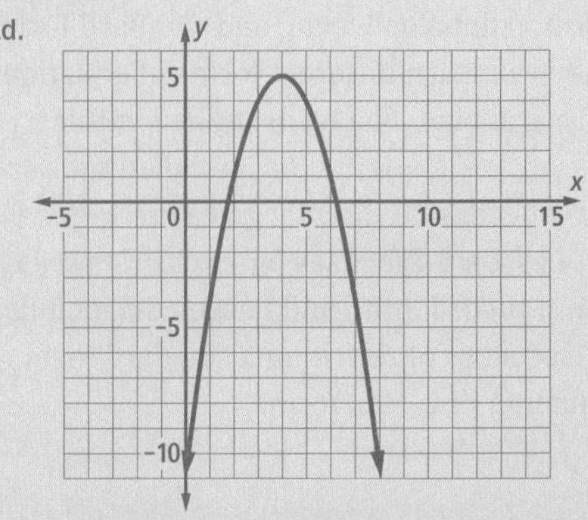

12. Find an equation for the translation image of $y = |x|$ graphed at the left below. $y = |x + 2| - 4$

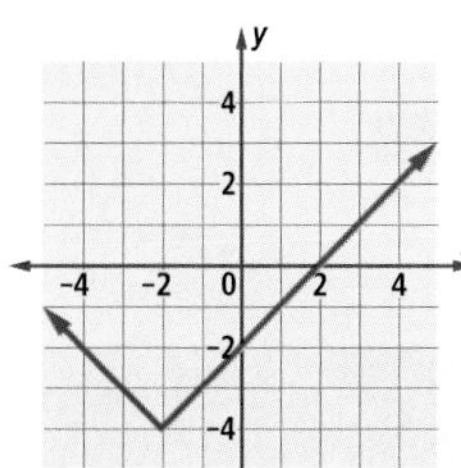

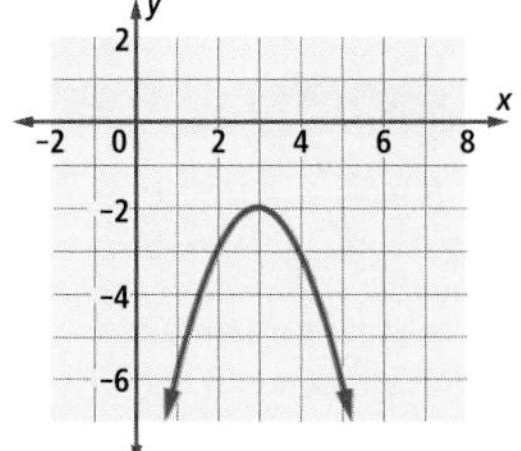

13. The parabola graphed at the right above is a translation image of $y = -x^2$. What is an equation for this parabola? $y = -(x - 3)^2 - 2$

APPLYING THE MATHEMATICS

14. On the first page of this chapter, an equation for the path of water from a drinking fountain is given as $y = -0.58x^2 + 2.7x$, where x and y are measured in inches. This equation is roughly equivalent to $y - 3.14 = -0.58(x - 2.33)^2$. From the second equation, how high does the water reach? 3.14 in.

Centennial Fountain was built in Chicago in 1989 and goes off every hour during the summer months.

15. Consider the graph of $y = -4x^2$. Write an equation for a translation image of the graph
    a. with vertex (0, 2).
    b. with vertex (2, 0).

16. a. Solve $x^2 = 81$. $x = 9$ or $x = -9$
    b. Solve $(x - 3)^2 = 81$. $x = 12$ or $x = -6$
    c. How are the solutions in Parts a and b related to the Graph-Translation Theorem?

17. One solution to $x^2 + 8x + 9 = 57$ is 4. Use this information to find a solution to $(x - 5)^2 + 8(x - 5) + 9 = 57$. $x = 9$

18. Find the x-intercepts and y-intercept of the graph of $y = |x + 3| - 5$. x-intercepts: 2 and -8, y-intercept: -2

19. **Fill in the Blanks** The point-slope form of a line, $y - y_1 = m(x - x_1)$, can be thought of as the image of the line with equation __?__ under the translation $T_{h,k}$, where $h =$ __?__ and $k =$ __?__. $y = mx$; x_1; y_1

15a. $y = -4x^2 + 2$

15b. $y = -4(x - 2)^2$

16c. x was replaced by $x - 3$, so the solutions for Part b are the solutions for Part a translated 3 units to the right.

Notes on the Questions

Question 16b This question can lead to rich discourse and many connections. Encourage students to describe how they solved this problem. Some may use purely numerical strategies, such as mentally finding 9 and −9 as solutions to Part a and adding 3 to each to get 12 and −6 for Part b. Others might use the Absolute Value–Square Root Theorem to take the square roots and get $|x - 3| = 9$, from which they solve the equation. Others may expand the square and use the Quadratic Formula. Still others might graph $y = (x - 3)^2$ and $y = 81$ and find the points of intersection graphically.

Question 17 When discussing this question, point out that the second equation is identical to the first except that x has been replaced by $x - 5$. This translates the graph five units to the right, so the solutions to the second equation are five greater than those to the first.

Question 19 This question extends the Graph-Translation Theorem to obtain the point-slope form of the equation for a line that students saw in Chapter 3.

Extension

Ask students to find enough ordered pairs that satisfy the equation $x^2 + y^2 = 25$ to sketch its graph. Ask students to describe the graph and then describe the effect of each of the following translations on the graph. The graph of $x^2 + y^2 = 25$ is a circle with center (0, 0) and radius 5.

a. $T_{4,0}$ The image is a circle with center (4, 0) and radius 5.

b. $T_{0,-3}$ The image is a circle with center (0, −3) and radius 5.

c. $T_{2,8}$ The image is a circle with center (2, 8) and radius 5.

d. $T_{h,k}$ The image is a circle with center (h, k) and radius 5.

4 Wrap-Up

Ongoing Assessment

Ask students to complete this table.

Equation of preimage	$T_{a,b}$	Replace x by ?, y by ?	Equation of image
$y = 5x^2$	$T_{-2,-5}$	$x + 2$, $y + 5$	$y + 5 = 5(x + 2)^2$
$y = \frac{2}{3}x^2$	$T_{3,-2}$	$x - 3$, $y + 2$	$y + 2 = \frac{2}{3}(x - 3)^2$
$y = -4x^2$	$T_{-7,-2}$	$x + 7$, $y + 2$	$y + 2 = -4(x + 7)^2$

Additional Answers

26. Answers vary. Sample: $h = -1$, $k = 1$

26a. yes

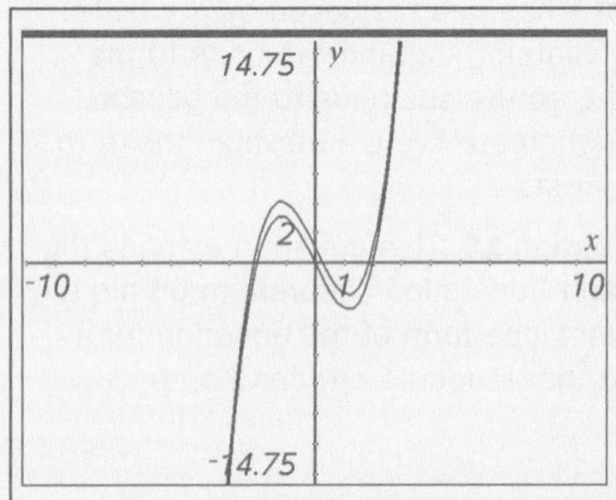

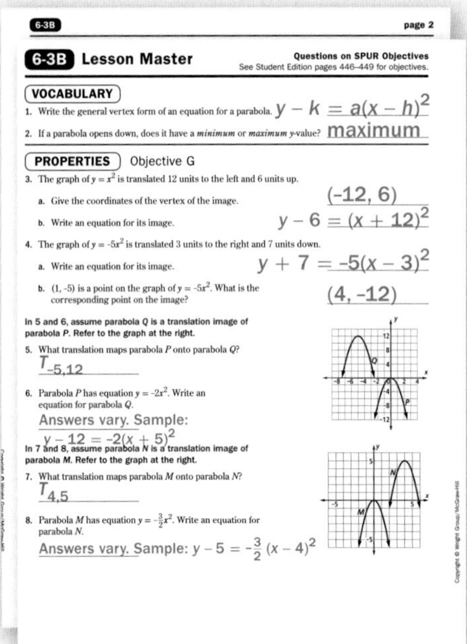

6-3B page 2

6-3B Lesson Master Questions on SPUR Objectives
See Student Edition pages 446–449 for objectives.

VOCABULARY

1. Write the general vertex form of an equation for a parabola. $y - k = a(x - h)^2$
2. If a parabola opens down, does it have a *minimum* or *maximum* y-value? maximum

PROPERTIES Objective G

3. The graph of $y = x^2$ is translated 12 units to the left and 6 units up.
   a. Give the coordinates of the vertex of the image. $(-12, 6)$
   b. Write an equation for its image. $y - 6 = (x + 12)^2$
4. The graph of $y = -5x^2$ is translated 3 units to the right and 7 units down.
   a. Write an equation for its image. $y + 7 = -5(x - 3)^2$
   b. $(1, -5)$ is a point on the graph of $y = -5x^2$. What is the corresponding point on the image? $(4, -12)$

In 5 and 6, assume parabola Q is a translation image of parabola P. Refer to the graph at the right.

5. What translation maps parabola P onto parabola Q? $T_{-5,12}$
6. Parabola P has equation $y = -2x^2$. Write an equation for parabola Q. Answers vary. Sample: $y - 12 = -2(x + 5)^2$

In 7 and 8, assume parabola N is a translation image of parabola M. Refer to the graph at the right.

7. What translation maps parabola M onto parabola N? $T_{4,5}$
8. Parabola M has equation $y = -\frac{3}{2}x^2$. Write an equation for parabola N. Answers vary. Sample: $y - 5 = -\frac{3}{2}(x - 4)^2$

264 Advanced Algebra

20. The parabola $y = 2(x - 4)^2 - 2$ is the image of the parabola $y = 2(x - 3)^2 + 5$ under the translation $T_{h,k}$. What are the values of h and k? $h = 1$; $k = -7$

REVIEW

In 21 and 22, solve and check. (Lesson 6-2)

21. $3 \cdot |2d + 3| = 21$
22. $-8x^2 = -162$

21. $d = 2$ or $d = -5$; $3|2(2) + 3| = 3|7| = 21$ and $3|2(-5) + 3| = 3|-7| = 21$

22. $x = 4.5$ or $x = -4.5$; $-8(4.5)^2 = -162$ and $-8(-4.5)^2 = -162$

23. The competition area for a judo contest consists of a d-meter by d-meter square surrounded by a 3-meter-wide border called the *safety area*. **(Lesson 6-1)**
    a. Write an expression in standard form for the total area of the competition area. $d^2 + 12d + 36$
    b. The rules of judo require $8 \le d \le 10$. What are the minimum and maximum areas a judo competition area can have? 196 m^2; 256 m^2

Judo emphasizes flexibility, energy, and balance, rather than brute strength.

24. A company makes two kinds of tires: model R (regular) and model S (snow). Each tire is processed on three machines, A, B, and C. To make one model R tire requires $\frac{1}{2}$ hour on machine A, 2 hours on B, and 1 hour on C. To make one model S tire requires 1 hour on A, 1 hour on B, and 4 hours on C. During the upcoming week, machine A will be available for at most 20 hours, machine B for at most 60 hours, and machine C for at most 60 hours. If the company makes a \$10 profit on each model R tire and a \$15 profit on each model S tire, how many of each tire should be made to maximize the company's profit? **(Lesson 5-9)** 26 regular, 6 snow or 20 regular, 10 snow
25. Simplify the expression $\frac{(x^2y)^2}{y^3}$. **(Previous Course)** $\frac{x^4}{y}$

EXPLORATION

26. Investigate how the Graph-Translation Theorem works with other functions. Graph $y = x^3 - 4x$ on your graphing utility. Pick values for h and k, write an equation for its image under each translation below, and graph the image. Verify that the image appears to be a translation image of $y = x^3 - 4x$. Try other values of h and k. See margin.
    a. $T_{0,k}$
    b. $T_{h,0}$
    c. $T_{h,k}$

QY ANSWER

The graph is the image under $T_{-40,15}$ of the graph of $y = x^2$. It has vertex $(-40, 15)$, is reflection-symmetric to $x = -40$, and opens up.

Additional Answers

26b. yes

14.75 y
2
x
-10
1
10
-14.75

26c. yes

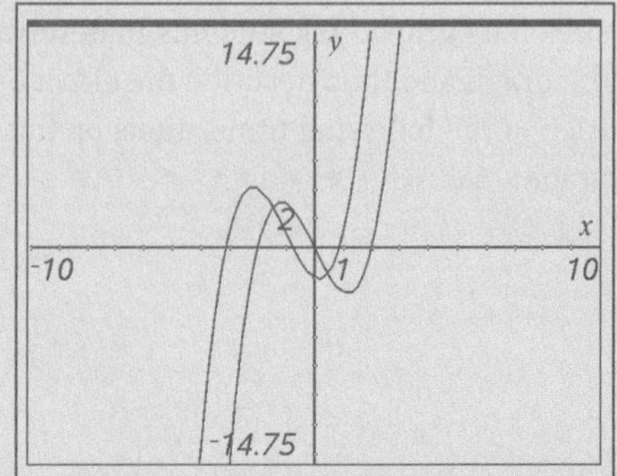

Lesson 6-4 The Graph of $y = ax^2 + bx + c$

BIG IDEA The graph of $y = ax^2 + bx + c$, $a \neq 0$, is a parabola that opens upward if $a > 0$ and downward if $a < 0$.

Standard Form for the Equation of a Parabola

Homer King hits a high-fly ball to deep center field. Ignoring air currents, which curve below most closely resembles the flight path of the ball?

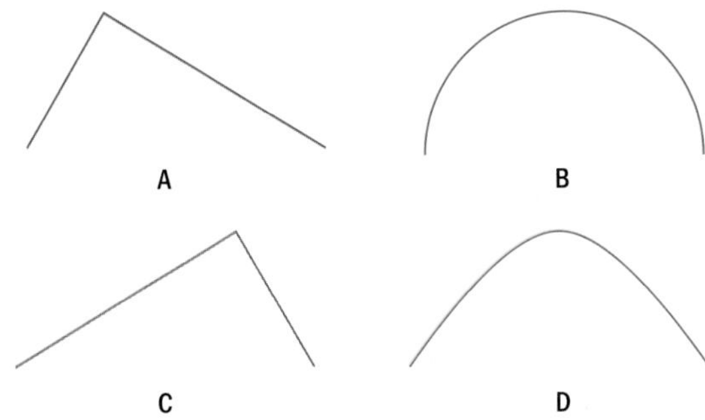

The answer is D, because high-fly balls and many other projectiles travel in parabolic paths. These paths have equations that can be put into the standard form of a quadratic function, $y = ax^2 + bx + c$. In general, any equation for a parabola that can be written in the vertex form $y - k = a(x - h)^2$ can be rewritten in the standard form $y = ax^2 + bx + c$.

Example 1

Show that the equation $y - 16 = 3(x - 5)^2$ can be rewritten in the form $y = ax^2 + bx + c$, and give the values of a, b, and c.

Solution Solve for y, then expand the binomial, distribute, and simplify.

(continued on next page)

Mental Math

Give an example of an equation whose graph contains (1, 3) and is

a. a line.

b. a hyperbola.

c. a parabola.

d. not a line, hyperbola, or parabola.

Answers vary. Sample:

a. $y = 3x$

b. $y = \frac{3}{x}$

c. $y = 3x^2$

d. $y = \frac{3}{x^2}$

Background

Applications of projectile motion include those situations in which a moving object is subject to constant acceleration—that is, objects whose height h at time t is given by an equation of the form

$$h = -\frac{1}{2}gt^2 + v_0t + h_0.$$

Such equations were first analyzed by Tartaglia and Galileo in the 16th century. They are of great importance historically, as they led to the invention of calculus by Newton and Leibniz, which paved the way for modern physics and mechanics.

The behavior of $h = -gt^2 + v_0t + h_0$ can be analyzed by converting the equation into vertex form. It may surprise many students that regardless of the values of the real numbers a, b, and c (where $a \neq 0$), the graph of $y = ax^2 + bx + c$ is a parabola.

(continued on next page)

Lesson 6-4

GOAL

Relate the graph of the parabola $y = ax^2 + bx + c$ to its vertex form $y = a(x - h)^2 + k$ and to problems involving paths of projectiles.

SPUR Objectives

B Convert quadratic equations from vertex to standard form.

G Use the Graph-Translation Theorem to interpret equations and graphs.

I Use quadratic equations to solve problems dealing with distance, velocity, and acceleration.

K Graph quadratic functions and interpret them.

Materials/Resources

- Lesson Masters 6-4A and 6-4B
- Resource Masters 2 and 102–104
- Quiz 1
- Stopwatch, meter stick, tape, rubber ball

HOMEWORK

Suggestions for Assignment

- Questions 1–25
- Question 26 (extra credit)
- Reading Lesson 6-5
- Covering the Ideas 6-5

Local Standards

1 Warm-Up

1. Suppose $mx + 3y + 6 = x - ky + 6$ for all x and y. What are the values of m and k? $m = 1$; $k = -3$
2. Suppose $3x^2 = ax^2$ for all x. *True or false:* $a = 3$ or $a = -3$. false
3. Suppose $(2x + y)^2 = ax^2 + bxy + cy^2$ for all x and y. Find a, b, and c. $a = 4$; $b = 4$; $c = 1$

2 Teaching

Notes on the Lesson

Example 1 The CAS display in the text shows 16 being added to each side of the equation $y - 16 = 3(x - 5)^2$. The result, shown in one step, is $y = 3x^2 - 30x + 91$. Note, however, that various CAS models may do this problem differently. For instance, the Casio ClassPad requires two steps to obtain the same result. On the ClassPad, you first add 16 and then use the expand command, as shown below. You may need to investigate how your students' CASs will handle this type of problem.

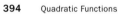

```
y-16=3(x-5)^2
                 y-16=3·(x-5)^2
ans+16
                 y=3·(x-5)^2+16
expand(ans)
                 y=3·x^2-30·x+91
```

Additional Example

Example 1 Show that the equation $y + 5 = 4(x + 3)^2$ can be rewritten in the form $y = ax^2 + bx + c$ and give the values of a, b, and c.
$y = 4(x + 3)^2 - 5$; $y = 4(x^2 + 6x + 9) - 5$; $y = 4x^2 + 24x + 36 - 5$; $y = 4x^2 + 24x + 31$; $a = 4$, $b = 24$, and $c = 31$

$y - 16 = 3(x - 5)^2$	
$y = 3(x - 5)^2 + 16$	Add 16 to both sides.
$y = 3(x^2 - 10x + 25) + 16$	Expand the binomial square.
$y = 3x^2 - 30x + 75 + 16$	Distribute the 3.
$y = 3x^2 - 30x + 91$	Arithmetic

So the original equation is equivalent to one in standard form with $a = 3$, $b = -30$, and $c = 91$.

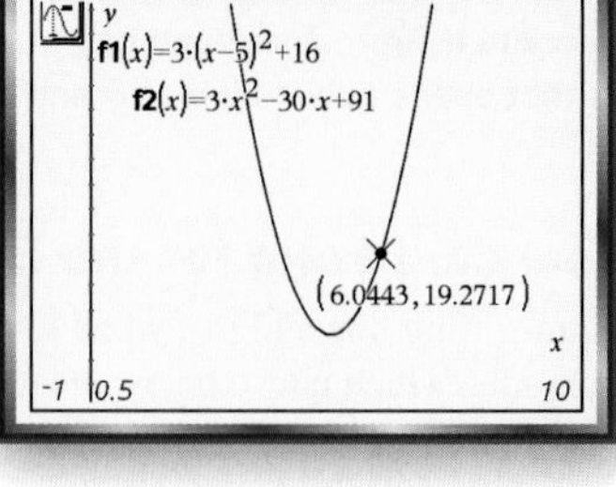

Check 1 Graph both $y = 3(x - 5)^2 + 16$ and $y = 3x^2 - 30x + 91$ on your graphng utility. Use the `trace` feature and toggle between graphs to see if the coordinates match. The graphs seem to be identical.

Check 2 Enter the original equation into a CAS. Add 16 to both sides of the equation.

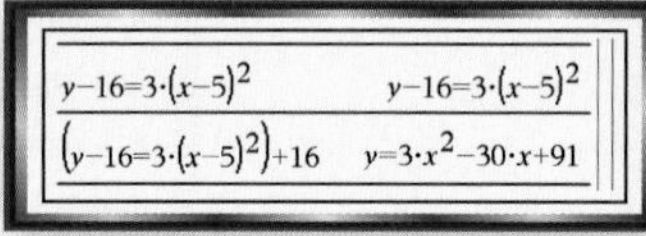
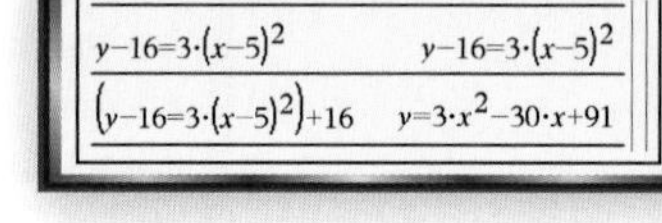

This CAS expands the right side automatically. It checks.

QY1

▸ QY1
In Example 1, subtract the final expression for y from the original expression for y. What do you get?

In general, to change vertex form to standard form, solve for y and expand.

$y - k = a(x - h)^2$	
$y = a(x - h)^2 + k$	Add k to each side.
$y = a(x^2 - 2hx + h^2) + k$	Square the binomial.
$y = ax^2 - 2ahx + ah^2 + k$	Use the Distributive Property.

This is in standard form, with $b = -2ah$ and $c = ah^2 + k$. With these substitutions, the equation becomes

$$y = ax^2 + bx + c.$$

Congruent Parabolas

Because the parabola determined by the equation $y - k = a(x - h)^2$ is a translation image of the parabola determined by the equation $y = ax^2$, the two parabolas are congruent. For all h and k, $y - k = a(x - h)^2$ can be written in standard form, so we have the following theorem.

The height vs. time application has a subtlety that is mentioned in the lesson. Consider Example 2. While the formula gives the height of the ball at a particular time, the graph is *not* congruent to the graph of the path of the ball because the ball loses velocity in the horizontal direction (and, furthermore, the units are different). However, both graphs are parabolas because the loss of speed over time is linear.

Activity This can be an unforgettable activity. We encourage you to explain the activity briefly, then let students explore the activity and discover its results and conclusions.

Parabola Congruence Theorem

The graph of the equation $y = ax^2 + bx + c$ is a parabola congruent to the graph of $y = ax^2$.

Recall that a *quadratic function* is any function f whose equation can be put in the form $f(x) = ax^2 + bx + c$, where $a \neq 0$. Thus, the graph of every quadratic function is a parabola, with y-intercept $f(0) = c$. Unless otherwise specified, the domain of a quadratic function is the set of real numbers. When $a > 0$, the range is the set of real numbers greater than or equal to its minimum value. When $a < 0$, the range is the set of real numbers less than or equal to its maximum value.

Applications of Quadratic Functions

Some applications of quadratic functions have been known for centuries. In the early 17th century, Galileo described the height of an object in free fall. Later that century, Isaac Newton derived his laws of motion and the law of universal gravitation. In developing his mathematical equations for the height of an object, Newton reasoned as follows:

- Gravity is a force that pulls objects near Earth downward. Without gravity, a ball thrown upward would continue traveling at a constant rate. Then its height would be (initial height) + (upward velocity) • (time). So, if it were thrown at 59 feet per second from an initial height of 4 feet, it would continue traveling at 59 feet per second, and its height after t seconds would be $4 + 59t$.
- Galileo had shown that gravity pulls the ball downward a total of $16t^2$ feet after t seconds. This effect can be subtracted from the upward motion without gravity. Therefore, after t seconds, its height in feet would be $4 + 59t - 16t^2$ feet. The number 16 in the expression is a constant for all objects falling at or near Earth's surface when the distances are measured in feet. When measured in meters, this number is 4.9.

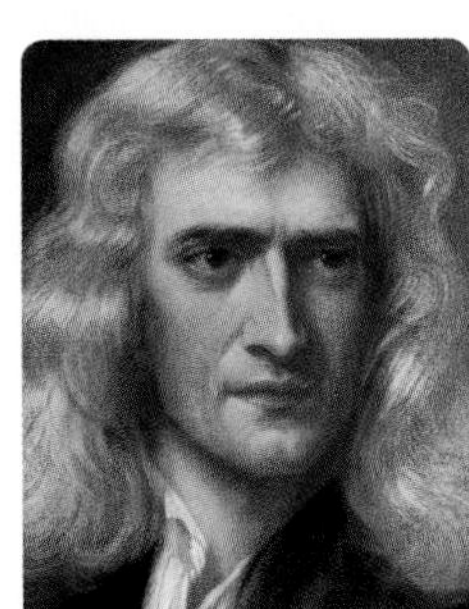

Sir Isaac Newton

Example 2

A thrown ball has height $h = -16t^2 + 59t + 4$ after t seconds.

a. Find h when $t = 0, 1, 2, 3,$ and 4.

b. Explain what the pairs (t, h) tell you about the height of the ball for $t = 0, 2,$ and 4.

(continued on next page)

Notes on the Lesson

Students may wonder how to determine where the parabola "turns," that is, the location of its vertex. Finding the exact location is covered in Lesson 6-5. In this lesson students may estimate the vertex from the graph; we also expect them to estimate the x-intercept(s) from the graph and to check by substitution that the value of y is 0 for those values of x. After studying the Quadratic Formula in Lesson 6-7, students should be able to express exact values for the x-intercepts.

Applications of quadratic functions It is important that students understand the exact definition of each variable in the general formula $h = -\frac{1}{2}gt^2 + v_0t + h_0$. (Emphasize the Note-Taking Tips on page 396.) List the variables on the board with a written identification of each. Stress that the subscript 0, as used in v_0 and h_0, indicates an initial state or condition, in these cases, the initial velocity and initial height.

Our perceptions of the shapes of graphs of parabolas are affected by the scales on the axes. Congruent parabolas may not look congruent when they are graphed with different scales. The confusion is due to two different ways of thinking about points. In looking at drawings, we think of points as locations, and a parabola is a set of locations. But on the coordinate plane, points are ordered pairs, and a parabola is a set of ordered pairs. Changing the scale on a graph may change apparent locations, but it does not change the set of ordered pairs.

ENGLISH LEARNERS

Vocabulary Development

Watch for students who refer to the time value $t = 0$ as "the start of time." Students should realize that $t = 0$ refers to an arbitrary moment in an experiment, such as throwing a ball or dropping a stone.

Additional Example

Example 2 Suppose a thrown ball has height $h = -16t^2 + 42t + 7$ after t seconds.

a. Find h when $t = 0, 1, 2, 3,$ and 4. 7; 33; 27; -11; -81

b. Explain what the pairs (t, h) tell you about the height of the ball for $t =$ 0, 2, and 4. At 0 sec, the ball is 7 ft above the ground; at 2 sec, the ball is 27 ft above the ground; at 4 sec, the ball is 81 ft below ground level (or has already hit the ground).

c. Graph the pairs (t, h) over the domain of the function.

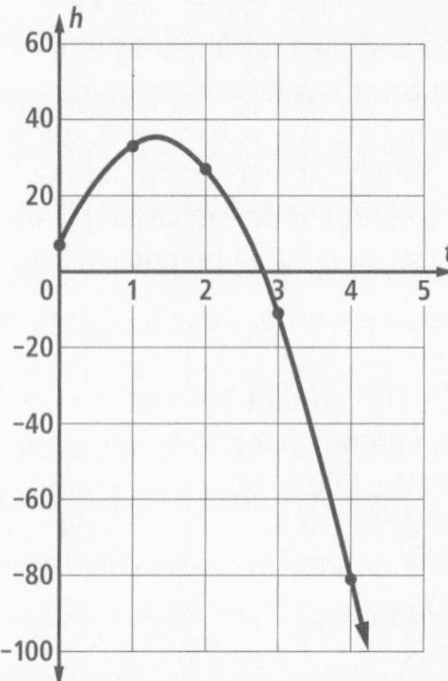

d. Is the ball moving at the same average rate between $t = 0$ and $t = 1$ as between $t = 1$ and $t = 2$? Justify your answer. No; the average rate of change between $t = 0$ and $t = 1$ is $\frac{33-7}{1-0} = 26\ \frac{\text{ft}}{\text{sec}}$. The average rate of change between $t = 1$ and $t = 2$ is $\frac{27-33}{2-1} = -6\ \frac{\text{ft}}{\text{sec}}$.

Note-Taking Tips

Although it may not affect how they write v_0 and h_0, students should understand that each subscript is the number zero (v_0 is the velocity when $t = 0$; h_0 is the height when $t = 0$), rather than the letter oh.

c. Graph the pairs (t, h) over the domain of the function.

d. Is the ball moving at the same average rate (speed) between $t = 0$ and $t = 1$ as between $t = 2$ and $t = 3$? Justify your answer.

Solution

a. Use the table feature on your graphing utility or substitute by hand.

t (sec)	h (ft)
0	4
1	47
2	58
3	37
4	-16

b. Each pair (t, h) gives the height h of the ball after t seconds. The pair (0, 4) means that at 0 seconds, the time of release, the ball is 4 feet above the ground. The pair (2, 58) means the ball is 58 feet high after 2 seconds. The pair (4, -16) means that after 4 seconds, the ball is 16 feet below ground level. Unless the ground is not level, it has already hit the ground.

c. The points in Part a are plotted at left below. The points do not tell much about the shape of the graph. More points are needed to show the parabola. By calculating h for other values of t, or by using a graphing utility, you can obtain a graph similar to the one at the right below. The graph is not a complete parabola because the domain of the function is $\{t | t \geq 0\}$.

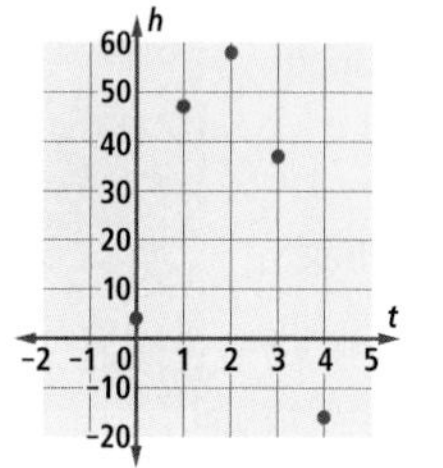

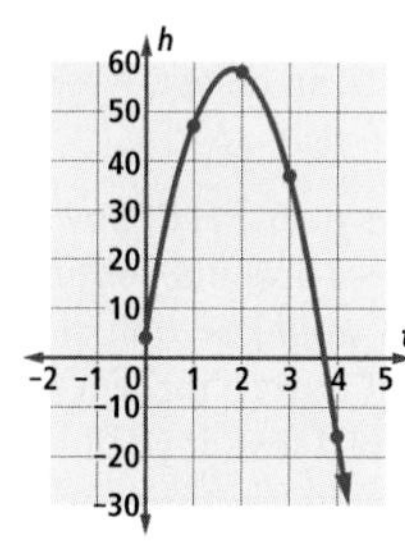

d. The average rate of change between two times is the change in height divided by the change in time. This is the slope of the line through the corresponding points on the graph.

The average rate of change between $t = 0$ and $t = 1$ is $\frac{47-4}{1-0} = 43\ \frac{\text{ft}}{\text{second}}$. The average rate of change between $t = 2$ and $t = 3$ is $\frac{37-58}{3-2} = -21\ \frac{\text{ft}}{\text{second}}$. (The ball is moving downward on this interval.) The rates are different, meaning the ball travels at different speeds during its flight.

By the Parabola Congruence Theorem, you know that the graph of $h = -16t^2 + 59t + 4$ is a translation image of the graph of $y = -16t^2$.

The equation in Example 2 is a special case of the following general formula that Newton developed for the height h of an object at time t seconds with an initial upward velocity v_0 and initial height h_0.

$$h = -\tfrac{1}{2}gt^2 + v_0t + h_0$$

Accommodating the Learner ↑

Ask students to find the values of a, b, and c for the standard form of the equation for the graph of $y = mx^2 + nx + p$ after the translation $T_{h,k}$ is applied. $y - k = m(x - h)^2 + n(x - h) + p$; $y - k = m(x^2 - 2xh + h^2) + nx - nh + p$; $y = mx^2 - 2mhx + nx + mh^2 - nh + p + k$; $y = mx^2 + (n - 2mh)x + (mh^2 - nh + p + k)$; $a = m$, $b = n - 2mh$, $c = mh^2 - nh + p + k$

Accommodating the Learner ↓

Show students the equation $y - k = p(x - h)^2$. Ask them to find the values of a, b, and c if that equation is rewritten in standard form. $y - k = p(x - h)2$; $y - k = p(x^2 - 2xh + h^2)$; $y = px^2 - 2phx + ph^2 + k$; $a = p$, $b = -2ph$, and $c = ph^2 + k$

In Example 2, $v_0 = 59\frac{\text{ft}}{\text{sec}}$, the height $h_0 = 4$ ft, and g is a constant denoting ***acceleration due to gravity***. Recall that *velocity* involves units like miles per hour, feet per second, or meters per second. Acceleration measures how fast the velocity changes. This "rate of change of a rate of change" involves units like feet per second per second (which is usually abbreviated $\frac{\text{ft}}{\text{sec}^2}$). The acceleration due to gravity varies depending on how close the object is to the center of a massive object. Ignoring the effects of air resistance, near the surface of Earth,

$$g \approx 32\frac{\text{ft}}{\text{sec}^2}, \quad \text{or} \quad g \approx 9.8\frac{\text{m}}{\text{sec}^2}.$$

Two common situations are important to note. First, if an object is dropped, not thrown or pushed, its initial velocity $v_0 = 0$. Second, if an object starts at ground level, its initial height $h_0 = 0$.

 QY2

▶ QY2

An object's height is modeled using the equation $h = -16t^2 + 24t + 4$. What is the initial velocity? (Do not forget the units.) From what height is it thrown?

Activity

MATERIALS stopwatch, meter stick, tape, rubber ball

Work with a partner to apply Newton's formula for free-falling objects.

Step 1 Copy the table below to record your data. Steps 1–5. Answers vary. Sample:

	Initial height h_0 (m)	Elapsed Time Trial 1 (sec)	Elapsed Time Trial 2 (sec)	Elapsed Time Trial 3 (sec)	Elapsed Time Average t (sec)
Partner 1	? 1.2	? 1.75	? 1.6	? 1.9	? 1.75
Partner 2	? 1	? 2.05	? 1.93	? 2.02	? 2.00

Step 2 Choose one partner to be the tosser and the other to be the measurer. The tosser chooses a comfortable height from which to toss the ball upward. The measurer records this height and marks it on the meter stick with tape so the tosser can try to consistently release the ball at the same height.

Step 3 The tosser throws the ball upward three times in succession from the height determined in Step 2. With the stopwatch, the measurer records the elapsed time, in seconds, from the initial release of the ball to when it first hits the ground.

Step 4 Reverse roles with your partner and repeat Steps 2 and 3.

Step 5 Calculate and record average times for each partner's tosses.

(continued on next page)

3 Assignment

Recommended Assignment

- Questions 1–25
- Question 26 (extra credit)
- Reading Lesson 6-5
- Covering the Ideas 6-5

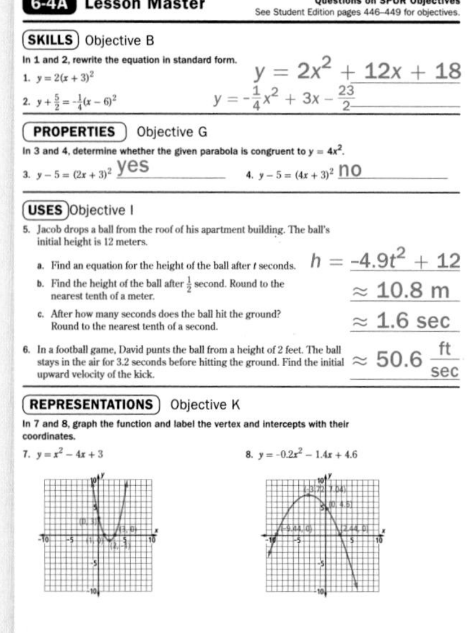

6-4A Lesson Master — Questions on SPUR Objectives. See Student Edition pages 446–449 for objectives.

SKILLS Objective B

In 1 and 2, rewrite the equation in standard form.

1. $y = 2(x + 3)^2$ $y = 2x^2 + 12x + 18$
2. $y + \frac{5}{2} = -\frac{1}{4}(x - 6)^2$ $y = -\frac{1}{4}x^2 + 3x - \frac{23}{2}$

PROPERTIES Objective G

In 3 and 4, determine whether the given parabola is congruent to $y = 4x^2$.

3. $y - 5 = (2x + 3)^2$ yes
4. $y - 5 = (4x + 3)^2$ no

USES Objective I

5. Jacob drops a ball from the roof of his apartment building. The ball's initial height is 12 meters.
   a. Find an equation for the height of the ball after t seconds. $h = -4.9t^2 + 12$
   b. Find the height of the ball after $\frac{1}{2}$ second. Round to the nearest tenth of a meter. ≈ 10.8 m
   c. After how many seconds does the ball hit the ground? Round to the nearest tenth of a second. ≈ 1.6 sec
6. In a football game, David punts the ball from a height of 2 feet. The ball stays in the air for 3.2 seconds before hitting the ground. Find the initial upward velocity of the kick. $\approx 50.6 \frac{\text{ft}}{\text{sec}}$

REPRESENTATIONS Objective K

In 7 and 8, graph the function and label the vertex and intercepts with their coordinates.

7. $y = x^2 - 4x + 3$
8. $y = -0.2x^2 - 1.4x + 4.6$

266 Advanced Algebra

Step 6 Use Newton's formula, $h = -\frac{1}{2}gt^2 + v_0t + h_0$ to calculate the initial upward velocity v_0 for each partner's average toss. (Hint: When did $h = 0$?) Then write an equation to describe each partner's average toss.

Step 7 The ball reaches it maximum height in a little less than half the time it takes the ball to hit the ground. Use your formula to estimate the maximum height of your average toss.

Step 6.
Answers vary. Sample: For partner 1, $v_0 \approx 7.89 \frac{\text{m}}{\text{sec}^2}$; $h = -4.9t^2 + 7.89t + 1.2$. For partner 2, $v_0 = 9.3 \frac{\text{m}}{\text{sec}^2}$; $h = -4.9t^2 + 9.3t + 1$.

Step 7.
Answers vary. Sample: for partner 1, about 4.4 m; for partner 2, about 5.4 m

Caution! The equation $h = -\frac{1}{2}gt^2 + v_0t + h_0$ models the height h of the object off the ground at time t. It *does not* describe the path of the object. However, Galileo showed that the actual path of an object thrown at any angle except straight up or straight down is almost parabolic, like the path of water on the second page of the chapter, and an equation for its path is a quadratic equation.

Questions

COVERING THE IDEAS

1. Write the standard form for the equation of a parabola with a vertical line of symmetry. $y = ax^2 + bx + c$

In 2 and 3, rewrite the equation in standard form.

2. $y = (x - 3)^2$ $y = x^2 - 6x + 9$
3. $y = -3(x + 4)^2 - 5$ $y = -3x^2 - 24x - 53$
4. **True or False** For any values of a, b, and c, the graph of $y = ax^2 + bx + c$ is congruent to the graph of $y = ax^2$. true

In 5–7, use the equation $h = -\frac{1}{2}gt^2 + v_0t + h_0$ for the height of a body in free fall.

5. Give the meaning of each variable.
   a. h b. g c. t d. v_0 e. h_0
6. What value of g should you use if v_0 is measured in $\frac{\text{ft}}{\text{sec}}$? $32 \frac{\text{ft}}{\text{sec}^2}$
7. What is the value of v_0 when an object is dropped? 0

5a. height
5b. acceleration due to gravity
5c. time
5d. initial velocity
5e. initial height

In 8–11, refer to the graph in Example 2.

8. About how high is the ball after 1.5 seconds? about 57 ft
9. When the ball hits the ground, what is the value of h? 0
10. At what times will the ball be 20 feet above the ground?
11. What is the average rate of change of the ball's height between 1 second and 3 seconds? $-5 \frac{\text{ft}}{\text{sec}}$

10. about 0.3 sec and 3.4 sec

Extension

Ask students to look again at Question 12.

a. Use the graph generated in Question 12c to find the value of t that results in the ball's maximum height. $t \approx 1.633$ sec

b. State the two values of t that are 0.5 second before and 0.5 second after your answer to Part a. $t = 1.133$; $t = 2.133$

c. Show that the average rate of change between the two values in Part b is 0. For $t = 1.133$, $h = -4.9(1.133)^2 + 16(1.133) + 20 = 31.84$, and for $t = 2.133$, $h = -4.9(2.133)^2 + 16(2.133) + 20 = 31.83$. Because the change in height is essentially 0 (depending on rounding), the average rate of change is 0.

12. Suppose a person throws a ball upward at a velocity of 16 $\frac{\text{m}}{\text{sec}}$ from the top of a 20-meter tall building.
    a. Write an equation to describe the height of the ball above the ground after t seconds.
    b. How high is the ball after 0.75 second?
    c. Use a graph to estimate the ball's maximum height.
    d. After 6 seconds, is the ball above or below ground level? Justify your answer.

APPLYING THE MATHEMATICS

13. Sketch $y = -x^2 + 4x + 6$ for $-2 \leq x \leq 6$. On your sketch of the graph, label the vertex and the x- and y-intercepts with approximate values. See margin.

14. Consider the function f defined by the equation $f(x) = x^2 + 3x - 10$.
    a. Sketch a graph of the function. See margin.
    b. Write an equation for the line of symmetry of the parabola.
    c. Estimate the coordinates of the lowest point on the parabola.

In 15 and 16, because the object is dropped, not thrown, its initial velocity is 0.

15. Suppose a penny is dropped from the top of Taipei 101, which in 2004 surpassed the Twin Petronas Towers in Malaysia as the world's tallest building. The roof of Taipei 101 is 1,474 feet above ground. 15b. See margin.
    a. Write an equation for the penny's height as a function of time.
    b. Graph your equation from Part a over an appropriate domain.
    c. Estimate how much time it would take the penny to fall to the ground.
    d. When the penny falls through the atmosphere, air resistance actually limits its velocity to a maximum of about 94 feet per second. If the penny traveled at a constant rate of 94 feet per second after 2.9 seconds, how much longer would it take to reach the ground?

16. In an article about education now often circulated as a joke, the late Dr. Alexander Calandra suggested one way to measure the height of a building with a barometer: drop the barometer from the top of the building and time its fall.
    a. Set up an equation for the barometer's height as a function of time, using h_0 for the initial height of the building. $h = -4.9t^2 + h_0$ or $h = -16t^2 + h_0$
    b. Suppose it takes 3.9 seconds for the barometer to hit the ground. Substitute values into the equation you wrote in Part a and solve for h_0. about 74.5 m or 243.4 ft

12a. $h = -4.9t^2 + 16t + 20$

12b. about 29.2 m above the ground

12c. about 33 m above the ground

12d. The equation predicts the ball's height to be -60.4 m, relative to ground level, after 6 sec. However, in real life the ball stops at ground level.

14b. $x = -1.5$

14c. (-1.5, -12.25)

15a. $h = -16t^2 + 1474$

15c. about 9.6 sec

15d. about 7.5 sec longer than the equation predicts

Taipei 101 in Taipei, Taiwan

d. Use the symmetry of the graph to explain your result in Part c. Answers vary. Sample: The graph is symmetric over the line $t = 1.633$, so points at equal horizontal distances from $t = 1.633$ have the same vertical values. Because the vertical values are the same, the difference between them is 0. In general, the average rate of change between any two symmetric points on a parabola is 0.

Notes on the Questions

Question 15 If students have difficulty writing the equation for Part a, remind them of the meaning of the variables in the height formula. In this case v_0, the initial velocity, is 0, and h_0, the initial height, is 1474 feet. In Part c, they should solve the equation for t when h, the height when the penny landed, is 0.

Additional Answers

13.

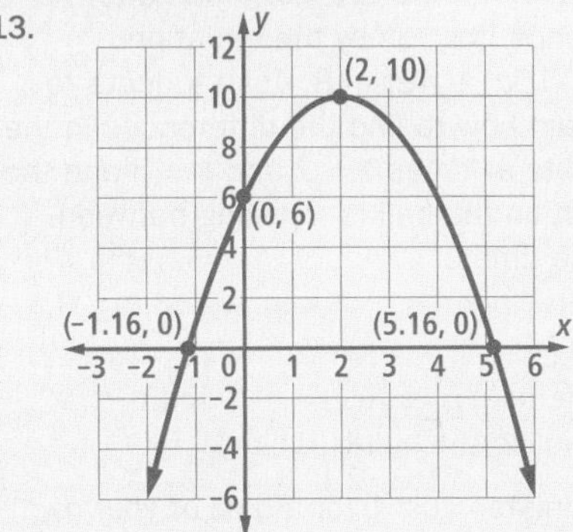

14a.

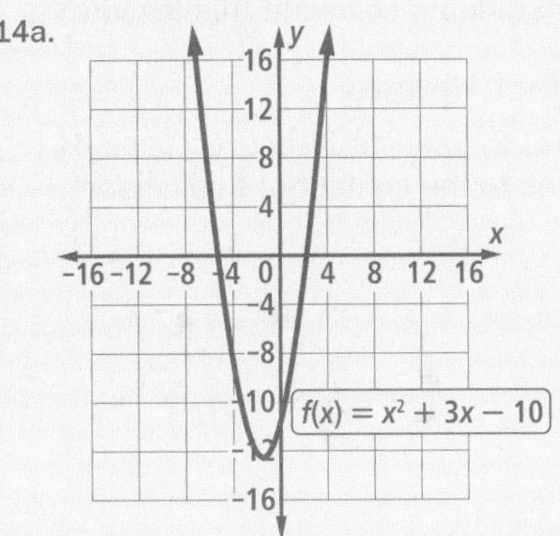

15b.

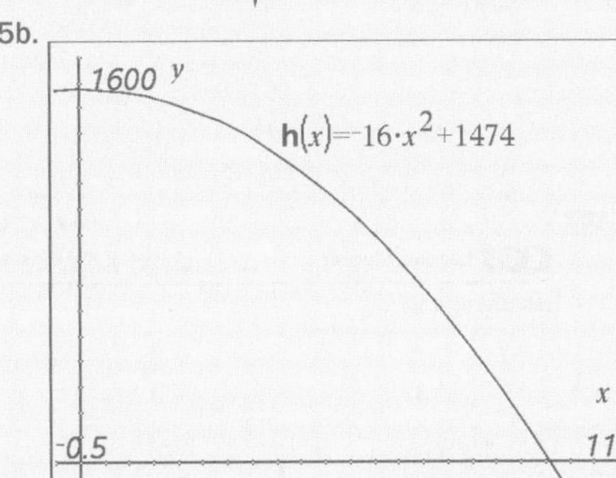

Notes on the Questions

Questions 23–25 You might want to set up a special review session for students who miss these questions.

Question 26 A student might expand this question into a project.

4 Wrap-Up

Ongoing Assessment

Suppose the height h of a ball after t seconds is given by the equation $h = -16t^2 + 48t + 8$. Ask students to explain how to find the differences in the heights at times $t = 2$ and $t = 3$ and the direction the ball is traveling between those times. Answers vary. Sample: The ordered pairs are (2, 40) and (3, 8). The difference in the heights is $40 - 8 = 32$ ft; the height is decreasing during that period, so the ball is falling.

Administer Quiz 1 (or a quiz of your own) after students complete this lesson.

Project Update

Project 2, *Satellite Dishes,* on page 441 relates to the content of this lesson.

6-4B Lesson Master — Questions on SPUR Objectives. See Student Edition pages 446–449 for objectives.

SKILLS Objective B

In 1–6, rewrite the equation in standard form.

1. $y + 6 = (x - 3)^2$ — $y = x^2 - 6x + 3$
2. $y - 1 = 2(x - 4)^2$ — $y = 2x^2 - 16x + 33$
3. $y = (x + 7)^2$ — $y = x^2 + 14x + 49$
4. $y = -3(x + 5)^2 + 8$ — $y = -3x^2 - 30x - 67$
5. $y + 14 = -x^2$ — $y = -x^2 - 14$
6. $y - 2 = \frac{2}{3}(x - 9)^2$ — $y = \frac{2}{3}x^2 - 12x + 56$

PROPERTIES Objective G

In 7–10, determine whether the given parabola is congruent to $y = 9x^2$.

7. $y - 6 = (9x + 1)^2$ — no
8. $y - 6 = (3x + 1)^2$ — yes
9. $y - 6 = \frac{1}{9}(9x + 1)^2$ — yes
10. $y - 6 = \frac{1}{9}(3x + 1)^2$ — no

USES Objective I

11. Suppose a ball is thrown upward from a height of 5 feet with an initial velocity of $35 \frac{\text{ft}}{\text{sec}}$.
    a. Write an equation relating the time t and the height h of the ball. $h = -16t^2 + 35t + 5$
    b. Find the height of the ball after 2 seconds. 11 ft
    c. Is the ball still in the air after 3 seconds? Explain. No; when $t = 3$, $h = -34$; when the ball is in the air, $h > 0$.
12. Yoko threw a stone upward at a speed of $10 \frac{\text{m}}{\text{sec}}$ while standing on a cliff 40 m above the ground.
    a. What was the height of the stone after 3 seconds? 25.9 m
    b. Estimate how long it took for the stone to touch the ground. ≈ 4 sec

Advanced Algebra 267

17. Find an equation in standard form for the image of the graph of $y = -\frac{1}{4}x^2$ under the translation $T_{4,2}$. $y = -\frac{1}{4}x^2 + 2x - 2$

REVIEW

In 18 and 19, two equations are given. 18–19. See margin.
 a. Graph both equations on the same set of axes.
 b. Describe how the graphs of the two equations are related. (Lesson 6-3)

18. $y = x^2$ and $y = (x + 3)^2 + 4$
19. $y = |x|$ and $y - 5 = |x - 2|$

20. A gallon of paint can cover an area of 450 square feet. Find the diameter of the largest circle that can be covered with a gallon of paint. (Lesson 6-2) about 23.94 ft

21. Write an inequality to describe the shaded region of the graph at the right. (Lessons 5-7, 3-4) $y \le \frac{2}{3}x + 4$

22. Solve the system $\begin{cases} A + B + C = 12 \\ 4A - 4B + 2C = -16 \\ 3A + 3B - C = 4 \end{cases}$. (Lesson 5-4) $A = -2, B = 6, C = 8$

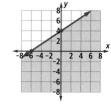

In 23–25, find n. (Previous Course)

23. $x^2 \cdot x^3 = x^n$ $n = 5$
24. $a^n \cdot a^{16} = a^{64}$ $n = 48$
25. $\frac{p^8}{p^2} = p^n$ $n = 6$

EXPLORATION

26. How do the values of a, b, and c affect the graph of $y = ax^2 + bx + c$? Here are two suggested methods for investigating:

Method 1 Use sliders on a DGS or CAS to adjust one coefficient, a, b, or c, at a time.

Method 2
 a. Start with $a = 1$ and $b = 6$. Then adjust c and record how the graph changes.
 b. Set $a = 1$ and $c = 4$, then adjust b and note the changes in the graph.
 c. Set $b = 6$ and $c = 4$, then adjust a and note the changes.

Is the transformation (motion) of the graph simple (like a translation or rotation) for each change of a, b, and c, or is it a compound motion? Which coefficients, if any, affect the graph's size as well as its position?

Answers vary. Sample: a controls the direction in which the parabola opens, as well as how steep it is and the location of the vertex. b controls the steepness and vertex location as well. c controls the y-intercept only. Thus, all three affect position, but only a and b affect size and shape.

QY ANSWERS

1. 0
2. 24 ft/sec; 4 ft

Additional Answers

18a.

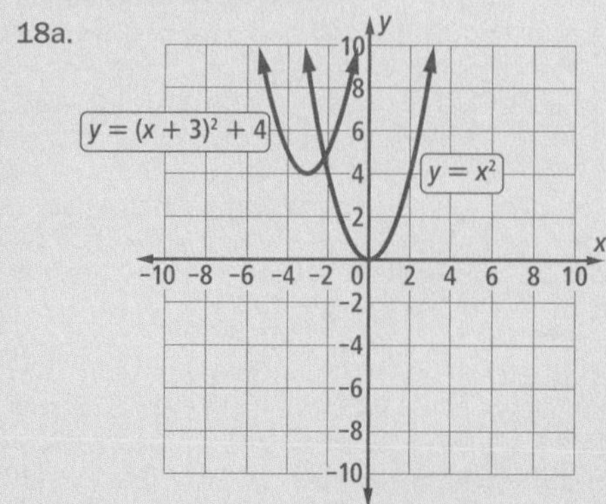

18b. The graph of $y = (x + 3)^2 + 4$ is the image of $y = x^2$ under the translation $T_{-3,4}$.

19a.

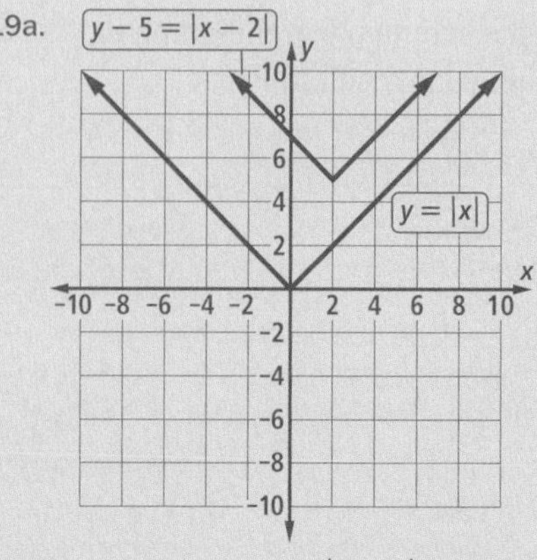

19b. The graph of $y - 5 = |x - 2|$ is the image of $y = |x|$ under the translation $T_{2,5}$.

Lesson 6-5 Completing the Square

Vocabulary

completing the square
perfect-square trinomial

BIG IDEA By adding a number to an expression of the form $x^2 + bx$, you can create a new expression that is the square of a binomial.

You have now seen two forms for an equation of a parabola.

Standard form $y = ax^2 + bx + c$

Vertex form $y - k = a(x - h)^2$ or $y = a(x - h)^2 + k$

Because each form is useful, being able to convert between forms is helpful. In Lesson 6-4 you saw how to convert vertex form to standard form. In this lesson, you will see how to convert standard form to vertex form.

Mental Math

How many solutions does a 2 × 2 system of linear equations have if the two equations in the system represent

a. oblique lines with different slopes? 1

b. one vertical line and one nonvertical line? 1

c. the same line? an infinite number

d. parallel lines with different y-intercepts? 0

What Is Completing the Square?

One method for converting standard form to vertex form is called **completing the square**. Remember that $(x + h)^2 = x^2 + 2hx + h^2$. The trinomial $x^2 + 2hx + h^2$ is called a **perfect-square trinomial** because it is the square of a binomial. At the right you can see that $x^2 + 2hx + h^2$ is the area of a square with side length $x + h$.

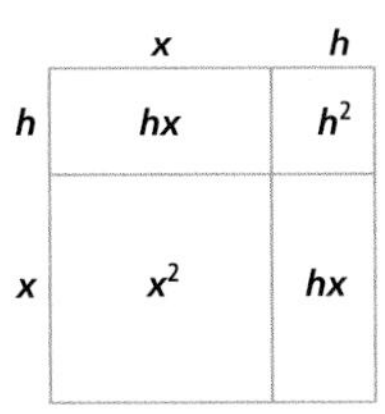

Area = $(x + h)^2 = x^2 + 2hx + h^2$

Example 1

a. What number should be added to $x^2 + 6x$ to make a perfect-square trinomial?

b. Write the perfect-square trinomial as the square of a binomial.

(continued on next page)

Lesson 6-5

GOAL

Practice converting quadratic expressions in standard form to vertex form; use the vertex form to determine the vertex of a graph.

SPUR Objectives

B Convert quadratic equations from standard to vertex form.

I Use quadratic equations to solve area problems or problems dealing with distance, velocity, and acceleration.

Materials/Resources

- Lesson Masters 6-5A and 6-5B
- Resource Masters 2, 3, 105, and 106

HOMEWORK

Suggestions for Assignment

- Questions 1–21
- Question 22 (extra credit)
- Reading Lesson 6-6
- Covering the Ideas 6-6

Local Standards

1 Warm-Up

1. Suppose $(3x - 4)^2 = ax^2 + bx + c$ for all x. What are the values of a, b, and c? $a = 9$; $b = -24$; $c = 16$

2. Suppose $n^2 + 400n + 12 = (n + k)^2 + t$ for all n. Find k and t. $k = 200$; $t = -39{,}988$

Background

This lesson uses a technique called *completing the square* to find the vertex of a parabola whose equation is given in standard form (see Example 2). Knowing the vertex allows us to accurately graph a parabola and solve some maximum or minimum problems (see Questions 9 and 14). On many calculators, there are commands (on the graph menu, the main menu, or both) for finding the minimum or maximum of a parabola. Although this use of calculators is not emphasized in the lesson, some students may benefit from their use; choose whatever method or technique that best suits your students. Another use of completing the square is to derive the Quadratic Formula, which appears in Lesson 6-7. A third use is to find key points on graphs of circles and other quadratic relations.

Solving quadratic equations by completing the square is not an objective in this book. The Quadratic Formula is a general

(continued on next page)

2 Teaching

Notes on the Lesson

You might begin the lesson by having students guess the number that needs to be added to the expressions $x^2 + 8x$, $x^2 - 2x$, or $x^2 + 30x$ to make each a perfect square. Most students will begin to see the pattern. Ask students to verbalize the pattern by giving the term needed to complete $x^2 + 7x$. The odd coefficient of x will force students to isolate the steps in the method they are using to find the term $\left(\frac{b}{2}\right)^2$.

Additional Example

Example 1

a. What number should be added to $x^2 + 14x$ to make a perfect-square trinomial? 49

b. Write the perfect-square trinomial as the square of a binomial. $(x + 7)^2$

Solution 1 Use geometry.

a. Draw a picture to represent $x^2 + 6x + \underline{\ ?\ }$. Since the sum of the areas of the two rectangles that are not squares must be $6x$, the area of each rectangle is $3x$. Think: What is the area of the missing square in the upper right corner that allows you to complete the larger square? (This is the reason this process is called "completing the square".) A square with area 9 would complete the larger square.

So, 9 must be added to $x^2 + 6x$ to make a perfect-square trinomial.

	x	3
3	$3x$	?
x	x^2	$3x$

Area $= x^2 + 6x + \underline{\ ?\ }$

b. In the picture at the right, the length of the side of the square is $x + 3$. So, $x^2 + 6x + 9 = (x + 3)^2$.

Solution 2 Use algebra.

a. Compare $x^2 + 6x + \underline{\ ?\ }$ with the perfect-square trinomial $x^2 + 2hx + h^2$. The first terms, x^2, are identical. To make the second terms equal, set

$$6x = 2hx.$$

So, $$h = 3.$$

The term added to make a perfect-square trinomial should be h^2, or 9.

b. Since $x^2 + 2xh + h^2 = (x + h)^2$, and you found in Part a that $h = 3$, $x^2 + 6x + 9 = (x + 3)^2$.

Check Apply the Binomial Square Theorem to expand $(x + 3)^2$.

$(x + 3)^2 = x^2 + 6x + 9$. It checks.

To generalize Example 1, consider the expression $x^2 + bx + \underline{\ ?\ }$. What goes in the blank so that the result is a perfect-square trinomial?

$$x^2 + bx + \underline{\ ?\ } = x^2 + 2hx + h^2$$

Because $b = 2h$, $h = \frac{b}{2}$. Then $h^2 = \left(\frac{b}{2}\right)^2$. This illustrates the following theorem.

Completing the Square Theorem

To complete the square on $x^2 + bx$, add $\left(\frac{b}{2}\right)^2$.

Proof $x^2 + bx + \left(\frac{b}{2}\right)^2 = x^2 + bx + \frac{b^2}{4} = \left(x + \frac{b}{2}\right)^2$

QY

▸ QY

What number should be added to $x^2 - 24x$ to make a perfect square trinomial?

theorem, and it would be a poor use of algebraic proof to derive individual cases again and again as if the general theorem did not exist. It would be as if we proved the Pythagorean Theorem for special cases every time we used it. It is possible to convert from the standard form to the vertex form without completing the square by equating coefficients, as in the Warm-Up Questions on pages 393 and 401. For instance, to convert $y = x^2 + 30x - 12$ to vertex form, set $x^2 + 30x - 12 = a(x - h)^2 + k$. Then, for all x, expanding the right side, $x^2 + 30x - 12 = ax^2 - 2ahx + (ah^2 + k)$. Thus $1 = a$, $30 = -2ah$, and $-12 = ah^2 + k$. Because $1 = a$, then $30 = -2h$ and $h = -15$. Next, substituting 1 for a and -15 for h results in $-12 = 225 + k$, so $k = -237$.

Thus, $x^2 + 30x - 12 = (x + 15)^2 - 237$. This method is used in Example 3, with an equation where the coefficient of x^2 is not 1. Some teachers prefer this method to complete the square.

Completing the Square to Find the Vertex of a Parabola

The Completing the Square Theorem can be used to transform an equation of a parabola from standard form into vertex form.

GUIDED

Example 2

a. **Rewrite the equation $y = x^2 + 12x + 3$ in vertex form.**

b. **Find the vertex of the parabola.**

Solution

a. Rewrite the equation so that only terms with x are on one side.

$$y - 3 = x^2 + 12x$$

Use the Completing the Square Theorem. Here,

$b =$ _?_, so $\left(\frac{b}{2}\right)^2 =$ _?_. 12; 36

Complete the square on $x^2 + 12x$.

$y - 3 +$ _?_ $= x^2 + 12x +$ _?_ Add $\left(\frac{b}{2}\right)^2$ to both sides. 36; 36

$y +$ _?_ $= x^2 + 12x +$ _?_ Simplify the left side. 33; 36

$y +$ _?_ $= (x +$ _?_$)^2$ Apply the Binomial Square Theorem. 33; 6

b. We can read the vertex from the vertex form of the equation. The vertex of the parabola is (_?_, _?_). -6; -33

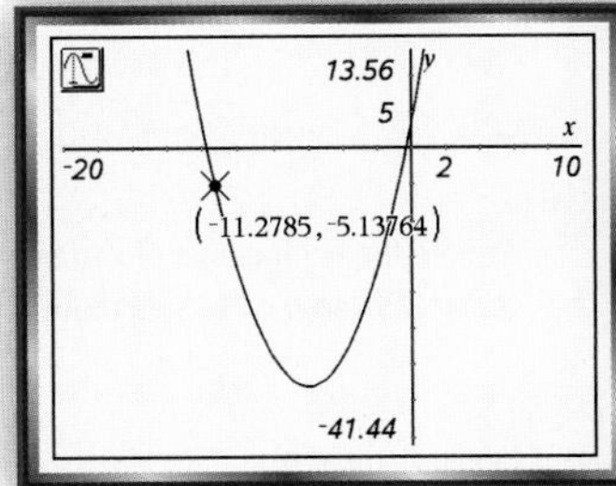

Check

a. Graph $y = x^2 + 12x + 3$ and the vertex form from Part a on the same set of axes in an appropriate window. Trace and toggle between the graphs for several values of x. They should be identical.

b. Trace to estimate the vertex on the graph.

Equating Expressions to Find the Vertex of a Parabola

Example 2 involves a parabola in which the coefficient of x^2 is 1. Example 3 shows how to find the vertex of a parabola if the coefficient of x^2 is not 1. This kind of expression occurs in describing heights of thrown objects and paths of projectiles.

Notes on the Lesson

In reviewing Example 2, emphasize that completing the square changes an equation in standard form, which is difficult to graph by hand, into an equivalent equation in vertex form, which is easier to graph by hand because of the Graph-Translation Theorem.

Additional Example

Example 2

a. Rewrite the equation $y = x^2 + 10x - 4$ in vertex form.

b. Find the vertex of the parabola.

Solution

a. Rewrite the equation so that only terms with x are on one side: $y +$ _?_ $= x^2 + 10x$. 4 Use the Completing the Square Theorem. Here, $b =$ _?_, so $\left(\frac{b}{2}\right)^2 =$ _?_. 10; 25 Thus, $y +$ _?_ $+$ _?_ $= x^2 + 10x +$ _?_ and $y +$ _?_ $= (x +$ _?_$)^2$. 4; 25; 25; 29; 5

b. We can read the vertex from the vertex form of the equation. The vertex of the parabola is _?_. (-5, -29)

Note-Taking Tips

Encourage students to include their own verbal description of $\left(\frac{b}{2}\right)^2$ with their notes for the Completing the Square Theorem. Some examples are "the square of half the coefficient of x" or "take half of the coefficient of the x term and square it."

Accommodating the Learner

Ask students to use the Completing the Square Theorem to solve the equation $x^2 + bx + c = 0$ for x. (You may want to mention to students that they will see a similar set of steps to solve $ax^2 + bx + c = 0$ in Lesson 6-7.) $x^2 + bx = -c$; $x^2 + bx + \left(\frac{b}{2}\right)^2 = \frac{b^2}{4} - c$; $\left(x + \frac{b}{2}\right)^2 = \frac{b^2 - 4c}{4}$; $x + \frac{b}{2} = \frac{\pm\sqrt{b^2 - 4c}}{2}$; $x = -\frac{b}{2} \pm \frac{\sqrt{b^2 - 4c}}{2}$ or $x = \frac{-b \pm \sqrt{b^2 - 4c}}{2}$.

Notes on the Lesson

Completing the square on an expression whose x^2 coefficient is not 1 is tricky for most students. This is why the solution to Example 3 equates coefficients rather than completing the square. If you would like to show your students how to solve Example 3 by completing the square, a solution is given below.

Steps:

1. $h = -16t^2 + 32t + 12$
2. $h - 12 = -16t^2 + 32t$
3. $\frac{h - 12}{-16} = t^2 - 2t$
4. $\frac{h - 12}{-16} + 1 = t^2 - 2t + 1$
5. $\frac{h - 12}{-16} + 1 = (t - 1)^2$
6. $h - 12 - 16 = -16(t - 1)^2$
7. $h - 28 = -16(t - 1)^2$

Reasons:

1. Given
2. Subtract 12 from each side.
3. Divide each side by -16, the coefficient of t^2.
4. Complete the square on the right side (and add 1 to *both* sides).
5. Rewrite the right side of the equation as the square of a binomial.
6. Multiply each side by -16.
7. Simplify.

Additional Example

Example 3 Suppose a ball is thrown straight up from a height of 6 feet with an initial velocity of 48 $\frac{\text{feet}}{\text{second}}$. Then the ball's height *y* after *x* seconds is given by the formula $y = -16x^2 + 48x + 6$.

a. Rewrite the formula in the vertex form of the equation for a parabola. $y = -16(x - 1.5)^2 + 42$ or $y - 42 = -16(x - 1.5)^2$

b. Find the maximum height of the ball and the time it takes the ball to reach that point. The vertex is (1.5, 42), so the maximum height is 42 ft, reached 1.5 sec after it is thrown.

Example 3

Suppose a ball is thrown straight up from a height of 12 feet with an initial velocity of 32 $\frac{\text{ft}}{\text{sec}}$. Then the ball's height *y* after *x* seconds is given by the formula $y = -16x^2 + 32x + 12$.

a. Rewrite the formula in the vertex form of the equation for a parabola.

b. Find the maximum height of the ball and the time it takes for the ball to reach that point.

Solution

a. Equate the given expression for *y* with the general vertex form.

$$-16x^2 + 32x + 12 = a(x - h)^2 + k$$

Enter this equation into a CAS. The CAS will automatically expand the square of the binomial, as shown here.

$-16 \cdot x^2+32 \cdot x+12=a \cdot (x-h)^2+k$
$-16 \cdot x^2+32 \cdot x+12=a \cdot x^2-2 \cdot a \cdot h \cdot x+a \cdot h^2+k$

The coefficients of x^2 on the two sides must be equal, so $a = -16$. Substitute this value for *a*.

$+32 \cdot x+12=a \cdot x^2-2 \cdot a \cdot h \cdot x+a \cdot h^2+k|a=-16$
$-16 \cdot x^2+32 \cdot x+12=-16 \cdot x^2+32 \cdot h \cdot x-16 \cdot h^2$

Add $16x^2$ to both sides.

$\cdot x+12=-16 \cdot x^2+32 \cdot h \cdot x-16 \cdot h^2+k)+16 \cdot x^2$
$32 \cdot x+12=32 \cdot h \cdot x-16 \cdot h^2+k$

Equate the coefficients of *x* to see that $32 = 32h$, so $h = 1$. Substitute this value for *h*.

$32 \cdot x+12=32 \cdot h \cdot x-16 \cdot h^2+k|h=1$
$32 \cdot x+12=32 \cdot x+k-16$

Add $-32x$ to both sides. Then add 16 to both sides. The display at the right show that $k = 28$.

$(32 \cdot x+12=32 \cdot x+k-16)+-32 \cdot x \quad 12=k-16$
$(12=k-16)+16 \quad 28=k$

Substitute back for *a*, *h*, and *k* in the square form.

$$y = -16(x - 1)^2 + 28, \text{ or}$$
$$y - 28 = -16(x - 1)^2$$

b. The vertex of this parabola is (1, 28). So the maximum height of the ball is 28 feet, 1 second after it is thrown.

Accommodating the Learner

Have students complete the following:

a. Show that the equations $y - 5 = (x - 4)^2$ and $y = x^2 - 8x + 21$ represent the same parabola. Answers vary. Sample: $y - 5 = (x - 4)^2$; $y - 5 = x^2 - 8x + 16$; $y = x^2 - 8x + 21$

b. What is the vertex of the parabola whose equation is $y = x^2 - 8x + 21$? (4, 5)

c. For what translation is the graph of $y = x^2 - 8x + 21$ the image of the graph of the graph of $y = x^2$? Write your answer as a mapping of the form $(x, y) \rightarrow (x + h, y + k)$ and as a translation $T_{h,k}$. $(x, y) \rightarrow (x + 4, y + 5)$; $T_{4,5}$

Check Graph $y = -16x^2 + 32x + 12$. Trace to estimate the maximum value of the parabola. It checks.

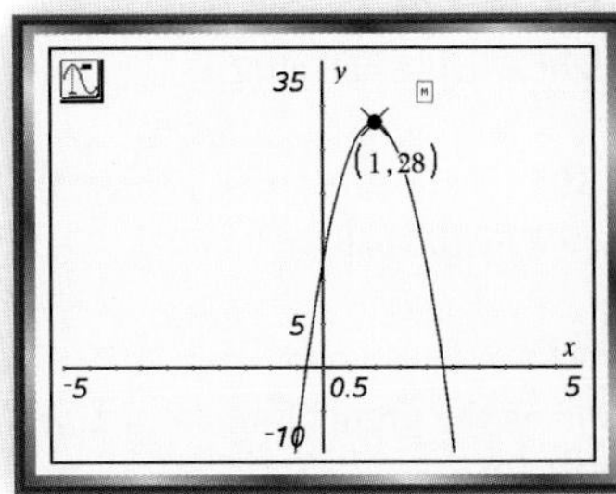

Questions

COVERING THE IDEAS

1. a. Give the sum of the areas of the three rectangles at right.
   b. What number must be added to this sum to complete the square?
   c. **Fill in the Blanks** Complete the equation $x^2 + \underline{\ ?\ }x + \underline{\ ?\ } = (x + \underline{\ ?\ })^2$. 16; 64; 8

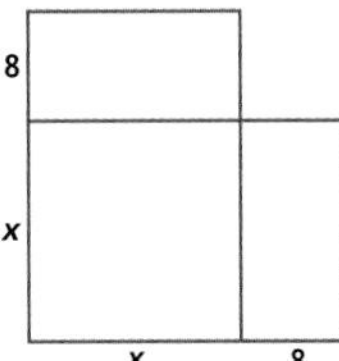

1a. $x^2 + 16x$

1b. 64

Fill in the Blanks In 2–5, find a number to make the expression a perfect-square trinomial.

2. $x^2 + 14x + \underline{\ ?\ }$ 49
3. $n^2 - n + \underline{\ ?\ }$ $\frac{1}{4}$
4. $z^2 - 30z + \underline{\ ?\ }$ 225
5. $t^2 + \frac{2}{3}t + \underline{\ ?\ }$ $\frac{1}{9}$

In 6 and 7, an equation in standard form is given.
  a. Rewrite the equation in vertex form.
  b. Find the vertex of the parabola represented by each equation.

6. $y = x^2 + 4x + 11$
7. $y = -2x^2 - 6x - 14$

6a. $y - 7 = (x + 2)^2$

6b. (-2, 7)

7a. $y + 9.5 = -2(x + 1.5)^2$

7b. (-1.5, -9.5)

8. Refer to Example 3. Generate a table of values for the equation $h = -16t^2 + 32t + 12$, or fill in a table like the one below by hand.

t	0	0.25	0.5	0.75	1.0	1.25	1.5	1.75	2
h	?	?	?	?	?	?	?	?	?

   a. The points in the table are symmetric to a vertical line through a particular point in the table. Which point? (1, 28)
   b. How does your answer to Part a compare to the vertex found in Example 3? The answer to Part a is the vertex.

8. See margin for table.

3 Assignment

Recommended Assignment

- Questions 1–21
- Question 22 (extra credit)
- Reading Lesson 6-6
- Covering the Ideas 6-6

Notes on the Questions

Questions 2–7 The term *completing the square* is used in two very different but related contexts in this lesson. In Questions 2–5, we *add* to complete the square, and the final expression is not equivalent to the given expression. Some students will wrongly extend this idea to Questions 6 and 7, where we *rewrite* the equations to find equations equivalent to those given. The geometric representation of completing the square in Example 1 may help students to see the difference. In *adding* to complete the square, we are filling in a missing square. In *rewriting* to complete the square, we are rewriting the area of the full square as the square of a binomial.

Additional Answers

8a.

t	h
0	12
0.25	19
0.5	24
0.75	27
1.0	28
1.25	27
1.5	24
1.75	19
2	12

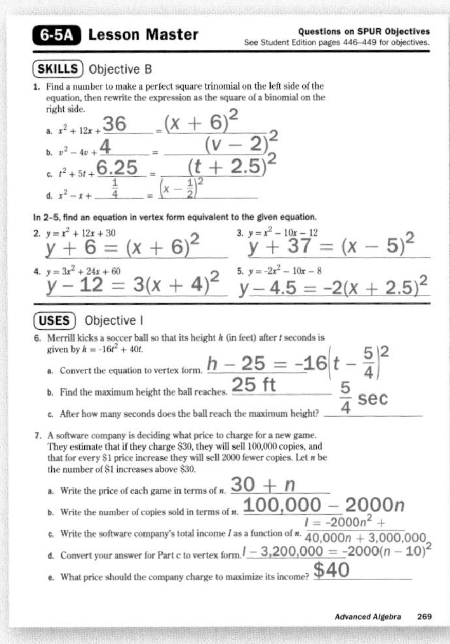

6-5A Lesson Master

Questions on SPUR Objectives
See Student Edition pages 446–449 for objectives.

SKILLS Objective B

1. Find a number to make a perfect square trinomial on the left side of the equation, then rewrite the expression as the square of a binomial on the right side.
   a. $x^2 + 12x +$ 36 = $(x + 6)^2$
   b. $v^2 - 4v +$ 4 = $(v - 2)^2$
   c. $t^2 + 5t +$ 6.25 = $(t + 2.5)^2$
   d. $x^2 - x +$ $\frac{1}{4}$ = $\left(x - \frac{1}{2}\right)^2$

In 2–5, find an equation in vertex form equivalent to the given equation.

2. $y = x^2 + 12x + 30$ $y + 6 = (x + 6)^2$
3. $y = x^2 - 10x - 12$ $y + 37 = (x - 5)^2$
4. $y = 3x^2 + 24x + 60$ $y - 12 = 3(x + 4)^2$
5. $y = -2x^2 - 10x - 8$ $y - 4.5 = -2(x + 2.5)^2$

USES Objective I

6. Merrill kicks a soccer ball so that its height h (in feet) after t seconds is given by $h = -16t^2 + 40t$.
   a. Convert the equation to vertex form. $h - 25 = -16\left(t - \frac{5}{4}\right)^2$
   b. Find the maximum height the ball reaches. 25 ft
   c. After how many seconds does the ball reach the maximum height? $\frac{5}{4}$ sec
7. A software company is deciding what price to charge for a new game. They estimate that if they charge $30, they will sell 100,000 copies, and that for every $1 price increase they will sell 2000 fewer copies. Let n be the number of $1 increases above $30.
   a. Write the price of each game in terms of n. $30 + n$
   b. Write the number of copies sold in terms of n. $100{,}000 - 2000n$
   c. Write the software company's total income I as a function of n. $I = -2000n^2 + 40{,}000n + 3{,}000{,}000$
   d. Convert your answer for Part c to vertex form. $I - 3{,}200{,}000 = -2000(n - 10)^2$
   e. What price should the company charge to maximize its income? $40

Advanced Algebra 269

Notes on the Questions

Questions 9 and 14 These questions offer one reason why knowing the vertex of a parabola is useful. One can find the highest point reached by a thrown ball or other projectile and also find the maximum value of functions related to economics. Question 14 may seem forced or unnatural, but the idea is fundamental in every business: Raising the price of an item decreases demand. The goal is to maximize profit, which is the product of sales and price.

Additional Answers

9d.

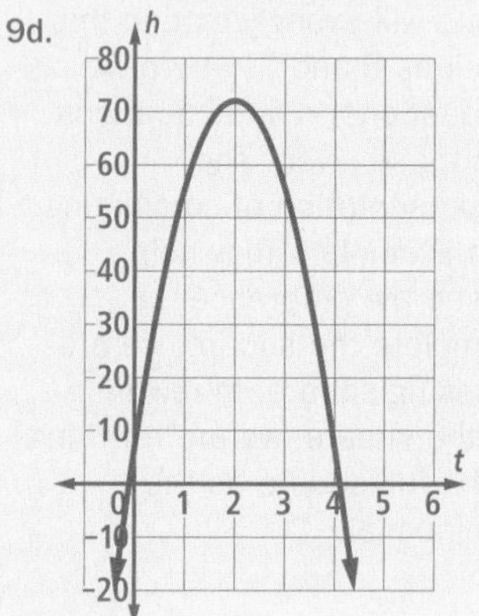

19a.

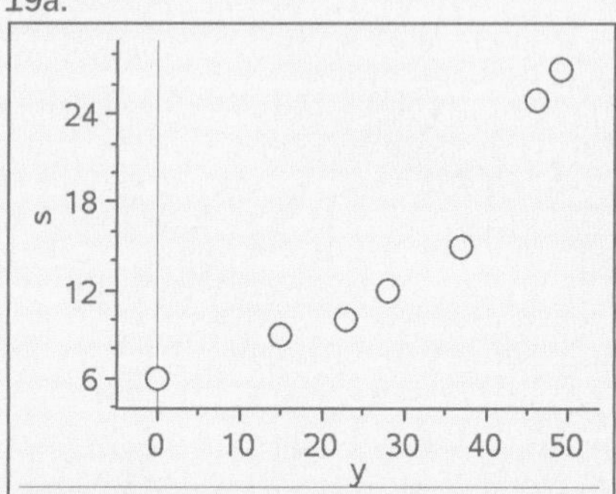

19b.

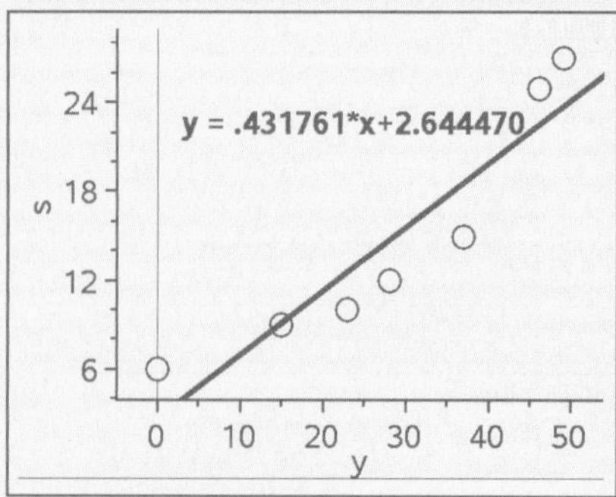

APPLYING THE MATHEMATICS

9. Suppose a ball is thrown straight up from a height of 8 feet with an initial upward velocity of 64 $\frac{\text{ft}}{\text{sec}}$.
   a. Write an equation to describe the height h of the ball after t seconds. $h = -16t^2 + 64t + 8$
   b. How high is the ball after 1 second? 56 ft
   c. Determine the maximum height attained by the ball by completing the square. 72 ft
   d. Sketch a graph your equation from Part a. See margin.
   e. How long will it take for the ball to land on the ground? about 4.1 sec
10. **Fill in the Blank** What is the missing term in the expression $x^2 + \frac{b}{a}x + \underline{\ ?\ }$ if the expression is a perfect-square trinomial? $\left(\frac{b}{2a}\right)^2$
11. Find an equation in vertex form equivalent to $y = 5x^2 - 2x + 15$. $y - 14.8 = 5(x - 0.2)^2$

In 12 and 13, consider the following. When a quadratic function is graphed, the second coordinate of the vertex of the parabola is always the minimum or maximum value of the function. Commands on some calculators may help you find those values. On one calculator these commands are `fMin` and `fMax`.

12. In the display at the right, `fMin` and `fMax` have been calculated. You are given the x-coordinate of the minimum point of the graph of $y = 3x^2 - 12x + 14$ and the x-coordinate of the maximum point of the graph of $y = -10x^2 + 60x$. Find the coordinates of the vertex of each parabola.

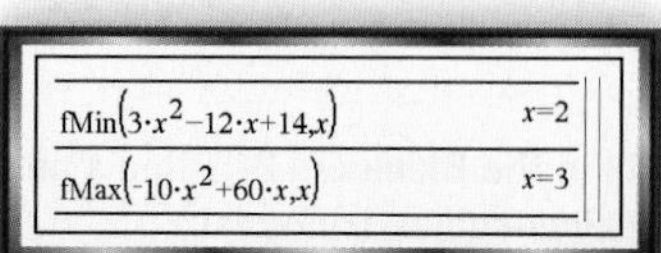

13. At the right, why is the x-coordinate of the minimum value stated as positive or negative infinity?

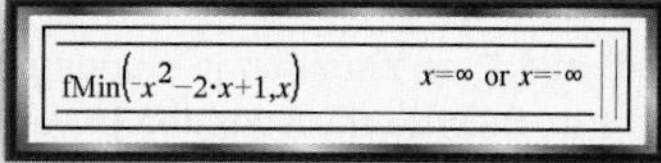

14. You run Twin Wheels bike-rental shop. You currently charge \$10 per day and average 56 rentals a day. In researching a price increase, you believe that for every fifty-cent increase in rental price you can expect to lose two rentals a day. Let n = the number of fifty-cent increases.
   a. Write an expression for the new price after n increases.
   b. Write an expression for the expected number of rentals after n increases. $56 - 2n$
   c. The total income for the day is equal to the price times the number of rentals. Multiply the expressions in Parts a and b to get an expression for the total daily income.
   d. Find the rental price that will maximize the total daily income. \$12 per day

12. (2, 2), (3, 90)

13. The parabola opens down and thus has no minimum.

14a. $10 + 0.5n$

14c. $(10 + 0.5n)(56 - 2n) = -n^2 + 8n + 560$

ENGLISH LEARNERS

Vocabulary Development

This lesson provides a natural opportunity to review the term *coefficient*. Students should understand that every algebraic term consists of variables (and their powers) and a coefficient, and any numbers or letters that do not represent variables must be (part of) the coefficient. For example, if the only variables are x, y, and z, then in the terms $5x$, $17sx^2y$, and $15\sqrt{3a^2}\,xz^2$ the coefficients are 5, $17s$, and $15\sqrt{3a^2}$, respectively. (Students will need to consider letters as coefficients when they solve $ax^2 + bx + c = 0$ in Lesson 6-7.)

REVIEW

15. Jailah tosses a ball upward from an initial height of 1.6 meters. The ball lands on the ground 4.8 seconds later. What was the upward velocity of Jailah's throw? **(Lesson 6-4)** $23.2\ \frac{\text{m}}{\text{sec}}$

16. Rewrite the equation $y = 4(3 - x)^2 - 8$ in standard form. **(Lesson 6-4)** $y = 4x^2 - 24x + 28$

17. On the coordinate grid at the right are the parabola with equation $y = -x^2$ and its image under a translation. **(Lessons 6-3, 4-10)**
    a. What translation maps the parabola with equation $y = -x^2$ onto the other parabola? $T_{1,4}$
    b. Write an equation for the image. $y = -(x - 1)^2$

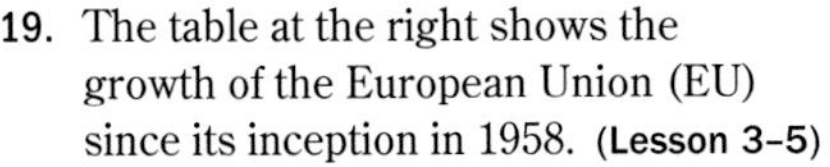

18. Solve the system $\begin{bmatrix} 1 & 0 & -1 \\ 2 & 1 & 3 \\ -1 & 4 & 0 \end{bmatrix}\begin{bmatrix} x \\ y \\ z \end{bmatrix} = \begin{bmatrix} 3 \\ 3 \\ -9 \end{bmatrix}$. **(Lesson 5-6)**

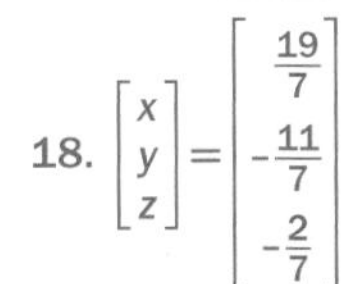

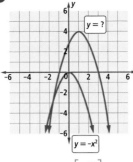

18. $\begin{bmatrix} x \\ y \\ z \end{bmatrix} = \begin{bmatrix} \frac{19}{7} \\ -\frac{11}{7} \\ -\frac{2}{7} \end{bmatrix}$

19. The table at the right shows the growth of the European Union (EU) since its inception in 1958. **(Lesson 3-5)**
    a. Draw a scatterplot of this data.
    b. Find an equation for the regression line, and draw the line on your scatterplot. a–b. See margin.
    c. How many member states does your regression line predict for the year 2058, the 100th anniversary of the founding of the EU? about 46 states

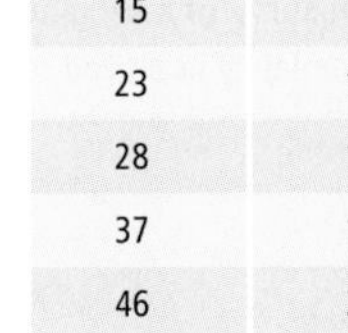

Years since 1958	Number of Member States
0	6
15	9
23	10
28	12
37	15
46	25
49	27

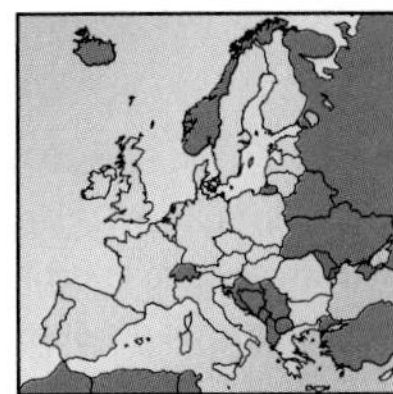

In 20 and 21, find x. (Previous Course)

20. $3^{2x} \cdot 3^4 = 3^{24}$ $x = 10$

21. $(2^x)^5 = 2^{25}$ $x = 5$

EXPLORATION

22. *MNOP* is a square with sides of length $a + b + c$. The areas of three regions inside *MNOP* are shown in the diagram.
    a. Find the areas of the other six regions. ab, b^2, bc, ac, bc, c^2
    b. Use the drawing to help you expand $(a + b + c)^2$.
    c. Make a drawing to illustrate the expansion of $(a + b + c + d)^2$.

22b. $a^2 + 2ab + 2ac + b^2 + 2bc + c^2$

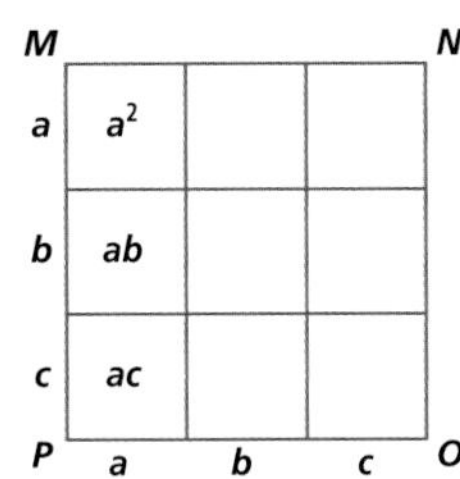

M	a	b	c	d	N
a	a^2	ab	ac	ad	
b	ab	b^2	bc	bd	
c	ac	bc	c^2	cd	
d	ad	bd	cd	d^2	
P					O

QY ANSWER

144

Notes on the Question

Question 19 This question sets up Lesson 6-6 on quadratic regression.

4 Wrap-Up

Ongoing Assessment

Have students work in small groups. Each group should select a value of b and write the equation of a parabola $y = x^2 + bx$ using that value. Then the members of the group should rewrite their equation in vertex form, find the vertex of the parabola, and check each other's work. Answers vary. Sample: If $b = 20$, then the equation is $y = x^2 + 20x$, which in vertex form is $y + 100 = (x + 10)^2$; the vertex is $(-10, -100)$.

Project Update

Project 5, *How High Does Your Parabola Go?*, on page 442 relates to the content of this lesson.

Extension

Ask students to use the result in Question 22, that $(a + b + c)^2 = a^2 + b^2 + c^2 + 2(ab + ac + bc)$, to expand the expression $((2a + 5b)^2 + (3a - 4b)^2)^2$.
$(4a^2 + 20ab + 25b^2 + 9a^2 - 24ab + 16b^2)^2 = (13a^2 - 4ab + 41b^2)^2 = (13a^2)^2 + (-4ab)^2 + (41b^2)^2 + 2[(13a^2) \cdot (-4ab) + (13a^2)(41b^2) + (-4ab)(41b^2)] = 169a^4 + 16a^2b^2 + 1681b^4 + 2(-52a^3b + 533a^2b^2 - 164ab^3) = 169a^4 - 104a^3b + 1082a^2b^2 - 328ab^3 + 1681b^4$

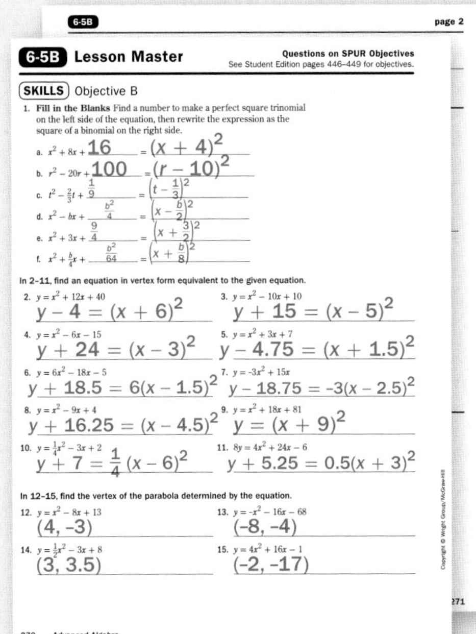

6-5B page 2

6-5B Lesson Master Questions on SPUR Objectives. See Student Edition pages 446–449 for objectives.

SKILLS Objective B

1. **Fill in the Blanks** Find a number to make a perfect square trinomial on the left side of the equation, then rewrite the expression as the square of a binomial on the right side.
    a. $x^2 + 8x + 16 = (x + 4)^2$
    b. $r^2 - 20r + 100 = (r - 10)^2$
    c. $t^2 - \frac{2}{3}t + \frac{1}{9} = \left(t - \frac{1}{3}\right)^2$
    d. $x^2 - bx + \frac{b^2}{4} = \left(x - \frac{b}{2}\right)^2$
    e. $x^2 + 3x + \frac{9}{4} = \left(x + \frac{3}{2}\right)^2$
    f. $x^2 + \frac{b}{4}x + \frac{b^2}{64} = \left(x + \frac{b}{8}\right)^2$

In 2–11, find an equation in vertex form equivalent to the given equation.

2. $y = x^2 + 12x + 40$ $y - 4 = (x + 6)^2$
3. $y = x^2 - 10x + 10$ $y + 15 = (x - 5)^2$
4. $y = x^2 - 6x - 15$ $y + 24 = (x - 3)^2$
5. $y = x^2 + 3x + 7$ $y - 4.75 = (x + 1.5)^2$
6. $y = 6x^2 - 18x - 5$ $y + 18.5 = 6(x - 1.5)^2$
7. $y = -3x^2 + 15x$ $y - 18.75 = -3(x - 2.5)^2$
8. $y = x^2 - 9x + 4$ $y + 16.25 = (x - 4.5)^2$
9. $y = x^2 + 18x + 81$ $y = (x + 9)^2$
10. $y = \frac{1}{4}x^2 - 3x + 2$ $y + 7 = \frac{1}{4}(x - 6)^2$
11. $8y = 4x^2 + 24x - 6$ $y + 5.25 = 0.5(x + 3)^2$

In 12–15, find the vertex of the parabola determined by the equation.

12. $y = x^2 - 8x + 13$ $(4, -3)$
13. $y = -x^2 - 16x - 68$ $(-8, -4)$
14. $y = \frac{1}{2}x^2 - 3x + 8$ $(3, 3.5)$
15. $y = 4x^2 + 16x - 1$ $(-2, -17)$

270 Advanced Algebra

Lesson 6-6

GOAL

Explore data sets that can be described either exactly or approximately by quadratic functions.

SPUR Objectives

J Fit a quadratic model to data.

Materials/Resources

- Lesson Masters 6-6A and 6-6B
- Resource Masters 2, 3, 107, and 108
- Old CD that can get scratched up, two $8\frac{1}{2}$-inch by 11-inch pieces of paper, quarter, CAS or graphing calculator

HOMEWORK

Suggestions for Assignment

- Questions 1–15
- Question 16 (extra credit)
- Reading Lesson 6-7
- Covering the Ideas 6-7

Local Standards

1 Warm-Up

Robin forgot the formula for the sum of the integers from 1 to n, but she knew that it was a quadratic function of n. If $f(x) = ax^2 + bx + c$ and $f(x)$ is the sum of the integers from 1 to x,

1. find numerical values for $f(1)$, $f(2)$, and $f(3)$. 1; 3; 6
2. find algebraic expressions for $f(1)$, $f(2)$, and $f(3)$ in terms of a, b, and c. $a + b + c$; $4a + 2b + c$; $9a + 3b + c$
3. Equate your answers to Warm-Ups 1 and 2 to obtain a 3 × 3 linear system in a, b, and c. $\begin{cases} a + b + c = 1 \\ 4a + 2b + c = 3 \\ 9a + 3b + c = 6 \end{cases}$
4. Solve the system in Warm-Up 3. $a = \frac{1}{2}$; $b = \frac{1}{2}$; $c = 0$

Lesson 6-6 Fitting a Quadratic Model to Data

Vocabulary

quadratic regression

BIG IDEA *Quadratic regression* is like linear regression in that it finds the model with the least sum of squares of differences from the given data points to the values predicted by the model.

In Chapter 3, you learned how to find an equation for the line through two points, and how to find a linear model for data that lie approximately on a straight line. You can also fit a *quadratic model* to data that lie approximately on a parabola. **Quadratic regression** fits a model of the form $y = ax^2 + bx + c$ to data.

Mental Math

Find the slope of the image of $3x + 2y = 7$ under the transformation.

a. $T_{6,-1}$ $-\frac{3}{2}$

b. R_{90} $\frac{2}{3}$

c. R_{270} $\frac{2}{3}$

d. $r_{y=x}$ $-\frac{2}{3}$

Activity

MATERIALS old CD that can get scratched up, two $8\frac{1}{2}$-inch by 11-inch pieces of paper, quarter, CAS or graphing calculator

You are going to investigate how the radius x of a circular object affects the probability y of the object landing completely in a fixed region when dropped.

Step 1 A CD like the one pictured at the right has 3 circles on it. Circle I represents the hole in the CD. Circle M (for middle) represents the start of the silver writing surface. Circle O represents the outer edge of the CD. Draw a line across the middle of your $8\frac{1}{2}$-by-11 piece of paper, dividing it into two $5\frac{1}{2}$-by-$8\frac{1}{2}$ rectangular targets.

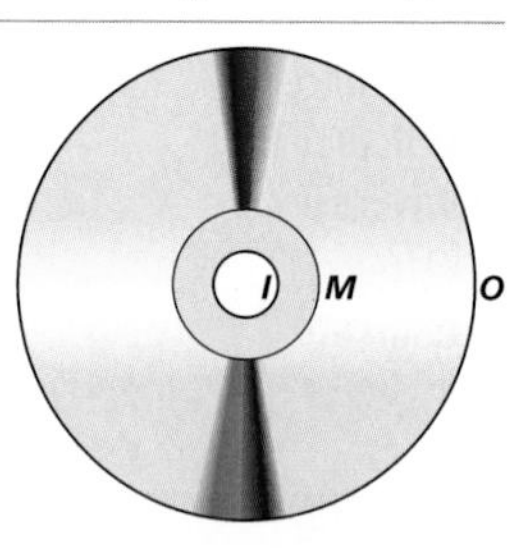

Step 2 On a separate sheet of paper, make four columns labeled Drop Number, I, M, and O. In the Drop Number column, write the integers 1 through 25. Place your divided sheet of $8\frac{1}{2}$-inch-by-11-inch paper on the floor and stand above it holding the CD waist high, parallel to the floor. Drop the CD.

Background

Some data fit a quadratic model. Three kinds of such data are found in this chapter: area, motion involving acceleration or deceleration, and the number of connections (such as the number of diagonals in a polygon).

Example There is exactly one quadratic function $f: x \to ax^2 + bx + c$ through three noncollinear points. To identify a quadratic model for a set of data with more than three points, the first step is to select three points to use. (This is directly analogous to fitting a linear function to data, as done in Lesson 3-6, where the first step is to select two points.) Students should be able to find an equation for the quadratic function either by solving a system or by using quadratic regression.

If the constraint that the parabola be a graph of a function is removed, then there are infinitely many parabolas through three points. Without more information, five coplanar points, no three of them collinear, determine a unique parabola.

If no part of the CD is touching the paper, drop it again. If any part of the CD is touching the paper, determine the score for each circle, *I*, *M*, and *O* as follows: If a circle on the CD lands completely inside one of the two rectangular targets, give it 1 point for that drop. Pictured below are the four possible situations and scores after a drop. The horizontal line represents either the edge of the paper or the line you drew on the paper.

Step 2
See Additional Answers section at the back of the book.

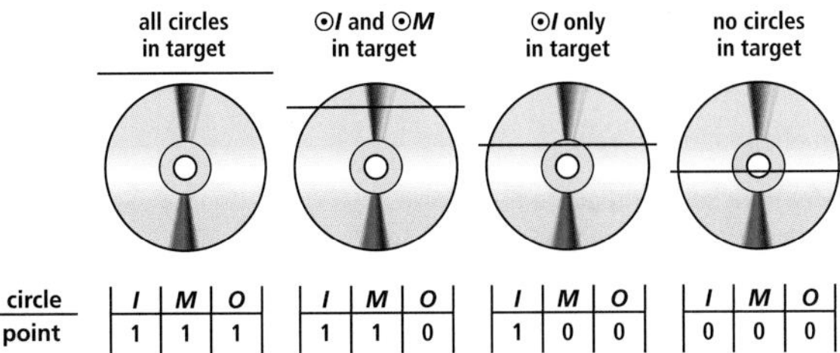

circle	I	M	O	I	M	O	I	M	O	I	M	O
point	1	1	1	1	1	0	1	0	0	0	0	0

Drop the CD 25 times and fill in your table.

Step 3 Calculate the relative frequency of a circle landing completely in a target. For example, if *M* has 16 points, then its relative frequency of points per drop is $\frac{16}{25}$. Record the frequencies in a table like the one at the right. The radii of circles on a standard CD have been filled in for you, but you should measure your CD to check. Answers vary. Samples given.

Circle	Radius (in.)	Relative Frequency
I	$\frac{5}{16}$	? $\frac{22}{25}$
M	$\frac{7}{8}$	? $\frac{14}{25}$
O	2	? $\frac{2}{25}$

Step 4 Create a scatterplot with three data points (radius, frequency) for *I*, *M*, and *O* on your calculator.

Choose the quadratic regression option from the appropriate menu. A sample is shown at the right. On this calculator, the graph of a quadratic model for the data is added to the scatterplot.

The calculator displays the equation for the quadratic model.

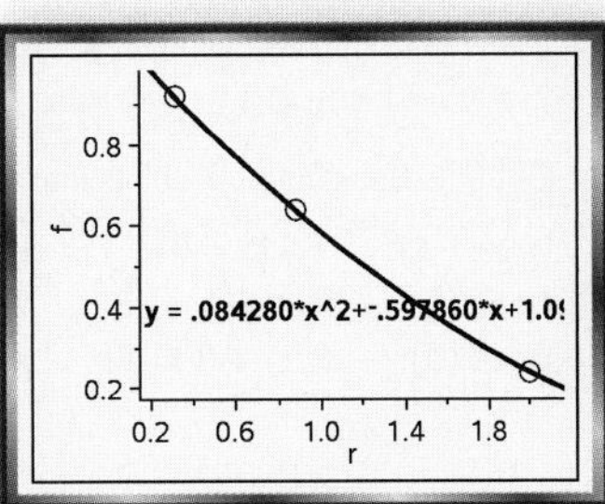

Step 5 Examine the scatterplot with the graph of the regression equation on it. How well does your model fit your data?

Step 6 Measure the diameter of a quarter and use your regression equation to predict the relative frequency of the quarter landing inside a target rectangle. Drop the quarter 25 times and see if the relative frequency is close to your prediction. Combine your results with other classmates. Compare the combined data with the prediction. Which value is closer to the predicted value—your own data or the combined data? See Additional Answers section at the back of the book.

Step 4
See Additional Answers section at the back of the book.

Step 5
Answers vary. Sample: This model seems to pass through all three of my data points.

2 Teaching

Notes on the Lesson

This lesson explores quadratic regression in two contexts. The first, in the Activity, fits a model to data from an experiment. The experiment yields different data each time it is performed, so students' models will be slightly different from each other. This is analogous to the situation for linear regression in Lesson 3-5. Quadratic regression gives a *quadratic of best fit;* this is analogous to the line of best fit in Lesson 3-5.

The second context, in the Example, is in the form of fitting a parabola through three ordered pairs. The model is exact, and while different points on a given parabola will yield different equations for the system, every system will give the same solution in terms of the values of *a*, *b*, and *c*.

Additional Answers can be found in the back of the book.

Fitting a quadratic model to a set of points is significant in the history of mathematics and statistics. Soon after the asteroid Ceres was discovered in 1801 by Giuseppe Piazzi, its location was lost. It was known that if Ceres went around the Sun, its orbit had to be an ellipse (with suitable adjustments for the gravities of bodies near it), and five points determine an ellipse. It was determined that Ceres had been seen and noted by others. These observations supplied more than five data points, and different five-point subsets of the available data gave slightly different orbits. So there was a question of how to calculate the best estimate of the real orbit of Ceres. In the process of tackling this problem, Gauss, the greatest mathematician of his time, discovered a fundamental use of the normal distribution. This is why a normal distribution is sometimes called a Gaussian distribution.

Additional Example

Example A parabola contains the points (-1, 8), (1, 2), and (3, 4). Find its equation. When $x = -1$, then $8 = a(-1)^2 + b(-1) + c$ or $8 = a - b + c$; when $x = 1$, then $2 = a(1)^2 + b(1) + c$ or $2 = a + b + c$; when $x = 3$, then $4 = a(3)^2 + b(3) + c$ or $4 = 9a + 3b + c$. So the system is $\begin{cases} 8 = a - b + c \\ 2 = a + b + c \\ 4 = 9a + 3b + c \end{cases}$. The solution is $a = 1$, $b = -3$, and $c = 4$. The resulting equation is $y = x^2 - 3x + 4$.

Note-Taking Tips

For a multistep process such as the one in the Example, encourage students to label and describe each step. For example, they might write the following:

1. Substitute each ordered pair into $y = ax^2 + bx + c$.
2. Write the result of Step 1 as a system of three equations.
3. Solve the system.
4. Use the solution to the system to write an equation for the parabola.
5. Check the three given ordered pairs in the final equation.

3 Assignment

Recommended Assignment

- Questions 1–15
- Question 16 (extra credit)
- Reading Lesson 6-7
- Covering the Ideas 6-7

Finding the Equation of a Given Parabola

You can apply the techniques of solving systems of equations you learned in Chapter 5 and the regression technique in the Activity to find an equation for any parabola on which you know three points.

Example

The parabola at the right contains the points (–1, 7), (1, -3) and (5, 1). Find its equation.

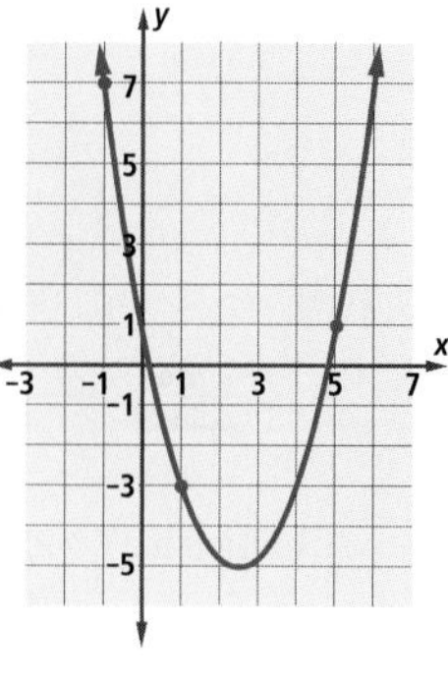

Solution 1 Use a system of equations.

Because the ordered pairs (x, y) are solutions of the equation $y = ax^2 + bx + c$, substitute to get 3 linear equations in a, b, and c.

When $x = -1$, $y = 7$: $7 = a(-1)^2 + b(-1) + c$
When $x = 1$, $y = -3$: $-3 = a(1)^2 + b(1) + c$
When $x = 5$, $y = 1$: $1 = a(5)^2 + b(5) + c$

So a, b, and c are solutions to the system $\begin{cases} 7 = a - b + c \\ -3 = a + b + c \\ 1 = 25a + 5b + c \end{cases}$.

You are asked to solve this system in Question 2.

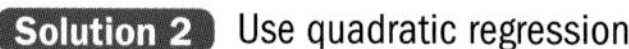

Solution 2 Use quadratic regression.

Enter the x-coordinates and y-coordinates into lists in your calculator and apply quadratic regression. One calculator gives the solution at the right, so the parabola has equation $y = x^2 - 5x + 1$.

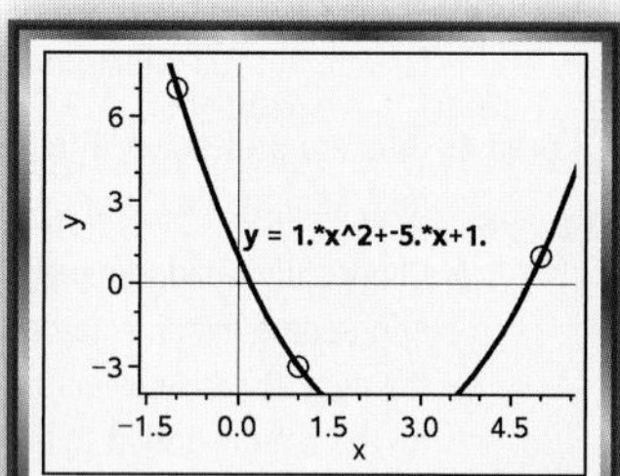

Check Substitute the points into the equation.

Does $(-1)^2 - 5(-1) + 1 = 7$? Yes.
Does $(1)^2 - 5(1) + 1 = -3$? Yes.
Does $(5)^2 - 5(5) + 1 = 1$? Yes; it checks.

Questions

COVERING THE IDEAS

1. Refer to the Activity.
   a. Write an equation for the function your quadratic regression describes. Answers vary. Sample: $y = 0.084x^2 - 0.669x + 1.081$
   b. Use the model from Part a to predict the probability of a mini CD with a radius of 4 centimeters landing completely inside one of the two rectangular targets. Answers vary. Sample: 0.236

Accommodating the Learner

Tell students that a parabola passes through the origin (not at its vertex) and the points (m, n) and (p, q).

a. Write the system of equations that will let you solve for the coefficients of the standard form of the equation for this parabola. The graph contains (0, 0), so $c = 0$. The system is $\begin{cases} n = m^2a + mb \\ q = p^2 + pb \end{cases}$.

b. Find the equation if one root is 4 and the minimum value is -8. The parabola contains (0, 0) and (4, 0), so the x-value of the vertex is halfway between 0 and 4, or 2; thus a third point is (2, -8). Using (4, 0) for (m, n) and (2, -8) for (p, q), the system is $\begin{cases} 0 = 16a + 4b \\ -8 = 4a + 2b \end{cases}$; the solution is $a = 2$, $b = -8$, so the equation of the parabola is $y = 2x^2 - 8x$.

2. Solve the system of the Example to find an equation for the parabola that contains the given points. $y = x^2 - 5x + 1$

In 3 and 4, solve a system of equations to write an equation for the parabola that contains the given points.

3. (4, -6), (-2, 30), (0, 10) $y = x^2 - 8x + 10$
4. (-1, -3), (5, 81), (2, 12) $y = 3x^2 + 2x - 4$

In 5 and 6, use quadratic regression to find an equation for the parabola that contains the given points.

5. (3, 2), (-1, 5), (8, 7) $y \approx 0.194x^2 - 1.14x + 3.7$
6. (-6, 5), (-1, 10), (3, 4) $y \approx -0.28x^2 - 0.94x + 9.3$

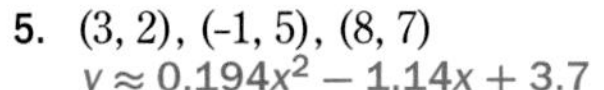

7b.

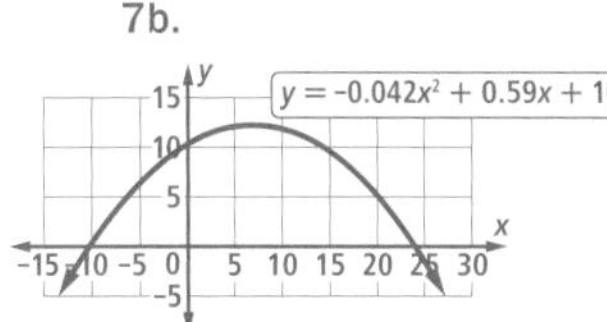

APPLYING THE MATHEMATICS

7. A quarterback threw a ball from 5 yards behind the line of scrimmage and a height of 6 feet. The ball was 10 feet high as it crossed the line of scrimmage. It was caught 20 yards past the line of scrimmage at a height of 5 feet off the ground.
   a. Find an equation that gives the height y of the ball (in feet) when it was x yards beyond the line of scrimmage.
   b. Graph the equation. a. $y = -0.042x^2 + 0.59x + 10$

Peyton Manning throwing for the Indianapolis Colts

8. In *The Greedy Triangle* by Marilyn Burns, an equilateral triangle keeps changing shape into a regular polygon with more and more sides. As the number of sides of a polygon increase, so do the number of diagonals of the polygon. Recall the formula for the number of diagonals in a polygon. If you have forgotten, you can derive it using quadratic regression.
   a. Count the number of diagonals in each polygon below and complete the table to the right.

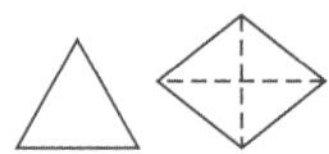

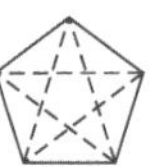

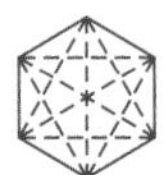

Shape	Number of Sides	Number of Diagonals
Triangle	? 3	? 0
Quadrilateral	? 4	? 2
Pentagon	? 5	? 5
Hexagon	? 6	? 9

   b. Use quadratic regression to find a model for the number of diagonals in a polygon. $d = 0.5n^2 - 1.5n$
   c. Is this model exact or approximate? exact
   d. Use the model to determine the number of diagonals in a 50-sided polygon. 1175 diagonals

Accommodating the Learner

Tell students that three other points on the parabola in the Example are (0, 1), (2, -5), and (3, -5).

1. Ask students to use those points to find a system of equations in a, b, and c. Using (0, 1): $1 = a(0)^2 + b(0) + c$ or $1 = c$; using (2, -5): $-5 = a(2)^2 + b(2) + c$ or $-5 = 4a + 2b + c$; using (3, -5): $-5 = a(3)^2 + b(3) + c$ or $-5 = 9a + 3b + c$.
   The system is $\begin{cases} 1 = c \\ -5 = 4a + 2b + c \\ -5 = 9a + 3b + c \end{cases}$.
2. Do they get the same system as in the Example? No
3. The values $a = 1$, $b = -5$, and $c = 1$ satisfy the system in the Example. Do they also satisfy the system that students found in Question 1? Does $1 = 1$? Yes. Does $-5 = 4(1) + 2(-5) + 1$? Yes. Does $-5 = 9(1) + 3(-5) + 1$? Yes. The points satisfy both systems.
4. What is the equation of the parabola? $y = x^2 - 5x + 1$

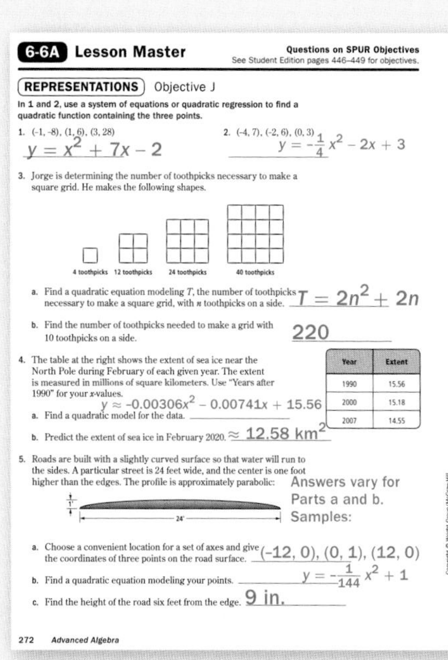

6-6A Lesson Master

Questions on SPUR Objectives
See Student Edition pages 446–449 for objectives.

REPRESENTATIONS Objective J

In 1 and 2, use a system of equations or quadratic regression to find a quadratic function containing the three points.

1. (-1, -8), (1, 6), (3, 28) $y = x^2 + 7x - 2$
2. (-4, 7), (-2, 6), (0, 3) $y = -\frac{1}{4}x^2 - 2x + 3$
3. Jorge is determining the number of toothpicks necessary to make a square grid. He makes the following shapes.

4 toothpicks 12 toothpicks 24 toothpicks 40 toothpicks

   a. Find a quadratic equation modeling T, the number of toothpicks necessary to make a square grid, with n toothpicks on a side. $T = 2n^2 + 2n$
   b. Find the number of toothpicks needed to make a grid with 10 toothpicks on a side. 220
4. The table at the right shows the extent of sea ice near the North Pole during February of each given year. The extent is measured in millions of square kilometers. Use "Years after 1990" for your x-values.

Year	Extent
1990	15.56
2000	15.18
2007	14.55

   a. Find a quadratic model for the data. $y \approx -0.00306x^2 - 0.00741x + 15.56$
   b. Predict the extent of sea ice in February 2020. ≈ 12.58 km^2
5. Roads are built with a slightly curved surface so that water will run to the sides. A particular street is 24 feet wide, and the center is one foot higher than the edges. The profile is approximately parabolic: Answers vary for Parts a and b. Samples:

1' 24'

   a. Choose a convenient location for a set of axes and give the coordinates of three points on the road surface. (-12, 0), (0, 1), (12, 0)
   b. Find a quadratic equation modeling your points. $y = -\frac{1}{144}x^2 + 1$
   c. Find the height of the road six feet from the edge. 9 in.

272 *Advanced Algebra*

Notes on the Questions

Question 9 This is the only question in the lesson in which students are asked to fit a parabola to more than three points. If students use only three points, following the Example in the lesson, you might wish to compare the models students obtain. If they use the first three planets, how good are their predictions for the last three? By comparing how small or large the squares of the residuals are (residuals are the difference between observed values and expected values), you can determine which is the best fit. Then compare the model given by quadratic regression with those used by students. Students should find that if they choose just three points to fit the data, it is best to use points spread over the data set rather than three "neighboring" points.

Questions 10–12 You might also ask for the vertex of the graph of each equation.

Additional Answers

9b. $p \approx 0.1081d^2 + 2.301d - 1.557$

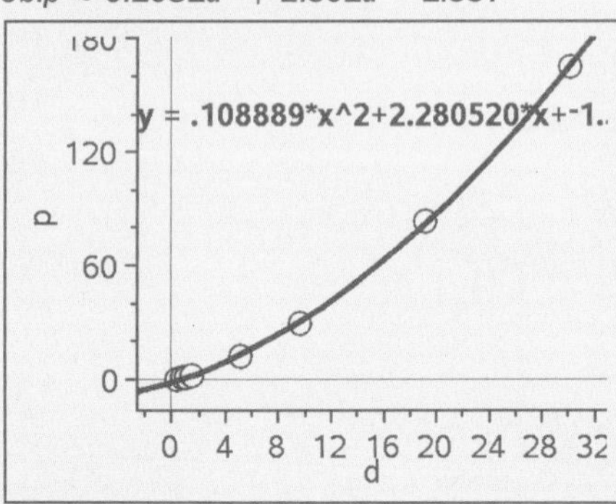

Yes; the model seems to pass through all the data points.

9. Shown below is a table of data on the eight major planets in our solar system. For each planet, the period of the orbit is given in Earth years and the average distance from the Sun is in astronomical units (AU). One AU is approximately the mean distance between Earth and the Sun. Each planet's distance from the Sun is not constant due to its elliptical orbit, so the average distance is given.

Planet	d = Avg. Distance From the Sun (AU)	P = Period of Orbit (in Earth years)
Mercury	0.39	0.24
Venus	0.72	0.62
Earth	1.00	1.00
Mars	1.52	1.88
Jupiter	5.20	11.86
Saturn	9.58	29.46
Uranus	19.20	84.01
Neptune	30.05	164.79

9a.

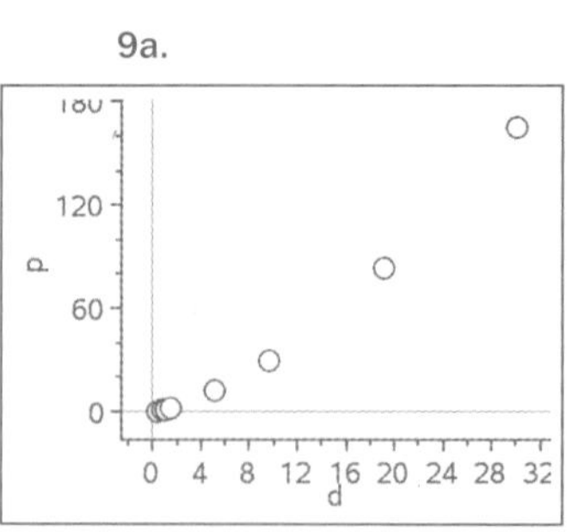
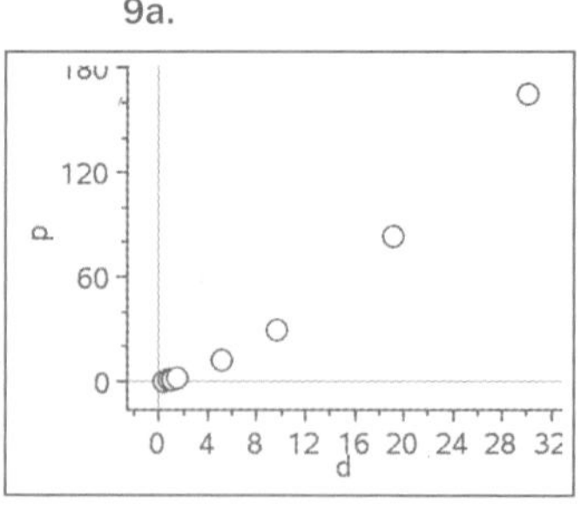

a. Create a scatterplot of the data. Use average distance d as the independent variable and period P as the dependent variable.

b. Fit a quadratic model to these data. Graph the model on the same axes as your scatterplot. Does the model seem like it fits the data? Why or why not? See margin.

c. Pluto, a dwarf planet, is an average 39.48 AU from the Sun. It takes Pluto 248.54 Earth years to orbit the Sun. Does Pluto fit your model?

d. Another dwarf planet, Sedna, or 2003 VB12, as it was originally designated, orbits the sun at an average distance of 90 AU. Use your model from Part b to predict how long it takes Sedna to orbit the Sun. about 1086 yr

9c. The model predicts about 258 yr for Pluto, so Pluto fits the model fairly well.

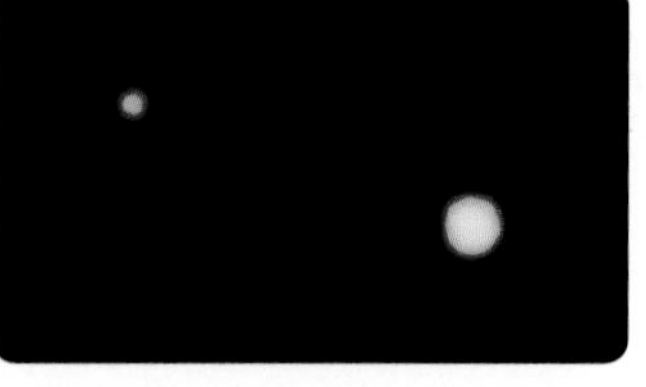

Pluto and one of its moons, Charon, are shown above. Sunlight takes about $5\frac{1}{2}$ hours to reach Pluto. Sunlight reaches Earth in about 8 minutes.

REVIEW

In 10–12, rewrite the equation in vertex form. (Lesson 6-5)

10. $y = x^2 - 14x + 53$ $y - 4 = (x - 7)^2$
11. $y = 3x^2 - 9x + 9$ $y - 2.25 = 3(x - 1.5)^2$
12. $y = x^2 - 4gx + 3g^2$ $y + g^2 = (x - 2g)^2$
13. Find an equation in standard form for the image of the parabola with equation $y = -2x^2$ under the translation $T_{-4, -0.5}$. (Lessons 6-3, 6-1) $y = -2x^2 - 16x - 32.5$

Extension

Show students the diagram at the right of a basketball player shooting a free throw. In the diagram, the ball is released at the ordered pair (15, 6) and goes through the hoop at the ordered pair (0, 10). Ask students to select a reasonable ordered pair for another point on the parabola and then find an equation that models the free throw.

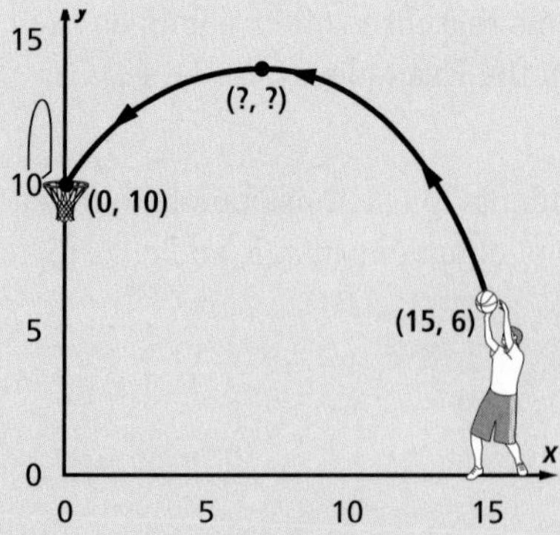

14. a. Find an equation for the line through points (a, b) and (b, a). 14a. $y = -x + a + b$

b. Use a rotation matrix to find an equation for the image of the line from Part a under a rotation of 90° about the origin. **(Lessons 4-9, 3-4)** $y = x + a + b$

15. The Moon is much less massive than Earth, and exerts less gravity. Near the surface of the Moon, the acceleration due to gravity is about $5.31 \frac{\text{ft}}{\text{sec}^2}$. Suppose an astronaut drops an object on the Moon from a height of 5 feet.

a. How long will it take the object to fall? about 1.37 sec

b. How long would it have taken the object to fall if it was dropped from the same height on Earth? **(Lesson 6-4)** about 0.56 sec

EXPLORATION

16. Follow these steps to determine the theoretical probabilities that the circles of the CD in the Activity will be in one of the rectangular target areas. Answers vary. Samples given.

a. Find the area of the region in which the center point of the CD can land so that the CD is touching the paper. about 184 in^2

b. Find the area of the region in which the center point of the CD can land so that circle *I* lands completely in one of the target areas. about 77 in^2

c. Let a be your answer to Part a, and b your answer to Part b. Calculate $\frac{b}{a}$. This number is the probability that the smallest circle is in the target area. 0.42

d. Repeat Parts b and c for the other two circles.

e. Do the probabilities seem to agree with the relative frequencies your class found?

16d. middle circle: about 51 in^2, 0.28; outer circle: about 13.5 in^2, 0.073

16e. Answers vary. Sample: The probability for the outer circle agrees fairly well with the relative frequency.

Answers vary. Sample: If the third ordered pair is (7, 14), then the system is

$$\begin{cases} 10 = c \\ 14 = 49a + 7b + c \\ 6 = 225a + 15b + c \end{cases}$$

The solution to this system is $a = -0.105$, $b = 1.30$, and $c = 10$, so the equation is $y = -0.105x^2 + 1.30x + 10$.

Notes on the Questions

Question 16 We encourage discussing this question after the Activity is completed.

4 Wrap-Up

Ongoing Assessment

Ask students to describe how to write a system of three equations to find an equation for a parabola through the given points (0, 10), (1, 3), and (4, –6). Answers vary. Sample: Use the ordered pairs to write three equations of the form $y = ax^2 + bx + c$. For (0, 10), $10 = a(0)^2 + b(0) + c$ or $10 = c$. For (1, 3), $3 = a(1)^2 + b(1) + c$ or $3 = a + b + c$. For (4, –6), $-6 = a(4)^2 + b(4) + c$ or $-6 = 16a + 4b + c$. Solve this system to find the coefficients in the equation for the parabola.

Project Update

Project 4, *How High Does Your Parabola Go?*, on page 442 relates to the content of this lesson.

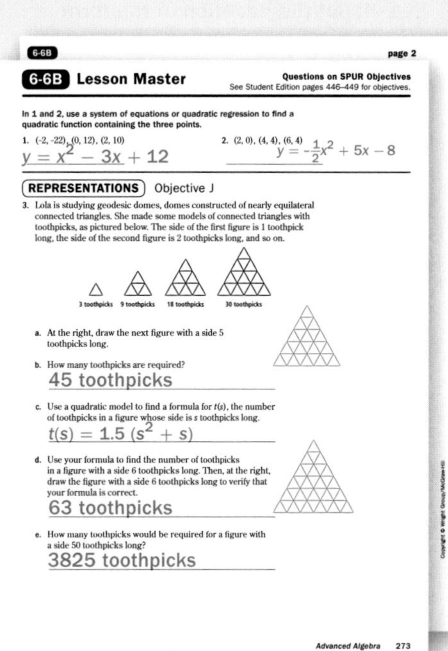
6-6B page 2

6-6B Lesson Master — Questions on SPUR Objectives. See Student Edition pages 446–449 for objectives.

In 1 and 2, use a system of equations or quadratic regression to find a quadratic function containing the three points.

1. (-2, -22), (0, 12), (2, 10) $y = x^2 - 3x + 12$

2. (2, 0), (4, 4), (6, 4) $y = -\frac{1}{2}x^2 + 5x - 8$

REPRESENTATIONS Objective J

3. Lola is studying geodesic domes, domes constructed of nearly equilateral connected triangles. She made some models of connected triangles with toothpicks, as pictured below. The side of the first figure is 1 toothpick long, the side of the second figure is 2 toothpicks long, and so on.

3 toothpicks 9 toothpicks 18 toothpicks 30 toothpicks

a. At the right, draw the next figure with a side 5 toothpicks long.

b. How many toothpicks are required? 45 toothpicks

c. Use a quadratic model to find a formula for $t(s)$, the number of toothpicks in a figure whose side is s toothpicks long. $t(s) = 1.5(s^2 + s)$

d. Use your formula to find the number of toothpicks in a figure with a side 6 toothpicks long. Then, at the right, draw the figure with a side 6 toothpicks long to verify that your formula is correct. 63 toothpicks

e. How many toothpicks would be required for a figure with a side 50 toothpicks long? 3825 toothpicks

Advanced Algebra 273

Copyright © Wright Group/McGraw-Hill

Lesson 6-7

GOAL

Motivate, prove, and apply the Quadratic Formula.

SPUR Objectives

C Solve quadratic equations.

I Use quadratic equations to solve problems dealing with distance, velocity, and acceleration.

Materials/Resources

- Lesson Masters 6-7A and 6-7B
- Resource Masters 2, 109, and 110
- Quiz 2

HOMEWORK

Suggestions for Assignment

- Questions 1–23
- Question 24 (extra credit)
- Reading Lesson 6-8
- Covering the Ideas 6-8

Local Standards

1 Warm-Up

In 1–4, put the equation in the form $ax^2 + bx + c = 0$ and indicate the values of a, b, and c.

1. $3x^2 - 4x = 10$ $3x^2 + (-4)x + (-10) = 0$; $a = 3$, $b = -4$, $c = -10$
2. $y = y^2$ $y^2 - y = 0$; $a = 1$, $b = -1$, $c = 0$
3. $1 + 2z^2 + 3z = 4 + 5z + 6z^2$ $4z^2 + 2z + 3 = 0$; $a = 4$, $b = 2$, $c = 3$
4. $(d - 14)^2 = (d + 6)^2$ $40d - 160 = 0$; $a = 0$, $b = 40$, $c = -160$; not quadratic

Lesson 6-7 The Quadratic Formula

Vocabulary

Quadratic Formula

▸ **BIG IDEA** The *Quadratic Formula* gives the solutions to any quadratic equation in standard form whose coefficients are known.

To help train outfielders, the coach of a baseball team (who is also a math teacher) uses a hitting machine. The machine hits a 4-foot-high pitch, and the ball travels toward the outfield along a nearly parabolic path. Let x be the distance along the ground (in feet) of the ball from home plate, and h be the height (in feet) of the ball at that distance. Using estimated heights of the ball at a various points along its path, he found the following regression equation to model the flight of the ball.

$$h = -0.00132x^2 + 0.545x + 4$$

If an outfielder leaps and catches a ball 10 feet off the ground, how far is he from home plate? To answer this, you can solve the flight equation when $h = 10$.

$$10 = -0.00132x^2 + 0.545x + 4$$

Subtract 10 from each side to rewrite the equation in standard form.

$$0 = -0.00132x^2 + 0.545x - 6$$

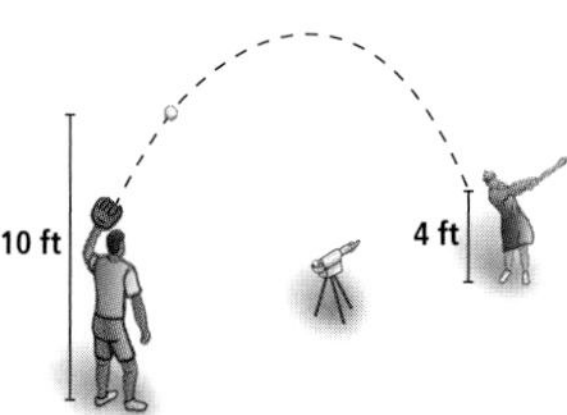

You could solve this equation by rewriting it in vertex form, but in previous courses you have probably used a formula that gives the solutions. The **Quadratic Formula** is a theorem that can be proved by completing the square, starting with a general quadratic equation in standard form.

Mental Math

Expand the binomial.

a. $(a - b)^2$ $a^2 - 2ab + b^2$

b. $(a - 3b)^2$ $a^2 - 6ab + 9b^2$

c. $(5a - 3b)^2$ $25a^2 - 30ab + 9b^2$

d. $(5a^4 - 3b^6)^2$ $25a^8 - 30a^4b^6 + 9b^{12}$

Quadratic Formula Theorem

If $ax^2 + bx + c = 0$ and $a \neq 0$, then $x = \frac{-b \pm \sqrt{b^2 - 4ac}}{2a}$.

The proof is given on the next page.

Background

This lesson's central idea is that the formula $x = \frac{-b \pm \sqrt{b^2 - 4ac}}{2a}$ gives the two solutions to the equation $ax^2 + bx + c = 0$ (where $a \neq 0$); furthermore, the formula provides the solution for any quadratic equation. The Quadratic Formula Theorem is one of the most important theorems in this course; every student should memorize it immediately.

Many students may have already worked with this formula but may not have been expected to derive it. A goal of this course is that students understand how the formula is derived, but we do not expect them to be able to re-create the derivation.

In going from Step 7 to Step 8 in the derivation of the Quadratic Formula, there are technically two possible values for the left side also, namely $x + \frac{b}{2a}$ and $-\left(x + \frac{b}{2a}\right)$.

Given the equation $ax^2 + bx + c = 0$, where $a \neq 0$.

Proof

1. $x^2 + \frac{b}{a}x + \frac{c}{a} = \frac{0}{a}$ — Divide both sides by a so the coefficient of x^2 is 1.
2. $x^2 + \frac{b}{a}x = -\frac{c}{a}$ — Add $-\frac{c}{a}$ to each side.
3. $x^2 + \frac{b}{a}x + \frac{b^2}{4a^2} = \frac{b^2}{4a^2} - \frac{c}{a}$ — Complete the square by adding $\left(\frac{1}{2} \cdot \frac{b}{a}\right)^2$ to both sides.
4. $\left(x + \frac{b}{2a}\right)^2 = \frac{b^2}{4a^2} - \frac{c}{a}$ — Write the left side as a binomial squared.
5. $\left(x + \frac{b}{2a}\right)^2 = \frac{b^2 - 4ac}{4a^2}$ — Add the fractions on the right side.
6. $\sqrt{\left(x + \frac{b}{2a}\right)^2} = \sqrt{\frac{b^2 - 4ac}{4a^2}}$ — Take the square roots of both sides.
7. $\left|x + \frac{b}{2a}\right| = \sqrt{\frac{b^2 - 4ac}{4a^2}}$ — Use the Absolute Value-Square Root Theorem.
8. $x + \frac{b}{2a} = \pm\frac{\sqrt{b^2 - 4ac}}{2a}$ — Use the definition of absolute value.
9. $x = \frac{-b \pm \sqrt{b^2 - 4ac}}{2a}$ — Add $-\frac{b}{2a}$ to both sides.

If you solve $ax^2 + bx + c = 0$ on a CAS, it is likely to display the solutions in a compound sentence.

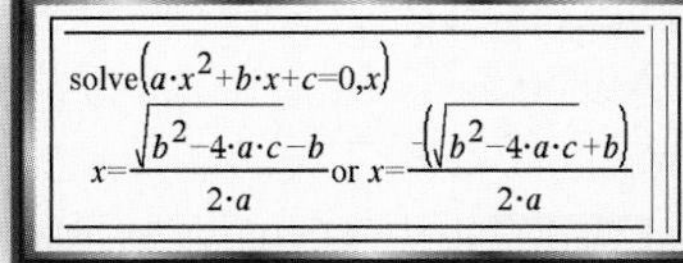

Using the Quadratic Formula

Example 1

To the nearest foot, how far from home plate was the outfielder when he leaped to catch the 10-ft high ball?

Solution Use the Quadratic Formula on the equation $0 = -0.00132x^2 + 0.545x - 6$.

Here $a = -0.00132$, $b = 0.545$, and $c = -6$.

$$x = \frac{-0.545 \pm \sqrt{(0.545)^2 - 4(-0.00132)(-6)}}{2(-0.00132)}$$

(continued on next page)

However, the second of these does not give rise to different solutions because Step 8 has a ± sign on the right side. Also between Step 7 and Step 8 we took the square root of a fraction by taking the square root of the numerator and denominator; each has two square roots, but one ± sign takes care of all possibilities.

ENGLISH LEARNERS

Vocabulary Development

When students read aloud the Quadratic Formula Theorem, encourage them to end their description with the phrase "all over $2a$." That can help them remember that each value of x is a fraction, with $-b \pm \sqrt{b^2 - 4ac}$ as the numerator and $2a$ as the denominator.

2 Teaching

Notes on the Lesson

Some teachers would say that an expression such as $-5x^2 - x + 10$ is not in $ax^2 + bx + c$ form because there is a subtraction sign between the first and second terms. They prefer students to write the expression as $-5x^2 + (-x) + 10$ to make more explicit the values of *a, b,* and c. We leave it to you to decide whether writing expressions in this way would be beneficial to your students.

When discussing the Quadratic Formula, emphasize that *one side of the equation must be zero*! This discourages students from incorrectly applying the formula.

The Quadratic Formula Theorem is important because it solves *any* quadratic equation. In particular, students who have learned to solve quadratics by factoring need to be aware of the weaknesses of that method compared to this formula. Stress that the ± sign in the formula means that there are possibly two solutions. Encourage students to separate the solutions, which is done in the Examples in this lesson.

Working with the Quadratic Formula provides a good opportunity to simplify expressions with square roots and to help students practice using calculators efficiently. For example, using the Quadratic Formula on $x^2 - x - 1 = 0$ yields $x = \frac{1 \pm \sqrt{5}}{2}$, and using it on the equivalent $3x^2 - 3x - 3 = 0$ yields $x = \frac{3 \pm \sqrt{45}}{6}$. Students should realize that these answers are identical. (You can make up other examples of this type by multiplying both sides of an equation by a constant and not reducing before applying the formula.)

Notes on the Lesson

Because many real-world situations lead to quadratic equations, a formula for solving a quadratic is an important tool. Two rather typical problems are given as examples: the path of a baseball in Example 1 and a problem involving the triangular numbers in Example 3.

Additional Examples

Example 1 Using the equation $h = -0.00132x^2 + 0.545x + 4$ to model the path of a ball, suppose an outfielder makes a "shoestring" catch and catches the ball when it is 2 feet above the ground. To the nearest foot, how far from home plate was the ball caught? $2 = -0.00132x^2 + 0.545x + 4$ or $0 = -0.00132x^2 + 0.545x + 2$, so $a = -0.00132$, $b = 0.545$, $c = 2$, and $x = \frac{-0.545 \pm \sqrt{0.3076}}{-0.00264}$; $x = -3.638$ or $x = 416.516$. The negative value is not applicable, so the outfielder caught the ball about 416.5 ft from home plate.

Example 2 Solve $3x^2 - 10x - 25 = 0$.

Solution Use the Quadratic Formula.

$a = \underline{\ ?\ }$, $b = \underline{\ ?\ }$, and $c = \underline{\ ?\ }$ 3; -10; -25 $x = \frac{-b \pm \sqrt{b^2 - 4ac}}{2a} = \underline{\ ?\ }$ $\frac{-(-10) \pm \sqrt{(-10)^2 - 4(3)(-25)}}{2(3)}$

$x = \underline{\ ?\ }$ $\frac{10 \pm \sqrt{400}}{6}$ So $x = \underline{\ ?\ }$ or $x = \underline{\ ?\ }$. 5; $-\frac{5}{3}$

Note-Taking Tips

Encourage students to record the observation, presented just above **Example 2**, that if $b^2 - 4ac$ is a perfect square, then the solutions to the quadratic equation are rational. Students will further explore the meaning of the value of $b^2 - 4ac$ in Lesson 6-10.

A calculator can approximate the two solutions in one step. Here are the intermediate steps

$$\approx \frac{-0.545 \pm \sqrt{0.265}}{-0.00264}$$

Estimate the square root and separate the solutions.

$x \approx \frac{-0.545 + 0.515}{-0.00264}$ or $x \approx \frac{-0.545 - 0.515}{-0.00264}$

$x \approx 11$ ft or $x \approx 402$ ft

The ball reaches a height of 10 feet in two places. The first is when the ball is on the way up and about 11 feet away from home plate. The second is when the ball is on the way down and about 402 feet from home plate. Between these distances the ball is over 10 feet high. An outfielder is unlikely to be 11 feet from home plate, so he was about 402 feet away.

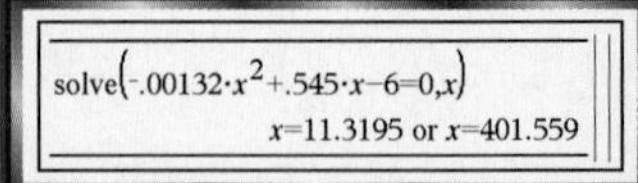

Check Use the `solve` command on a CAS.

In Example 1, the number $b^2 - 4ac$ is not a perfect square. When this is the case, there are no rational number solutions to the equation. When $b^2 - 4ac$ is a perfect square, as it is in Example 2, the solutions are always rational.

GUIDED

Example 2

Solve $5x^2 + 13x - 6 = 0$.

Solution Use the Quadratic Formula.

$a = \underline{\ ?\ }$ 5 $b = \underline{\ ?\ }$ 13 $c = \underline{\ ?\ }$ -6

$x = \frac{-b \pm \sqrt{b^2 - 4ac}}{2a}$

$x = \frac{-(?) \pm \sqrt{(?)^2 - 4(?)(?)}}{2(?)}$ 13; 13; 5; -6 / 5

$x = \frac{? \pm \sqrt{?}}{?}$ -13; 289 / 10

So, $x = \frac{? + ?}{?}$ -13, 17 / 10 or $x = \frac{? - ?}{?}$ -13, 17 / 10

$x = \underline{\ ?\ }$ $\frac{2}{5}$ or $x = \underline{\ ?\ }$ -3

A quadratic equation must be in standard form before the Quadratic Formula can be applied.

Accommodating the Learner

1. Suppose the two roots of $ax^2 + bx + c = 0$ are x_1 and x_2. Use the results of the Quadratic Formula Theorem to find an expression for the sum of the roots, $x_1 + x_2$. $x_1 + x_2 = \frac{(-b + \sqrt{b^2 - 4ac}) + (-b - \sqrt{b^2 - 4ac})}{2a} = \frac{-2b}{2a} = -\frac{b}{a}$

2. Use your result from Question 1 to find the sum of the roots for the equation $2x^2 - 5x - 12 = 0$. $a = 2$ and $b = -5$, so $x_1 + x_2 = -\frac{b}{a} = -\frac{-5}{2} = \frac{5}{2}$

3. Verify your answer in Question 2 by solving the equation $2x^2 - 5x - 12 = 0$ and adding the roots. The roots are $x = -\frac{3}{2}$ and $x = 4$; the sum of the roots is $\frac{5}{2}$, which is the same as the answer to Question 2.

(See Extension on page 417 for a similar exercise on the sum of the roots.)

Example 3

Recall that the explicit formula for the sequence t_n of triangular numbers is $t_n = \frac{n(n+1)}{2}$. Is 101,475 a triangular number? If it is, which term of the sequence is it?

Solution Set $t_n = 101{,}475$ and solve for n.

$$t_n = \frac{n(n+1)}{2} = 101{,}475$$

Put the equation in standard form.

$$n(n+1) = 202{,}950 \quad \text{Multiply both sides by 2.}$$

$$n^2 + n = 202{,}950 \quad \text{Expand.}$$

$$n^2 + n - 202{,}950 = 0 \quad \text{Add -202,950 to both sides.}$$

Use the Quadratic Formula with $a = 1$, $b = 1$, and $c = -202{,}950$.

$$n = \frac{-1 \pm \sqrt{1^2 - 4(1)(-202{,}950)}}{2(1)}$$

$$n = \frac{-1 \pm \sqrt{811{,}801}}{2}$$

$$n = \frac{-1 \pm 901}{2}$$

$$n = -451 \text{ or } n = 450$$

Because 450 is a positive integer, 101,475 is the 450th triangular number.

 QY

> **QY**
> Use the explicit formula for the triangular numbers to check the solution to Example 3.

Questions

COVERING THE IDEAS

1. If $ax^2 + bx + c = 0$, and $a \neq 0$, write the two values of x in terms of a, b, and c as a compound sentence.

In 2–4 refer to the proof of the Quadratic Formula.

2. Why must a be nonzero in the Quadratic Formula?
3. Why is it necessary to divide both sides by a in the first step?
4. Write $x^2 + \frac{b}{a}x + \frac{b^2}{4a^2}$ as the square of a binomial. $\left(x + \frac{b}{2a}\right)^2$

In 5 and 6, a quadratic equation is given. Solve each using the Quadratic Formula.

5. $10z^2 + 13z + 3 = 0$ $z = -1$ or $z = -\frac{3}{10}$
6. $2n^2 - 11n + 12 = 0$ $n = \frac{3}{2}$ or $n = 4$

1. $x = \frac{-b + \sqrt{b^2 - 4ac}}{2a}$ or $x = \frac{-b - \sqrt{b^2 - 4ac}}{2a}$
2. The variable a appears in the denominator, and division by zero is undefined.
3. to make the coefficient of x^2 1 in order to complete the square

Additional Example

Example 3 Use the explicit formula $t_n = \frac{n(n+1)}{2}$ for the sequence of triangular numbers. Is 70,876 a triangular number? If it is, which term of the sequence is it? $\frac{n(n+1)}{2} = 70{,}876$; $n^2 + n = 141{,}752$ or $n^2 + n - 141{,}752 = 0$. Using the Quadratic Formula with $a = 1$, $b = 1$, and $c = -141{,}752$, then $n = \frac{-1 \pm \sqrt{1^2 - 4(1)(-141{,}752)}}{2}$, $n = \frac{-1 \pm 753}{2}$, $n = -377$ or $n = 376$; the number 70,876 is the 376th triangular number.

3 Assignment

Recommended Assignment

- Questions 1–23
- Question 24 (extra credit)
- Reading Lesson 6-8
- Covering the Ideas 6-8

Extension

1. Suppose the roots of $ax^2 + bx + c = 0$ are x_1 and x_2. Use the results of the Quadratic Formula Theorem to find an expression for the product of the roots, $x_1 \cdot x_2$. $x_1 \cdot x_2 = \left(\frac{-b + \sqrt{b^2 - 4ac}}{2a}\right)\left(\frac{-b - \sqrt{b^2 - 4ac}}{2a}\right) = \frac{b^2 - (b^2 - 4ac)}{4a^2} = \frac{4ac}{4a^2} = \frac{c}{a}$
2. Use your result from Question 1 to find the product of the roots for the equation $2x^2 - 5x - 12 = 0$. $a = 2$ and $c = -12$, so $x_1 \cdot x_2 = \frac{c}{a} = \frac{-12}{2} = -6$
3. Verify your answer in Question 2 by solving the equation $2x^2 - 5x - 12 = 0$ and multiplying the roots. The roots are $x = -\frac{3}{2}$ and $x = 4$; the product of the roots is -6, which is the same as the answer to Question 2.

(See Accommodating the Learner Up on page 416 for a similar exercise on the sum of the roots.)

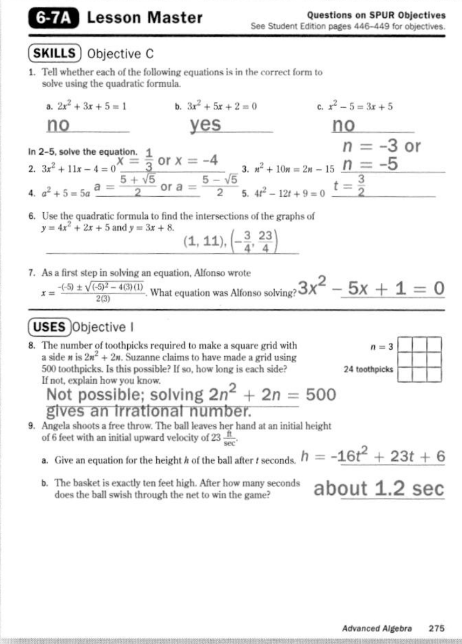
6-7A Lesson Master

Questions on SPUR Objectives
See Student Edition pages 446–449 for objectives.

SKILLS Objective C

1. Tell whether each of the following equations is in the correct form to solve using the quadratic formula.
   a. $2x^2 + 3x + 5 = 1$ no
   b. $3x^2 + 5x + 2 = 0$ yes
   c. $x^2 - 5 = 3x + 5$ no

In 2–5, solve the equation.

2. $3x^2 + 11x - 4 = 0$ $x = \frac{1}{3}$ or $x = -4$
3. $n^2 + 10n = 2n - 15$ $n = -3$ or $n = -5$
4. $a^2 + 5 = 5a$ $a = \frac{5 + \sqrt{5}}{2}$ or $a = \frac{5 - \sqrt{5}}{2}$
5. $4t^2 - 12t + 9 = 0$ $t = \frac{3}{2}$
6. Use the quadratic formula to find the intersections of the graphs of $y = 4x^2 + 2x + 5$ and $y = 3x + 8$. $(1, 11), \left(-\frac{3}{4}, \frac{23}{4}\right)$
7. As a first step in solving an equation, Alfonso wrote $x = \frac{-(-5) \pm \sqrt{(-5)^2 - 4(3)(1)}}{2(3)}$. What equation was Alfonso solving? $3x^2 - 5x + 1 = 0$

USES Objective I

8. The number of toothpicks required to make a square grid with a side n is $2n^2 + 2n$. Suzanne claims to have made a grid using 500 toothpicks. Is this possible? If so, how long is each side? If not, explain how you know. Not possible; solving $2n^2 + 2n = 500$ gives an irrational number.
   $n = 3$
   24 toothpicks
9. Angela shoots a free throw. The ball leaves her hand at an initial height of 6 feet with an initial upward velocity of 23 $\frac{\text{ft}}{\text{sec}}$.
   a. Give an equation for the height h of the ball after t seconds. $h = -16t^2 + 23t + 6$
   b. The basket is exactly ten feet high. After how many seconds does the ball swish through the net to win the game? about 1.2 sec

Advanced Algebra 275

Notes on the Questions

Questions 8 and 10 Students can check their answers by drawing and tracing a graph.

Question 15 Students can solve this problem by factoring the quadratics using a CAS. (This lesson's Accommodating the Learner Up and Extension activities also explore the sum and product of the roots of a quadratic equation, as does Project 1.)

Additional Answers

13. $t_n = \frac{n(n+1)}{2} = 10{,}608$

$n(n+1) = 21{,}216$

$n^2 + n = 21{,}216$

$n^2 + n - 21{,}216 = 0$

$n = \frac{-1 \pm \sqrt{1^2 - 4(1)(-21{,}216)}}{2(1)}$

$n = \frac{-1 \pm \sqrt{84{,}865}}{2}$

n is not an integer; therefore, 10,608 cannot be a triangular number.

15a. Q_1: $x = -2$ or $x = -3$; Q_2: $x = -3$ or $x = -4$; Q_3: $x = -4$ or $x = -5$; Q_4: $x = -5$ or $x = -6$; Q_5: $x = -6$ or $x = -7$

15b. Q_1: 6, -5; Q_2: 12, -7; Q_3: 20, -9; Q_4: 30, -11; Q_5: 42, -13

15c. The sum of the solutions is equal to $-b$, and the product of the solutions is equal to c.

16a. $m = 1 \pm 2\sqrt{2} \approx -1.83$ or 3.83; Answers vary. Sample: m-intercepts of the graph of the equation

16d.

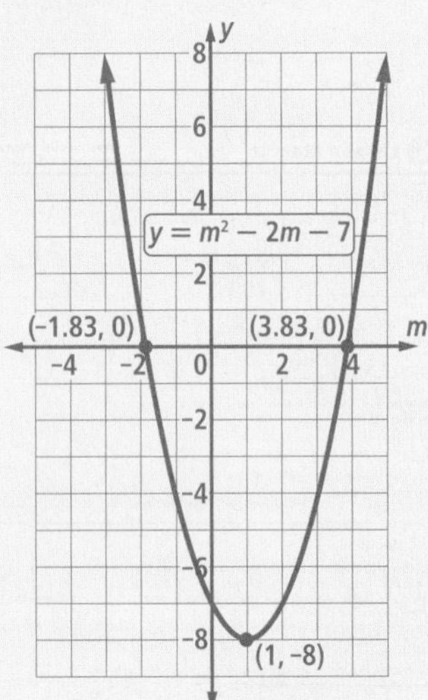

In 7–10, consider the equation $h = -0.00132x^2 + 0.545x + 4$ from the beginning of the lesson. The left field wall at Fenway Park in Boston is 37 ft tall and 310 ft from home plate.

7. What do x and h represent?
8. Would a ball on the path of this example be a home run? (That is, would it have gone over the left field wall?) yes
9. Trace a graph of the equation to find the maximum height reached by the ball.
10. How far from home plate would the ball hit the ground, if the outfielder missed it? about 420.1 ft away
11. Refer to Example 2. How do your solutions change when you solve $5x^2 - 13x - 6 = 0$ instead? The solutions are the opposites of the solutions from Example 2; $x = -\frac{2}{5}$ or $x = 3$.

In 12 and 13, refer to Example 3.

12. Use a CAS to check the solution for Example 3.
13. Show that 10,608 is not a triangular number. See margin.

Fenway Park, home to the Boston Red Sox

7. x represents the distance along the ground in feet of the ball from home plate, and h represents the height in feet of the ball at that distance.

9. about 60.25 ft

12.

$\text{solve}\left(\frac{n\cdot(n+1)}{2}=101475, n\right)$ $\quad n=-451$ or $n=450$

APPLYING THE MATHEMATICS

14. What is another way to solve $ax^2 + bx + c = 0$, $a \neq 0$, besides using the Quadratic Formula or a CAS? complete the square or graph
15. Consider this sequence of quadratic equations.

Q_1: $x^2 + 5x + 6 = 0$
Q_2: $x^2 + 7x + 12 = 0$
Q_3: $x^2 + 9x + 20 = 0$
Q_4: $x^2 + 11x + 30 = 0$
Q_5: $x^2 + 13x + 42 = 0$

 a. Solve each quadratic equation. a–c. See margin.
 b. Find the product and the sum of each set of answers in Part a.
 c. What is the connection between the solutions to the quadratic equations and the coefficients of the quadratic equations?

16. Consider the parabola with equation $y = m^2 - 2m - 7$.
 a. Find the values of m for which $y = 0$. What are these values called? See margin.
 b. Find the vertex of this parabola. (1, -8)
 c. Give an equation for its axis of symmetry. $m = 1$
 d. Sketch a graph of the parabola. See margin.

17. The graphs of $y = 6x^2 + x + 2$ and $y = 4$ are shown at the right. Use the Quadratic Formula to find the points of intersection. $\left(-\frac{2}{3}, 4\right)$ and $\left(\frac{1}{2}, 4\right)$

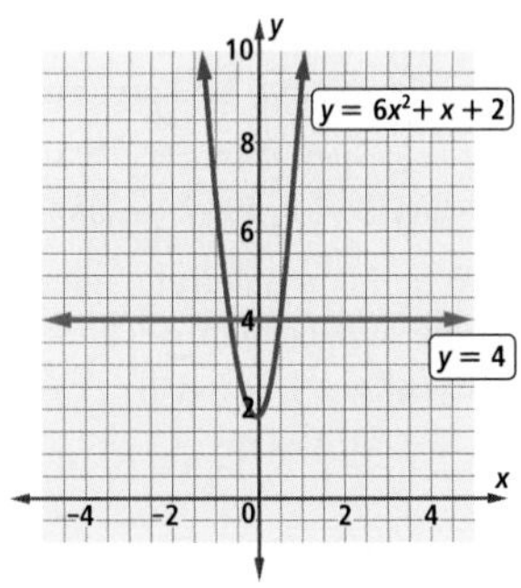

Accommodating the Learner

Ask students to rewrite the steps on the left side of the proof of the Quadratic Formula Theorem if $a = 1$—that is, for the equation $x^2 + bx + c = 0$.

1. $x^2 + bx + c = 0$
2. $x^2 + bx = -c$
3. $x^2 + bx + \frac{b^2}{4} = \frac{b^2}{4} - c$
4. $\left(x + \frac{b}{2}\right)^2 = \frac{b^2}{4} - c$
5. $\left(x + \frac{b}{2}\right)^2 = \frac{b^2 - 4c}{4}$
6. $\sqrt{\left(x + \frac{b}{2}\right)^2} = \sqrt{\frac{b^2 - 4c}{4}}$
7. $\left|x + \frac{b}{2}\right| = \sqrt{\frac{b^2 - 4c}{4}}$
8. $x + \frac{b}{2} = \pm\sqrt{\frac{b^2 - 4c}{4}}$
9. $x = \frac{-b \pm \sqrt{b^2 - 4c}}{2}$

18. **Fill in the Blanks** Given $ax^2 + bx + c = 0$, where $a \neq 0$, provide the missing algebra in this alternate proof of the Quadratic Formula that does not use completing the square. See margin.
    a. Multiply both sides by $4a$. __?__

    Recognize that the terms $4a^2x^2 + 4abx$ are initial terms of the binomial square $(2ax + b)^2$.

    b. Replace $4a^2x^2 + 4abx$ with $(2ax + b)^2 - b^2$. (Explain why $-b^2$ is added in this step.) __?__
    c. Add $b^2 - 4ac$ to both sides. $(2ax + b)^2 = b^2 - 4ac$
    d. Take the square roots of both sides. __?__
    e. Use the Absolute Value-Square Root Theorem. $|2ax + b| = \sqrt{b^2 - 4ac}$
    f. Use the definition of absolute value. __?__
    g. Add $-b$ to both sides. $2ax = -b \pm \sqrt{b^2 - 4ac}$
    h. Divide both sides by $2a$. __?__

REVIEW

19. Solve a system of equations to write an equation for the parabola that contains the points (-1, -7), (0, 3), and (3, 9). (Lesson 6-6)

    19. $y = -2x^2 + 8x + 3$

20. A ball is thrown straight up from a height of 1.5 meters with initial upward velocity of $6\frac{\text{m}}{\text{s}}$. Find the maximum height of the ball and the time the ball takes to reach this height. (Lessons 6-5, 6-4) about 3.32 m, about 0.61 sec

21. Let $M = \begin{bmatrix} 4 & 12 \\ -8 & x \end{bmatrix}$. For what value or values of x does M^{-1} not exist? (Lesson 5-5) $x = -24$

22. State the domain and range of the function f when $f(x) = -\frac{\sqrt{2}}{x}$. (Lesson 2-6) domain: $\{x \mid x \neq 0\}$; range: $\{y \mid y \neq 0\}$

23. a. Let $g_n = 1 + (-1)^n$. Calculate g_1, g_2, g_3, and g_4.
    b. Describe how to quickly know g_n for any positive integer n.
    c. What is g_{7532}? (Lesson 1-8) 2

    23a. $g_1 = 0$; $g_2 = 2$; $g_3 = 0$; $g_4 = 2$

    23b. $g_n = 0$ for all odd integers n, and $g_n = 2$ for all even integers n.

EXPLORATION

24. Find out what you can about the formula used to solve the general cubic equation $ax^3 + bx^2 + cx + d = 0$. See margin.

QY ANSWER

Does $t_{450} = \frac{450(450 + 1)}{2} = 101{,}475$? $\frac{450 \cdot 451}{2} = \frac{202{,}950}{2} = 101{,}475$. It checks.

Notes on the Questions

Question 18 Although completing the square is not used, students *do* have to recognize the square of a binomial.

4 Wrap-Up

Ongoing Assessment

Ask students to tell the values of *a*, *b*, and *c* for the quadratic equation $ax^2 + bx + c = 0$ if the solutions are $x = \frac{-3 \pm \sqrt{3^2 - 4(8)(-5)}}{2(8)}$. Comparing the solutions to $x = \frac{-b \pm \sqrt{b^2 - 4ac}}{2a}$, you can see that $a = 8$, $b = 3$, and $c = -5$. (The quadratic equation would be $8x^2 + 3x - 5 = 0$.)

Administer Quiz 2 (or a quiz of your own) after students complete this lesson.

Project Update

Project 1, *Sum and Product of Roots,* on page 441 relates to the content of this lesson.

Additional Answers

18a. $4a^2x^2 + 4abx + 4ac = 0$

18b. $(2ax + b)^2 - b^2 + 4ac = 0$; $-b^2$ is added to balance the b^2 that was added to $4a^2x^2 + 4abx$ to complete the square.

18d. $\sqrt{(2ax + b)^2} = \sqrt{b^2 - 4ac}$

18f. $2ax + b = \pm\sqrt{b^2 - 4ac}$

18h. $x = \frac{-b \pm \sqrt{b^2 - 4ac}}{2a}$

Additional Answers

24. Answers vary: Sample: A method commonly used to solve cubics was first introduced by Girolamo Cardano in the 1500s. Start with the equation $ax^3 + bx^2 + cx + d = 0$. Then substitute $y - \frac{b}{3a}$ for x to "depress" the cubic and eliminate the x^2 term. The result is an equation of the form $y^3 + Ay = B$. More substitutions can then be made to convert this depressed cubic into a quadratic that can be solved with the Quadratic Formula. Back substitutions can then be made to obtain a general formula, but the solutions to a general cubic are not usually written that way because the formula is so complicated and hard to work with.

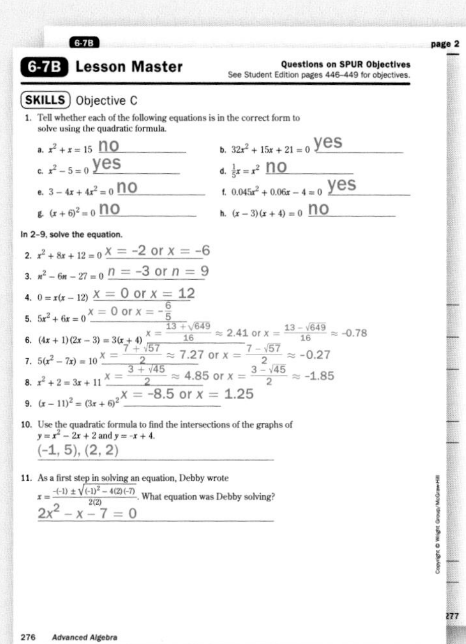

6-7B page 2

6-7B Lesson Master Questions on SPUR Objectives
See Student Edition pages 446–449 for objectives.

SKILLS Objective C

1. Tell whether each of the following equations is in the correct form to solve using the quadratic formula.
    a. $x^2 + x = 15$ no
    b. $32x^2 + 15x + 21 = 0$ yes
    c. $x^2 - 5 = 0$ yes
    d. $\frac{1}{5}x = x^2$ no
    e. $3 - 4x + 4x^2 = 0$ no
    f. $0.045x^2 + 0.06x - 4 = 0$ yes
    g. $(x + 6)^2 = 0$ no
    h. $(x - 3)(x + 4) = 0$ no

In 2–9, solve the equation.

2. $x^2 + 8x + 12 = 0$ $x = -2$ or $x = -6$
3. $n^2 - 6n - 27 = 0$ $n = -3$ or $n = 9$
4. $0 = x(x - 12)$ $x = 0$ or $x = 12$
5. $5x^2 + 6x = 0$ $x = 0$ or $x = -\frac{6}{5}$
6. $(4x + 1)(2x - 3) = 3(x + 4)$ $x = \frac{13 + \sqrt{649}}{16} \approx 2.41$ or $x = \frac{13 - \sqrt{649}}{16} \approx -0.78$
7. $5(x^2 - 7x) = 10$ $x = \frac{7 + \sqrt{57}}{2} \approx 7.27$ or $x = \frac{7 - \sqrt{57}}{2} \approx -0.27$
8. $x^2 + 2 = 3x + 11$ $x = \frac{3 + \sqrt{45}}{2} \approx 4.85$ or $x = \frac{3 - \sqrt{45}}{2} \approx -1.85$
9. $(x - 11)^2 = (3x + 6)^2$ $x = -8.5$ or $x = 1.25$

10. Use the quadratic formula to find the intersections of the graphs of $y = x^2 - 2x + 2$ and $y = -x + 4$.
    (-1, 5), (2, 2)

11. As a first step in solving an equation, Debby wrote $x = \frac{-(-1) \pm \sqrt{(-1)^2 - 4(2)(-7)}}{2(2)}$. What equation was Debby solving?
    $2x^2 - x - 7 = 0$

276 Advanced Algebra 277

Lesson 6-8

GOAL

Introduce *i* and its multiples; explore the fundamental operations on multiples of *i*.

SPUR Objectives

C Solve quadratic equations.

E Perform operations with complex numbers.

Materials/Resources

- Lesson Masters 6-8A and 6-8B
- Resource Masters 111 and 112
- Calculator

HOMEWORK

Suggestions for Assignment

- Questions 1–39
- Question 40 (extra credit)
- Reading Lesson 6-9
- Covering the Ideas 6-9

Local Standards

1 Warm-Up

1. Write the product $(12 + 7\sqrt{2}) \cdot (9 - 10\sqrt{2})$ in $a + b\sqrt{2}$ form. $-32 - 57\sqrt{2}$
2. Generalize Warm-Up 1. $(a + b\sqrt{2})(c + d\sqrt{2}) = (ac + 2bd) + (ad + bc)\sqrt{2}$

Lesson 6-8 Pure Imaginary Numbers

Vocabulary

imaginary number
$\sqrt{k}$
$\sqrt{-1}$, i
pure imaginary number

BIG IDEA The square roots of negative numbers are *pure imaginary numbers* and are all multiples of $\sqrt{-1}$, defined as the number *i*.

Square Roots of Negative Numbers

Consider the quadratic equation $x^2 = 900$. You can solve it for x as follows.

$x^2 = 900$	
$\sqrt{x^2} = \sqrt{900}$	Take square roots.
$\lvert x\rvert = 30$	Use the Absolute Value-Square Root Theorem.
$x = \pm 30$	Solve the absolute value equation.

Now consider the quadratic equation $x^2 = -900$. You know that the solution cannot be a real number because the square of a real number is never negative. However, if you followed the solution above you might write:

$$x^2 = -900$$
$$\sqrt{x^2} = \sqrt{-900}$$
$$|x| = ?$$

So far, $\sqrt{x}$ has only been defined for $x \geq 0$. If you try to evaluate $\sqrt{-900}$ on a calculator you may see an error message, or you may see $30 \cdot i$, as shown below. The difference is whether or not your calculator is in complex number mode.

Mental Math

Solve for *x*.

a. $|x| = 4$

b. $|x - 3| = 4$

c. $|2x - 3| = 4$

a. $x = 4$ or $x = -4$

b. $x = 7$ or $x = -1$

c. $x = 3.5$ or $x = -0.5$

Background

For many years, the concept of imaginary numbers was difficult for mathematicians to accept and explain logically, even though they were able to devise rules that made computation with such numbers relatively easy. Now, most mathematicians consider imaginary numbers to be as "real" as any other kind of number.

The use of the word *imaginary* to describe the square root of a negative number is unfortunate, for these numbers have numerous real-world applications. The term *imaginary number* is used to describe only the nonreal numbers that can be written in the form *bi*. (In this lesson, we call such numbers "pure imaginary numbers.") The term *complex number* is broader, describing all numbers that can be written in the form $a + bi$. The latter term is introduced in Lesson 6-9 and is universally used by mathematicians.

A Brief History of *i*

Why does a calculator display $30 \cdot i$ when it is in complex number mode? The symbol i was first used in the 18th century, but work with square roots of negative numbers started sooner. Until the 1500s, mathematicians were puzzled by square roots of negative numbers. They knew that if they solved certain quadratics, they would get negative numbers under the radical sign. However, they did not know what to do with them!

One of the first to work with these numbers was the Italian mathematician Girolamo Cardano. In a book called *Ars Magna* ("Great Art") published in 1545, Cardano reasoned as follows: When k is positive, the equation $x^2 = k$ has two solutions, $\sqrt{k}$ and $-\sqrt{k}$. If we solve the equation $x^2 = -k$ in the same way, then the two solutions are $\sqrt{-k}$ and $-\sqrt{-k}$. In this way, he defined symbols for the square roots of negative numbers. Cardano called these square roots of negatives "fictitious numbers."

Girolamo Cardano

Working in the 1600s, the French mathematician and philosopher René Descartes called them **imaginary numbers** in contrast to the numbers everyone understood, which he called "real numbers."

In his book *De Formulis Differentialibus Angularibus,* written in 1777, the Swiss mathematician Leonhard Euler wrote, "in the following I shall denote the expression $\sqrt{-1}$ by the letter i so that $i \cdot i = -1$."

Today, people around the world build on the work of Cardano, Descartes, and Euler and use the following definitions.

Definition of $\sqrt{k}$ when K Is Negative

When $k < 0$, the two solutions to $x^2 = k$ are denoted $\sqrt{k}$ and $-\sqrt{k}$.

By the definition, when $k < 0$, $\left(\sqrt{k}\right)^2 = k$. This means that we can say, for *all* real numbers r,

$$\sqrt{r} \cdot \sqrt{r} = r.$$

Suppose $k = -1$. Then we define the number i to be one of the two square roots of -1. That is, i is defined as follows.

Definition of *i*

$i = \sqrt{-1}$

Thus, i is a solution to $x^2 = -1$. The other solution is $-\sqrt{-1}$, which we call $-i$. That is, $i^2 = -1$ and $(-i)^2 = -1$.

2 Teaching

Notes on the Lesson

By this time, most students have heard of the number *i*, even if they know nothing about it. They will be curious about its properties and may think it is far more difficult to work with than it is.

Encourage students to write out all the steps when multiplying or dividing square roots of negatives, as is done in Example 3. This will help them to avoid errors.

Accommodating the Learner

Tell students that a is a real number. Ask them to verify that ai and $-ai$ are both square roots of $-a^2$. Answers vary. Sample: Because $(ai)(ai) = a^2i^2 = -a^2$, ai is a square root of $-a^2$. Also, because $(-ai)(-ai) = (-1)^2a^2i^2 = (1)(a^2)(-1) = -a^2$, $-ai$ is a square root of $-a^2$.

ENGLISH LEARNERS

Vocabulary Development

This lesson provides a natural opportunity to review the different kinds of numbers that make up the real number system. Ask students to name the sets of numbers within the real number system. natural numbers, whole or counting numbers, rational numbers, and irrational numbers Students should understand that pure imaginary numbers are the first set of numbers they have studied that are *not* part of the system of real numbers.

Notes on the Lesson

This is an appropriate time to remind students that the meaning a word has in mathematics may be quite different from other, more general meanings. For example, there is nothing "negative" about negative numbers, nor is there anything "irrational" about irrational numbers. Similarly, there is nothing "imaginary" about imaginary numbers.

Additional Examples

Example 1 Solve $x^2 = -625$. $x = i\sqrt{625}$ or $x = -i\sqrt{625}$, so $x = 25i$ or $x = -25i$.

Example 2

a. Show that $i\sqrt{10}$ is a square root of -10. $(i\sqrt{10})(i\sqrt{10}) = i \cdot i \cdot \sqrt{10} \cdot \sqrt{10} = i^2 \cdot 10 = (-1)(10) = -10$, so $i\sqrt{10}$ is a square root of -10.

b. What is the other square root of -10? $-i\sqrt{10}$

Multiples of i, such as $7i$, are called **pure imaginary numbers**. By the definition of i, $7i = 7\sqrt{-1}$. If we assume that multiplication of imaginary numbers is commutative and associative, then

$$\begin{aligned}(7i)^2 &= 7i \cdot 7i \\ &= 7^2 \cdot i^2 \\ &= 49 \cdot (-1) \\ &= -49.\end{aligned}$$

So $7i$ is a square root of -49. We write $7i = \sqrt{-49}$ and $-7i = \sqrt{-49}$. The following theorem generalizes this result.

Square Root of a Negative Number Theorem

If $k < 0$, $\sqrt{k} = i\sqrt{-k}$.

Thus all square roots of negative numbers are multiples of i.

QY1

▸ QY1
Write $\sqrt{-36}$ as a multiple of i.

Example 1

Solve $x^2 = -900$.

Solution Apply the definition of $\sqrt{k}$ when k is negative.

$x = \sqrt{-900}$ or $x = -\sqrt{-900}$

Now use the Square Root of a Negative Number Theorem.

$x = i\sqrt{900}$ or $x = -i\sqrt{900}$

Simplify.

$x = 30i$ or $x = -30i$

Check Use a CAS in complex mode to solve the equation. On some machines, you use the `csolve` command to display complex solutions to equations. This CAS uses the `solve` command and gives the solution at the right. It checks.

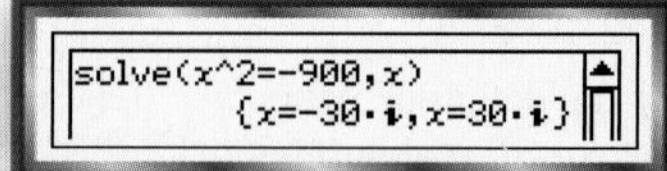

Example 2

a. Show that $i\sqrt{5}$ is a square root of –5.

b. What is the other square root of –5?

Solution

a. Multiply $i\sqrt{5}$ by itself. Assume the Commutative and Associative Properties.

Accommodating the Learner

In the Square Root of a Negative Number Theorem, "If $k < 0$, then $\sqrt{k} = i\sqrt{-k}$," ask students to describe and explain which values or expressions are real numbers and which are pure imaginary numbers.
Answers vary. Sample: In the first phrase, "If $k < 0$," k is a real, negative number. So $\sqrt{k}$ represents the square root of a negative number, which must be a pure imaginary number. In the expression $i\sqrt{-k}$, because k is a real, negative number, then $-k$ is a real, positive number, and $\sqrt{-k}$ represents the positive square root of that real, positive number. So $\sqrt{-k}$ is a real number. Finally, $i\sqrt{-k}$ represents the product of $\sqrt{-1}$ and the positive square root of $-k$ (a real number), so it is a pure imaginary number.

$i\sqrt{5} \cdot i\sqrt{5} = i \cdot i \cdot \sqrt{5} \cdot \sqrt{5}$
$= i^2 \cdot 5$
$= -1 \cdot 5$
$= -5$

b. Take the opposite of the square root from Part a. The other square root of -5 is $-i\sqrt{5}$.

 QY2

Due to the long history of quadratic equations, solutions to them are described in different ways. The following all refer to the same numbers.

the solutions to $x^2 = -5$

the square roots of -5

$\sqrt{-5}$ and $-\sqrt{-5}$

$i\sqrt{5}$ and $-i\sqrt{5}$

The last two forms could also be written $\sqrt{5}i$ and $-\sqrt{5}i$ as a CAS displays them. On handwritten materials and in textbooks you commonly see $i\sqrt{5}$ to clearly show that the i is not underneath the radical sign.

▶ QY2

Use a CAS to show that $-i\sqrt{5}$ is a square root of -5.

Operations with Pure Imaginary Numbers

The Commutative, Associative, and Distributive Properties of Addition and Multiplication are true for all imaginary numbers, as are all theorems based on these postulates. Consequently, you can use them when working with multiples of i, just as you would when working with multiples of any real numbers.

Example 3

Simplify the following.

a. $(5i)(3i)$ b. $\sqrt{-16} - \sqrt{-64}$ c. $\sqrt{-2} + \sqrt{-2}$ d. $\frac{\sqrt{-100}}{\sqrt{-81}}$

Solution

a. $(5i)(3i) = 15i^2 = 15 \cdot -1 = -15$

b. $\sqrt{-16} - \sqrt{-64} = 4i - 8i = -4i$

c. $\sqrt{-2} + \sqrt{-2} = i\sqrt{2} + i\sqrt{2} = 2i\sqrt{2}$

d. $\frac{\sqrt{-100}}{\sqrt{-81}} = \frac{10i}{9i} = \frac{10}{9}$

Notes on the Lesson

Even after discussing Example 3 and doing the Activity, many students, when faced with negative numbers under separate radicals, will multiply those negative numbers before taking the square root. You may need to stress several times that imaginary numbers are different from real numbers, and thus we cannot assume that all properties that hold true for real numbers will also hold true for imaginary numbers.

Additional Example

Example 3 Simplify the following.

a. $(7i)(-10i)$ $-70i^2 = 70$

b. $-\sqrt{-25} - \sqrt{-100}$ $-5i - 10i = -15i$

c. $\sqrt{-3} + \sqrt{-3}$ $i\sqrt{3} + i\sqrt{3} = 2i\sqrt{3}$

d. $\frac{\sqrt{-25}}{\sqrt{-64}}$ $\frac{5i}{8i} = \frac{5}{8}$

Note-Taking Tips

When students record in their notes that $\sqrt{a} \cdot \sqrt{b} \neq \sqrt{ab}$ for negative numbers, encourage them to include specific counterexamples (such as the ones in the Activity).

Additional Answers

Activity

Step 2: Addition and subtraction of imaginary numbers, and multiplication of an imaginary number by a real scalar, result in an imaginary number, but multiplication of two imaginary numbers results in a real number.

Step 3: 10; 10; yes; If $4 \geq 0$ and $25 \geq 0$, then $\sqrt{4} \cdot \sqrt{25} = \sqrt{100} = 10$.

Step 4: $10i$; 10; yes; If $a \geq 0$ and $b < 0$, then $\sqrt{a} \cdot \sqrt{b} = \sqrt{a} \cdot i\sqrt{-b}$, and $ab < 0$ so $\sqrt{ab} = i\sqrt{a(-b)} = \sqrt{a} \cdot i\sqrt{-b}$. no; $-4 < 0$ and $-25 < 0$, and $\sqrt{-4} \cdot \sqrt{-25} \neq \sqrt{-4 \cdot -25}$, so this is a counterexample.

3 Assignment

Recommended Assignment

- Questions 1–39
- Question 40 (extra credit)
- Reading Lesson 6-9
- Covering the Ideas 6-9

6-8A Lesson Master — Questions on SPUR Objectives. See Student Edition pages 446–449 for objectives.

SKILLS Objective C

In 1–3, give all solutions, both real and imaginary.

1. Solve for x. a. $x^2 = 9$ $x = 3$ or $x = -3$
   b. $x^2 = -9$ $x = 3i$ or $x = -3i$
2. Solve for a. a. $a^2 = 21$ $a = \sqrt{21}$ or $a = -\sqrt{21}$
   b. $a^2 = -21$ $a = \sqrt{21}\,i$ or $a = -\sqrt{21}\,i$
3. Solve for p. a. $(p - 0.2)^2 = 0.81$ $p = 1.1$ or $p = -0.7$
   b. $(p - 0.2)^2 = -0.81$ $p = 0.9i + 0.2$ or $p = -0.9i + 0.2$
4. Solve $3x^2 + 363 = 0$. Write the solutions
   a. with a radical sign. $x = \sqrt{-121}$ or $x = -\sqrt{-121}$
   b. without a radical sign. $x = 11i$ or $x = -11i$

SKILLS Objective E

In 5–7, simplify the expression.

5. $\sqrt{-81} = 9i$ 6. $\sqrt{-2209} = 47i$ 7. $-\sqrt{-\frac{9}{16}} = -\frac{3}{4}i$

In 8 and 9, evaluate $\sqrt{b^2 - 4ac}$ for the given values of a, b, and c.

8. $a = 10, b = 8, c = 2$ $4i$ 9. $a = -2, b = -3, c = -5$ $\sqrt{31}\,i$

In 10–17, perform the indicated operations and simplify the result.

10. $7i - 3i + 5i = 9i$ 11. $3\sqrt{-4} - 2\sqrt{-25} = -4i$
12. $(3i)(5i) = -15$ 13. $\sqrt{-16} \cdot \sqrt{-49} = -28$
14. $\frac{18i}{3i} = 6$ 15. $\frac{\sqrt{-144}}{\sqrt{-81}} = \frac{4}{3}$
16. $\frac{17i - 12i}{10i} = \frac{1}{2}$ 17. $\frac{\sqrt{-16} + \sqrt{-9}}{5} = \frac{7}{5}i$
18. Give examples for values of a and b so that: Answers vary. Samples are given.
    a. $\sqrt{a} \cdot \sqrt{b} = \sqrt{ab}$ $a = 3, b = 12$ b. $\sqrt{a} \cdot \sqrt{b} \neq \sqrt{ab}$ $a = -3, b = -12$
19. **Multiple Choice** The square of a pure imaginary number is C.
    A always a pure imaginary number
    B always a positive real number
    C always a negative real number
    D a real number that could be either positive or negative

278 *Advanced Algebra*

In operating with imaginary numbers in radical form, be sure to follow the order of operations, treating the square root as a grouping symbol.

Activity

MATERIALS calculator

Work with a partner to calculate with imaginary numbers.

Step 1 Make sure that your calculator is in complex mode. Use your calculator to write each answer in $a + bi$ form.

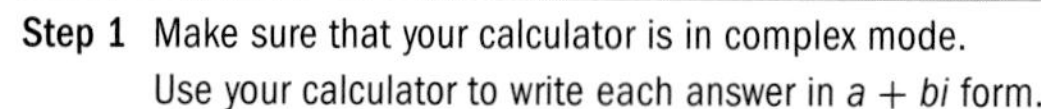

$(4i)(25i)$	$4i - 5i$	$\sqrt{-4} - \sqrt{-25}$	$\frac{\sqrt{-4}}{\sqrt{25}}$	$\sqrt{-4} \cdot \sqrt{25}$	$\sqrt{-4} \cdot \sqrt{-25}$
? -100	? $-i$	? $-3i$	? $\frac{2i}{5}$	? $10i$	? -10

Step 2 Look for patterns in your results from Step 1. When are the results real numbers and when are they imaginary?

Step 3 Calculate $\sqrt{4} \cdot \sqrt{25}$ and $\sqrt{4 \cdot 25}$. Do your results support the property $\sqrt{a}\,\sqrt{b} = \sqrt{ab}$ for nonnegative real numbers? Why or why not? Steps 2–4. See margin.

Step 4 Calculate $\sqrt{-4 \cdot 25}$ and $\sqrt{-4 \cdot -25}$. Now look at your Step 1 results for $\sqrt{-4} \cdot \sqrt{25}$ and $\sqrt{-4} \cdot \sqrt{-25}$. Does $\sqrt{a}\,\sqrt{b} = \sqrt{ab}$ if either a or b, but not both, is a negative real number? Does $\sqrt{a}\,\sqrt{b} = \sqrt{ab}$ if both a and b are both negative real numbers? Why or why not?

In the Activity, $\sqrt{-4 \cdot -25} = \sqrt{100} = 10$. You can verify that $\sqrt{-4} \cdot \sqrt{-25} = 10$ by hand as follows.

$$\begin{aligned}\sqrt{-4} \cdot \sqrt{-25} &= i\sqrt{4} \cdot i\sqrt{25} \\ &= 2 \cdot 5 \cdot i \cdot i \\ &= 10i^2 \\ &= -10\end{aligned}$$

So $\sqrt{-4 \cdot -25} \neq \sqrt{-4} \cdot \sqrt{-25}$ is a counterexample showing that the property $\sqrt{a}\,\sqrt{b} = \sqrt{ab}$ *does not hold* for *nonnegative* real numbers a and b.

Questions

COVERING THE IDEAS

1. **True or False** All real numbers have square roots. true
2. Write the solutions to $x^2 = -4$. $x = \pm 2i$

3. **Multiple Choice** About when did mathematicians begin to use roots of negative numbers as solutions to equations? C
   A sixth century B twelfth century
   C sixteenth century D twenty-first century
4. Who first used the term *imaginary number*? Descartes
5. Who was the first person to suggest using i for $\sqrt{-1}$? Euler

In 6 and 7, True or False.

6. For all real numbers x, $\sqrt{-x} < 0$. false
7. If $b > 0$, $\sqrt{-b} = i\sqrt{b}$. true

In 8 and 9, solve for x.
a. **Write the solutions to each equation with a radical sign.**
b. **Write the solutions without a radical sign.**

8. $x^2 + 25 = 0$
9. $x^2 + 16 = 0$
10. **True or False** $i\sqrt{7}$ is a square root of -7. Justify your answer.
11. Show that $-6i$ is a square root of -36.
12. Show that $\sqrt{-3}\sqrt{-27} \neq \sqrt{81}$. $i\sqrt{3} \cdot i\sqrt{27} = i^2\sqrt{81} = -\sqrt{81} \neq \sqrt{81}$

In 13–15, simplify.

13. $\sqrt{-53}$ $i\sqrt{53}$
14. $\sqrt{-121}$ $11i$
15. $-\sqrt{72}$ $-6\sqrt{2}$

In 16–21, perform the indicated operations. Give answers as real numbers or multiples of i.

16. $-2i + 7i$ $5i$
17. $10i - 3i$ $7i$
18. $(4i)(17i)$ -68
19. $3\sqrt{-16} + \sqrt{-64}$ $20i$
20. $\dfrac{\sqrt{-81}}{\sqrt{-9}}$ 3
21. $-\sqrt{-49} + \sqrt{-49}$ 0

In 22–24, simplify the product.

22. $\sqrt{-5} \cdot \sqrt{-5}$ -5
23. $\sqrt{-10} \cdot \sqrt{-30}$ $-10\sqrt{3}$
24. $\sqrt{3} \cdot \sqrt{-3}$ $3i$
25. a. Does $\sqrt{-3 \cdot 27} = \sqrt{-3} \cdot \sqrt{27}$? yes
    b. Does your answer in Part a provide a counterexample to $\sqrt{a}\sqrt{b} = \sqrt{ab}$ for $a < 0$ and $b > 0$? no
26. For what real number values of x and y does $\sqrt{xy} \neq \sqrt{x}\sqrt{y}$? $x < 0, y < 0$

8a. $x = \sqrt{-25}$ or $x = -\sqrt{-25}$
8b. $x = 5i$ or $x = -5i$
9a. $x = \sqrt{-16}$ or $x = -\sqrt{-16}$
9b. $x = 4i$ or $x = -4i$
10. true; $i\sqrt{7} \cdot i\sqrt{7} = i^2 \cdot 7 = -7$.
11. $(-6i)^2 = (-6)^2 i^2 = 36(-1) = -36$

APPLYING THE MATHEMATICS

In 27 and 28, simplify.

27. $\sqrt{-477{,}481}$ $691i$
28. $\dfrac{5i + 9i}{2i}$ 7

Notes on the Questions

Questions 25, 26, 29, and 30
Remind students that providing a counterexample is an easy way to prove that a statement is false.

Notes on the Questions

Question 29 and 30 Students will see in the next lesson that any two conjugate complex numbers are counterexamples for these statements.

Question 40 This is an important question. Students should learn that every fourth power of i repeats. (The Extension on this page explores the pattern for negative integer powers of i.)

4 Wrap-Up

Ongoing Assessment

Ask students to show the steps to simplify each of these expressions.

a. $(3i)(12i)$ $(3)(12)(i)(i) = 36i^2 = 36(-1) = -36$

b. $3i - 12i$ $i(3 - 12) = i(-9) = -9i$

c. $\sqrt{-9} - \sqrt{-36}$ $i\sqrt{9} - i\sqrt{36} = 3i - 6i = -3i$

d. $\frac{\sqrt{-9}}{\sqrt{-64}}$ $\frac{i\sqrt{9}}{i\sqrt{64}} = \frac{3i}{8i} = \frac{3}{8}$

6-8B page 2

6-8B Lesson Master Questions on SPUR Objectives
See Student Edition pages 446–449 for objectives.

SKILLS Objective C

In 1–9, solve for x. Give all solutions, both real and imaginary.

1. a. $x^2 = 900$ $x = 30$ or $x = -30$
   b. $x^2 = -900$ $x = 30i$ or $x = -30i$
2. a. $x^2 = -14$ $x = i\sqrt{14}$ or $x = -i\sqrt{14}$
   b. $x^2 = 14$ $x = \sqrt{14}$ or $x = -\sqrt{14}$
3. a. $5x^2 = -20$ $x = 2i$ or $x = -2i$
   b. $5x^2 = 20$ $x = 2$ or $x = -2$
4. a. $-8x^2 = 24$ $x = i\sqrt{3}$ or $x = -i\sqrt{3}$
   b. $8x^2 = 24$ $x = \sqrt{3}$ or $x = -\sqrt{3}$
5. a. $x^2 + 8 = 28$ $x = -\sqrt{20} = -2\sqrt{5}$ or $x = \sqrt{20} = 2\sqrt{5}$
   b. $x^2 + 8 = -28$ $x = 6i$ or $x = -6i$
6. a. $x^2 - 8 = 28$ $x = 6$ or $x = -6$
   b. $x^2 - 8 = -28$ $x = i\sqrt{20} = 2i\sqrt{5}$ or $x = -i\sqrt{20} = -2i\sqrt{5}$
7. a. $3x^2 + 17 = 130$ $x = \sqrt{\frac{113}{3}}$ or $x = -\sqrt{\frac{113}{3}}$
   b. $3x^2 + 17 = -130$ $x = 7i$ or $x = -7i$
8. a. $3x^2 - 17 = 130$ $x = 7$ or $x = -7$
   b. $3x^2 - 17 = -130$ $x = i\sqrt{\frac{113}{3}}$ or $x = -i\sqrt{\frac{113}{3}}$
9. a. $(x - 1)^2 + 20 = 5$ $x = 1 + i\sqrt{15}$ or $x = 1 - i\sqrt{15}$
   b. $(x + 5)(x - 5) = -31$ $x = i\sqrt{6}$ or $x = -i\sqrt{6}$
10. Solve $b^2 - 12 = -13$. Write the solutions
    a. with a radical sign. $b = \sqrt{-1}$ or $b = -\sqrt{-1}$
    b. without a radical sign. $b = i$ or $b = -i$
11. Solve $x^2 + 8 = -8$. Write the solutions
    a. with a radical sign. $x = \sqrt{-16}$ or $x = -\sqrt{-16}$
    b. without a radical sign. $x = 4i$ or $x = -4i$

280

Advanced Algebra 279

In 29 and 30, True or False. If false, give a counterexample.

29. The sum of any two imaginary numbers is imaginary.
30. The product of any two imaginary numbers is imaginary.
31. Verify your solutions to $x^2 = -4$ in Question 2 by using the Quadratic Formula to solve $x^2 + 0x + 4 = 0$.
32. Solve $9y^2 + 49 = 0$ using the Quadratic Formula.

In 33 and 34, solve the equation.

33. $a^2 + 12 = 5$ $a = \pm i\sqrt{7}$
34. $(b - 5)^2 + 13 = 9$ $b = 5 \pm 2i$

REVIEW

In 35 and 36, solve for x using the Quadratic Formula. (Lesson 6-7)

35. $8x^2 - 2x - 15 = 0$
36. $x^2 + dx - 2d^2 = 0$
37. Use quadratic regression to find an equation of the parabola that contains the points (2, 523.3), (4, 1126.3), and (8, 2338.3). (Lesson 6-6) $y = 0.25x^2 + 300x - 77.7$
38. A chef reports that with 5 kilograms of flour, 12 loaves of bread and 6 pizza crusts can be made. With 2 kilograms of flour, 1 loaf of bread and 10 pizza crusts can be made. How much flour is needed to make one loaf of bread? How much is needed for one pizza crust? (Lesson 5-4) $\frac{1}{3}$ kg; $\frac{1}{6}$ kg

39. Consider the function graphed below. Give its domain and range. (Lesson 1-4)

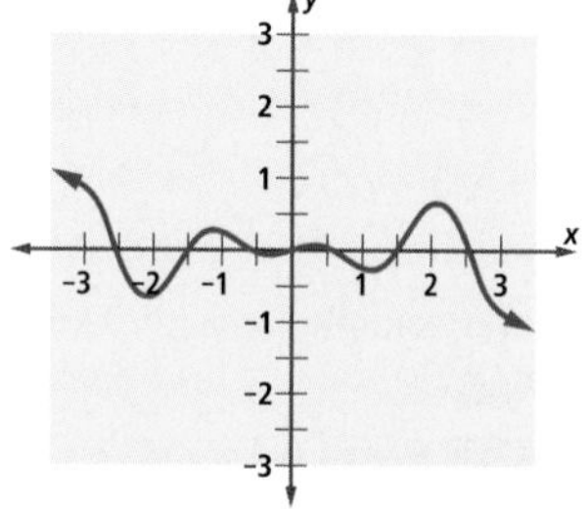

EXPLORATION

40. By definition, $i^2 = -1$. So $i^3 = i^2 \cdot i = -1 \cdot i = -i$ and $i^4 = i^3 \cdot i = -i \cdot i = -i^2 = -(-1) = 1$. Continue this pattern to evaluate and simplify each of i^5, i^6, i^7, and i^8. Generalize your result to predict the value of i^{2009}, i^{2010}, and i^{2020}. Explain how to simplify any positive power of i.
i, -1, $-i$, 1; i, -1, 1; because $i^4 = 1$, divide the exponent by 4, and use the remainder in the pattern as follows: remainder 1: i; remainder 2: -1; remainder 3: $-i$; remainder 0: 1.

29. False; $2i + -2i = 0$, 0 is a real number.
30. False; $i \cdot 5i = -5$, -5 is a real number.
31. $x = \frac{0 \pm \sqrt{0 - 4(1)(4)}}{2(1)} = \pm\frac{i\sqrt{16}}{2} = \pm 2i$
32. $y = \frac{0 \pm \sqrt{0 - 4(9)(49)}}{2(9)} = \pm\frac{i\sqrt{1764}}{18} = \pm\frac{7i}{3}$
35. $x = \frac{3}{2}$ or $x = -\frac{5}{4}$
36. $x = d$ or $x = -2d$
39. domain: all real numbers; range: all real numbers

QY ANSWERS

1. $6i$
2.

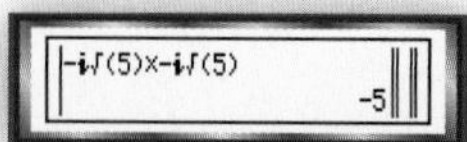

Extension

Question 40 asks students to evaluate i^n for $n = 3, 4, 5, \ldots$ and to identify a pattern for successive positive powers of i.

1. Ask students to extend that question. Simplify the negative powers of i (i.e., i^{-1}, i^{-2}, i^{-3}, ...). $i^{-1} = \frac{1}{i} = -i$; $i^{-2} = \frac{1}{i^2} = -1$; $i^{-3} = \frac{1}{i} \cdot \frac{1}{i^2} = i$; $i^{-4} = \frac{1}{i^2} \cdot \frac{1}{i^2} = 1$; ...
2. Do those powers follow the same pattern as the one in Question 40? Answers vary. Sample: The same pattern appears for the negative powers of i as for the positive powers of i (and $i^0 = 1$); that pattern is ..., 1, i, -1, $-i$, 1, ...

Lesson 6-9 Complex Numbers

Vocabulary

complex number
real part, imaginary part
equal complex numbers
complex conjugate

▶ **BIG IDEA** *Complex numbers* are numbers of the form $a + bi$, where $i = \sqrt{-1}$, and are operated with as if they are polynomials in i.

Many aspects of an electrical charge, such as voltage (electric potential) and current (movement of an electric charge), affect the performance and safety of the charge. When working with these two quantities, electricians find it easier to combine them into one number Z, called *impedance*. Impedance in an alternating-current (AC) circuit is the amount, usually measured in ohms, by which the circuit resists the flow of electricity. The two-part number Z is the sum of a real number and an imaginary number, and is called a *complex number*.

Mental Math

Write an inequality to represent the sentence.

a. The weight w of my carry-on luggage must be less than 30 pounds.

b. A medium-size sock can be worn by anyone with a shoe size s from 7 to 10.

c. To ride this roller coaster, your height h must be at least 54 inches.

a. $w < 30$

b. $7 \le s \le 10$

c. $h \ge 54$

What Are Complex Numbers?

Recall from the previous lesson that the set of numbers of the form bi, where b is a real number, are called *pure imaginary numbers*. When a real number and a pure imaginary number are added, the sum is called a *complex number*.

Definition of Complex Number

A **complex number** is a number of the form $a + bi$, where a and b are real numbers and $i = \sqrt{-1}$.

In the complex number $a + bi$, a is the **real part** and b is the **imaginary part**. For example, $-8.5 - 4i$ is a complex number in which the real part is -8.5 and the imaginary part is -4 (not $4i$ or $-4i$).

We say that $a + bi$ and $c + di$ are **equal complex numbers** if and only if their real parts are equal and their imaginary parts are equal. That is, $a + bi = c + di$ if and only if $a = c$ and $b = d$. For example, if $x + yi = 2i - 3$, then $x = -3$ and $y = 2$.

 QY1

▶ **QY1**

If $a + bi = -4 + \sqrt{-3}$, what is a and what is b?

Background

What are complex numbers? A common error is to think that bi is the imaginary part of the complex number $a + bi$. Emphasize that both the real and the imaginary parts of complex numbers are real numbers.

Operations with complex numbers Many books *define* the addition and multiplication of complex numbers and then deduce their properties. We take another approach: We *assume*, as we did with real numbers, that addition and multiplication in the set of complex numbers satisfy the customary (field) properties. From those assumptions, we derive rules for adding and multiplying complex numbers.

It is customary to write the answer to a complex number computation in the form $a + bi$, so that the real and imaginary parts of the complex number are evident.

(continued on next page)

Lesson 6-9

GOAL

Define and introduce operations on the set of complex numbers, including addition, subtraction, multiplication, and division.

SPUR Objectives

E Perform operations with complex numbers.

Materials/Resources

- Lesson Masters 6-9A and 6-9B
- Resource Masters 2, 113, and 114

HOMEWORK

Suggestions for Assignment

- Questions 1–29
- Question 30 (extra credit)
- Reading Lesson 6-10
- Covering the Ideas 6-10

Local Standards

1 Warm-Up

1. Multiply both the numerator and the denominator of $\frac{30 + 17\sqrt{3}}{4 - 12\sqrt{3}}$ by $30 - 17\sqrt{3}$. What is the effect? $\frac{33}{732 - 428\sqrt{3}}$; it rationalizes the numerator.
2. Multiply both the numerator and the denominator of $\frac{30 + 17\sqrt{3}}{4 - 12\sqrt{3}}$ by $4 + 12\sqrt{3}$. What is the effect? $\frac{732 + 428\sqrt{3}}{-416}$; it rationalizes the denominator.

2 Teaching

Notes on the Lesson

Although the rules for the sum and product of two complex numbers follow easily from the field properties, it takes many steps for a rigorous proof. Here is such a proof, but even here we have sometimes combined steps. Notice how many field properties are used.

$(a + bi) + (c + di)$

$= a + (bi + c) + di$ Assoc. Prop. of Add.

$= a + (c + bi) + di$ Com. Prop. of Add.

$= (a + c) + (bi + di)$ Assoc. Prop. of Add.

$= (a + c) + (ib + id)$ Com. Prop. of Mult.

$= (a + c) + i(b + d)$ Distrib. Prop.

$= (a + c) + (b + d)i$ Com. Prop. of Mult.

$(a + bi)(c + di)$

$= (a + bi)c + (a + bi)di$ Distrib. Prop.

$= c(a + bi) + di(a + bi)$ Com. Prop. of Mult.

$= (ca + cbi) + ((di)a + (di)(bi))$ Distrib. Prop.

$= ca + cbi + dia + dibi$ Assoc. Prop. of Add. and Mult.

$= ac + adi + bci + bdii$ Assoc. and Com. Prop. of Add. and Mult.

$= ac + adi + bci + bd(-1)$ def. of i

$= ac + adi + bci + (-bd)$ Mult. Prop. of -1

$= ac + (-bd) + adi + bci$ Assoc. and Com. Prop. of Add.

$= ac + (-bd) + (ad + bc)i$ Distrib. Prop. and Com. Prop. of Mult.

$= ac - bd + (ad + bc)i$ def. of subtraction

$= (ac - bd) + (ad + bc)i$ Assoc. Prop. of Add.

Operations with Complex Numbers

All of the assumed properties of addition, subtraction, multiplication, and division of real numbers hold for complex numbers.

Properties of Complex Numbers Postulate

In the set of complex numbers:

1. Addition and multiplication are commutative and associative.
2. Multiplication distributes over addition and subtraction.
3. $0 = 0i = 0 + 0i$ is the additive identity; $1 = 1 + 0i$ is the multiplicative identity.
4. Every complex number $a + bi$ has an additive inverse $-a + -bi$ and a multiplicative inverse $\frac{1}{a + bi}$ provided $a + bi \neq 0$.
5. The addition and multiplication properties of equality hold.

You can use the properties to operate with complex numbers in a manner consistent with the way you operate with real numbers. You can also operate with complex numbers on a CAS.

Activity

Step 1 Add the complex numbers.

$(2 + 3i) + (6 + 9i) =$ ___?___ $8 + 12i$

$(4 - 3i) + (7 + 5i) =$ ___?___ $11 + 2i$

$(-16 + 5i) + (4 - 8i) =$ ___?___ $-12 - 3i$

$(2+3i)+(6+9i)$

Step 2 Subtract the complex numbers.

$(4 - 3i) - (6 + 5i) =$ ___?___ $-2 - 8i$

$(-2 + i) - (7 + 9i) =$ ___?___ $-9 - 8i$

$(8 - 4i) - (1 - i) =$ ___?___ $7 - 3i$

Step 3 Describe, in words and using algebra, how to add and subtract two complex numbers.

Step 4 Check your answer to Step 3 by calculating $(a + bi) + (c + di)$ and $(a + bi) - (c + di)$ on a CAS.

Step 3. You can use the Commutative and Associative Properties to add or subtract the real parts and then add or subtract the imaginary parts; $(a + bi) + (c + di) = (a + c) + (b + d)i$ or $(a + bi) - (c + di) = (a - c) + (b - d)i$

Step 4.

$a+b\cdot i+c+d\cdot i$	$a+c+(b+d)\cdot i$
$a+b\cdot i-(c+d\cdot i)$	$a-c+(b-d)\cdot i$

In the Activity, you should have seen that the sum or difference of two complex numbers is a complex number whose real part is the sum or difference of the real parts and whose imaginary part is the sum or difference of the imaginary parts.

The Distributive Property can also be used to multiply a complex number by a real number or by a pure imaginary number.

The last paragraph of the lesson points out a "nonproperty" of nonreal complex numbers: They cannot be positive or negative. Still, some students will wonder why a complex number such as $2 + 3i$ is not considered positive. Ask students to multiply $2 + 3i$ by itself. They should get $-5 + 12i$. The square of a positive number should be positive; do they want $-5 + 12i$ to be considered positive? Ask them to calculate the third and fourth powers of $2 + 3i$, which are $-46 + 9i$ and $-119 - 120i$, respectively. Surely the fourth power looks like it should be negative. The point of doing these computations is to see that if you label any nonreal complex number as positive, when you start taking powers of that number, you get numbers that do not look so "positive."

Example 1

Put $4i(8 + 5i)$ in $a + bi$ form.

Solution

$4i(8 + 5i) = 4i(8) + 4i(5i)$	Distributive Property
$= 32i + 20(i^2)$	Associative and Commutative Properties of Multiplication
$= 32i + 20(-1)$	Definition of i
$= -20 + 32i$	Commutative Property of Addition

Check Multiply on a CAS. It checks.

In Example 1, notice that i^2 was simplified using the fact that $i^2 = -1$. Generally, you should write answers to complex number operations in $a + bi$ form. Most calculators use this form as well.

To multiply complex numbers, think of them as linear expressions in i and multiply using the Distributive Property. Then use $i^2 = -1$ to simplify your answer.

Example 2

Multiply and simplify $(6 - 2i)(4 + 3i)$.

Solution

$(6 - 2i)(4 + 3i) = 24 + 18i - 8i - 6i^2$	Distributive Property (Expand.)
$= 24 + 10i - 6i^2$	Distributive Property (Combine like terms.)
$= 24 + 10i - 6(-1)$	Definition of i
$= 30 + 10i$	Arithmetic

 QY2

▶ QY2

Multiply $(4 + 3i)(4 - 3i)$.

Conjugate Complex Numbers

The complex numbers $4 + 3i$ and $4 - 3i$ in QY 2 are *complex conjugates* of each other. In general, the **complex conjugate** of $a + bi$ is $a - bi$. Notice that the product $(4 + 3i)(4 - 3i)$ is a real number. In Question 23, you are asked to prove that the product of any two complex conjugates is a real number.

Note-Taking Tips

When students record in their notes the Properties of Complex Numbers Postulate, encourage them to include a few examples of each property using specific complex numbers.

Additional Examples

Example 1 Write $7i(9 - 6i)$ in $a + bi$ form. $42 + 63i$

Example 2 Multiply and simplify: $(5 + 7i)(6 - 2i)$. $30 - 10i + 42i - 14i^2 = 44 + 32i$

Notes on the Lesson

Conjugate complex numbers The term *complex conjugate* is also used in Lesson 6-10, so it should be discussed here.

Accommodating the Learner

Ask students to express the multiplicative inverse of $a + bi$ in $a + bi$ form. $\frac{1}{a+bi} = \frac{1}{a+bi} \cdot \frac{a-bi}{a-bi} = \frac{a-bi}{a^2+b^2} = \frac{a}{a^2+b^2} + \frac{-b}{a^2+b^2}i$

ENGLISH LEARNERS

Vocabulary Development

For the complex number $a + bi$, you may have to help some students understand the subtle difference between the convention that, while a is called the *real part* and b is called the *imaginary part*, both a and b must be real numbers.

Notes on the Lesson

The various kinds of complex numbers Many students may be familiar with hierarchical diagrams of this type that are based on inclusion, perhaps for various types of angles, triangles, and quadrilaterals. Emphasize that, as in any hierarchy, each type of number is an example of any higher type. Every integer is a complex number, every irrational number is a real number, and so on.

Additional Example

Example 3 Simplify $\frac{5-2i}{3+4i}$.

Solution Multiply the numerator and denominator by $3 - 4i$, the conjugate of $3 + 4i$.

$$\frac{5-2i}{3+4i} = \frac{5-2i}{3+4i} \cdot \frac{3-4i}{3-4i} = \frac{(5-2i)(3-4i)}{(3+4i)(3-4i)} = \frac{?}{?} = \frac{?}{9-16(\ ?\ )} = \frac{?}{25} + \frac{?}{25}i$$

$\frac{15-20i-6i+8i^2}{9-12i+12i-16i^2}$; $7 - 26i$; i^2; 7; -26

Complex conjugates are useful when dividing complex numbers. To divide two complex numbers, multiply both numerator and denominator by the conjugate of the denominator. This gives a real number in the denominator that you can then divide into each part of the numerator.

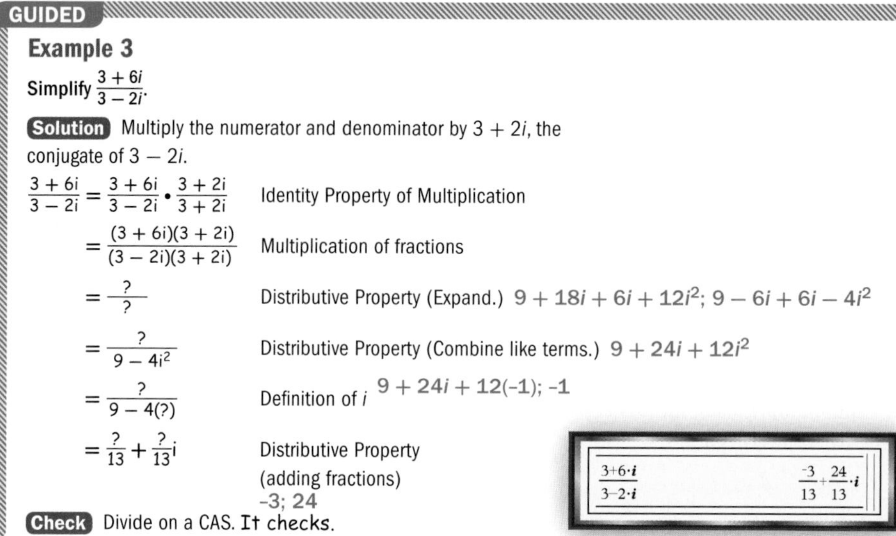

GUIDED

Example 3

Simplify $\frac{3+6i}{3-2i}$.

Solution Multiply the numerator and denominator by $3 + 2i$, the conjugate of $3 - 2i$.

$\frac{3+6i}{3-2i} = \frac{3+6i}{3-2i} \cdot \frac{3+2i}{3+2i}$ Identity Property of Multiplication

$= \frac{(3+6i)(3+2i)}{(3-2i)(3+2i)}$ Multiplication of fractions

$= \frac{?}{?}$ Distributive Property (Expand.) $9 + 18i + 6i + 12i^2$; $9 - 6i + 6i - 4i^2$

$= \frac{?}{9-4i^2}$ Distributive Property (Combine like terms.) $9 + 24i + 12i^2$

$= \frac{?}{9-4(?)}$ Definition of i $9 + 24i + 12(-1)$; -1

$= \frac{?}{13} + \frac{?}{13}i$ Distributive Property (adding fractions) -3; 24

Check Divide on a CAS. It checks.

$\frac{3+6\cdot i}{3-2\cdot i}$ $\frac{-3}{13}+\frac{24}{13}\cdot i$

The Various Kinds of Complex Numbers

Because $a + 0i = a$, every real number a is a complex number. Thus, the set of real numbers is a subset of the set of complex numbers. Likewise, every pure imaginary number bi equals $0 + bi$, so the set of pure imaginary numbers is also a subset of the set of complex numbers.

The diagram at the right is a *hierarchy of number sets*. It shows how the set of complex numbers includes some other number sets.

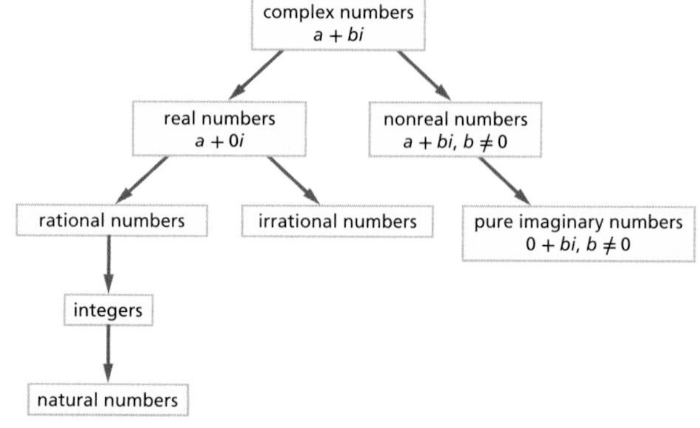

Accommodating the Learner

Ask students to write the square of the complex number $a + bi$ in $a + bi$ form.
$(a + bi)^2 = (a + bi)(a + bi) = a^2 + 2abi + b^2i^2 = (a^2 - b^2) + (2ab)i$

Applications of Complex Numbers

The first use of the term *complex number* is generally credited to Carl Friedrich Gauss. Gauss applied complex numbers to the study of electricity. Later in the 19th century, applications using complex numbers were found in geometry and acoustics. In the 1970s, complex numbers were used in a new field called *dynamical systems*.

Recall that electrical impedance Z is defined as a complex number involving voltage V and current I. A complex number representing impedance is of the form $Z = V + Ii$.

The total impedance Z_T of a circuit made from two connected circuits is a function of the impedances Z_1 and Z_2 of the individual circuits. Two electrical circuits may be connected *in series* or *in parallel*. In a series circuit, $Z_T = Z_1 + Z_2$. In a parallel circuit, $Z_T = \frac{Z_1Z_2}{Z_1+Z_2}$. Thus, to find the total impedance in a parallel circuit, you need to multiply and divide complex numbers.

GUIDED

Example 4

Find the total impedance in a parallel circuit if $Z_1 = 3 + 2i$ ohms and $Z_2 = 5 - 4i$ ohms.

Solution Substitute the values of Z_1 and Z_2 into the impedance formula for parallel circuits.

$Z_T = \frac{Z_1Z_2}{Z_1+Z_2}$

$Z_T = \frac{(3+2i)(5-4i)}{? + ?}$ Substitution $3 + 2i$; $5 - 4i$

$= \frac{? + ?i}{? - ?i}$ 23; -2; 8; 2

$= \frac{? + ?i}{? - ?i} \cdot \frac{? + ?i}{? + ?i}$ Multiply numerator and denominator by the conjugate of the denominator. 23; -2; 8; 2; 8; 2; 8; 2

$Z_T = \frac{?}{68}$ $188 + 30i$ Definition of i and arithmetic

The total impedance is $\frac{?}{68}$ ohms. $188 + 30i$

parallel circuit

series circuit

The basic properties of inequality that hold for real numbers do not hold for nonreal complex numbers. For instance, if you were to assume $i > 0$, then multiplying both sides of the inequality by i, you would get $i \cdot i > 0 \cdot i$, or $-1 > 0$, which is not true. If you assume $i < 0$, then multiply both sides by i, you get (changing the direction) $i \cdot i > 0 \cdot i$, or again $-1 > 0$. Except for those complex numbers that are also real numbers, there are no positive or negative complex numbers.

Notes on the Lesson

Applications of complex numbers To understand why complex numbers are used in describing impedance requires trigonometry and a geometric picture of what it means to multiply by i. The idea is as follows: Alternating current has two pulses. Think of graphs of the sine and cosine functions. One pulse is 90° after the other. Multiplication by i moves a pulse 90°, so by using a complex number to represent impedance, one can deal with both pulses.

Additional Example

Example 4 Find the total impedance in a parallel circuit if $Z_1 = 1 + i$ ohms and $Z_2 = 2 - 6i$ ohms.

Solution Substitute the values of Z_1 and Z_2 into the impedance formula for parallel circuits: $Z_T = \frac{Z_1Z_2}{Z_1 + Z_2}$.

$Z_T = \frac{(1+i)(2-6i)}{? + ?}$. $(1 + i)$; $(2 - 6i)$

$= \frac{? - ?i}{? - ?i}$ 8; 4; 3; 5

$= \frac{? - ?i}{? - ?i} \cdot \frac{? + ?i}{? + ?i}$; 8; 4; 3; 5; 3; 5; 3; 5

$Z_T = \frac{?}{34}$. $44 + 28i$

The total impedance is $\frac{?}{34}$ ohms. $44 + 28i$

Extension

Ask students to express the sum, difference, product, and quotient of the complex numbers $m + ni$ and $p + qi$ in $a + bi$ form.

Sum: $(m + p) + (n + q)i$

Difference: $(m - p) + (n - q)i$

Product: $(mp - nq) + (mq + np)i$

Quotient: $\frac{mp + nq}{p^2 + q^2} + \frac{np - mq}{p^2 + q^2}i$

3 Assignment

Recommended Assignment

- Questions 1–29
- Question 30 (extra credit)
- Reading Lesson 6-10
- Covering the Ideas 6-10

Notes on the Questions

You might have students check any paper-and-pencil computations with their calculators. Students are often surprised to learn that their calculators can perform operations with complex numbers.

Questions 12 and 13 You may wish to generalize these questions. What is the result (in $x + yi$ form) when $a + bi$ is divided by $c + di$? $\frac{ac + bd}{c^2 + d^2} + \frac{bc - ad}{c^2 + d^2}i$ (This idea is also treated in the Extension on page 431.)

Question 19 If z and w are complex numbers and both zw and $z + w$ are real numbers, then either (1) z and w are complex conjugates, or (2) z and w are both real numbers. If only zw is a real number, then either (1) z is a real multiple of the complex conjugate of w, or (2) z and w are both real numbers.

6-9A Lesson Master

Questions on SPUR Objectives
See Student Edition pages 446–449 for objectives.

VOCABULARY

In 1 and 2, give a. the real part and b. the imaginary part of each complex number.

1. $6 - 8i$ a. 6 b. -8
2. $\sqrt{3} + \pi i$ a. $\sqrt{3}$ b. π

In 3 and 4, write the complex conjugate of each number.

3. $9 - 24i$ $9 + 24i$
4. $m + ni$ $m - ni$

SKILLS Objective E

In 5–8, perform the indicated operations and write the result in $a + bi$ form.

5. $(6 - i)(5 + 2i) =$ $32 + 7i$
6. $(4 + 3i)^2 =$ $7 + 24i$
7. $(2 + 6i)(2 - 6i) =$ $40 + 0i$
8. $\frac{1+i}{2+6i} =$ $\frac{1}{5} - \frac{1}{10}i$

In 9–14, let $Z_1 = 3 + 5i$ and $Z_2 = 2 + i$. Perform the indicated operations and write the result in $a + bi$ form.

9. $Z_1 + 3Z_2 =$ $9 + 8i$
10. $Z_2 - Z_1 =$ $-1 - 4i$
11. $Z_1Z_2 =$ $1 + 13i$
12. $Z_2(3 - Z_1) =$ $5 - 10i$
13. $(Z_1)^2 =$ $-16 + 30i$
14. $\frac{Z_1}{Z_2} =$ $\frac{11}{5} + \frac{7}{5}i$
15. Evaluate $\frac{-b + \sqrt{b^2 - 4ac}}{2a}$ and $\frac{-b - \sqrt{b^2 - 4ac}}{2a}$ when $a = 1$, $b = 8$, and $c = 17$.
   a. $\frac{-b + \sqrt{b^2 - 4ac}}{2a} =$ $-4 + i$
   b. $\frac{-b - \sqrt{b^2 - 4ac}}{2a} =$ $-4 - i$
16. Recall that in electrical engineering, the total impedance Z_T of a circuit made from two circuits connected in parallel is $Z_T = \frac{Z_1Z_2}{Z_1 + Z_2}$ where Z_1 and Z_2 are the impedances of the individual circuits. Find the total impedance of a circuit with $Z_1 = -4 + i$ ohms and $Z_2 = 3 - 4i$ ohms.
   $-\frac{49}{10} - \frac{43}{10}i = -4.9 - 4.3i$

Advanced Algebra 281

Questions

COVERING THE IDEAS

1. **Fill in the Blank** A complex number is a number of the form $a + bi$ where a and b are ___?___ numbers. real

In 2–4, give the real and imaginary parts of each complex number.

2. $5 + 17i$
3. $-4 + i\sqrt{5}$
4. i

In 5–8, rewrite the expression as a single complex number in $a + bi$ form.

5. $(7 + 3i) - (4 - 2i)$ $3 + 5i$
6. $(5 + 2i)(6 - i)$ $32 + 7i$
7. $(5 + 2i)(5 - 2i)$ 29
8. $(9 + i\sqrt{2}) + (12 - 3i\sqrt{2})$
9. What is the complex conjugate of $a + bi$? $a - bi$
10. Provide reasons for each step.

$(9 + 5i)(7 + 2i) = 63 + 18i + 35i + 10i^2$ a. ___?___
$= 63 + 53i + 10i^2$ b. ___?___
$= 63 + 53i + 10(-1)$ c. ___?___
$= 53 + 53i$ d. ___?___

11. Find the complex conjugate of each number.
   a. $5 + 2i$ $5 - 2i$ b. $3i$ $-3i$ c. $-2 - 3i$ $-2 + 3i$ d. 4 4

In 12 and 13, write in $a + bi$ form.

12. $\frac{5+2i}{4-i}$ $\frac{18}{17} + \frac{13}{17}i$
13. $\frac{13}{2+3i}$ $2 - 3i$
14. Two electrical circuits have impedances $Z_1 = 8 + 4i$ ohms and $Z_2 = 7 - 4i$ ohms. Find the total impedance if these two circuits are connected
   a. in series. 15
   b. in parallel. $\frac{24}{5} - \frac{4}{15}i$
15. **True or False** Every real number is also a complex number. true
16. Name two fields in which complex numbers are applied.

APPLYING THE MATHEMATICS

17. Write $\sqrt{-25}$ in $a + bi$ form. $5i$ or $0 + 5i$
18. If $Z_1 = -4 + i$ and $Z_2 = 1 - 2i$, write each expression in $a + bi$ form.
   a. $2Z_1 - Z_2$
   b. $3Z_1Z_2$
   c. $\frac{Z_1}{Z_2}$
19. Find two nonreal complex numbers that are not complex conjugates and whose
   a. sum is a real number.
   b. product is a real number.

2. real part: 5; imaginary part: 17

3. real part: -4; imaginary part: $\sqrt{5}$

4. real part: 0; imaginary part: 1

8. $21 - 2i\sqrt{2}$

10a. Distributive Property

10b. Distributive Property (Combine like terms.)

10c. Definition of i

10d. Commutative Property of Addition; arithmetic

16. Answers vary. Sample: electronics, acoustics

18a. $-9 + 4i$

18b. $-6 + 27i$

18c. $-\frac{6}{5} - \frac{7}{5}i$

19a. Answers vary. Sample: $3 + 2i$, $8 - 2i$

19b. Answers vary. Sample: $3i$, $5i$

Additional Answers

20b, c.

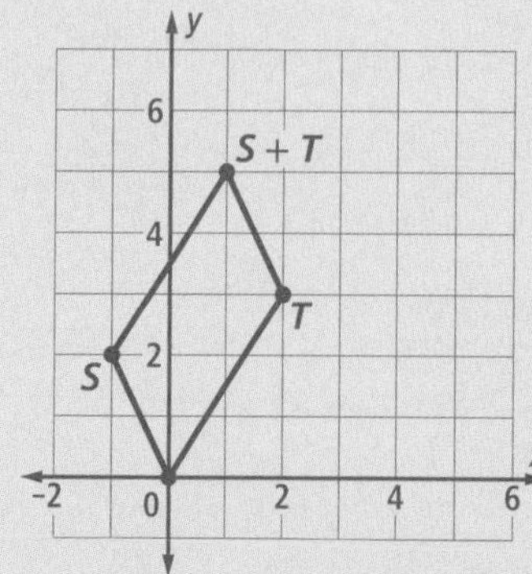

27. Answers vary. Sample: By the definition of absolute value, the distance beween x and $\frac{-b}{2a}$ is $\sqrt{\frac{b^2 - 4ac}{4a^2}}$, and this means that the difference between x and $\frac{-b}{2a}$ could be $\sqrt{\frac{b^2 - 4ac}{4a^2}}$ or its opposite. So, when absolute value signs are removed, a $\pm$ sign must be added.

28. $g(x) = \begin{cases} x + 2, x \geq -2 \\ -x - 2, x < -2 \end{cases}$

20. A complex number $a + bi$ is graphed as the point (a, b) with the x-axis as the real axis and the y-axis as the imaginary axis.
   a. Refer to the graph at the right. S and T are the graphs of which complex numbers? S: $-1 + 2i$, T: $2 + 3i$
   b. Graph $S + T$. See margin.
   c. Connect (0, 0), S, $S + T$, and T to form a quadrilateral. What type of quadrilateral is formed? parallelogram

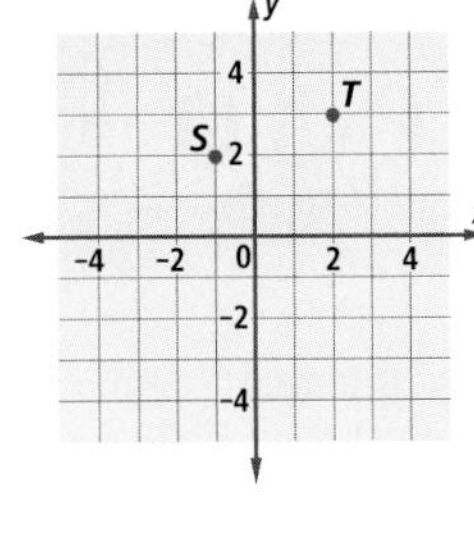

21. a. Solve the equation $x^2 - 6x + 13 = 0$ using the Quadratic Formula. Write the solutions in $a + bi$ form. $3 + 2i$, $3 - 2i$
   b. How are the solutions to the equation $x^2 - 6x + 13 = 0$ related to each other? They are complex conjugates.

In 22 and 23, consider the complex numbers $a + bi$ and $a - bi$.

22. Find their sum and explain why it is a real number.

23. Find their product and explain why it is a real number.

24. Prove that, if two circuits connected in parallel have impedances Z_1 and Z_2 and the total impedance is Z_T, then $\frac{1}{Z_T} = \frac{1}{Z_1} + \frac{1}{Z_2}$.

22. $2a$; because a is a real number, $2a$ is a real number.

23. $a^2 + b^2$; because a and b are real numbers, $a^2 + b^2$ is a real number.

24. $Z_T = \frac{Z_1Z_2}{Z_1+Z_2}$;
$\frac{1}{Z_T} = \frac{Z_1+Z_2}{Z_1Z_2} =$
$\frac{Z_1}{Z_1Z_2} + \frac{Z_2}{Z_1Z_2} =$
$\frac{1}{Z_2} + \frac{1}{Z_1} = \frac{1}{Z_1} + \frac{1}{Z_2}$

REVIEW

In 25 and 26, solve. Write the solutions as real numbers or multiples of i. (Lesson 6-8)

25. $a^2 - 3 = -8$ $a = i\sqrt{5}$ or $-i\sqrt{5}$ 26. $-r^2 = 196$ $r = 14i$ or $-14i$

27. Explain where the $\pm$ comes from in Step 8 of the derivation of the Quadratic Formula in Lesson 6-7. **(Lesson 6-2)** See margin.

28. Write a piecewise definition for the function g with equation $g(x) = |x + 2|$. **(Lessons 6-2, 3-4)** See margin.

29. The two graphs at the right show the relationships between a dependent variable R and independent variables m and p. Find an equation for R in terms of m and p. (You may leave the constant of variation as k.) **(Lesson 2-8)** $R = \frac{km^2}{p}$

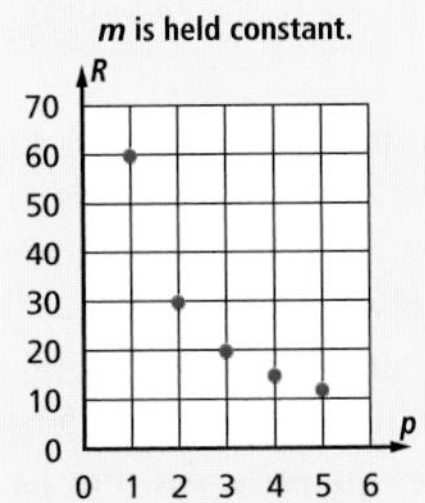
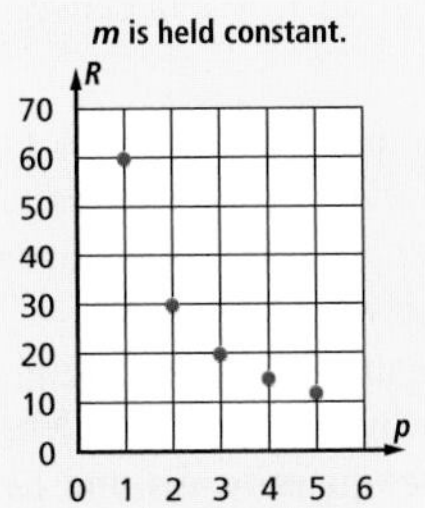

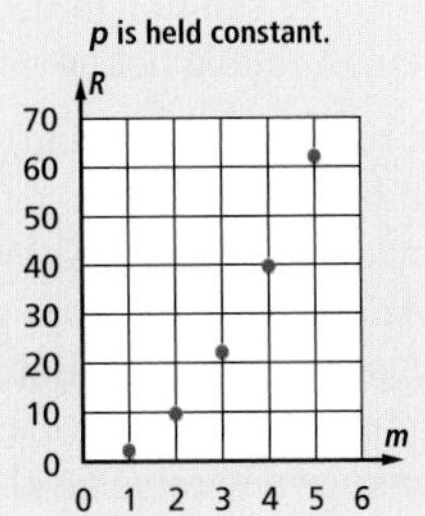

EXPLORATION

30. Refer to Question 20. a–c. See margin.
   a. Graph $z = 1 + i$ as the point (1, 1).
   b. Compute and graph z^2, z^3, and z^4.
   c. What pattern emerges? Predict where z^5, z^6, z^7, and z^8 will be.

QY ANSWERS

1. $a = -4, b = \sqrt{3}$
2. 25

Notes on the Questions

Question 21 This question should be discussed because it leads into the ideas of Lesson 6-10.

Question 24 The relationship among the reciprocals of impedance in a parallel circuit is the fundamental property from which the formula $Z_T = \frac{Z_1Z_2}{Z_1 + Z_2}$ was derived.

4 Wrap-Up

Ongoing Assessment

Have students work in groups. In each group, two students should each write a complex number, such as $5 + 3i$ or $2 - i$. Then all students in the group should simplify the two ratios formed by the two complex numbers $\left(\frac{5 + 3i}{2 - i}\right.$ and $\left.\frac{2 - i}{5 + 3i}\right)$ and write them in $a + bi$ form. Answers vary. Sample: $\frac{5 + 3i}{2 - i} = \frac{7 + 11i}{5}$ or $\frac{7}{5} + \frac{11}{5}i$; $\frac{2 - i}{5 + 3i} = \frac{7 - 11i}{34}$ or $\frac{7}{34} - \frac{11}{34}i$

Project Update

Project 3, *Representing Complex Numbers as Points*, on page 441 relates to the content of this lesson.

Additional Answers

30a. and 30b.

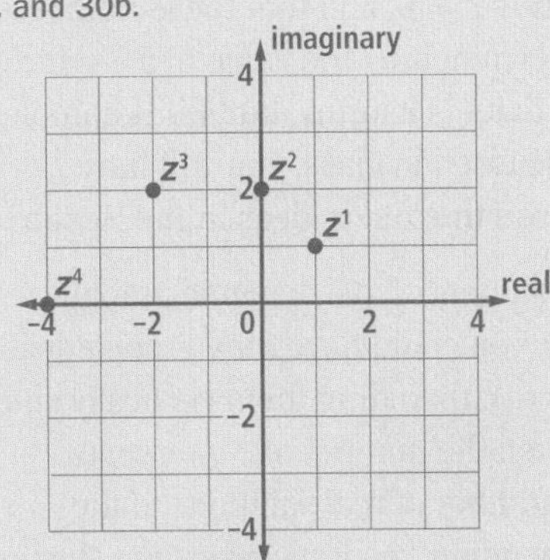

30b. $z^2 = 2i$; $z^3 = -2 + 2i$; $z^4 = -4$

30c. Answers vary. Sample: The points appear to be on a spiral: $z^5 = (-4, -4)$, $z^6 = (0, -8)$, $z^7 = (8, -8)$, and $z^8 = (16, 0)$.

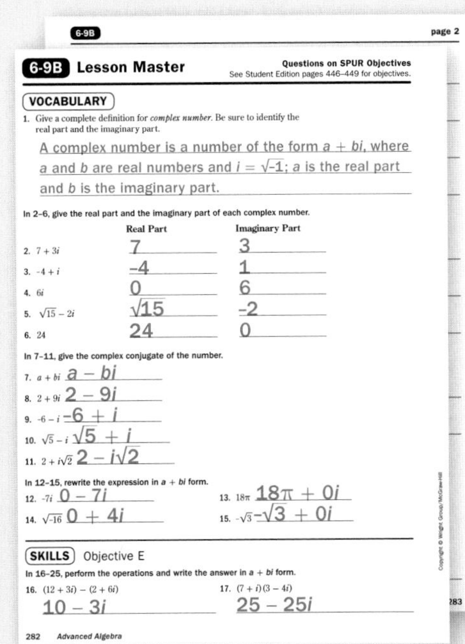

6-9B page 2

6-9B Lesson Master

Questions on SPUR Objectives
See Student Edition pages 446–449 for objectives.

VOCABULARY

1. Give a complete definition for *complex number*. Be sure to identify the real part and the imaginary part.
A complex number is a number of the form $a + bi$, where a and b are real numbers and $i = \sqrt{-1}$; a is the real part and b is the imaginary part.

In 2–6, give the real part and the imaginary part of each complex number.

	Real Part	Imaginary Part
2. $7 + 3i$	7	3
3. $-4 + i$	-4	1
4. $6i$	0	6
5. $\sqrt{15} - 2i$	$\sqrt{15}$	-2
6. 24	24	0

In 7–11, give the complex conjugate of the number.

7. $a + bi$ $a - bi$
8. $2 + 9i$ $2 - 9i$
9. $-6 - i$ $-6 + i$
10. $\sqrt{5} - i$ $\sqrt{5} + i$
11. $2 + i\sqrt{2}$ $2 - i\sqrt{2}$

In 12–15, rewrite the expression in $a + bi$ form.

12. $-7i$ $0 - 7i$
13. 18π $18\pi + 0i$
14. $\sqrt{-16}$ $0 + 4i$
15. $-\sqrt{3}$ $-\sqrt{3} + 0i$

SKILLS Objective E

In 16–25, perform the operations and write the answer in $a + bi$ form.

16. $(12 + 3i) - (2 + 6i)$ $10 - 3i$
17. $(7 + i)(3 - 4i)$ $25 - 25i$

282 Advanced Algebra

283

Lesson

6-10

GOAL

Provide students an extra day to practice calculating solutions to quadratic equations; introduce the concept of the discriminant and its relation to the number and the nature of the roots of a quadratic equation; put together earlier ideas of the chapter concerning graphs of quadratic functions.

SPUR Objectives

C Solve quadratic equations.

H Use the discriminant of a quadratic equation to determine the nature of the solutions to the equation.

K Graph quadratic functions and interpret them.

L Use the discriminant of a quadratic equation to determine the number of *x*-intercepts of a graph of the associated quadratic function.

Materials/Resources

- Lesson Masters 6-10A and 6-10B
- Resource Masters 2 and 115–117

HOMEWORK

Suggestions for Assignment

- Questions 1–22
- Question 23 (extra credit)
- Self-Test

Local Standards

Lesson

6-10 Analyzing Solutions to Quadratic Equations

Vocabulary

discriminant
roots of an equation
zeros of a function

BIG IDEA You can determine whether the solutions to a quadratic equation with real coefficients are real or not real by calculating a value called the *discriminant* of the quadratic.

A Brief History of Quadratics

As early as 1700 BCE, ancient mathematicians considered problems that today would be solved using quadratic equations. The Babylonians described solutions to these problems using words that indicate they had general procedures for solving them similar to the Quadratic Formula. However, the ancients had neither our modern notation nor the notion of complex numbers. The history of the solving of quadratic equations helped lead to the acceptance of irrational numbers, negative numbers, and complex numbers.

The Pythagoreans in the 5th century BCE thought of x^2 as the area of a square with side x. So if $x^2 = 2$, as in the square pictured here, then $x = \sqrt{2}$. The Greeks proved that $\sqrt{2}$ was an irrational number, so a long time ago people realized that irrational numbers have meaning. But they never considered the negative solution to the equation $x^2 = 2$ because lengths could not be negative.

1
x

Writings of Indian and Arab mathematicians from 800 to 1200 CE indicate that they could solve quadratic equations. The Arab mathematician Al-Khowarizmi, in 825 CE in his book ***Hisab al-jabr w'al muqabala*** (from which we get the word "algebra"), solved quadratics like the Babylonians. His contribution is that he did not think of the unknown as having to stand for a length. Thus, the unknown became an abstract quantity. Around 1200, Al-Khowarizmi's book was translated into Latin by Fibonacci, and European mathematicians had a method for solving quadratics.

Mental Math

a. What size change is represented by the matrix $\begin{bmatrix} 3 & 0 \\ 0 & 3 \end{bmatrix}$?

b. Give a matrix for $S_{4.2}$.

c. What scale change is represented by the matrix $\begin{bmatrix} 0.5 & 0 \\ 0 & 6 \end{bmatrix}$?

d. Give a matrix for $S_{7,2}$.

a. S_3

b. $\begin{bmatrix} 4.2 & 0 \\ 0 & 4.2 \end{bmatrix}$

c. $S_{0.5,6}$

d. $\begin{bmatrix} 7 & 0 \\ 0 & 2 \end{bmatrix}$

Background

This lesson helps students connect algebraic and graphical solutions for quadratic equations.

Predicting the number of real solutions to a quadratic equation By working through the Activity, many students will "discover" the Discriminant Theorem. That is, they will see that the number of *x*-intercepts of a graph of a quadratic function with equation $y = ax^2 + bx + c$ is related to the number of real solutions to the corresponding quadratic equation $ax^2 + bx + c = 0$, and that these numbers are determined by the value of $b^2 - 4ac$. The Activity is lengthy, but if it is completed and discussed in class, you will have addressed the major ideas in the lesson.

If your students have dynamic graphing utilities, you could have then graph equations (a) and (d), then drag them vertically and note when the number of *x*-intercepts, or the number of real solutions to the corresponding quadratic equation, changes

Mathematicians began using complex numbers in the 16th century because these numbers arose as solutions to quadratic and higher-degree equations. In the 19th century, Gauss brought both geometric and physical meaning to complex numbers. The geometric meaning built on Descartes' coordinate plane. Physical meanings of complex numbers occur in a variety of engineering and physics applications. In 1848, Gauss was the first to allow the *coefficients* in his equations to be complex numbers. Today, complex numbers are used in virtually all areas of mathematics.

Predicting the Number of Real Solutions to a Quadratic Equation

Activity

Work in groups of three. Record all the results for Steps 1, 2 and 4 in a single table like the one below. For Steps 1–4, divide the six equations in the table equally among the group members.

$y = ax^2 + bx + c$	Number of x-intercepts of Graph	Solutions to $ax^2 + bx + c = 0$	Number of Real Solutions to $ax^2 + bx + c = 0$	Value of $b^2 - 4ac$
a. $y = 4x^2 - 24x + 27$	? 2	? $x = 1.5, 4.5$	? 2	? 144
b. $y = 4x^2 - 24x + 36$	? 1	? $x = 3$	? 1	? 0
c. $y = 4x^2 - 24x + 45$	? 0	? $x = 3 \pm \frac{3}{2}i$	? 0	? -144
d. $y = -6x^2 + 36x - 54$	? 1	? $x = 3$	? 1	? 0
e. $y = -6x^2 + 36x - 48$	? 2	? $x = 2, 4$	? 2	? 144
f. $y = -6x^2 + 36x - 60$	? 0	? $x = 3 \pm i$	? 0	? -144

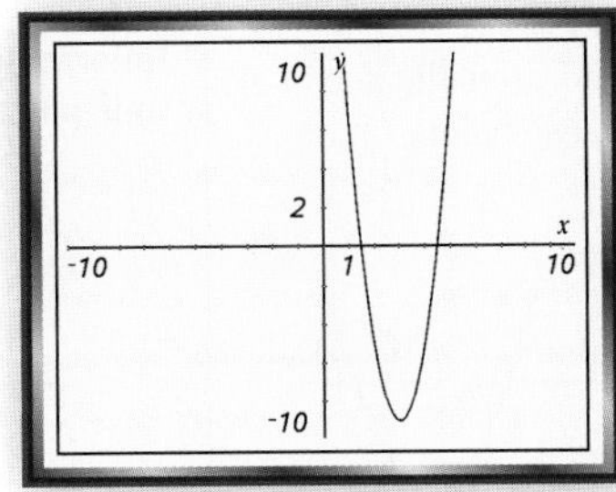

Step 1 Graph each quadratic equation and record the number of x-intercepts of its graph.

Step 2 Solve each equation using the Quadratic Formula and record how many of the solutions are real.

Step 3 Describe any patterns you see in the table so far. See margin.

Step 4 When $ax^2 + bx + c = 0$, the value of the expression $b^2 - 4ac$ can be used to predict the number of real solutions to the quadratic equation. This value is the **discriminant** of the quadratic equation. Calculate and record the discriminant for each equation in the table. Make a conjecture about the relationship between the number of real solutions and the value of the discriminant. See margin.

(continued on next page)

to 2, 1, and 0. Some graphing utilities can even be set up to show how the value of $b^2 - 4ac$ changes as the graph is dragged.

How many real solutions does a quadratic equation have? The Quadratic Formula may be applied to any quadratic equation. However, in this lesson, we restrict our attention to those quadratic equations with real coefficients. Only when the coefficients are real numbers does the Discriminant Theorem hold.

ENGLISH LEARNERS
Vocabulary Development

To help students remember that the discriminant is $b^2 - 4ac$, not $\sqrt{b^2 - 4ac}$, emphasize that the discriminant for *any* quadratic equation is always a real number. Therefore, the discriminant cannot be $\sqrt{b^2 - 4ac}$ because that expression is not always a real number.

1 Warm-Up

In 1–3, graph the function defined by the equation and determine the number of x-intercepts.

1. $f(x) = x^2 - 18x + 6$ 2 x-intercepts;

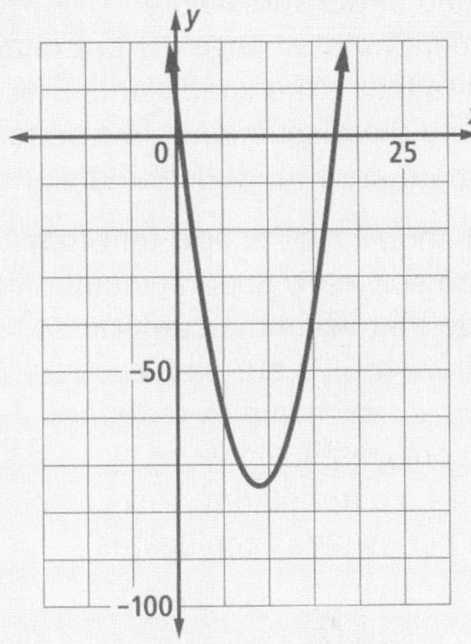

2. $g(x) = x^2 - 18x + 100$ 0 x-intercepts;

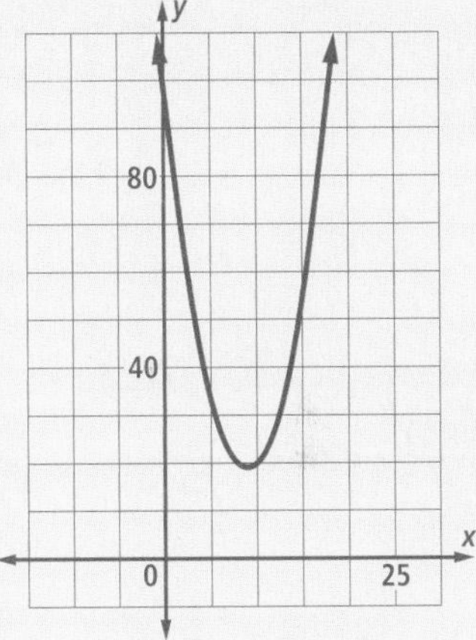

3. $h(x) = x^2 - 18x + 81$ 1 x-intercept;

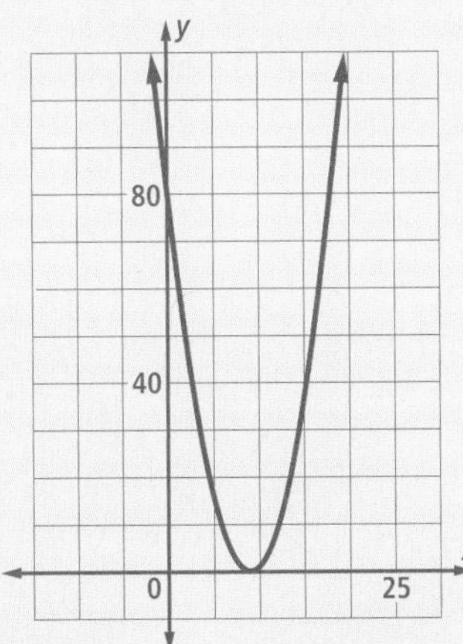

Optional: Have students calculate $D = b^2 - 4ac$ for each expression and see that $D > 0$ in Warm-Up 1, $D < 0$ in Warm-Up 2, and $D = 0$ in Warm-Up 3.

2 Teaching

Notes on the Lesson

Be sure that students note that the discriminant of $ax^2 + bx + c = 0$ is $b^2 - 4ac$ and *not* $\sqrt{b^2 - 4ac}$. (This idea is expanded in the Vocabulary Development note on page 435.) Explain to students that if the coefficients are rational and the discriminant is a perfect square, there are two rational roots.

Students should realize now that they are able to solve any quadratic equation. Emphasize that when the coefficients of $ax^2 + bx + c = 0$ are real, such as in Example 1, any complex roots are complex conjugates. However, when the coefficients are not all real, any complex roots are not complex conjugates.

Step 5 **a.** Have each person make three new quadratic equations of the form $y = ax^2 + bx + c$, where a, b, and c are real numbers and $a \neq 0$. One equation should have two real solutions, one should have one real solution, and the third should have no real solutions.

b. Add each of the equations in Part a to the table, then graph them on your graphing utility. Solve each equation, then record the number of x-intercepts, the number of real solutions, the values of the real solutions, and the value of the discriminant in the table.

c. Do the nine additions to the table support your conjecture from Step 4? yes

Step 5a–b. Answers vary. Check students' work.

How Many Real Solutions Does a Quadratic Equation Have?

Now consider the general quadratic equation. When the coefficients a, b, and c are real numbers and $a \neq 0$, the Quadratic Formula gives the following two solutions to $ax^2 + bx + c = 0$: $x = \frac{-b \pm \sqrt{b^2 - 4ac}}{2a}$.

QY

> **QY**
> Write the two solutions to the Quadratic Formula as a compound sentence.

Because a and b are real numbers, the numbers $-b$ and $2a$ are real, so only $\sqrt{b^2 - 4ac}$ could possibly not be real. It is because of this property that the number $b^2 - 4ac$ is called the discriminant. It allows you to discriminate the *nature of the solutions* to the equation, as shown below.

If $b^2 - 4ac$ is positive, then $\sqrt{b^2 - 4ac}$ is a positive number. There are two real solutions. The graph of $y = ax^2 + bx + c$ intersects the x-axis in two points.

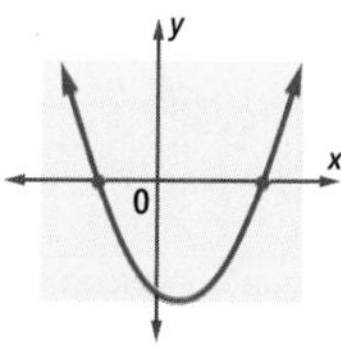

$y = ax^2 + bx + c$
$b^2 - 4ac > 0$
two real solutions

If $b^2 - 4ac$ is zero, then $\sqrt{b^2 - 4ac} = \sqrt{0} = 0$. Then $x = \frac{-b \pm 0}{2a} = \frac{-b}{2a}$, and there is only one real solution. The graph of $y = ax^2 + bx + c$ intersects the x-axis in one point.

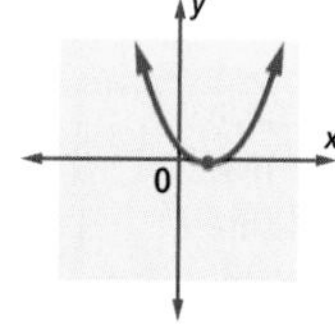

$y = ax^2 + bx + c$
$b^2 - 4ac = 0$
one real solution

If $b^2 - 4ac$ is negative, then $\sqrt{b^2 - 4ac}$ is an imaginary number. There will then be two nonreal solutions. Furthermore, because these solutions are of the form $m + ni$ and $m - ni$, they are complex conjugates. The graph of $y = ax^2 + bx + c$ does not intersect the x-axis.

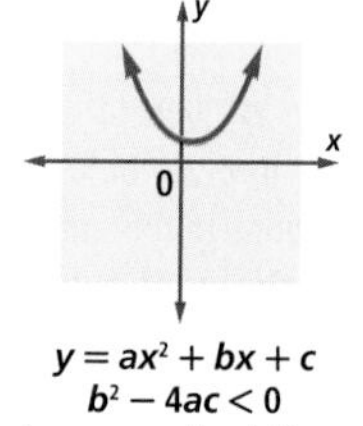

$y = ax^2 + bx + c$
$b^2 - 4ac < 0$
two nonreal solutions

Accommodating the Learner

Ask students to look at the discriminant $b^2 - 4ac$ and give a relationship between a and c that results in a quadratic equation that has two real roots. Answers vary. Sample: If a and c have opposite signs, then $b^2 - 4ac$ must be positive, so the roots will be two real numbers.

The graphs on the previous page are drawn for positive a, so the parabolas open up. Solutions to quadratic (and other) equations are also called **roots of the equation** $ax^2 + bx + c = 0$, or **zeros of the function** represented by the equation $y = ax^2 + bx + c$. The number i allows you to write square roots of negative numbers as complex solutions. You saw in the Activity that the number of real roots of each quadratic equation equals the number of x-intercepts. To summarize, the results of the Activity should be consistent with the following theorem.

Discriminant Theorem

Suppose a, b, and c are real numbers with $a \neq 0$.
Then the equation $ax^2 + bx + c = 0$ has:
(i) two real solutions, if $b^2 - 4ac > 0$.
(ii) one real solution, if $b^2 - 4ac = 0$.
(iii) two complex conjugate solutions, if $b^2 - 4ac < 0$.

GUIDED

Example 1

Determine the nature of the roots of each equation.

a. $4x^2 - 4x + 1 = 0$
b. $25x^2 + 6x + 4 = 0$
c. $3x^2 + 5x - 14 = 0$

Solution Use the Discriminant Theorem. Let $D = b^2 - 4ac$.

a. Here $a = 4$, $b = -4$, and $c = 1$. So $D = (-4)^2 - 4(4)(1) = 0$.
Thus, the equation has __?__ real root. 1

b. Here $a = 25$, $b = 6$, and $c = 4$, so $D =$ __?__. -364
Because D is negative, the equation has __?__ real roots. 0

c. Here $a =$ __?__, $b =$ __?__, and $c =$ __?__; so $D =$ __?__ > 0. 3; 5; -14; 193
So, this equation has __?__ real roots. Because D is not a perfect square, the roots are irrational. 2

Check Use a graphing utility. Let $f1(x) = 4x^2 - 4x + 1$, $f2(x) = 25x^2 + 6x + 4$, and $f3(x) = 3x^2 + 5x - 14$. The number of real solutions should equal the number of x-intercepts of the graph.

a. The graph of $f1$ has __?__ x-intercept. So, the equation has __?__ real root. It checks. 1; 1

b. The graph of $f2$ has __?__ x-intercepts. So, the equation has __?__ real roots. It checks. 0; 0

c. The graph of $f3$ has __?__ x-intercepts. So, the equation has __?__ real roots. It checks. 2; 2

Note-Taking Tips

Encourage students to include in their notes the relationship between *roots, zeros,* and *x-intercepts,* as well as the appropriate context for using each term. For example, students might write the following:

- The solutions of $ax^2 + bx + c = 0$ are the *roots of the equation.*
- The x-values where the graph of the function with equation $y = ax^2 + bx + c$ crosses the x-axis are the *x-intercepts of the graph* or the *zeros of the function.*

Additional Example

Example 1 Determine the nature of the roots of each equation.

a. $6x^2 + 2x + 5 = 0$

b. $9x^2 - 12x + 4 = 0$

c. $3x^2 + x - 2 = 0$

Solution

Use the Discriminant Theorem.
Let $D = b^2 - 4ac$.

a. $a = 6$, $b = 2$, and $c = 5$, so $D = (2)^2 - 4(6)(5) = -116$. Because D is negative, the equation has __?__ real roots. zero

b. $a = 9$, $b = -12$, and $c = 4$, so $D =$ __?__. The equation has __?__ real root. 0; one

c. $a = 3$, $b = 1$, and $c = -2$, so $D =$ __?__. This equation has __?__ real roots. Because D is __?__, the roots are __?__.
25; two; a perfect square; rational

Accommodating the Learner

Refer students to the Accommodating the Learner Up activity on page 416, which asked for an expression for the sum of the roots of a quadratic equation with real coefficients.

1. Does that expression work for any value of the discriminant? Yes, the sum of the roots is always $-\frac{b}{a}$.

2. How can you use the expression for the sum of the roots to find the x-coordinate of the vertex of the parabola?
Answers vary. Sample: To find the x-coordinate of the vertex, which is always halfway between the roots, calculate one-half of the sum of the roots. So the x-coordinate of the vertex is $x = \frac{1}{2} \cdot -\frac{b}{a}$ or $x = -\frac{b}{2a}$.

Notes on the Lesson

Example 2 This example uses the Discriminant Theorem in a practical way. If students had found that the value of the discriminant was positive, they should have realized that the basketball was 10 feet high at two different times. If the value of the discriminant had been 0, there would have been a single such time, the highest point of the path. Because the value of the discriminant is negative, there was no such time. Students can check their answers by graphing.

Additional Example

Example 2 The equation $h = -0.4x^2 + 2x + 2$ models the path of a ball, where x is the horizontal distance in feet that the ball has traveled and h is the ball's height in feet above the ground. Use the Discriminant Theorem to determine whether the ball ever reaches a height of 4 feet. The ball reaches 4 ft if there are real values of x such that $4 = -0.4x^2 + 2x + 2$ or $0 = -0.4x^2 + 2x - 2$. The discriminant is $2^2 - 4(-0.4)(-2) = 0.8$. Because D is positive, there are two real solutions to the equation. The ball reaches a height of 4 ft two times.

3 Assignment

Recommended Assignment

- Questions 1–22
- Question 23 (extra credit)
- Self-Test

Notes on the Questions

Question 4 As you discuss the questions in this lesson, you might want to emphasize four aspects of the same idea: the number of times the graph intersects the x-axis, the number of x-intercepts, the number of real solutions, and the value of the discriminant. The discriminant gives information about the other three values.

Applying the Discriminant Theorem

The number of real solutions to a quadratic equation can tell you something about the situation that led to the equation. The following example shows how.

Example 2

Eight-year old Allie Oop, an aspiring basketball player, shoots five feet from the hoop. She is trying to get the ball above the rim, which is set at a height of 10 feet. She releases the ball from an initial height of 4 feet. The following equation models the path of the ball, where x is the horizontal distance in feet that the ball has traveled and h is the ball's height in feet above the ground.

$$h = -0.4x^2 + 3x + 4$$

Use the Discriminant Theorem to determine whether Allie's ball ever reaches the height of the rim.

Solution The ball will reach the rim if there are real values of x for which

$$10 = -0.4x^2 + 3x + 4.$$

First, rewrite the equation in standard form. $0 = -0.4x^2 + 3x - 6$

Then calculate the value of the discriminant. $3^2 - 4(-0.4)(-6) = -0.6$

The discriminant $D = -0.6$. Because D is negative, there are no real solutions to this equation. This means that the ball will not reach the height of the rim.

Questions

COVERING THE IDEAS

1. What is the relationship between the number of x-intercepts of the graph of a quadratic function and the number of real solutions to the corresponding quadratic equation? They are equal.
2. Why did the Pythagoreans think there was only one solution to $x^2 = 2$? They considered the solution to be a length, and lengths cannot be negative.
3. Consider the equation $ax^2 + bx + c = 0$, where a, b, and c are real numbers.
   a. What is its discriminant? $b^2 - 4ac$
   b. What are its roots? $\frac{-b \pm \sqrt{b^2-4ac}}{2a}$
4. The discriminant of an equation $ax^2 + bx + c = 0$ is 0. What does this indicate about the graph of $y = ax^2 + bx + c$? The graph has one x-intercept.

5. **Matching** Match the idea about quadratics at the left with the estimated length of time that idea has been understood.
   a. geometric and physical meanings to complex numbers v
   b. problems in which the unknown could be an abstract quantity iv

   i. about 3700 years
   ii. about 1400 years
   iii. about 1750 years
   iv. about 1150 years
   v. about 150 years

In 6 and 7, a quadratic expression is given.
   a. Set the expression equal to 0. Use the discriminant to determine the nature of the roots to the equation.
   b. Set the expression equal to *y*. How many *x*-intercepts does the graph of the equation have?

6. $2x^2 - 3x + 7$
7. $x^2 - 10x + 9$

8. a. Solve $2s^2 - 3s + 7 = 0$, and write the solutions in $a + bi$ form.
   b. **True or False** The roots of this equation are complex conjugates.

9. Sketch a graph of a quadratic function $y = ax^2 + bx + c$, with $a > 0$ and a negative discriminant similar to one of the three graphs on page 436. See margin.

In 10 and 11, a graph of a quadratic function $f : x \rightarrow ax^2 + bx + c$ is given.
   a. Tell whether the value of $b^2 - 4ac$ is positive, negative, or zero.
   b. Tell how many real roots the equation $f(x) = 0$ has.

10.

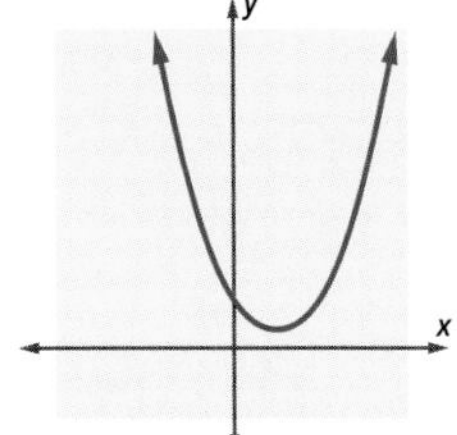

11.

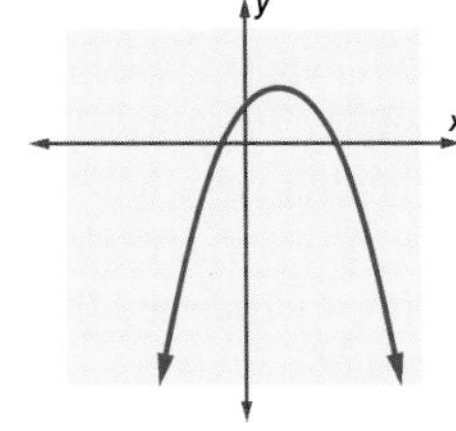

12. Without drawing a graph, tell whether the x-intercepts of $y = 2.5x^2 - 10x + 6.4$ are rational or irrational. Justify your answer.

13. Refer to Example 2. Allie practices her shot, but it never reaches the rim, so her father lowers the hoop to 9 feet. Now will the ball reach the height of the rim? Justify your answer.
   Yes; the discriminant D of $0 = -0.4x^2 + 3x - 5$ is 1. Because D is positive there are real solutions, and the ball will reach the height of the rim.

6a. $2x^2 - 3x + 7 = 0$; $b^2 - 4ac = -47$, so the roots are complex conjugates.

6b. $2x^2 - 3x + 7 = y$; 0 x-intercepts

7a. $x^2 - 10x + 9 = 0$; $b^2 - 4ac = 64$, so there are 2 real roots.

7b. $x^2 - 10x + 9 = y$; 2 x-intercepts

8a. $s = \frac{3}{4} + \frac{\sqrt{47}}{4}i$ or $s = \frac{3}{4} - \frac{\sqrt{47}}{4}i$

8b. true

10a. negative

10b. 0

11a. positive

11b. 2

12. Rational; $D = (-10)^2 - 4 \cdot 2.5 \cdot 6.4 = 36$; since the discriminant is a perfect square, the x-intercepts are rational.

Notes on the Questions

Question 5 Students may wonder why quadratics were so important in ancient times. The main reason was their applications to problems involving area and to other situations associated with multiplication. Many applications of multiplication tended to lead to applications of quadratics.

Additional Answers

9. Answers vary. Sample:

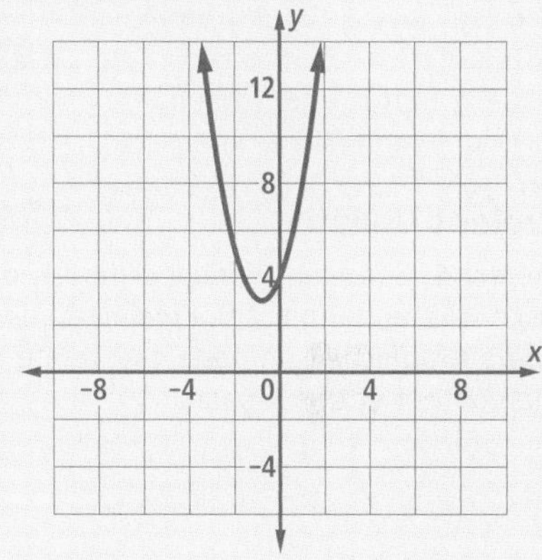

Extension

The second paragraph on page 434 shows that you can represent a segment of length $\sqrt{2}$ by constructing a right isosceles triangle whose legs are 1 unit in length. Ask students to extend that diagram by creating additional right triangles, each with one leg of length 1 unit and the other leg the length of the previous hypotenuse, as shown at the right. Ask students what numbers are represented by the lengths of the hypotenuse segments. The hypotenuse segments have lengths $\sqrt{2}$, $\sqrt{3}$, $\sqrt{4}$, $\sqrt{5}$, and so on.

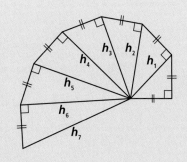

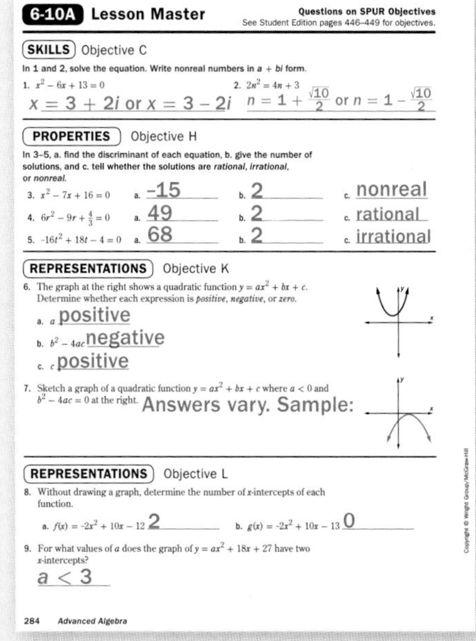
6-10A Lesson Master

Questions on SPUR Objectives
See Student Edition pages 446–449 for objectives.

SKILLS Objective C

In 1 and 2, solve the equation. Write nonreal numbers in $a + bi$ form.

1. $x^2 - 6x + 13 = 0$ $x = 3 + 2i$ or $x = 3 - 2i$
2. $2n^2 = 4n + 3$ $n = 1 + \frac{\sqrt{10}}{2}$ or $n = 1 - \frac{\sqrt{10}}{2}$

PROPERTIES Objective H

In 3–5, a. find the discriminant of each equation, b. give the number of solutions, and c. tell whether the solutions are *rational*, *irrational*, or *nonreal*.

3. $x^2 - 7x + 16 = 0$ a. -15 b. 2 c. nonreal
4. $6r^2 - 9r + \frac{4}{3} = 0$ a. 49 b. 2 c. rational
5. $-16t^2 + 18t - 4 = 0$ a. 68 b. 2 c. irrational

REPRESENTATIONS Objective K

6. The graph at the right shows a quadratic function $y = ax^2 + bx + c$. Determine whether each expression is *positive*, *negative*, or *zero*.
   a. a positive
   b. $b^2 - 4ac$ negative
   c. c positive

7. Sketch a graph of a quadratic function $y = ax^2 + bx + c$ where $a < 0$ and $b^2 - 4ac = 0$ at the right. Answers vary. Sample:

REPRESENTATIONS Objective L

8. Without drawing a graph, determine the number of x-intercepts of each function.
   a. $f(x) = -2x^2 + 10x - 12$ 2
   b. $g(x) = -2x^2 + 10x - 13$ 0

9. For what values of a does the graph of $y = ax^2 + 18x + 27$ have two x-intercepts?
   $a < 3$

284 *Advanced Algebra*

4 Wrap-Up

Ongoing Assessment

Ask students to describe how to calculate the discriminant of a quadratic equation and tell what the value of the discriminant says about the roots. Answers vary. Sample: Write the equation in standard form, then calculate $b^2 - 4ac$ to get the value of the discriminant. If the discriminant is negative, there are no real roots; if the discriminant is zero, there is one real root; if the discriminant is positive, there are two real roots. (If the discriminant is a perfect square, the solutions are rational numbers.)

Project Update

Project 1, *Sum and Product of Roots,* on page 441 and Project 6, *Finding Complex Roots Graphically,* on page 442 relate to the content of this lesson.

6-10B page 2

6-10B Lesson Master **Questions on SPUR Objectives** See Student Edition pages 446–449 for objectives.

SKILLS Objective C

In 1–8, solve the equation. Write nonreal numbers in $a + bi$ form.

1. $2x^2 - 7x + 15 = 0$ $x = \frac{7}{4} + \frac{\sqrt{71}}{4}i$ or $x = \frac{7}{4} - \frac{\sqrt{71}}{4}i$
2. $3x = 7 + 5x^2$ $x = \frac{3}{10} + \frac{\sqrt{131}}{10}i$ or $x = \frac{3}{10} - \frac{\sqrt{131}}{10}i$
3. $-4(2n^2 - 2n) = 3(n + 6)$ $n = \frac{5}{16} + \frac{\sqrt{551}}{16}i$ or $n = \frac{5}{16} - \frac{\sqrt{551}}{16}i$
4. $t^2 - 1 = 0$ $t = 1$ or $t = -1$
5. $2x^2 - x + 15 = 0$ $x = \frac{1}{4} + \frac{\sqrt{119}}{4}i$ or $x = \frac{1}{4} - \frac{\sqrt{119}}{4}i$
6. $2h^2 - h - 15 = 0$ $h = 3$ or $h = -\frac{5}{2}$
7. $(3m + 1)^2 - 5 = 0$ $m = -\frac{1}{3} + \frac{\sqrt{5}}{3}$ or $m = -\frac{1}{3} - \frac{\sqrt{5}}{3}$
8. $16x^2 - 72x + 81 = 0$ $x = 2.25$

PROPERTIES Objective H

In 9–16, a. find the discriminant of each equation, b. give the number of solutions, and c. tell whether the solutions are *rational, irrational,* or *nonreal.*

		a.	b.	c.
9.	$x^2 - 3x + 6 = 0$	-15	2	nonreal
10.	$2r^2 - r - 40 = 0$	321	2	irrational
11.	$t^2 - 8t + 16 = 0$	0	1	rational
12.	$5x^2 - 6x - 11 = 0$	256	2	rational
13.	$15x^2 - 3x + 7 = 0$	-411	2	nonreal
14.	$15h^2 - 11h - 14 = 0$	961	2	rational
15.	$x^2 + x + 1 = 0$	-3	2	nonreal
16.	$x^2 - x - 1 = 0$	5	2	rational

17. The graph at the right shows a quadratic function $y = ax^2 + bx + c$. Determine whether each expression is *positive, negative,* or *zero.*
   a. a negative
   b. $b^2 - 4ac$ zero
   c. c negative

Advanced Algebra 285

APPLYING THE MATHEMATICS

In 14 and 15, True or False. If true, explain why; if false, give a counterexample.

14. The y-intercept of every parabola that has an equation of the form $y = ax^2 + bx + c$ is $(0, b)$. false; $y = 2x^2 + 4x + 6$
15. Whenever a parabola opens down and its vertex is above the x-axis, its discriminant must be positive.
16. a. Find the value(s) of k for which the graph of the equation $y = x^2 + kx + 6.25$ will have exactly one x-intercept.
    b. Check your answer to Part a by graphing. See margin.
17. Can a quadratic equation have two real roots, one rational and the other irrational? Why or why not?

15. True; the graph intersects the x-axis in two points, so there are two real roots.

16a. $k = -5$ or $k = 5$

17. No. Explanations vary. Sample: If one root is rational, then by the Quadratic Formula $x = \frac{a + \sqrt{b}}{c}$, where a, $\sqrt{b}$, and c are rational numbers. The other root, $\frac{a - \sqrt{b}}{c}$ would have to be rational because addition, subtraction, and division of rational numbers result in a rational number.

REVIEW

18. Write $\frac{49 + 28i}{2 + 3i}$ in $a + bi$ form by hand. **(Lesson 6-9)** $14 - 7i$
19. Solve the equation $x^2 - 8x + 25 = 0$. Write the solutions in $a + bi$ form. **(Lesson 6-9)** $x = 4 + 3i$ or $x = 4 - 3i$
20. Find all the *fourth* roots of 16, that is, the square roots of the square roots of 16. **(Lesson 6-8)** 2, -2, $2i$, $-2i$
21. Penny drops a penny from the top of a 1200-foot building. At the exact moment Penny drops the penny, her sister Ellie gets on an elevator at a height of 300 feet which travels upward at a constant rate of 30 $\frac{\text{feet}}{\text{second}}$. Ignore air resistance. **(Lessons 6-4, 5-2, 3-1)**
    a. Write an equation for the height p in feet of Penny's penny as a function of the time t in seconds after it is dropped. $p = -16t^2 + 1200$
    b. Write an equation for Ellie's height m as a function of t. $m = 300 + 30t$
    c. Graph your two equations from Parts a and b and use the graph to determine at what time are Ellie and the penny at the same height above the ground. $t \approx 6.62$ sec; See margin for graph.
22. The trim around a square window is 2 inches wide. The total length of one side of the window including trim is x inches. Find an expression in standard form for the area of just the window without trim. **(Lesson 6-1)** $x^2 - 8x + 16$

EXPLORATION

23. The word "algebra" comes from the Arabic "al-jabr." What does "al-jabr" mean and what does that meaning have to do with algebra?

23. Al-jabr is the process of transposing subtracted terms to the other side of the equation. It is one of the operations used to solve equations.

QY ANSWER

$x = \frac{-b + \sqrt{b^2 - 4ac}}{2a}$ or $x = \frac{-b - \sqrt{b^2 - 4ac}}{2a}$

Additional Answers

16b.

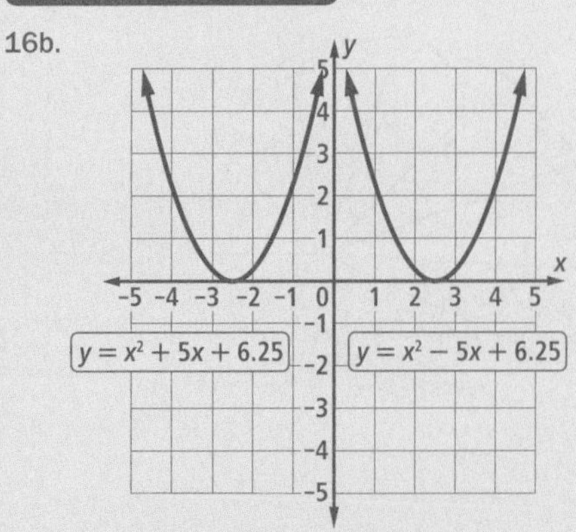

21c.

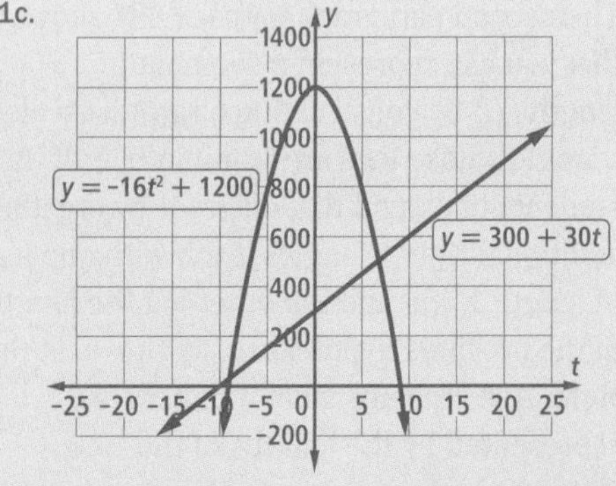

Chapter 6 Projects

1 Sum and Product of Roots

Checking solutions to quadratic equations can be tedious, but there is an easier way to check than by substitution. The method checks the sum and the product of the roots. Look back over some quadratic equations you have solved. Let r_1 and r_2 be the roots of the equation $ax^2 + bx + c = 0$. For each equation, calculate $r_1 + r_2$ and $r_1 \cdot r_1$. What patterns do you notice? Can you prove that your generalizations hold for all quadratics? Use your results to check some of the solutions to quadratic equations in this chapter.

2 Satellite Dishes

Satellite dishes are in the shape of three-dimensional parabolas called *paraboloids*. Find out how satellite dishes work. Why are they in the shape of paraboloids? What determines their dimensions? How are light, sound, or radio waves reflected from the satellite dish? Write a report summarizing your findings.

3 Representing Complex Numbers as Points

The use of the coordinate plane to represent complex numbers is often attributed to Gauss, but the plane defined by one real axis and one imaginary axis is called an *Argand plane* after Jean-Robert Argand (b. 1768). Yet record has it that the Argand plane was first proposed by an amateur mathematician named Caspar Wessel (b. 1745). Research Argand or Wessel and describe their careers and accomplishments.

4 Minimum Distance

Use a DGS.

a. Graph the line $y = 3x$ and plot the dynamic point $(x, 3x)$ on the line.

b. Plot the point (a, b) not on the line in Part a. Construct a line segment from (a, b) to $(x, 3x)$.

c. Calculate the distance from (a, b) to $(x, 3x)$. Call it d. Plot the result as the ordered pair (x, d) for various values of x.

d. Make a conjecture about what an equation describing the graph of all possible ordered pairs (x, d) in Part c might be.

e. When is the distance between $(x, 3x)$ and (a, b) minimized?

Project Rubric

Advanced	Student correctly provides all of the details asked for in the project as well as additional correct independent conclusions.
Proficient	Student correctly provides all of the details asked for in the project.
Partially proficient	Student correctly provides some of the details asked for in the project or provides all details with some inaccuracies.
Not proficient	Student correctly provides few of the details asked for in the project or provides all details with many inaccuracies.
No attempt	Student makes little or no attempt to complete the project.

Chapter 6

The projects relate to the content of the lessons of this chapter as follows:

Project	Lesson(s)
1	6-7, 6-10
2	6-4
3	6-9
4	6-2
5	6-5, 6-6
6	6-10

1 Sum and Product of Roots

Students were asked about parts of this project in the Accommodating the Learner Up and Extension activities of Lesson 6-7. Also, the Accommodating the Learner Up activity in Lesson 6-10 asked students to relate the sum of the roots to the vertex for a parabola. Encourage students to incorporate all of these ideas in their project.

2 Satellite Dishes

Encourage students to describe *how* paraboloids work and *why* they are used. Paraboloids take signals that arrive as parallel rays and focus them to a single point. When signals from a distant transmitter arrive at a satellite dish, those signals approximate parallel rays.

3 Representing Complex Numbers as Points

You might want to ask students to make timelines showing the two mathematicians' accomplishments so they can be easily compared.

4 Minimum Distance

Some students may want to extend this project by showing the steps that lead to the following statements:

a. An equation for the line through (a, b) that is perpendicular to $y_1 = 3x$ is $y_2 = -\frac{1}{3}x + \frac{a + 3b}{3}$.

b. The intersection of y_1 and y_2 is $\left(\frac{a + 3b}{10}, \frac{3a + 9b}{10}\right)$.

c. The distance between (a, b) and $\left(\frac{a + 3b}{10}, \frac{3a + 9b}{10}\right)$ is

$$\sqrt{\left(\frac{9a - 3b}{10}\right)^2 + \left(\frac{-3a + b}{10}\right)^2} = \sqrt{\frac{9a^2 - 6ab + b^2}{10}} = \sqrt{\frac{(3a - b)^2}{10}} = \frac{(3a - b)}{10}\sqrt{10}.$$

5 How High Does Your Parabola Go?

Ask students to compare the height-and-distance relationship for water coming from a hose, fountain, or water cannon with the height-and-distance relationship for a thrown baseball or football. Answers vary. Sample: If you throw a ball, using a constant throwing strength, into the air at various angles, one angle will maximize the distance the ball travels. This is analogous to water coming out of a hose or cannon at different angles.

6 Finding Complex Roots Graphically

After students present this project to the class, you may want to give students another quadratic equation with complex roots and ask them to solve the equation without using the Quadratic Formula.

Sample answers for projects are in the Solution Manual in the Electronic Teacher's Edition.

5 How High Does Your Parabola Go?

You can make a parabolic shape from water flowing out of a hose or fountain. The curvature and maximum height of the parabola affect the distance at which the parabolic path of the water hits the ground. Work with a partner. Use a hose with a strong, consistent flow of water.

a. Make the water flow from the hose in a parabolic path and try to get the water to reach as high in the air as possible while maintaining the parabolic shape. Have your partner take a picture of the "parabolic" water flow and measure height of the hose opening and the horizontal distance from the hose opening to the point the water flow hits the ground.

b. Place a coordinate system on your photo. Make sure to fit the coordinate system so it reflects the height and distance you measured. Estimate some other points on the water's path and use them to determine the equation of your parabola. How high was the water to the nearest inch?

c. Switch roles and try the experiment again.

d. Compare the horizontal distances and heights to which the water traveled. How do these measures seem to be related?

6 Finding Complex Roots Graphically

Real roots of quadratic equations can be found graphically by finding the x-intercepts of the graph of the equation. Complex roots can also be found graphically.

a. Graph $y = 2(x - 2)^2 + 4.5$ and $y = -2(x - 2)^2 + 4.5$ on the same set of axes. How are the graphs of these two equations related?

b. Find the x-intercepts of the graph of $y = -2(x - 2)^2 + 4.5$. These are the solutions to $0 = -2(x - 2)^2 + 4.5$.

c. The solutions you found in Part b can be expressed in $a \pm b$ form, when a is the x-coordinate of the vertex of the graph of the equation. Find the vertex of the parabola and use it to write your answer to Part b in $a \pm b$ form.

d. Solve $0 = 2(x - 2)^2 + 4.5$. Express the solutions in $a \pm bi$ form. How are the solutions related to your answer to Part c?

e. Generalize Parts a–d to explain how you can find complex solutions to quadratic equations graphically.

Notes

Chapter 6 Summary and Vocabulary

- The simplest **quadratic equation** is of the form $x^2 = k$. If $k > 0$, there are two real solutions, $\sqrt{k}$ and $-\sqrt{k}$. When $k < 0$, the solutions are the imaginary numbers $i\sqrt{-k}$ and $-i\sqrt{-k}$, where, by definition, $\sqrt{-1} = i$. Any number of the form $a + bi$, where a and b are real numbers, is a **complex number**. Complex numbers are added, subtracted, and multiplied using the properties that apply to operations with real numbers and polynomials.

- Areas, paths of objects, and relations between the initial velocity of an object and its height over time lead to problems involving quadratic equations and functions. A projectile's height h above the ground on a planet with gravity g at time t after being launched with initial velocity v_0 from an initial height h_0 satisfies

$$h = \frac{1}{2}gt^2 + v_0t + h_0.$$

- When a, b, and c are real numbers and $a \neq 0$, the graph of the general quadratic equation $y = ax^2 + bx + c$ is a parabola. Using a process known as **completing the square,** this equation can be rewritten in **vertex form** $y - k = a(x - h)^2$. This parabola is a translation image of the parabola $y = ax^2$ you studied in Chapter 2. Its vertex is (h, k), its line of symmetry is $x = h$, and it opens up if $a > 0$ and opens down if $a < 0$. If data involving two variables are graphed in a scatterplot that appears to be part of a parabola, you can use three points on the graph to set up a system of equations that will allow you to find a, b, and c in the equation $y = ax^2 + bx + c$.

- The values of x for which $ax^2 + bx + c = 0$ can be found by using the **Quadratic Formula**:

$$x = \frac{-b \pm \sqrt{b^2 - 4ac}}{2a}.$$

- The expression $b^2 - 4ac$ in the formula is the **discriminant** of the quadratic equation, and reveals the nature of its roots.

Vocabulary

6-1
quadratic expression
quadratic equation
quadratic function
standard form of a quadratic
binomial

6-2
absolute value
absolute-value function
square root
rational number
irrational number

6-3
corollary
vertex form
axis of symmetry
minimum, maximum

6-5
completing the square
perfect-square trinomial

6-6
quadratic regression

6-7
Quadratic Formula

6-8
imaginary number
*$\sqrt{k}$
*$\sqrt{-1}$, i
*pure imaginary number

6-9
*complex number
*real part, imaginary part
*equal complex numbers
*complex conjugate

6-10
*discriminant
*root of an equation
*zeros of a function

Chapter 6

Summary and Vocabulary

The Summary gives an overview of the entire chapter and provides an opportunity for students to consider the material as a whole. Thus, the Summary can be used to help students relate and unify the concepts presented in the chapter.

Vocabulary words and symbols are listed by lesson to provide a checklist of concepts that students must know. Emphasize to students that they should read the vocabulary list carefully before starting the Self-Test on page 445. If students do not understand the meaning of a vocabulary word, they should refer back to the indicated lesson.

Theorems and Properties covered in the chapter are listed below the Summary with page references included to lead students back to the location in the chapter where the theorem or property is stated.

Additional Answers

1. $y - 21 = x^2 - 10x$
   $y - 21 + 25 = x^2 - 10x + 25$
   $y + 4 = (x - 5)^2$

3. $0 = x^2 - 10x + 21$
   $x = \frac{10 \pm \sqrt{(-10)^2 - 4(1)(21)}}{2} = \frac{10 \pm 4}{2}$
   $x = \frac{10 + 4}{2} = 7$ or $x = \frac{10 - 4}{2} = 3$
   The x-intercepts are 7 and 3.

4. $5i \cdot i = 5i^2 = -5$

5. $\sqrt{-12} \cdot \sqrt{-3} = i\sqrt{12} \cdot i\sqrt{3} = i^2\sqrt{36} = -6$

6. $\frac{6 + \sqrt{-64}}{3} = \frac{6 + i\sqrt{64}}{3} = \frac{6 + 8i}{3} = 2 + \frac{8}{3}i$

7. $(1 + 5i)(-4 + 3i) =$
   $-4 - 20i + 3i + 15i^2 = -19 - 17i$

8. $6 - 5i - (2 + 5i) =$
   $6 - 5i - 2 - 5i = 4 - 10i$

10. $y - 3 = -(x + 4)^2$ is in vertex form, so the vertex is $(-4, 3)$. Because $a = -1 < 0$, the graph will open down. It is symmetric to the line $x = -4$, and the y-intercept is $-16 + 3 = -13$.

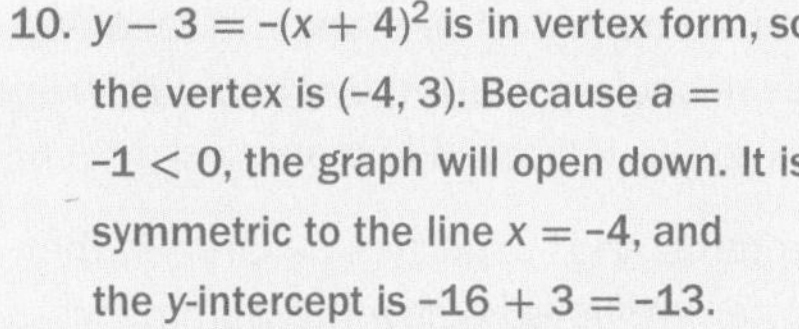

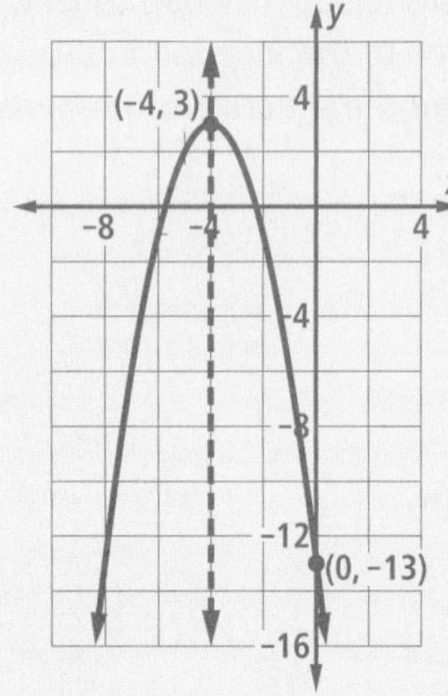

11. From the vertex form of the equation, the vertex is $(-4, 3)$. Since $a < 0$, the parabola opens down. So, the domain is all real numbers and the range is $\{y \mid y \leq 3\}$.

12. $t + 12 = 21$ or $t + 12 = -21$
    $t = 9$ or $t = -33$

13. $\sqrt{(6s + 5)^2} = 9$, so $|6s + 5| = 9$.
    $6s + 5 = 9$ or $6s + 5 = -9$
    $s = \frac{2}{3}$ or $s = -\frac{7}{3}$

- If $b^2 - 4ac > 0$, there are two real solutions, as shown below.

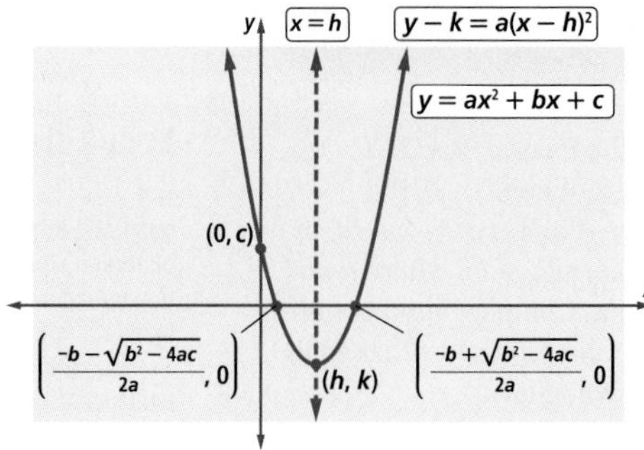

- If $b^2 - 4ac = 0$, there is exactly one solution and the vertex of the parabola is on the x-axis. If a, b, and c are rational numbers and the discriminant is a perfect square, then the solutions are rational numbers.
- If $b^2 - 4ac < 0$, there are no real solutions and the parabola does not intersect the x-axis. The nonreal solutions are **complex conjugates**.

Postulates, Theorems, and Properties

Binomial Square Theorem (p. 376)
Absolute Value-Square Root Theorem (p. 381)
Graph-Translation Theorem (p. 387)
Parabola-Translation Theorem (Graph-Translation Corollary) (p. 388)
Parabola Congruence Theorem (p. 395)
Completing the Square Theorem (p. 402)
Quadratic Formula Theorem (p. 414)
Square Root of a Negative Number Theorem (p. 422)
Properties of Complex Numbers Postulate (p. 428)
Discriminant Theorem (p. 437)

Chapter 6 Self-Test

Take this test as you would take a test in class. You will need a calculator. Then use the Selected Answers section in the back of the book to check your work.

In 1–3, consider the parabola with equation $y = x^2 - 10x + 21$. 1 and 3. See margin.

1. Rewrite the equation in vertex form.
2. What is the vertex of this parabola? (5, -4)
3. What are the x-intercepts of this parabola?

In 4–7, perform the operations and put the answer in $a + bi$ form. 4–7. See margin.

4. $5i \cdot i$
5. $\sqrt{-12} \cdot \sqrt{-3}$
6. $\frac{6 + \sqrt{-64}}{3}$
7. $(1 + 5i)(-4 + 3i)$
8. If $z = 6 - 5i$ and $w = 2 + 5i$, write $z - w$ in $a + bi$ form. See margin.
9. **Multiple Choice** How does the graph of $y - 3 = -(x + 4)^2$ compare to the graph of $y = -x^2$? It is translated: C
   - A 4 units to the right and 3 units down.
   - B 4 units to the right and 3 units up.
   - C 4 units to the left and 3 units up.
   - D 4 units to the left and 3 units down.
10. Graph $y - 3 = -(x + 4)^2$. See margin.
11. If $f(x) = -(x + 4)^2 + 3$, find the domain and range of f. See margin.

In 12–15, solve the equation. Show your work.

12. $|t + 12| = 21$
13. $\sqrt{(6s + 5)^2} = 9$
14. $17 = (y + 18)^2$
15. $3x^2 + 18x = 4x + 5$

12–15. See margin.

16. This statement is false: $\sqrt{x} = |x|$ for all real values of x. Correct it. See margin.
17. Expand: $(2a - 5)^2 + (2a + 5)^2$. $4a^2 - 20a + 25 + 4a^2 + 20a + 25 = 8a^2 + 50$
18. The discriminant of an equation $ax^2 + bx + c = 0$ is negative. What does this indicate about the solutions of the equation? The solutions are not real.
19. Consider the graph of $y = ax^2 + bx + c$. How many x-intercepts does the graph have if its discriminant is
   a. -2? 0 b. 0? 1 c. 17? 2

In 20 and 21, suppose the height h in feet of a ball at time t seconds is given by $h = -16t^2 + 28t + 6$. 20–21. See margin.

20. How high is the ball after 1.5 seconds?
21. When does the ball hit the ground?
22. A 12-foot by 16-foot rectangular garden has an x-foot wide walkway that surrounds it on all sides. Write an expression for the area of the walkway. See margin.
23. **Multiple Choice** The graph of each equation is a parabola. Which parabola is not congruent to the others? See margin.
   - A $y = (x + 4)^2$
   - B $y = 4x^2$
   - C $y + 4 = x^2$
   - D $y + 2 = x^2$
24. If circles are drawn so that every circle intersects every other circle, there is a pattern to the maximum number of intersection points. 24a. See margin.
   a. Draw a scatterplot of these data.
   b. Fit a quadratic model to these data.
   c. Predict in how many points 17 circles will intersect if every circle intersects every other circle. $f(17) = 17^2 - 17 = 272$ points

   24b. See margin.

Number of Circles n	Maximum Number of Intersections $f(n)$
1	0
2	2
3	6
4	12
5	20

Additional Answers

21. $0 = -16t^2 + 28t + 6$

$t = \frac{-28 \pm \sqrt{784 - 4 \cdot (-16) \cdot 6}}{-32}$

$t = \frac{-28 \pm \sqrt{1168}}{-32}$

$t \approx -0.193$ or $t \approx 1.943$

In this situation, only $t = 1.943$ sec makes sense. So the ball hit the ground after about 1.9 sec.

22. $(16 + 2x)(12 + 2x) - 16 \cdot 12 =$ $192 + 56x + 4x^2 - 192 = 4x^2 + 56x$

23. B; the coefficient of x^2 in B is 4, but the coefficient of x^2 in A, C, and D is 1, so B has a narrower graph.

24a.

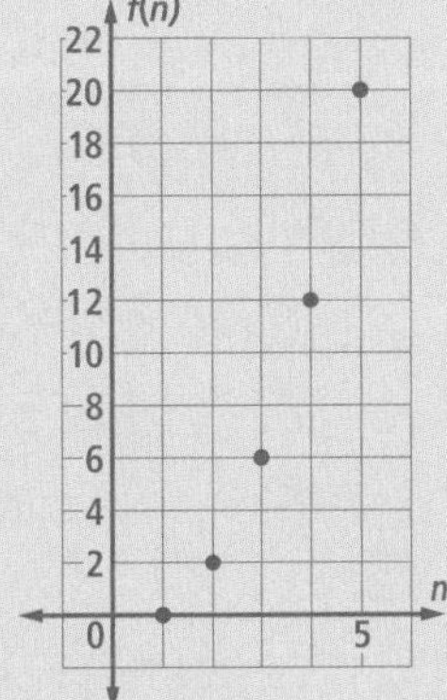

24b. $f(n) = n^2 - n$

Self-Test

For the development of mathematical competence, feedback and correction, along with the opportunity for practice, are necessary. The Self-Test provides the opportunity for feedback and correction; the Chapter Review provides additional opportunities for practice. We cannot overemphasize the importance of these end-of-chapter materials. It is at this point that the material gels for many students, allowing them to solidify skills and understanding. In general, student performance should improve after these pages.

Assign the Self-Test as a one-night assignment. Worked-out solutions for all questions are in the Selected Answers section of the student book. Encourage students to take the Self-Test honestly, grade themselves, and then be prepared to discuss the test in class.

Advise students to pay special attention to those Chapter Review questions (pages 446–449) that correspond to the questions they missed on the Self-Test.

Additional Answers

14. $17 = y^2 + 36y + 324$

$0 = y^2 + 36y + 307$

$y = \frac{-36 \pm \sqrt{1296 - 4 \cdot 1 \cdot 307}}{2}$

$y = \frac{-36 \pm \sqrt{68}}{2}$

$y = -18 \pm \sqrt{17}$

15. $3x^2 + 14x - 5 = 0$

$x = \frac{-14 \pm \sqrt{196 - 4 \cdot 3 \cdot (-5)}}{6}$

$x = \frac{-14 \pm \sqrt{196 + 60}}{6}$

$x = \frac{-14 \pm 16}{6}$

$x = \frac{1}{3}$ or $x = \frac{-10}{3}$

16. By the Absolute Value-Square Root Theorem, $\sqrt{x^2} = |x|$ for all real values of x.

20. $h = -16(1.5)^2 + 28(1.5) + 6$

$h = -36 + 42 + 6$

$h = 12$ ft

Chapter Review

The main objectives for the chapter are organized in the Chapter Review under the four types of understanding this book promotes: Skills, Properties, Uses, and Representations.

Whereas end-of-chapter material may be considered optional in some texts, in UCSMP *Advanced Algebra* we have selected these objectives and questions with the expectation that they will be covered. Students should be able to answer these questions with about 85% accuracy after studying the chapter.

You may assign these questions over a single night to help students prepare for a test the next day or you may assign the questions over a two-day period. If you work the questions over two days, we recommend assigning the evens for homework the first night so that students get feedback in class the next day, and then assigning the odds the night before the test because the answers are provided to the odd-numbered questions in the Selected Answers section at the back of the book.

It is effective to ask students which questions they still do not understand and use the day as a total class discussion of the material that the class finds most difficult.

Resources

- Assessment Resources:
  Chapter 6 Test Forms A–D;
  Chapter 6 Test, Cumulative Form;
  Comprehensive Test, Chapters 1–6

Technology Resources

Teacher's Assessment Assistant, Ch. 6
Electronic Teacher's Edition, Ch. 6

Chapter 6 Chapter Review

SKILLS
PROPERTIES
USES
REPRESENTATIONS

SKILLS Procedures used to get answers

OBJECTIVE A Expand products and squares of binomials. (Lesson 6-1)

In 1–8, expand.

1. $(7p + 2)(p - 3)$ $7p^2 - 19p - 6$
2. $(r + 2q)(r - q)$ $r^2 + rq - 2q^2$
3. $6(3w - 2)(2w + 1)$ $36w^2 - 6w - 12$
4. $(3x + \sqrt{2})(3x - \sqrt{2})$ $9x^2 - 2$
5. $(a + b)^2$ $a^2 + 2ab + b^2$
6. $(2x + 1)^2$ $4x^2 + 4x + 1$
7. $13(y - 3)^2$ $13y^2 - 78y + 117$
8. $7(s + t)^2 - 3(s - t)^2$ $4s^2 + 20st + 4t^2$

OBJECTIVE B Convert quadratic equations from vertex to standard form, and vice versa. (Lessons 6-4, 6-5)

In 9 and 10, rewrite in standard form.

9. $y = 5(x + 1)^2$ $y = 5x^2 + 10x + 5$
10. $y + 3 = 0.25(x - 4)^2$ $y = 0.25x^2 - 2x + 1$

In 11 and 12, write each equation in vertex form.

11. $y = x^2 + 9x - 5$ $y + \frac{101}{4} = \left(x + \frac{9}{2}\right)^2$
12. $3y = 7x^2 - 6x + 5$ $y - \frac{26}{21} = \frac{7}{3}\left(x - \frac{3}{7}\right)^2$
13. **Multiple Choice** Which equation is equivalent to $y - 1 = 2(x - 1)^2$? C
    - A $y = 2x^2 + 4x - 3$
    - B $y = 2x^2 + 4x + 3$
    - C $y = 2x^2 - 4x + 3$
    - D $y = 2x^2 - 4x - 3$

OBJECTIVE C Solve quadratic equations. (Lessons 6-2, 6-7, 6-8, 6-10)

In 14–22, solve.

14. $(x - 3)^2 = 0$ $x = 3$
15. $r^2 - 26 = 0$ $r = \pm\sqrt{26}$
16. $d^2 = -24$ $d = \pm 2i\sqrt{6}$
17. $-25 = y^2$ $y = \pm 5i$
18. $2x^2 + x - 1 = 0$ $x = \frac{1}{2}$ or $x = -1$
19. $3 - s^2 - 5s = 6$ $s = \frac{-5 \pm \sqrt{13}}{2}$
20. $z^2 + 2z - 8 = 7$ $z = -5$ or $z = 3$
21. $k^2 = 6k - 9$ $k = 3$
22. $2x(x - 2) = -1 + x^2 - 2x$ $x = 1$

OBJECTIVE D Solve absolute-value equations. (Lesson 6-2)

In 23–28, solve.

23. $|11 - y| = 15$ $y = -4$ or $y = 26$
24. $|s + 3| = 5$ $s = 2$ or $s = -8$
25. $-\sqrt{(3x + 2)^2} = -5$ $x = 1$ or $x = -\frac{7}{3}$
26. $\sqrt{(x - 2)^2} = 3$ $x = 5$ or $x = -1$
27. $|4t - 20| = 0$ $t = 5$
28. $|96 - A| = -4$ no solution

OBJECTIVE E Perform operations with complex numbers. (Lesson 6-8, 6-9)

In 29–34, simplify.

29. $-i^2$ 1
30. $\sqrt{-49}$ $7i$
31. $\sqrt{-9} \cdot \sqrt{-25}$ -15
32. $\sqrt{-7} \cdot \sqrt{7}$ $7i$
33. $2i \cdot 3i$ -6
34. $3\sqrt{-4} + \sqrt{-9}$ $9i$

In 35 and 36, write the conjugate.

35. $8 - 3i$ $8 + 3i$
36. $-7i$ $7i$

In 37–42, suppose $r = 7 - i$ and $s = 3i + 2$. Evaluate and simplify.

37. rs $17 + 19i$

38. s^2 $-5 + 12i$

39. $2r - s$ $12 - 5i$

40. $ir + 3s - i$ $7 + 15i$

41. $\frac{r}{s}$ $\frac{11 - 23i}{13}$

42. $\frac{is}{r}$ $\frac{-23 + 11i}{50}$

PROPERTIES Principles behind the mathematics

OBJECTIVE F Apply the definition of absolute value and the Absolute Value-Square Root Theorem. (Lesson 6-2)

43. For which real numbers x is $|x| - x > 0$? $x < 0$

44. For which real numbers x is $|x| = -\pi$? none

In 45–47, use the Absolute Value-Square Root Theorem to simplify.

45. $\sqrt{(11 + 5)^2}$ 16

46. $-\sqrt{t^2}$ $-|t|$

47. $-\sqrt{(-3)^2} + \sqrt{5^2}$ 2

OBJECTIVE G Use the Graph-Translation Theorem to interpret equations and graphs. (Lessons 6-3, 6-4)

48. The preimage graph of $y = x^2$ is translated 50 units to the right and 300 units up. What is an equation for its image? $y - 300 = (x - 50)^2$

49. Describe how the graphs of $y = |x|$ and $y = |x + 2|$ are related.

50. **Multiple Choice** Which of the following is not true for the graph of the equation $y - 3 = -\frac{1}{2}(x + 1)^2$? D

A The vertex is (-1, 3).

B The maximum point is (-1, 3).

C The equation of the axis of symmetry is $x = -1$.

D The graph opens up.

49. The graph of $y = |x + 2|$ is the image of the graph of $y = |x|$ under $T_{-2,0}$

51b. $y - 0.6 = \frac{3}{4}(x - 0.9)^2$

51. Assume parabola A is congruent to parabola B in the graph below.

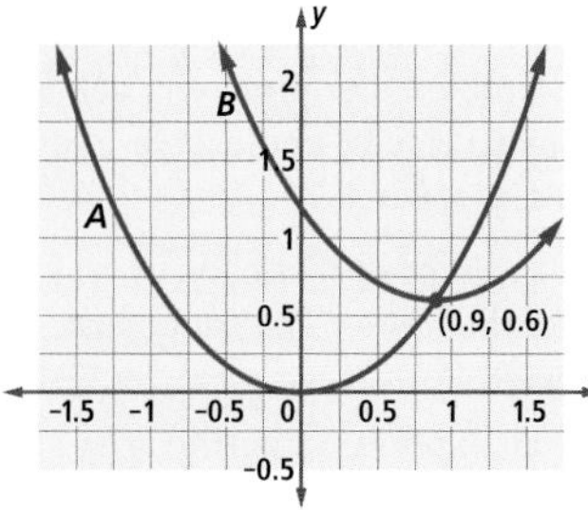

a. What translation maps parabola A onto parabola B? $T_{0.9, 0.6}$

b. What is an equation for parabola B if parabola A has equation $y = \frac{3}{4}x^2$?

52. Compare the solutions to $4 = (x - 1)^2$ with the solutions to $x^2 = 4$.

53. Compare the solutions to $(k + 2)^2 = 25$ with the solutions to $k^2 = 25$.

54. The graph of $y = (5x + 3)^2$ is congruent to the graph of $y = ax^2$. What is a? $a = 25$

OBJECTIVE H Use the discriminant of a quadratic equation to determine the nature of the solutions to the equation. (Lesson 6-10)

In 55–57, an equation is given.

a. Evaluate its discriminant.

b. Give the number of real solutions.

c. Tell whether the solutions are rational, irrational, or nonreal. 55–57. See margin.

55. $6x^2 + 9x + 1 = 0$

56. $z^2 = 81z + 81$

57. $5 + k = k^2 + 9$

52. The solutions to $4 = (x - 1)^2$ are the solutions to $x^2 = 4$ under a horizontal shift to one unit to the right.

53. The solutions to $(k + 2)^2 = 25$ are the solutions to $k^2 = 25$ under a horizontal shift of two units to the left.

Additional Answers

55a. 57

55b. 2

55c. irrational

56a. 6885

56b. 2

56c. irrational

57a. 15

57b. 0

57c. nonreal

USES Applications of mathematics in real-world situations

OBJECTIVE I Use quadratic equations to solve area problems or problems dealing with distance, velocity, and acceleration. (Lessons 6-1, 6-4, 6-5, 6-7)

58. A framed mirror is 28 inches by 34 inches, including the frame. The frame is w inches wide. a. $4w^2 - 124w + 952$
    a. Write an expression for the area of the mirror without the frame.
    b. If the area of the mirror is 85% of the total area, how wide is the frame? about 1.2 in.

In 59 and 60, use the equation, $h = -16t^2 + v_0t + h_0$ for the height h in feet of an object after t seconds. Ignore wind resistance.

59. A ball is thrown directly upward from an initial height of 5 feet at an initial velocity of 37 feet per second.
    a. Estimate to the nearest hundredth the highest point reached by the ball. 26.39 ft
    b. To the nearest hundredth of a second, when does the ball reach its highest point? after 1.16 sec
    c. How far from the ground will the ball be after 2 seconds? 15 ft

60. A ball is dropped from the top of a building that is 1000 feet tall. To the nearest tenth of a second, how long after it is dropped will the ball reach the ground? 7.9 sec

61a. Answers vary. Sample: $y \approx x^2 + 23.2x + 11.7$
61b. about 121 frogs
61c. The model does not take into account the initial number of frogs released. If the model's prediction of the twentieth ring were correct, there would be more than 1000 frogs found.
63a. $y = 76.68x^2 + 2254x + 314{,}255$, where y is the population x years after 1980.

REPRESENTATIONS Pictures, graphs, or objects that illustrate concepts

OBJECTIVE J Fit a quadratic model to data. (Lesson 6-6)

61. A researcher marked four evenly-spaced concentric circles on a field. She then released 1000 frogs and returned an hour later to count how many frogs were in each circle. She found 200 frogs: 11 frogs in the inner circle, 38 frogs in the first ring, 60 frogs in the second ring, and 91 frogs in the third ring. The researcher then created another evenly spaced concentric circle and repeated the experiment.
    a. Fit a model to the data that can predict the number of frogs in the fourth ring.
    b. How many frogs should the researcher expect to find in the fourth ring?
    c. Why will the model overestimate the number of frogs in the 20th concentric circle?

62. Consider the sequence {1, 5, 12, 22, 35,...}, where differences between consecutive terms increase by 3.
    a. Use quadratic regression to write an explicit formula for the terms of this sequence. $y = 1.5x^2 - 0.5x$
    b. Find the 23rd term in this sequence. 782

63. In 1980, Omaha, Nebraska, had a population of 314,255. By 1990, the population had increased to 344,463. The population continued to increase and reached 390,007 by 2000.
    a. Write a quadratic equation that models Omaha's population growth starting in 1980.
    b. Use your equation to predict Omaha's population in 2010. 450,887
    c. Based on your model, in which year will Omaha's population first exceed 1 million? 2061

OBJECTIVE K Graph quadratic functions and absolute-value functions and interpret them. (Lessons 6-2, 6-3, 6-4, 6-10)

In 64–67, sketch a graph of the function, and label the vertex and x-intercepts with their coordinates.

64. $y = 3x^2 + 18x$ 64–66. See margin.

65. $y - 6 = -\frac{1}{3}(x + 3)^2$

66. $y - 7 = |x - 2|$

67. $y + 1 = 2x^2$

68. The height of a ball thrown upward at time t is shown on the graph below.

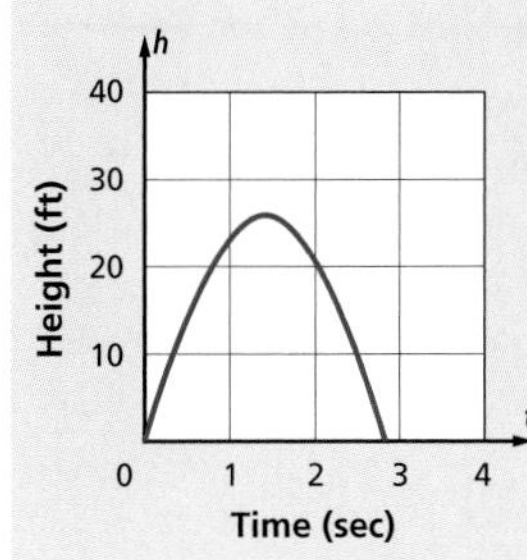

a. About when did the ball get to its maximum height? after about 1.5 sec

b. About how high did the ball get?

c. About when was the ball 10 feet high? after about 0.3 sec and 2.6 sec

67.

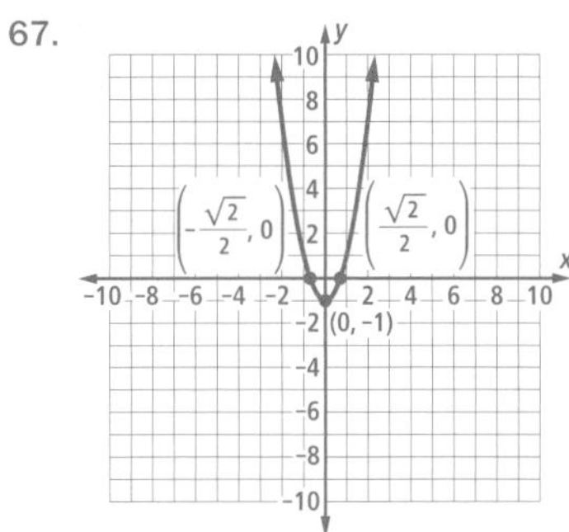

68b. about 25 ft

In 69 and 70, refer to the parabolas shown below.

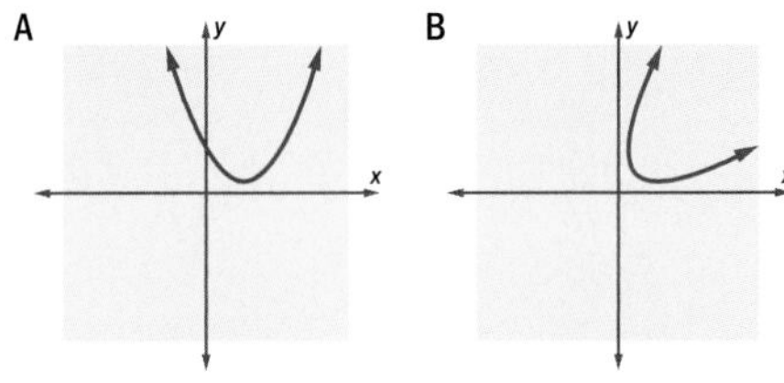

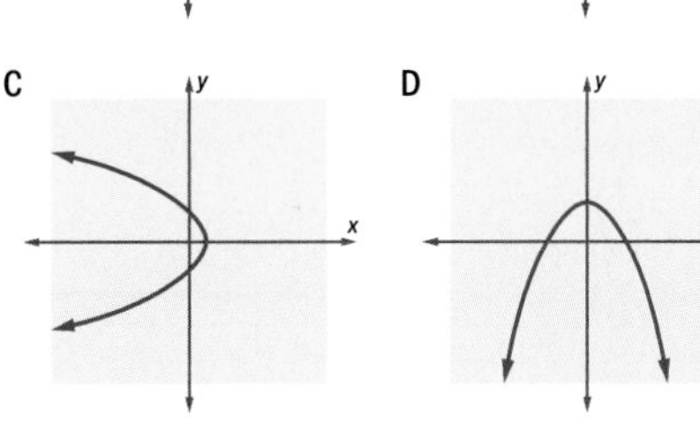

69. Which graph is of the form $y - k = a(x - h)^2$ with h positive? A

70. Which graph is of the form $y - k = a(x - h)^2$ with a negative? D

OBJECTIVE L Use the discriminant of a quadratic equation to determine the number of x-intercepts of a graph of the associated quadratic function. (Lesson 6-10)

In 71 and 72, give the number of x-intercepts of the graph of the parabola.

71. $y = 7x^2 + 5x - 13$ 2

72. $y = \frac{1}{7}(x + 3)^2 - 6$ 2

73. Does the parabola $y = 3x^2 - 9x$ ever intersect the line $y = -1$? Explain your reasoning.

74. How many x-intercepts does the graph of $y = -\frac{1}{5}(x - t)^2$ have when $t \neq 0$? one

73. Yes; the vertex of the parabola is $\left(\frac{3}{2}, -\frac{27}{4}\right)$, which is below the line $y = -1$. The parabola opens up, so the parabola intersects the horizontal line $y = -1$.

Assessment

Evaluation The *Assessment Resources* provide four forms of the Chapter 6 Test. Forms A and B present parallel versions of a short-answer format. Form C consists of four to six short-response questions that cover the SPUR objectives from Chapter 6. Form D offers performance assessment that covers a subset (or even just one) of the SPUR objectives for the chapter. The fifth type of test is a Chapter 6 Test, Cumulative Form. About 50% of this test covers Chapter 6, and the remaining 50% covers the previous chapters evenly.

Feedback After students have taken the test for Chapter 6 and you have scored the results, return the tests to students for discussion. Class discussion on the questions that caused trouble for most students can be very effective in identifying and clarifying misunderstandings. You might want to have them note the items they missed and work either in groups or at home to correct them. It is important for students to receive feedback on every chapter test, and we recommend that students see and correct their mistakes before proceeding too far into the next chapter.

Suggestions for Assignment Assign Lesson 7-1 for homework the evening of the test. It gives students work to do after they have completed the test and keeps the class moving. If you do not do this, you may cover one less chapter over the course of the year.

Additional Answers

65.

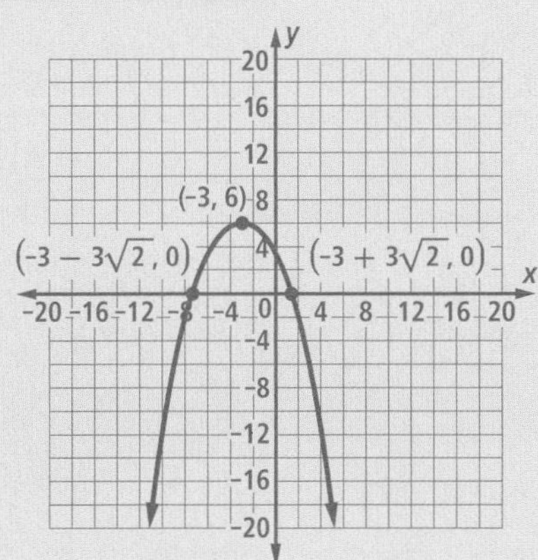

66.

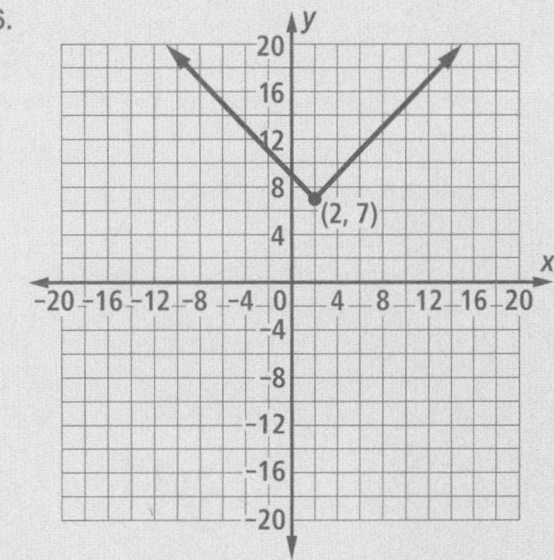

Additional Answers

64.

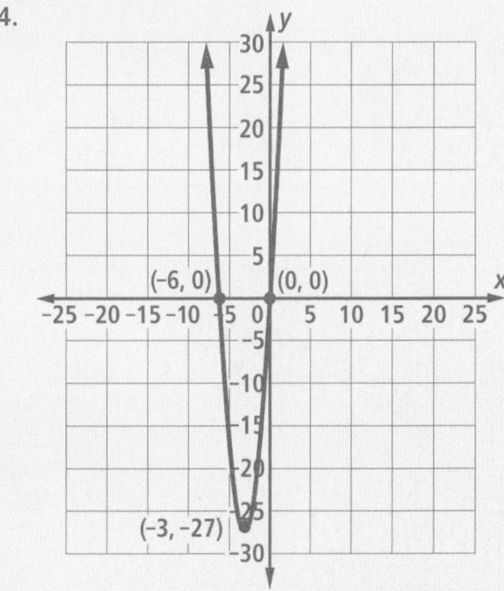

Properties

Algebra Properties from Earlier Courses

Selected Properties of Real Numbers

For any real numbers a, b, and c:

Postulates of Addition and Multiplication (Field Properties)

	Addition	*Multiplication*
Closure property	$a + b$ is a real number.	ab is a real number.
Commutative property	$a + b = b + a$	$ab = ba$
Associative property	$(a + b) + c = a + (b + c)$	$(ab)c = a(bc)$
Identity property	There is a real number 0 with $0 + a = a + 0 = a$.	There is a real number 1 with $1 \cdot a = a \cdot 1 = a$.
Inverse property	There is a real number $-a$ with $a + -a = -a + a = 0$.	If $a \neq 0$, there is a real number $\frac{1}{a}$ with $a \cdot \frac{1}{a} = \frac{1}{a} \cdot a = 1$.
Distributive property	$a(b + c) = ab + ac$	

Postulates of Equality

Reflexive property	$a = a$
Symmetric property	If $a = b$, then $b = a$.
Transitive property	If $a = b$ and $b = c$, then $a = c$.
Substitution property	If $a = b$, then a may be substituted for b in any arithmetic or algebraic expression.
Addition property	If $a = b$, then $a + c = b + c$.
Multiplication property	If $a = b$, then $ac = bc$.

Postulates of Inequality

Trichotomy property	Either $a < b$, $a = b$, or $a > b$.
Transitive property	If $a < b$ and $b < c$, then $a < c$.
Addition property	If $a < b$, then $a + c < b + c$.
Multiplication property	If $a < b$ and $c > 0$, then $ac < bc$. If $a < b$ and $c < 0$, then $ac > bc$.

Postulates of Powers

For any nonzero bases a and b and integer exponents m and n:

Product of Powers property	$b^m \cdot b^n = b^{m+n}$
Power of a Power property	$(b^m)^n = b^{mn}$
Power of a Product property	$(ab)^m = a^m b^m$
Quotient of Powers property	$\frac{b^m}{b^n} = b^{m-n}$
Power of a Quotient property	$\left(\frac{a}{b}\right)^m = \frac{a^m}{b^m}$

Selected Theorems of Graphing

The set of points (x, y) satisfying $Ax + By = C$, where A and B are not both 0, is a line.

The line with equation $y = mx + b$ has slope m and y-intercept b.

Two nonvertical lines are parallel if and only if they have the same slope.

Two nonvertical lines are perpendicular if and only if the product of their slopes is -1.

The set of points (x, y) satisfying $y = ax^2 + bx + c$ is a parabola.

Selected Theorems of Algebra

For any real numbers a, b, c, and d (with denominators of fractions not equal to 0):

Multiplication Property of Zero	$0 \cdot a = 0$
Multiplication Property of -1	$-1 \cdot a = -a$
Opposite of an Opposite Property	$-(-a) = a$
Opposite of a Sum	$-(b + c) = -b + -c$
Distributive Property of Multiplication over Subtraction	$a(b - c) = ab - ac$
Addition of Like Terms	$ac + bc = (a + b)c$
Addition of Fractions	$\frac{a}{c} + \frac{b}{c} = \frac{a+b}{c}$
Multiplication of Fractions	$\frac{a}{b} \cdot \frac{c}{d} = \frac{ac}{bd}$
Equal Fractions	$\frac{ac}{bc} = \frac{a}{b}$
Means-Extremes	If $\frac{a}{b} = \frac{c}{d}$, then $ad = bc$.
Binomial Square	$(a + b)^2 = a^2 + 2ab + b^2$
Extended Distributive Property	To multiply two polynomials, multiply each term in the first polynomial by each term in the second, and then add the products.
Zero Exponent	If $b \neq 0$, then $b^0 = 1$.
Negative Exponent	If $b \neq 0$, then $b^{-n} = \frac{1}{b^n}$.
Zero Product	$ab = 0$ if and only if $a = 0$ or $b = 0$.
Absolute Value-Square Root	$\sqrt{a^2} = \|a\|$
Product of Square Roots	If $a \geq 0$ and $b \geq 0$, then $\sqrt{ab} = \sqrt{a} \cdot \sqrt{b}$.
Quadratic Formula	If $ax^2 + bx + c = 0$ and $a \neq 0$, then $x = \frac{-b \pm \sqrt{b^2 - 4ac}}{2a}$.

Geometry Properties from Earlier Courses

In this book, the following symbols are used:

Symbol	Meaning
a, b, c	sides
A	area
B	area of base
b_1, b_2	bases
C	circumference
d	diameter
d_1, d_2	diagonals
h	height
ℓ	length
ℓ	slant height (in conics)
L.A.	lateral area
n	number of sides
p	perimeter
r	radius
s	side
S.A.	surface area
V	volume
w	width

Two-Dimensional Figures

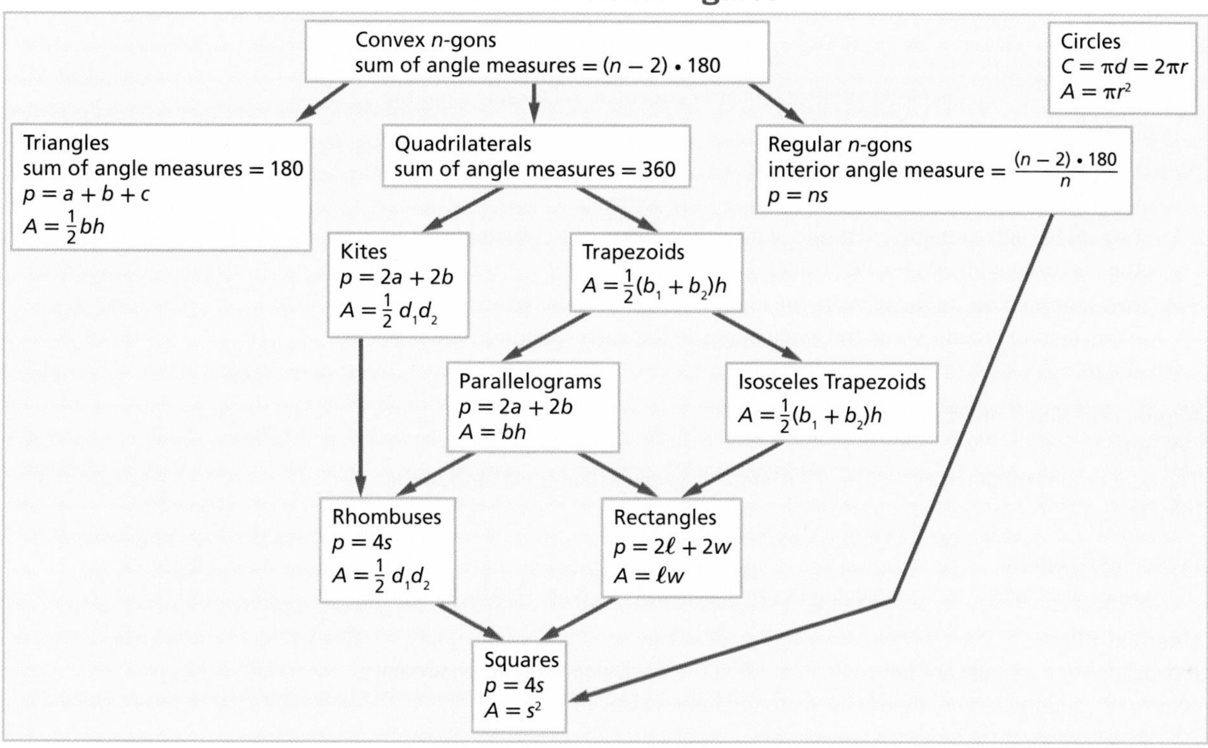

Three-Dimensional Figures

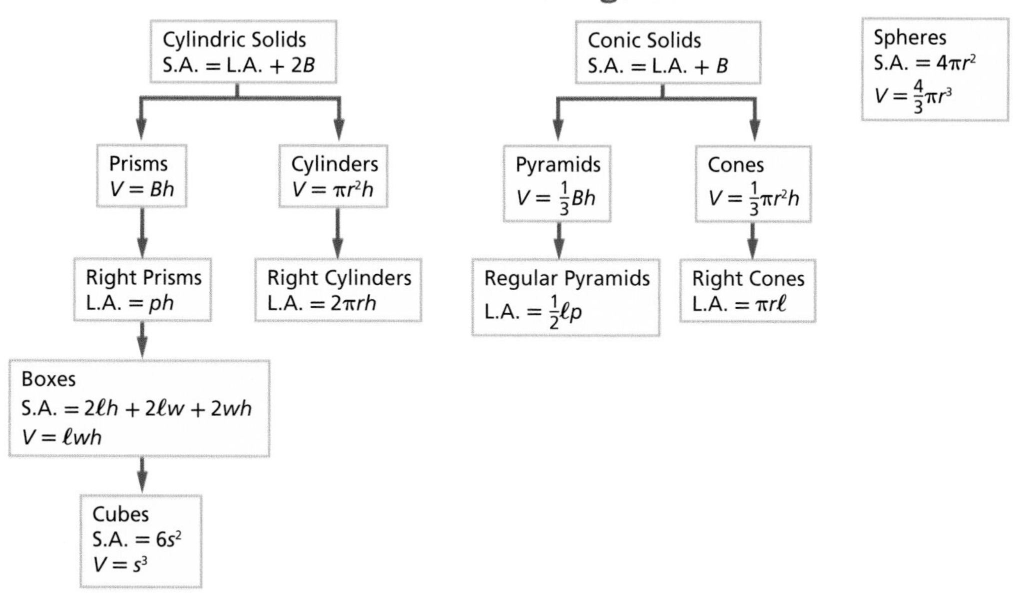

Selected Theorems of Geometry

Parallel Lines

Two lines are parallel if and only if:

1. corresponding angles have the same measure.
2. alternate interior angles are congruent.
3. alternate exterior angles are congruent.
4. they are perpendicular to the same line.

Triangle Congruence

Two triangles are congruent if:

SSS three sides of one are congruent to three sides of the other.

SAS two sides and the included angle of one are congruent to two sides and the included angle of the other.

ASA two angles and the included side of one are congruent to two angles and the included side of the other.

AAS two angles and a nonincluded side of one are congruent to two angles and the corresponding nonincluded side of the other.

SsA two sides and the angle opposite the longer of the two sides of one are congruent to two sides and the angle opposite the corresponding side of the other.

Angles and Sides of Triangles

Triangle Inequality

The sum of the lengths of two sides of a triangle is greater than the length of the third side.

Isosceles Triangle

If two sides of a triangle are congruent, the angles opposite those sides are congruent.

Unequal Sides

If two sides of a triangle are not congruent, then the angles opposite them are not congruent, and the larger angle is opposite the longer side.

Unequal Angles

If two angles of a triangle are not congruent, then the sides opposite them are not congruent, and the longer side is opposite the larger angle.

Pythagorean Theorem

In any right triangle with legs a and b and hypotenuse c, $a^2 + b^2 = c^2$.

30-60-90 Triangle

In a 30-60-90 triangle, the sides are in the extended ratio $x : x\sqrt{3} : 2x$.

45-45-90 Triangle

In a 45-45-90 triangle, the sides are in the extended ratio $x : x : x\sqrt{2}$.

Parallelograms

A quadrilateral is a parallelogram if and only if:

1. one pair of sides is both parallel and congruent.
2. both pairs of opposite sides are congruent.
3. both pairs of opposite angles are congruent.
4. its diagonals bisect each other.

Quadrilateral Hierarchy

If a figure is of any type in the hierarchy pictured at the right, it is also of all types above it to which it is connected.

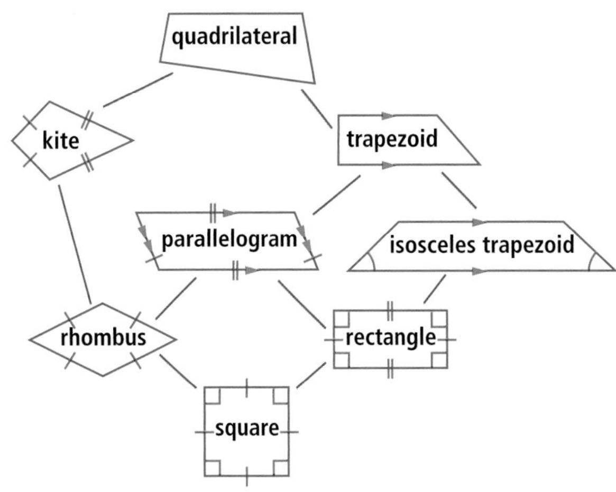

Properties of Transformations

A-B-C-D

Every isometry preserves angle measure, betweenness, collinearity, and distance.

Two-Reflection for Translations

If $m \parallel n$, the translation $r_n \circ r_m$ has magnitude two times the distance between m and n in the direction from m perpendicular to n.

Two-Reflection for Rotations

If m intersects ℓ, the rotation $r_m \circ r_\ell$ has a center at the point of intersection of m and ℓ, and has a magnitude twice the measure of an angle formed by these lines, in the direction from ℓ to m.

Isometry

Every isometry is a transformation that is a reflection or a composite of reflections.

Size-Change

Every size change with magnitude k preserves angle measure, betweenness, and collinearity; a line is parallel to its image; distance is multiplied by k.

Fundamental Theorem of Similarity

If two figures are similar with ratio of similitude k, then:

1. corresponding angle measure are equal.
2. corresponding lengths and perimeters are in the ratio k.
3. corresponding areas and surface areas are in the ratio k^2.
4. corresponding volumes are in the ratio k^3.

Triangle Similarity

Two triangles are similar if:

1. three sides of one are proportional to three sides of the other (SSS).
2. the ratios of two pairs of corresponding sides are equal and the included angles are congruent (SAS).
3. two angles of one are congruent to two angles of the other (AA).

Coordinate Plane Formulas

For all $A = (x_1, y_1)$ and $B = (x_2, y_2)$:

Distance formula	$AB = \sqrt{(x_2 - x_1)^2 + (y_2 - y_1)^2}$
Midpoint formula	The midpoint of $\overline{AB}$ is $\left(\frac{x_1 + x_2}{2}, \frac{y_1 + y_2}{2}\right)$.

For all points (x, y):

reflection over the x-axis	$(x, y) \rightarrow (x, -y)$
reflection over the y-axis	$(x, y) \rightarrow (-x, y)$
reflection over $y = x$	$(x, y) \rightarrow (y, x)$
size change of magnitude k, center $(0, 0)$	$(x, y) \rightarrow (kx, ky)$
translation h units horizontally, k units verically	$(x, y) \rightarrow (x + h, y + k)$

Theorems

Advanced Algebra Theorems

Chapter 1

Rules for Order of Operations *(Lesson 1-1, p. 8)*

1. Perform operations within parentheses or other grouping symbols from the innermost group out.
2. Within grouping symbols or if there are no grouping symbols:
   a. Take powers from left to right.
   b. Multiply and divide in order from left to right.
   c. Add and subtract in order from left to right.

Distributive Property *(Lesson 1-6, p. 41)*
For all real numbers a, b, and c, $c(a + b) = ca + cb$.

Opposite of a Sum Theorem *(Lesson 1-6, p. 44)*
For all real numbers a and b, $-(a + b) = -a + -b = -a - b$.

Chapter 2

The Fundamental Theorem of Variation
(Lesson 2-3, p. 88)

1. If $y = kx^n$, that is, y varies *directly* as x^n, and x is multiplied by c, then y is multiplied by c^n.
2. If $y = \frac{k}{x^n}$, that is, y varies *inversely* as x^n, and x is multiplied by a nonzero constant c, then y is divided by c^n.

Slope of $y = kx$ Theorem *(Lesson 2-4, p. 95)*
The graph of the direct-variation function with equation $y = kx$ has constant slope k.

Converse of the Fundamental Theorem of Variation *(Lesson 2-8, p. 122)*

a. If multiplying every x-value of a function by c results in multiplying the corresponding y-values by c^n, then y varies directly as the nth power of x, that is, $y = kx^n$.
b. If multiplying every x-value of a function by c results in dividing the corresponding y-values by c^n, then y varies inversely as the nth power of x, that is, $y = \frac{k}{x^n}$.

Chapter 3

Parallel Lines and Slope Theorem
(Lesson 3-1, p. 154)
Two non-vertical lines are parallel if and only if they have the same slope.

Standard Form of an Equation of a Line Theorem *(Lesson 3-3, p. 163)*
The graph of $Ax + By = C$, where A and B are not both zero, is a line.

Point-Slope Theorem *(Lesson 3-4, p. 170)*
If a line contains the point (x_1, y_1) and has slope m, then it has the equation $y - y_1 = m(x - x_1)$.

***n*th Term of an Arithmetic Sequence Theorem** *(Lesson 3-8, p. 197)*
The nth term a_n of an arithmetic (linear) sequence with first term a_1 and constant difference d is given by the explicit formula $a_n = a_1 + (n - 1)d$.

Constant-Difference Sequence Theorem
(Lesson 3-8, p. 198)
The sequence defined by the recursive formula

$$\begin{cases} a_1 \\ a_n = a_{n-1} + d, \text{ for integers } n \geq 2 \end{cases}$$

is the arithmetic sequence with first term a_1 and constant difference d.

Chapter 4

Size Change Theorem *(Lesson 4-4, p. 244)*
$\begin{bmatrix} k & 0 \\ 0 & k \end{bmatrix}$ is the matrix for S_k.

Pythagorean Distance Formula *(Lesson 4-4, p. 245)*
If $A = (x_1, y_1)$ and $B = (x_2, y_2)$, then
$AB = \sqrt{|x_2 - x_1|^2 + |y_2 - y_1|^2}$.

Scale Change Theorem *(Lesson 4-5, p. 251)*
$\begin{bmatrix} a & 0 \\ 0 & b \end{bmatrix}$ is a matrix for $S_{a,b}$.

Matrix for r_y Theorem *(Lesson 4-6, p. 256)*
$\begin{bmatrix} -1 & 0 \\ 0 & 1 \end{bmatrix}$ is the matrix for r_y.

Matrix Basis Theorem *(Lesson 4-6, p. 257)*
Suppose A is a transformation represented by a 2×2 matrix. If $A : (1, 0) \rightarrow (x_1, y_1)$ and $A : (0, 1) \rightarrow (x_2, y_2)$, then A has the matrix $\begin{bmatrix} x_1 & x_2 \\ y_1 & y_2 \end{bmatrix}$.

Matrices for r_x, $r_{y=x}$, and $r_{y=-x}$ Theorem *(Lesson 4-6, p. 259)*

1. $\begin{bmatrix} 1 & 0 \\ 0 & -1 \end{bmatrix}$ is the matrix for r_x.
2. $\begin{bmatrix} 0 & 1 \\ 1 & 0 \end{bmatrix}$ is the matrix for $r_{y=x}$.
3. $\begin{bmatrix} 0 & -1 \\ -1 & 0 \end{bmatrix}$ is the matrix for $r_{y=-x}$.

Matrices and Composites Theorem *(Lesson 4-7, p. 265)*
If $M1$ is the matrix for transformation T_1, and $M2$ is the matrix for transformation T_2, then $M2M1$ is the matrix for $T_2 \circ T_1$.

Composite of Rotations Theorem *(Lesson 4-8, p. 270)*
A rotation of $b°$ following a rotation of $a°$ with the same center results in a rotation of $(a + b)°$. In symbols, $R_b \circ R_a = R_{a+b}$.

Matrix for R_{90} Theorem *(Lesson 4-8, p. 270)*
$\begin{bmatrix} 0 & -1 \\ 1 & 0 \end{bmatrix}$ is the matrix for R_{90}.

Perpendicular Lines and Slopes Theorem *(Lesson 4-9, p. 276)*
Two lines with slopes m_1 and m_2 are perpendicular if and only if $m_1m_2 = -1$.

Parallel Lines and Translations Theorem *(Lesson 4-10, p. 282)*
Under a translation, a preimage line is parallel to its image.

Chapter 5

Addition Property of Inequality *(Lesson 5-1, p. 303)*
For all real numbers a, b, and c, if $a < b$, then $a + c < b + c$.

Multiplication Property of Inequality *(Lesson 5-1, p. 303)*
For all real numbers a, b, and c, if $a < b$ and $c > 0$, then $ac < bc$; if $a < b$ and $c < 0$, then $ac > bc$.

Substitution Property of Equality *(Lesson 5-3, p. 314)*
If $a = b$, then a may be substituted for b in any arithmetic or algebraic expression.

Inverse Matrix Theorem *(Lesson 5-5, p. 329)*
If $ad - bc \neq 0$ and $M = \begin{bmatrix} a & b \\ c & d \end{bmatrix}$,

then $M^{-1} = \begin{bmatrix} \frac{d}{ad - bc} & \frac{-b}{ad - bc} \\ \frac{-c}{ad - bc} & \frac{a}{ad - bc} \end{bmatrix}$.

System-Determinant Theorem *(Lesson 5-6, p. 338)*
An $n \times n$ system of linear equations has exactly one solution if and only if the determinant of the coefficient matrix is *not* zero.

Linear-Programming Theorem *(Lesson 5-9, p. 356)*
The feasible region of every linear-programming problem is convex, and the maximum or minimum quantity is determined at one of the vertices of this feasible region.

Chapter 6

Binomial Square Theorem *(Lesson 6-1, p. 376)*
For all real numbers x and y,
$(x + y)^2 = x^2 + 2xy + y^2$ and
$(x - y)^2 = x^2 - 2xy + y^2$.

Absolute Value-Square Root Theorem *(Lesson 6-2, p. 381)*
For all real numbers x, $\sqrt{x^2} = |x|$.

Graph-Translation Theorem *(Lesson 6-3, p. 387)*
In a relation described by a sentence in x and y, the following two processes yield the same graph:

1. replacing x by $x - h$ and y by $y - k$;
2. applying the translation $T_{h,k}$ to the graph of the original relation.

Parabola-Translation Theorem *(Lesson 6-3, p. 388)*
The image of the parabola with equation $y = ax^2$ under the translation $T_{h,k}$ is the parabola with the equation

$$y - k = a(x - h)^2$$
or
$$y = a(x - h)^2 + k.$$

Parabola Congruence Theorem *(Lesson 6-4, p. 395)*
The graph of the equation $y = ax^2 + bx + c$ is a parabola congruent to the graph of $y = ax^2$.

Completing the Square Theorem *(Lesson 6-5, p. 402)*
To complete the square on $x^2 + bx$, add $\left(\frac{b}{2}\right)^2$.

Quadratic Formula Theorem *(Lesson 6-7, p. 414)*
If $ax^2 + bx + c = 0$ and $a \neq 0$, then $x = \frac{-b \pm \sqrt{b^2 - 4ac}}{2a}$.

Square Root of a Negative Number Theorem *(Lesson 6-8, p. 422)*
If $k < 0$, $\sqrt{k} = i\sqrt{-k}$.

Properties of Complex Numbers Postulate *(Lesson 6-9, p. 428)*
In the set of complex numbers:

1. Addition and multiplication are commutative and associative.
2. Multiplication distributes over addition and subtraction.
3. $0 = 0i = 0 + 0i$ is the additive identity; $1 = 1 + 0i$ is the multiplicative identity.
4. Every complex number $a + bi$ has an additive inverse $-a + -bi$ and a multiplicative inverse $\frac{1}{a + bi}$ provided $a + bi \neq 0$.
5. The addition and multiplication properties of equality hold.

Discriminant Theorem *(Lesson 6-10, p. 437)*
Suppose a, b, and c are real numbers with $a \neq 0$. Then the equation $ax^2 + bx + c = 0$ has:

(i) two real solutions if $b^2 - 4ac > 0$.
(ii) one real solution if $b^2 - 4ac = 0$.
(iii) two complex conjugate solutions if $b^2 - 4ac < 0$.

Chapter 7

Probability of Repeated Independent Events *(Lesson 7-1, p. 454)*
If an event has probability p, and if each occurrence of the event is independent of all other occurrences, then the probability that the event occurs n times in a row is p^n.

Product of Powers Postulate *(Lesson 7-2, p. 459)*
For any nonnegative base b and nonzero real exponents m and n, or any nonzero base b and integer exponents m and n, $b^m \cdot b^n = b^{m+n}$.

Quotient of Powers Theorem *(Lesson 7-2, p. 460)*
For any positive base b and real exponents m and n, or any nonzero base b and integer exponents m and n, $\frac{b^m}{b^n} = b^{m-n}$.

Power of a Product Postulate *(Lesson 7-2, p. 460)*
For any nonnegative bases a and b and nonzero real exponent m, or any nonzero bases a and b and integer exponent m, $(ab)^m = a^m b^m$.

Power of a Quotient Theorem *(Lesson 7-2, p. 461)*
For any positive bases a and b and real exponent n, or any nonzero bases a and b and integer exponent n, $\left(\frac{a}{b}\right)^n = \frac{a^n}{b^n}$.

Zero Exponent Theorem *(Lesson 7-2, p. 461)*
If b is a nonzero real number, $b^0 = 1$.

Power of a Power Postulate *(Lesson 7-2, p. 462)*
For any nonnegative base b and nonzero real exponents m and n, or any nonzero base b and integer exponents m and n, $(b^m)^n = b^{mn}$.

Negative Exponent Theorem *(Lesson 7-3, p. 467)*
For any positive base b and real exponent n, or any nonzero base b and integer exponent n, $b^{-n} = \frac{1}{b^n}$.

Annual Compound Interest Formula *(Lesson 7-4, p. 473)*
Let P be the amount of money invested at an annual interest rate r compounded annually. Let A be the total amount after t years. Then $A = P(1 + r)^t$.

General Compound Interest Formula *(Lesson 7-4, p. 473)*
Let P be the amount invested at an annual interest rate r compounded n times per year. Let A be the amount after t years. Then $A = P\left(1 + \frac{r}{n}\right)^{nt}$.

Recursive Formula for a Geometric Sequence
(Lesson 7-5, p. 479)
Let r be a nonzero constant. The sequence g defined by the recursive formula $\begin{cases} g_1 = x \\ g_n = rg_{n-1}, \text{ for integers } n \geq 2 \end{cases}$ is the geometric, or exponential, sequence with first term x and constant multiplier r.

Explicit Formula for a Geometric Sequence
(Lesson 7-5, p. 481)
In the geometric sequence g with first term g_1 and constant ratio r, $g_n = g_1(r)^{n-1}$, for integers $n \geq 1$.

Number of Real Roots Theorem *(Lesson 7-6, p. 488)*
Every positive real number has:
2 real nth roots when n is even.
1 real nth root when n is odd.
Every negative real number has:
0 real nth roots when n is even.
1 real nth root when n is odd.
Zero has:
1 real nth root.

$\frac{1}{n}$ Exponent Theorem *(Lesson 7-6, p. 489)*
When $x \geq 0$ and n is an integer greater than 1, $x^{\frac{1}{n}}$ is an nth root of x.

Rational Exponent Theorem *(Lesson 7-7, p. 493)*
For any nonnegative real number x and positive integers m and n,
$x^{\frac{m}{n}} = \left(x^{\frac{1}{n}}\right)^m$, the mth power of the positive nth root of x, and
$x^{\frac{m}{n}} = (x^m)^{\frac{1}{n}}$, the positive nth root of the mth power of x.

Chapter 8

Inverse-Relation Theorem *(Lesson 8-2, p. 524)*
Suppose f is a relation and g is the inverse of f. Then:
1. If a rule for f exists, a rule for g can be found by switching x and y in the rule for f.
2. The graph of g is the reflection image of the graph of f over the line with equation $y = x$.
3. The domain of g is the range of f, and the range of g is the domain of f.

Inverse Functions Theorem *(Lesson 8-3, p. 530)*
Two functions f and g are inverse functions if and only if:
1. For all x in the domain of f, $g(f(x)) = x$, and
2. For all x in the domain of g, $f(g(x)) = x$.

Power Function Inverse Theorem
(Lesson 8-3, p. 532)
If $f(x) = x^n$ and $g(x) = x^{\frac{1}{n}}$ and the domains of f and g are the set of *nonnegative* real numbers, then f and g are inverse functions.

Root of a Power Theorem *(Lesson 8-4, p. 539)*
For all positive integers $m \geq 2$ and $n \geq 2$,
$\sqrt[n]{x^m} = \left(\sqrt[n]{x}\right)^m = x^{\frac{m}{n}}$ when $x \geq 0$.

Root of a Product Theorem *(Lesson 8-5, p. 546)*
For any nonnegative real numbers x and y, and any integer $n \geq 2$, $(xy)^{\frac{1}{n}} = x^{\frac{1}{n}} \cdot y^{\frac{1}{n}}$ (power form) and $\sqrt[n]{xy} = \sqrt[n]{x} \cdot \sqrt[n]{y}$ (radical form).

***n*th Root of a Product Theorem** *(Lesson 8-7, p. 559)*
When $\sqrt[n]{x}$ and $\sqrt[n]{y}$ are defined and are real numbers, then $\sqrt[n]{xy}$ is also defined and $\sqrt[n]{xy} = \sqrt[n]{x} \cdot \sqrt[n]{y}$

Chapter 9

Exponential Change Model *(Lesson 9-2, p. 589)*
If a positive quantity a is multiplied by b ($b > 0$, $b \neq 1$) in each unit period, then after a period of length x, the amount of the quantity is ab^x.

Continuously Compounded Interest Formula
(Lesson 9-3, p. 597)
If an amount P is invested in an account paying an annual interest rate r compounded continuously, the amount A in the account after t years is $A = Pe^{rt}$.

Log_b of b^n Theorem *(Lesson 9-9, p. 636)*
For every positive base $b \neq 1$, and any real number n, $\log_b b^n = n$.

Logarithm of 1 Theorem *(Lesson 9-9, p. 636)*
For every positive base $b \neq 1$, $\log_b 1 = 0$.

Logarithm of a Product Theorem *(Lesson 9-9, p. 637)*
For any positive base $b \neq 1$ and positive real numbers x and y, $\log_b(xy) = \log_b x + \log_b y$.

Logarithm of a Quotient Theorem *(Lesson 9-9, p. 638)*
For any positive base $b \neq 1$ and for any positive real numbers x and y, $\log_b\left(\frac{x}{y}\right) = \log_b x - \log_b y$.

Logarithm of a Power Theorem *(Lesson 9-9, p. 639)*
For any positive base $b \neq 1$ and for any positive real number x and any real number n, $\log_b(x^n) = n \log_b x$.

Change of Base Theorem *(Lesson 9-10, p. 646)*
For all positive real numbers a, b, and t, $b \neq 1$ and $t \neq 1$, $\log_b a = \frac{\log_t a}{\log_t b}$.

Chapter 10

Pythagorean Identity Theorem *(Lesson 10-5, p. 688)*
For all θ, $(\cos\theta)^2 + (\sin\theta)^2 = 1$.

Supplements Theorem *(Lesson 10-7, p. 701)*
For all θ in degrees, $\sin\theta = \sin(180° - \theta)$.

Law of Sines Theorem *(Lesson 10-7, p. 702)*
In any triangle ABC, $\frac{\sin A}{a} = \frac{\sin B}{b} = \frac{\sin C}{c}$.

Law of Cosines Theorem *(Lesson 10-8, p. 706)*
In any triangle ABC, $c^2 = a^2 + b^2 - 2ab\cos C$.

Chapter 11

Extended Distributive Property *(Lesson 11-2, p. 739)*
To multiply two polynomials, multiply each term in the first polynomial by each term in the second and add the products.

Difference of Squares Factoring Theorem
(Lesson 11-3, p. 747)
For all a and b, $a^2 - b^2 = (a + b)(a - b)$.

Binomial Square Factoring Theorem
(Lesson 11-3, p. 747)
For all a and b, $a^2 + 2ab + b^2 = (a + b)^2$ and $a^2 - 2ab + b^2 = (a - b)^2$.

Zero-Product Theorem *(Lesson 11-4, p. 752)*
For all a and b, $ab = 0$ if and only if $a = 0$ or $b = 0$.

Factor Theorem *(Lesson 11-4, p. 753)*
$x - r$ is a factor of $P(x)$ if and only if $P(r) = 0$, that is, r is a zero of P.

Rational-Root (or Rational-Zero) Theorem
(Lesson 11-5, p. 761)
Suppose that all the coefficients of the polynomial function described by $f(x) = a_n x^n + a_{n-1}x^{n-1} + \ldots + a_2x^2 + a_1x + a_0$ are integers with $a_n \neq 0$ and $a_0 \neq 0$. If $\frac{p}{q}$ is a root of $f(x)$ in lowest terms, then p is a factor of a_0 and q is a factor of a_n.

The Fundamental Theorem of Algebra
(Lesson 11-6, p. 766)
Every polynomial equation $P(x) = 0$ of any degree ≥ 1 with complex number coefficients has at least one complex number solution.

Number of Roots of a Polynomial Equation Theorem *(Lesson 11-6, p. 768)*
Every polynomial equation of degree n has exactly n roots, provided that multiple roots are counted according to their multiplicities.

Polynomial-Difference Theorem *(Lesson 11-7, p. 773)*
$y = f(x)$ is a polynomial function of degree n if and only if, for any set of x-values that form an arithmetic sequence, the nth differences of corresponding y-values are equal and the $(n - 1)$st differences are not equal.

Chapter 12

Focus and Directrix of a Parabola Theorem
(Lesson 12-1, p. 801)
For any nonzero real number a, the graph of $y = ax^2$ is the parabola with focus at $\left(0, \frac{1}{4a}\right)$ and directrix at $y = -\frac{1}{4a}$.

Circle Equation Theorem *(Lesson 12-2, p. 806)*
The circle with center (h, k) and radius r is the set of points (x, y) that satisfy $(x - h)^2 + (y - k)^2 = r^2$.

Interior and Exterior of a Circle Theorem
(Lesson 12-3, p. 812)
Let c be the circle with center (h, k) and radius r. Then the interior of c is described by $(x - h)^2 + (y - k)^2 < r^2$ and the exterior of c is described by $(x - h)^2 + (y - k)^2 > r^2$.

Equation for an Ellipse Theorem
(Lesson 12-4, p. 818)
The ellipse with foci $(c, 0)$ and $(-c, 0)$ and focal constant $2a$ has equation $\frac{x^2}{a^2} + \frac{y^2}{b^2} = 1$, where $b^2 = a^2 - c^2$.

Length of Axes of an Ellipse Theorem
(Lesson 12-4, p. 820)
In the ellipse with equation $\frac{x^2}{a^2} + \frac{y^2}{b^2} = 1$, $2a$ is the length of the horizontal axis and $2b$ is the length of the vertical axis.

Circle Scale-Change Theorem *(Lesson 12-5, p. 826)*
The image of the unit circle with equation $x^2 + y^2 = 1$ under $S_{a,b}$ is the ellipse with equation $\left(\frac{x}{a}\right)^2 + \left(\frac{y}{b}\right)^2 = 1$.

Graph Scale-Change Theorem *(Lesson 12-5, p. 827)*
In a relation described by a sentence in x and y, the following two processes yield the same graph:
1. replacing x by $\frac{x}{a}$ and y by $\frac{y}{b}$;
2. applying the scale change $S_{a,b}$ to the graph of the original relation.

Area of an Ellipse Theorem *(Lesson 12-5, p. 828)*
An ellipse with semimajor and semiminor axes of lengths a and b has area $A = \pi ab$.

Equation for a Hyperbola Theorem
(Lesson 12-6, p. 832)
The hyperbola with foci $(c, 0)$ and $(-c, 0)$ and focal constant $2a$ has equation $\frac{x^2}{a^2} - \frac{y^2}{b^2} = 1$, where $b^2 = c^2 - a^2$.

Asymptotes of a Hyperbola Theorem
(Lesson 12-6, p. 834)
The asymptotes of the hyperbola with equation $\frac{x^2}{a^2} - \frac{y^2}{b^2} = 1$ are $\frac{y}{b} = \pm\frac{x}{a}$, or $y = \pm\frac{b}{a}x$.

Attributes of $y = \frac{k}{x}$ Theorem *(Lesson 12-7, p. 841)*
The graph of $y = \frac{k}{x}$ or $xy = k$ is a hyperbola. When $k > 0$, this hyperbola has vertices $\left(\sqrt{k}, \sqrt{k}\right)$ and $\left(-\sqrt{k}, -\sqrt{k}\right)$, foci $\left(\sqrt{2k}, \sqrt{2k}\right)$ and $\left(-\sqrt{2k}, -\sqrt{2k}\right)$, and focal constant $2\sqrt{2k}$. The asymptotes of the graph are $x = 0$ and $y = 0$.

Chapter 13

Arithmetic Series Formula *(Lesson 13-1, p. 871)*
In an arithmetic sequence $a_1, a_2, a_3, ..., a_n$ with constant difference d, $\sum_{i=1}^{n} a_i = \frac{n}{2}(a_1 + a_n) = \frac{n}{2}(2a_1 + (n-1)d)$.

Finite Geometric Series Formula
(Lesson 13-2, p. 878)
Let S_n be the sum of the first n terms of the geometric sequence with first term g_1 and constant ratio $r \neq 1$. Then $S_n = \frac{g_1(1 - r^n)}{1 - r}$.

Number of Permutations Theorem
(Lesson 13-4, p. 890)
There are $n!$ permutations of n distinct objects.

Factorial Product Theorem *(Lesson 13-4, p. 890)*
For all $n \geq 1$, $n! = n \cdot (n-1)!$.

Combination Counting Formula *(Lesson 13-4, p. 892)*
The number ${}_nC_r$ of subsets, or combinations, of r elements that can be formed from a set of n elements is given by the formula ${}_nC_r = \frac{n!}{r!(n-r)!}$.

Pascal's Triangle Explicit Formula
(Lesson 13-5, p. 899)
If n and r are integers with $0 \leq r \leq n$, then $\binom{n}{r} = {}_nC_r = \frac{n!}{r!(n-r)!}$.

Binomial Theorem *(Lesson 13-6, p. 905)*
For all complex numbers a and b, and for all integers n and r with $0 \leq r \leq n$, $(a + b)^n = \sum_{r=0}^{n} \binom{n}{r} a^{n-r} b^r$.

Binomial Probability Theorem *(Lesson 13-7, p. 913)*
Suppose an experiment has an outcome with probability p, so that the probability the outcome does not occur is $q = 1 - p$. Then in n independent repetitions of the experiment, the probability that the outcome occurs r times is $\binom{n}{r} p^r q^{n-r}$.

CAS Commands

The Computer Algebra System (CAS) commands used in this course and examples of their use are given below. Each command must be followed by a number, variable, expression, or equation, usually enclosed in parentheses.

Command	Description	Example
Define	A rule for a function is stored under the name indicated. Values of that function can then be calculated by entering the function's name followed by the value of the independent variable in parentheses.	Define $f(n)=2000\cdot n-1400$ *Done* $f(4)$ 6600
| (such that)	Variable values that appear after the symbol are substituted into an expression, inequality, or equation that appears before the symbol.	$r=\frac{\sqrt{v}}{\sqrt{h\cdot\pi}}\|v=500000$ $\quad r=\frac{500\cdot\sqrt{2}}{\sqrt{h\cdot\pi}}$
solve	An equation, inequality, or system is solved for an indicated variable or variables. All real solutions are given.	$\text{solve}\left(y=\frac{1}{2}\cdot x-5 \text{ and } y=2\cdot x-1,\{x,y\}\right)$ $x=\frac{-8}{3} \text{ and } y=\frac{-19}{3}$
expand	The Distributive Property is applied to products and powers of mathematical expressions.	$\text{expand}((72+w)\cdot(24+2\cdot w))$ $2\cdot w^2+168\cdot w+1728$
DelVar	Any stored values for the indicated variable are deleted from memory.	DelVar a *Done*
cSolve	An equation or inequality is solved for an indicated variable. All complex solutions are given.	$\text{cSolve}(z^4=81,z)$ $z=3\cdot i$ or $z=-3\cdot i$ or $z=-3$ or $z=3$
factor	A polynomial is factored over the rational numbers. On some CAS, if ",x" is added to the end of the polynomial, it is factored over the real numbers.	$\text{factor}(x^4-14\cdot x^2+45)$ $(x-3)\cdot(x+3)\cdot(x^2-5)$ $\text{factor}(x^4-14\cdot x^2+45,x)$ $(x-3)\cdot(x+3)\cdot(x+\sqrt{5})\cdot(x-\sqrt{5})$
cFactor	A polynomial is factored over the complex numbers.	$\text{cFactor}(x^2+36,x)$ $\quad (x+-6\cdot i)\cdot(x+6\cdot i)$
rfactor	On some CAS, a polynomial is factored over the real numbers.	rfactor(x^2-14) $(x+\sqrt{14})\cdot(x-\sqrt{14})$

Selected Answers

Chapter 1

Lesson 1-1 (pp. 6-13)

Mental Math **a.** 49 in^2 **b.** 24 cm^2 **c.** 9 ft **d.** 40 mm
Guided Example 2 **Step 1:** 1; -1; 3; -4; 3 **Step 2:** 1; 49; 3 **Step 3:** -6; 6 **Step 4:** -1 **Guided Example 3** **a.** 33; 9.53; $\frac{6}{100}$ or 0.06; 0.06; 33; 9.53; 18.87; 18.87 **b.** $\frac{ptu}{1000}$

Questions

1. 1975 **3.** Answers vary. Sample: An equation must include an equal sign, but an algebraic expression does not include a verb. **5.** Answers vary. Sample: e^{rt} **7. a.** Yes; it is an algebraic sentence that includes an equal sign. **b.** Answers vary. Sample: Yes; it can be considered a formula solved for c^2. **9.** $306 - 60m$ **11.** \$28.02 **13. a.** $C + 372t$ **b.** $C + 12bt$ **15.** 4.2 **17.** -48.1 **19.** (e) **21.** (b) **23.** (d) **25.** C **27. a.** $x = -9$ **b.** $2(-9) = 4(-9) + 18$; $-18 = -36 + 18$; $-18 = -18$. The answer checks.

Lesson 1-2 (pp. 14-19)

Mental Math **a.** x^9 **b.** a^5 **c.** not possible **d.** n^{14}

Questions

1. Answers vary. Sample: A function is a set of ordered pairs where no two pairs have the same first coordinate. **3.** Answers vary. Sample: A mathematical model is a description of a real situation using the language and concepts of mathematics. For example, the equation $x + y + z = 180$ models the relationship among the angle measures in a triangle. **5.** Yes; for every ordered pair (r, C), each value of r determines only one value for C. **7.** No; one x-value generates two different y-values. **9. a.** D is the dependent variable. You cannot know the measure of the interior vertex angles if you do not know how many sides the polygon has. **b.** 120 **c.** Answers vary. Sample: A regular hexagon can be split into six equilateral triangles. Each of the triangles has interior angles that sum to 180°. Since they are equilateral, they are also equiangular. So, each interior angle of each triangle has measure 60°. Therefore, each interior angle of the hexagon has measure 120°.

11. $p = 75$ **13.** No; it is not the graph of a function because there are two y-values for every x-value except -1 and 1. **15.** $\frac{b}{m}$dollars **17.** KL outfits **19.** $\frac{g}{m}n$ eggs

Lesson 1-3 (pp. 20-25)

Mental Math **a.** \$8.85 **b.** \$88.50 **c.** \$8.85 **d.** \$26.55
Activity **Step 1:** $y = \sqrt{5^2 - x^2}$ **Step 3:** 3; 4.03702; $\sqrt{25 - \pi^2}$; $\sqrt{25 - 9 \cdot c^2}$
Step 4: Answers vary. Sample: Error: Nonreal answer. $25 - 36 = -11$, for which there exists no real square root.

Questions

1. f of x **3.** A of x equals $\frac{1}{2}x$ times the quantity 5 minus x. **5.** 4.80 **7.** 29.85 **9.** 186.8 **11.** Answers vary. Sample: define $t(c) = 1.8c + 32$ **13. a.** -12 **b.** 18 **15. a.** r **b.** 288π **c.** $36\pi R^3$

17. a.

X	h(x)	g(x)	h(x) – g(x)
-4	16	0.06	15.94
-2	4	0.25	3.75
-0.5	0.25	0.71	-0.46
0.5	0.25	1.41	-1.16
2.5	6.25	5.66	0.59
3	9	8	1
3.5	12.25	11.31	0.94
4.5	20.25	22.63	-2.38
10	100	1024	-924

b. No; the table shows, for example, that $h(-5) < g(-5)$. **c.** Answers vary. Sample: The var key should display the currently stored variables and functions in your CAS memory. **d.** Answers vary. Sample: Yes; the calculator uses a different icon to represent stored functions and stored variables. **e.** The calculator does not evaluate the function. **19.** 2000, 2003, 2004, 2005, 2006 **21. a.** 12 **b.** -212 **c.** 2.42916 **d.** $|4b| + (4b - 2)^3$ **23.** No; because one brother has more than one sibling. **25. a.** $y = 6$ **b.** $x = -4$ **c.** $y = k, x = h$

Lesson 1-4 (pp. 26-32)

Mental Math **a.** 2 units **b.** 1 square unit **c.** 5 units
Activity **Step 4:** (70, 478.33) **Step 5:** $C(75) = 356.25$, $S(75) = 543.75$; new window: $0 \le x \le 75, 0 \le y \le 545$
Step 7: No; you do not need to consider negative values because cars and SUVs cannot travel at a negative speed or stop in a negative number of feet. **Step 9:** Minimum value of $C \approx -5$; minimum value of $S \approx -3$

Questions
1. $\{x | 0 \leq x \leq 70\}$ **3.** Use the TRACE function on your graphing utility to estimate $C(45)$. **5.** Answers vary. Sample: $0 \leq x \leq 55, 0 \leq y \leq 310$ **7.** $\{x \mid 0 \leq x \leq 8\}$; $\{y \mid 2 \leq y \leq 5\}$ **9.** integer, rational number, real number
11. irrational number, real number
13. Answers vary. Sample: -29
15. a. $\{y \mid 0 \leq y \leq 24\}$ **b.** 17 years **c.** $7 \leq d \leq 12$
d. yes **Tree Age vs. Trunk Diameter**

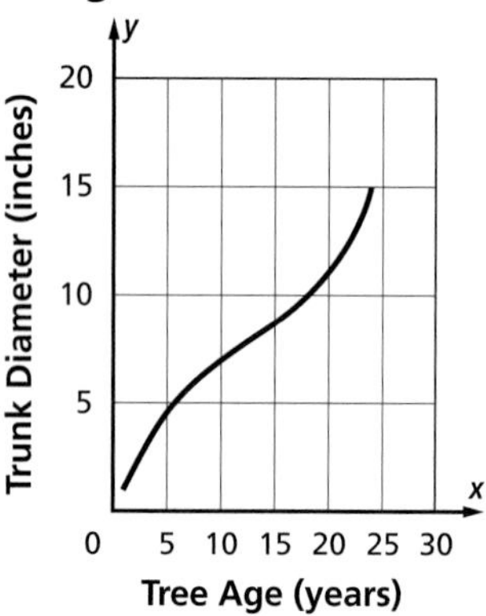

17. a. 5 **b.** $\{x \mid x \text{ is a real number}\}$; $\{y \mid y = 5\}$ **19. a.** 4 **b.** $x = 7$ **21. a.**

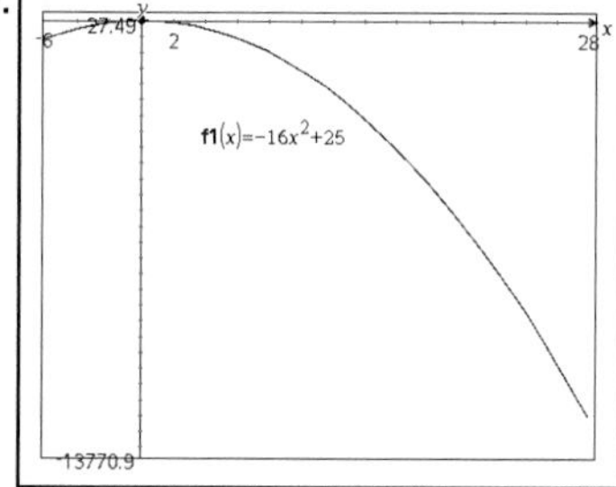

b. 5.64 ft **23.** 5050 **25.** $r = 261; \frac{1}{3}(261) - 27 = 60$

Lesson 1-5 (pp. 33-39)

Mental Math a. 70 mph **b.** 315 miles **c.** 3 hours **d.** 5:30 PM
Guided Example 1 a. $d; t$ **b.** 0; 210; 0; 12 **c.** 6; 6; 60; 6 **d.** 90; 90 **e.** 45; 60; 45; 60; t
Activity Step 4: t days; $D(t)$ inches; no; negative values of x do not make sense because x represents elapsed time.
Step 5: $D(6) = 3.75$ in. **Step 6:** $D(2) = 5.75$ in.
Questions
1. 0 miles; The graph shows this because the rightmost point is (210, 0), and the coordinate 0 indicates distance from home. **3.** 12 **5. a.** 4 **b.** -2 **7. a.** 5.19 in. **b.** After 5.6 days **9.** (1, 8); (1.5, 6.75); (2, 5); (2.5, 2.75); (3, 0) **11.** Yes; domain: {-3, -2, -1, 0, 1, 2, 3}; range: {-0.1, -0.06, -0.03, 0, 0.03, 0.06, 0.1} **13.** Yes; domain: {-6, -4, -2, 0, 2, 4, 6}; range: {0, 1, 2, 3} **15.** 2,160,000
17. a. -5, 0, 3, 4, 3, 0, -5

b.

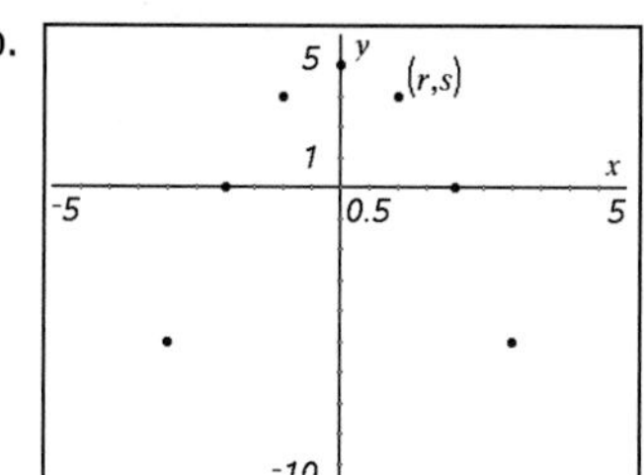

Yes; each value of r is paired with a single value of s.

c.

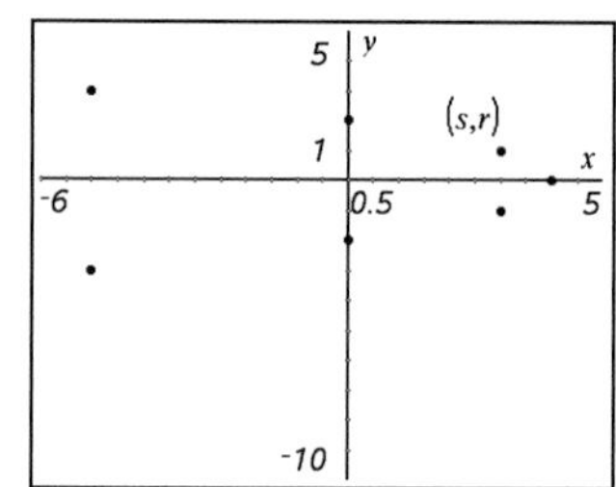

No; certain values of s are paired with more than one value of r. **19.** $\{x \mid 0 \leq x \leq 100\}$; $\{G(x) \mid 0 \leq G(x) \leq 20\}$
21. Yes; $f: x \rightarrow 2x - \pi x^2$ **23.** 7,698,000,000 km^2

Lesson 1-6 (pp. 40-46)

Mental Math a. 18 **b.** 120 **c.** $28xy$
Guided Example 2 465; $0.93d$; $0.28d$; 465; $0.28d$; 85; 303.57; 303.57; 196.43; \$550; \$303.57; \$196.43
Guided Example 4 $-5a$; -7; $5a$; $-8a$; 19; $8a$; 2.375
Questions
1. 45,600 in^3 **3.** 13.9; if she has 122 nickels, her collection is worth \$13.90. **5.** $y = 8$ **7.** $x = 1.5$ **9.** Answers vary. Sample: 24; $x = \frac{120}{19}$ **11. a.** $x = 4$ **b.** $3(4) - (4 + 1) = 7$
13. 52 **15.** $0 < A < 200$ **17.** $t = \frac{72}{5}$ **19.** $z = 10$
21. a. $\frac{17}{20}$ **b.** $n = 47$ **23.** about \$1,000,000 million
25. 1990 through 2000 **27.** 12.0 cm

Lesson 1-7 (pp. 47-52)

Mental Math a. 4 **b.** 4 **c.** 5
Questions
1. $\approx$ 1,963.5 cm^3 **3.**

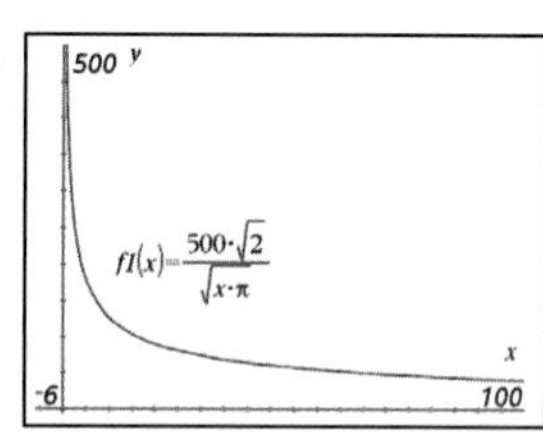

5. V; B and h. **7.** $r = \frac{65t}{c} + 65 = 65(\frac{t}{c} + 1)$ **9.** B
11. a. $S = \frac{R}{0.5P}$ **b.** 40 feet **13.** $k = 0.75$ **15.** $b_1 = \frac{2A}{h} - b^2$
17. a. $x = 16$ **b.** $x = -32$ **c.** $x = \frac{-480}{7}$

19. a.

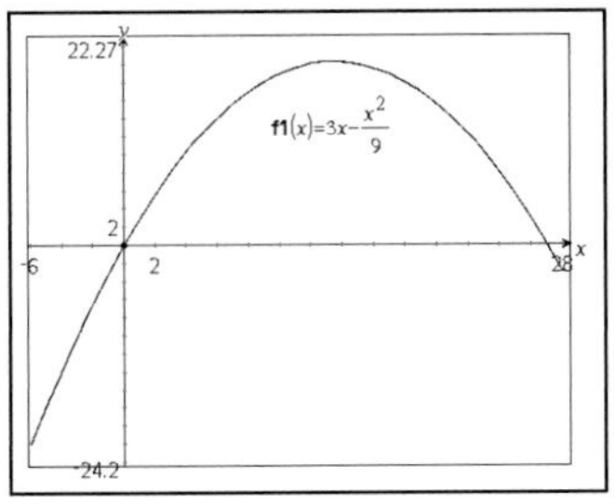

b. all real numbers; all real numbers ≤ 20.25
c. $\{f(x) \mid \frac{50}{9} \leq f(x) \leq 14\}$

Lesson 1-8 (pp. 53-59)

Mental Math a. 0 **b.** 0 **c.** 36 **d.** 6 **e.** 81

Activity Step 1:

Number of Dots
1
3
6
10
15

Step 2:

Number of Dots
21
28
36
45

Step 3: For each term number there corresponds only one number of dots.

Guided Example 2 Solution 1 a. 28,700; 29,876.70; 31,101.64; 32,376.81; 33,704.26 **b.** 1,532,865.74 **c.** 1,532,865.74; \$1,532,865.74 **Solution 2 a.** 1; 1; 5 **b.** 1,532,865.74 **c.** \$1,532,865.74

Questions

1. a. term **b.** 21 **3.** 210 **5. a.**

b. 1, 4, 9, 16, 25 **c.** $S_n = n^2$
7. 4.3, 1.3, -1.7, -4.7

9. a.

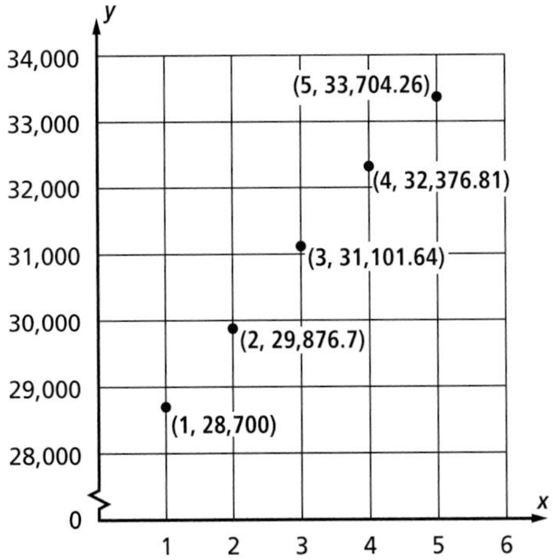

b. No; non-integer values are not part of the domain of the function.

11. a.

Term Number	Value of term
4	$C_4 = \frac{4^2(4+1)^2}{4} = 100$
5	$C_5 = \frac{5^2(5+1)^2}{4} = 225$
6	$C_6 = \frac{6^2(6+1)^2}{4} = 441$
7	$C_7 = \frac{7^2(7+1)^2}{4} = 784$

b. the sum of the first seven cubes **13. a.** (1, 2), (2, 4), (3, 6), (4, 10), (5, 18), (6, 34) **b.** $S_n = 2 + 2^{n-1}$, for all $n > 1$ **15.** $s = \frac{d+13}{7}$ **17. a.** $r = \frac{7}{3}$ **b.** $5\left(\frac{7}{3}\right) - \left(2\left(\frac{7}{3}\right) + 1\right) = 6$
19. a. t must be a whole number. **b.** 12.5, 14, 15.5, 17
c.

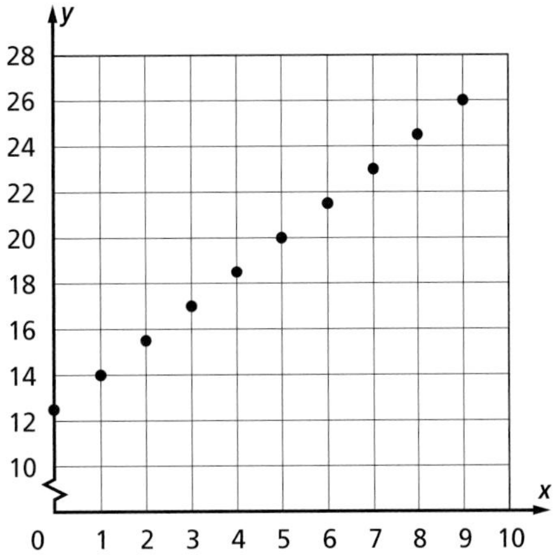

Self-Test (64-65)

1. 2.13 **2.** The first statement says that the value of the function $f(x)$ evaluated at $x = a$ is 7, whereas the second statement says that the value of the function $f(x)$ evaluated at $x = 7$ is a. **3.** $g(-2) = 17$ and $g(2) = 3$. **4.** domain: $\{x \mid -2 \leq x \leq 6\}$; range: $\{y \mid 2 \leq y \leq 6\}$. **5. a.** 5 **b.** $x = -1.3$ and $x = 2$. **6.** 135 **7.** B **8.** $s = \frac{m}{4}$ **9.** $5(7x - 4) = 50$; $7x - 4 = 10$; $7x = 14$; $x = 2$ **10.** $3.2a = 0.75 + 1.2a$; $2a = 0.75$; $a = 0.375$ **11.** $p + 0.2(1200 - p) = 244.4p$; $p + 0.2 \cdot 1200 - 0.2p = 244.4p$; $240 = 243.6p$; $p \approx 0.985$ **12.** 101cm^3 **13.** $\{V \mid 0 < V \leq 200\pi\}$.
14. a. $V = \frac{1}{3}\pi r^2 h$; $h = \frac{V}{\left(\frac{1}{3}\right)\pi r^2}$; $h = \sqrt{\frac{3V}{\pi r^2}}$ **b.** $V = \frac{1}{3}\pi r^2 h$; $r^2 = \frac{3V}{\pi h}$; $r = \sqrt{\frac{3V}{\pi h}}$ **15.** domain: $\{0, 4, 8, 16\}$; range: $\{7, 8, 9, 11\}$.
16. B, C **17.** No; it is not a function because $x = 9$ corresponds to both $y = 7$ and $y = 4$. **18.** Yes; it is a function; each x-value defines just one y-value.
19. a. $a_1 = -4^1 + 2 = -2$; $a_2 = -4^2 + 2 = -14$; $a_3 = -4^3 + 2 = -62$; $a_4 = -4^4 + 2 = -254$; $a_5 = -4^5 + 2 = -1022$. **b.** -16,382

20. 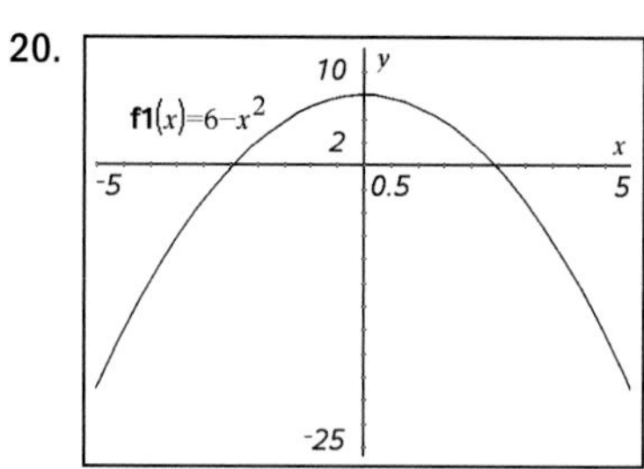

a. $\{f(t) \mid -19 \leq f(t) \leq 6\}$. b. $x \approx -2.45$ and $x \approx 2.45$.

21.

x	-6	-4	-2	0	2
y	-192	-48	-12	-3	-0.75

a. The first ordered pairs are (-6, -192), (-4, -48), (-2, -12), (0, -3), (2, -0.75). b. $x = 2$ 22. a. $W(10) = -4$; the wind-chill index with a 10 mph wind at 10°F is -4°F. b. $A = -20$ 23. a. (-1, 0), (0, 2), (1, 3), (2, 2), (3, 0). b. Yes; there is only one y-value for each x-value. c. domain: {-1, 0, 1, 2, 3}; range:{0, 2, 3}. 24. about 149,000 more people 25. C 26. about 0.000772 27. $T = \frac{1}{4}T + \frac{1}{10}T + 195$; $T = \frac{7}{20}T + 195$; $\frac{13}{20}T = 195$; $T = \frac{20}{13} \cdot 195 = 300$; 300 tickets 28. The value of c does not change because $a^2 + b^2 = b^2 + a^2 = c^2$. This corresponds to the geometric situation of a reflection, where the orientation of the triangle shifts, but its lengths do not change.

Self-Test Correlation Chart

The chart below keys the **Self-Test** questions to the objectives in the **Chapter Review** at the end of the chapter. This will enable you to locate those **Chapter Review** questions that correspond to questions missed on the **Self-Test**. The lesson where the material is covered is also indicated on the chart.

Question	1	2	3	4	5	6	7	8	9	10
Objective(s)	B	B	B	H	H	B	D	D	C	C
Lesson(s)	1-3	1-3	1-3	1-4, 1-5	1-4, 1-5	1-3	1-7	1-7	1-6	1-6
Question	**11**	**12**	**13**	**14**	**15**	**16**	**17**	**18**	**19**	**20**
Objective(s)	C	A	H	D	H	G	G	G	E	H, L
Lesson(s)	1-6	1-1	1-4, 1-5	1-7	1-4, 1-5	1-2, 1-5	1-2, 1-5	1-2, 1-5	1-8	1-4, 1-5, 1-8
Question	**21**	**22**	**23**	**24**	**25**	**26**	**27**	**28**		
Objective(s)	L	J	G, H	J	F	A	K	I		
Lesson(s)	1-4, 1-5, 1-8	1-3, 1-4	1-2, 1-4, 1-5	1-3, 1-4	1-7	1-1	1-6	1-7		

Chapter Review (pp. 66-69)

1. 119.1016 3. $d = 44.1$ m 5. -15 7. a. $h: x \rightarrow 12x - 2\sqrt{x}$ b. 102 9. a. $f(x) = 4 - 27x$ b. -212 11. $x = \frac{1}{15}$; $12\left(\frac{1}{15}\right) = \frac{4}{5}$ 13. $v = 3$; $-\frac{5}{3} = \frac{4}{3} - 3$ 15. $s = -3$; $3 + 5(-3) = 4(2(-3) + 3)$ 17. $m = \frac{48}{79}$; $\left(\frac{48}{79 \cdot 8}\right) + \left(\frac{48}{79 \cdot 6}\right) - 2 = -3\left(\frac{48}{79}\right)$ 19. $t = \frac{12 - x}{6}$ 21. $h = \frac{3A}{\pi\left(r_1{}^2 - r_2{}^2\right)}$ 23. Answers vary. Sample: It is not solved for s because s appears on both sides of the equal sign. 25. -9, -15, -21, -27, -33 27. 18 29. $r = -\frac{\sqrt{3-v}}{\sqrt{h\pi}}$ or $\frac{\sqrt{3-v}}{\sqrt{h\pi}}$; $r = \frac{\sqrt{3-v}}{\sqrt{h\pi}}$ 31. B 33. no 35. Yes; each x-value defines a single y-value. 37. No; an x-value defines two y-values. 39. {-2,-1,0,1,2}; {-1} 41. all real numbers; all real numbers 43. all real numbers; all nonnegative real numbers 45. $g(-3) = 1$ 47. If m_1 and m_2 are switched, F has the same value. This implies that the magnitude of the gravitational force that m_2 exerts on m_1 is equal to that exerted by m_1 on m_2. 49. D 51. 240 ft

53. a.

Time (months)	Balance (dollars)
1	200
2	235
3	270
4	305
5	340
6	375

b. $B(t) = 200 + 35(t - 1)$ 55. 629,797; the difference between the population of Wisconsin and the population of Minnesota in 1980 57. a. $d = \frac{W - 4000}{200}$ b. 50 days 59. 10 hours

61. a.

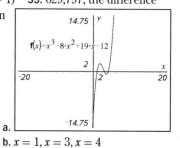

b. $x = 1, x = 3, x = 4$

63. 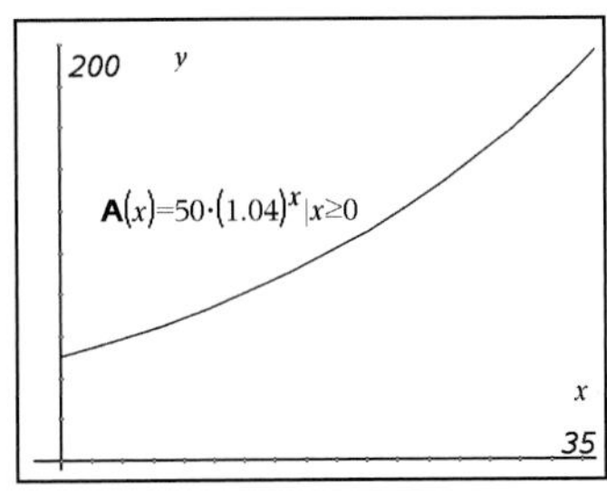

$\{A(x) \mid A(x) \geq 50\}$

65. a.

x	f(x)
1	1
1.2	0.757
1.4	0.330
1.6	-0.359
1.8	-1.419

b. 1.6 **c.** C

Chapter 2

Lesson 2-1 (pp. 72–78)

Mental Math **a.** $\frac{7}{9}$ **b.** $\frac{4}{7}$ **c.** $\frac{1}{3} - \frac{1}{4}$ **d.** $\frac{1}{2} + \frac{1}{4} + \frac{1}{6}$

Guided Example 2 *b; g;* 729; 2; 729; 64; $\frac{729}{64}$; *b;* $\frac{729}{64}$; *g;* $\frac{729}{64}$; 10; 11,390,625; 11,390,625

Questions

1. Answers vary. Sample: The weekly salary of a person varies directly with how many hours that person works that week. **3.** y; x^2; 5 **5.** 118.1 mm **7. a.** B **b.** B **9.** 2.09 cm **11.** 7,235.1744 **13. a.** $d = kt$ **b.** 2.4 miles

15. a.

s	1	2	3	4	5	6	7	8	9	10
A	6	24	54	96	150	216	294	384	486	600

b. 4 **c.** 4 **d.** 4 **e.** quadruples **f.** increases by a factor of 9 **17. a.** 784 feet **b.** 2.28 seconds **19.** No; $x = -1$ is paired with two different y-values.

21. a. Answers vary. Sample:

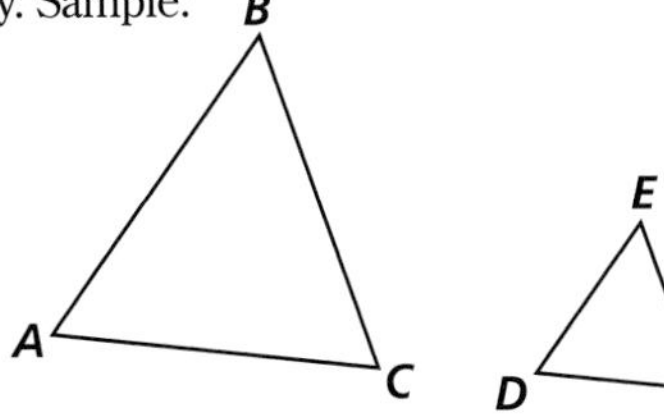

b. They are equal.
23. 5^6

Lesson 2-2 (pp. 79–85)

Mental Math **a.** 8 **b.** 0.32 **c.** $18n^2$ **d.** $18n^2 - 6$

Guided Example 3 d^2; 4; 40; 40; 4^2; 40; 16; 640; 640; 640; 6^2; 17.8

Questions

1. number of workers **3.** A **5.** 3.28 m **7.** 7.9 lumens; it is approximately 0.44 times as intense (or, it is 2.25 times softer). **9.** 187.5 **11. a.**

w	2	3	4	5	6	7	8	9	10	11	12	15	20
t	24	16	12	9.6	8	6.9	6	5.3	4.8	4.4	4	3.2	2.4

b. is halved **c.** is divided by 3 **d.** $t = \frac{48}{w}$, so $\frac{\frac{48}{3w}}{\frac{48}{w}} = \frac{48 \cdot w}{48 \cdot 3w} = \frac{1}{3}$
13. inversely **15.** inversely **17.** 137.9 lb
19. x^7; Quotient of Powers Property: $\frac{x^m}{x^n} = x^{m-n}$

21. a.

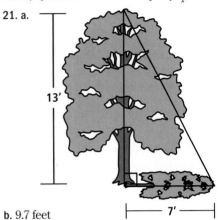

13′
7′

b. 9.7 feet

Lesson 2-3 (pp. 86–92)

Mental Math **a.** 1200 ft^3 **b.** 80 ft **c.** 20

Activity Step 1.

Size	Mean Radius r (cm)	r^3 (cm^3)	Ratio of Raius to Mini's Radius	Ratio of r^3 to Mini's r^3	Production Cost Estimate
Mini	0.7	0.343	1:1	1:1	$\frac{1}{2}$ cent
Regular	1.4	2.744	2:1	8:1	
Jumbo	2.1	9.261	3:1	27:1	

Step 2. a. 2; 8; 8; 4 **b.** 27; 13.5; 3 **c.** 32 cents; The radius ratio is 4, so the cost ratio is 4^3.
$4^3\left(\frac{1}{2}\text{ cent}\right) = 64\left(\frac{1}{2}\text{ cent}\right) = 32$ cents

Size	Mean Radius r (cm)	r^3 (cm^3)	Ratio of Raius to Mini's Radius	Ratio of r^3 to Mini's r^3	Production Cost Estimate
Super Jumbo	2.8	21.952	4:1	64:1	32 cents

Step 3. c^3 **Step 4.** inversely **a.**

Size	Radius r (cm)	Ratio of r^3 to Mini's r^3	Number of Pops n in a Carton
Mini	0.7	1:1	270
Regular	1.4	8:1	33
Jumbo	2.1	27:1	10
Super Jumbo	2.8	64:1	4

b. decrease; 8; 8; 33 **c.** dividing; 3; third; dividing; 4; third
Step 5. c^3
Guided Example 2 Solution 1. 18; 18; 5832; 5832
Solution 2. $18d$; 18^3; kd^3; 5832; 5832
Questions
1. 13.5 cents **3.** 4 **5.** divided by c^n **7.** The ancient rodent was $3.2^3 = 32.8$ times as heavy. **9.** When x is doubled, y is multiplied by 16. This is because $16 = 2^4$. **11. a.** The volume is multiplied by 512. **b.** The volume is divided by 8. **13. a.** Their weight would be about 12^3, or 1728, times as great. **b.** Their surface area would be about 12^2, or 144, times as great. **15.** 5:3
17. Let y_1 = original value before multiplying x by c. Let y_2 = value when x is multiplied by c. To find y_2, x must be multiplied by c.

$y_1 = \frac{k}{x^n}$	Definition of inverse variation
$y_2 = \frac{k}{(cx)^n}$	Definition of y_2
$y_2 = \frac{k}{c^n x^n}$	Product of Powers Postulate
$y_2 = \frac{1}{c^n} \cdot \frac{k}{x^n}$	Associative and Commutative Properties of Multiplication
$y_2 = \frac{1}{c^n} \cdot y_1$	Substitution of y_1 for $\frac{k}{x^n}$
$y_2 = \frac{y_1}{c^n}$	Definition of division

19. C **21. a.** cn cents **b.** $\frac{d}{2}m$ cents **23.** 10.85

Lesson 2-4 (pp. 93-99)

Mental Math a. 0.0145 **b.** $-\sqrt{2}$ **c.** $\frac{7}{11}$ and 0.0145 **d.** 17 and 512
Activity Step 1. The value of y increases with respect to x. The graph becomes steeper. **Step 2.** The value of y decreases with respect to x. The graph becomes steeper in a downward direction. **Step 3.** The graph is horizontal. **Step 4.** Answers vary. Sample: Let $k = 3$. Then $y_1 = 3$. Slope = 3. They are all the same number.
Questions
1. (x_1, y_1) and (x_2, y_2) **3.** dependent; independent **5.** For every 5 seconds it takes to hear thunder, you are 1 mile farther away from where the lightning struck. **7.** positive; negative **9.** line; k; (0, 0) **11.** 60 miles per hour **13.** Answers vary. Sample: For $k = 3$, $A = (1, 3)$. The point $B = (2, 6)$ is also on the line $y = 3x$. Using A and B, the slope is $\frac{6-3}{2-1} = 3$. This is the same slope found using A and O, and it is equal to k. **15.** No; the rate of change between the first two points is $\frac{1}{3}$, and the rate of change between second and third points is 1.

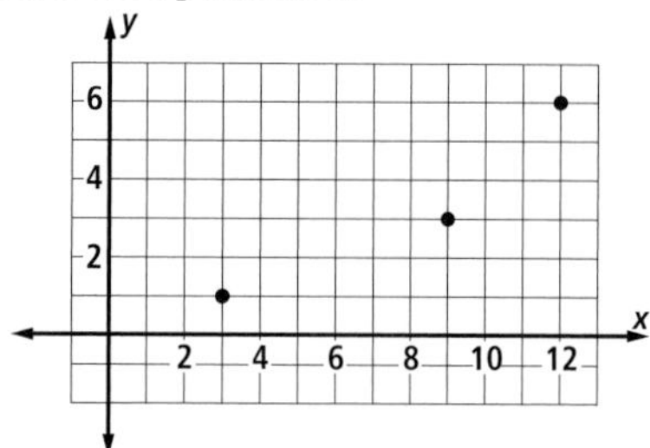

17. a: $y = -4x$; b: $y = 4x$; c: $y = \frac{1}{4}x$; d: $y = -\frac{1}{4}x$
19. a. $\frac{41}{21}$ **b.** $-\frac{17}{3}$ **21.** 9:25 **23.** direct **25.** neither

Lesson 2-5 (pp. 100-105)

Mental Math a. 22 cents **b.** \$1.88 **c.** \$2.20 **d.** \$4.15
Activity Step 1. $y = k(1)^2$, so $y = k$. **Step 3.** It becomes narrower. **Step 4.** It becomes the x-axis. $A = (1, 0)$. **Step 5.** It becomes narrower. When k is negative, the graph is reflected over the x-axis.
Questions
1. a. 1.5; As speed increases from 10 to 20 miles per hour, braking distance increases by 1.5 ft for each mph, on average. **b.** 5.5; As speed increases from 50 to 60 miles per hour, braking distance increases by 5.5 ft for each mph, on average. **c.** $\frac{d-b}{c-a}$; As speed increases from a to c miles per hour, braking distance increases by $\frac{d-b}{c-a}$ ft for each mph, on average. **3.** parabola **5.** domain: set of all real numbers, range: $\{y \mid y \leq 0\}$ **7. a.** $k > 0$ **b.** $k < 0$ **9. a.** A, s **b.** $\frac{\sqrt{3}}{4}$ **11. a.** Substituting (0, 0) into $y = kx^2$ gives the true statement $0 = 0$ for all values of k. **b.** Substitute 1 for x: $f(1) = k(1)^2 = k$, so $k = f(1)$ in this equation. **13.** Yes; each 4-inch beam will be half as strong as the 8-in. beam because strength is directly proportional to width.
15. a.

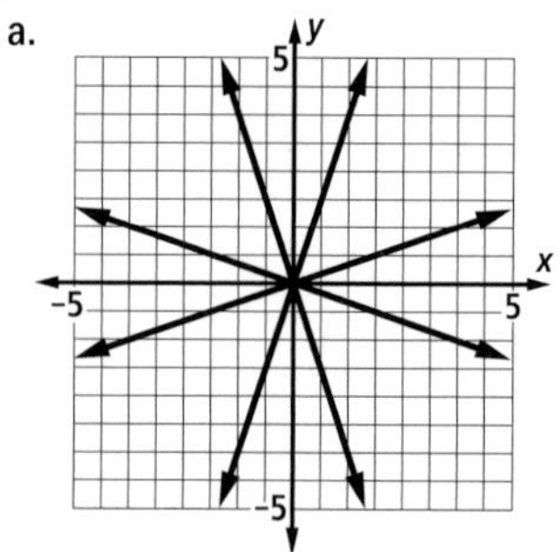

b. 3; $\frac{1}{3}$; $-\frac{1}{3}$; -3 **c.** $y = \frac{1}{3}x$; $y = -3x$ or $y = -\frac{1}{3}x$; $y = 3x$
17. a. The domain of any sequence is the set of positive numbers. **b.** 3818, 4035, 4258, 4487, 4722 **19. a.** Answers vary. Samples: A, B, C, D, E, K, M, T, U, V, W, Y
b. Answers vary. Samples: H, I, O, X

Lesson 2-6 (pp. 106–113)

Mental Math **a.** 108 **b.** 18 **c.** 72 **d.** 108

Activity 1 **Step 2.** y approaches 0. **Step 3.** y approaches 0. **Step 4.** No; the numerator is 10, thus y could never equal 0. **Step 5.** No; it is not possible to divide by 0, so 0 is not in the domain of the function. **Step 6.** Yes, the graphs have the same behavior. None of the graphs intersect the x- or y-axis.

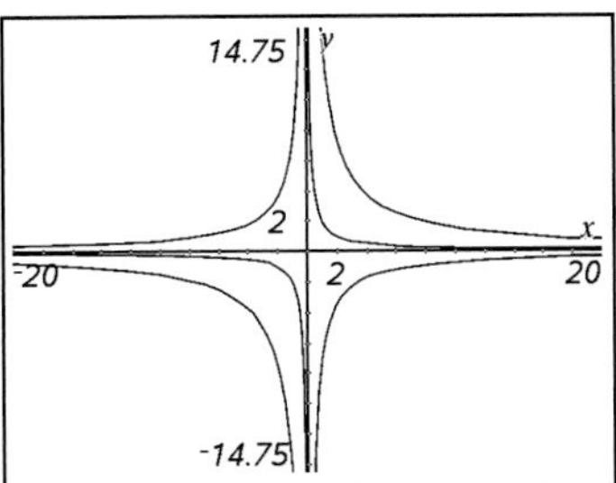

Activity 2 **Step 1.** It is not possible for the function values to be negative, since the denominator must be positive. **Step 2.** y approaches 0. **Step 3.** y approaches 0. **Step 4.** No; the numerator is 10, thus y could never equal 0. **Step 5.** No; it is not possible to divide by 0. **Step 6.** It goes to infinity. The denominator keeps getting smaller, causing the function values to become greater and greater.

Questions

1. It is not possible to divide by 0. **3.** hyperbola **5. a.** $-\frac{3}{2}$; 1

b.

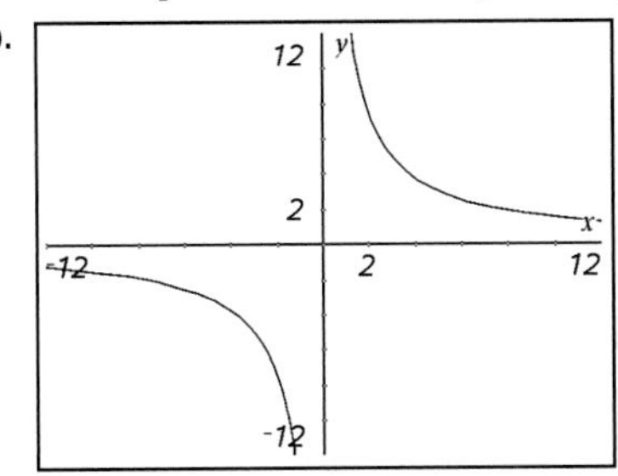

7. a. no **b.** yes **9.** The y-coordinates get larger and larger. **11. a.** ii **b.** iii **c.** i **d.** iv **13. a.** 4; 2; $\frac{12}{8} = 1.5$; $\frac{12}{10} = 1.2$ **b.** $y = \frac{12}{x}$, x = number of kids, y = number of cookies each kid gets **c.** There cannot be a fractional number of kids. **15. a.**

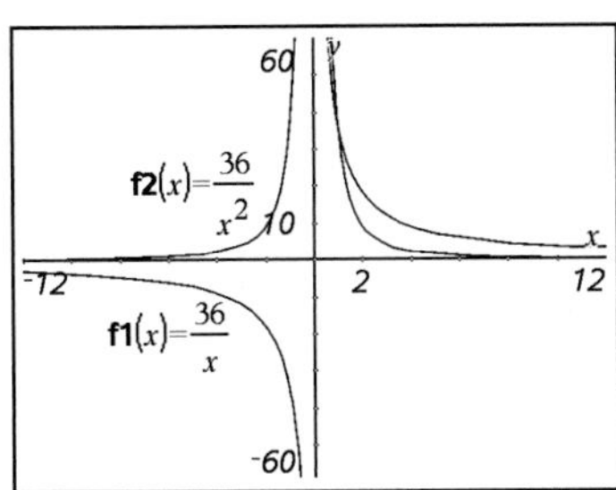

Answers vary. Both graphs have two branches, but the branches of the graph of f are in Quadrants I and III, whereas the branches of the graph of g are in Quadrants I and II.

b. -6, -7; the average rate of change of g is more negative than the average rate of change of f. **c.** $-\frac{1}{2}$, $-\frac{1}{8}$; the average rate of change of g is less negative than the average rate of change of f. **17.** $y = -3x^2$ **19. a.** $\frac{4.75}{3} \approx 1.58$ **b.** $1.58^3 \approx 3.94$ **c.** According to the Fundamental Theorem of Variation, the answer to Part b is the cube of the answer to Part a. **21.** C **23. a.** independent variable: time; dependent variable: temperature

b.

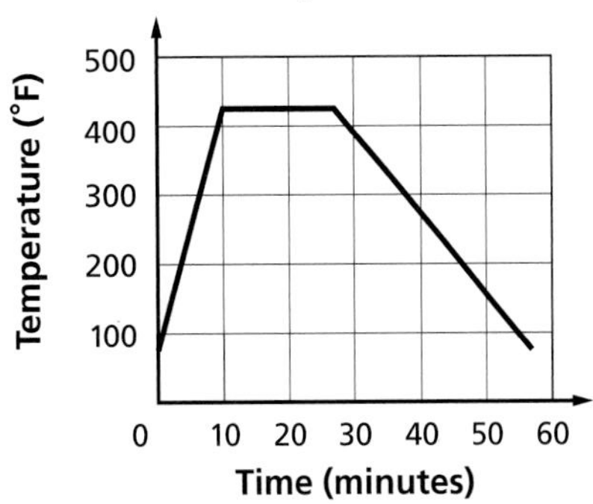

c. domain: 0 to 57; range: 75° to 425°

Lesson 2-7 (pp. 114–120)

Mental Math **a.** 2 **b.** 4 **c.** \$10.12 **d.** no

Guided Example 1 **Solution** 4.9; 1; 4.9; 4.9 **Check** 4.9; 11.0; 19.6; 30.6; 44.1

Activity **Step 1.** $k = 10{,}115$; $d = \frac{10{,}115}{w^2}$ **Step 2.** No; only $w = 85$ lb has the same value, but the other points do not fit very well. **Step 3.** $k = 119$; $d = \frac{119}{w}$ **Step 4.** The values are not exactly the same, but they are closer than the first equation. **Step 5.** Yes; the values that the second equation gives are much closer to the experimental results.

Questions

1. After it is dropped from the top of a cliff, the distance d a ball has fallen varies directly as the square of the time t. **3.** about 10.1 sec **5.** Answers vary. Sample: Jenna's data shows that when $w = 80$, $d = 1.5$, but the model gives $d = 1.58$. **7.** 5.95 yd; no, this is too long for a seesaw to be safe **9. a.** i **b.** $k = 14.3$ **c.** $V = 200.2 \text{ in}^3$ **11. a.** iv **b.** $k = 12$ **c.** No; if this were true, I would have to increase with d, which is not what the data indicate. **d.** $I = 0.12$ **13.** Matt will need to sit 2.5 times as far from the pivot as Pat sits. Sample: Matt weighs 80 lb, Pat weighs 200 lb, and Pat is 3 feet from the pivot. Since $d = \frac{k}{w}$, $3 = \frac{k}{200}$ and $k = 600$. Then Matt's distance is $d = \frac{600}{80} = 7.5$, and $3 \cdot 2.5 = 7.5$. **15.** E **17.** C **19.** The value of y is multiplied by $3^{23} = 94{,}143{,}178{,}827$. **21. a.** $f(1999) = 8{,}698{,}000$ **b.** 2002

Lesson 2-8 (pp. 121–128)

Mental Math **a.** (2, 7) **b.** (4, 9.5) **c.** (5, 3)

Guided Example 1 Answers vary. Sample: (1, 9) 9; 1; 9; *M*; 9; *w*; Answers vary. Sample:

w	1	2	3	4	5	6
M	9	18	27	36	45	54

directly; *w*

Guided Example 3 Answers vary. Sample answers are given. 1, 212; 2, 106; 3, 71; $\frac{1}{2}$; 2; about $\frac{1}{3}$; 3; inversely; *d*; *d*; 212; 1; 212; $M = \frac{212}{d}$;

d	1	2	3	4	5	6
M	212	106	70.7	53	42.4	35.3

inversely; *d*

Questions

1. w, t, d **3.** 32 lb **5.** a straight line **7.** When *d* doubles, *M* is divided by 2, not 4. **9.** numerator **11. a.** *P* varies directly as *w*. When *w* is multiplied by about $\frac{4}{3}$ to go from $w = 75$ to $w = 99$, *P* is multiplied by $\frac{12.9}{9.8} \approx \frac{4}{3}$. **b.** *P* varies inversely as h^2. **c.** 17.6 psi; by the table in Part b, $P = 70.2$ when $w = 1.5$, so when *w* is doubled to 3, $P = \frac{70.2}{4} \approx 17.6$ by the Fundamental Theorem of Variation. **d.** $P = \frac{kw}{h^2}$
13 a. none **b.** none **c.** $x = 0, y = 0$ **d.** $x = 0, y = 0$
15. $r = \frac{512}{729} \approx 0.7$

Lesson 2-9 (pp. 129–135)

Mental Math **a.** 20 **b.** 10 **c.** 16

Guided Example 3 **a.** hr^2 **b.** 6; 2; 24; 3.142 **c.** π **d.** $3.142hr^2$ or πhr^2 **e.** cylinder

Questions

1. a. Combined variation is a situation in which both direct and inverse variations occur together. **b.** In joint variation a quantity varies directly as a power of two or more independent variables, but in combined variation there is both direct and inverse variation. **3.** 13.7 mph **5. a.** $k \approx 3.4$ **b.** No; she used $k = 3.4$ instead of 3.14 or π. **7. a.** *F* varies jointly as *m* and *a*. **b.** $k = 1$ **9. a.** $V = khw\ell$ **b.** rectangular **c.** $k = 1$ **11. a.** $C = kL(R_o^2 - R_i^2)$ **b.** $k = 165.33$ **c.** $C = 165.33L(R_o^2 - R_i^2)$ **d.** \$32.40 **e.** dollars per cubic foot

13. a.

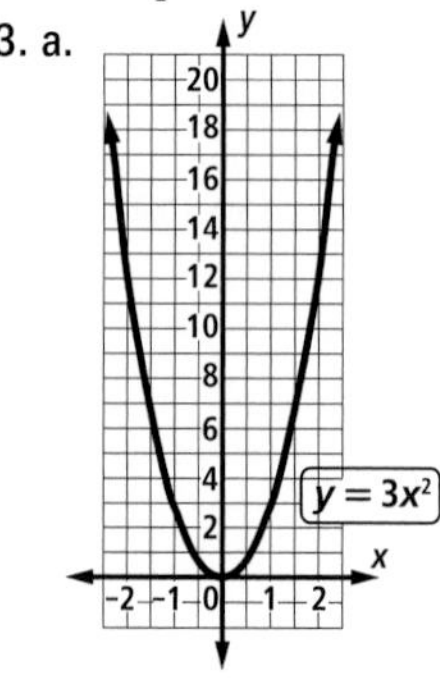

b. parabola **c.** 9 **d.** No; the rate of change between x_1 and x_2 increases as the values of x_1 and x_2 increase.
15. $k = \frac{wy}{xz}$ **17.** 118.7

Self-Test (pp. 140–142)

1. Direct variation means that *n* and ℓ increase together. *n* is the dependent variable and ℓ is the independent variable, so the equation is $n = k\ell$. **2.** Direct variation means that *w* increases as d^4 increases, and inverse variation means that *w* decreases as L^2 increases. *w* is the dependent variable and *d* and *L* are the independent variables, so the equation is $w = \frac{kd^4}{L^2}$. **3.** By the form of the equation, we know that *s* is the dependent variable, *p* is the independent variable, and *k* is the constant of variation. Because p^4 is in the denominator, this means that as p^4 increases, *s* decreases. So, to express this equation, we say: *s* varies inversely as p^4. **4.** The equation described is $T = ks^3w^2$. Given $s = 2$ and $w = 1$, $T = 10$, thus $10 = k(2^3)(1^2)$ and $k = \frac{5}{4}$. Therefore we can rewrite the equation as $T = \frac{5}{4}s^3w^2$. So for $s = 8$ and $w = \frac{1}{2}$, $T = \frac{5}{4}(8)^3\left(\frac{1}{2}\right)^2 = 160$. **5.** From the equation we can see that *y* varies inversely as x^2. Therefore, by the Fundamental Theorem of Variation, doubling the *x*-value divides the *y*-value by 4. For example, the points (1, 5) and $\left(2, \frac{5}{4}\right)$ satisfy the equation. **6.** If *y* is multiplied by 8 when *x* is doubled, this implies that *y* and *x* are directly related. As the cube of 2 is 8, we see that *y* varies directly as the cube of *x*. A general equation to express this relationship is $y = kx^3$. **7.** The average rate of change can be found by plugging the points into the formula $m = \frac{y_2 - x_2}{x_2 - x_1}$. Here we get $m = \frac{16-4}{4-2} = \frac{12}{2} = 6$. **8. a.** False; for inverse variation equations $y = \frac{k}{x^n}$, there is no value for *y* when $x = 0$. **b.** False; if *y* varies directly with x^n, where $n > 1$, the rate of change will not be constant. **9. a.** parabola; $k > 0$ **b.** The opening of the parabola grows wider. **10.** $\{d \mid d \neq 0\}$. Since 0 cannot be in the denominator of a fraction, d^2 cannot equal 0, and thus $d \neq 0$. *d* is defined for all other real numbers. **11. a.** Directly; the volume of the sphere will increase as the radius increases. **b.** Inversely; the more expensive the stock, the fewer shares of stock you can buy. **12. a.** Answers vary. Sample:

x	y
0	0
1	-0.5
2	-1
3	-1.5
4	-2
5	-2.5

b.

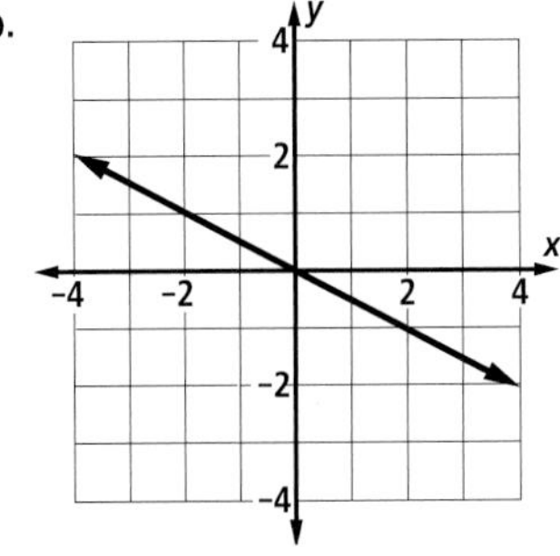

c. We can use two points from the table to find the slope. Because the slope is constant, any two points will work. Therefore, $m = \frac{-2-(-1)}{4-2} = -\frac{1}{2}$.

13. a.

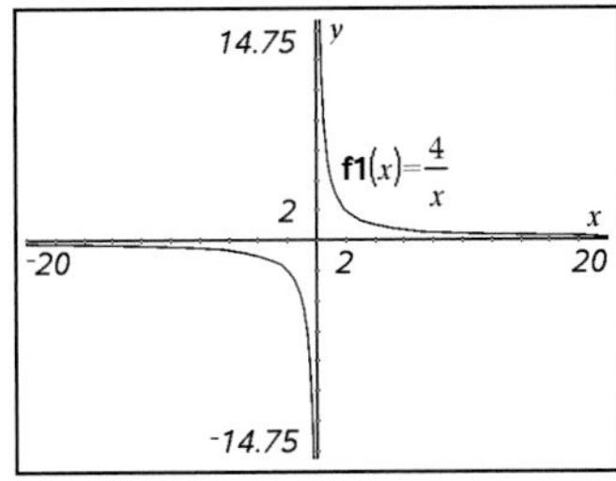

b. $x = 0, y = 0$ 14. a. B; the answer cannot be A or D because both of these graphs would have constant slope. The answer cannot be C because the *y*-values of this function must be positive, but the graph shown does not have this property. b. Because you cannot have 0 in the denominator, $x \neq 0$, but all other values of *x* are in the domain. Likewise $y \neq 0$, but all other values of *y* are in the range.

15. a.

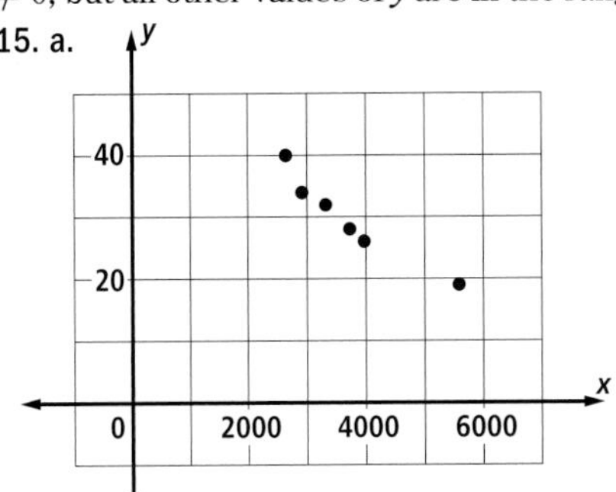

b. $F = \frac{k}{w}$. As *w* doubles, *F* is halved. Find the constant of variation by plugging in a pair of values. Answers vary. Sample: $40 = \frac{k}{2655}$, $k = 106{,}200$. c. Plug in 5900 for the weight to find that according to the model, $F = \frac{106{,}200}{5900} = 18$ mpg. d. The model shows that as vehicle weight increases, fuel economy decreases. 16. *V* is the dependent variable, and because its graph with *g* is a parabola, it is related to *g* as follows: $V = kg^2$. Its graph with *h* is a line, so it is related to *h* as follows: $V = kh$. Because *V* varies jointly with *g* and *h*, we can combine these two equations into the general equation $V = kg^2h$. 17. a. Because height is inversely proportional to the square of the radius by the Fundamental Theorem of Variation, as *r* doubles, *h* will be divided by 4. So when *r* increases from 5 cm to 10 cm, *h* will decrease from 10 cm to $\frac{10}{4} = 2.5$ cm. b. In general, if two cylinders have the same volume and the radius of one is double the radius of the other, their heights are related in the ratio 1:4. 18. a. If Paula is right, then the equation that fits is $m = kd^3$. Therefore, plugging in the given points, $k = \frac{6.0 \cdot 10^{24}}{(12{,}700)^3} = 2.9 \cdot 10^{12}$. Thus the equation would be $m = 2.9 \cdot 10^{12}d^3$. b. The model from Part a predicts Jupiter's mass to be 1331 times the mass of Earth, because $11^3 = 1331$. Thus Jupiter's mass would be about $8.0 \cdot 10^{27}$ kg. c. Answers vary. Sample: Not all planets are made of the same materials. Jupiter is less dense than Earth; therefore, their masses cannot vary directly as their volumes alone. 19. a. $d = kt$; the data appear to lie on a line, so *d* varies directly with time, not the square of time. b. Answers vary slightly, depending on the data point chosen. Sample: $41 = 30k$, $k = \frac{41}{30}$, $d = \frac{41}{30}t$. c. Answers vary slightly. Sample: $d = \frac{41}{30}(180) = 246$ in. d. Answers vary slightly. Sample: 50 ft = 600 in., $600 = \frac{41}{30}t$, $t \approx 439$ minutes, or 7 hours, 19 minutes.

Self-Test Correlation Chart

Question	1	2	3	4	5	6	7	8	9	10
Objective(s)	A	A	A	B	D	D	C	E	E	E
Lesson(s)	2-1, 2-2, 2-9	2-1, 2-2, 2-9	2-1, 2-2, 2-9	2-1, 2-2, 2-9	2-3, 2-8	2-3, 2-8	2-4, 2-5	2-4, 2-5, 2-6	2-4, 2-5, 2-6	2-4, 2-5, 2-6

Question	11	12	13	14	15	16	17	18	19
Objective(s)	F	C, I	E, I	E, J	G, H, I	H	F	F, G	F, G, H
Lesson(s)	2-1, 2-2	2-4, 2-5, 2-6	2-4, 2-5, 2-6	2-4, 2-5, 2-6	2-1, 2-2, 2-4, 2-5, 2-6, 2-7, 2-8, 2-9	2-7, 2-8	2-1, 2-2	2-1, 2-2, 2-9	2-1, 2-2, 2-7, 2-8, 2-9

Chapter Review (pp. 143-147)

1. $y = kx$ **3.** $z = kxt$ **5.** directly; x; inversely; the square of v **7.** y varies inversely as the third power of w. **9.** $y = 49$ **11.** $y = \frac{1}{3}$ **13.** $\frac{32}{7}$ **15.** 8 **17.** $-\frac{1}{40}$ **19.** y is tripled. **21.** y is multiplied by 3^n. **23.** divided by c^n **25.** y is multiplied by $\frac{a^n}{b^n}$. **27.** parabola **29.** B, D **31.** true **33.** $x = 0$ **35.** $n = k\ell^2$ **37.** $F = \frac{k}{d^2}$ **39.** directly **41.** inversely **43.** only 0.0225 min, or about 1.35 sec **45.** 500,000,000 seconds, or about 16 yr **47.** ≈ 944.58 lb

49. a.

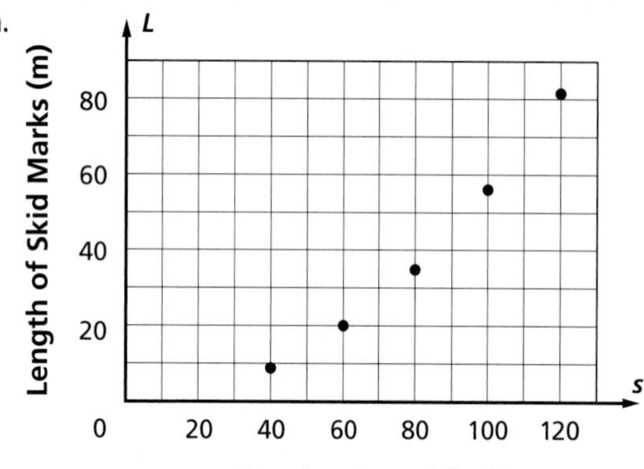

b. $L = kS^2$ **c.** $k = \frac{9}{1600}$; $L = \left(\frac{9}{1600}\right)S^2$ **d.** $L \approx 126.6$ m

51. $P = kdD$; because the points on both graphs lie on straight lines, P varies directly D, and also as d. Therefore, P varies jointly as D and d.

53. a.

q	p
0	undef
1	2
2	5
3	0.222
4	0.125
5	0.8
6	0.056

b.

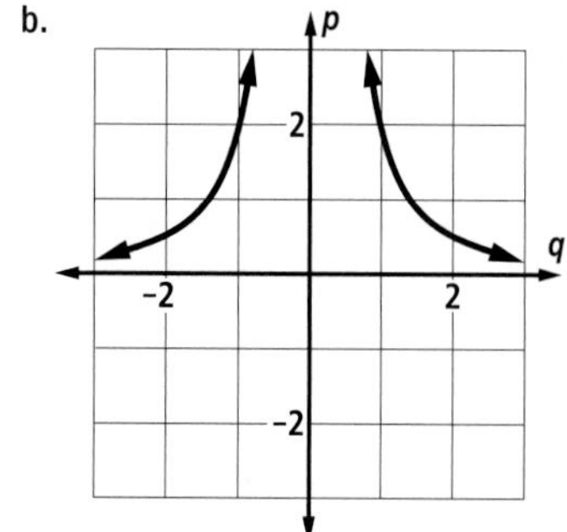

55.

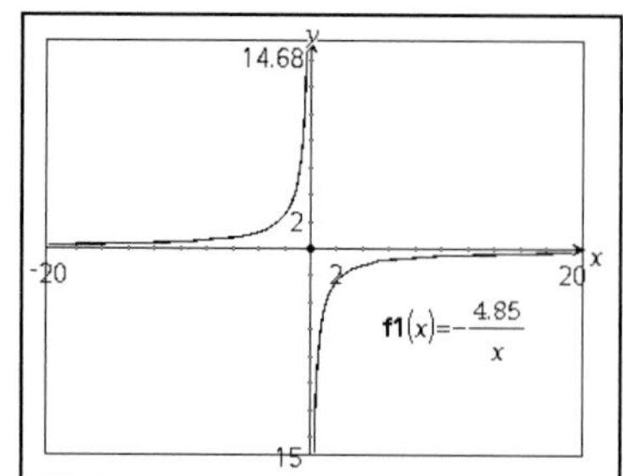

57. The branches pull away from the y-axis. **59.** C **61.** negative

Chapter 3

Lesson 3-1 (pp. 150-156)

Mental Math **a.** 31 or 32 **b.** 17 **c.** 14

Guided Example 2 **a.** 26; $8t$ **b.** $26 - 8t$; $\frac{13}{4}$; $3\frac{1}{4}$ **c.** 26; -8

Questions

1. m; b **3.** 1 minute, 45 seconds **5.** y-intercept; slope **7.** $\frac{1}{2}$ **9.** $y = \frac{2}{3}x - 3$ **11.** a, c, and e; b and d **13. a.** $y = 0.03x + 29.99$ **b.** 0.03; 29.99; The slope is the constant rate per minute, the y-intercept is the initial condition, the monthly service fee. **c.** \$34.07 **15.** 1

17.

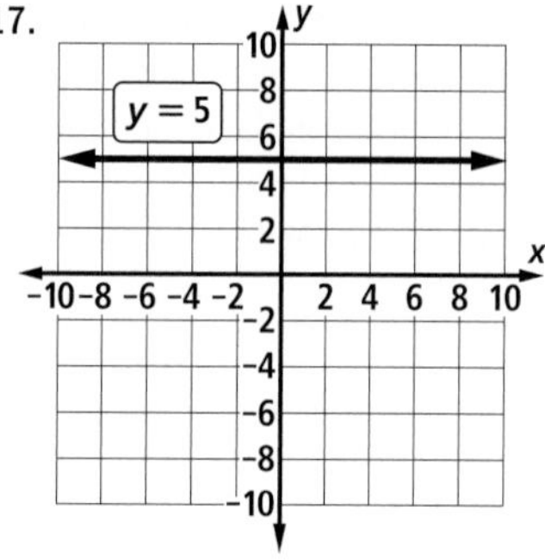

19. a. Answers vary. Sample: (1, -180), (4, 180), (5, 300), (7, 540) **b.** $T = 120D - 300$ **c.** \$28,080 **21.** joint **23.** combined **25. a.** inversely **b.** $n = 1$ **27.** $y = 48 - 6x$

Lesson 3-2 (pp. 157-162)

Mental Math **a.** $-12 < x < 12$ **b.** $-6 < x < 6$ **c.** $-4 < x < 8$ **d.** $x \leq -4$ or $x \geq 8$

Activity **Step 1.** $2.5b + 2d = 30$ **Step 2.** $d = 15 - 1.25b$ **Step 4.** (0, 15), (4, 10), (8, 5), (12, 0)

Guided Example 1 **a.** 30: 3,:4, continuous **b.** \$6: \$3: \$30: buying 3 adult tickets and 4 child tickets; discrete

Questions

1. a. linear combination **b.** Answers vary. Sample: Biking 600 miles, with P hours at 15 mph and L hours at 12 mph **3.** $0.5T + 0.75S + 1.25K$ **5. a.** $b + t = 12$ **b.** discrete **7. a.** $5.2x$ **b.** $7.8y$ **c.** $5.2x + 7.8y$ **d.** $5.2x + 7.8y = 3.6$ **e.** approximately 0.19 L **9. a.** nonnegative integers **b.** \$190 **c.** $25L + 15S = 225$

d.

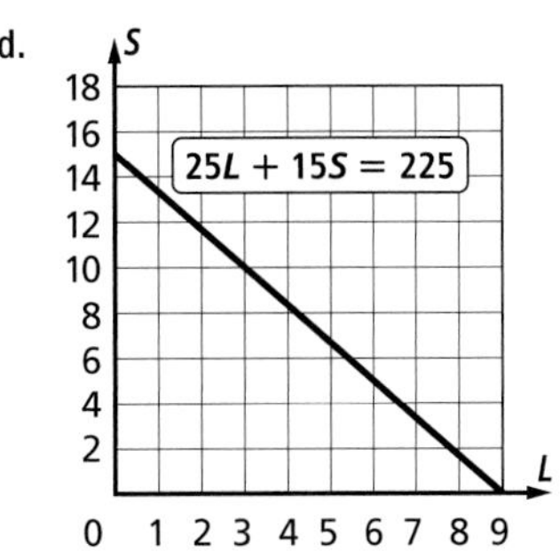

e.

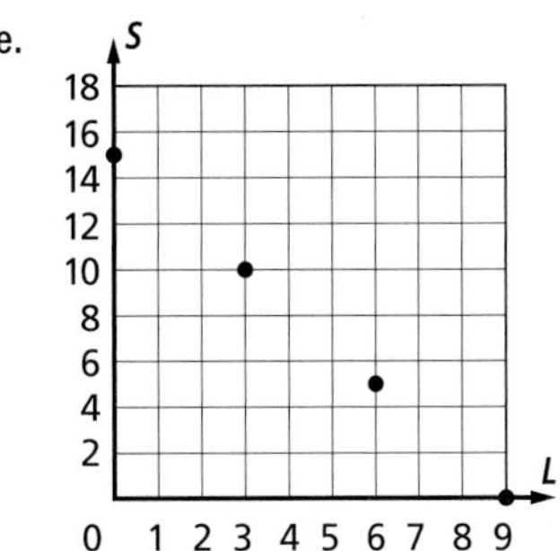

f. (0, 15), (3, 10), (6, 5), (9, 0) **11.** $\frac{5}{3}$ lb **13.** $t = ksr$ and $r = pm$, where k and p are constants. So then by substitution, $t = kpsm$. Let $a = kp$. Then a is a constant and $t = asm$, so t varies jointly with s and m. **15. a.** $w = kh^3$ **b.** $\frac{1}{173} = \frac{1}{4913}$

Lesson 3-3 (pp. 163-168)

Mental Math a. $c = kn$ **b.** $p = klw$ **c.** $t = \frac{k}{n}$ **d.** $d = \frac{kt}{a^2}$
Guided Example 3 $y = -\frac{8}{3}x + 8$; $y = -\frac{8}{3}x + 8$; $y = -\frac{8}{3}x + 4$; $y = -\frac{8}{3}x + 2$; (1) and (2); (3) and (4); (1); (2); (1); (2)

Questions

1. a. line **b.** vertical **c.** horizontal **3.** It is undefined.
5. a. 9 **b.** 4

c.

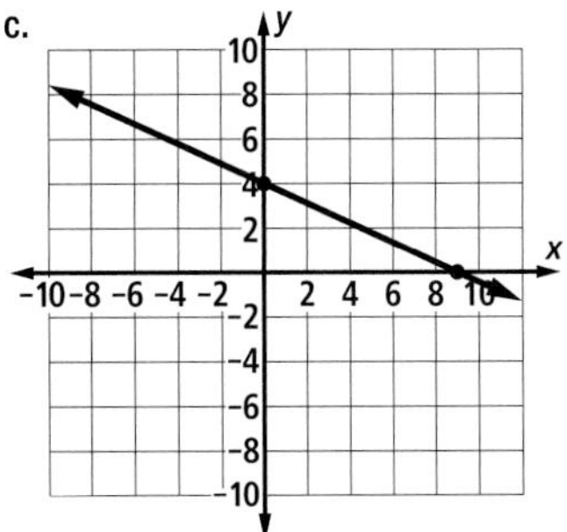

7. a. $\frac{C}{A}$; there is no x-intercept. **b.** $\frac{C}{B}$; there is no y-intercept
9. 42 **11. a.**

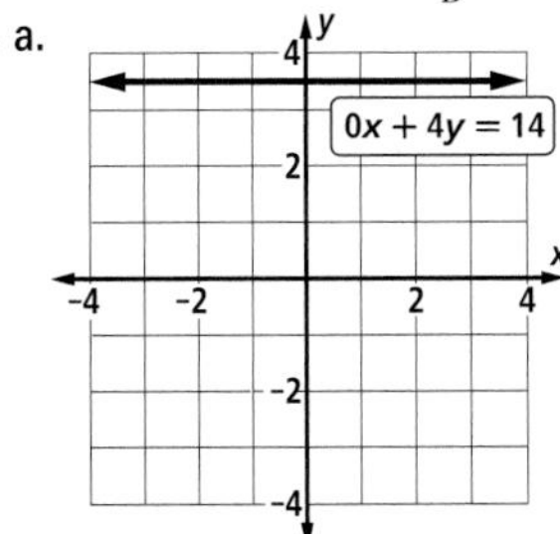

b. Answers vary. Sample: (0, 3.5), (5, 3.5) **c.** 0
13. $x = 17$ **15. a.** $y = -\frac{A}{B}x + \frac{C}{B}$; $y = -\frac{A}{B}x + \frac{D}{B}$
b. The slopes are equal, so the lines are parallel or are the same line. **c.** The intercepts are different, so the lines cannot be the same line and are thus parallel.
d. If equations for two lines are written in standard form with the same coefficients of x and y but different right sides, then the lines are unique and parallel.
e. Answers vary. Sample: $16x - 13y = 15$, $16x - 13y = 20$
17. $0.50P + H$ **19. a.** $400 - 60t = d$ **b.** constant decrease
21. Answers vary. Samples: **a.** $\{h \mid 0 \le h \le 16\}$ **b.** $\{d \mid 0 < d\}$. **c.** $\{t \mid -20 \le t \le 50\}$.

Lesson 3-4 (pp. 169-175)

Mental Math a. $\frac{2}{3}$ **b.** $\frac{3}{11}$ **c.** $\frac{b}{b+r+w}$
Guided Example 2 $-\frac{9}{2}$; 7; $-\frac{9}{2}$; 4; $y = -\frac{9}{2}x + 25$

Questions

1. 2 **3.** false **5.** Compute the slope and then use either point in the point slope form $y - y_1 = m(x - x_1)$.
7. $y = 6x + \sqrt{3}$ **9.** $y + 3 = \frac{12}{7}(x + 2)$ **11. a.** $c = 1.45s + 30$
b. \$30 **c.** \$175 **13. a.** 0.759398
b. `Define ptslope(a,b,m)=m·(x-a)+b`
c. $y = 0.759398x - 10.7376$ **d.** `Define line2pt(a,b,c,d)=ptslope(a,b,slope(a,b,c,d))`
e. yes **15. a.** $w = f(x) = \begin{cases} x + 10, \text{ for } 3 \le x \le 12 \\ \frac{5}{12}x + 17, \text{ for } 12 < x \le 60 \end{cases}$
b. 29.5 pounds **17.** not 0; 0 **19.** D **21. a.** $r_3 = 1700$
b. r sub seven equals negative one thousand three hundred twenty-seven.

Lesson 3-5 (pp. 176-181)

Mental Math a. 2.5 **b.** 0 **c.** 0.144 **d.** -0.8
Activity 1 Step 1. Answers vary. Sample:

Number of Squares	Score
240	5083
45	859
12	366
165	3115
174	3407
216	4257
165	3269
69	1409
225	4612
209	4097
225	4524
315	6340
210	4388
248	4807
150	2794

Step 2. Answers vary. Sample:

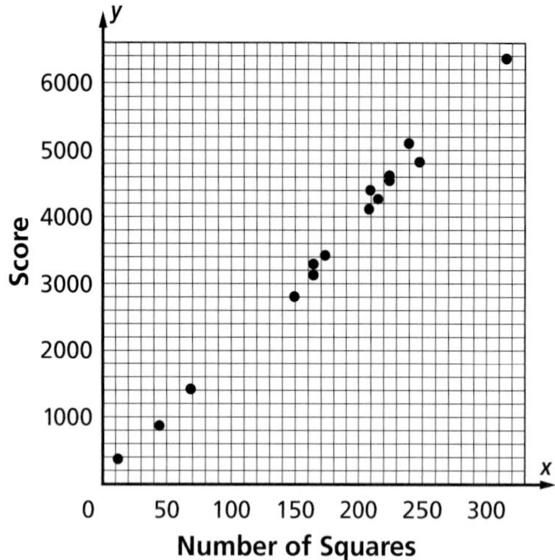

Yes, the data points appear to have a linear pattern.

Step 3. Answers vary. Sample:

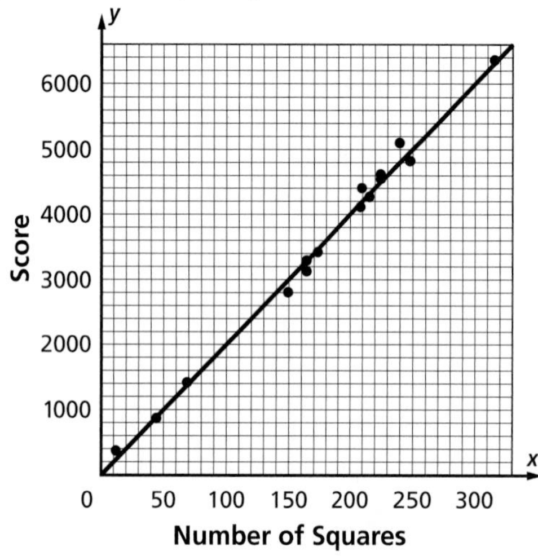

Step 4. Answers vary. Sample: (200, 4000), (300, 6000). In this case the equation is $y = 20x$. **Step 5.** Answers vary. Sample: Using the equation in the previous step would give a score of 2000.

Activity 2 Step 3. Answers vary. Sample: $y = 0.4829x - 29.90$ **Step 4.** Answers vary. Sample: It is very close to the regression line.

Step 5. Answers vary. Sample: At $x = 20$, the predictions differ by 0.01242. When $x = 80$, the prediction from the movable line differs from the value in the table by ≈ 0.73, and the prediction from the regression line differs from the value in the table by ≈ 0.74.

Questions

1. The student captured 48 squares, for a score of 985 points. **3. a.** 19 **b.** 19 points are scored for every square captured. **c.** 35 **d.** The player starts with 35 points. **e.** no **5. a.** $y = -\frac{4}{3}x + \frac{16}{3}$ **b.** $y = -\frac{4}{3}x + \frac{16}{3}$

7.

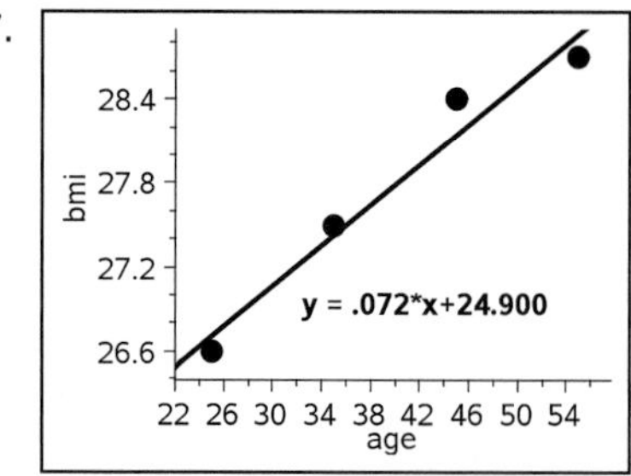

9. $y = 11.74x + 204.3$ **11. a.** $-\frac{5}{2}x + 3$ **b.** $-\frac{5}{2}x - \frac{9}{2}$ **13. a.** -6, 7, -8, 9 **b.** negative **15. a.** $-\frac{11}{9}$ **b.** $\frac{5}{7}$ **c.** $\frac{3a+5}{7-8a}$ **d.** $-\frac{200}{897} \approx -0.22$

Lesson 3-6 (pp. 182-188)

Mental Math a. 31.5 **b.** 5007 **c.** 22 **d.** the set of positive integers

Guided Example 1 113; 154; 154; 195; 195;236; 154; 195; 236

Guided Example 2 10,000; 400; 1

Guided Example 5 A1; $= \frac{A1}{2}$; A2; A3; A6; 64; 32; 16; 8; 4; 2

Questions

1. The answer of the last input **3.** a set of statements that indicate the first (or first few) terms and tell how the next term is calculated from the previous term or terms.

5. $\begin{cases} b_1 = 64 \\ b_{n+1} = \frac{1}{2}b_n, \text{ for integers } n = \{1, 2, 3, 4, 5\} \end{cases}$

7. a. -2, 6, 14, 22, 30 **b.** $\begin{cases} a_1 = -2 \\ a_n = a_{n-1} + 8, \text{ for } n \geq 2 \end{cases}$

9. Answers vary. Sample: If the formula did not have two parts, you would be missing either the initial condition or the instructions for how to calculate the following terms.

11. $\begin{cases} t_1 = -2 \\ t_{n+1} = t_n - 2, \text{ for } n \geq 1 \end{cases}$

13.a. $\begin{cases} S_1 = 8 \\ S_n = S_{n-1} + 2, \text{ for } 2 \leq n \leq 25 \end{cases}$ **b.** 34 seats

15. Yes; for each n there is a unique S_n. **17. a.** The initial term of the sequence is 6.42, and each subsequent term in the sequence is 2.73 less than the previous term.

b. $\begin{cases} a_1 = 6.42 \\ a_n = a_{n-1} - 2.73, \text{ for } n \geq 2 \end{cases}$ **c.** -12.69

19. Yes; there appears to be a linear relationship between attendance and payroll.

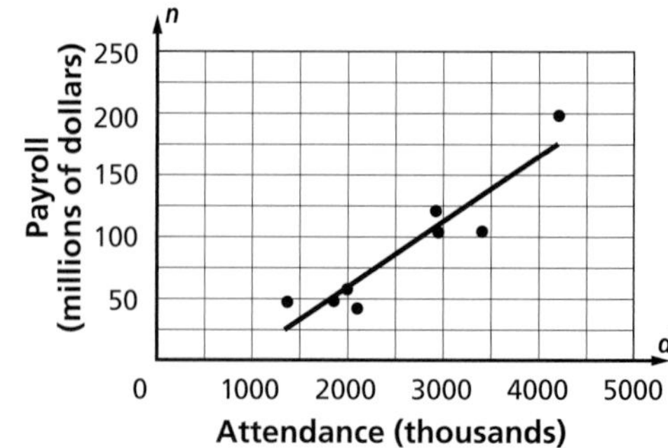

21. a.

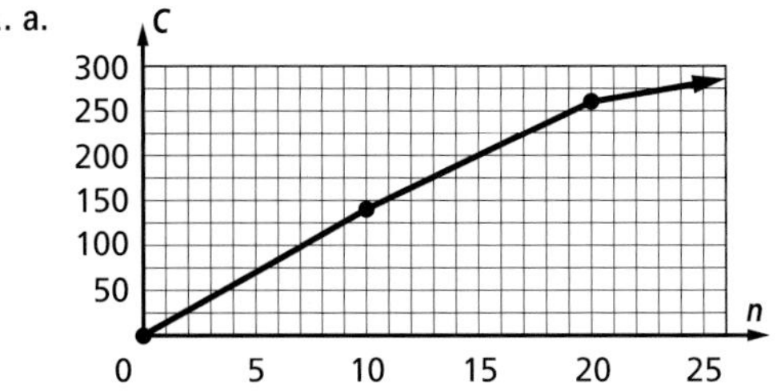

b. $C = \begin{cases} 14n \text{ for } 0 \le n \le 10 \\ 12n + 20, \text{ for } 10 < n \le 20 \\ 10n + 60, \text{ for } 20 < n \end{cases}$

23. a. After 3 seconds, the object has fallen 44.1 feet.
b. No; the object cannot fall for a negative amount of time.

Lesson 3-7 (pp. 189-195)

Mental Math a. $21x$ **b.** $21x$ **c.** $6x - 18y$

Guided Example 1 a.

n	a_n
1	-2
2	2
3	6
4	10
5	14
6	18

b.

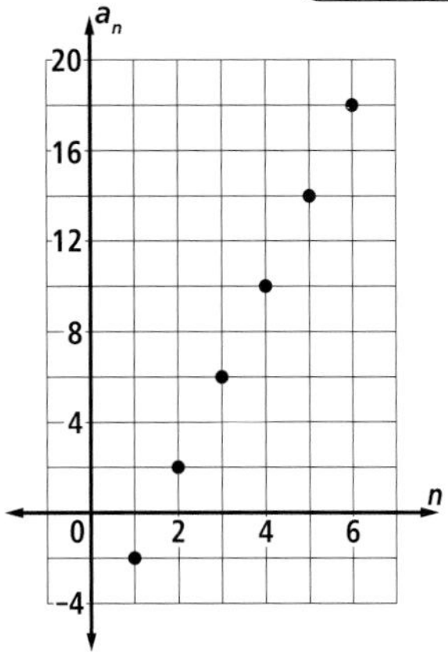

Questions

1. a. 34 **b.** $\begin{cases} a_1 = -2 \\ a_{n+1} = a_n + 4, \text{ for } n \ge 1 \end{cases}$ **3.** D

5. a. 55 **b.** 5 **c.** 5 **7. a.** $\begin{cases} b_1 = 10 \\ b_{n+1} = 1.2b_n, \text{ for } n \ge 1 \end{cases}$

b.

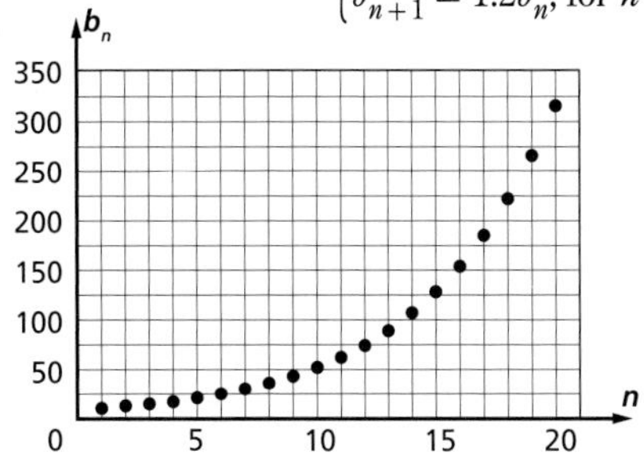

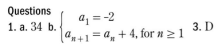

c. 22 days **9. a.**

n	b_n
1	$500
2	$575
3	$650
4	$725
5	$800
6	$875

b. $\begin{cases} b_1 = 500 \\ b_n = b_{n-1} + 75, \text{ for } n \ge 2 \end{cases}$

c.

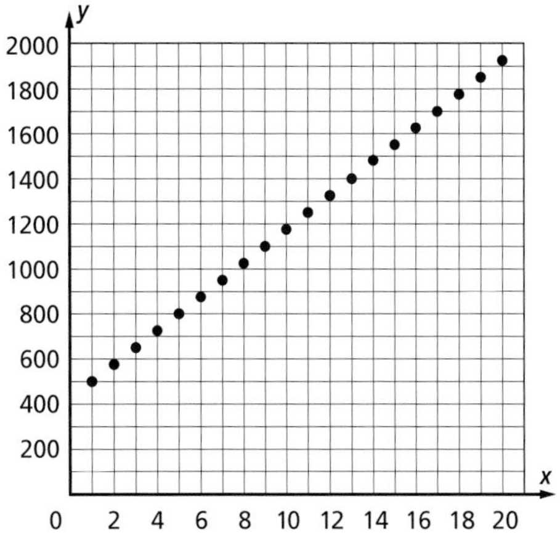

d. Yes; All the points lie on the line $y = 500 + 75n$ because Kamilah saves the same amount every week.

11. a.

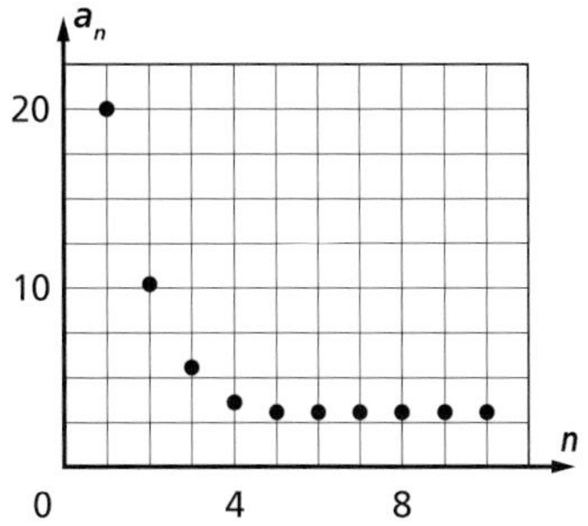

b. The numbers get smaller and closer to 3.

c.

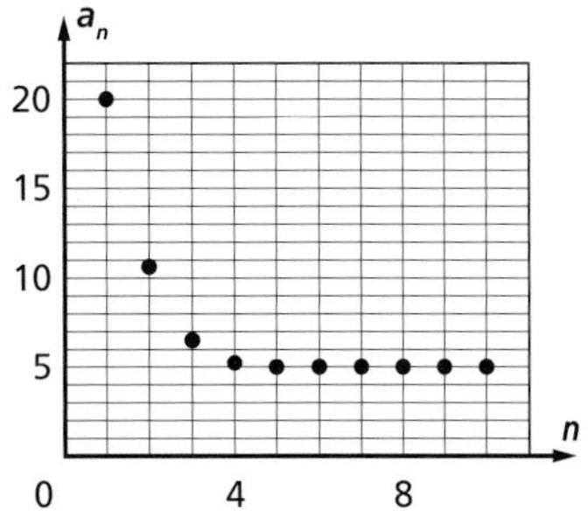

The numbers get smaller and closer to 5. The only change in the answer between the two formulas is in the numbers that the sequences approached.

13. a. one third of b. $\begin{cases} b_1 = 81 \\ b_n = \frac{1}{3}b_{n-1}, \text{ for } n \geq 2 \end{cases}$

c. $1, \frac{1}{3}, \frac{1}{9}, \frac{1}{27}$ 15. E

17. a.

n	s_n
1	1
2	2
3	4
4	7
5	12
6	20
7	33
8	54
9	88
10	143
11	232
12	376
13	609
14	986

b. $s_n = F_{n+2} - 1$ c. Answers vary. Sample: If we let t_n be the sum of the squares of the first n Fibonacci numbers, then a table for t_n is as follows:

n	t_n
1	1
2	2
3	6
4	15
5	40
6	104
7	273
8	714
9	1870
10	4895
11	12,816
12	33,552
13	87,841
14	229,970

An equation for t_n is $t_n = F_n \cdot F_{n+1}$.

Lesson 3-8 (pp. 196–202)

Mental Math a. parabola b. line c. none of these d. hyperbola

Questions

1. 151 3. $a_n = a_1 + (n - 1)d$ 5. a. $a_n = 12 + (n - 1)4$
b. $\begin{cases} a_1 = 12 \\ a_n = a_{n-1} + 4, \text{ for integers } n \geq 2 \end{cases}$ c. 196
7. $\begin{cases} a_1 = 1.3 \\ a_n = a_{n-1} + 0.3, \text{ for integers } n \geq 2 \end{cases}$
9. a. $\begin{cases} t_1 = 12 \\ t_n = t_{n-1} + 7, \text{ for integers } n \geq 2 \end{cases}$ b. 544
11. $\begin{cases} a_1 = -70 \\ a_{n+1} = a_n + 22.5, \text{ for integers } n \geq 1 \end{cases}$
13. $a_n = 13 - 4(n - 1)$
15. \$400 17. a. 15.85, 15.71, 15.56
b. $r_n = 15.85 - 0.14545(n-1)$, or $r_n = 16 - 0.14545n$
19. $T_1 = \frac{1(1+1)}{2} = 1$; $T_2 = \frac{2(2+1)}{2} = 3 = 1 + 2$; $T_3 = \frac{3(3+1)}{2} = 6 = 3 + 3$ 21. E 23. a. $k = -\frac{1}{2}$
b. k is the slope of the line.

Lesson 3-9 (pp. 203–209)

Mental Math a. 10, 12 b. -1, -7 c. 1, -1

Guided Example 1 a. 5 b. greatest integer; -5 c. 3.1416; π; 4; d. smallest integer; 13; 13

Guided Example 4 6; 0.18; 18

Questions

1. \$1.38 3. Answers vary. Sample: $\lceil x \rceil$ means the smallest integer greater than or equal to x. It is called the ceiling function because the ceiling of a room is the *smallest* (or *next up*) level of the building that is above that room.
5. 12 7. 7 9. a. domain: set of all real numbers; range: set of all integers b. domain: set of all positive real numbers; range: {2.50, 2.90, 3.30, ...} 11. a. 1 b. 2 c. r rounds to the greatest integer less than or equal to $x + 0.5$.
13. $750 - g\left\lfloor \frac{750}{g} \right\rfloor$ 15. a. yes b. $5.10 + 1.15\left\lceil \frac{a}{100} \right\rceil$
17. a. Answers vary. Sample: Monday b. Thursday
c. Monday 19. a. $\begin{cases} a_1 = \sqrt{2} \\ a_n = a_{n-1} + 2\sqrt{3}, \text{ for } n \geq 2 \end{cases}$
b. $a_n = \sqrt{2} + 2\sqrt{3}(n - 1)$ c. $\sqrt{2} + 200\sqrt{3}$
21. a. $y - 2 = 2.5(x - 2)$ b. $y + 3 = 2.5x$
c. $y = 2.5(x - 2) + 2 = 2.5x - 5 + 2 = 2.5x - 3$

Self-Test (pp. 213–214)

1.

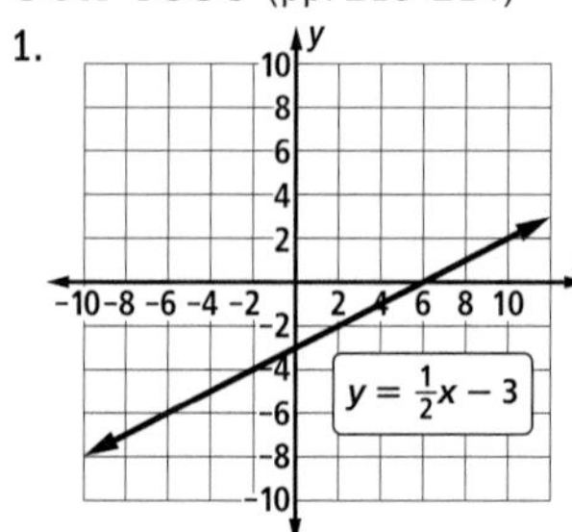

2. a. $\frac{5}{3}$, since $-3y = 10 - 5x$, $y = -\frac{10}{3} + \frac{5}{3}x$ b. x-intercept: 2, y-intercept: $-\frac{10}{3}$; $5x - 3(0) = 10$, $x = 2$; $5(0) - 3y = 10$, $y = -\frac{10}{3}$ 3. constant decrease; as the x-value increases, the y-value decreases 4. $m = \frac{7-3}{-2-5} = -\frac{4}{7}$, so an equation in point-slope form is $y - 7 = -\frac{4}{7}(x + 2)$. 5. The line will have the same slope, $-\frac{2}{3}$. Use point-slope form: $y - 3 = -\frac{2}{3}(x + 6)$. 6. a. vertical lines, division by zero is undefined b. horizontal lines, there is no vertical change 7. H hot dogs cost $2.25H$, and T tacos cost $3.75T$, so the total amount is $2.25H + 3.75\,T$. 8. The constant change is $-\frac{1}{3}$ and the initial condition is 310; $h = 310 - \frac{1}{3}t$ 9. a. Explicit; you can find the value of a_n directly by plugging in the value of n. b. $a_1 = 50 - 3(1 - 1) = 50$; $a_2 = 50 - 3(2 - 1) = 47$; $a_3 = 50 - 3(3 - 1) = 44$; $a_4 = 50 - 3(4 - 1) = 41$; $a_5 = 50 - 3(5 - 1) = 38$ c. Yes; there is a constant difference of 3 between consecutive terms 10. a. $C = 23.50 + 0.08(m - 200)$; $C = 23.50 + 0.08(453 - 200)$; $C = \$43.74$ b. $C = \begin{cases} 23.50, & 0 \le m \le 200 \\ 23.50 + 0.08(m - 200), & m > 200 \end{cases}$

11. a. 29, 47, 76, 123 since $11 + 18 = 29$, $18 + 29 = 47$, $29 + 47 = 76$, $47 + 76 = 123$

b. $\begin{cases} L_1 = 1 \\ L_2 = 3 \\ L_{n+2} = L_n + L_{n+1}, n \ge 1 \end{cases}$ 12. $m = \frac{305.4 - 273.2}{90 - 32} = \frac{32.2}{58} = 0.56$; $K - 273.2 = 0.56(F - 32)$; $K - 273.2 = 0.56F - 17.9$; $K = 0.56F + 255.3$ 13. $a_n = -25 - 20(n - 1)$, because -20 is the common difference between terms and -25 is the initial term. 14. B; each piece has a steeper slant than the previous one.

15.

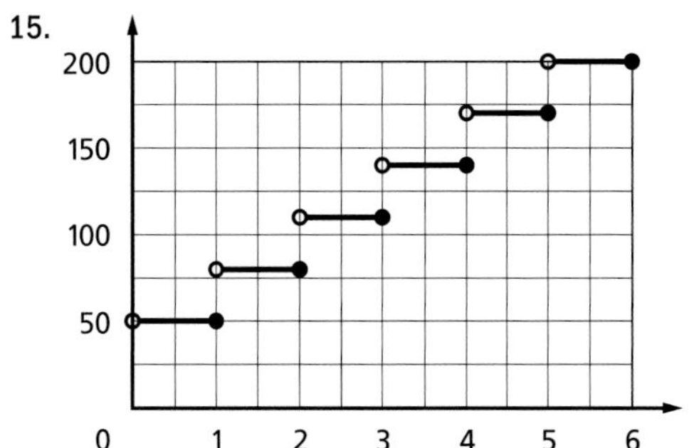

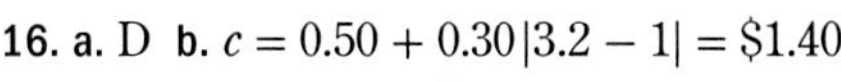
16. a. D b. $c = 0.50 + 0.30|3.2 - 1| = \$1.40$

17.

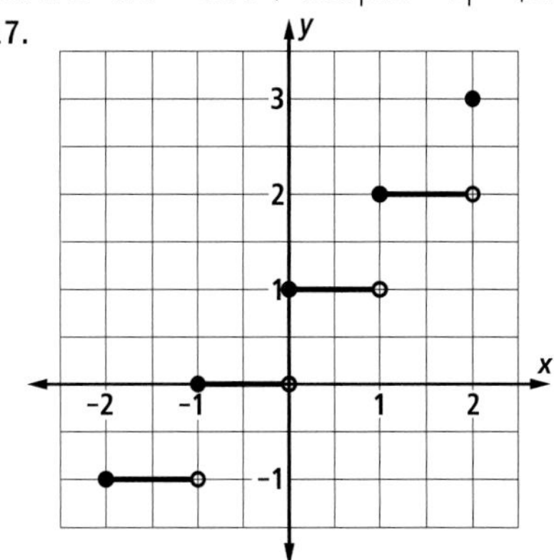

18. a. $y \approx -0.875x + 75.9$ b. $y \approx -0.874\,(42) + 75.9 \approx 39.2$ c. (80, 8.9); It means that the regression line gives a less accurate prediction for an 80-year-old. d. Answers vary. People who are ages 80–100 have many more health factors affecting their life expectancy than people who are younger.

Self-Test Correlation Chart

Question	1	2	3	4	5	6	7	8	9	10
Objective(s)	M	A	G	M	B	E	H	G	D, F	K
Lesson(s)	3-1, 3-3	3-1, 3-3	3-1, 3-8	3-1, 3-3	3-4	3-1, 3-2, 3-3	3-2	3-1, 3-8	3-6, 3-8	3-4, 3-9
Question	**11**	**12**	**13**	**14**	**15**	**16**	**17**	**18**		
Objective(s)	D, L	I	D	N	N	C, K	N	J		
Lesson(s)	3-6, 3-7, 3-8	3-4	3-6, 3-8	3-4, 3-7, 3-9	3-4, 3-7, 3-9	3-4, 3-9	3-4, 3-7, 3-9	3-5		

Chapter Review (pp. 215-219)

1. a. 3 b. 4 c. -12 3. a. 0 b. no x-intercept c. -17 5. a. $\frac{6}{5}$ b. $-\frac{1}{3}$ c. $\frac{2}{5}$ 7. $y - 10 = \frac{2}{5}(x + 5)$ 9. $y = -(x + 3) + 4$, or $y = -x + 1$ 11. a. 13 b. -13 13. 8 15. a. $a_n = 37 + (n - 1)(-21) = -21n + 58$ for integers $n \ge 1$

b. $\begin{cases} a_1 = 37 \\ a_n = a_{n-1} - 21, \text{ for integers } n \ge 2 \end{cases}$

c. -26, -47, -68, -89, -110 17. a. $a_n = -\frac{11}{12} + \frac{n}{4}$ for integers $n \ge 1$ b. $-\frac{2}{3}, -\frac{5}{12}, -\frac{1}{6}, \frac{1}{12}, \frac{1}{3}$ 19. true 21. $-\frac{b}{m}$ 23. Answers vary. Sample: $(x + 4, y - 3)$ 25. It is a set of collinear points. 27. no 29. yes 31. 0.8 33. a. $p = 44 - 2t$ b. 9 hours 35. a. $A + B$ b. $2.5A + 6.25B$ c. $0.75 = 2.5A + 6.25B$ d. Answers vary. Sample: (0.3, 0), (0, 0.12), (0.25, 0.02) 37. 70 mL

39. a.

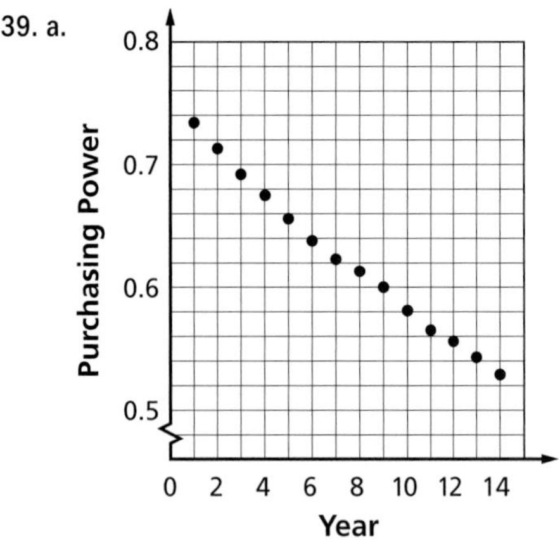

b. $y \approx -0.016x + 0.790$ **c.** Yes; the decrease in the purchasing power is relatively stable from year to year.

41. $C = \begin{cases} 0.99d \text{ for } d \leq 20 \\ 19.80 + 0.89(d - 20) \text{ for } d > 20 \end{cases}$ **43. a.** 3 mph

b. 3 mph **c.** $d = \begin{cases} 3t, \text{ for } t \leq 0.5 \\ 1.5, \text{ for } 0.5 < t \leq 6.5 \\ -3t + 21, \text{ for } 6.5 < t \leq 6.75 \\ 0.75, \text{ for } 6.75 < t \leq 7.5 \\ -3t + 23.25, \text{ for } 7.5 < t \leq 7.75 \end{cases}$

d. Her speed walking home was the same. We can use the graph to calculate the rate of change of d with respect to t to see this. In both cases she walked at 3 mph.

45. a. $\begin{cases} a_1 = 2300 \\ a_n = a_{n-1} - 26, \text{ for integers } n \geq 2 \end{cases}$

b. $a_n = 2326 - 26n$ for integers $n \geq 1$ **c.** Yes; she will have 246 nuts left at the end of the winter.

47.

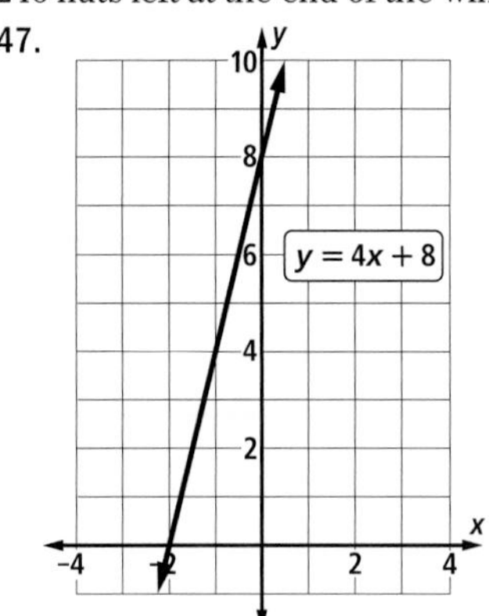

49.

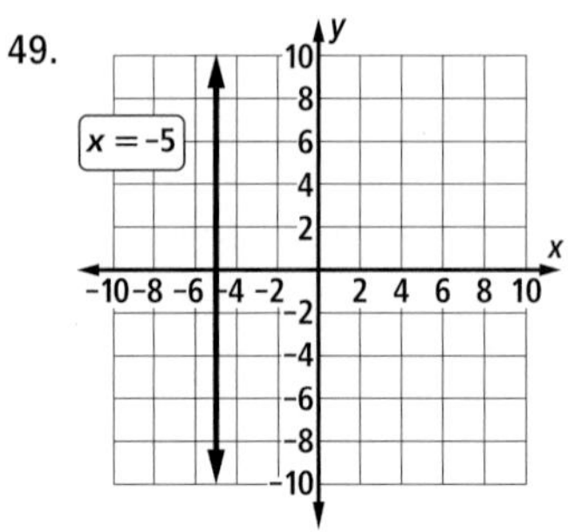

51. negative **53.** Answers vary. Sample: $y = -\frac{1}{3}x - 1$

55. a.

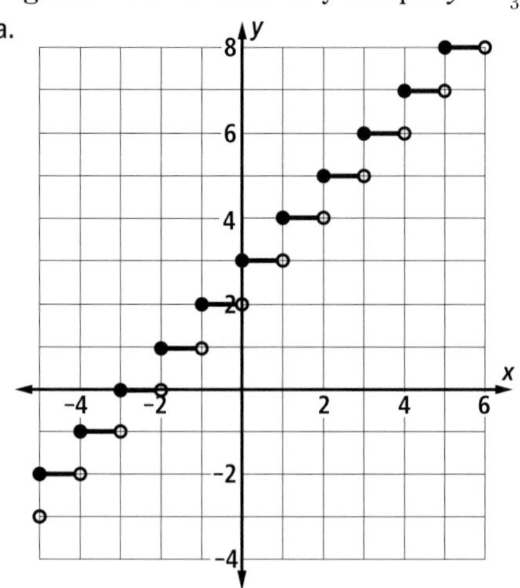

b. Domain: set of all real numbers; range: set of all integers

57. $a_n = 6n - 4$

Chapter 4

Lesson 4-1 (pp. 222-227)

Mental Math a. $y = 4x + 2.5$ **b.** $x = -7$ **c.** $y = \frac{1}{3}x + \frac{9}{10}$ **d.** $y = 12$

Guided Example a. 3.5; 1.9; 3.4; 1.9; 3.9; 2.8; 3.5; 3.4; 3.9; 1.9; 1.9; 2.8; **b.** 3; 2; 3 × 2; 2; 3; 2 × 3

Activity Step 1. Answers vary.

Sample: $\begin{bmatrix} 3 & 6 & 4 & -2.5 & -5 \\ -5 & -1 & 5 & 4 & -0.75 \end{bmatrix}$

Step 2. Answers vary.

Sample: $\begin{bmatrix} 6 & 4 & -2.5 & -5 & 3 \\ -1 & 5 & 4 & -0.75 & -5 \end{bmatrix}$

and $\begin{bmatrix} -2.5 & -5 & 3 & 6 & 4 \\ 4 & -0.75 & -5 & -1 & 5 \end{bmatrix}$

Step 4.

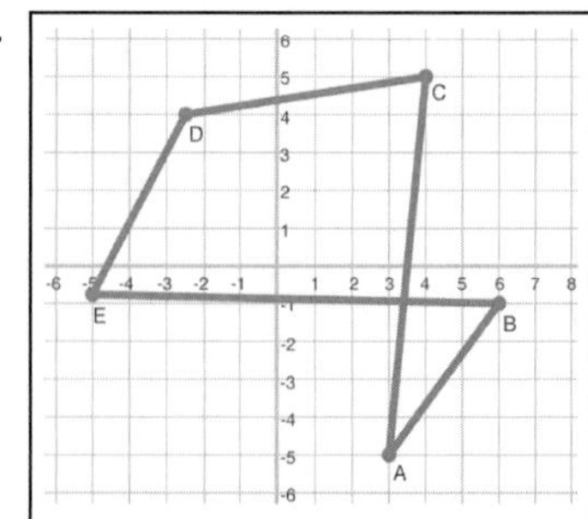

$BACDE$ is not a polygon because $\overline{AC}$ intersects $\overline{BE}$.

Questions

1. A matrix is a rectangular arrangement of objects.

3. Answers vary. Sample: Find the matrix command and enter the dimensions.

5.

	1980	1985	1990	2000
Males	3.5	3.3	3.4	3.9
Females	1.9	1.8	1.9	2.8

7. a. $\begin{bmatrix} x \\ y \end{bmatrix}$ **b.** a point matrix

9. $\begin{matrix} A & B & C \end{matrix}$ $\begin{bmatrix} -3 & 5 & -2 \\ 4 & 1 & -2 \end{bmatrix}$ **11. a.** 4×2 **b.** the number of law degrees earned in 2000 **c.** the total number of professional degrees in Medicine, Dentistry, Law, and Theology earned by women in 2000 **13.** -3; 0.1

15. a.

	A	E	I	O	U
English	0.08	0.13	0.07	0.08	0.03
SCRABBLE	0.09	0.12	0.09	0.08	0.04

b. Answers vary. Sample: Go to the matrix prompt and then specify the 2 by 5 dimensions and enter the elements in their appropriate location.

17.

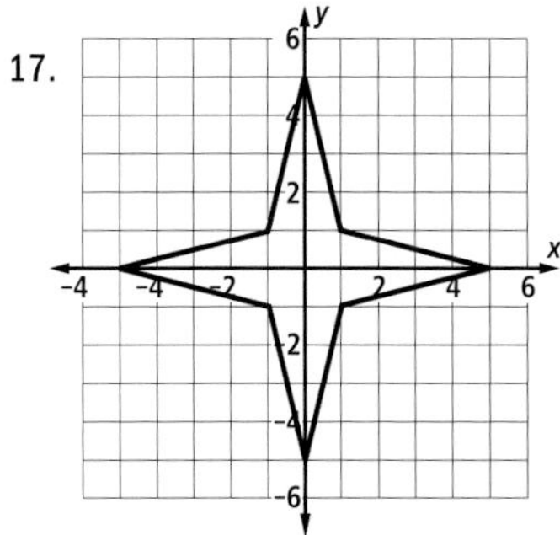

This is a nonconvex polygon. **19.** $a_n = 50 - 2n$ **21.** The lengths of the edges of *A* are 3 times as long as the lengths of the edges of *B*.

Lesson 4-2 (pp. 228–234)

Mental Math a. \$11.00 **b.** \$12.50 **c.** \$10.75 **d.** $4.5p + 3.25s + 3c$

Activity Step 2. $\begin{bmatrix} 2a & 2b & 2c \\ 2d & 2e & 2f \end{bmatrix}$ **Step 3.** $\begin{bmatrix} 3a & 3b & 3c \\ 3d & 3e & 3f \end{bmatrix}$

Step 4. $\begin{bmatrix} 4a & 4b & 4c \\ 4d & 4e & 4f \end{bmatrix}$; The coefficients seem to be increasing by 1 each time I add the original matrix.

Step 5. $\begin{bmatrix} 2a & 2b & 2c \\ 2d & 2e & 2f \end{bmatrix}$ **Step 6.** $\begin{bmatrix} 3a & 3b & 3c \\ 3d & 3e & 3f \end{bmatrix}$

Step 7. $\begin{bmatrix} 4a & 4b & 4c \\ 4d & 4e & 4f \end{bmatrix}$; Again, the coefficients seem to be increasing by 1. **Step 8.** Answer vary. Sample: Yes; Steps 4 and 7 show that the result of adding a matrix to itself a certain number of times is the same as multiplying the original matrix by the number of times you added it.

Questions

1. No; in order to add two matrices, they must have the same dimensions. The two matrices in question have different dimensions. **3.** $\begin{bmatrix} 5 & -15 \\ -6 & 3 \end{bmatrix}$ **5.** $\begin{bmatrix} -1 & -3 \\ -\frac{9}{2} & 10 \end{bmatrix}$

7. $\begin{bmatrix} 6 & 8 & 4 & 3 & 1 \\ 7 & 8 & 5 & 2 & 5 \\ 13 & 1 & 1 & 4 & 4 \\ 12 & 1 & 9 & 4 & 2 \end{bmatrix}$; The matrix represents the cars at Rusty's Car Dealership that were not damaged by the hailstorm. **9. a.** false **b.** $B - C = \begin{bmatrix} -1 & -1 \\ -1 & -1 \end{bmatrix}$; $C - B = \begin{bmatrix} 1 & 1 \\ 1 & 1 \end{bmatrix}$ **11. a.** $M = \begin{bmatrix} 2 & -2 & 6 & -101 \\ -3 & 3 & -36 & 57 \\ -2 & 2 & -12 & 113 \\ -4 & 4 & -76 & 47 \end{bmatrix}$

b. the difference in points scored against each team in 2006 from 2005 **c.** 2 means New England had 2 more wins in 2006 compared to 2005; -2 represents the 2 fewer losses New England had in 2006 compared to 2005; 6 represents how many more points New England scored in 2006 compared to 2005; -101 represents how many fewer points against New England were incurred in 2006 compared to 2005 **13. a.** $k = \frac{1}{3}$ **b.** $l = 3$ **15.** $a = 4, b = 63, c = -29, d = -5$ **17.** $\begin{bmatrix} 0 & 0 & -1 \\ 0 & 4 & 0 \end{bmatrix}$

19.

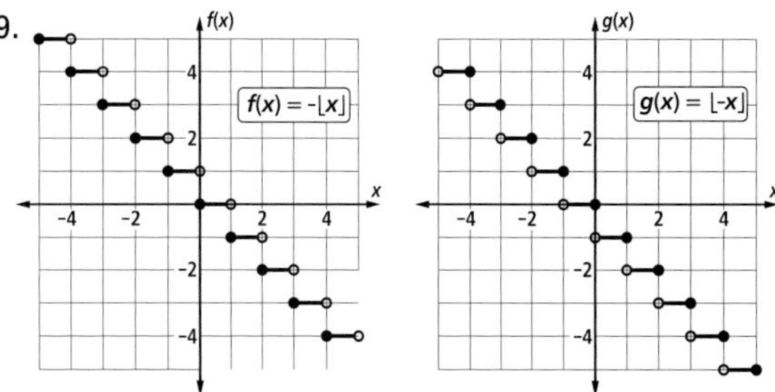

Answers vary. Sample: $f(x) = -\lfloor x \rfloor$ is always 1 greater than $g(x) = \lfloor -x \rfloor$ for all values of x, except when x is an integer, in which case $f(x) = g(x)$. **21. a.** Area $= 4x \cdot 0.5x = 2x^2$

b.

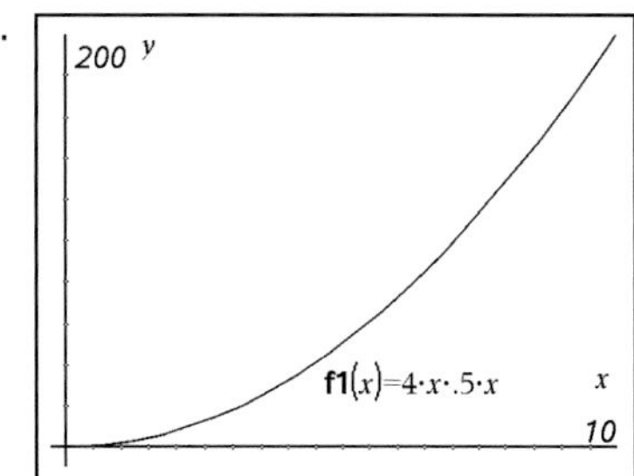

c. $\{x \mid x > 0\}$ **d.** the set of real numbers

e. 200 y; f1(x)=4·x·.5·x; x; -10; 1; 10

Lesson 4-3 (pp. 235-241)

Mental Math a. \$2.50 **b.** \$4.80 **c.** \$14.80

Guided Example 2 2; 3; 6; 3 • -1; 1 • 2 + 3 • 4; -2 • 5; -2 • 2 + 4 • 4; 2; 14; -14; 12

Activity Step 2. [358] **Step 3.** [358] **Step 4.** The Associative Property of Multiplication

Questions

1. 3 **3.** \$11 • 1 + \$17 • 5 + \$18 • 3 = \$150 **5.** [-23]

7. a. No; the number of elements in a row of B is not the same as the number of elements in a column of A. **b.** Matrix multiplication is not commutative.

9. $\begin{bmatrix} 4 & 6 \\ -1 & 8 \end{bmatrix} \cdot \begin{bmatrix} 7 & 3 \\ 5 & 1 \end{bmatrix} = \begin{bmatrix} 58 & 18 \\ 33 & 5 \end{bmatrix}$

$\begin{bmatrix} 7 & 3 \\ 5 & 1 \end{bmatrix} \cdot \begin{bmatrix} 4 & 6 \\ -1 & 8 \end{bmatrix} = \begin{bmatrix} 25 & 66 \\ 19 & 38 \end{bmatrix}$

11.

	TTB	TB	TB
Wt.	1.5	5	12
Vol.	1	1	0.6

	Store 1	Store 2
TTB	20	60
TB	50	10
BB	12	15

	Store 1	Store 2
Wt.	424	320
Vol.	77.2	19

13. a. $\begin{bmatrix} x+y \\ x+y \end{bmatrix}$; A is moved to the right y units and up x units to B.

b. $\begin{bmatrix} x \\ y \end{bmatrix}$; $B = A$ **c.** $\begin{bmatrix} y \\ x \end{bmatrix}$; A's coordinates are switched to get B.

d. $\begin{bmatrix} -y \\ x \end{bmatrix}$; the y-coordinate of A is changed to its opposite and then the coordinates are switched to get B. **e.** $\begin{bmatrix} 2x \\ 2y \end{bmatrix}$; A's coordinates are doubled to get B. **15.** $x = 3$

17. $\begin{bmatrix} 0 & 0 \\ 0 & 0 \end{bmatrix}$ **19.** 4×3 **21. a.** square **b.** $K' = (0.5, 1.5)$; $L' = (-2, 1.5)$; $M' = (-2, 4)$; $N' = (0.5, 4)$ **c.** Square; it is a size-change image of $KLMN$, and size-change images are similar to their preimages.

Lesson 4-4 (pp. 242-248)

Mental Math a. true **b.** true **c.** false **d.** true

Activity Step 1. $\begin{bmatrix} 4 & 6 & 6 & 3 & 4 \\ 2 & 2 & 6 & 4 & 4 \end{bmatrix}$

Step 2. $\begin{bmatrix} 2 & 0 \\ 0 & 2 \end{bmatrix}\begin{bmatrix} 4 & 6 & 6 & 3 & 4 \\ 2 & 2 & 6 & 4 & 4 \end{bmatrix} = \begin{bmatrix} 8 & 12 & 12 & 6 & 8 \\ 4 & 4 & 12 & 8 & 8 \end{bmatrix}$;

$\begin{bmatrix} \frac{1}{3} & 0 \\ 0 & \frac{1}{3} \end{bmatrix}\begin{bmatrix} 4 & 6 & 6 & 3 & 4 \\ 2 & 2 & 6 & 4 & 4 \end{bmatrix} = \begin{bmatrix} \frac{4}{3} & 2 & 2 & 1 & \frac{4}{3} \\ \frac{2}{3} & \frac{2}{3} & 2 & \frac{4}{3} & \frac{4}{3} \end{bmatrix}$

Step 3. The coordinates of $N'U'M'E'R'$ are each 2 (or $\frac{1}{3}$) times the corresponding coordinates of the original $NUMER$.

Step 4.

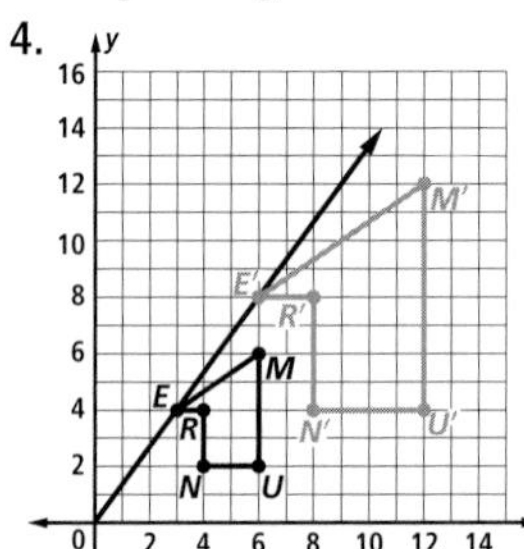

Step 5. $\frac{OE'}{OE} = 2\left(\text{or } \frac{1}{3}\right)$ **Step 6.** $\frac{OR'}{OR} = 2\left(\text{or } \frac{1}{3}\right)$; $\frac{ON'}{ON} = 2\left(\text{or } \frac{1}{3}\right)$; $\frac{OM'}{OM} = 2\left(\text{or } \frac{1}{3}\right)$; $\frac{OU'}{OU} = 2\left(\text{or } \frac{1}{3}\right)$ **Step 7.** The vertices of $N'U'M'E'R'$ are k times the vertices of the original $NUMER$.

Guided Example 2 Missing numbers along top rows of matrices, left to right: 4, -1, 1, 4; Missing numbers along bottom rows of matrices, left to right: 0, 4, 8, -12, 8, 4

Questions

1. a. $N'U'M'E'R'$ is similar to $NUMER$, with sides four times as long. **b.** $N'U'M'E'R'$ is similar to $NUMER$, with sides half as long. **c.** $N'U'M'E'R'$ is identical to $NUMER$.

3. The size change of magnitude 1.2 and center (0, 0) maps (4, 3.4) onto (4.8, 4.08). **5.** C **7.** $\begin{bmatrix} \frac{1}{4} & 0 \\ 0 & \frac{1}{4} \end{bmatrix}$

9. always **11.** always **13.** $\begin{bmatrix} 2768 & 0 \\ 0 & 2768 \end{bmatrix}$ **15. a.** $\begin{bmatrix} \frac{5}{2} & 0 \\ 0 & \frac{5}{2} \end{bmatrix}$

b. 1 **c.** 1 **d.** yes, by the Parallel Lines and Slope Theorem **17. a.**

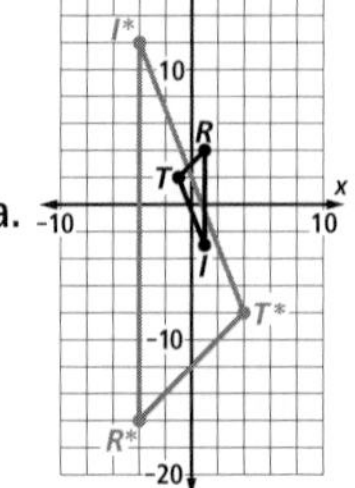

b. $\triangle T^*R^*I^*$ is the rotation image of $\triangle T'R'I'$ under a half turn.

19. a. 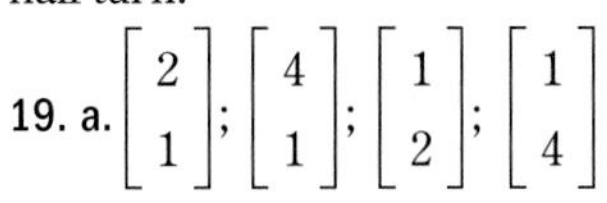
$\begin{bmatrix} 2 \\ 1 \end{bmatrix}; \begin{bmatrix} 4 \\ 1 \end{bmatrix}; \begin{bmatrix} 1 \\ 2 \end{bmatrix}; \begin{bmatrix} 1 \\ 4 \end{bmatrix}$

b.

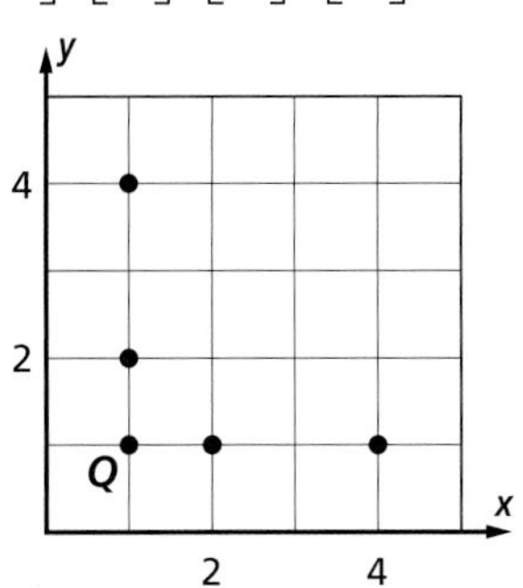

21. a. $\ell = \frac{V}{wh}$ **b.** V; w; h **c.** $\frac{5}{18}$

Lesson 4-5 (pp. 249–254)

Mental Math a. I and II **b.** II and IV **c.** III and IV **d.** I and III
Guided Example 1 4; 0.5; 4; 0.5; 20; 3; 24; 0
Activity Step 1. See first graph in Guided Example 1.

Step 2. $S1 \cdot M = \begin{bmatrix} 0 & 20 & 24 \\ 2 & 3 & 0 \end{bmatrix}$ **Step 3.** See second graph in Example 1. $S1$ represents the scale change $S_{4,0.5}$.

Step 4. $S2 \cdot M = \begin{bmatrix} 0 & 6 & 7.2 \\ 12 & 18 & 0 \end{bmatrix}$

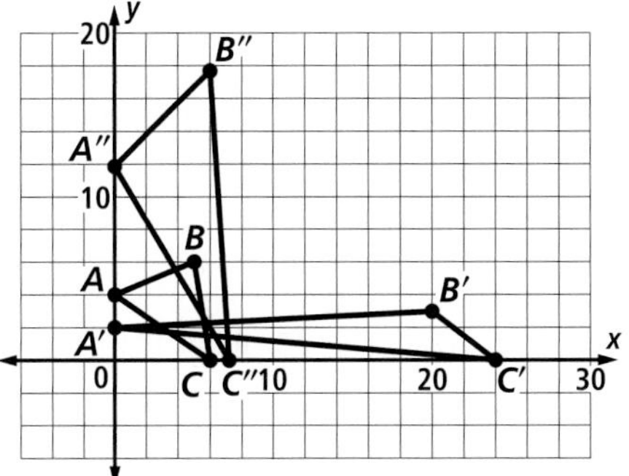

Step 5. $S2$ represents the scale change $S_{1.2,3}$.

Step 6. The matrix $\begin{bmatrix} a & 0 \\ 0 & b \end{bmatrix}$ represents the scale change $S_{a,b}$.

Questions

1. $\left(0.8x, \frac{4}{7}y\right)$ **3. a.** (12, 15) **b.** $S_{4,2}$ stretches horizontally by a factor of 4 and stretches vertically by a factor of 2. **5.** $A' = (-6, 10)$, $B' = (0, 14)$, $C' = (12, 2)$, $D' = (-12, -2)$ **7.** false **9.** size; S_8 **11.** Answers vary. Sample: Move F right to make the image 3 times as wide, and move E down to make the image 0.75 times as small.

13. a.

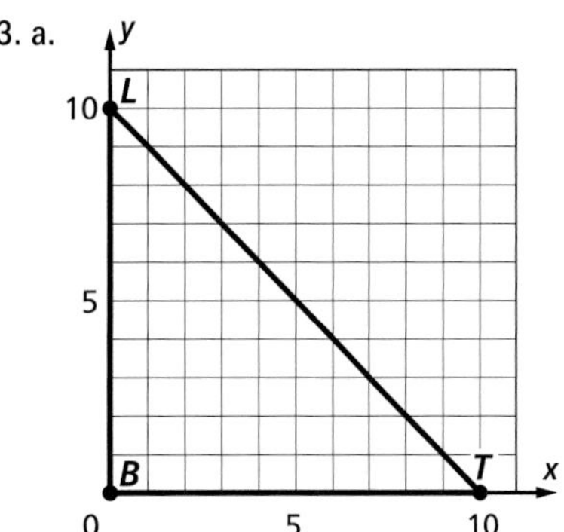

$\triangle BLT$ is an isosceles right triangle. **b.** $\triangle B'L'T' = \begin{bmatrix} 0 & 0 & 40 \\ 0 & 12 & 0 \end{bmatrix}$

c.

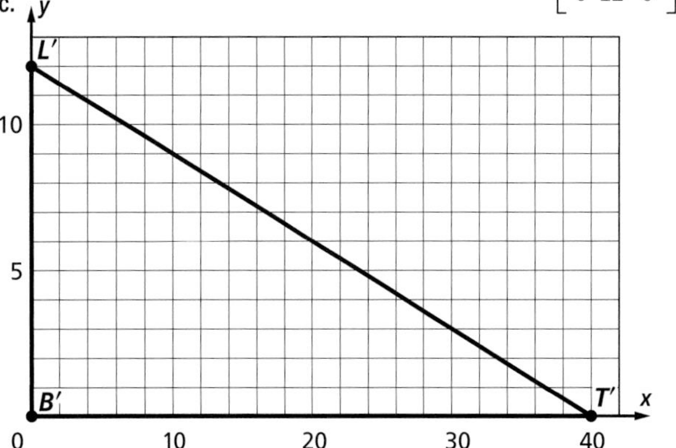

$\triangle B'L'T'$ is also a right triangle but it is scalene, not isosceles. **15. a.** $S_{5,7}$ **b.** $F = (5,2)$, $O = (1,4)$, $O = (4,-1)$ **c.** $\frac{F'O'}{FO} \approx 5.5$, $\frac{O'R'}{OR} \approx 6.5$ **d.** No; the transformation given here is a scale change that is not a size change. The figure and its image are not similar triangles, so the ratios will not be the same. **17. a.** 4 **b.** $\frac{1}{2}$ **c.** $\begin{bmatrix} 2 & 0 \\ 0 & 2 \end{bmatrix}$; 2

19. $a_n = a_1 + d(n - 1)$ **21. a.** Answers vary. Sample: distance, angle measure, and collinearity **b.** An isometry is a transformation that preserves distance. Answers vary. Sample: rotation and translation

Lesson 4-6 (pp. 255–261)

Mental Math a. no **b.** no **c.** yes **d.** yes

Guided Example 2 0; 1; 0; 1; 1; 0 $\begin{bmatrix} 0 & 1 \\ 1 & 0 \end{bmatrix}$

Activity Step 4. The corresponding points have the same x-coordinate and opposite y-coordinates; reflection over the x-axis. **Step 5.** Corresponding points have x- and y-coordinates switched; reflection over the line $y = x$; corresponding points have x- and y-coordinates switched, and each coordinate is multiplied by –1; reflection over the line $y = -x$.

Questions

1. (-30, -150) **3.** $\overline{AA'}$ **5.** $r_x: (x, y) \to (x, -y)$; $r_x(x, y) = (x, -y)$
7. D **9.** B **11.** true **13.** (4, 6); $y = x$; (6, 4)

15. $\begin{bmatrix} 0 & -1 \\ -1 & 0 \end{bmatrix}\begin{bmatrix} y \\ x \end{bmatrix} = \begin{bmatrix} 0(x) + -1(y) \\ -1(x) + 0(y) \end{bmatrix}\begin{bmatrix} -y \\ -x \end{bmatrix}$

17. a. (1, -6) **b.** $\begin{bmatrix} 0.5 & 0 \\ 0 & 2 \end{bmatrix}$ **c.** a scale change in which horizontal distances are halved and vertical distances are doubled **19. a.** $\sqrt{|4 + 2|^2 + |4 - 3|^2} = \sqrt{37}$
b. $\sqrt{|2 + 1|^2 + |2 - \frac{3}{2}|^2} = \frac{\sqrt{37}}{2}$ **c.** no
21. a. $A = 6x^2$ **b.** $x = \sqrt{\frac{A}{6}}$

Lesson 4-7 (pp. 262-268)

Mental Math a. 10 **b.** 5 **c.** 20
Activity Step 4. a counterclockwise rotation 90° about (0, 0)
Step 5. $M = \begin{bmatrix} 0 & -1 \\ 1 & 0 \end{bmatrix}$

Step 6. 

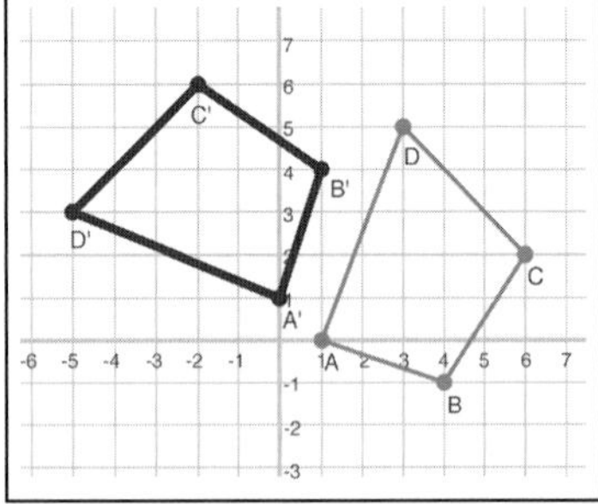

The image of $ABCD$ after applying the transformation described by M is the same as $A''B''C''D''$ from Step 3.

Questions
1. a. 2 × 2 **b.** closure under multiplication **3.** $\begin{bmatrix} 5 & 2 \\ \sqrt{8} & \pi \end{bmatrix}$
5. a. yes **b.** yes **c.** Answers vary.
Sample: $\begin{bmatrix} 1 & 2 \\ 3 & 4 \end{bmatrix}\begin{bmatrix} 5 & 6 \\ 7 & 8 \end{bmatrix} \neq \begin{bmatrix} 5 & 6 \\ 7 & 8 \end{bmatrix}\begin{bmatrix} 1 & 2 \\ 3 & 4 \end{bmatrix}$ **7.** B **9.** A
11. He changed the order of the matrices being multiplied, and matrix multiplication is not always commutative.
13. No; one is a rotation of 90°, the other of -90°. You can also show this with matrices:

$$\begin{bmatrix} 1 & 0 \\ 0 & -1 \end{bmatrix}\begin{bmatrix} 0 & 1 \\ 1 & 0 \end{bmatrix} = \begin{bmatrix} 0 & 1 \\ -1 & 0 \end{bmatrix} \neq \begin{bmatrix} 0 & -1 \\ 1 & 0 \end{bmatrix} = \begin{bmatrix} 0 & 1 \\ 1 & 0 \end{bmatrix}\begin{bmatrix} 1 & 0 \\ 0 & -1 \end{bmatrix}$$

15. a. $\begin{bmatrix} 0 & 1 \\ -1 & 0 \end{bmatrix}$ **b.** $\begin{bmatrix} 0 & -6 & -6 \\ -1 & -1 & -2 \end{bmatrix}$ **c.** They are the same.
A -90° rotation is equivalent to a 270° rotation.
17. a. $\begin{bmatrix} -\frac{1}{2} & -2 & -2 & -\frac{3}{2} \\ 0 & -\frac{1}{2} & 1 & \frac{5}{2} \end{bmatrix}$ **b.** no **c.** yes

19. a. $AB = \begin{bmatrix} ae + bg & af + bh \\ ce + dg & cf + dh \end{bmatrix}$; $BA = \begin{bmatrix} ae + cf & be + df \\ ag + ch & bg + dh \end{bmatrix}$
b. No, it is not. For instance, $ae + bg$ does not necessarily equal $bg + dh$. **21.** Answers vary. Sample: (0, 0), (1, 1), and (2, 2) **23.** $\begin{bmatrix} \frac{3}{2} & 0 \\ 0 & \frac{3}{2} \end{bmatrix}$ **25. a.** $9s + 15r = 78$
b.

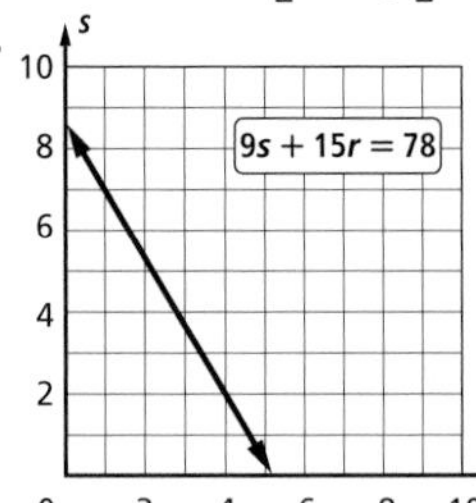

2 sale movies and 4 regular movies or 7 sale movies and 1 regular movie

Lesson 4-8 (pp. 269-273)

Mental Math a. $h = \frac{3v}{\pi r^2}$ **b.** $t = \sqrt{\frac{h}{4.9}}$ **c.** $k = \frac{Md}{wt^2}$ **d.** $x = \frac{y - 12}{4}$
Activity Step 2. 70° **Step 3.** 82° **Step 4.** 152° **Step 5.** -152°
Guided Example a. $\begin{bmatrix} -1 & 0 \\ 0 & -1 \end{bmatrix}$ **b.** 180; $\begin{bmatrix} -1 & 0 \\ 0 & -1 \end{bmatrix}$; $\begin{bmatrix} 0 & 1 \\ -1 & 0 \end{bmatrix}$

Questions
1. clockwise **3. a.** 135° **b.** $R_{90} \circ R_{45} = R_{135}$
5. R_{90}: $\begin{bmatrix} 0 & -1 \\ 1 & 0 \end{bmatrix}$; R_{180}: $\begin{bmatrix} -1 & 0 \\ 0 & -1 \end{bmatrix}$; R_{270}: $\begin{bmatrix} 0 & 1 \\ -1 & 0 \end{bmatrix}$; R_{360}: $\begin{bmatrix} 1 & 0 \\ 0 & 1 \end{bmatrix}$
7. $\begin{bmatrix} -2 & -8 & -8 & -2 \\ -3 & -3 & -9 & -9 \end{bmatrix}$ **9. a.** $\begin{bmatrix} 0 & 1 \\ 1 & 0 \end{bmatrix}$ **b.** $\begin{bmatrix} 0 & -1 \\ -1 & 0 \end{bmatrix}$
c. Matrix multiplication is not commutative; composition of transformations is not commutative. **11. a.** $\begin{bmatrix} -4 & 0 \\ 0 & 0.25 \end{bmatrix}$
b. a horizontal stretch of magnitude 4 and a vertical shrink of magnitude 0.25 **13.** false **15.** about 10,920,000 people

Lesson 4-9 (pp. 274-279)

Mental Math a. 70 **b.** 20 **c.** $\frac{950 - 5n}{10}$
Activity Step 1. $\begin{bmatrix} -8 & 5 \\ 3 & -1 \end{bmatrix}$ **Step 2.** $R1 = \begin{bmatrix} 0 & -1 \\ 1 & 0 \end{bmatrix}$

Step 3. Answers vary. Sample: The segments look perpendicular.

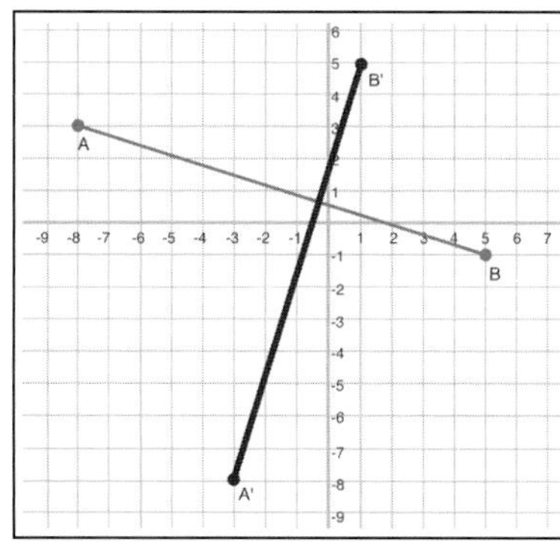

Step 4. The slope of $\overline{AB} = -\frac{4}{13}$; the slope of $\overline{A'B'} = \frac{13}{4}$; the slopes are negative reciprocals of each other.

Guided Example $\frac{2}{5}$; $-\frac{5}{2}$; $y + 3 = -\frac{5}{2}(x - 4)$

Questions

1. $\begin{bmatrix} x_1 & x_2 \\ y_1 & y_2 \end{bmatrix}$ **3.** true **5.** false **7.** $y = -\frac{5}{3}x + 11$

9. $y - 10 = -\frac{1}{4}(x + 5)$ **11.** Answers vary. Sample: Lines with slopes of zero will never satisfy the condition $m_1m_2 = -1$. **13.** $x = 6$ **15. a.** 90° **b.** $A' = (2, -6)$ and $B' = (0, 5)$ **c.** slope of $\overleftrightarrow{AB} = \frac{2}{11}$; slope of $\overleftrightarrow{A'B'} = -\frac{11}{2}$ **d.** (slope of $\overleftrightarrow{AB}$)$\cdot$(slope of $\overleftrightarrow{A'B'}$) = -1, so the two lines are perpendicular

17. a. || **b.** Answers vary. Sample:

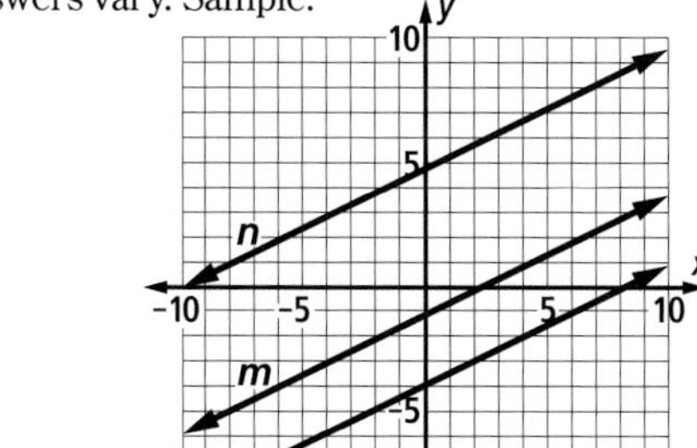

19. a. ⊥ **b.** Answers vary. Sample:

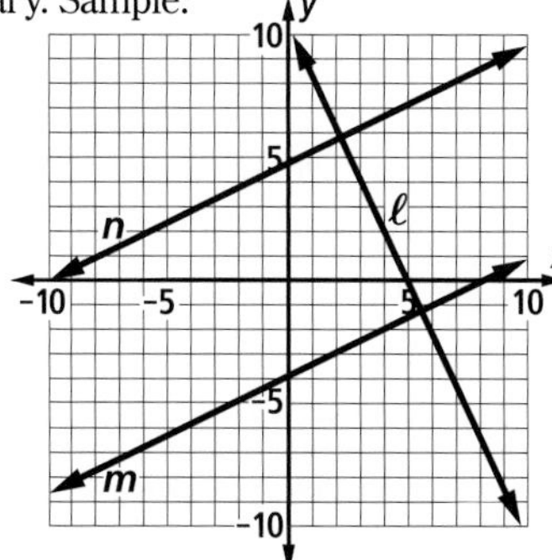

21. a. perpendicular **b.** neither **c.** parallel **d.** parallel **e.** parallel **f.** neither **23.** $\begin{bmatrix} 1 & 0 \\ 0 & 1 \end{bmatrix}$ **25.** B

Lesson 4-10 (pp. 280-285)

Mental Math a. r_x **b.** $r_{y=x}$ **c.** R_{-90} or R_{270}

Activity Step 1. $D = \begin{bmatrix} 4 & 4 & 4 \\ 3 & 3 & 3 \end{bmatrix}$ **Step 2.** the difference in the x-coordinates of $\triangle ABC$ and $\triangle A'B'C'$ **Step 3.** the difference in the y-coordinates of $\triangle ABC$ and $\triangle A'B'C'$

Step 4. $D + M = \begin{bmatrix} 5 & 5 & 7 \\ 1 & 5 & 5 \end{bmatrix}$; $D + M$ represents $\triangle A'B'C'$, the image of $\triangle ABC$ shifted 4 units to the right and 3 units up.

Step 5. $(x + 4, y + 3)$

Guided Example 1 a. 6 – 8; 2 + 2; 8 – 8; 4 + 2; 0; 6; 5 – 8; 5 + 2; -3; 7; $\begin{bmatrix} -8 & -8 \\ 2 & 2 \end{bmatrix}$; $\begin{bmatrix} 8 & 5 \\ 4 & 5 \end{bmatrix}$; $\begin{bmatrix} 0 & -3 \\ 6 & 7 \end{bmatrix}$

b.

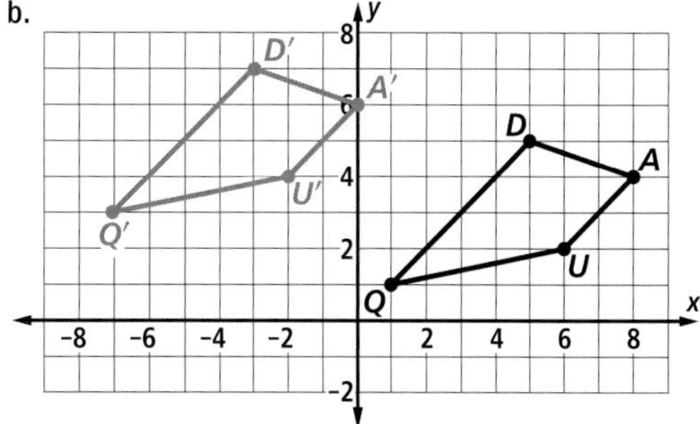

Guided Example 2 3; 2; -6; 3; 2; -6; 3; -12

Questions

1. a. $T_{4,3}(x, y) = (x + 4, y + 3)$ **b.** $T_{-4,-3}(x, y) = (x - 4, y - 3)$

3. h; k **5.** $\begin{bmatrix} -3 & 5 & -12 \\ -5 & -2 & 5 \end{bmatrix}$ **7. a.** $\frac{3}{7}$ **b.** $\frac{3}{7}$

c. Yes; their slopes are equal so the two lines are parallel.

9. a. $T_{2,-4}$ **b.** slope of $\overline{BC}$ = slope of $\overline{B'C'} = -\frac{2}{3}$ **c.** $BC = B'C' = \sqrt{13}$ **d.** parallelogram **11. a.** $T_{5,8}$ **b.** yes **c.** yes, because matrix addition is commutative

13. $T_{-2,-1}$, $T_{-2,1}$, $T_{1,2}$, $T_{1,-2}$, $T_{-1,-2}$, $T_{2,-1}$ **15. a.** $(-y + h, x + k)$; $(-y - k, x + h)$ **b.** No, the two images in Part a are not equal.

17. a. $\begin{bmatrix} -1 & 0 \\ 0 & -1 \end{bmatrix}$ **b.** $\begin{bmatrix} -1 & 0 \\ 0 & -1 \end{bmatrix}$; yes

19. a. $\begin{array}{c} \\ S \\ M \\ L \end{array} \begin{array}{c} \text{blue gray tan} \\ \begin{bmatrix} 8 & 8 & 8 \\ 12 & 12 & 12 \\ 8 & 8 & 8 \end{bmatrix} \end{array}$ **b.** $\begin{bmatrix} 0 & 0 & 1 \\ 2 & 1 & 0 \\ 0 & 1 & 0 \end{bmatrix}$ **c.** $\begin{bmatrix} 8 & 8 & 7 \\ 10 & 11 & 12 \\ 8 & 7 & 8 \end{bmatrix}$

Self-Test (pp. 291-292)

1. $\begin{array}{c} H \quad U \quad L \quad K \\ \begin{bmatrix} -2 & 5 & -2 & -4 \\ 4 & 1 & -2 & 2 \end{bmatrix} \end{array}$

2. a.

	Jicamaport	Okraville	Potatotown
first-class	16	4	2
economy	107	180	321

b.

	first-class	economy
Jicamaport	16	107
Okraville	4	180
Potatotown	2	321

3. The product will exist when the number of columns in the left matrix is equal to the number of rows in the right matrix. This the the case for AB, BA, AC, and CB.

4. $BA = \begin{bmatrix} (5\cdot2)+(-2\cdot4)+\left(-1\cdot-\frac{1}{2}\right) & (5\cdot0)+(-2\cdot(-2)+\left(-1\cdot\frac{1}{2}\right) \\ \left(\frac{1}{8}\cdot2\right)+(6\cdot4)+\left(5\cdot-\left(\frac{1}{2}\right)\right) & \left(\frac{1}{8}\cdot0\right)+(6\cdot(-2))+\left(5\cdot\frac{1}{2}\right) \end{bmatrix}$

$= \begin{bmatrix} 2.5 & 3.5 \\ 21.75 & -9.5 \end{bmatrix}$

5. not possible; A and C have different dimensions

6. $\frac{1}{3}B = \begin{bmatrix} \frac{1}{3}\cdot5 & \frac{1}{3}\cdot(-2) & \frac{1}{3}\cdot(-1) \\ \frac{1}{3}\cdot\frac{1}{8} & \frac{1}{3}\cdot6 & \frac{1}{3}\cdot5 \end{bmatrix} = \begin{bmatrix} \frac{5}{3} & -\frac{2}{3} & -\frac{1}{3} \\ \frac{1}{24} & 2 & \frac{5}{3} \end{bmatrix}$

7. Answers vary. Sample: Multiplication by $\begin{bmatrix} 1 & 0 \\ 0 & 1 \end{bmatrix}$ maps each point $\begin{bmatrix} x \\ y \end{bmatrix}$ onto itself. 8. No; $m_1 = 5$, $m_2 = \frac{1}{5}$, and $m_1m_2 = 5\cdot\frac{1}{5} = 1$. For perpendicular lines, $m_1m_2 = -1$.

9. For $m_1 \cdot \frac{1}{7} = -1$, $m = -7$, $y - (-1) = -7(x - \frac{3}{4})$; $y = -7x + \frac{3}{4}$

10. The matrix for $r_y \circ R_{270}$ is $\begin{bmatrix} -1 & 0 \\ 0 & 1 \end{bmatrix}\begin{bmatrix} 0 & 1 \\ -1 & 0 \end{bmatrix} =$

$\begin{bmatrix} (-1\cdot0)+(0\cdot(-1)) & (-1\cdot1)+(0\cdot0) \\ (0\cdot0)+(1\cdot(-1)) & (0\cdot1)+(1\cdot0) \end{bmatrix} = \begin{bmatrix} 0 & -1 \\ -1 & 0 \end{bmatrix}$

11. $P = (3, -5)$ maps onto $P' = (8, -10)$, so the translation is $T_{5,-5}$.

12.

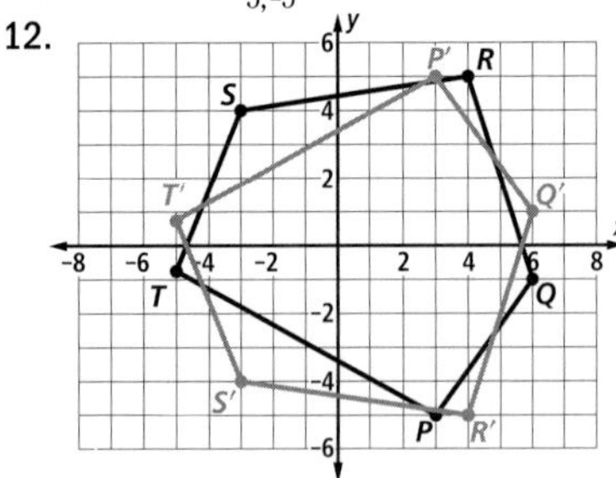

13. $\begin{bmatrix} (38\cdot4)+(135\cdot6.5)+(169\cdot5) \\ (84\cdot4)+(101\cdot6.5)+(152\cdot5) \\ (84\cdot4)+(118\cdot6.5)+(135\cdot5) \\ (67\cdot4)+(236\cdot6.5)+(34\cdot5) \end{bmatrix} =$

Movie 1	1874.5
Movie 2	1752.5
Movie 3	1778
Movie 4	1972

14. $\begin{bmatrix} 42+5 & 15+2 \\ 10+3 & 2+1 \\ 7+0 & 1+3 \\ 4+2 & 0+0 \end{bmatrix} =$

	fiction	non-fiction
Paperbacks	47	17
Hardbacks	13	3
Audiotapes	7	4
Audio CDs	6	0

15. $\begin{bmatrix} 2 & 0 \\ 0 & 2 \end{bmatrix} = \begin{bmatrix} 2 & -9 \\ 7 & 5 \end{bmatrix} = \begin{bmatrix} (2\cdot2)+(0\cdot-9) & (2\cdot-9)+(0\cdot5) \\ (0\cdot2)+(2\cdot7) & (0\cdot-9)+(2\cdot5) \end{bmatrix}$

$= \begin{bmatrix} 4 & -18 \\ 14 & 10 \end{bmatrix} = 2\begin{bmatrix} 2 & -9 \\ 7 & 5 \end{bmatrix}$ 16. $\begin{bmatrix} 0 & -1 \\ 1 & 0 \end{bmatrix}$

17. The reflection of $\triangle XYZ$ over the y-axis gives a triangle with vertices $X' = (4, 5)$, $Y' = (-2, 6)$, and $Z' = (3, 1)$.

18. $R_{270}(x) = (5,4)$, $R_{270}(y) = (6,-2)$, $R_{270}(z) = (1,3)$

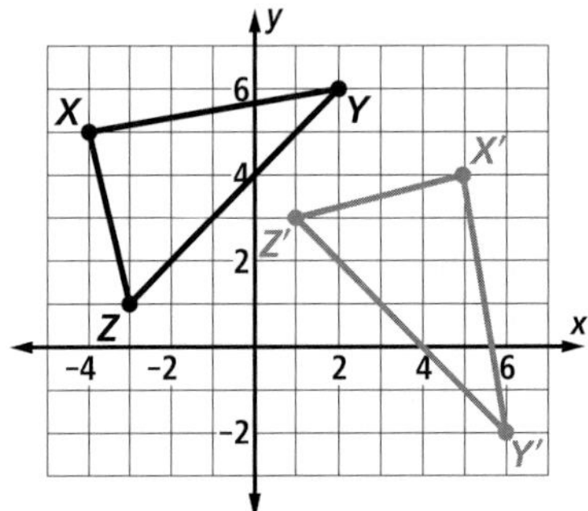

19. a. $\begin{bmatrix} 2 & 0 \\ 0 & 2 \end{bmatrix}\begin{bmatrix} 2 & -9 \\ 7 & 5 \end{bmatrix} = \begin{bmatrix} 2.5\cdot4 & 1\cdot4 & -6\cdot4 \\ -5\cdot3 & 4\cdot3 & -12\cdot3 \end{bmatrix} =$

$\begin{bmatrix} 10 & 4 & -24 \\ -15 & 12 & -36 \end{bmatrix}$

b. $\begin{bmatrix} 2.5 & 1 & -6 \\ -5 & 4 & -12 \end{bmatrix} + \begin{bmatrix} 2.5 & 2.5 & 2.5 \\ -1 & -1 & -1 \end{bmatrix} =$

$\begin{bmatrix} 2.5+2.5 & 1+2.5 & -6+2.5 \\ -5-1 & 4-1 & -12-1 \end{bmatrix} = \begin{bmatrix} 5 & 3.5 & -3.5 \\ -6 & 3 & -13 \end{bmatrix}$

20. true 21. False; Examples vary. Sample: $y = x$ rotated $135°$ is the line $y = 0$. $m_1m_2 = (1 \cdot 0) = 0 \neq -1$.

22. a. $S_7(a, b) = (7a, 7b)$ b. $PQ = \sqrt{|3-2|^2 + |9-5|^2} = \sqrt{17}$; $S_7(2, 5) = (7 \cdot 2, 7 \cdot 5) = (14, 35)$; $S_7(3, 9) = (7\cdot3, 7\cdot9) = (21, 63)$; $P'Q' = \sqrt{|21-14|^2 + |63-35|^2} = \sqrt{833}$; $\frac{\sqrt{833}}{\sqrt{17}} = \sqrt{\frac{833}{17}} = \sqrt{49} = 7$. Thus, $P'Q' = 7PQ$.

23. $m_2 = \frac{9-5}{3-2} = 4$; $m_1 \cdot 4 = -1$; $m_1 = -\frac{1}{4}$; midpoint $= \left(\frac{2+3}{2}, \frac{5+9}{2}\right) = \left(\frac{5}{2}, 7\right)$; $y - 7 = -\frac{1}{4}\left(x - \frac{5}{2}\right)$

Self-Test Correlation Chart

Question	1	2	3	4	5	6	7	8
Objective(s)	A	I	E	C	B, E	B	E	H
Lesson(s)	4-1	4-1	4-2, 4-3, 4-7	4-3	4-2, 4-3, 4-7	4-2	4-2, 4-3, 4-7	4-9, 4-10
Question	**9**	**10**	**11**	**12**	**13**	**14**	**15**	**16**
Objective(s)	D	G	F	K	J	J	B	G
Lesson(s)	4-9	4-4, 4-5, 4-6, 4-7, 4-8, 4-10	4-4, 4-5, 4-6, 4-8, 4-9, 4-10	4-4, 4-5, 4-6, 4-7, 4-8, 4-10	4-2, 4-3	4-2, 4-3	4-2	4-4, 4-5, 4-6, 4-7, 4-8, 4-10
Question	**17**	**18**	**19**	**20**	**21**	**22**	**23**	
Objective(s)	G	K	G	F	F	F	D	
Lesson(s)	4-4, 4-5, 4-6, 4-7, 4-8, 4-10	4-4, 4-5, 4-6, 4-7, 4-8, 4-10	4-4, 4-5, 4-6, 4-7, 4-8, 4-10	4-4, 4-5, 4-6, 4-8, 4-9, 4-10	4-4, 4-5, 4-6, 4-8, 4-9, 4-10	4-4, 4-5, 4-6, 4-8, 4-9, 4-10	4-9	

Chapter Review (pp. 293-297)

1. a. $\begin{bmatrix} 4 \\ 5 \end{bmatrix}$ **b.** $\begin{bmatrix} 3 \\ -4 \end{bmatrix}$ **c.** $\begin{bmatrix} -4 \\ 1 \end{bmatrix}$ **d.** $\begin{bmatrix} -2 \\ -4 \end{bmatrix}$ **e.** $\begin{bmatrix} 3 \\ 1 \end{bmatrix}$

3. $\begin{bmatrix} 4 & -2 & -2 \\ 3 & 1 & 3 \\ -4 & -4 & 7 \end{bmatrix}$ **5.** $\begin{bmatrix} -6 & 0 & -3 \\ -9 & -5 & -1 \\ 4 & 7 & -4 \end{bmatrix}$ **7.** $p = 3; q = 3$

9. $\begin{bmatrix} 1 & 12 \\ 15 & 0 \end{bmatrix}$ **11.** $\begin{bmatrix} 22 & 19 \\ -8 & 34 \end{bmatrix}$ **13.** $p = 4; q = 2$ **15.** $y = -3x + 1$

17. $y = -\frac{5}{3}x + \frac{7}{3}$ **19. a.** true **b.** Answers vary.

Sample: $\left(\begin{bmatrix} 4 & 3 \\ 7 & 1 \end{bmatrix}\begin{bmatrix} 2 & 9 \\ -1 & -3 \end{bmatrix}\right)\begin{bmatrix} -4 \\ -4 \end{bmatrix} = \begin{bmatrix} 4 & 3 \\ 7 & 1 \end{bmatrix}\left(\begin{bmatrix} 2 & 9 \\ -1 & -3 \end{bmatrix}\begin{bmatrix} -4 \\ -4 \end{bmatrix}\right)$

21. a. false **b.** Answers vary. Sample:

$\begin{bmatrix} 1 & 2 \\ 3 & 4 \end{bmatrix} - \begin{bmatrix} 5 & 6 \\ 7 & 8 \end{bmatrix} \neq \begin{bmatrix} -4 & -4 \\ -4 & -4 \end{bmatrix} \neq \begin{bmatrix} 5 & 6 \\ 7 & 8 \end{bmatrix} - \begin{bmatrix} 1 & 2 \\ 3 & 4 \end{bmatrix}$

23. $m = 1; n = 7$ **25.** $\begin{bmatrix} 1 & 0 \\ 0 & 1 \end{bmatrix}$ **27.** C

29. $\sqrt{(2x_2 - 2x_1)^2 + (2y_2 - 2y_1)^2} = \sqrt{4(x_2 - x_1)^2 + 4(y_2 - y_1)^2} = 2\sqrt{(x_2 - x_1)^2 + (y_2 - y_1)^2}$

31. $2x + 3y = 67$ **33.** $\begin{bmatrix} 1 & 0 \\ 0 & 1 \end{bmatrix}$; the identity transformation

35. a. $\begin{bmatrix} -1 & 0 \\ 0 & 1 \end{bmatrix}$ **b.** r_y **37. a.** S_2 **b.** Multiply the matrix of the points for *FIG* by the size change matrix $\begin{bmatrix} 2 & 0 \\ 0 & 2 \end{bmatrix}$.

39. F **41.** $\begin{bmatrix} 2 & -1 & 4 & 3 \\ -0.7 & 0 & 1 & -5 \end{bmatrix}$ **43.** $\begin{bmatrix} 0 & -4 & 3 \\ 2 & 0 & 2 \end{bmatrix}$

45. No; their slopes are not equal. **47.** Answers vary. Sample: (1, 8) **49.**

	CC/DC Fraud	non-delivery	investment fraud
	240	410	2000
	427.50	585	2694.99

51. The element in the second row and first column. (1:01)

53. a. $\begin{bmatrix} 822 & 456 & 977 \\ 784 & 739 & 879 \end{bmatrix}$ **b.** *Harry Potter* (original)

c. *The Matrix* sequel **55.** $B = \begin{bmatrix} 9 & 11 & 2 \\ 5 & 7 & 5 \end{bmatrix}; P = \begin{bmatrix} 1 \\ 2 \\ 3 \end{bmatrix}; BP = \begin{bmatrix} 37 \\ 34 \end{bmatrix}$

57. a.

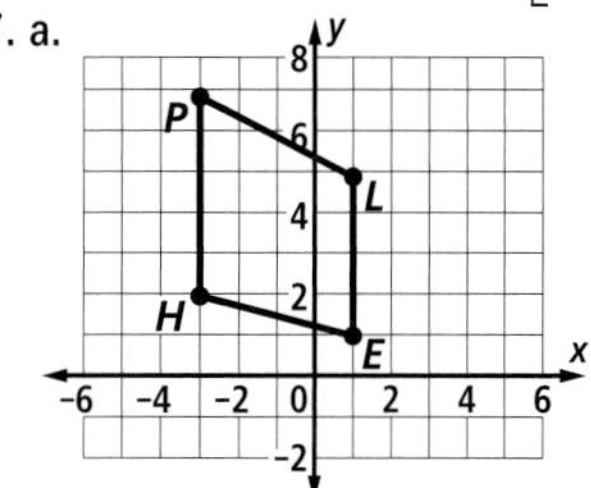

b. $\begin{bmatrix} -6 & 2 & 2 & -6 \\ 6 & 3 & 15 & 21 \end{bmatrix}$

c.

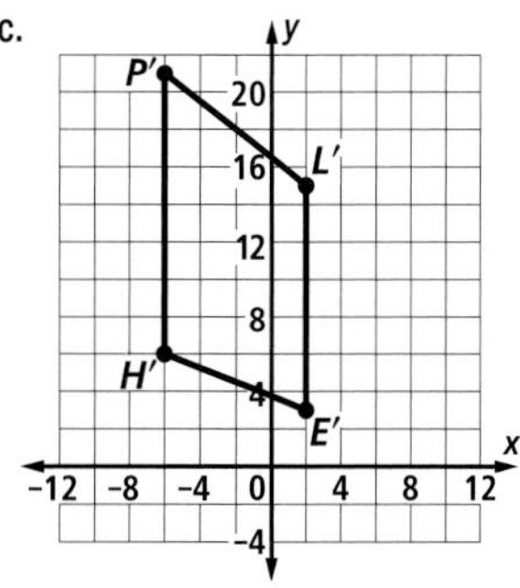

d. No; magnitude is not the same for the horizontal and vertical directions.

59. a.

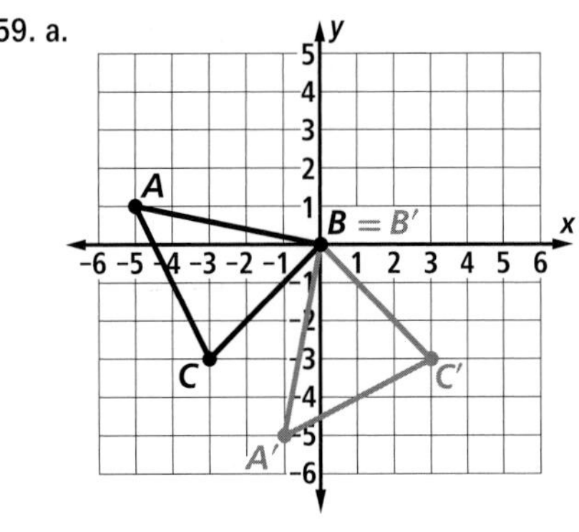

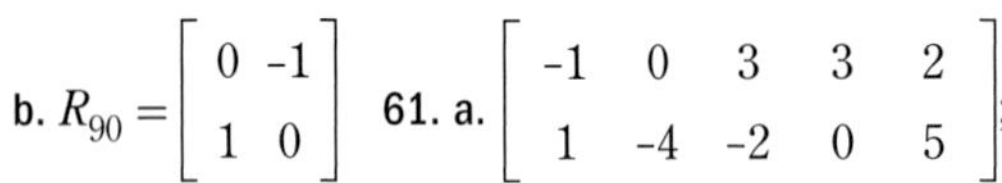

b. $R_{90} = \begin{bmatrix} 0 & -1 \\ 1 & 0 \end{bmatrix}$ **61. a.** $\begin{bmatrix} -1 & 0 & 3 & 3 & 2 \\ 1 & -4 & -2 & 0 & 5 \end{bmatrix}$;

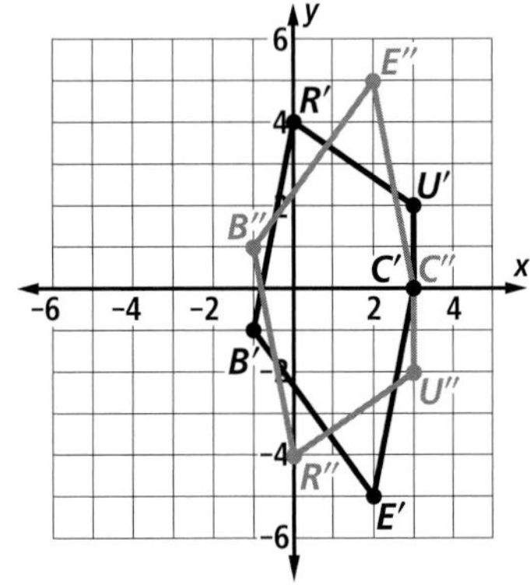

b. Yes; reflection is a congruence transformation.
c. Yes; reflections preserve angle measure and slope.

Chapter 5

Lesson 5-1 (pp. 300-306)

Mental Math **a.** {7,11} **b.** the set of all integers **c.** Ø **d.** the set of all real numbers

Activity Step 1.

Compound Sentence Entry	CAS Output
$x > 4$ and $x \le 8$	$4 < x \le 8$
$x > 4$ or $x \le 8$	true
$a < 5$ and $a < 20$	$a < 5$
$a < 5$ or $a < 20$	$a < 20$
$n < 0$ and $n > 5$	false
$n < 0$ or $n > 5$	$n < 0$ or $n > 5$

Step 2. *True* is displayed when all real numbers satisfy the compound sentence, and *false* is displayed when no real numbers satisfies the compound sentence.
Step 3. Compound sentences involving the word *or* include more values in their solution set than compound sentences involving the word *and* because solutions to *or* sentences only have to satisfy half the sentence.

Step 4.

Stored Variable	Compound Sentence Entry	CAS Output
$3 \rightarrow x$	$x > 4$ and $x \le 8$	false
$3 \rightarrow x$	$x > 4$ or $x \le 8$	true
$1 \rightarrow a$	$a < 5$ and $a < 20$	true
$1 \rightarrow a$	$a < 5$ or $a < 20$	true
$2 \rightarrow n$	$n < 0$ and $n > 5$	false
$2 \rightarrow n$	$n < 0$ or $n > 5$	false

Step 5. When the stored value satisfies the compound sentence, the output is *true*; when the stored value does not satisfy the compound sentence, the output is *false*.

Questions

1. $h < 4$

3. $9\frac{29}{60} \le h \le 14\frac{48}{60}$

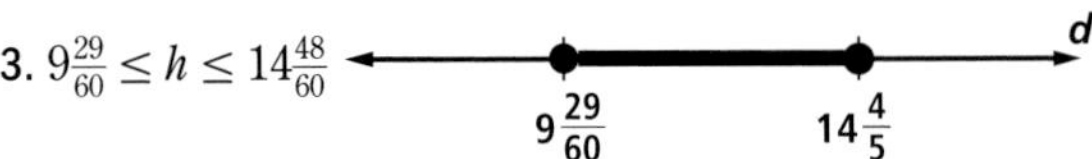

5. B **7. a.** intersection **b.** union

9.

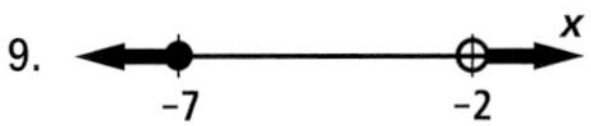

11. Steel Dragon 2000 **13.** multiply; divide; reverse

15. $m < -0.28$ (number line: -5 -4 -3 -2 -1 0 1, m)

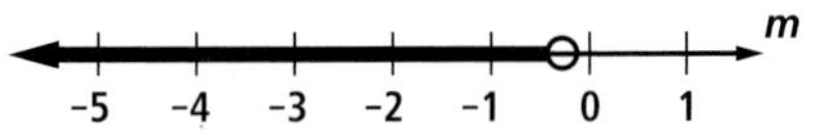

17. a. $0 \le r \le 61$ **b.** $0 \le r \le 6$ **19.** $\{m \mid -\frac{1}{3} \le m < 3\}$ (number line: $-\frac{1}{3}$, 3, m)

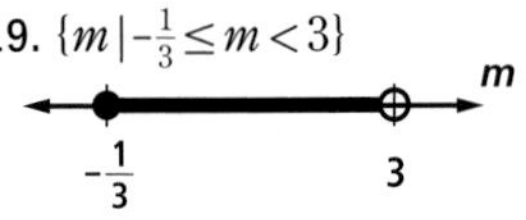

21. Answers vary. Sample: $T_{0,8}$
23. C

Lesson 5-2 (pp. 307-313)

Mental Math **a.** 9 times as much **b.** 1.44 times as much **c.** 2 times as tall

Guided Example 3 **Solution 1.** $-3x$; -3; 3; -5; 15; -1.75; 12.25; 1; 4
Solution 2. -1.75; 12.25; 1; 4

Questions

1. A system is a set of conditions joined by the word *and*.

3. a.

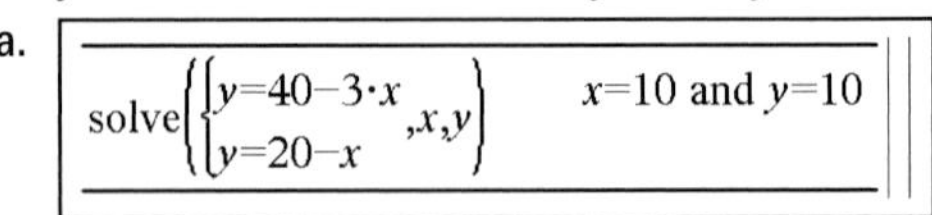

$\text{solve}\left(\begin{cases} y=40-3\cdot x \\ y=20-x \end{cases}, x, y\right)$ $x=10$ and $y=10$

b.

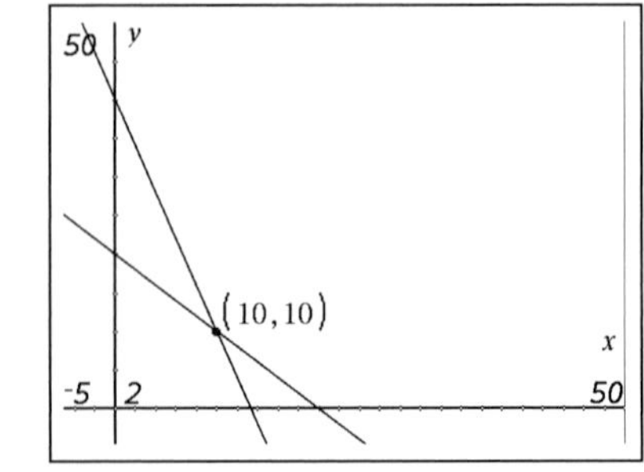

c. Answers vary. The "solve" command because it involved fewer steps. **5. a.** $x = -3, y = -3$

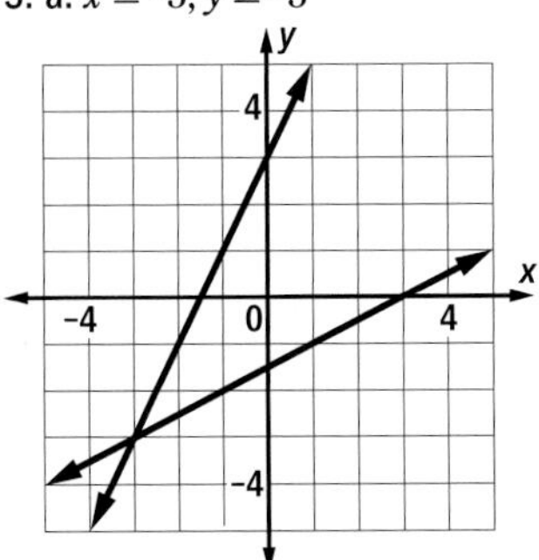

b. Answers vary. Sample: The lines have their x- and y-intercepts exchanged.

c.

$\text{solve}\left(y=\frac{1}{2}\cdot x-1.5 \text{ and } y=2\cdot x+3, x, y\right)$

$x=^-3. \text{ and } y=^-3.$

7. a. Answers vary. Sample: The graphing utility shows more decimal places for the y-coordinate, so 11.2 must be a rounded value. **b.** Answers vary. Sample: No, this is also an estimate. Since the solution involves the irrational number π, no exact decimal answer can be written. **9. a.** 2 **b.** (0.85, 1.45), (-2.35, 11.05) **c.** $2(0.85)^2 \approx 1.45$; $-3(0.85) + 4 = 1.45$; $2(-2.35)^2 \approx 11.05$; $-3(-2.35) + 4 = 11.05$ **11. a.** 2 **b.** (-0.76, 7), (0.76, 7) **c.** $(0.76)^2 \cdot 7 \approx 4$; $(-0.76)^2 \cdot 7 \approx 4$

13. a

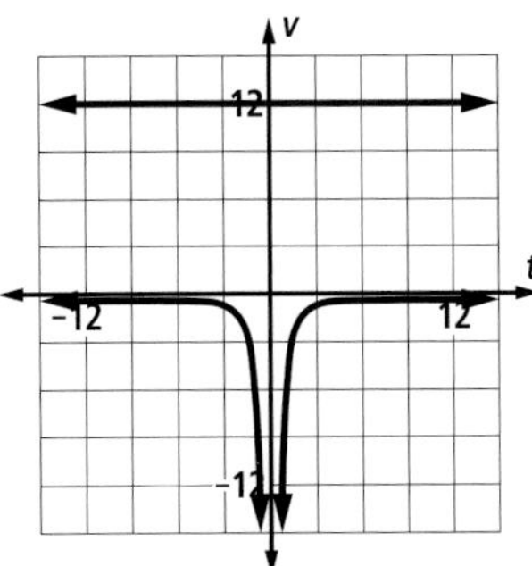

b. 0 **c.** no solutions

15. yes; The graphs of $xy = 1740$ and $x + y = 89$ intersect in two points, (29,60) and (60,29).

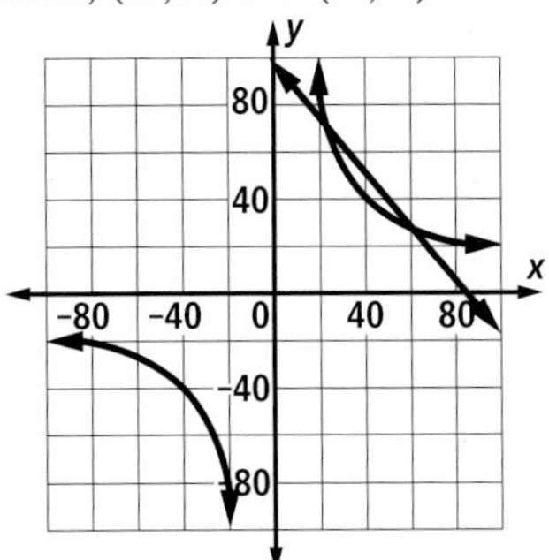

17. $x > -\frac{3}{4}$

19. $\begin{bmatrix} -4 & -1 \\ 1 & -4 \end{bmatrix}$ **21.** $\frac{ea-f}{1.5} = \frac{2}{3}(ea - f)$

Lesson 5-3 (pp. 314-320)

Mental Math **a.** $4x + 4$ **b.** $8 + \sqrt{34}$ **c.** $2L + 10$ **d.** $\frac{n\sqrt{3}}{2}$

Activity Step 1. $\begin{cases} H + V = 600 \\ H = 4V \end{cases}$ **Step 2.** $H = 4V$; $4V + V = 600$; $V = 600 - H$; $H = 4(600 - H)$; **Step 3.** $V = 120$; $H = 480$; the home team gets 480 tickets and the visiting team gets 120 tickets. **Step 4.** Answers vary. Sample: Yes; one substitution was easier because it required less arithmetic. **Step 5.** The CAS command substitutes $4V$ for H in the first equation. **Step 6.** $V = 120$ **Step 7.** $H = 480$

$h=4\cdot v|v=120 \qquad h=480$

Guided Example 1 $2M$; $5M$; $2M$; $5M$; 20; 40; 100; 40; 20; 100; yes; yes; yes

Questions

1. If $a = b$, then a may be substituted for b in any arithmetic or algebraic expression. **3.** one **5.** $-12 = 4(-3)$; $(-12)(-3) = 36$; the original equations are both true when the values are substituted. **7.** $x = 3, y = -2, z = \frac{1}{2}$ **9. a.** no solution **b.** inconsistent

c.

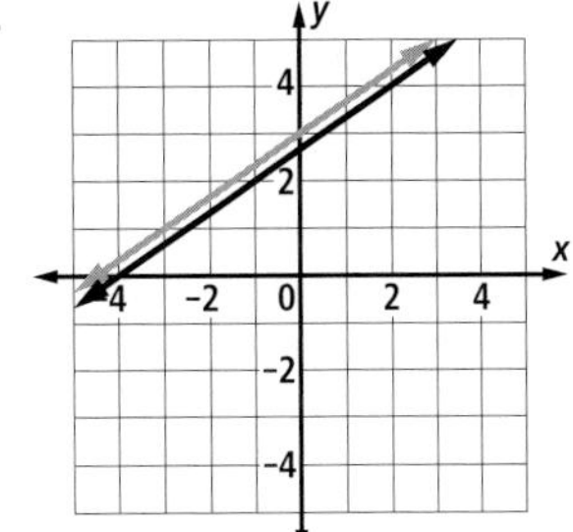

11. There are either no solutions, one solution, or infinitely many solutions. **13. a.** There are no solutions. **b.** inconsistent

c.

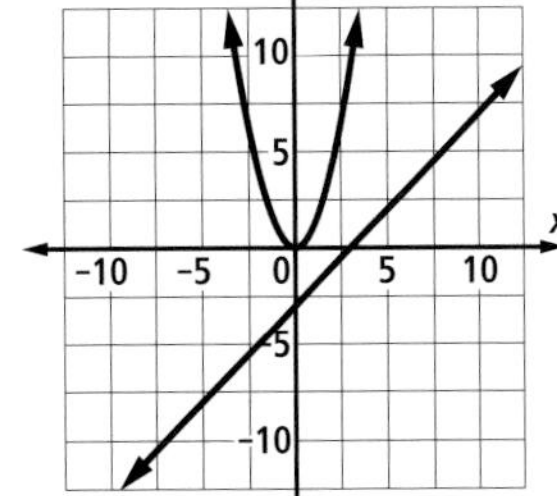

15. a. Answers vary. Sample: $\begin{cases} S = 2C \\ G = 4C \\ S + G + C = 50 \end{cases}$

b. $C = \frac{50}{7}$, $G = \frac{200}{7}$, $S = \frac{100}{7}$; use about 14.3 yd^3 of sand, 28.6 yd^3 of gravel, and 7.1 yd^3 of cement.
17. a. $0.09x \le 20$ b. $x \le 222.2$ c. 222 one page flyers
19. a. domain: all real numbers except 0; range: all real numbers except 0 b. domain: all real numbers; range: all real numbers less than or equal to 0 c. domain: all real numbers except 0; range: all positive real numbers d. domain: all real numbers; range: all real numbers

Lesson 5-4 (pp. 321-327)

Mental Math a. $39p + 4s$ dollars b. $3d_1 + 6d_2$ dollars c. $xd_1 + yd_2$ dollars
Activity Step 2. $9c + 2p = 50$ and $65c + 45p = 800$
Step 3. Answers vary. Sample: To eliminate c, multiply the second equation by $\frac{-1}{5}$ and multiply the first equation by $\frac{13}{9}$. To eliminate p, multiply the first equation by -45 and the second equation by 2. Step 4. Answers vary. Sample: $\frac{-55}{9p} = \frac{-790}{9}$; $-275c = -650$ Step 5. $p = \frac{158}{11}$; $c = \frac{26}{11}$; she should eat about 14.4 ounces of pasta and 2.4 ounces of chicken for dinner. Step 6. Answers vary. Sample: The easier variable to eliminate is usually the one where the coefficients have factors in common. Using a CAS can make this easier.
Guided Example 2 $7x$; $2y$; $-6x$; $6y$; -54; $-4x$; $7y$; $7x$; $2y$; 31; $49y$; -238; $28x$; 124; $57y$, -2; -20; 5; 12; 3; 5; -2; 3; 5; -2; 3
Questions
1. Addition and Multiplication Properties of Equality, Distributive Property 3. a. p b. $p = 14.36$; $c = 2.36$ c. (2.36, 14.36) 5. a. $\begin{cases} 5h + r = 50 \\ 80h + 95 = 800 \end{cases}$ b. 10 oz of chicken, 0 oz of fries 7. $u = 5$ and $v = -2$
9. $x = 6$, $y = 2$, and $z = -3$ 11. inconsistent 13. \$4.25
15. a. Answers vary. Sample: Multiply the first equation by -3 and the second equation by 2. b. Answers vary. Sample: Multiply the first equation by -2. c. $y = -2$, $z = 3$, and $x = 5$ d. true 17. (-14, -10, 1)
19. $\begin{bmatrix} 4x + 3y \\ -2x + 6y \end{bmatrix}$ 21. a. $3\begin{bmatrix} 4 & -6 & 5.5 \\ 0 & 3 & 0 \end{bmatrix} - 2\begin{bmatrix} 7 & 2 & 0 \\ 0 & 0 & -1 \end{bmatrix}$
b. $\begin{bmatrix} -2 & -22 & 16.5 \\ 0 & 9 & 2 \end{bmatrix}$

Lesson 5-5 (pp. 328-335)

Mental Math a. $\frac{1}{6}$ b. $\frac{1}{2}$ c. $\frac{1}{2}$ d. 1
Activity 1 Step 2. $\begin{bmatrix} 5.5 & 2.5 \\ 3.5 & 1.5 \end{bmatrix}$ Step 3. $\begin{bmatrix} 1 & 0 \\ 0 & 1 \end{bmatrix}$ Step 4. $\begin{bmatrix} 1 & 0 \\ 0 & 1 \end{bmatrix}$
Guided Example a. -2; -4; -1; 6; -2; 6; 4; -1; -8; $\frac{6}{-8}$; $\frac{-4}{-8}$; $\frac{1}{-8}$; $\frac{-3}{4}$; $\frac{1}{2}$; $\frac{-1}{8}$; $\frac{1}{4}$
b. 5; 10; 3; 6; 5; 6; 10; 3; 0; 0; no inverse
Activity 2 Step 1. 13, 5, 27, 9, 14, 27, 20, 8, 5, 27, 16, 1, 18, 11
Step 3. 5, 9, 27, 8, 27, 1, 11, 13, 27, 14, 20, 5, 16, 18, 27
Step 5. 1, 51, 145, 110, 23, 119, 201, 145, 85, 88, 79, 154, 16, 41, 47, 134, 141, 92, 183, 157
Step 6. $e^{-1} = \begin{bmatrix} -\frac{5}{31} & \frac{8}{31} \\ \frac{2}{31} & \frac{3}{31} \end{bmatrix}$; $e^{-1} \cdot V =$
$\begin{bmatrix} 13 & 5 & 27 & 5 & 9 & 27 & 8 & 27 & 1 & 11 \\ 5 & 20 & 13 & 27 & 14 & 20 & 5 & 16 & 18 & 27 \end{bmatrix}$ Step 7. PASS MATH
Questions
1. a. 1 b. 0 c. $\begin{bmatrix} 1 & 0 \\ 0 & 1 \end{bmatrix}$ 3. a. $\begin{bmatrix} 1 & 0 \\ 0 & 1 \end{bmatrix}$ b. $\begin{bmatrix} 1 & 0 \\ 0 & 1 \end{bmatrix}$
5. a. when $ad - bc \ne 0$ b. $\begin{bmatrix} \frac{d}{ad-bc} & \frac{-b}{ad-bc} \\ \frac{-c}{ad-bc} & \frac{a}{ad-bc} \end{bmatrix}$ 7. 75, $\begin{bmatrix} \frac{2}{25} & -\frac{3}{25} \\ \frac{7}{75} & \frac{2}{75} \end{bmatrix}$
9. $\begin{bmatrix} \frac{d}{ad-bc} & \frac{-b}{ad-bc} \\ \frac{-c}{ad-bc} & \frac{a}{ad-bc} \end{bmatrix}\begin{bmatrix} a & b \\ c & d \end{bmatrix} = \begin{bmatrix} \frac{da}{ad-bc} + \frac{-bc}{ad-bc} & \frac{db}{ad-bc} + \frac{-bd}{ad-bc} \\ \frac{-ca}{ad-bc} + \frac{ac}{ad-bc} & \frac{-cb}{ad-bc} + \frac{ad}{ad-bc} \end{bmatrix}$
$= \begin{bmatrix} \frac{ad-bc}{ad-bc} & \frac{0}{ad-bc} \\ \frac{0}{ad-bc} & \frac{ad-bc}{ad-bc} \end{bmatrix} = \begin{bmatrix} 1 & 0 \\ 0 & 1 \end{bmatrix}$
11. 54, 190, 35, 127, 42, 150, 31, 114, 62, 221, 33, 129, 15, 54, 26, 96, 49, 185 13. Answers vary. Sample: $\begin{bmatrix} 2 & 6 \\ 1 & 3 \end{bmatrix}$
15. a. $\begin{bmatrix} 0 & -1 \\ 1 & 0 \end{bmatrix}\begin{bmatrix} 0 & 1 \\ -1 & 0 \end{bmatrix} = \begin{bmatrix} 1 & 0 \\ 0 & 1 \end{bmatrix}$;
$\begin{bmatrix} 0 & 1 \\ -1 & 0 \end{bmatrix}\begin{bmatrix} 0 & -1 \\ 1 & 0 \end{bmatrix} = \begin{bmatrix} 1 & 0 \\ 0 & 1 \end{bmatrix}$ b. They are inverses.
If you rotate an object 90° and then 270° or vice versa, you end up in the same place where you started. c. It is the matrix for R_{180}, $\begin{bmatrix} -1 & 0 \\ 0 & -1 \end{bmatrix}$, because $R_{180} \cdot R_{180} = R_{360}$.
17. a. $\begin{cases} 50e + 30d = 160 \\ 10e = 20 \\ 0.75d + 0.75b = 3 \end{cases}$ b. $e = 2$; $d = 2$; $b = 2$;
2 energy bars, 2 energy drink bottles, and 2 bottles of water c. Answers vary. Sample: I used the substitution method because it was easy to solve the second equation for e. 19. a. $d = 60t$
b.

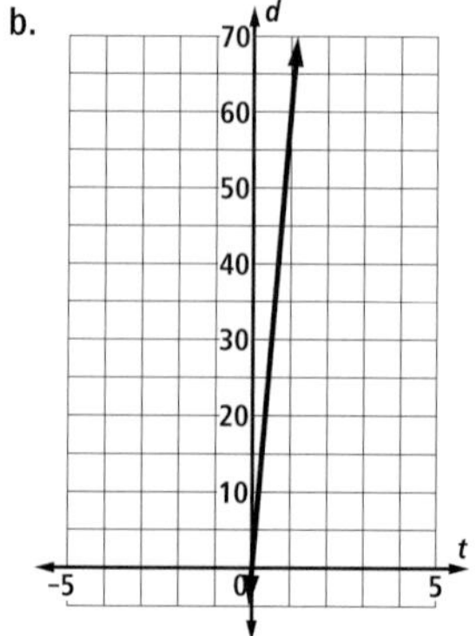

Lesson 5-6 (pp. 336-341)

Mental Math **a.** 4 **b.** 2 **c.** 11 **d.** $ad - bc$

Guided Example 1 $\begin{bmatrix} \frac{2}{7} & \frac{1}{14} \\ -\frac{1}{7} & \frac{3}{14} \end{bmatrix}$; $\begin{bmatrix} \frac{2}{7} & \frac{1}{14} \\ -\frac{1}{7} & \frac{3}{14} \end{bmatrix}$; $\begin{bmatrix} \frac{2}{7} & \frac{1}{14} \\ -\frac{1}{7} & \frac{3}{14} \end{bmatrix}$; $\begin{bmatrix} 1 & 0 \\ 0 & 1 \end{bmatrix}$; $\begin{bmatrix} 4 \\ -2 \end{bmatrix}$; $\begin{bmatrix} 4 \\ -2 \end{bmatrix}$; 4, -2

Questions

1. a. $\begin{bmatrix} 0.5 & -1 \\ 3 & 8 \end{bmatrix}\begin{bmatrix} x \\ y \end{bmatrix} = \begin{bmatrix} 1.75 \\ 5 \end{bmatrix}$ **b.** about (2.71, -0.39)

3. zero; The determinant of the coefficient matrix is 0, and (2, 2) satisfies the first equation but not the second. **5.** infinitely many; the determinant of the coefficient matrix is 0 and (2, 2) satisfies both equations.

7. $\begin{bmatrix} x \\ y \\ z \end{bmatrix} = \begin{bmatrix} -1 \\ 0 \\ 8 \end{bmatrix}$ **9.** $\begin{bmatrix} 3 & 5 \\ 1 & 1 \end{bmatrix}\begin{bmatrix} s \\ n \end{bmatrix} = \begin{bmatrix} 3943 \\ 937 \end{bmatrix}$; $\begin{bmatrix} s \\ n \end{bmatrix} = \begin{bmatrix} 371 \\ 566 \end{bmatrix}$; 371 student tickets and 566 non-student tickets **11.** No; you need three equations to find three unknowns.

13. $n = -12$ **15.** $(w, x, y, z) = (-1, 1, 2, 4)$ **17. a.** $\begin{bmatrix} 1 & -1 \\ 0 & 1 \end{bmatrix}$

b. $\begin{bmatrix} 1 & -1 \\ 0 & 1 \end{bmatrix}\begin{bmatrix} 1 & 1 \\ 0 & 1 \end{bmatrix} = \begin{bmatrix} 1 & 1 \\ 0 & 1 \end{bmatrix}\begin{bmatrix} 1 & -1 \\ 0 & 1 \end{bmatrix} = \begin{bmatrix} 1 & 0 \\ 0 & 1 \end{bmatrix}$

19. $y = -\frac{5}{8}x$

Lesson 5-7 (pp. 342-347)

Mental Math **a.** $8 + 0.5m$ in. **b.** 9.5 in. **c.** 6.5 in. **d.** 9 in.

Guided Example 2 Answers vary. Sample: 0; 0; above; Answers vary. Sample: 0; 0; Answers vary. Sample: does not; below

Questions

1. half-planes; boundary **3.** below **5. a.** ii **b.** i **c.** iii

7.

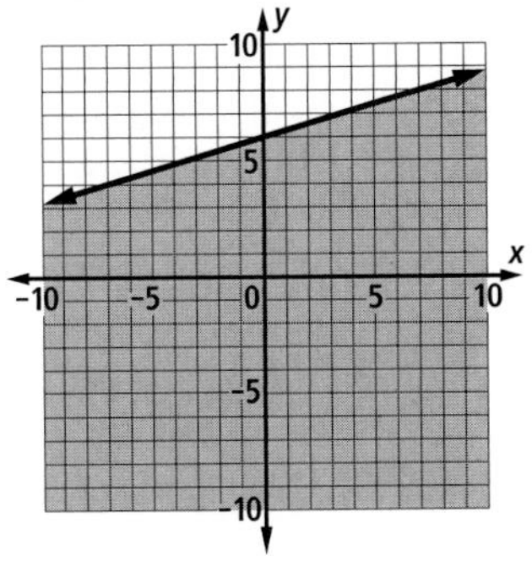

9. 8 **11.** 3 **13.** $-3x + 2y \le 12$ **15. a.** yes **b.** yes **c.** no **17.** No; a single x value is paired with multiple y values. **19.** Yes; it has exactly one solution.

21. $\{w \mid 2 < w \le 4.5\}$

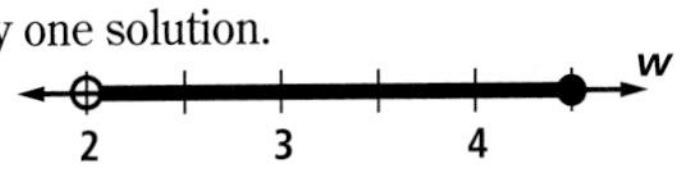

Lesson 5-8 (pp. 348-354)

Mental Math **a.** $p \le 12$ **b.** $c > -3$ **c.** $23 < x \le 31$ **d.** $t < 0.7$ or $t > 0.9$

Activity **Step 1.** $2T + C \le 12$ **Step 2** $2T + 2C \le 16$

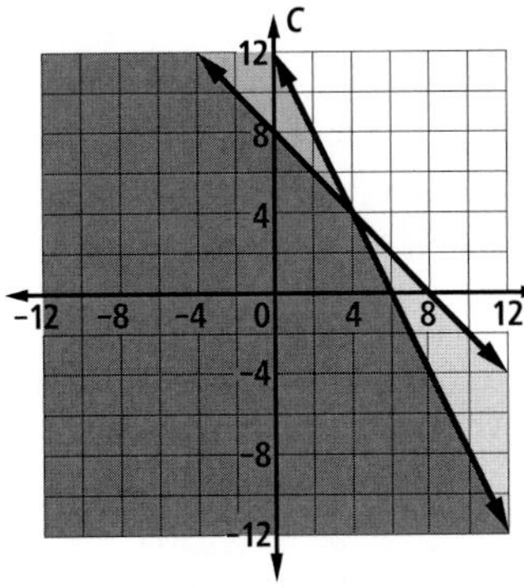

Step 3.

(T, C)	Satisfies Long Block Inequality	Satisfies Square Block Inequalit
(2, 4)	yes	yes
(6, 2)	no	yes
(2, 7)	yes	no
(5, 4)	no	no

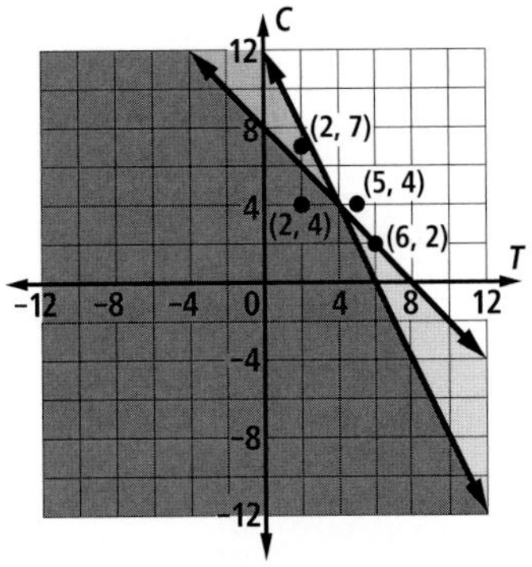

Step 4. (2, 4); It appears in the region where the solutions to the two inequalities overlap.

Guided Example 1 **a.** 2000; L; $2000L$; $1500R$; $1500R$; $2000L$; $1500R$; $2000L$; $15R$; $20L$ **b.** 30; 40; 50; 20; 30; 40; 50; 20

Questions

1. intersection **3. a.** not possible; not enough long blocks or square blocks **b.** possible **c.** possible **d.** not possible; not enough square blocks **5. a.** $\begin{cases} 2T + C = 12 \\ 2T + 2C = 16 \end{cases}$ **b.** (4, 4)

7. a. \$160,000 **b.** \$100,000 **c.** \$107,500

9. a.

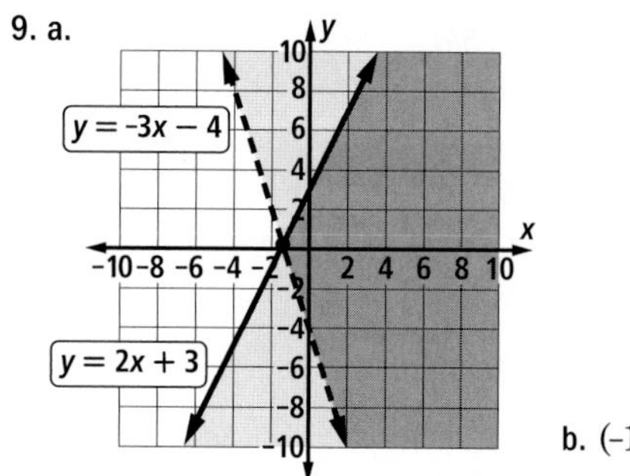

b. (-1.4, 0.2)

11. a. 0; 0; 40; $1.25S + 2.5L$

b.

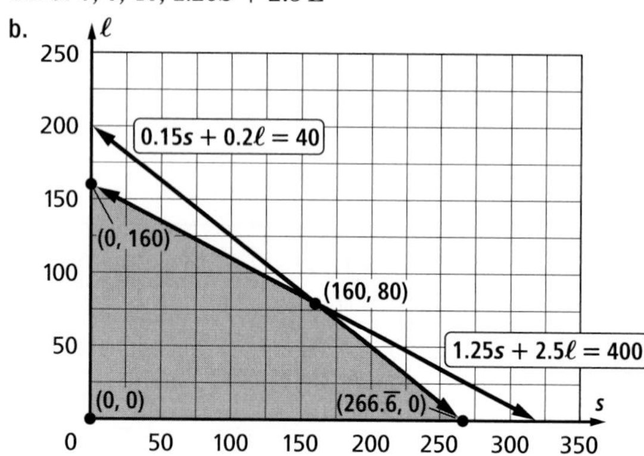

13. a. $\begin{cases} x \le 40 \\ 2x + 2y \le 100 \\ 2.5x + 3.5y \le 150 \\ x \ge 0 \\ y \ge 0 \end{cases}$

b.

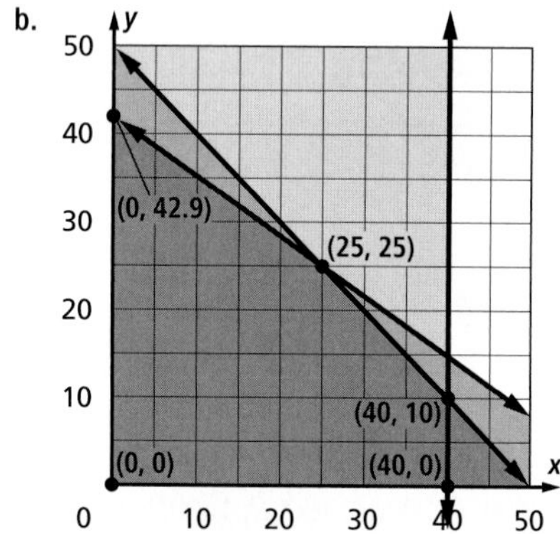

15.

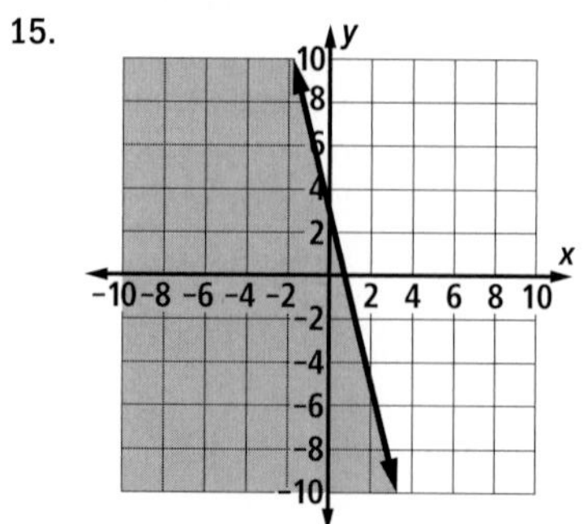

17. false 19. $52x$ to $53x + 265$ minutes

Lesson 5-9 (pp. 355-361)

Mental Math a. \$45 b. \$45 c. \$75 d. \$95

Activity Step 1. Numbers for empty cells of table. Top row table: $5x$; $3y$; Middle row table: $2x$; $6y$; 130; Bottom row table: $2.5x$; $4y$; 120; $\begin{cases} 5x + 3y \le 115 \\ 2x + 6y \le 130 \\ 2.5x + 4y \le 120 \\ x \ge 10 \\ y \ge 1 \end{cases}$

Step 2.

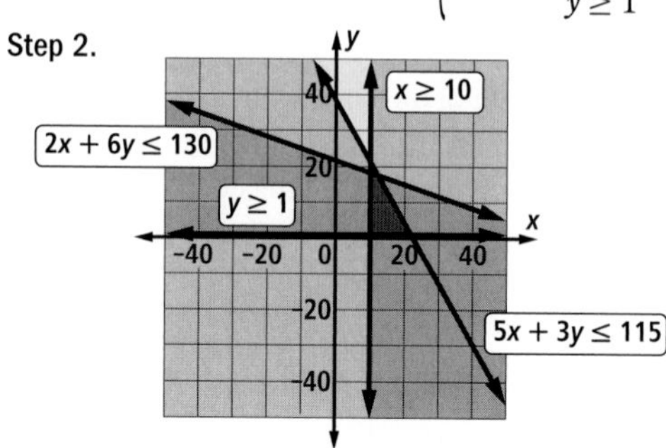

$2x + 6y = 130$; $5x + 3y = 115$; $2x + 6y = 130$; $5x + 3y = 115$; $2.5x + 4y \le 120$ does not help define the feasible region.

Step 3. (10,1), $(10, \frac{55}{3})$, (22.4, 1), (12.5, 17.5)

Step 4. $R = 20x + 15y$ **Step 5.** $R_1 = 20(10) + 15(1) = 215$; $R_2 = 20(10) + 15(18) = 470$; $R_3 = 20(22) + 15(1) = 455$; $R_4 = 20(12) + 15(17) = 495$; **Step 6.** To maximize profits, 12 centerpieces and 17 topiaries should be made. \$495 would be made from the sales.

Questions

1. a. revenue, $R = 900T + 600C$ b. \$5100 c. possible combinations of tables and chairs d. true 3. He proved the Linear-Programming Theorem. 5. (12, 17); It means that they should make 12 centerpieces and 17 topiaries. 7. a procedure for solving large linear programming problems 9. a. (7, 10) b. (1, 2)

11. a. Let M = trays of muffins, N = loaves of nut bread $\begin{cases} \frac{9}{16}M + \frac{1}{2}N \le 50 \\ \frac{3}{4}M + \frac{3}{4}N \le 48 \\ \frac{3}{4}M + \frac{1}{6}N \le 15 \\ M \ge 0 \\ N \ge 0 \end{cases}$

b.

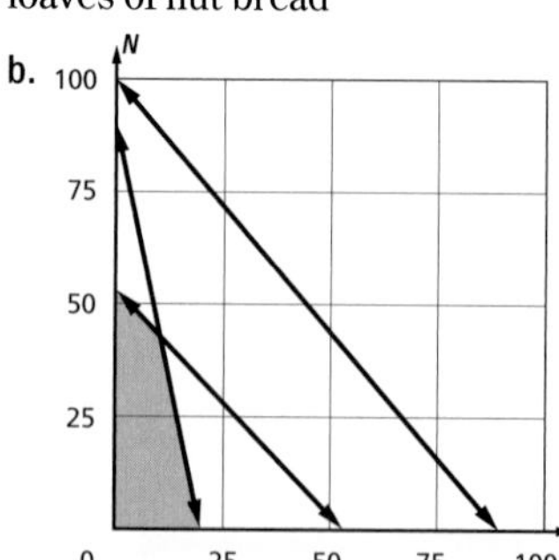

$\frac{9}{16}M + \frac{1}{2}N = 50$ is not a boundary of the feasible region. The feasible set is the set of lattice points in the shaded region. c. 53 loaves of nut bread and 0 trays of muffins

13.

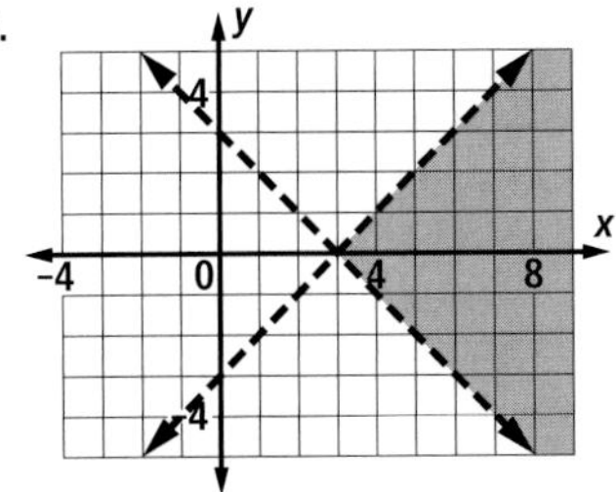

15. $y \geq -\frac{2}{3}x + 2$ 17. $(s, A) = (2, 4)$ or $(-4, 16)$

Self-Test (pp. 365-366)

1. $n > -3$ 2.

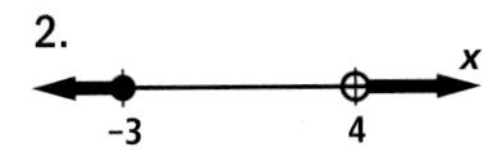

3. Estimating the intersection points from the graph, the solutions are approximately (-1.7, -2.8) and (1.2, -1.4). 4. This system is inconsistent because there is no solution. The system describes two lines that do not intersect because they are parallel. 5. Substituting the first two equations into the third yields $3(q + 4) - 2(3q) = 3$, or $-3q + 12 = 3$, so $q = 3$. Substituting this value back into the first two equations gives $p = 3(3) = 9$ and $r = 3 + 4 = 7$. Thus, the solution to this system is $p = 9$, $q = 3$, $r = 7$. Substituting these values back into the system of equations confirms this solution: $9 = 3 \cdot 3$; $7 = 3 + 4$; $3 \cdot 7 - 2 \cdot 9 = 3$. 6. Multiplying the first equation by 2, multiplying the second by 7, and subtracting yields $-53y = -74 \Rightarrow y = \frac{74}{53}$. Substituting this into either equation yields $x = \frac{38}{53}$. We can substitute to check: $7\left(\frac{38}{53}\right) + 5\left(\frac{74}{53}\right) = 12$ and $2\left(\frac{38}{53}\right) + 9\left(\frac{74}{53}\right) = 14$.

7. a. $\begin{cases} H + P = 20 \\ 7.83H + 11.50P = 200 \end{cases}$; H is the number of pounds of organic hazelnuts and P is the number of pounds of organic pecans. b. Solving the first equation for H and substituting into the second yields $7.83(20 - P) + 11.50P = 200$, $P \approx 11.8$. The first equation then implies $H = 20 - P \approx 8.2$. Thus, about 11.8 pounds of organic pecans must be mixed with about 8.2 pounds of organic hazelnuts to obtain 20 pounds of mixed nuts worth \$10 per pound.

8. a. $\begin{bmatrix} 3 & 2 \\ -2 & 7 \end{bmatrix}$ b. Because $(3)(7) - (2)(-2) = 25 \neq 0$, the Inverse Matrix Theorem says that the inverse of the coefficient matrix is $\begin{bmatrix} \frac{7}{25} & \frac{-2}{25} \\ \frac{2}{25} & \frac{3}{25} \end{bmatrix}$.

c. $\begin{bmatrix} 3 & 2 \\ -2 & 7 \end{bmatrix}\begin{bmatrix} x \\ y \end{bmatrix} = \begin{bmatrix} 24 \\ 39 \end{bmatrix}\begin{bmatrix} \frac{7}{25} & \frac{-2}{25} \\ \frac{2}{25} & \frac{3}{25} \end{bmatrix}\begin{bmatrix} 3 & 2 \\ -2 & 7 \end{bmatrix}\begin{bmatrix} x \\ y \end{bmatrix} =$

$\begin{bmatrix} \frac{7}{25} & \frac{-2}{25} \\ \frac{2}{25} & \frac{3}{25} \end{bmatrix}\begin{bmatrix} 24 \\ 39 \end{bmatrix}\begin{bmatrix} 1 & 0 \\ 0 & 1 \end{bmatrix}\begin{bmatrix} x \\ y \end{bmatrix} = \begin{bmatrix} \frac{18}{5} \\ \frac{33}{5} \end{bmatrix}$; $x = \frac{18}{5}, y = \frac{33}{5}$

9. a. Answers vary. Sample: $\begin{bmatrix} 1 & 1 \\ 1 & 1 \end{bmatrix}$ b. The determinant of the matrix is zero: $(1)(1) - (1)(1) = 0$.
10. First, graph the boundary $y = -\frac{5}{2}x - 2$ with a dotted line, then shade above it.

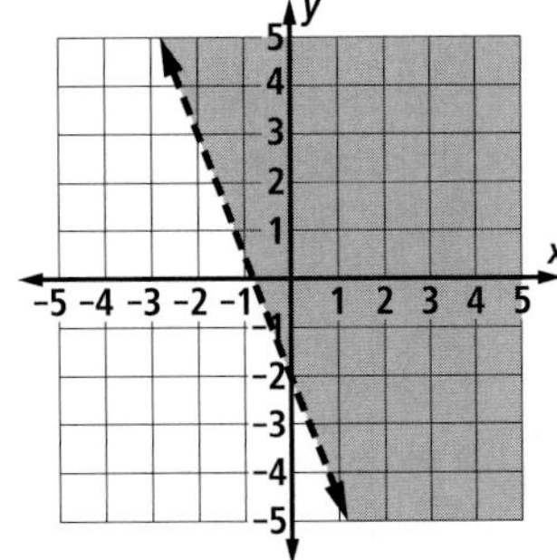

11. $y < -x$ and $y \geq -2$

12. a. no b. yes c. no 13. $\begin{cases} \frac{1}{3}e + \frac{1}{6}c \leq 48 \\ \frac{1}{6}e + \frac{1}{3}c \leq 64 \\ e \geq 0 \\ c \geq 0 \end{cases}$

b. vertices: (0, 0); (0, 144); (160, 64); (192, 0)

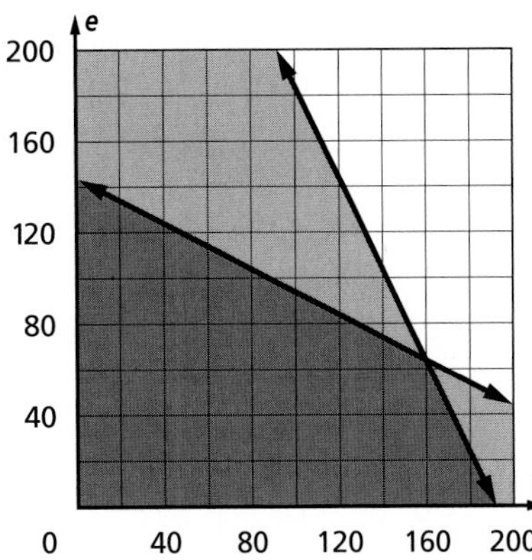

c. The Linear-Programming Theorem states that one of the vertices from Part b will maximize $15e + 12c = profits$. Substituting each vertex's values into this profit expression, we find that the company maximizes its profits at \$2880 by making 160 Cool Contemporary shelves and 64 Olde English shelves.

Self-Test Correlation Chart

Question	1	2	3	4	5	6	7	8
Objective(s)	H	H	I	D	A	A	F	B, C
Lesson(s)	5-1	5-1	5-2	5-2, 5-3, 5-4, 5-6	5-3, 5-4	5-3, 5-4	5-2, 5-3, 5-4, 5-6	5-5, 5-6
Question	**9**	**10**	**11**	**12**	**13**			
Objective(s)	B	J	K	E	G			
Lesson(s)	5-5	5-7	5-8	5-8, 5-9	5-9			

Chapter Review (pp. 367-371)

1. D **3.** $x = -12, y = 4$ **5.** $x = \frac{47}{2}, y = -9$ **7.** $a = -\frac{8}{5}, b = \frac{6}{5}, c = -\frac{2}{5}$ **9. a.** 4 **b.** $\begin{bmatrix} \frac{1}{4} & 0 \\ 0 & 1 \end{bmatrix}$ **11. a.** 0 **b.** does not exist

13. $\begin{bmatrix} \frac{3}{13} & \frac{-2}{13} \\ \frac{5}{13} & \frac{1}{13} \end{bmatrix}$ **15.** The determinant equals 0.

17. $\begin{bmatrix} 3 & -4 \\ 4 & -6 \end{bmatrix}\begin{bmatrix} x \\ y \end{bmatrix} = \begin{bmatrix} 12 \\ 48 \end{bmatrix}; \begin{bmatrix} x \\ y \end{bmatrix} = \begin{bmatrix} -60 \\ -48 \end{bmatrix}$

19. $\begin{bmatrix} 2 & -5 \\ 3 & -6 \end{bmatrix}\begin{bmatrix} m \\ n \end{bmatrix} = \begin{bmatrix} 4 \\ -3 \end{bmatrix}; \begin{bmatrix} m \\ n \end{bmatrix} = \begin{bmatrix} -13 \\ -6 \end{bmatrix}$

21. No; they have different solutions. **23.** an inconsistent system **25. a.** consistent **b.** 1 **27. a.** consistent **b.** 2 **29.** Answers vary. Sample: $t = 1$ **31.** false **33. a.** Yes; this is a convex region. **b.** No; the region is not convex. **c.** Yes; the region is convex. **d.** No; the region is not convex. **35.** Yes; it is a vertex. **37.** The tank must contain 60% from the first source and 40% from the second source. **39.** 7 oz of meat and 4 oz of vegetables

41. a. $\begin{cases} c \geq 0 \\ r \geq 0 \\ c \leq 30{,}000 \\ c + r \leq 40{,}000 \\ 185c + 225r \leq 8{,}500{,}000 \end{cases}$

b.

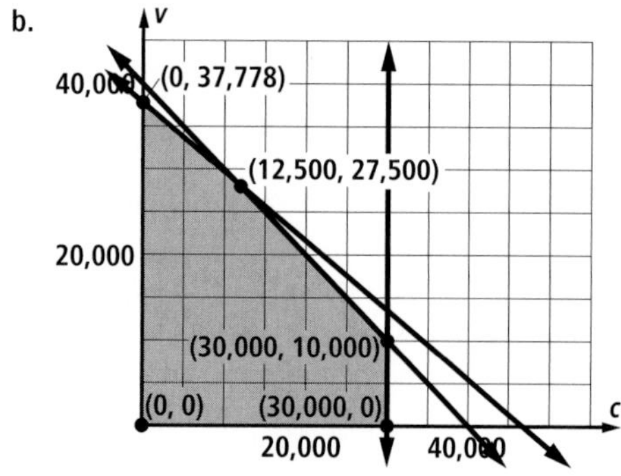

(0, 0), (30,000, 10,000), (12,500, 27,500), (0, 37,777.7)

c. (12,500, 27,500)

43. a.

b. $\{t \mid 48 < t \leq 99\}$

45. $x < -4$

47. $t \leq 5$

49.

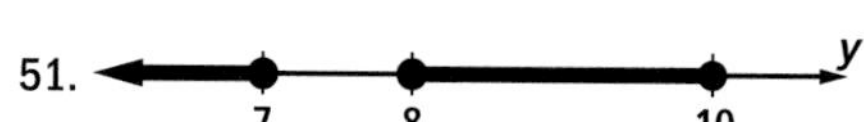

51.

53. (2.3, 4.1)

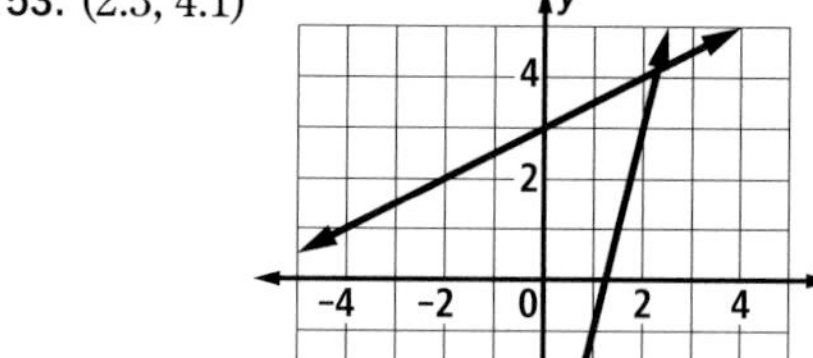

55. no solutions

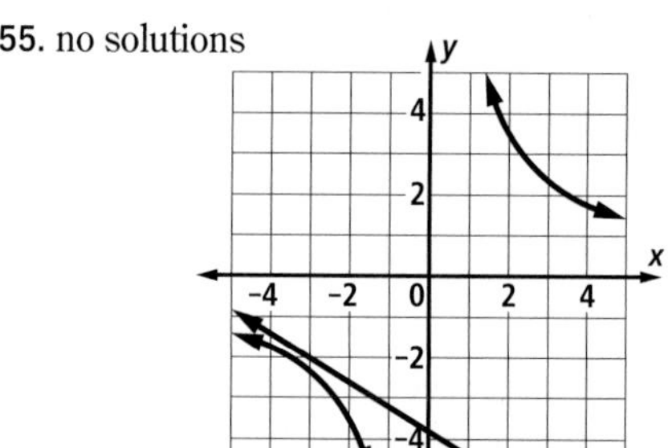

57.

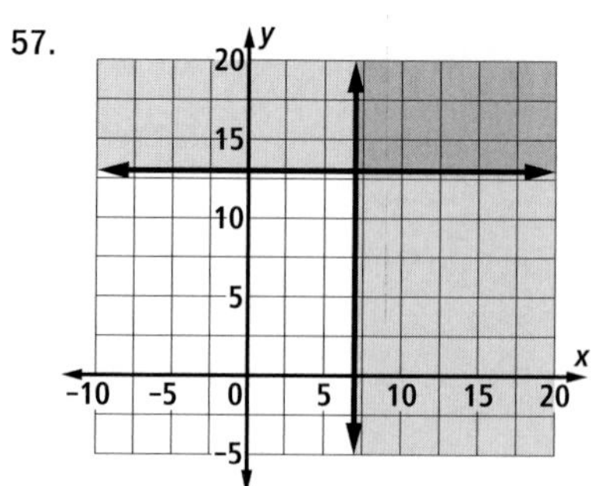

59.

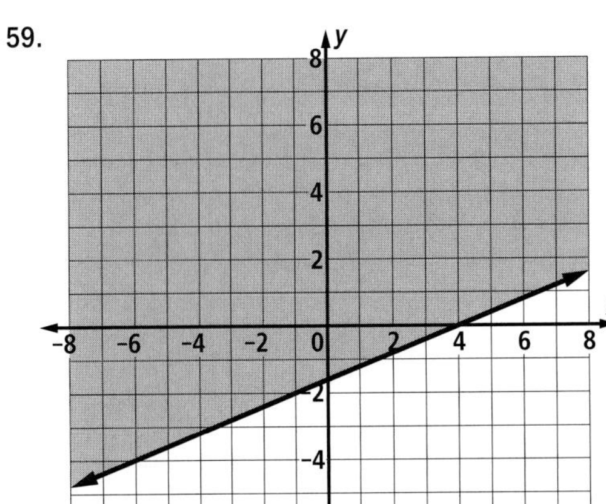

61.

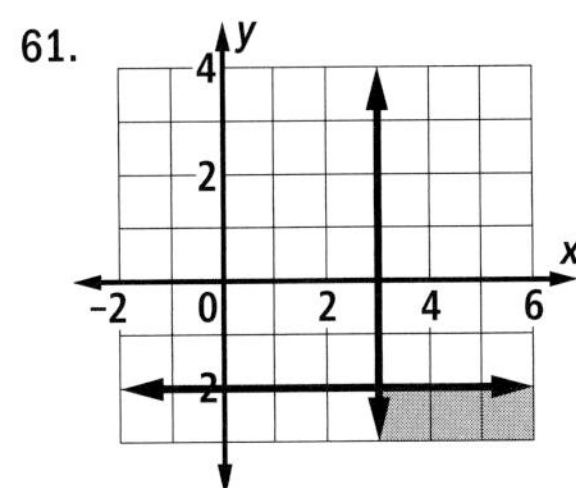

63.

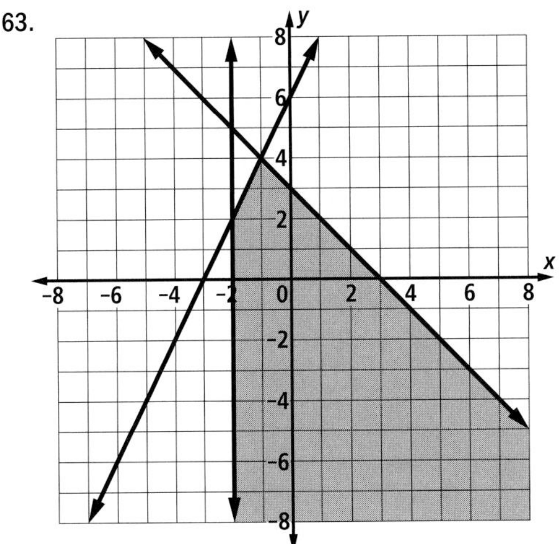

65. C

Chapter 6

Lesson 6-1 (pp. 374-379)

Mental Math **a.** 21 ft^2 **b.** 58.5 ft^2 **c.** 37.5 ft^2 **d.** 44 ft^2

Guided Example 3 **a.** $15 - s$; $15 - s$; 15; s, 15; 15; 15; 30; 225; $15 - s$; s^2 **b.** $15 - s$; 225; $30s$; s^2; $30s\pi$; $s^2\pi$; $30\pi s - \pi s^2$

Questions

1. B; it is not a second-degree equation. **3.** Answers vary. Sample: square, circle **5. a.** $6x^2 + 31xy + 35y^2$

b.

```
expand((3·x+5·y)·(2·x+7·y))
                    6·x^2+31·x·y+35·y^2
```

7. a. $6y^2 - 7y + 2$

b.

```
expand((1-2·y)·(2-3·y))      6·y^2-7·y+2
```

9. 169 **11.** $p^2 + 2pw + w^2$ **13.** $(x - y)^2 = (x - y)(x - y)$, Definition of second power; $= (x - y)x - (x - y)y$, Distributive Property; $= x^2 - yx - xy + y^2$, Distributive Property; $= x^2 - 2xy + y^2$, Commutative and Associative Properties **15.** $p^2 - 2p + 1$ **17. a.** $4w^2 + 224w + 1200$ **b.** $4w^2 + 224w$ **19.** $4t^2 - \frac{4}{3}kt + \frac{1}{9}k^2$ **21. a.** $x^2 + 12x + 32$ **b.** about 189 tiles **c.** about 16% **d.** about 23% **23.** $h = 10$ **25. a.** -5.25 million visits/yr **b.** 0.129 billion dollars/yr **27. a.**

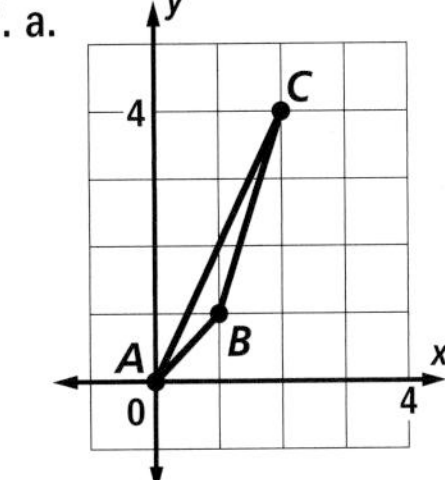

b.

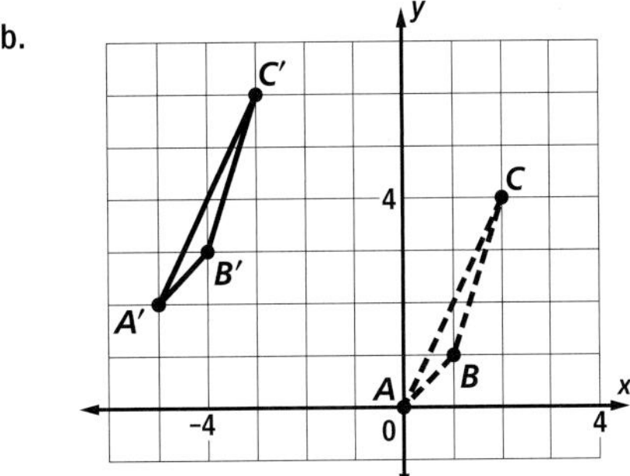

c. The transformation translates $\triangle ABC$ 5 units to the left and 2 units up.

Lesson 6-2 (pp. 380-385)

Mental Math **a.** \$3000 **b.** \$3400 **c.** \$2500

Activity **Step 1.** Answers vary. Sample:

	x	$f(x)$	$g(x)$
$x < -10$	-15	15	15
$-10 \le x \le -1$	-6	6	6
$-1 < x < 0$	$-\frac{1}{2}$	$\frac{1}{2}$	$\frac{1}{2}$
$x = 0$	0	0	0
$0 < x < 1$	$\frac{1}{3}$	$\frac{1}{3}$	$\frac{1}{3}$
$1 \le x \le 10$	7	7	7
$x > 10$	12	12	12

Step 2. $f(x) = g(x)$ for all real numbers x.

Step 3.

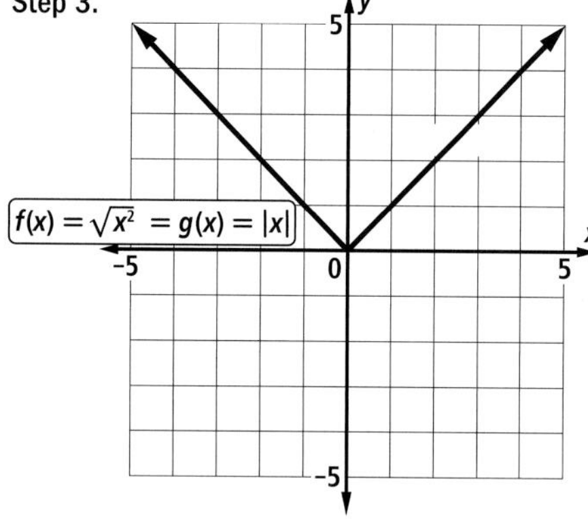

Step 4. The graphs are the same.

Questions

1. a. 17.8 **b.** 17.8 **c.** -17.8 **d.** -17.8 **3.** No; consider $x \neq 0$. Then $|x| > 0$, so $-|x| < 0$ and $|x| \neq -|x|$. **5.** $|x| = 90$ **7.** $n = -1$ or $n = -6$ **9.** A **11.** ± 27 **13.** 4.51 **15.** irrational **17.** rational, 6 **19.** irrational **21. a.** $1.5 \geq |p - 442.5|$ **b.** 444 g **23.** a pizza with about a 13.4" diameter **25.** Answers vary. Sample: Each small square with dimensions $\sqrt{3} \times \sqrt{3}$ has an area of $(\sqrt{3})^2 = 3$. So the large square, which is made up of four small squares, has an area of $4 \cdot 3 = 12$. You can also find the area of the large square by squaring its side length: $(\sqrt{3} + \sqrt{3})^2 = (2\sqrt{3})^2$. So $(2\sqrt{3})^2 = 12$. Taking the square root of both sides gives $2\sqrt{3} = \sqrt{12}$. (Since the side length must be positive, the absolute value can be ignored.) **27.** $64 - x^2$

29. a.

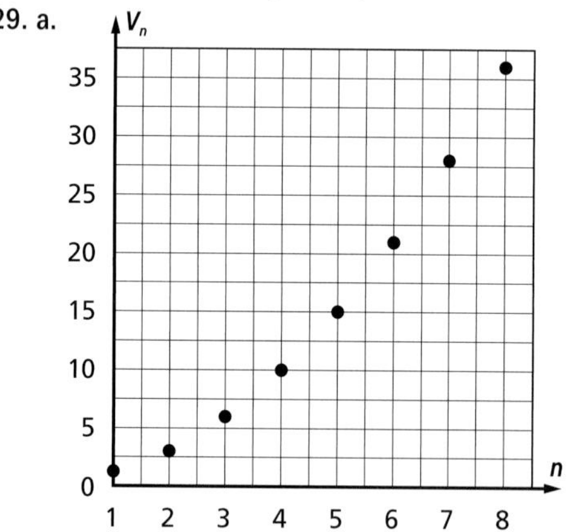

b. $v_{n+1} = v_n + (n + 1)$, for integers $n \geq 1$

Lesson 6-3 (pp. 386-392)

Mental Math a. 16 **b.** 100 **c.** 63 **d.** 441

Activity Step 1. Group B

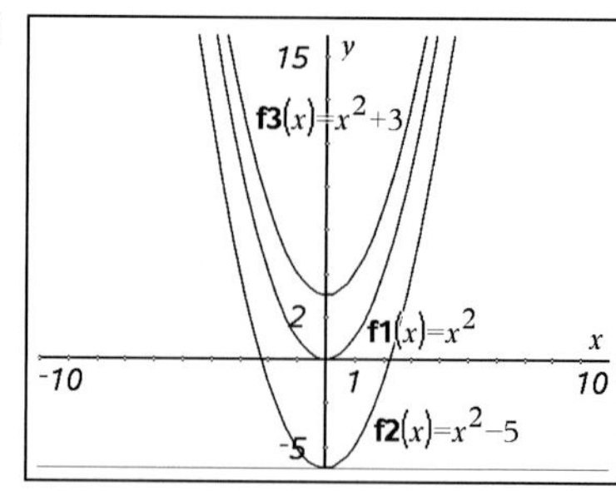

Group C

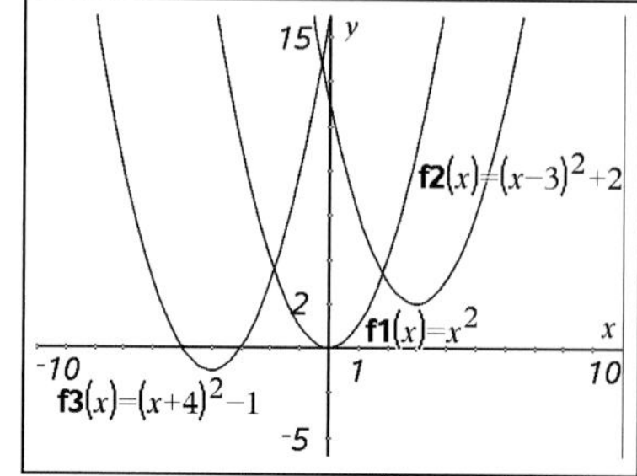

Step 2. Group A: $f2$ is a translation of $f1$ four units to the right; $f3$ is a translation of $f1$ two units to the left; Group B: $f2$ is a translation of $f1$ five units down; $f3$ is a translation of $f1$ three units up; Group C: $f2$ is a translation of $f1$ three units to the right and two units up; $f3$ is a translation of $f1$ four units to the left and one unit down.

Step 3. a. translation 5 units to the left **b.** translation 1 unit down **c.** translation 2 units to the left and 5 units down **Step 4. a.** translation h units horizontally (to the right if h is positive, to the left if h is negative) **b.** translation k units vertically (up if k is positive, down if k is negative) **c.** translation h units horizontally and k units vertically **Step 5.** The conjecture is true.

Guided Example 2 a. $x + 3$; $y - 5$; $T_{-3,5}$; -3; 5 **b.** $x = 0$; -3 **c.** -2; -2; 3; 3; (-3, 5); 3; -3

Questions

1. The translation $T_{5,0}$ maps the first graph onto the second. **3. a.** $(x + 7, y)$ **b.** $y = (x - 7)^2$ **5.** $y = \frac{7}{5}(x - 4)^2 - 7$ **7.** true **9. a.** $x = -5$ **b.** $x = h$ **11. a.** (4, 5) **b.** $x = 4$ **c.** down **d.**

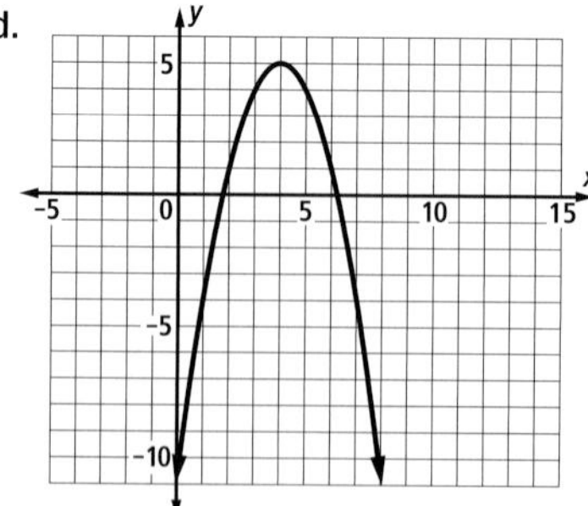

13. $y = -(x - 3)^2 - 2$ **15. a.** $y = -4x^2 + 2$ **b.** $y = -4(x - 2)^2$ **17.** $x = 9$ **19.** $y = mx$; x_1; y_1 **21.** $d = 2$ or $d = -5$; $3|2(2) + 3| = 3|7| = 21$ and $3|2(-5) + 3| = 3|-7| = 21$ **23. a.** $d^2 + 12d + 36$ **b.** 196 m²; 256 m² **25.** $\frac{x^4}{y}$

Lesson 6-4 (pp. 393-400)

Mental Math **a.** Answers vary. Sample: $y = 3x$ **b.** Answers vary. Sample: $y = \frac{3}{x}$ **c.** Answers vary. Sample: $y = 3x^2$ **d.** Answers vary. Sample: $y = \frac{3}{x^2}$

Activity Answers vary. Sample: **Steps 1–5.**

	Initial Height h_0 (m)	Elapsed Time Trial 1 (sec)	Elapsed Time Trial 2 (sec)	Elapsed Time Trial 3 (sec)	Elapsed Time Average (t) (sec)
Partner 1	1.2	1.75	1.6	1.9	1.75
Partner 2	1	2.05	1.93	2.02	2.00

Step 6. Answers vary. Sample : For partner 1, $v_0 \approx 7.89 \frac{\text{m}}{\text{sec}^2}$; $h = -4.9t^2 + 7.89t + 1.2$. For partner 2, $v_0 = 9.3 \frac{\text{m}}{\text{sec}^2}$; $h = -4.9t^2 + 9.3t + 1$.

Step 7. Answers vary. Sample: for partner 1, about 4.4 m; for partner 2, about 5.4 m

Questions

1. $y = ax^2 + bx + c$ **3.** $y = -3x^2 - 24x - 53$ **5. a.** height **b.** acceleration due to gravity **c.** time **d.** initial velocity **e.** initial height **7.** 0 **9.** 0 **11.** $-5 \frac{\text{ft}}{\text{sec}}$

13.

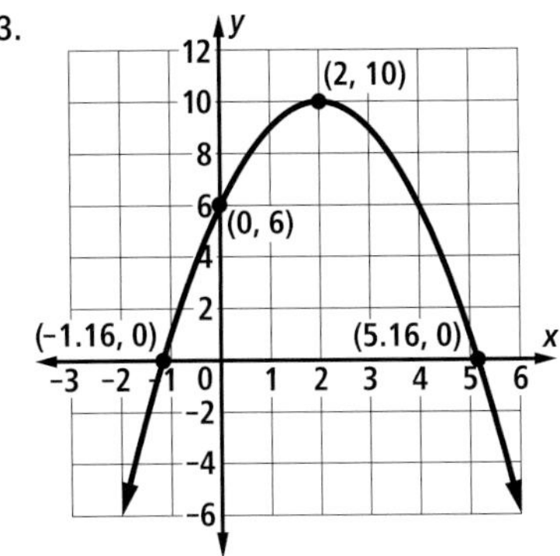

15. a. $h = -16t^2 + 1474$

b.

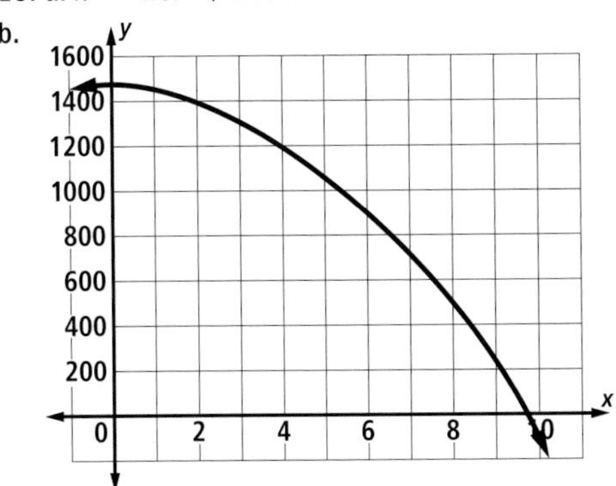

c. about 9.6 sec **d.** about 7.5 sec longer than the equation predicts **17.** $y = -\frac{1}{4}x^2 + 2x - 2$

19. a.

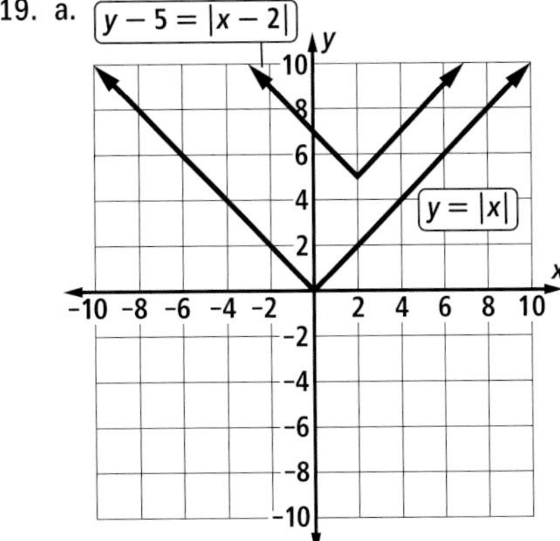

b. The graph of $y - 5 = |x - 2|$ is the image of $y = |x|$ under the translation $T_{2,5}$. **21.** $y \le \frac{2}{3}x + 4$ **23.** $n = 5$ **25.** $n = 6$

Lesson 6-5 (pp. 401-407)

Mental Math **a.** 1 **b.** 1 **c.** an infinite number **d.** 0

Guided Example 2 **a.** 12; 36; 36; 36; 33; 36; 33; 6 **b.** -6; -33

Questions

1. a. $x^2 + 16x$ **b.** 64 **c.** 16; 64; 8 **3.** $\frac{1}{4}$ **5.** $\frac{1}{9}$

7. a. $y + 9.5 = -2(x + 1.5)^2$ **b.** (-1.5, -9.5)

9. a. $h = -16t^2 + 64t + 8$ **b.** 56 ft **c.** 72 ft

d.

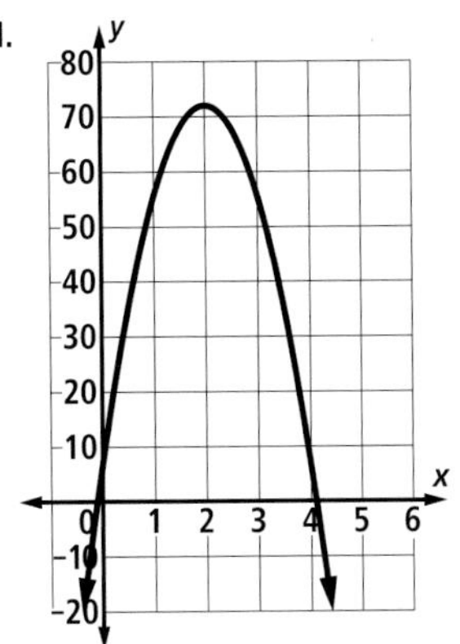

e. about 4.1 sec **11.** $y - 14.8 = 5(x - 0.2)^2$ **13.** The parabola opens down and thus, has no minimum. **15.** $23.2 \frac{\text{m}}{\text{sec}}$ **17. a.** $T_{1,4}$ **b.** $y = -(x - 1)^2 + 4$

19. a.

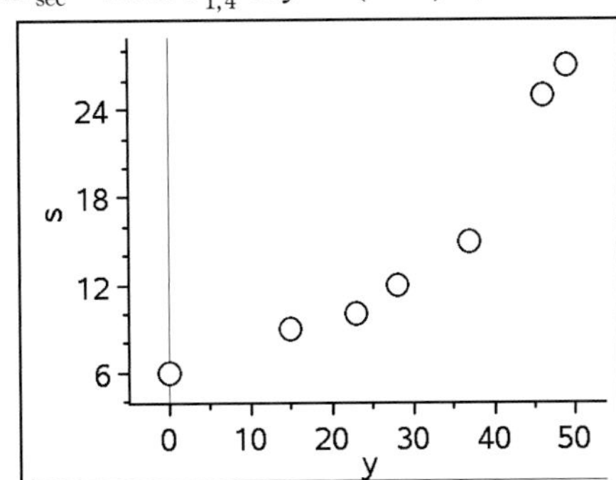

b.

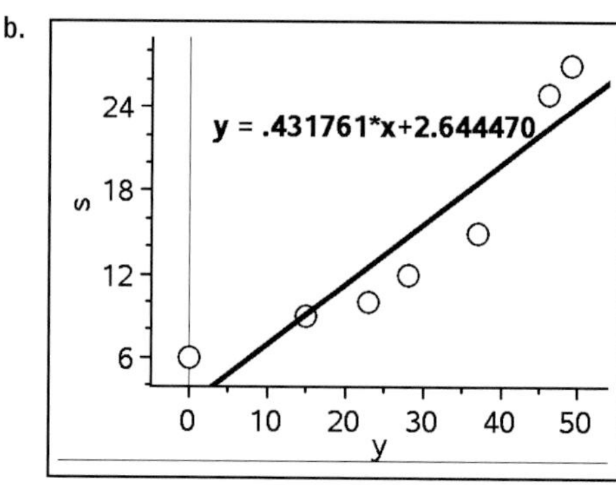

c. about 46 states **21.** $x = 5$

Lesson 6-6 (pp. 408–413)

Mental Math **a.** $-\frac{3}{2}$ **b.** $\frac{2}{3}$ **c.** $\frac{2}{3}$ **d.** $-\frac{2}{3}$

Activity: Answers vary. Samples are given.

Step 2.

Drop #	I	M	O
1	0	0	0
2	1	0	0
3	1	1	0
4	1	1	0
5	1	1	0
6	1	0	0
7	1	1	0
8	1	1	0
9	1	1	0
10	1	1	0
11	1	0	0
12	1	1	1
13	0	0	0
14	1	1	0
15	0	0	0
16	1	0	0
17	1	1	0
18	1	1	0
19	1	0	0
20	1	1	0
21	1	0	0
22	1	1	0
23	1	1	1
24	1	0	0
25	1	0	0

Step 3. $I: \frac{22}{25}$; $M: \frac{14}{25}$; $O: \frac{2}{25}$

Step 4.

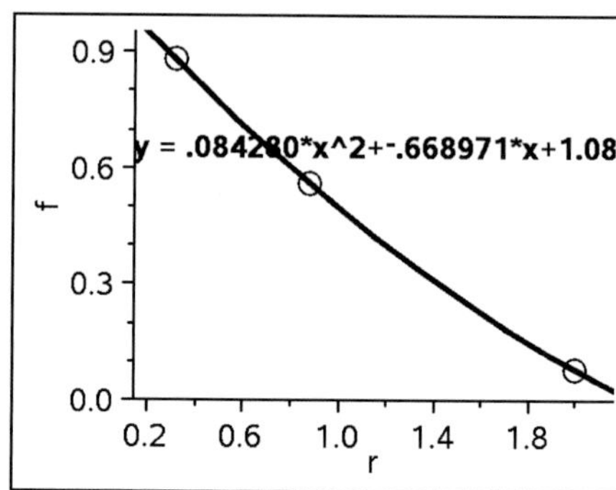

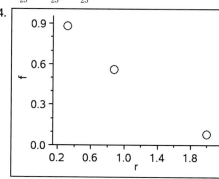

Step 5. Answers vary. Sample: This model seems to pass through all three of my data points. **Step 6.** Answers vary. Sample: Quarter radius = $\frac{15}{32}$ in.; prediction $\approx$ 0.786; relative frequency = $\frac{19}{25}$ = 0.76; This value is close to the predicted value. The value from the combined data is even closer to the predicted value.

Questions

1. a. Answers vary. Sample: $y = 0.084x^2 - 0.669x + 1.081$
b. Answers vary. Sample: 0.236 **3.** $y = x^2 - 8x + 10$
5. $y \approx 0.194x^2 - 1.14x + 3.7$ **7. a.** $y = -0.042x^2 + 0.59x + 10$
b.

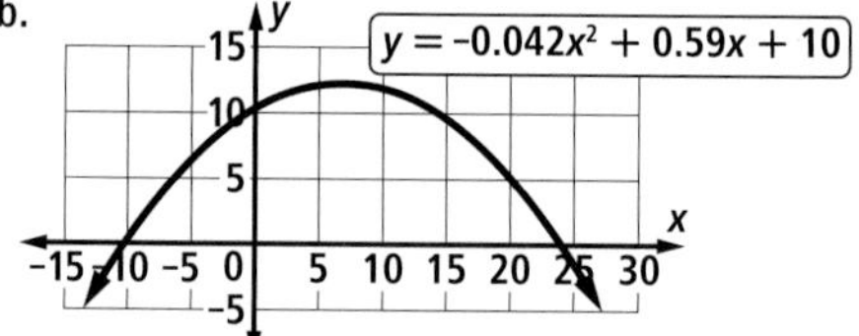

9. a.

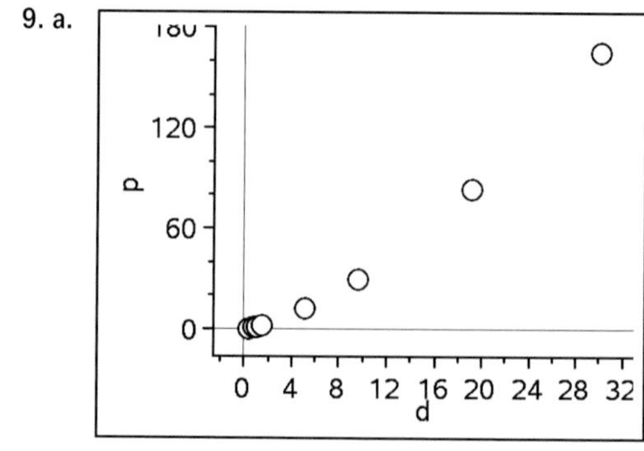

b. $p \approx 0.1081d^2 + 2.301d - 1.557$

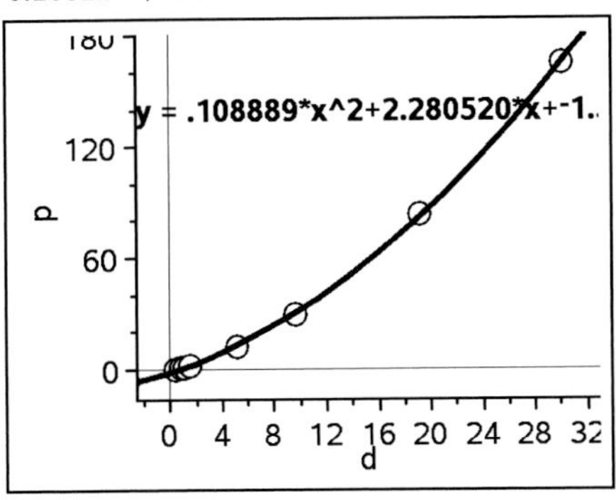

Yes; the model seems to pass through all the data points. **c.** The model predicts about 258 yr for Pluto, so Pluto fits the model fairly well. **d.** about 1,081 yr **11.** $y - 2.25 = 3(x - 1.5)^2$ **13.** $y = -2x^2 - 16x - 32.5$ **15. a.** about 1.37 sec **b.** about 0.56 sec

Lesson 6-7 (pp. 414-419)

Mental Math a. $a^2 - 2ab + b^2$ **b.** $a^2 - 6ab + 9b^2$ **c.** $25a^2 - 30ab + 9b^2$ **d.** $25a^8 - 30a^4b^6 + 9b^{12}$

Guided Example 2 5; 13; -6; 13; 13; 5; -6; 5; -13; 289; 10; -13; 17; 10; -13; 17; 10; $\frac{2}{5} - 3$

Questions

1. $x = \frac{-b+\sqrt{b^2-4ac}}{2a}$ or $x = \frac{-b-\sqrt{b^2-4ac}}{2a}$. **3.** to make the coefficient of x^2 1 in order to complete the square **5.** $z = -1$ or $z = -\frac{3}{10}$ **7.** x represents the distance along the ground in feet of the ball from home plate, and h represents the height in feet of the ball at that distance. **9.** about 60.25 ft **11.** The solutions are the opposites of the solutions from Example 2; $x = -\frac{2}{5}$ or $x = 3$. **13.** $t_n = \frac{n(n+1)}{2} = 10{,}608$; $n(n+1) = 21{,}216$; $n^2 + n = 21{,}216$; $n^2 + n - 21{,}216 = 0$; $n = \frac{-1 \pm \sqrt{1^2 - 4(1)(-21{,}216)}}{2(1)}$; $n = \frac{-1 \pm \sqrt{84{,}865}}{2}$; n is not an integer, therefore it cannot be a triangular number. **15. a.** Q_1: $x = -2$ or $x = -3$; Q_2: $x = -3$ or $x = -4$; Q_3: $x = -4$ or $x = -5$; Q_4: $x = -5$ or $x = -6$; Q_5: $x = -6$ or $x = -7$ **b.** Q_1: 6, -5; Q_2: 12, -7; Q_3: 20, -9; Q_4: 30, -11; Q_5: 42, -13 **c.** The sum of the solutions is equal to $-b$, and the product of the solutions is equal to c. **17.** $\left(-\frac{2}{3}, 4\right)$ and $\left(\frac{1}{2}, 4\right)$ **19.** $y = -2x^2 + 8x + 3$ **21.** $x = -24$ **23. a.** $g_1 = 0$; $g_2 = 2$; $g_3 = 0$; $g_4 = 2$ **b.** $g_n = 0$ for all odd integers n, and $g_n = 2$ for all even integers n. **c.** 0

Lesson 6-8 (pp. 420-426)

Mental Math a. $x = 4$ or $x = -4$ **b.** $x = 7$ or $x = -1$ **c.** $x = 3.5$ or $x = -0.5$

Activity Step 1. -100; $-i$; $-3i$; $\frac{2i}{5}$; $10i$; -10 **Step 2.** Addition and subtraction of imaginary numbers, and multiplication of an imaginary number by a real scalar, result in an imaginary number, but multiplication of two imaginary numbers results in a real number. **Step 3.** 10; 10; yes; $4 \ge 0$ and $25 \ge 0$, and $\sqrt{4} \cdot \sqrt{25} = \sqrt{100} = 10$. **Step 4.** $10i$; 10; yes; If $a \ge 0$ and $b < 0$, then $\sqrt{a} \cdot \sqrt{b} = \sqrt{a} \cdot i\sqrt{-b}$, and $ab < 0$ so $\sqrt{ab} = i\sqrt{a(-b)} = \sqrt{a} \cdot i\sqrt{-b}$. No; $-4 < 0$ and $-25 < 0$, and $\sqrt{-4} \cdot \sqrt{-25} \ne \sqrt{-4 \cdot -25}$, so this is a counterexample.

Questions

1. true **3.** C **5.** Euler **7.** true **9. a.** $x = \sqrt{-16}$ or $x = -\sqrt{-16}$ **b.** $x = 4i$ or $x = -4i$ **11.** $(-6i)^2 = (-6)^2 i^2 = 36(-1) = -36$ **13.** $i\sqrt{53}$ **15.** $-6\sqrt{2}$ **17.** $7i$ **19.** $20i$ **21.** 0 **23.** $-10\sqrt{3}$ **25. a.** yes **b.** no **27.** $691i$ **29.** False; $2i + -2i = 0$, 0 is a real number. **31.** $x = \frac{0 \pm \sqrt{0 - 4(4)(1)}}{2(1)} = \pm\frac{i\sqrt{16}}{2} = \pm 2i$ **33.** $a = \pm i\sqrt{7}$ **35.** $x = \frac{3}{2}$ or $x = -\frac{5}{4}$ **37.** $y = 0.25x^2 + 300x - 77.7$ **39.** domain: all real numbers; range: all real numbers

Lesson 6-9 (pp. 427-433)

Mental Math a. $w < 30$ **b.** $7 \le s \le 10$ **c.** $h \ge 54$

Activity Step 1. $8 + 12i$; $11 + 2i$; $-12 - 3i$ **Step 2.** $-2 - 8i$; $-9 - 8i$; $7 - 3i$ **Step 3.** You can use the Commutative and Associative Properties to add or subtract the real parts and then add or subtract the imaginary parts; $(a + bi) + (c + di) = (a + c) + (b + d)i$ or $(a + bi) - (c + di) = (a - c) + (b - d)i$

Step 4.

$a+b\cdot i+c+d\cdot i$	$a+c+(b+d)\cdot i$
$a+b\cdot i-(c+d\cdot i)$	$a-c+(b-d)\cdot i$

Guided Example 3 $9 + 18i + 6i + 12i^2$; $9 - 6i + 6i - 4i^2$; $9 + 24i + 12i^2$; $9 + 24i + 12(-1)$; -1; -3; 24

Guided Example 4 $3 + 2i$; $5 - 4i$; 23; -2; 8; 2; numerators: 23, -2, 8, 2; denominators: 8, 2, 8, 2; $188 + 30i$; $188 + 30i$

Questions

1. real **3.** real part: -4; imaginary part: $\sqrt{5}$ **5.** $3 + 5i$ **7.** 29 **9.** $a - bi$ **11. a.** $5 - 2i$ **b.** $-3i$ **c.** $-2 + 3i$ **d.** 4 **13.** $2 - 3i$ **15.** true **17.** $5i$ or $0 + 5i$ **19. a.** Answers vary. Sample: $3 + 2i$, $8 - 2i$ **b.** Answers vary. Sample: $3i$, $5i$ **21. a.** $3 + 2i$, $3 - 2i$ **b.** They are complex conjugates. **23.** $a^2 + b^2$; Because a and b are real numbers, $a^2 + b^2$ is a real number. **25.** $a = i\sqrt{5}$ or $-i\sqrt{5}$ **27.** Answers vary. Sample: By the definition of absolute value, the distance between x and $\frac{-b}{2a}$ is $\sqrt{\frac{b^2-4ac}{4a^2}}$, and this means that the difference between x and $\frac{-b}{2a}$ could be $\sqrt{\frac{b^2-4ac}{4a^2}}$ or its opposite. So, when absolute value signs are removed, a $\pm$ sign must be added. **29.** $R = \frac{km^2}{P}$

Lesson 6-10 (pp. 434-440)

Mental Math a. S_3 **b.** $\begin{bmatrix} 4.2 & 0 \\ 0 & 4.2 \end{bmatrix}$ **c.** $S_{0.5,6}$ **d.** $\begin{bmatrix} 7 & 0 \\ 0 & 2 \end{bmatrix}$

Activity

$y = ax^2 + bx + c$	Number of *x*-Intercepts of Graph	Solutions to $ax^2 + bx + c = 0$	Number of Real Solutions to $ax^2 + bx + c = 0$	Value of $b^2 - 4ac$
a. $y = 4x^2 - 24x + 27$	2	$x = 1.5, 4.5$	2	144
b. $y = 4x^2 - 24x + 36$	1	$x = 3$	1	0
c. $y = 4x^2 - 24x + 45$	0	$x = 3 \pm \frac{3}{2}i$	0	-144
d. $y = -6x^2 - 36x - 48$	1	$x = 3$	1	0
e. $y = -6x^2 - 36x - 54$	2	$x = 2, 4$	2	144
f. $y = -6x^2 - 36x - 60$	0	$3 \pm i$	0	-144

Step 3. Answers vary. Sample: the number of *x*-intercepts is equal to the number of real solutions. **Step 4.** Answers vary. Sample: When the discriminant is positive, there are two real solutions. When the discriminant is zero, there is one real solution. When the discriminant is negative, there are no real solutions. **Step 5a-b.** Answers vary. Check students' work. **Step 5c.** yes

Guided Example Solution a. 1 **b.** -364; 0 **c.** 3; 5; -14, 193; 2

Check a. 1; 1 **b.** 0; 0 **c.** 2; 2

Questions

1. They are equal. **3. a.** $b^2 - 4ac$ **b.** $\frac{-b \pm \sqrt{b^2 - 4ac}}{2a}$ **5. a.** v **b.** iv **7. a.** $x^2 - 10x + 9 = 0$; $b^2 - 4ac = 64$, so there are 2 real roots. **b.** $x^2 - 10x + 9 = y$; 2 *x*-intercepts
9. Answers vary. Sample:

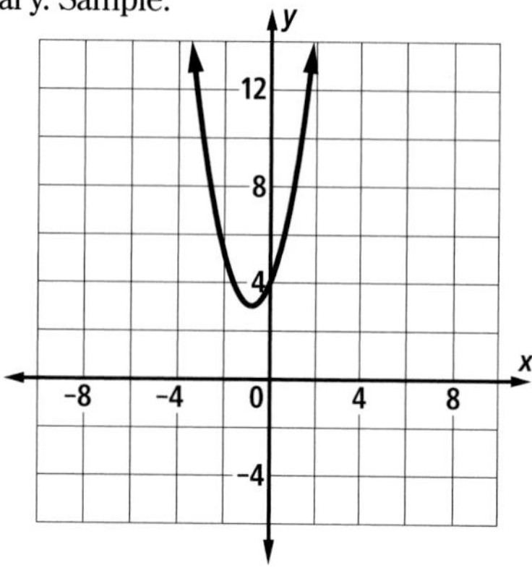

11. a. positive **b.** 2 **13.** Yes; the discriminate *D* of $0 = -0.4x^2 + 3x - 5$ is 1. Because *D* is positive there are real solutions, and the ball will reach the height of the rim. **15.** True; the graph intersects the *x*-axis in two points, so there are two real roots. **17.** No; Explanations vary. Sample: If one root is rational, then by the quadratic formula $x = \frac{a \pm \sqrt{b}}{c}$, where a, $\sqrt{b}$, and c are rational numbers. The other root, $\frac{a - \sqrt{b}}{c}$ would have to be rational because addition, subtraction, and division of rational numbers result in a rational number. **19.** $x = 4 + 3i$ or $x = 4 - 3i$
21. a. $p = -16t^2 + 1200$ **b.** $m = 300 + 30t$
c. $t \approx 6.62$ seconds

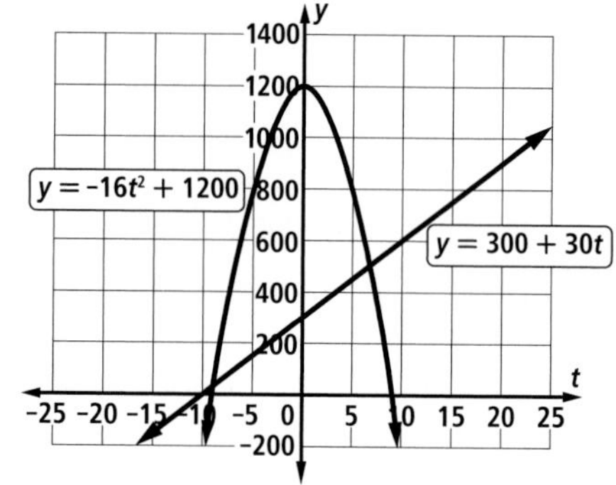

Self-Test (p. 445)

1. $y - 21 = x^2 - 10x$; $y - 21 + 25 = x^2 - 10x + 25$; $y + 4 = (x - 5)^2$ **2.** (5, -4) **3.** $0 = x^2 - 10x + 21$; $x = \frac{10 \pm \sqrt{(-10)-4(1)(21)}}{2} = \frac{10 \pm 4}{2}$; $x = \frac{10+4}{2} = 7$ or $x = \frac{10-4}{2} = 3$. The *x*-intercepts are 7 and 3. **4.** $5i \cdot i = 5i^2 = -5$ **5.** $\sqrt{-12} \cdot \sqrt{-3} = i\sqrt{12} \cdot i\sqrt{3} = i^2\sqrt{36} = -6$ **6.** $\frac{6 + \sqrt{-64}}{3} = \frac{6 + i\sqrt{64}}{3} = \frac{6 + 8i}{3} = 2 + \frac{8}{3}i$ **7.** $(1 + 5i)(-4 + 3i) = -4 - 20i + 3i + 15i^2 = -19 - 17i$ **8.** $6 - 5i - (2 + 5i) = 6 - 5i - 2 - 5i = 4 - 10i$ **9.** C
10. $y - 3 = -(x + 4)^2$ is in vertex form, so the vertex is (-4, 3). Because $a = -1 < 0$, the graph will open down, it is symmetric about $x = -4$, and the *y*-intercept is $y = -16 + 3 = -13$.

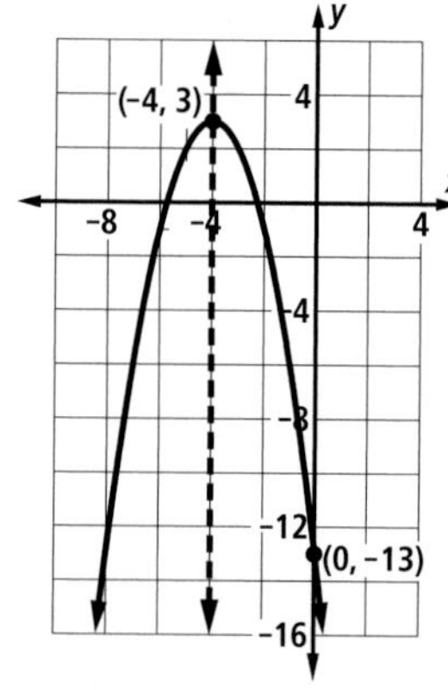

11. From the vertex form of the equation, the vertex is (-4, 3). Since $a < 0$, the parabola opens down. So, the domain is all real numbers and the range is $\{y \mid y \leq 3\}$.

13. $\sqrt{(6s+5)^2} = 9 \Rightarrow |6s+5| = 9$; $6s+5 = 9$, $s = \frac{2}{3}$; or $(6s+5) = -9$, $s = -\frac{7}{3}$ 14. $17 = y^2 + 36y + 324$; $0 = y^2 + 36y + 307$; $y = \frac{-36 \pm \sqrt{1296 - 4 \cdot 1 \cdot 307}}{2}$; $y = \frac{-36 \pm \sqrt{68}}{2}$; $y = -18 \pm \sqrt{17}$ 15. $3x^2 + 14x - 5 = 0$; $x = \frac{-14 \pm \sqrt{196 - 4 \cdot 3 \cdot (-5)}}{6}$; $x = \frac{-14 \pm \sqrt{196 + 60}}{6}$; $x = \frac{-14 \pm 16}{6}$; $x = \frac{1}{3}$, $x = \frac{-10}{3}$ 16. By the Absolute Value-Square Root Theorem, $\sqrt{x^2} = |x|$ for all real values of x. 17. $4a^2 - 20a + 25 + 4a^2 + 20a + 25 = 8a^2 + 50$ 18. The solutions are not real. 19. a. 0 b. 1 c. 2 20. $h = -16(1.5)^2 + 28(1.5) + 6$ $h = -36 + 42 + 6$ $h = 12$ feet 21. $0 = -16t^2 + 28t + 6$; $t = \frac{-28 \pm \sqrt{784 - 4 \cdot (-16) \cdot 6}}{-32}$; $t = \frac{-28 \pm \sqrt{1168}}{-32}$; $t \approx -0.193$, $t \approx 1.943$; In this situation, only $t = 1.943$ seconds makes sense. So the ball hit the ground after about 1.9 sec. 22. $(16 + 2x)(12 + 2x) - 16 \cdot 12 = 192 + 56x + 4x^2 - 192 = 4x^2 + 56x$

23. B; the coefficient of x^2 in B is 4, but the coefficient of x^2 in A, C, and D is 1, so B has a narrower graph.

24. a.

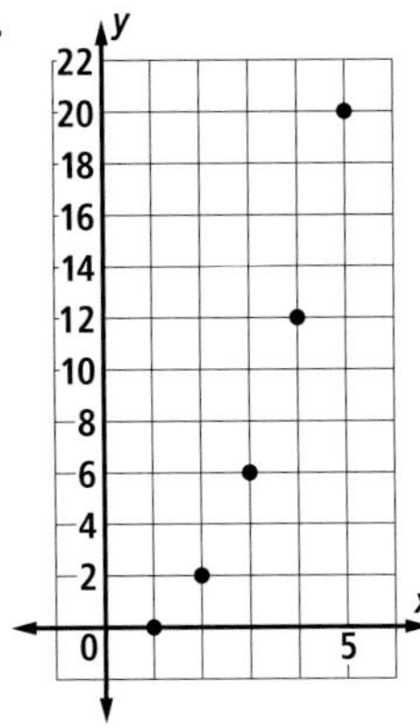

b. $f(n) = n^2 - n$ c. 272 points

Self-Test Correlation Chart

Question	1	2	3	4	5	6	7	8
Objective(s)	B	B	C	E	E	E	E	E
Lesson(s)	6-4, 6-5	6-4, 6-5	6-2, 6-7, 6-8, 6-10	6-8, 6-9	6-8, 6-9	6-8, 6-9	6-8, 6-9	6-8, 6-9

Question	9	10	11	12	13	14	15	16
Objective(s)	G	K	G	D	C	C	C	F
Lesson(s)	6-3, 6-4	6-2, 6-3, 6-4, 6-10	6-3, 6-4	6-2	6-2, 6-7, 6-8, 6-10	6-2, 6-7, 6-8, 6-10	6-2, 6-7, 6-8, 6-10	6-2

Question	17	18	19	20	21	22	23	24
Objective(s)	A	H	L	I	I	I	G	J
Lesson(s)	6-1	6-10	6-10	6-1, 6-4, 6-5, 6-7	6-1, 6-4, 6-5, 6-7	6-1, 6-4, 6-5, 6-7	6-3, 6-4	6-6

Chapter Review (pp. 446–449)

1. $7p^2 - 19p - 6$ 3. $36w^2 - 6w - 12$ 5. $a^2 + 2ab + b^2$ 7. $13y^2 - 78y + 117$ 9. $y = 5x^2 + 10x + 5$ 11. $y + \frac{101}{4} = \left(x + \frac{9}{2}\right)^2$ 13. C 15. $r = \pm\sqrt{26}$ 17. $y = \pm 5i$ 19. $s = \frac{-5 \pm \sqrt{13}}{2}$ 21. $k = 3$ 23. $y = -4$ or $y = 26$ 25. $x = 1$ or $x = -\frac{7}{3}$ 27. $t = 5$ 29. 1 31. -15 33. -6 35. $8 + 3i$ 37. $17 + 19i$ 39. $12 - 5i$ 41. $\frac{11 - 23i}{13}$ 43. $x < 0$ 45. 16 47. 2 49. The graph of $y = |x+2|$ is the image of the graph of $y = |x|$ under $T_{-2,0}$. 51. a. $T_{0.9,0.6}$ b. $y - 0.6 = \frac{3}{4}(x - 0.9)^2$ 53. The solutions to $(k+2)^2 = 25$ are the solutions to $k^2 = 25$ under a horizontal shift of two units to the left. 55. a. 57 b. 2 c. irrational 57. a. 15 b. 0 c. nonreal 59. a. 26.39 ft b. after 1.16 sec c. 15 ft 61. a. Answers vary. Sample: $y \approx x^2 + 23.2x - 11.7$ b. about 121 frogs c. The model does not take into account the initial number of frogs released. If the model's prediction of the twentieth ring were correct, there would be more than 1000 frogs found. 63. a. $y = 76.68x^2 + 2254x + 314{,}255$, where y is the population x years after 1980. b. 450,887 c. 2061

65.

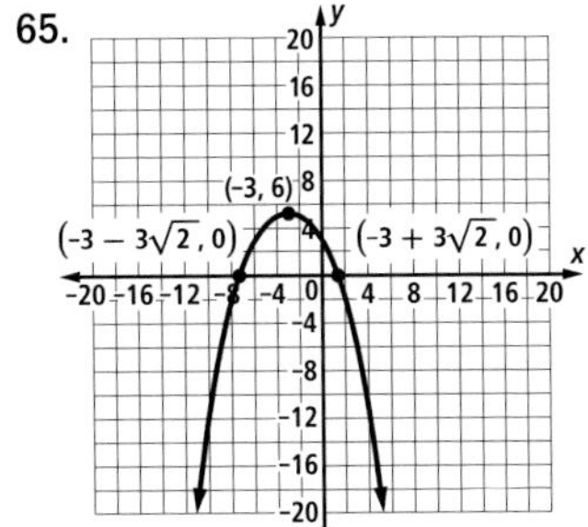

67.

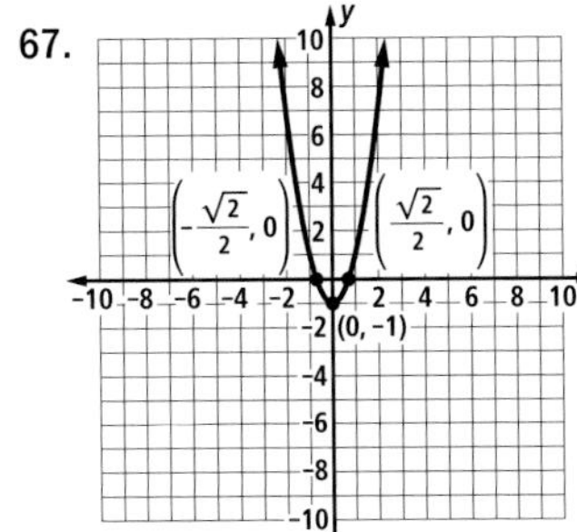

69. A 71. 2 73. Yes; the vertex of the parabola is $\left(\frac{3}{2}, -\frac{27}{4}\right)$, which is below the line $y = -1$. The parabola opens up, so the parabola intersects the horizontal line $y = -1$.

Glossary

A

absolute deviation The difference $|x_i - \mu|$, where x_i is an element of a data set and μ is the mean of the set. (884)

absolute value The operation or function defined by $|x| = \begin{cases} x \text{ when } x \geq 0 \\ -x \text{ when } x < 0 \end{cases}$; geometrically, the distance of x from 0 on a number line. (380)

absolute-value function The function with equation $f(x) = |x|$. (380)

acceleration The rate of change of the velocity of an object. (12)

algebraic expression See *expression.* (6)

algebraic sentence A sentence in which expressions are related by equality or inequality. (6)

angle of depression The angle between the line of sight and the horizontal when the line of sight points down. (672)

angle of elevation The angle between the horizontal base of an object and the observer's line of sight to the object when the line of sight points up. (665)

annual percentage yield, or APY The rate of interest earned after all the compoundings have taken place in one year. Also called *effective annual yield* or *yield.* (475)

argument of a function The domain variable in a function. (21)

arithmetic mean See *mean of a data set.* (883)

arithmetic sequence A sequence with a constant difference between consecutive terms. Also called *linear sequence.* (196)

arithmetic series An indicated sum of successive terms of an arithmetic sequence. (869)

asymptote A line approached by the graph of a function. (581)

asymptotes of a hyperbola The two lines that are approached by the points on the branches of a hyperbola as the points get farther from the foci. (107)

axis of symmetry of a parabola The line through the focus of a parabola perpendicular to the directrix. (388, 798)

B

base x in the expression x^n. (452)

bel A unit of sound intensity; 10 bels is a decibel. (616)

binomial An expression with two terms. A polynomial with two terms. (375, 738)

binomial coefficients The coefficients of terms in the expansion of $(a + b)^n$, often displayed as the numbers in Pascal's Triangle. (906)

binomial distribution A probability function P resulting from calculations of binomial probabilities. Also called *binomial probabilty distribution.* (923)

binomial expansion The result of writing the power of a binomial as a sum. (903)

binomial experiment A situation in which n independent trials occur, and each trial has exactly two mutually exclusive outcomes. (912)

binomial probability distribution See *binomial distribution.* (923)

boundary of a half plane The line in a plane that separates the half-plane from another mutually exclusive half-plane. (342)

branches of a hyperbola The two separate parts of the graph of a hyperbola. (107)

C

ceiling function The step function $f(x) = \lceil x \rceil$, the least integer greater than or equal to x. Also called *least-integer function* or *rounding-up function.* (204)

ceiling symbol The symbol $\lceil x \rceil$ indicating the least integer greater than or equal to x. (204)

center of a circle The fixed point from which the set of points of the circle are at a given distance. (804)

center of a rotation In a rotation, a point that coincides with its image. (269)

center of a size change The point in a size change of magnitude $k \neq 1$ that coincides with its image. (242)

center of an ellipse The intersection of the axes of an ellipse. (819)

circle The set of all points in a plane at a given distance from a fixed point. (804)

closure The property of an operation on elements of a set S when all the results of performing the operation are elements of S. (262)

coefficient matrix A matrix that contains the coefficients of the variables in a system of equations. (336)

coefficients of a polynomial The numbers a_n, a_{n-1}, a_{n-2}, ..., a_0 in the polynomial $a_n x^n + a_{n-1}x^{n-1} + a_{n-2}x^{n-2} + ... + a_0$. (730)

combination Any choice of r objects from n objects when the order of the objects does not matter. (892)

combined variation A situation in which direct and inverse variations occur together. (129)

common logarithm A logarithm to the base 10. Also called *common log.* (609)

common logarithm function The function that maps x onto $\log_{10}x$ for all positive numbers x. Also called the *logarithm function to the base 10.* (611)

completing the square A technique used to transform a quadratic from $ax^2 + bx + c$ form to $a(x - h)^2 + k$ form.
(401)

complex conjugate For any complex number $a + bi$, the difference $a - bi$. (429)

complex number A number that can be written in the form $a + bi$, where a and b are real numbers and $i = \sqrt{-1}$. (427)

composite $g \circ f$ For two functions f and g, the function that maps x onto $g(f(x))$ and whose domain is the set of all values in the domain of f for which $f(x)$ is in the domain of g. (517)

composite of two transformations Given transformation T_1 that maps figure G onto figure G' and transformation T_2 that maps figure G' onto figure G'', the transformation that maps G onto G'', the composite of T_1 and T_2, written $T_2 \circ T_1$. (263)

composition See *function composition.* (517)

compound sentence A sentence in which two clauses are connected by the word *and* or by the word *or.* (300)

compounding The process of earning interest on the interest of an investment. (473)

concentric circles Circles with the same center but different radii. (804)

conic section The intersection of a plane and a double cone. (838)

conjugate For any expression of the form $a + \sqrt{b}$, the expression $a - \sqrt{b}$. (553)

consistent system A system that has one or more solutions. (316)

constant-decrease situation A situation in which a quantity y decreases by a constant amount for every fixed increase in x. (150)

constant difference In an arithmetic sequence, the difference of two consecutive terms. (196)

constant-increase situation A situation in which a quantity y increases by a constant amount for every fixed increase in x. (150)

constant of variation The nonzero real constant k in the equation $y = kx^n$ or $y = \frac{k}{x^n}$ or other equation of a function of variation. (72)

constant matrix A matrix that contains the constants on the right sides of the equations in a system. (336)

constant multiplier The constant in a geometric sequence. Also called *constant ratio.* (479)

constant ratio In a geometric sequence, the ratio of successive terms. Also called *constant multiplier.* (480)

constant term, constant In the polynomial $a_n x^n + a_{n-1}x^{n-1} + a_{n-2}x^{n-2} + ... + a_0$, the number a_0. (730)

constraint A restriction on a variable or variables in a situation. (299)

continuous change model The equation $N(t) = N_0 e^{rt}$, where N_0 is the initial amount and r is the growth factor over a time t. (598)

continuous compounding The limit of the process of earning interest with periods of compounding approaching zero. Also called *instantaneous compounding.* (596)

convex region A region of the plane in which any two points of the region can be connected by a line segment which lies entirely in the region. (354)

coordinate plane A plane in which there is a one-to-one correspondence between the points in the plane and the set of ordered pairs of real numbers. (33)

corollary A theorem that follows immediately from another theorem. (388)

correlation coefficient A number between -1 and 1 that indicates how well a linear equation fits data. (181)

cosine function The correspondence $\theta \rightarrow \cos\theta$ that maps a number θ onto its cosine. (663)

cosine of θ (cos θ) In a right triangle with acute angle θ, $\cos\theta = \frac{\text{length of leg adjacent to }\theta}{\text{length of hypotenuse}}$, the x-coordinate of the image of (1, 0) under R_θ, the rotation with center (0, 0) and magnitude θ. (663, 684)

counterexample An instance which shows a generalization to be false. (424)

counting numbers See *natural numbers.* (29)

$\cos^{-1} x$ The number between 0 and 180°, or between 0 and π, whose cosine is x. (671)

cube of x The third power of x, x^3. (454)

cube root A cube root t of x, denoted $\sqrt[3]{x}$, is a solution to the equation $t^3 = x$. (487)

cubic polynomial A polynomial of a single variable with degree 3, such as $ax^3 + bx^2 + cx + d$. (731)

cubing function A function f with equation $f(x) = x^3$. (454)

D

data set A collection of elements in which an element may appear more than once. (883)

decade growth factor The ratio of an amount in a specific year to the amount ten years earlier. (542)

decibel (dB) A measure of relative sound intensity; $\frac{1}{10}$ of a bel. (615)

default window The window that is set on an automatic grapher by the manufacturer. (28)

degree of a polynomial in a single variable The largest exponent of the variable in a polynomial. (730)

degree of a polynomial in several variables The largest sum of the exponents of the variables in any term in a polynomial expression. (738)

dependent variable A variable whose value always depends on the value(s) of other variable(s). (15)

depreciation The decrease in value over time of manufactured goods. (587)

determinant of a 2 × 2 matrix For the matrix $M = \begin{bmatrix} a & b \\ c & d \end{bmatrix}$, the number $ad - bc$. (331)

deviation For each value of an independent variable, the difference $p - a$ between the value p of the dependent variable predicted by a model and the actual value a. (178)

difference of two matrices For two matrices A and B with the same dimensions, their difference $A - B$ is the matrix in which each element is the difference of the corresponding elements in A and B. (230)

dimensions of a matrix A matrix with m rows and n columns has dimensions $m \times n$. (222)

direct-variation equation An equation in which one variable is a multiple of another variable or product of variables. (72)

direct-variation function A function that can be described by a formula of the form $y = kx^n$, $k \neq 0$ and $n > 0$. (73)

directly proportional to The situation in which y varies directly as x^n. Also called *varies directly as.* (73)

directrix of a parabola The line such that the distance from it to any point on the parabola is equal to the distance from that point to the focus. (798)

discrete function A function whose domain can be put into one-to-one correspondence with a finite or infinite set of integers, with gaps or intervals between successive values in the domain. (57)

discrete graph A graph that is made up of unconnected points. (57)

discrete set A set in which there is a positive distance greater than some fixed amount between any two elements of the set. (108)

discriminant of a quadratic equation For the equation $ax^2 + bx + c = 0$, the value of the expression $b^2 - 4ac$. (435)

domain of a function The set of values which are allowable substitutions for the independent variable. (27)

double cone The surface generated by a line rotating about an axis that contains a point on the line. (797)

double inequality A sentence that has two inequality symbols. (301)

double root The root of a quadratic equation when the discriminant is 0; the root of a quadratic equation that has only one solution; a root r of a polynomial in x for which $(x - r)^2$ is a factor, but not $(x - r)^3$. Also called a *root with multiplicity 2.* (767)

E

e The constant 2.7182818459... that the sequence of numbers of the form $\left(1 + \frac{1}{n}\right)^n$ approaches as n increases without bound; the base of natural logarithms. (596)

element of a matrix Each object in a matrix. (222)

ellipse Given two points F_1 and F_2 (the *foci*) and a positive number d, the set of points P in a plane for which $PF_1 + PF_2 = d$. (817)

equal complex numbers Two complex numbers with equal real parts and equal imaginary parts. (427)

equal matrices Two matrices that have the same dimensions and in which corresponding elements are equal. (223)

equation A sentence stating that two expressions are equal. (9)

equivalent formulas Two or more formulas for which all values of the variables that satisfy one formula satisfy the other(s). (48)

Euler's $f(x)$ notation Notation in which $f(x)$ represents the value of a function f with argument x. (20)

evaluating an expression Substituting numbers for the variables in an expression and calculating a result. (8)

expanding a polynomial Writing a power of a polynomial or the product of polynomials as a sum. (739)

explicit formula for *n*th term A formula that describes any term in a sequence in terms of its position in the sequence. (54)

exponent n in the expression b^n. (452)

exponential curve The graph of an exponential function. (582)

exponential decay A situation described by an exponential function in which the growth factor is between zero and 1, in which $f(x)$ decreases as x increases. (587)

exponential function A function f with the equation $f(x) = ab^x$ $(a \neq 0, b > 0, b \neq 1)$. (582)

exponential growth A situation described by an exponential function where the growth factor is greater than one. (582)

exponential growth model If a quantity a has growth factor b for each unit period, then after a period of length x, there will be ab^x. (580)

exponential sequence See *geometric sequence.* (479)

exponentiation See *powering.* (452)

expression A combination of numbers, variables, and operations that stands for a number. Also called *algebraic expression.* (6)

exterior of a circle The region outside a circle; the set of points whose distance from the center of the circle is greater than the radius. (811)

extraneous solution A possible solution that is obtained from an equation-solving procedure but that does not check in the original equation. (563)

F

$f(x)$ notation The notation used to describe functions, read "f of x." (20)

factor A number or expression which evenly divides a given expression. (745)

factored form of a polynomial A polynomial written as a product of two or more factors. (745)

factorial For any integer $n \geq 2$, the product of the integers from 1 through n, denoted by $n!$. (890)

factorial symbol, ! The symbol used to represent the product of the integers n through 1. (890)

factoring a polynomial The process of rewriting a polynomial as a product of two or more factors. (745)

fair coin, fair die A coin or die that has an equal probability of landing on each of its sides. Also called *unbiased coin* or *unbiased die.* (910)

feasible region The set of solutions to a system of linear inequalities. Also called *feasible set.* (349)

feasible set See *feasible region.* (349)

Fibonacci sequence The sequence 1, 1, 2, 3, 5, 8, 13, … . A recursive definition is

$$\begin{cases} F_1 = 1 \\ F_2 = 1 \\ F_n = F_{n-1} + F_{2n-2} \text{ for } n \geq 3 \end{cases} \quad .$$ (192)

field properties The assumed properties of addition and multiplication of real numbers. **(S1)**

floor function The step function $f(x) = \lfloor x \rfloor$, indicating the greatest integer less than or equal to x. Also called *greatest-integer function*, *int function*, or *rounding-down function*. **(204)**

floor symbol The symbol $\lfloor x \rfloor$ indicating the greatest integer less than or equal to x. **(204)**

focal constant The constant sum of the distances from any point P on an ellipse to the foci. For a hyperbola, the absolute value of the difference of the distances from a point on a hyperbola to the two foci of the hyperbola. **(817, 832)**

focus, plural *foci* For a parabola, the point along with the directrix from which a point is equidistant. The two points from which the sum (ellipse) or difference (hyperbola) of distances to a point on the conic section is constant. **(798, 817, 832)**

formula A sentence stating that a single variable is equal to an expression with one or more different variables on the other side. **(9)**

function A set of ordered pairs (x, y) in which each first component x of the pair is paired with exactly one second component y. A relation in which no two ordered pairs have the same first component x. **(15)**

function composition The operation that results from first applying one function, then another; denoted by the symbol $\circ$. **(517)**

G

general form of a quadratic relation An equation of the form $Ax^2 + Bxy + Cy^2 + Dx + Ey + F = 0$, where A, B, C, D, E, and F are real numbers and at least one of A, B, or C is not zero. **(796)**

geometric mean The nth root of the product of n numbers. **(537)**

geometric sequence A sequence in which each term after the first is found by multiplying the previous term by a constant. Also called *exponential sequence*. **(479)**

geometric series An indicated sum of successive terms of a geometric sequence. **(877)**

gravitational constant The acceleration of a moving object due to gravity, often denoted by g. Near Earth's surface, $g \approx 32 \frac{\text{ft}}{\text{sec}^2} \approx 9.8 \frac{\text{m}}{\text{sec}^2}$. **(12)**

greatest common monomial factor The monomial with the greatest coefficient and highest degree that is a factor of all the terms of a polynomial. **(746)**

greatest integer function See *floor function*. **(204)**

growth factor In the exponential function $y = ab^x$ with $a > 0$, the base b. **(582)**

H

half-life The amount of time required for a quantity in an exponential decay situation to decay to half its original value. **(588)**

half-plane Either of the two sets of points, or regions, separated by a line in a plane. **(342)**

hierarchy A diagram that shows how various ideas are related, with a direction that moves from more specific to more general. **(S5)**

horizontal asymptote A horizontal line that is approached by a graph as the values of x get very large or very small. **(107)**

horizontal line A line with an equation of the form $y = b$. **(153)**

horizontal-line test The inverse of a function is itself a function if and only if no horizontal line intersects the graph of the function in more than one point. **(525)**

horizontal magnitude The number a in the scale change that maps (x, y) onto (ax, by). **(249)**

horizontal scale change The stretching or shrinking of a figure in only the horizontal direction; a transformation which maps (x, y) onto (kx, y). **(249)**

hyperbola The graph of a function with equation of the form $y = \frac{k}{x}$, where $k \neq 0$. For any two points F_1 and F_2 (the *foci* of the hyperbola) and d (the *focal constant* of the hyperbola) with $0 < d < F_1F_2$, the set of points P in a plane that satisfy $|PF_1 - PF_2| = d$. **(107, 832)**

I

i One of the two square roots of -1, denoted by $\sqrt{-1}$. **(421)**

identity A relationship that is true for all values of variables in a domain. **(688)**

identity function The function with equation $f(x) = x$. **(454)**

2 × 2 identity matrix The matrix $\begin{bmatrix} 1 & 0 \\ 0 & 1 \end{bmatrix}$, which maps each point $\begin{bmatrix} x \\ y \end{bmatrix}$ of a figure onto itself. (244)

3 × 3 identity matrix The matrix $\begin{bmatrix} 1 & 0 & 0 \\ 0 & 1 & 0 \\ 0 & 0 & 1 \end{bmatrix}$, which maps each point $\begin{bmatrix} x \\ y \\ z \end{bmatrix}$ of a figure onto itself. (268)

identity transformation The size-change transformation of magnitude 1; the transformation in which each point coincides with its image. (244)

image The result of applying a transformation to a preimage. (242)

imaginary number A number that is the square root of a negative real number. (421)

imaginary part Of the complex number $a + bi$, bi. (427)

imaginary unit The complex number i. (421)

inconsistent system A system that has no solutions. (316)

independent events Two or more events in which the occurrence of one event does not affect the probabilities the other events occur. (453)

independent variable In a formula, a variable upon whose value other variables depend. (15)

index The subscript used for a term in a sequence indicating the position of the term in the sequence. (54)

inequality A sentence containing one of the symbols $<, >, \leq, \geq, \neq$, or $\approx$. (303)

index variable The variable i under the Σ sign in summation notation. Also called *index.* (871)

input A value of the independent variable in a function. (15)

interval The set of numbers x such that $x \leq a$ or $a \leq x \leq b$, where the $\leq$ can be replaced by $<, >$, or $\geq$. (301)

int function See *floor function.* (204)

integers The set of numbers {... , -3, -2, -1, 0, 1, 2, 3, ...}; the set of natural numbers and their opposites. (29)

interior of a circle The region inside a circle; the set of points whose distance from the center of the circle is less than the radius. (811)

intersection of two sets The set consisting of those values common to both sets. (301)

inverse cosine function, $\cos^{-1}$ For the function that maps x onto $\cos x$, restricted to the domain $0 \leq x \leq \pi$ or $0 \leq x \leq 180°$, the function that maps $\cos x$ onto x. (671)

inverse function, f^{-1} The inverse relation formed by switching the coordinates of each ordered pair of f, when this inverse is itself a function. A function that when composed with another function gives the identity function. (529, 531)

inverse matrices Two matrices whose product is the identity matrix. (328)

inverse of a relation The relation obtained by switching the coordinates of each ordered pair in the relation. (523)

inverse sine function, $\sin^{-1}$ For the function that maps x onto $\sin x$, restricted to the domain $-\frac{\pi}{2} \leq x \leq \frac{\pi}{2}$, the function that maps $\sin x$ onto x. (670)

inverse-square curve The graph of $y = \frac{k}{x^2}$. (108)

inverse tangent function, $\tan^{-1}$ For the function that maps x onto $\tan x$, restricted to the domain $-\frac{\pi}{2} \leq x \leq \frac{\pi}{2}$, the function that maps $\tan x$ onto x. (671)

inverse-variation function A function that can be described by a formula of the form $y = \frac{k}{x^n}$, for $k \neq 0$ and $n > 0$. (79)

inversely proportional to The situation in which y varies indirectly with x^n. Also called *varies inversely as.* (80)

irrational number A real number that is not rational, that is, cannot be expressed as a simple fraction or ratio of the form $\frac{a}{b}$, where a and b are integers and $b \neq 0$. (29, 383)

irreducible polynomial See *prime polynomial.* (748)

J

joint variation A situation in which one quantity varies directly as the product of two or more independent variables, but not inversely as any variable. (132)

L

lattice point A point in a solution set whose coordinates are both integers. (344)

leading coefficient In the polynomial $a_n x^n + a_{n-1}x^{n-1} + a_{n-2}x^{n-2} + \ldots + a_0$, the number a_n. (730)

line of reflection The line over which a figure is reflected. **(255)**

line of sight An imaginary line from one position to another, or in a particular direction. **(672)**

line of best fit A line that best fits a set of data, found by using regression. Also called *least-squares line* or *regression line.* **(177)**

line of reflection See *reflecting line.* **(255)**

line of symmetry For a figure F, a line m such that the reflection image of F over m is F itself. **(102)**

linear combination The sum of the multiples of two or more variables. **(157)**

linear-combination method A method of solving systems that involves adding multiples of the given equations. **(321)**

linear function A function whose graph is a line or part of a line. A function f with the equation $f(x) = ax + b$, where a and b are real numbers. **(151)**

linear inequality An inequality in which both sides are linear expressions. **(342)**

linear polynomial A polynomial of the first degree. **(731)**

linear-programming problem A problem of maximizing or minimizing a quantity based on solutions to a system of linear inequalities. **(356)**

linear regression A method that uses all the data points to find the line of best fit for those points. **(177)**

linear scale A scale with units spaced so that the distance between successive units is constant. **(617)**

linear sequence See *arithmetic sequence.* **(196)**

log of *x* to the base 10 See *logarithm of x to the base 10.* **(608)**

logarithm function to the base 10 See *common logarithm function.* **(611)**

logarithm function with base *b*, $\log_b x$ The inverse of the exponential function with base b, $f(x) = b^x$; the function that maps x onto $\log_b x$ for all positive numbers x. **(624)**

logarithm of *x* to the base 10 y is the logarithm of x to the base 10, written $y = \log_{10} x$, if and only if $10^y = x$. Also called *log of x to the base 10* or *log base 10 of x.* **(608)**

logarithm of *a* to the base *b* Let $b > 0$ and $b \neq 1$. Then x is the logarithm of a to the base b, written $x = \log_b a$, if and only if $b^x = a$. **(622)**

logarithmic curve The graph of a function of the form $y = \log_b x$. **(611)**

logarithmic equation An equation of the form $y = \log_b x$. **(610)**

logarithmic scale A scale in which the scale values are the exponents of the powers. **(615)**

M

matrix subtraction If two matrices A and B have the same dimensions, their difference $A - B$ is the matrix whose element in each position is the difference of the corresponding elements in A and B. **(230)**

magnitude of a size change In the size change that maps (x, y) onto (kx, ky), the number k. Also called *size-change factor.* **(242)**

magnitude of a rotation In a rotation, the amount that the preimage is turned about the center of rotation, measured in degrees from –180° (clockwise) to 180° (counterclockwise), $m\angle POP'$, where P' is the image of P under the rotation and O is its center. **(269)**

major axis of an ellipse The segment that contains the foci of the ellipse and has two vertices of the ellipse as its endpoints. **(819)**

mapping A synonym for *function.* Also called *map.* **(22)**

mapping notation The notation $f: x \rightarrow y$ for a function f. **(22)**

mathematical model A mathematical graph, sentence, or idea that parallels some or all of the structure of a real situation. **(16)**

matrix A rectangular arrangement of objects or numbers, its *elements.* **(222)**

matrix addition If two matrices A and B have the same dimensions, their sum $A + B$ is the matrix in whose element in each position is the sum of the corresponding elements in A and B. **(228)**

matrix form of a system A representation of a system using matrices. The matrix form for $\begin{cases} ax + by = e \\ cx + dy = f \end{cases}$ is $\begin{bmatrix} a & b \\ c & d \end{bmatrix} \cdot \begin{bmatrix} x \\ y \end{bmatrix} = \begin{bmatrix} e \\ f \end{bmatrix}$. **(336)**

matrix multiplication If A is an $m \times n$ matrix and B is an $n \times p$ matrix, the product $A \cdot B$, or AB, is the $m \times p$ matrix whose element in row i and column j is the product of row i of A and column j of B. (237)

matrix product The result of matrix multiplication. (237)

maximum The greatest value of a data set or function. (388)

mean absolute deviation, *m.a.d.* The mean of the absolute deviations in a data set. (884)

mean of a data set The result of dividing the sum of the numbers in a data set by the number of numbers in the set. (883)

measure of center A number which in some sense is at the "center" of a data set; the mean or median of a data set. Also called *measure of central tendency.* (884)

measure of spread A number, like standard deviation, which describes the extent to which elements of a data set are dispersed or spread out. (884)

median When the terms of a data set are placed in increasing order, if the set has an odd number of terms, the middle term; if the set has an even number of terms, the average of the two terms in the middle. (537)

method of finite differences The use of successive calculations of differences of values of polynomial functions to determine whether a polynomial function of a particular degree can be an exact model for a set of points. (774)

minimum The least value of a set or function. (388)

minor axis of an ellipse The segment that has two vertices of the ellipse as its endpoints and does not contain the foci. (819)

mode The number or numbers which occur most often in a data set. (608)

model for an operation A pattern that describes many uses of that operation. (7)

monomial A polynomial with one term. (738)

multiplicity of a root For a root r in an equation $P(x) = 0$, the highest power of the factor $x - r$. (767)

N

natural logarithm of *m* n is the natural logarithm of m, written $n = \ln m$, if and only if $m = e^n$. (629)

natural numbers The set of numbers {1, 2, 3, 4, 5, ...}, sometimes also including 0. Also called the *counting numbers.* (29)

normal curve The graph of a normal distribution. (924)

normal distribution A function whose graph is the image of the graph of $y = \frac{1}{\sqrt{2\pi}}e^{\left(\frac{-x^2}{2}\right)}$ under a composite of translations or scale transformations. (924)

normalized scores See *standardized scores.* (925)

***n*th-power function** The function defined by $f(x) = x^n$, where n is a positive integer. (454)

***n*th root** Let n be an integer greater than 1. Then b is an nth root of x if and only if $b^n = x$. (486)

***n*th term** The term occupying the nth position in the listing of a sequence. The general term of a sequence. (197)

O

oblique line A line that is neither horizontal nor vertical.

one-to-one correspondence A mapping in which each member of one set is mapped to a distinct member of another set, and vice versa. (242)

order of operations A set of rules used to evaluate expressions, specifically: 1. Perform operations within grouping symbols from inner to outer; 2. Take powers from left to right; 3. Do multiplications or divisions from left to right; 4. Do additions or subtractions from left to right. (8)

output A value of the dependent variable in a function. (15)

P

parabola For a line ℓ and a point F not on ℓ, the set of all points in the plane of ℓ and F equidistant from F and ℓ. (102, 798)

paraboloid A 3-dimensional figure created by rotating a parabola in space around its axis of symmetry. (801)

parallax angle for a star Let P and Q be two positions on Earth and let S be the position of a star. Then the parallax angle θ is half the measure of $\angle PSQ$. (676)

Pascal's Triangle The sequence satisfying

1. $\binom{n}{0} = \binom{n}{n} = 1$ for all integers $n \geq 0$ and
2. $\binom{n+1}{r+1} = \binom{n}{r} + \binom{n}{r+1}$ for all integers $0 \leq r \leq n$.

The triangular array

$$\begin{array}{c} 1 \\ 1\ 2\ 1 \\ 1\ 3\quad 3\ 1 \\ 1\ 4\quad 6\quad 4\ 1 \\ 1\ 5\quad 10\quad 10\quad 5\ 1 \\ \vdots \end{array}$$

where if x and y are located next to each other on a row, the element just below and directly between them is $x + y$. **(898, 867)**

perfect-square trinomial A trinomial of the form $a^2 + 2ab + b^2$ or $a^2 - 2ab + b^2$; the square of a binomial. **(401)**

period The horizontal translation of smallest positive magnitude that maps the graph of a function onto itself. **(694)**

periodic function A function whose graph can be mapped to itself by a horizontal translation. **(694)**

permutation An arrangement of objects in which order matters. **(889)**

pH scale A logarithmic scale used to measure the acidity of a substance. **(618)**

piecewise linear Relating to a function or graph that is described as a union of segments or other subsets of lines. **(171)**

pitch The measure of the steepness of the slant of a roof. **(51)**

point matrix A 2×1 matrix. **(224)**

point-slope form of a linear equation For a line, an equation of the form $y - y_1 = m(x - x_1)$, where (x_1, y_1) is a point on the line with slope m. **(170)**

polynomial equation An equation of the form $y = a_n x^n + a_{n-1}x^{n-1} + ... + a_1 x^1 + a_0$, where n is a positive integer and $a_n \neq 0$. **(729)**

polynomial function A function of the form $P: x \rightarrow P(x)$, where $P(x)$ is a polynomial. **(731)**

polynomial in *x* of degree *n* An expression of the form $a_n x^n + a_{n-1}x^{n-1} + ... + a_1 x^1 + a_0$, where n is a positive integer and $a_n \neq 0$. **(730)**

polynomial model A polynomial equation which fits a data set. **(772)**

power The expression x^n; the result of the operation of powering, or exponentiation. **(452)**

powering An operation by which a variable is raised to a power. Also called *exponentiation.* **(452)**

preimage An object to which a transformation is applied. **(242)**

prime polynomial Over a set of numbers, a polynomial that cannot be factored into polynomials of lower degree whose coefficients are in the set. Also called *irreducible polynomial.* **(748)**

principal The original amount of money invested. **(473)**

probability distribution A function that maps a set of events onto their probabilities. Also called *probability function.* **(923)**

probability of an event If a situation has a total of t equally likely outcomes and e of these outcomes satisfy conditions for a particular event, then the probability of the event is $\frac{e}{t}$. **(453)**

pure imaginary numbers Multiples of the complex number i. **(422)**

Q

quadratic equation An equation that involves quadratic expressions. **(374)**

quadratic equation in two variables An equation of the form $Ax^2 + Bxy + Cy^2 + Dx + Ey + F = 0$, where A, B, C, D, E, and F are real numbers and at least one of A, B, or C is not zero. **(374)**

quadratic expression An expression that contains one or more terms in its variables, such as x^2, y^2, or xy, but no higher powers of x and y. **(374)**

quadratic form An expression of the form $Ax^2 + Bxy + Cy^2 + Dx + Ey + F$. **(374)**

Quadratic Formula If $ax^2 + bx + c = 0$ and $a \neq 0$, then $x = \frac{-b \pm \sqrt{b^2 - 4ac}}{2a}$. **(414)**

quadratic function A function f with an equation of the form $f(x) = ax^2 + bx + c$. **(374)**

quadratic polynomial A polynomial of a single variable with degree 2. **(731)**

quadratic regression A process of finding the model with the least sum of squares of differences from the given data points to the values predicted by the model. (408)

quadratic system A system that involves polynomial sentences of degrees 1 and 2, at least one of which is a quadratic sentence. (844)

quadratic-linear system A quadratic system with at least one linear sentence. (844)

quadratic-quadratic system A system that involves two or more quadratic sentences. (851)

quartic equation A fourth degree polynomial equation. (766)

quartic polynomial A polynomial of a single variable with degree 4. (731)

quintic equation A fifth degree polynomial equation. (766)

R

radian A measure of an angle, arc, or rotation such that π radians = 180 degrees. (712)

radical symbol The symbol $\sqrt{\ }$, as in $\sqrt{2x}$ or $\sqrt[3]{9}$. (537)

radius The distance between any point on a circle and the center of the circle. (804)

random numbers Numbers which have the same probability of being selected. (928)

range of a function The set of values of the dependent variable that can result from all possible substitutions for the independent variable. (27)

rate of change See *slope*. (94)

ratio of similitude In two similar figures, the ratio between a length in one figure and the corresponding length in the other. (245)

rational number A number that can be represented as a simple fraction or ratio of the form $\frac{a}{b}$, where a and b are integers and $b \neq 0$. (29, 383)

rationalizing the denominator The process of rewriting a fraction so that its denominator is a rational number. (551)

real function A function whose independent and dependent variables stand for only real numbers. (26)

real numbers Those numbers that can be represented by finite or infinite decimals. (29)

real part Of the complex number $a + bi$, the real number a. (427)

rectangular hyperbola A hyperbola with perpendicular asymptotes. (842)

recursive formula A set of statements that indicates the first term (or first few terms) of a sequence and tells how the next term is calculated from the previous term or terms. Also called *recursive definition*. (183)

reflecting line The line over which a point is reflected. Also called *line of reflection*. (255)

reflection A transformation under which the image of a point P over a reflecting line m is (1) P itself, if P is on m; (2) the point P' such that m is the perpendicular bisector of the segment connecting P with P' that maps a figure to its reflection image. (255)

reflection image of a point *A* over a line *m* The point A if A is on m and the point A' such that m is the perpendicular bisector of $\overline{AA'}$ if A is not on m. (255)

reflection-symmetric Coinciding with a reflection image of itself. (102)

regression line See *line of best fit*. (177)

relation Any set of ordered pairs. (15)

root of a polynomial For a polynomial function P, a zero of the equation $P(x) = 0$. Also called *zero of a polynomial*. (752)

root with multiplicity 2 See *double root*. (767)

roots of an equation Solutions to an equation. (437)

rotation A transformation with a center O under which the image of O is O itself and the image of any other point P is the point P' such that $m\angle POP'$ is a fixed number (its *magnitude*). (269)

rounding-down function See *floor function*. (204)

rounding-up function See *ceiling function*. (204)

row A horizontal list in a table, rectangular array, or spreadsheet. (222)

row-by-column multiplication The process of obtaining an element in the product of two matrices in which a row matrix is multiplied by a column matrix. (236)

S

scalar multiplication An operation leading to the product kA of a scalar k and a matrix A, in which each element of kA is k times the corresponding element in A. (230)

scalar product The result of scalar multiplication. (230)

scale change The stretching or shrinking of a figure in either a horizontal direction only, in a vertical direction only, or in both directions. A horizontal scale change of magnitude a and a vertical scale change of magnitude b maps (x, y) onto (ax, by), and is denoted by $S_{a,b}$. (249)

scatterplot A plot with discrete points used to display a data set. (178)

semicircle A half-circle. (806)

semimajor axis Half the major axis of an ellipse. (820)

semiminor axis Half the minor axis of an ellipse. (820)

sequence A function whose domain is the set of all positive integers or the set of positive integers from a to b. (53)

set-builder notation The notation $\{x| \ldots\}$ read "the set of all x such that ... ." Also written $\{x: \ldots\}$ (27)

series An indicated sum of terms in a sequence. (869)

shrink A scale change in the horizontal (or vertical) direction in which the absolute value of the magnitude is less than 1. (249)

sigma, Σ The Greek letter that indicates a sum. (871)

sigma notation, Σ-notation A shorthand notation used to restate a series. Also called *summation notation*. (871)

similar figures Two figures such that one is the image of the other under a composite of isometries (reflections, rotations, translations, glide reflections) and size changes. (245)

simple fraction A fraction of the form $\frac{a}{b}$, where a and b are integers and $b \neq 0$. (383)

simple interest The amount of interest I earned when calculated using the formula $I = Prt$, where P is the principal, r is the rate, and t is the time. (477)

sine function The correspondence $\theta \rightarrow \sin\theta$ that maps a number onto its sine. (663)

sine of θ (sin θ) In a right triangle with acute angle θ, $\sin\theta = \frac{\text{length of leg opposite } \theta}{\text{length of hypotenuse}}$; the y-coordinate of the image of (1, 0) under R_θ, the rotation with center (0, 0) and magnitude θ. (663, 684)

sine wave A curve that is the image of the graph of the sine function s: $\theta \rightarrow \sin\theta$ by any composite of translations, scale changes, or reflections. (695)

singular matrix A matrix whose multiplicative inverse does not exist. (330)

sinusoidal Pertaining to sine waves. (695)

size change The transformation that maps the point (x, y) onto (kx, ky); a transformation with center O such that the image of O is O itself and the image of any other point P is the point P' such that $OP' = k \cdot OP$ and P' is on ray OP if k is positive, and on the ray opposite ray OP if k is negative. (242)

$\sin^{-1} x$ The number between -90° and 90°, or between $-\frac{\pi}{2}$ and $\frac{\pi}{2}$, whose sine is x. (670)

size change factor *See magnitude of a size change.* (242)

slope The slope of a line through two points (x_1, y_1) and (x_2, y_2) is the quantity $\frac{y_2 - y_1}{x_2 - x_1}$. Also called *rate of change*. (94)

slope-intercept equation of a line An equation of the form $y = mx + b$, where m is the slope of the line and b is its y-intercept. (151)

solution set of a system The intersection of the solution sets of the individual sentences in a system. (307)

solving a sentence Finding all solutions to a sentence. (40)

solving a triangle Using theorems from geometry and trigonometry to find all the missing measures of sides and angles of a triangle. (700)

square matrix A matrix with the same number of rows and columns. (328)

square root A square root x of t is a solution to $x^2 = t$. The positive square root of a positive number x is denoted $\sqrt{x}$. (381)

square root function The function f with equation $f(x) = \sqrt{x}$, where x is a nonnegative real number. (537)

squaring function The function f with equation $f(x) = x^2$. (454)

standard deviation, *s.d.* Let S be a data set of n numbers $\{x_1, x_2, ..., x_n\}$. Let μ be the mean of S. Then the standard deviation, $s.d.$, of S is given by

$$s.d. = \sqrt{\frac{\sum_{i=1}^{n}(x_i - \mu)^2}{n}}.$$ **(885)**

standard form for an equation of a line An equation for a line in the form $Ax + By = C$, where A and B are not both zero. **(159)**

standard form of an equation for a parabola An equation for a parabola in the form $y = ax^2 + bx + c$, where $a \neq 0$. **(374)**

standard form of a polynomial A polynomial written in the form $a_nx^n + a_{n-1}x^{n-1} + ... + a_1x^1 + a_0$, where n is a positive integer and $a_n \neq 0$. **(730)**

standard form of a quadratic equation An expression of the form $ax^2 + bx + c = 0$, where $a \neq 0$. **(374)**

standard form of an equation for a hyperbola An equation for a hyperbola in the form $\frac{x^2}{a^2} - \frac{y^2}{b^2} = 1$, where $b^2 = c^2 - a^2$, the foci are $(c, 0)$ and $(-c, 0)$ and the focal constant is $2a$. **(833)**

standard form of an equation for a quadratic relation An equation of the form $Ax^2 + Bxy + Cy^2 + Dx + Ey + F = 0$, where $A, B, C, D, E,$ and F are real numbers and at least one of A, B, or C is nonzero. **(839)**

standard form of an equation for an ellipse An equation for an ellipse in the form $\frac{x^2}{a^2} + \frac{y^2}{b^2} = 1$, where $b^2 = a^2 - c^2$, the foci are $(c, 0)$ and $(-c, 0)$ and the focal constant is $2a$. **(818)**

standard normal curve The graph of a normal distribution. **(924)**

standard position for an ellipse The position of an ellipse centered at the origin with its foci on an axis. **(818)**

standard window The default window of a grapher that shows all four quadrants at a reasonably close scale. **(28)**

standardized scores Scores whose distribution is normal with a predetermined mean and standard deviation. **(925)**

statistical measure A single number which is used to describe an entire set of numbers.

step function A piecewise function whose graph looks like a series of steps, such as the graph of the function with equation $y = \lfloor x \rfloor$. **(204)**

stretch A scale change in the horizontal (or vertical) direction in which the absolute value of the magnitude is greater than 1; that is, $|a| > 1$ (or $|b| > 1$). **(249)**

subscript A number or variable written below and to the right of a variable. **(54)**

subset A set whose elements are all from a given set. **(891)**

substitution method A method of solving systems in two or more variables by solving one equation for one variable, substituting the expression for that variable into the other equation(s), and solving the resulting equation(s). **(314)**

subtraction of matrices Given two matrices A and B having the same dimensions, their difference $A - B$ is the matrix whose element in each position is the difference of the corresponding elements in A and B. **(230)**

sum of two matrices For two matrices A and B with the same dimensions, the matrix $A + B$ in which each element is the sum of the corresponding elements in A and B. **(228)**

summation notation A shorthand notation used to denote a series. Also called *sigma notation* or *Σ-notation*. **(871)**

system A set of conditions joined by the word "and"; a special kind of compound sentence. **(307)**

T

$\tan^{-1} x$ The number between 0° and 180°, or between 0 and π whose tangent is x. **(671)**

tangent function The correspondence that maps a number x onto its tangent. **(663)**

tangent line A line that intersects a circle or ellipse in exactly one point. **(846)**

tangent of θ ($\tan \theta$) In a right triangle with acute angle θ, $\tan \theta = \frac{\text{length of leg opposite } \theta}{\text{length of leg adjacent to } \theta}$; $\tan \theta = \frac{\sin \theta}{\cos \theta}$, provided $\cos \theta \neq 0$. **(663)**

term of a polynomial Any one of the separate addends in a polynomial. **(730)**

term of a sequence An element of a sequence. **(53)**

theorem In a mathematical system, a statement that has been proved. **(88)**

transformation A one-to-one correspondence between the points of a preimage and the points of an image. (242)

translation A transformation for all x and y that maps (x, y) onto $(x + h, y + k)$ denoted by $T_{h,k}$. (281)

trial One repetition of an experiment. (912)

triangular number An element of the sequence 1, 3, 6, 10, ..., whose nth term is $\frac{n(n+1)}{2}$. (54)

triangulation The process of determining the location of points using triangles and trigonometry. (703)

trigonometric ratios The ratios of the lengths of the sides in a right triangle. (663)

trinomial A polynomial with three terms. (738)

U

union of two sets The set consisting of those elements in either one or both sets. (302)

unit circle The circle with center at the origin and radius 1 unit. (683)

unit fraction A simple fraction with 1 in its numerator. (918)

V

value of a function For a function f, if $y = f(x)$, the value of y. (21)

variable A symbol that can be replaced by any one of a set of numbers or other objects. (6)

varies directly as See *directly proportional to.* (72)

varies inversely as See *inversely proportional to.* (80)

velocity The rate of change of distance with respect to time. (52)

vertex form of an equation of a parabola An equation of the form $y - k = a(x - h)^2$ where (h, k) is the vertex of the parabola. (388)

vertex of a parabola The intersection of a parabola with its axis of symmetry. (102, 798)

vertical asymptote A vertical line that is approached by the graph of a relation as the values of x approach a particular real number. (107)

vertical line A line in the plane with an equation of the form $x = b$. (153)

vertical magnitude The number b in the scale change that maps (x, y) onto (ax, by). (249)

vertical scale change A transformation that maps (x, y) onto (x, by). (249)

vertices of an ellipse The endpoints of the major and minor axes of the ellipse. (819)

vertices of a hyperbola The points of intersection of a hyperbola and the line containing its foci. (832)

vinculum The bar in a fraction or a radical symbol. (8)

W

whole numbers The set of numbers {0, 1, 2, 3, 4, 5, ... }. (29)

window The part of the coordinate grid shown on the screen of an automatic grapher. (27)

X

x-axis The line in the coordinate plane in which the second coordinates of points are 0. (152)

x-intercept The x-coordinate of the point at which a graph crosses the x-axis. (152)

Y

y-axis The line in the coordinate plane in which the first coordinates of points are 0. (255)

y-intercept The y-coordinate of the point at which a graph crosses the y-axis. (151)

yield See *annual percentage yield.* (475)

Z

zeros of a function For a function f, a value of x for which $f(x) = 0$. (437)

zero of a polynomial See *root of a polynomial.* (752)

zoom A feature on an automatic grapher which enables the window of a graph to be changed without keying in interval endpoints for x and y. (32)

Index

D

E

H

I

J

K

L

M

N

Q

T

U

V

W

X

Y

Z

Photo Credits

Illustration Credits

McGraw Hill Companies, Inc. would like to thank the following illustrator for his contributions: Garry Nichols

Photo Credits

Chapters 1–6

Cover, back: ©Peter J. Robinson/photolibrary; **vi** (l) ©Tomislav Forgo/Shuttterstock, (r) ©Pete Saloutos/zefa Corbis; **vii** (l) ©Tim Tadder/Corbis, (r) ©S.P. Gillette/Corbis; **viii** (l) ©Paul Gilham/Getty Images Sport/Getty Images, (r) ©Sam Kittner/National Geographic/Getty Images; **ix** (l) ©Corbis/SuperStock, (r) ©The Granger Collection, New York; **x** (l) ©Somos Images/Corbis, (r) ©Allen Wallace/Photonica/Getty Images; **xi** (l) ©age fotostock/SuperStock, (r) ©Dennis di Cicco/Corbis; **xii** ©David Madison/The Image Bank/Getty Images; **3** ©Glenn Bartley/All Canada Photos/Getty images; **4-5** ©Tomislav Forgo/Shuttterstock; **7** Courtesy Robert Beerbohm/blbcomics.com; **12** Courtesy Corby Waste/NASA/JPL-Caltech; **16** ©Hannamariah/Shutterstock; **19** ©Nancy R. Cohen/Getty Images; **20** ©The Granger Collection; **21** ©Burke/Triolo/Brand X Pictures; **25** ©Michael-John Wolfe/Shutterstock; **27** ©Stephen Aaron Rees/Shutterstock; **32** ©2008 The Associated Press; **36** ©Tim Platt/Iconica/Getty Images; **39** ©Chuck Pefley/Alamy; **40** ©Image Source Pink/Alamy; **42** ©Chris Hondros/Getty Images Sport/Getty Images; **43** ©Ronald Martinez/Getty Images Sport/Getty Images; **45** ©Image100/Corbis/Punchstock; **51** ©Michael Gunther/www.art-and-archaeology.com; **56** ©Jeff Greenberg/PhotoEdit; **58** Courtesy Mitsumasa Anno/Penguin Group Inc.; **59** ©Hybrid Medical Animation/Photo Researchers, Inc. **60** (l) ©The Bridgeman Art Library, (r) ©Mike Flippo/Shutterstock; **61** ©Mitch Hrdlicka/Getty Images; **70-71** (t) ©Pete Saloutos/zefa Corbis; **71** (b) ©Seb Rogers/Alamy; **77** ©Stock Image/SuperStock; **85** ©Jonathan Daniel/Getty Images Sport/Getty Images; **86** ©Jennifer Westmoreland/Shutterstock; **89** ©Science/Illustration Carin L. Cain; **92** ©Photodisc/Getty Images; **93** ©Don Farrall/Photodisc/Getty Images; **104** ©CreativeAct-Technology Series/Alamy; **112** Courtesy NASA; **117** ©Oliver Furrer/Brand X/Corbis; **119** ©Michael Steele/Getty Images Sport/Getty Images; **130** (t, b) ©Ramiro Posada; **136** (l) ©Tme & Life Pictures/Getty Images, (r) ©Caroline J. Clarke/Shutterstock; **137** ©Lebrecht Music & Arts; **148-149** ©Tim Tadder/Corbis; **150** ©www.RoadsideArchitecture.com; **161** © Image Club; **168** ©Scenics of America/PhotoLink/Getty Images; **181** ©2008 The Associated Press; **185** ©Jim McIsaac/Getty Images Sport/Getty Images; **194** ©Eric Isselee/Shutterstock; **202** ©2008 The Associated Press; **206** ©fotog/Tetra Images/Getty Images; **210** ©Peter Weber/Shutterstock; **211** ©Duomo/Corbis; **220-221** ©S.P. Gillette/Corbis; **225** ©Kalev Leetaru; **226** ©Peter M. Fisher/Corbis/Veer; **228** ©Luigi Petro/Alamy; **233** ©2008 The Associated Press; **235** ©FoodCollection/SuperStock; **240** ©Andrey Kozachenko/Shutterstock; **246** ©Mark Segal/Stone/Getty Images; **249** ©Daryl Benson/Photographer's Choice/Getty Images; **259** ©Glenn Bartley/All Canada Photos/Getty images; **265** ©Big House Productions/Photodisc/Getty Images; **267** ©PhotoAlto/Laurence Mouton/Getty Images; **273** ©Lynn Radeka/SuperStock; **278** (t) ©G. Brad Lewis/Photo Resource Hawaii, (c) ©J Marshall/Tribaleye Images/Alamy, (b) ©Robin Bath/Alamy; **279** ©Royalty-Free/Corbis; **282** ©rfx/Shutterstock; **285** Courtesy University of Chicago; **286** (l) Courtesy Library of Congress, (c) ©akg-images, (r) ©Laurence Monneret/Getty Images; **287** Courtesy NASA; **298** (l) ©Photodisc/Getty Images; **298-299** ©Paul Gilham/Getty Images Sport/Getty Images; **302** ©fine art/Alamy; **305** ©SuperStock, Inc./SuperStock; **312** ©Ariel Skelley/Blend Images/Getty Images; **313** ©David Papas/UpperCut Images/Getty Images; **319** ©Andrew Turner/Camfaud Concrete Pumps Ltd.; **322** ©Sylvain Grandadam/Stone/Getty Images; **326** ©2008 The Associated Press; **331** ©Stephen Kallis, Jr.; **335** ©Travel Ink/Gallo Images/Getty Images; **340** ©2008 The Associated Press; **347** ©U.S. Geological Survey; **352** ©Shalom Ormsby/Stone/Getty Images; **353** ©Mark Weiss/Stone/Getty Images; **356** ©Ted Spiegel/Corbis; **362** (l) ©age fotostock/SuperStock; (r) ©Ian Waldie/Getty Images News/Getty Images; **363** ©Corbis/SuperStock; **372-373** (t) ©Sam Kittner/National Geographic/Getty Images; **373** (b) ©Phillip James Corwin/Corbis; **377** ©age fotostock/SuperStock; **378** ©image100/SuperStock; **390** ©VisionsofAmerica/Joe Sohm/Digital Vision/Getty Images; **391** ©Kim Karpeles/Alamy; **392** ©2008 The Associated Press; **395** ©The Granger Collection, New York; **397** ©flashfilm/Taxi Japan/Getty Images; **399** ©Peter Vanderwarker/The Image Bank/Getty Images; **411** ©2008 The Associated Press; **412** ©AURA/STSci; **418** ©Della Huff; **421** ©North Wind/North Wind Picture Archives; **426** ©Ablestock/Alamy; **431** (t, b) ©Doug Martin/Photo Researchers, Inc.; **438** ©it Stock/PunchStock; **441** ©Thinkstock/PunchStock; **442** ©Ken Welsh/ArtLife Images

Chapters 7–13

450-451 (t) ©Corbis/SuperStock; **451** (b) ©Leslie Richard Jacobs/Corbis; **453** ©Kent Larsson/Stone+/Getty Images; **458** ©2008 The Associated Press; **463** Courtesy NASA/ESA; **464** ©Michael Fay/National Geographic/Getty Images; **470** (t) ©Spectral-Design/Shutterstock; (b) ©FPG Intl./Taxi/Getty Images; **474** ©Keith Brofsky/Getty Images; **475** ©Robert Brenner/PhotoEdit; **476** ©2008 The Associated Press; **478** ©Copestello/Shutterstock; **479** ©Fallon London; **487** Photononstop/Superstock; **491** ©Corbis/SuperStock; **496** ©Car Culture/Getty Images; **498** ©Julie Mowbray/Alamy; **501** ©Blend Images/SuperStock; **502** (t) ©Digital Vision/Getty Images; (b) ©image100/Punchstock; **503** ©G.K. & Vikki Hart/Getty Images; **504** ©The Granger Collection, New York; **505** (l) ©Steve Dunwell/Getty Images; (r) ©Melba Photo Agency/PunchStock; **506** ©RubberBall Productions; **514-515** ©The Granger Collection, New York; **516** ©Thinkstock/JupiterImages; **522** Courtesy NASA, The Hubble Heritage Team, STSci,AURA; **526** Courtesy NASA, ESA, and The Hubble Heritage Team; **536** ©2008 The Associated Press; **538** ©Keith Weller/U.S. Department of Agriculture/Photo Researchers, Inc.; **541** NASA/JPL-Caltech/Cornell University; **544** ©Italian School/The Bridgeman Art Library/Getty Images; **549** ©2008 The Associated Press; **561** image100/SuperStock; **566** Collection of the Australian National Maritime Museum; **568** ©FPG/Taxi/Getty Images; **569** ©2008 The Associated Press; **578-579** ©Somos Images/Corbis; **580** ©Steve Shott/Dorling Kindersley/Getty Images; **583** ©Lawrence Livermore National Laboratory; **585** ©Sean Sprague/Painet; **586** ©Wil Meinderts/Foto Natura/Minden Pictures; **589** ©Burke/Triolo/Brand X Pictures/Jupiterimages; **592** ©Neil Emmerson/Robert Harding World Imagery/Corbis; **594** ©Maximilian Weinzierl/Alamy; **597** ©Dimitri Vervitsiotis/Digital Vision/Getty Images; **602** ©Blend Images/SuperStock; **607** ©arabianEye/Getty Images; **613** ©David Paul Morris/Getty Images News/Getty Images; **616** ©William Radcliffe/Science Faction/Getty Images; **618** ©Adam Teitelbaum/AFP/Getty Images; **619** ©AFP/Getty Images; **620** ©Rob Gendler; **621** ©Peter Cade/Iconica/Getty Images; **628** ©Atlas Photo Bank/Photo Researchers, Inc.; **629** ©The Old Calculator Museum; **631** ©Comstock Images/PictureQuest; **633** ©Pradeep Subramanian; **634** ©Science & Society Picture Library; **638** ©Stephen Dunn/Getty Images Sport/Getty Images; **642** (t, b) Courtesy Scripophily; **644** ©2008 The Associated Press; **648** ©David Young-Wolff/PhotoEdit; **649** (l) ©Nassyrov Rusian/Shutterstock, (r) ©Mark Harwood/Stone/Getty Images; **650** (l) ©2008 The Associated Press, (r) ©Photononstop/SuperStock; **651** ©Dennis Galante/Taxi/Getty Images; **660-661** ©Allen Wallace/Photonica/Getty Images; **665** ©Alan Becker/Photographer's Choice/Getty Images; **668** (t) ©Photodisc/PunchStock, (b) ©Kirk Treakle/Alamy; **673** ©Lee Foster/Lonely Planet Images/Getty Images; **678** ©North Wind/North Wind Picture Archives; **680** ©North Wind/North Wind Picture Archives; **686** ©Jason Hirschfeld/Getty Images News/ Getty Images; **692** ©Corbis/SuperStock; **695** ©The Granger Collection, New York; **696** ©Royalty-Free/Corbis; **698** Courtesy NASA/JPL-Caltech/Cornell; **705** ©Travel Ink/Getty Images; **710** ©2008 The Associated Press; **718** ©Alan Gallery/Alamy; **719** (l) ©kolvenbach/Alamy, (r) ©North Wind/North Wind Picture Archives; **728** (b) ©Dynamic Graphics Value/SuperStock; **728-729** (t) ©age fotostock/SuperStock; **735** ©Ken Chernus/Taxi/Getty Images; **736** ©Photodisc/SuperStock; **737** ©The McGraw-Hill Companies, Inc.; **743** ©C Squared Studios/Getty Images; **758** ©Andy Sacks/Stone/Getty Images; **766** ©The Granger Collection, New York; **781** ©Jorg Greuel/The Image Bank/Getty Images; **784** ©Comstock/Punchstock; **786** ©2008 Masterfile Corporation; **787** ©Jeffrey Coolidge/The Image Bank/Getty Images; **796-797** ©Dennis di Cicco/Corbis; **801** ©Sun Baked; **802** ©Mark Darley/Esto Photographics; **808** ©Allthesky.com Astrophotography; **809** ©2008 The Associated Press; **810** ©Herbert Hartmann/The Image Bank/Getty Images; **812** ©The Bridgeman Art Library/Getty Images; **174** Courtesy NASA; **823** ©David S. Gunderson; **829** © J.B. Spector/Museum of Science & Industry; **831** (l) ©amana images inc./Alamy, (r) ©Kamee14u/Shutterstock; **837** ©Richard Thornton/Shutterstock; **842** ©William H. Edwards/Stone/Getty Images; **848** ©VisionsofAmerica/Joe Sohm/Digital Vision/Getty Images; **849** ©Stephen Schauer/Riser/Getty Images; **852** ©Kraig Scarbinsky/Riser/Getty Images; **854** ©age fotostock/SuperStock; **856** (l) ©2008 The Associated Press, (r) ©Luis Veiga/Photographer's Choice/Getty Images; **857** ©Antonio M. Rosario/The Image Bank/Getty Images; **866-867** ©David MadisonThe Image Bank/Getty Images; **874** ©Purestock/Getty Images; **879** ©Alex Mares-Manton/Asia Images/Getty Images; **881** ©Nick Vedros & Assoc./Stone/Getty Images; **886** ©NBAE/Getty Images; **887** ©The Granger Collection, New York; **889** ©Jeff Greenberg/Alamy; **892** ©Paul Burns/Lifesize/Getty Images; **894** ©Garry Gay/Photographer's Choice/Getty Images; **901** ©Influx Productions/Photodisc/Getty Images; **904** ©Bettmann/Corbis; **909** ©Mario Bruno/Shutterstock; **911** ©2008 The Associated Press; **913** ©Royalty-Free/Corbis; **914** ©WIN-Initiative/Getty Images; **915** ©Cadence Gamache; **916** ©Ingram Publishing/SuperStock; **919** ©Ian Mckinnell/Photographer's Choice/Getty Images; **921** ©Juniors Bildarchiv/Alamy; **927** ©2008 The Associated Press; **928** ©RubberBall/SuperStock; **929** ©Joan Kerrigan/Shutterstock.

Symbols

Symbol	Meaning
$\{x \mid x > n\}$	the set of all x such that x is greater than n
$-x$	opposite of x
$\cap$	intersection
$\cup$	union
$f(x)$	function notation read "f of x"
$f: x \rightarrow y$	function notation read "f maps x onto y"
A'	image of A
S_k	size change of magnitude k
$S_{a,b}$	scale change with horizontal magnitude a and vertical magnitude b
r_x	reflection over the x-axis; transformation with matrix $\begin{bmatrix} 1 & 0 \\ 0 & -1 \end{bmatrix}$
r_y	reflection over the y-axis; transformation with matrix $\begin{bmatrix} -1 & 0 \\ 0 & 1 \end{bmatrix}$
$r_{y=x}$	reflection over the line $y = x$; transformation with matrix $\begin{bmatrix} 0 & 1 \\ 1 & 0 \end{bmatrix}$
r_m	reflection over the line m
R_θ	rotation of magnitude θ *counterclockwise* with center at the origin
R_{180}	rotation of magnitude 180°; transformation with matrix $\begin{bmatrix} -1 & 0 \\ 0 & -1 \end{bmatrix}$
R_{90}	rotation of magnitude 90°; transformation with matrix $\begin{bmatrix} 0 & -1 \\ 1 & 0 \end{bmatrix}$
$T_2 \circ T_1$	composite of transformations T_1 and T_2
$T_{h,k}$	translation of h units horizontally and k units vertically
$\parallel$	parallel
$\perp$	perpendicular
$\begin{bmatrix} a & b \\ c & d \end{bmatrix}$	2 × 2 matrix
M^{-1}	inverse of matrix M
$\det M$	determinant of matrix M
$\sqrt{\ }$	radical sign; square root
$\sqrt[n]{x}$	the largest real nth root of x
i	$\sqrt{-1}$
$\sqrt{-k}$	a solution of $x^2 = -k$, $k > 0$
$a + bi$	a complex number, where a and b are real numbers
$g \circ f$	composite of functions f and g
$g(f(x))$	value at x of the composite of functions f and g
$\lvert x \rvert$	absolute value of x
$\lfloor x \rfloor$	greatest integer less than or equal to x
$\lceil x \rceil$	least integer greater than or equal to x
f^{-1}	inverse of a function f read "f inverse"
a^b, a^b	the bth power of a
$\log_b a$	logarithm of a to the base b
e	2.71828...
$\ln x$	natural logarithm of x
$m\angle ABC$	measure of angle ABC
$\sin \theta$	sine of θ
$\cos \theta$	cosine of θ
$\tan \theta$	tangent of θ
rad	radian
a_n	"a sub n"; the nth term of a sequence
$\sum_{i=1}^{n} 1$	the sum of the integers from 1 to n
S_n	the sum of the first n terms of a sequence
$x!$	x factorial
$\binom{n}{r}$, ${}_nC_r$	the number of ways of choosing r objects from n objects
`int`	greatest integer calculator command
`seq`	sequence calculator command
`det`	determinant of a matrix calculator command
`fMax`, `fMin`	maximum or minimum function value calculator command
`stDevPop`	standard deviation calculator command
`nCr`	combination calculator command

Additional Answers

Chapter 3

Lesson 3-5
Questions Page 181

10b.

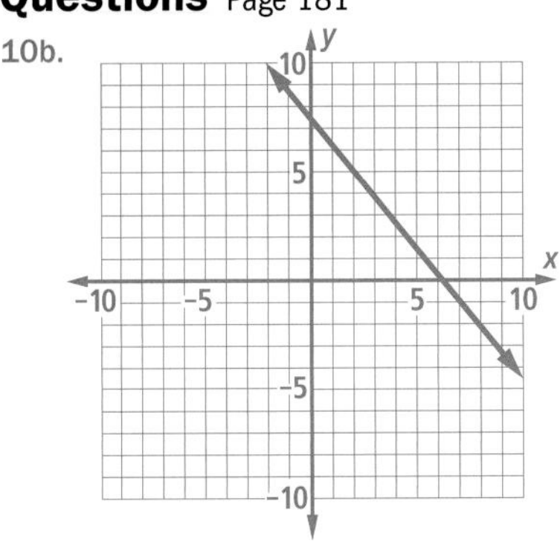

14a.

x	f1(x):...	
	25*x-5	
0.	-50.	
1.	-25.	
2.	0.	
3.	25.	
4.	50.	
5.	75.	

$f1(x):=25\cdot x-50$

14b.

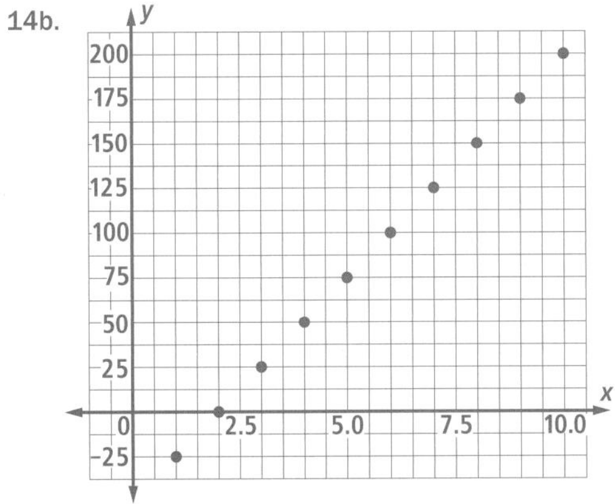

Lesson 3-6
Questions Page 188

24a. $\begin{cases} a_1 = 1 \\ a_n = a_{n-1} + 2 - 1 \text{ for } n \geq 2 \end{cases}$

24b. Answers vary. Sample: For all of the progress we make in life, we sometimes need to take one step back before moving forward due to some setback or obstacle.

Chapter 4

Lesson 4-2
Questions Page 234

19.

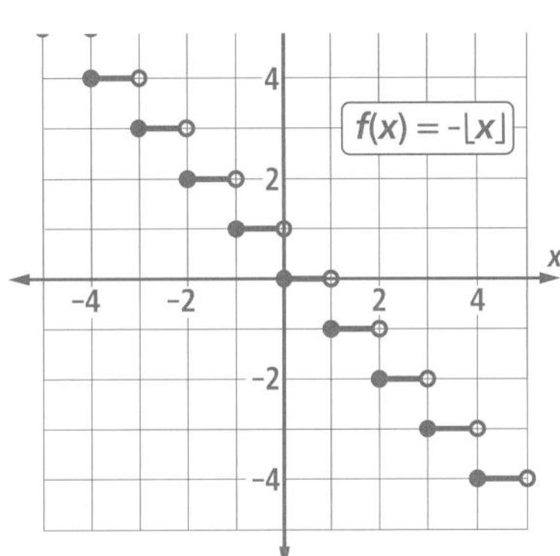

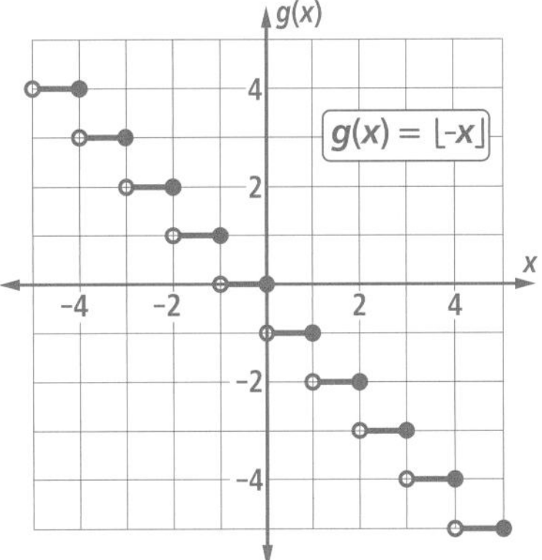

Answers vary. Sample: $f(x) = -\lfloor x \rfloor$ is always 1 greater than $g(x) = \lfloor -x \rfloor$ for all values of x, except when x is an integer, in which case $f(x) = g(x)$.

Lesson 4-4
Activity Page 243

Step 4

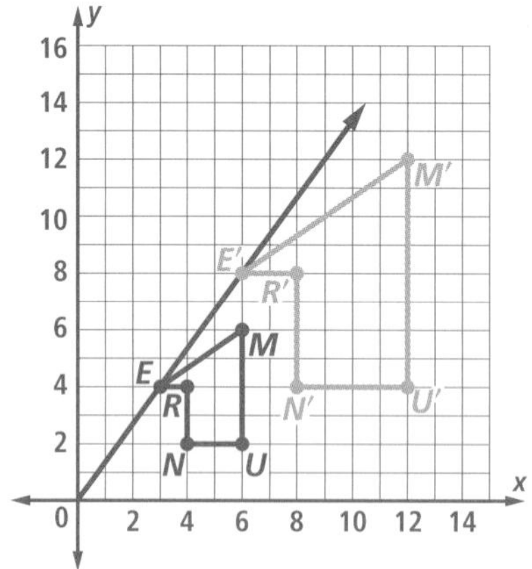

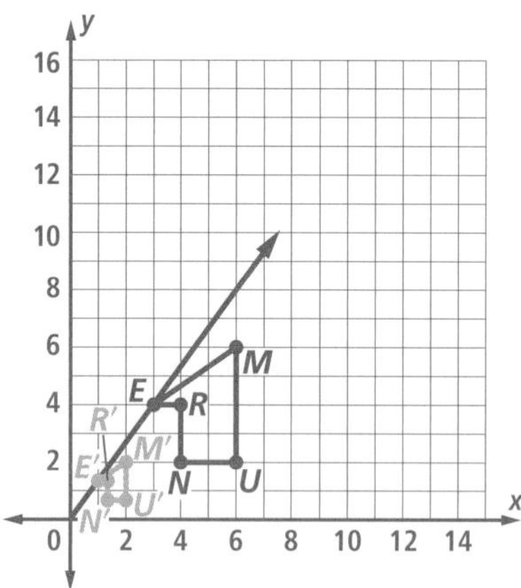

Lesson 4-7
Questions Page 268

26a. Answers vary. Sample: Closure does hold for multiplication of 3 × 3 matrices. The dimensions of the product matrix are the number of rows of the first matrix by the number of columns of the second matrix. Since both of these values are 3, the resulting matrix is 3 × 3.

26b. $\begin{bmatrix} 1 & 0 & 0 \\ 0 & 1 & 0 \\ 0 & 0 & 1 \end{bmatrix}$,

$$\begin{bmatrix} 1 & 0 & 0 \\ 0 & 1 & 0 \\ 0 & 0 & 1 \end{bmatrix}\begin{bmatrix} a & b & c \\ d & e & f \\ g & h & i \end{bmatrix} = \begin{bmatrix} a & b & c \\ d & e & f \\ g & h & i \end{bmatrix}$$

26c. Answers vary. Sample: The commutative property does not hold.

$$\begin{bmatrix} 1 & 0 & 0 \\ 0 & 3 & 0 \\ 2 & 0 & 3 \end{bmatrix}\begin{bmatrix} 0 & 2 & 4 \\ 0 & 0 & 3 \\ 0 & 1 & 2 \end{bmatrix} = \begin{bmatrix} 0 & 2 & 4 \\ 0 & 0 & 9 \\ 0 & 7 & 14 \end{bmatrix}$$

$$\begin{bmatrix} 0 & 2 & 4 \\ 0 & 0 & 3 \\ 0 & 1 & 2 \end{bmatrix}\begin{bmatrix} 1 & 0 & 0 \\ 0 & 3 & 0 \\ 2 & 0 & 3 \end{bmatrix} = \begin{bmatrix} 8 & 6 & 12 \\ 6 & 0 & 9 \\ 4 & 3 & 6 \end{bmatrix}$$

26d. Answers vary. Sample: The associative property seems to hold.

$$\left(\begin{bmatrix} 0 & 0 & 2 \\ 0 & 3 & 0 \\ 4 & 0 & 0 \end{bmatrix}\begin{bmatrix} 1 & 2 & 1 \\ 1 & 1 & 1 \\ 1 & 2 & 1 \end{bmatrix}\right)\begin{bmatrix} 1 & 2 & 1 \\ 1 & 1 & 1 \\ 1 & 2 & 1 \end{bmatrix} =$$

$$\begin{bmatrix} 2 & 4 & 2 \\ 3 & 3 & 3 \\ 4 & 8 & 4 \end{bmatrix}\begin{bmatrix} 1 & 2 & 1 \\ 1 & 1 & 1 \\ 1 & 2 & 1 \end{bmatrix} = \begin{bmatrix} 8 & 12 & 8 \\ 9 & 15 & 9 \\ 16 & 24 & 16 \end{bmatrix}$$

$$\begin{bmatrix} 0 & 0 & 2 \\ 0 & 3 & 0 \\ 4 & 0 & 0 \end{bmatrix}\left(\begin{bmatrix} 1 & 2 & 1 \\ 1 & 1 & 1 \\ 1 & 2 & 1 \end{bmatrix}\begin{bmatrix} 1 & 2 & 1 \\ 1 & 1 & 1 \\ 1 & 2 & 1 \end{bmatrix}\right) =$$

$$\begin{bmatrix} 0 & 0 & 2 \\ 0 & 3 & 0 \\ 4 & 0 & 0 \end{bmatrix}\begin{bmatrix} 4 & 6 & 4 \\ 3 & 5 & 3 \\ 4 & 6 & 4 \end{bmatrix} = \begin{bmatrix} 8 & 12 & 8 \\ 9 & 15 & 9 \\ 16 & 24 & 16 \end{bmatrix}$$

Lesson 4-8
Questions Page 273

16a. $\begin{bmatrix} a^2 + bc & ab + bd \\ ac + dc & bc + d^2 \end{bmatrix}$

16b. $a^2 + bc = 0$; $ab + bd = -1$; $ac + dc = 1$; $bc + d^2 = 0$

16c. Combining the first and last equation we see that $a^2 + bc = bc + d^2$, so $a^2 = d^2$. Looking at the second equation, we have $b(a + d) = 1$, so $a + d = \frac{-1}{b} \neq 0$, and $a \neq -d$.

16d. From Part c, we have $a + d = \frac{-1}{b}$, and from the third equation we have $a + d = \frac{1}{c}$, so $\frac{1}{c} = \frac{-1}{b}$ and $b = -c$.

16e. $\begin{bmatrix} \frac{1}{\sqrt{2}} & -\frac{1}{\sqrt{2}} \\ \frac{1}{\sqrt{2}} & \frac{1}{\sqrt{2}} \end{bmatrix}$; $\begin{bmatrix} -\frac{1}{\sqrt{2}} & \frac{1}{\sqrt{2}} \\ -\frac{1}{\sqrt{2}} & -\frac{1}{\sqrt{2}} \end{bmatrix}$

16f. R_{225}

Chapter 6

Lesson 6-3
Activity Page 386

Step 1

Group B

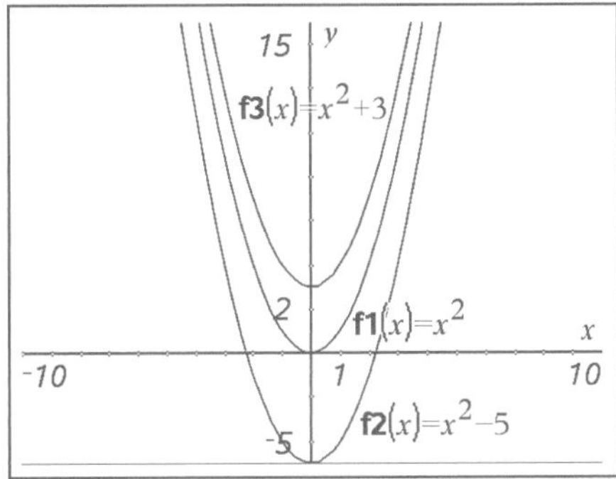

Group C

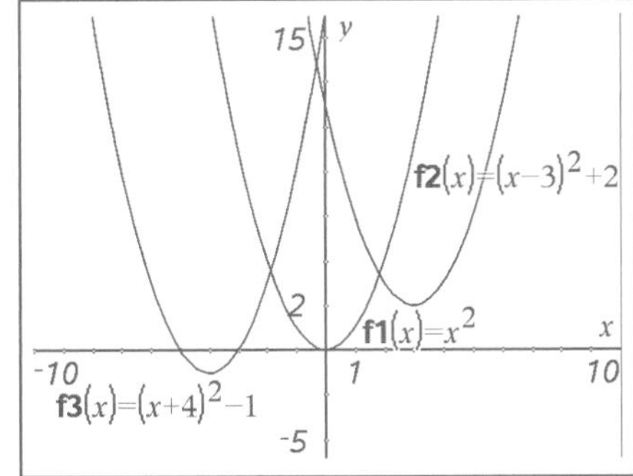

Step 2

Group A: *f*2 is a translation of *f*1 four units to the right; *f*3 is a translation of *f*1 two units to the left; Group B: *f*2 is a translation of *f*1 five units down; *f*3 is a translation of *f*1 three units up; Group C: *f*2 is a translation of *f*1 three units to the right and two units up; *f*3 is a translation of *f*1 four units to the left and one unit down.

Step 4

a. translation h units horizontally (to the right if h is positive, to the left if h is negative)

b. translation k units vertically (up if k is positive, down if k is negative)

c. translation h units horizontally and k units vertically

Lesson 6-6
Activity Page 408

Answers vary. Sample:

Step 2:

Drop #	I	M	O
1	0	0	0
2	1	0	0
3	1	1	0
4	1	1	0
5	1	1	0
6	1	0	0
7	1	1	0
8	1	1	0
9	1	1	0
10	1	1	0
11	1	0	0
12	1	1	1
13	0	0	0
14	1	1	0
15	0	0	0
16	1	0	0
17	1	1	0
18	1	1	0
19	1	0	0
20	1	1	0
21	1	0	0
22	1	1	0
23	1	1	1
24	1	0	0
25	1	0	0

Step 4

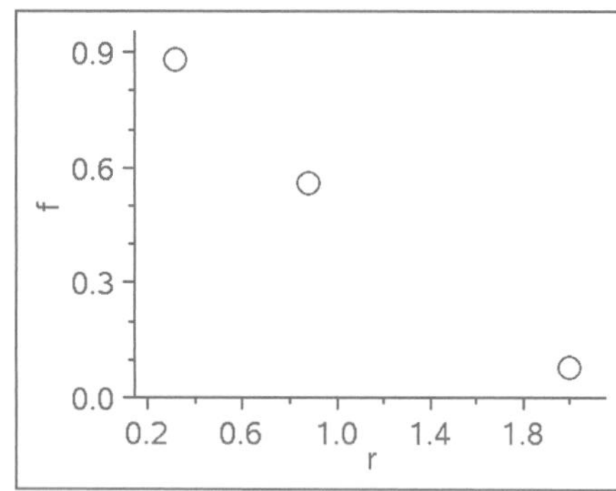

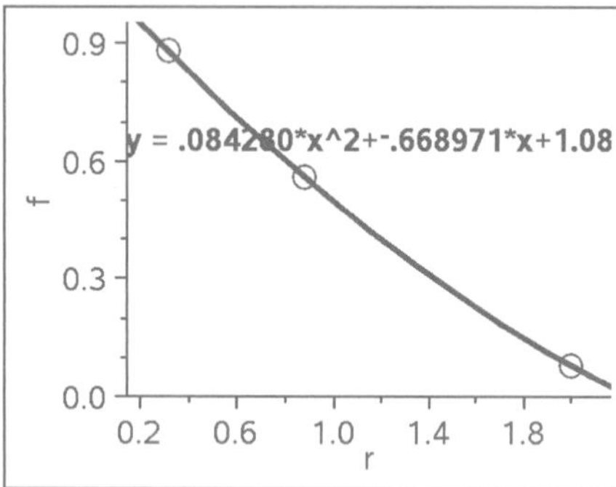

Step 6

Answers vary. Sample: Quarter radius $= \frac{15}{32}$ in.; prediction ≈ 0.786; relative frequency $= \frac{19}{25} = 0.76$; This value is close to the predicted value. The value from the combined data is even closer to the predicted value.

Lesson 6-10

Activity Page 435

Step 3

The number of x-intercepts of the graph is the same as the number of solutions to $ax^2 + bx + c = 0$ if the solutions are real. If the solutions to $ax^2 + bx + c = 0$ are imaginary, there are no x-intercepts.

Step 4

If the discriminant is 0, there is one intercept. If the discriminant is greater than 0, there are two intercepts. If the discriminant is less than 0, there are no intercepts.